Krishna's

Calculus of Finite Differences
&
Numerical Analysis

(Computer Fundamentals with Programming in C)

(For IAS, IFS, PCS, CSIR (Net) Graduate and Post-Graduate Students of Science and Engineering of Various Indian Universities)

Revised Edition

As per UGC Syllabus

By

Prof. P.P. Gupta
Ex. Director
Dr. K.N. Modi Institute of
Engineering and Technology,
Modinagar

G.S. Malik
Ex. Sr. Lecturer
Department of Mathematics,
M.M.P.G. College,
Modinagar

J.P. Chauhan
M.Sc. (Mathematics)
C.C.S. University, Meerut

KRISHNA Prakashan Media (P) Ltd.
KRISHNA HOUSE, 11, Shivaji Road, Meerut-250 001 (U.P.), India

Krishna's

Calculus of Finite Differences & Numerical Analysis

First Edition: 1980

Thirty Ninth Revised & Enlarged Edition: 2011

Forty Second Edition: 2015

Forty Sixth Edition: 2022

Edition: 2025

Book Code : 214-46 (E)

[redacted] [redacted]

Published by : **Sugam Rastogi & Kanupriya Rastogi**
for **KRISHNA** Prakashan Media (P) Ltd.
11, Shivaji Road, Meerut – 250 001 (U.P.) India.
Phones: 91.121.2644766, 2642946, 4026111, 4026112; Fax: 91.121.2645855
Website: www.krishnaprakashan.com
E-mail: info@krishnaprakashan.com

Typesetting : Krishna Graphic Arts, Meerut (V.S., V.K.)

Printed at : Citizen Offset, Meerut

Jai Shri Radhey Shyam

Dedicated

to

Lord

Krishna

Authors & Publishers

Preface to the Latest Edition

The book entitled **Calculus of Finite Differences and Numerical Analysis,** ha been written with a prime object to take care of fast development in the knowledge the subject and to meet the requirements of the students of **M.A./M.Sc.** (Third and Four semester course / final year course) in Mathematics of All Indian Universities. The top covered in this book are strictly according to the **UGC Model Curriculum 2002** whi has been adopted by most of the Indian Universities.

Nearly every definition is followed by examples illustrating the use of abstract concept i some fairly concrete situations. This device makes the book suitable for self-study. Th arrangement of the material is such that the book can also serve as a reference for mor advanced mathematicians.

The problems which are given at the end of each chapter, can also be solved by the methods developed in the book. The book contains some routine problems and also important theorems which complement the material in the text; they are accompanied by hints for their solution.

A large number of new problems of **I.A.S. P.C.S, I.F.S, C.S.I.R. (Net) and GATE** have been added in many chapters. It has been tried to strike a balance among the various point of view.

Possible Course Outlines: Most instructions which used this test for a course in **Programming in 'C'** are covered in chapter 19 and **Numerical Analysis** with solution of Partial Differential Equations is covered from chapter 18.

I would like to thank the students: past & present, colleagues and others for their constructive ideas and valuable assistance.

The Job is not yet complete, there is and would always be hope for improvement and we invite comments and suggestions to make this book more purposeful.

—J.P. Chauhan

Syllabus

Programming in C and Numerical Analysis

BMH 303 (a and b) **UGC MODEL CURRICULUM**

B.A./B.Sc. (HONS), M.A./M.Sc. Mathematics (Final Year)

PROGRAMMING IN C

Programmer's Model of a Computer, Algorithms, Flow Charts, Data Types, Arithmetic and Input/Output Instructions, Decisions Control Structures, Decision Statements, Logical and Conditional Operators, Loop, Case Control Structures, Functions, Recursions, Preprocessors, Arrays, Puppetting of Strings, Structures, Pointers, File Formating.

NUMERICAL ANALYSIS

Solution of Equations: Bisection, Secant, Regula Falsi, Newton's Method, Roots of Polynomials.

Interpolation:
Lagrange and Hermite Interpolation, Divided Differences, Difference Schemes Interpolation Formulas using Differences.

Numerical Differentiation
Numerical Quadrature: Newton-Cote's Formulas, Gauss Quadrature Formulas, Chebychev's Formulas.

Linear Equations: Direct Methods for Solving Systems of Linear Equations (Guass Elimination, LU Decomposition, Cholesky Decomposition), Iterative Methods (Jacobi, Gauss-Seidel, Relaxation Methods).

The Algebraic Eigen Value Problem: Jacobi's Method, Given's Method, Householder's Method, Power Method, QR Method, Lanczos' Method.

Ordinary Differential Equations: Euler Method, Single-step Methods, Runge-Kutta's Method, Multi-Step Methods, Milne-Simpson Method, Methods Based on Numerical Integration, Methods Based on Numerical Differentiation, Boundary Value Problems, Eigen Value Problems.

Approximation: Different Types of Approximation, Least Square Polynomial Approximation, Polynomial Approximation using Orthogonal Polynomials, Approximation with Trigonometric Functions, Exponential Functions, Chebychew Polynomials, Rational Functions.

Detailed Contents

Chapter-14 Matrix Inversion...(601–630)

Chapter-15 Eigen Values and Eigen Vectors...........................(631–664)

Chapter-16 Bernoulli and Euler Polynomials..............................(665–682)

Chapter-17 Curve Fitting and Principle of Least Squares.....(683–714)

Chapter-18 Numerical Solution of Partial Differential Equations...(715–772)

Chapter-19 Computer Fundamentals with Programming in C.........(773–900)

ooo

Theory | Solved Examples | Problem Set

Chapter 1

The Calculus of Finite Differences

Finite differences, formulae, error effect, properties and formulae of the operators, E, Δ, ∇, Factorial notation, Differences of zero, Leibnitz's rule, Error effect on tabular value.

1.1 Finite Differences

Introduction

In applied mathematics, the solution of a problem generally consists of numbers which satisfy some kind of equation; theoretically these numbers may be specified by the equation; but in practice it is found that even in the simplest cases (for example $x = \sqrt{2}$) it is not possible to write down an exact decimal representative of the solution. *Numerical methods are very important tools to provide practical methods for calculating the solutions of problems to applied mathematics to a desired degree of accuracy.* The wide use of electronic computers for solving problems in various fields of engineering, scientific, industry etc. has further enhanced the scope of numerical methods.

Let $y = f(x)$ for $a \le x \le b$: This statement from numerical point of view means that one or more values of $f(x)$ exist corresponding to every value of x in the given range. In case $f(x)$ is specified by a given explicit formula, we can compute the value or values of $f(x)$ corresponding to some given value of x by simply substituting the value of x in the formula. If it is not the case, even then we can find an approximate representative of the function; this is done with the help of calculus of finite differences. *The calculus of finite differences deals with the changes in the values of the function (dependent variable) due to changes in the independent variable.* Again through this we study the relations of the values which the function assumes, whenever the independent variable changes by finite jumps whether equal or unequal. Here, we shall study the case when independent variable changes by equal intervals.

1.2 Differences

Consider the function $y = f(x) = \cos x$, then the values of y corresponding to different values of x are obtained by putting the various values of x on the right hand side of the equation, *e.g.*,

$x°$	$\cos x°$
0°	1.0000
20°	0.9397
40°	0.7660
60°	0.5000
80°	0.1736

Now, if instead of numerical values of x differing by 20°, let the consecutive values of x be $a, a+h, a+2h, \ldots, a+nh$ differing by h, the values of $y = f(x)$ corresponding to the values of x are

$$f(a), f(a+h), f(a+2h), \ldots, f(a+nh)$$

The values of the independent variable x are called ***Arguments*** and corresponding value of dependent variable y is called ***Entry***.

1.2.1 Forward or Descending Difference

Now $\quad f(a+h) - f(a), f(a+2h) - f(a+h), \ldots$

$$f(a+nh) - f(a+\overline{n-1}\,h)$$

are called the ***first differences*** of the function $y = f(x)$ and we denote these differences by $\Delta f(a), \Delta f(a+h), \ldots \Delta f(a+\overline{n-1}\,h)$ respectively

i.e.

$$\left.\begin{aligned} \Delta f(a) &= f(a+h) - f(a) \\ \Delta f(a+h) &= f(a+2h) - f(a+h) \\ &\cdots\cdots\cdots\cdots\cdots \\ \Delta f(a+\overline{n-1}\,h) &= f(a+nh) - f(a+\overline{n-1}\,h) \end{aligned}\right\} \quad \ldots(1)$$

where Δ is called the ***forward or descending difference*** operator and $\Delta f(a), \Delta f(a+h)$ are called ***first forward differences***.

In general, the first forward difference is defined by

$$\Delta f(x) = f(x+h) - f(x)$$

The differences of the first forward differences given by (1) are called the ***second forward differences*** and denoted by $\Delta^2 f(a), \Delta^2 f(a+h)$, etc.

Therefore, we have

$$\Delta^2 f(a) = \Delta f(a+h) - \Delta f(a)$$
$$= [f(a+2h) - f(a+h)] - [f(a+h) - f(a)]$$
$$= f(a+2h) - 2f(a+h) + f(a)$$

Similarly

$$\Delta^2 f(a+h) = \Delta f(a+2h) - \Delta f(a+h)$$
$$= [f(a+3h) - f(a+2h)] - [f(a+2h) - f(a+h)]$$
$$= f(a+3h) - 2f(a+2h) + f(a+h)$$

In general, we have

$$\Delta^2 f(x) = \Delta f(x+h) - \Delta f(x)$$
$$= [f(x+2h) - f(x+h)] - [f(x+h) - f(x)]$$
$$= f(x+2h) - 2f(x+h) + f(x)$$

Again, differences of the second forward differences are called ***third forward differences*** and are given by $\Delta^3 f(a), \Delta^3 f(a+h)$ etc.

i.e., $$\Delta^3 f(a) = \Delta^2 f(a+h) - \Delta^2 f(a)$$
$$= f(a+3h) - 3f(a+2h) + 3f(a+h) - f(a)$$

and so on.

In general, the nth forward difference is given by

$$\Delta^n f(x) = \Delta^{n-1} f(x+h) - \Delta^{n-1} f(x)$$

Note 1: $f(a)$, the first entry is termed as the **leading term** and the differences $\Delta f(a)$, $\Delta^2 f(a)$, $\Delta^3 f(a), \ldots$ are known as the **leading differences.**

Note 2: It should be kept in mind that Δ is an operator, Δ^2 is not the square of the operator Δ but it is repetition of the operator Δ.

1.2.2 Backward or Ascending Differences

The differences

$$f(a+h) - f(a),\ f(a+2h) - f(a+h), \ldots,\ f(a+nh) - f(a+\overline{n-1}h)$$

are called ***first backward differences*** and these are denoted by $\nabla f(a+h), \nabla f(a+2h), \ldots,$ $\nabla f(a+nh)$ respectively so that $\nabla f(a+h) = f(a+h) - f(a)$;

$$\nabla f(a+2h) = f(a+2h) - f(a+h) \text{ etc.,}$$

where ∇ is called the ***backward difference operator***.

We observe that forward differences are defined by points to the right of x while backward differences are defined by points to the left of x.

The differences of first backward differences are said to be second backward differences and are denoted by $\nabla^2 f(a+2h), \nabla^2 f(a+3h)$, etc.

i.e., $$\nabla^2 f(a+2h) = \nabla f(a+2h) - \nabla f(a+h)$$
$$= [f(a+2h) - f(a+h)] - [f(a+h) - f(a)]$$
$$= f(a+2h) - 2f(a+h) + f(a)$$

In general, first backward difference is given by

$$\nabla f(x) = f(x) - f(x-h)$$

and second backward difference is given by

$$\nabla^2 f(x) = \nabla f(x) - \nabla f(x-h)$$
$$= [f(x) - f(x-h)] - [f(x-h) - f(x-2h)]$$
$$= f(x) - 2f(x-h) + f(x-2h)$$

In the same way it can be shown that the nth backward difference of $y = f(x)$ is given by

$$\nabla^n f(x) = \nabla[\nabla^{n-1} f(x)]$$
$$= \nabla^{n-1} f(x) - \nabla^{n-1} f(x-h)$$

Solved Examples

Example 1· *If Δ and ∇ be the first descending difference operator and first ascending difference operator respectively of a function $f(x)$, show that $(\Delta - \nabla) \equiv \Delta\nabla$*

[Bilaspur 2010; Agra 2004, 2007; Bhopal 2005, 2007, 2009]

Solution: By the definition, we have

$$\Delta f(x) = f(x+h) - f(x)$$

and $$\nabla f(x) = f(x) - f(x-h),$$

where h is interval of differencing.

Now $$\Delta\nabla f(x) = \Delta[\nabla f(x)] = \Delta[f(x) - f(x-h)]$$
$$= \Delta f(x) - \Delta f(x-h)$$
$$= \Delta f(x) - [f(x) - f(x-h)]$$
$$= \Delta f(x) - \nabla f(x) = (\Delta - \nabla) f(x)$$

or $$\Delta\nabla \equiv \Delta - \nabla$$

1.3 Difference Formulae

1. The ***differences of constant function*** are zero *i.e.* $\Delta c = 0$ where c is constant. By definition we have $\Delta c = c - c = 0$.

2. *The **operator Δ is commutative** in its operation as regards constants i.e.* $\Delta c = c\,\Delta$

we have $(\Delta c)\, f(x) = \Delta c\, f(x) = c\,\{f(x+h) - f(x)\}$

i.e., $= c\,\Delta f(x)$

$\Rightarrow$ $\Delta c = c\,\Delta$

3. ***Δ is distributive.*** If $f(x)$ and $g(x)$ are two functions of x then

$$\Delta [f(x) + g(x)] = [\Delta f(x) + \Delta g(x)]$$

4. If a and b are constants, then

$$\Delta [af(x) + bg(x)] = a\Delta f(x) + b\Delta g(x)$$

5. ***Indices law** holds for the operator Δ*

$$\Delta^n [\Delta^m f(x)] = \Delta^{m+n} f(x) = \Delta^{n+m} f(x)$$

6. The finite difference of a product of two functions is given by

$$\Delta [f(x)\, g(x)] = f(x+h)\, \Delta g(x) + g(x)\, \Delta f(x)$$

Proof: $\Delta [f(x)\, g(x)] = f(x+h)\, g(x+h) - f(x)\, g(x)$

$$= f(x+h)\, g(x+h) - f(x+h)\, g(x)$$

$$+ f(x+h)\, g(x) - f(x)\, g(x)$$

$$= f(x+h)\, [g(x+h) - g(x)]$$

$$+ g(x)\, [f(x+h) - f(x)]$$

$$\therefore \quad \Delta [f(x)\, g(x)] = f(x+h)\, \Delta g(x) + g(x)\, \Delta f(x)$$

7. The finite difference of a quotient of two functions is given by

$$\Delta \left[\frac{f(x)}{g(x)}\right] = \frac{g(x)\, \Delta f(x) - f(x)\, \Delta g(x)}{g(x+h)\, g(x)}$$

Proof: $\Delta \left[\frac{f(x)}{g(x)}\right] = \frac{f(x+h)}{g(x+h)} - \frac{f(x)}{g(x)} = \frac{f(x+h)\, g(x) - f(x)\, g(x+h)}{g(x+h)\, g(x)}$

$$= \frac{[f(x+h)\, g(x) - f(x)\, g(x)] - [g(x+h)\, f(x) - f(x)\, g(x)]}{g(x+h)\, g(x)}$$

$$= \frac{g(x)\,[f(x+h) - f(x)] - f(x)\,[g(x+h) - g(x)]}{g(x+h)\,g(x)}$$

$$\therefore \quad \Delta\left[\frac{f(x)}{g(x)}\right] = \frac{g(x)\,\Delta f(x) - f(x)\,\Delta g(x)}{g(x+h)\,g(x)}$$

8. $\Delta e^x = e^{x+h} - e^x = e^x\,(e^h - 1)$

9. $\Delta \log x = \log(x+h) - \log(x) = \log \dfrac{x+h}{x} = \log\left(1 + \dfrac{h}{x}\right)$

[Rajasthan 2002, 2007]

10. $\Delta \sin(ax+b) = \sin[a(x+h)+b] - \sin(ax+b)$

$$= 2\sin\frac{ah}{2}\cos\left[a\left(x+\frac{h}{2}\right)+b\right]$$

$$= 2\sin\frac{ah}{2}\sin\left[ax+b+\frac{ah+\pi}{2}\right]$$

Similarly, we have

$$\Delta \cos(ax+b) = -2\sin\left(\frac{ah}{2}\right)\sin\left[a\left(x+\frac{h}{2}\right)+b\right]$$

$$= 2\sin\frac{ah}{2}\cos\left[ax+b+\frac{ah+\pi}{2}\right]$$

and $\quad \Delta \tan(ax+b) = \sin ah \sec(ax+b)\sec[a(x+h)+b]$

1.4 Fundamental Theorem of Difference Calculus

If $f(x)$ be a polynomial of nth degree in x, then the nth difference of $f(x)$ is constant and $\Delta^{n+1} f(x) = 0$.

[Avadh 2005, 2007, 2009; Delhi 2005, 2008; M.D.U. (Rohtak) 2007, 2009]

Proof: Consider n^{th} degree polynomial

$$f(x) = a_0 + a_1 x + a_2 x^2 + \ldots + a_n x^n,$$

where n is a positive integer and $a_0, a_1, .., a_n$ are constants.

By the definition of operator Δ, we have $\Delta f(x) = f(x+h) - f(x)$

$$= [a_0 + a_1(x+h) + a_2(x+h)^2 + \ldots + a_n(x+h)^n]$$

$$- [a_0 + a_1 x + a_2 x^2 + \ldots + a_n x^n]$$

$$= a_1 h + a_2[(x+h)^2 - x^2] + a_3[(x+h)^3 - x^3] + \ldots$$

$$+ a_n[(x+h)^n - x^n)]$$

$$= a_1 h + a_2 [{}^2C_1\, xh + h^2] + a_3 [{}^3C_1\, x^2 h + {}^3C_2\, xh^2 + h^3] + \ldots$$

$$+ a_n [{}^nC_1\, x^{n-1} h + {}^nC_2\, x^{n-2} h^2 + \ldots + {}^nC_n\, h^n]$$

$$= b_1 + b_2 x + b_3 x^2 + \ldots + b_{n-1} x^{n-2} + na_n hx^{n-1} \qquad \ldots(1)$$

where $b_1, b_2, \ldots, b_{n-1}$ are constant coefficients. From (1), we observe that first difference of a polynomial of nth degree is again a polynomial of $(n-1)^{th}$ degree *i.e.* $\Delta f(x)$ is one degree less than the degree of $f(x)$.

Again $\Delta^2 f(x) = \Delta f(x+h) - \Delta f(x)$

$$= b_1 + b_2 (x+h) + b_3 (x+h)^2 + \ldots + b_{n-1} (x+h)^{n-2}$$

$$+ nha_n (x+h)^{n-1} - [b_1 + b_2 x + \ldots + nha_n x^{n-1}]$$

$$= b_2 h + b_3 [(x+h)^2 - x^2] + \ldots + b_{n-1} [(x+h)^{n-2} - x^{n-2}]$$

$$+ nha_n [(x+h)^{n-1} - x^{n-2}]$$

$$= b_2 h + b_3 [{}^2C_1\, hx + h^2] + \ldots + b_{n-1} [{}^{n-2}C_1\, x^{n-3} h + \ldots$$

$$+ {}^{n-2}C_{n-2} h^{n+2}] + nha_n [{}^{n-1}C_1 x^{n-2} h + {}^{n-1}C_2 x^{n-3} h^2 + \ldots + h^{n-1}]$$

$$= C_2 + C_3 x + C_4 x^2 + \ldots + C_{n-1} x^{n-3} + n(n-1) h^2 a_n x^{n-2} \qquad \ldots(2)$$

We observe that (2) is a polynomial of degree $(n-2)$.

Thus by continuing the process, we will get a polynomial of zero degree for the nth difference

i.e., $$\Delta^n f(x) = n(n-1)(n-2)\ldots 1.\, h^n a_n x^{n-n} = (n)!\, h^n a_n x^0 = (n)!\, h^n a_n$$

Thus n^{th} difference is a constant and so all higher differences are each zero *i.e.* $(n+1)^{th}$ and higher difference of a polynomial of nth degree are zero.

> **Note:** The converse of the above theorem is also true, namely if the nth differences of a tabulated function are constant when values of the independent variable are taken at equal intervals, the function is a polynomial of degree n.

1.5 The Difference Table

While using higher differences, a useful table called the *difference table is given below.*

Argument x	Entry $y = f(x)$	First differences $\Delta f(x)$	Second differences $\Delta^2 f(x)$
a	$f(a)$		
		$f(a+h) - f(a) = \Delta f(a)$	
$a+h$	$f(a+h)$		$\Delta f(a+h) - \Delta f(a) = \Delta^2 f(a)$
		$f(a+2h) - f(a+h) = \Delta f(a+h)$	
$a+2h$	$f(a+2h)$		$\Delta f(a+2h) - \Delta f(a+h) = \Delta^2 f(a+h)$
		$f(a+3h) - f(a+2h) = \Delta f(a+2h)$	
$a+3h$	$f(a+3h)$		$\Delta f(a+3h) - \Delta f(a+2h) = \Delta^2 f(a+2h)$
		$f(a+4h) - f(a+3h) = \Delta f(a+3h)$	
$a+4h$	$f(a+4h)$		

Similarly, we can find third differences and so on. The above table is also called ***forward differences table*** since we have taken here forward differences.

Backward Difference Table

Argument x	Entry $y = f(x)$	First differences $\nabla f(x)$	Second differences $\nabla^2 f(x)$
a	$f(a)$		
		$f(a+h) - f(a) = \nabla f(a+h)$	
$a+h$	$f(a+h)$		$\nabla f(a+2h) - \nabla f(a+h) = \nabla^2 f(a+2h)$
		$f(a+2h) - f(a+h) = \nabla f(a+2h)$	
$a+2h$	$f(a+2h)$		$\nabla f(a+3h) - \nabla f(a+2h) = \nabla^2 f(a+3h)$
		$f(a+3h) - f(a+2h) = \nabla f(a+3h)$	
$a+3h$	$f(a+3h)$		$\nabla f(a+4h) - \nabla f(a+3h) = \nabla^2 f(a+4h)$
		$f(a+4h) - f(a+3h) = \nabla f(a+4h)$	
$a+4h$	$f(a+4h)$		

The above two tables are also called ***diagonal forward*** and ***diagonal backward*** difference tables since the differences are shown in diagonal pattern. Sometimes the more compact tables called ***Horizontal forward difference*** table and ***Horizontal backward*** difference tables are used.

Horizontal Forward Difference Table

Argument x	Entry $y = f(x)$	1st differences $\Delta f(x)$	2nd differences $\Delta^2 f(x)$	3rd differences $\Delta^3 f(x)$
a	$f(a)$	$\Delta f(a)$	$\Delta^2 f(a)$	$\Delta^3 f(a)$
$a+h$	$f(a+h)$	$\Delta f(a+h)$	$\Delta^2 f(a+h)$	$\Delta^3 f(a+h)$
$a+2h$	$f(a+2h)$	$\Delta f(a+2h)$	$\Delta^2 f(a+2h)$	
$a+3h$	$f(a+3h)$	$\Delta f(a+3h)$		
$a+4h$	$f(a+4h)$			

Similarly, we can write fourth differences.

Horizontal Backward Difference Table

Argument x	Entry $y = f(x)$	1st differences $\nabla f(x)$	2nd differences $\nabla^2 f(x)$	3rd differences $\nabla^3 f(x)$
a	$f(a)$			
$a+h$	$f(a+h)$	$\nabla f(a+h)$		
$a+2h$	$f(a+2h)$	$\nabla f(a+2h)$	$\nabla^2 f(a+2h)$	
$a+3h$	$f(a+3h)$	$\nabla f(a+3h)$	$\nabla^2 f(a+3h)$	$\nabla^3 f(a+3h)$
$a+4h$	$f(a+4h)$	$\nabla f(a+4h)$	$\nabla^2 f(a+4h)$	$\nabla^3 f(a+4h)$

Similarly, we can write fourth differences.

1.5.1 Effect of an Error in a Tabular Value

Suppose $f(x_0), f(x_1), f(x_2), \ldots, f(x_n)$ are the true values of a function $f(x)$ and suppose that the value $f(x_3)$ is in error by quantity ε so that erroneous value of $f(x_3)$ is $f(x_3)+\varepsilon$. Then the table will be as follows.

$f(x)$	$\Delta f(x)$	$\Delta^2 f(x)$	$\Delta^3 f(x)$
$f(x_0)$	$\Delta f(x)$		
$f(x_1)$	$\Delta f(x_0)$	$\Delta^2 f(x)$	
$f(x_2)$	$\Delta f(x_1)$	$\Delta^2 f(x_0)$	$\Delta^3 f(x)$
$f(x_3)+\varepsilon$	$\Delta f(x_2)+\varepsilon$	$\Delta^2 f(x_1)+\varepsilon$	$\Delta^3 f(x_0)+\varepsilon$
$f(x_4)$	$\Delta f(x_3)-\varepsilon$	$\Delta^2 f(x_2)-2\varepsilon$	$\Delta^3 f(x_1)-3\varepsilon$
$f(x_5)$	$\Delta f(x_4)$	$\Delta^2 f(x_3)+\varepsilon$	$\Delta^3 f(x_2)+3\varepsilon$
$f(x_6)$	$\Delta f(x_5)$	$\Delta^2 f(x_4)$	$\Delta^3 f(x_3)-\varepsilon$

If we carefully observe the above difference table, we see that

1. The effect of an error goes on increasing with the succession.
2. The coefficients of ε's are the binomial coefficients with alternating signs.
3. In various difference columns of the difference table, the algebraic sum of the errors is zero.
4. The maximum error occurs in the same line as the erroneous tabular value.

With these points in mind we will try to locate the error, *i.e.*, its source and so on. In case there are two or more errors, the successive differences will be irregular and it will not be possible to locate the errors in the tabular values.

Example 2: *Locate the error in the second columns of the following difference table:*

x	$f(x)$	$\Delta f(x)$	$\Delta^2 f(x)$	$\Delta^3 f(x)$	$\Delta^4 f(x)$
3.60	0.112046	8158			
3.61	0.120204	8146	–12		
3.62	0.128350	8112	–34	–22	
3.63	0.136462	8138	26	60	82
3.64	0.144600	8102	–36	–62	–122
3.65	0.152702	8086	–16	20	82
3.66	0.160788	8069	–17	–1	–21
3.67	0.168857	8051	–18	–1	0
3.68	0.176908				

Solution: It is obvious from the above difference table that irregularity starts in each column on the horizontal lines corresponding to $x = 3.63$. From the pattern of differences in table of 1.5.1

We have $-4\varepsilon = .000082$,

so the error is nearly equal to $\varepsilon = -.000020$.

Thus the true value of $f(x)$ at $x = 3.63$ is

$$0.136462 - (-0.000020) = 0.136462 + 0.000020 = 0.136482$$

Now replacing $f(x)$ at $x = 3.63$ by $.136482$, we have found that the 3rd difference will be practically constant.

1.5.2 To Express any Value of the Function in Terms of Leading Term and the Leading Differences of Difference Table

To show that

$$f(a+nh) = f(a) + {}^nC_1\,\Delta f(a) + {}^nC_2\,\Delta^2 f(a) + \ldots + {}^nC_n\,\Delta^n f(a)$$

We know that $\Delta f(a) = f(a+h) - f(a)$

$$\therefore \quad f(a+h) = f(a) + \Delta f(a) \quad \ldots(1)$$

Again $f(a+2h) = f(a+h) + \Delta f(a+h)$

$$= f(a) + \Delta f(a) + \Delta[f(a) + \Delta f(a)] \quad \text{from (1)}$$

$$= f(a) + 2\Delta f(a) + \Delta^2 f(a) \quad \ldots(2)$$

Similarly, $f(a+3h) = f(a+2h) + \Delta f(a+2h)$

$$= f(a) + 2\Delta f(a) + \Delta^2 f(a) + \Delta[f(a) + 2\Delta f(a) + \Delta^2 f(a)]$$

$$= f(a) + 3\Delta f(a) + \Delta^2 f(a) + \Delta^3 f(a) \quad \ldots(3)$$

Now assume that $f(a+nh) = f(a) + {}^nC_1\,\Delta f(a) + {}^nC_2\,\Delta^2 f(a) + \ldots + \Delta^n f(a)$ be true for any value n. We shall now show that this result is true for the next integer $n+1$.

Now, $f(a+\overline{n+1}\,h) = f(a+nh) + \Delta f(a+nh)$

$$= [f(a) + {}^nC_1\,\Delta f(a) + {}^nC_2\,\Delta^2 f(a) + \ldots + \Delta^n f(a)]$$

$$+ \Delta[f(a) + {}^nC_1\,\Delta f(a) + {}^nC_2\,\Delta^2 f(a) + \ldots + \Delta^n f(a)]$$

$$= f(a) + [{}^nC_1\,\Delta f(a) + \Delta f(a)] + [{}^nC_1\Delta^2 f(a) + {}^nC_2\,\Delta^2 f(a)] + \ldots$$

$$+ \Delta^{n+1} f(a)$$

$$= f(a) + {}^{(n+1)}C_1\,\Delta f(a) + {}^{(n+1)}C_2\,\Delta^2 f(a) + \ldots + \Delta^{n+1} f(a)$$

$$[\because \; {}^nC_r + {}^nC_{r+1} = {}^{(n+1)}C_{r+1}]$$

Hence, the result is true for $n = n+1$; the result is also true for $n = 2$ and 3.

Thus for all integral values of n, we have

$$\mathbf{f(a+nh) = f(a) + {}^nC_1\,\Delta f(a) + {}^nC_2\,\Delta^2 f(a) + \ldots + {}^nC_n\,\Delta^n f(a)}$$

1.6 The Operator E [Meerut 2004, 2006]

The shift operator E is given by the rule

$$E[f(x)] = f(x+h) \quad \text{...(1)}$$

Again, we know that

$$\Delta f(x) = f(x+h) - f(x) = Ef(x) - f(x) \quad \text{...(2)}$$

Thus from (2), we have

$$Ef(x) = \Delta f(x) + f(x)$$

or
$$E[f(x)] = (\Delta + 1) f(x), \quad \text{...(3)}$$

Since $f(x)$ is arbitrary, so omitting it from (3), we get

$$E \equiv 1 + \Delta \quad \text{or} \quad \Delta \equiv E - 1$$ **[Meerut 2005]**

It should be noted here that in the identify $E \equiv 1I + \Delta$, I is a symbol of operation just like E and Δ and stands for $I\, f(x) = f(x)$.

Again $E^n f(x) = EE \dots E\, f(x)$ (n-times) $= f(x+nh)$

Like wise, we have $E^{-1}\{f(x)\} = f[x + (-1)h] = f(x-h)$

1.7 Properties of the Operators E and Δ

(i) Operators E and Δ are distributive **[Agra 2002, Indore 2004, 2008]**

Consider a function $u(x)$ which is the sum of the functions $f(x)$, $g(x)$ and $p(x)$,...

i.e., $$u(x) = f(x) + g(x) + p(x) + \dots \quad \text{...(1)}$$

Then $$Eu(x) = f(x+h) + g(x+h) + p(x+h) + \dots$$

[The interval of differencing is taken as h]

$$= Ef(x) + Eg(x) + Ep(x) + \dots$$ *i.e.* E is distributive.

Again $$\Delta u(x) = \Delta\{f(x) + g(x) + p(x) + \dots]$$

$$= [f(x+h) + g(x+h) + p(x+h) + \dots] - [f(x) + g(x) + p(x) + \dots]$$

$$= \{f(x+h) - f(x)\} + \{g(x+h) - g(x)\} + \{p(x+h) - p(x)\} + \dots$$

$$= \Delta f(x) + \Delta g(x) + \Delta p(x) + \dots$$

which shows that Δ is also distributive.

(ii) E and Δ are commutative with regard to constants

i.e. $E[Cf(x)] = CEf(x)$

and $\Delta[Cf(x)] = C\Delta f(x)$

where C is constant **[I.A.S. 2001]**

$$E[Cf(x) = Cf(x+h), \text{ the interval of differencing being } h,$$

$$= CE\, f(x)$$

Again $$\Delta[Cf(x)] = Cf(x+h) - Cf(x) = C\,\Delta\, f(x)$$

(iii) E and Δ obey the law of indices

i.e. $E^m E^n f(x) = E^{m+n} f(x)$

and $\Delta^m . \Delta^n f(x) = \Delta^{m+n} f(x)$

$$E^m . E^n f(x) = E^m f(x+nh) = f(x+n.h+nh)$$

$$= f[x+\overline{m+n}\,h) = E^{m+n} f(x).$$

and $$\Delta^m \Delta^n f(x) = (\Delta\,\Delta \ldots m \text{ times})(\Delta\,\Delta \ldots n \text{ times}) f(x)$$

$$= \{\Delta\,\Delta \ldots (m+n) \text{ times}\} f(x) = \Delta^{m+n} f(x)$$

(iv) E and Δ are not commutative w.r.t. variables

i.e., if $u(x) = f(x)\,g(x)$

then $Eu(x) \neq f(x)\,Eg(x)$

and $\Delta u(x) \neq f(x)\,\Delta g(x)$

(v) $E[af(x) + bg(x)] = aEf(x) + bEg(x)$

(vi) $E\nabla \equiv \nabla E \equiv \Delta$

(vii) $E^0 f(x) = f(x)$

(viii) $E^{-n} f(x) = f(x - nh)$

(ix) $E^2 f(x) \neq \{Ef(x)\}^2$

(x) If $\Delta f(x) = 0$ then it does not mean that either $\Delta = 0$ or $f(x) = 0$

(xi) Operators E and Δ can not stand without operand.

(xii) $(1+\Delta)(1-\nabla) \equiv 1$ **[Meerut 2002, 2004; Rohilkhand 2003, 2007]**

Now, $(1+\Delta)(1-\nabla) f(x) = (1+\Delta)\{(1-\nabla) f(x)\}$

$$= (1+\Delta)\{f(x) - \nabla f(x)\}$$

$$= (1+\Delta)[f(x) - \{f(x) - f(x-h)\}]$$

$$= (1+\Delta) f(x-h)$$

$$= Ef(x-h) \qquad [\because \; E \equiv 1+\Delta]$$

$$= f(x) = 1.\, f(x).$$

$\Rightarrow$ $(1+\Delta)(1-\nabla) f(x) = 1.\, f(x), \forall\, f(x)$

$\Rightarrow$ $(1+\Delta)(1-\nabla) \equiv 1.$ Proved.

1.8 Relation Between Operator E of Finite Differences and Differential Coefficient D of Differential Calculus

[Rajasthan 2001, 2002, 2008; Bhopal 2007]

The operator Δ is an analogous to the operator D *i.e.* $\frac{d}{dx}$ of differential calculus. In calculus of finite differences, we deal with ratio of simultaneous increments of mutually dependent quantities whereas in differential calculus, we find the limit of such ratios when the increment tends to zero *i.e.*

$$\frac{d}{dx} f(x) = Df(x) = \lim_{h \to 0} \frac{f(x+h) - f(x)}{h}$$

Again by Taylor's theorem, we have

$$f(x+h) = f(x) + hf'(x) + \frac{h^2}{2!} f''(x) + \ldots = f(x) + hDf(x) + \frac{h^2}{2!} D^2 f(x) + \ldots$$

$$= \left(1 + hD + \frac{h^2}{2!} D^2 + \ldots\right) f(x) = e^{hD} f(x). \qquad \ldots(1)$$

From calculus of finite differences $f(x+h) = Ef(x)$. ...(2)

Hence from (1) and (2), $E \equiv e^{hD} \equiv 1 + \Delta$

or $$hD = \log(1+\Delta) = \left(\Delta - \frac{\Delta^2}{2} + \frac{\Delta^3}{3} - \ldots\right)$$

or $$D = \frac{1}{h}\left[\Delta - \frac{\Delta^2}{2} + \frac{\Delta^3}{3} - \ldots\right].$$

1.9 One or More Missing Terms

We may use either of the following two methods to find the values of the missing terms:

***Method* 1:** Suppose n values out of $(n+1)$ values of $y = f(x)$ are given for $(n+1)$ value of x, the values of x being equidistant. Let the unknown value be M. Now construct the difference table. Since only n values of y are known, we can assume $y = f(x)$ to be a polynomial of degree $(n-1)$ in x. Now equating to zero the nth difference we get the value of M.

***Method* 2:** In case, we know the value of the difference then

$$\Delta^n f(x) = \sum_{i=0}^{n} (-1)^{n-i}\, {}^nC_i f(x+ih),$$

can be used to estimate the missing terms. Let $f(x)$ be a polynomial of $(n-1)^{th}$ degree in x, thus $\Delta^n f(x) = 0$ for all x.

$$\therefore \quad \sum_{i=0}^{n} (-1)^{n-i}\, {}^nC_i f(x+ih) = 0$$

From this equation, we can find the value of the missing term.

1.10 Factorial Notation

The product of factors in which the first factor is x and the successive factors decrease by a constant difference is known as a factorial function and is denoted by $x^{(n)}$, where n is a positive integer. These functions play an important role in the theory of finite differences. With the help of these functions we can find the various order differences directly and by simple rule of differentiation.

$$x^{(n)} = x(x-1)(x-2)\ldots(x-\overline{n-1}) \quad \ldots(1)$$

[when the interval of differencing is unity.]

$$x^{(n)} = x(x-h)(x-2h)\ldots(x-\overline{n-1}h) \quad \ldots(2)$$

[when the interval of differencing is h.]

Again from (1)

$$x^{(n)} = \frac{x\,(x-1)\,(x-2)\ldots(x-\overline{n-1})\,(x-n)\,!}{(x-n)\,!} = \frac{x\,!}{(x-n)\,!}\,;\,(x>n).$$

To show that $\Delta^n x^{(n)} = n\,!\,h^n$ and $\Delta^{n+1}\, x^{(n)} = 0$.

$$\Delta\, x^{(n)} = (x+h)^{(n)} - x^{(n)}.$$

$$= (x+h)\,(x+h-h)\,(x+h-2h)\ldots(x+h-\overline{n-1}\,h)$$

$$-\,[x\,(x-h)\ldots(x-\overline{n-1}\,h)]$$

$$= (x+h)\,(x)\,(x-h)\ldots(x-\overline{n-2}\,h) - x\,(x-h)\ldots$$

$$(x-\overline{n-2}\,h)\,(x-\overline{n-1}\,h)$$

$$= x\,(x-h)\ldots(x-\overline{n-2}\,h)\,[(x+h)-(x-\overline{n-1}\,h]$$

$$= x^{(n-1)}\,[x+h-x+nh-h] = nh\,x^{(n-1)} \qquad \ldots(3)$$

or equivalently $\dfrac{\Delta\, x^{(n)}}{\Delta\, x} = n\,x^{(n-1)}$ (since $\Delta\, x = h$).

Again $\quad \Delta^2 x^{(n)} = \Delta\,.\,\Delta\, x^{(n)} = nh\,\Delta\, x^{(n-1)}$ from (3)

$$= nh\,\Delta\,[x\,(x-h)\ldots(x-\overline{n-2}\,h)]$$

$$= nh\,[(x+h)\,(x)\,(x-h)\ldots(x+h-\overline{n-2}\,h)]$$

$$-\,[x\,(x-h)\ldots(x-\overline{n-2}\,h)]$$

$$= nh\,[x\,(x-h)\ldots(x-\overline{n-3}\,h)\,(x+h\,x+\overline{n-2}\,h)]$$

$$= n\,(n-1)\,h^2\,x\,(x-h)\ldots(x-\overline{n-3}\,h)$$

$$= n\,(n-1)\,h^2\,x^{(n-2)}.$$

Proceeding in the same manner, we get

$$\Delta^{n-1}\, x^{(n)} = n\,(n-1)\ldots 2\,.\,h^{n-1}\,x.$$

$$\therefore \quad \Delta^n x^{(n)} = n\,(n-1)\ldots 2\,.\,h^{n-1}\,\Delta x$$

$$= n\,(n-1)\ldots 2\,.\,h^{n-1}\,(x+h-x)$$

$$= n\,(n-1)\ldots 2\,.1\,.\,h^n$$

or $\quad \Delta^n\, \mathbf{x}^{(n)} = (\mathbf{n})\,!\,\mathbf{h}^n. \qquad \ldots(4)$

Again $\Delta^{n+1}\, x^{(n)} = \Delta\,(n\,!\,h^n) = n\,!\,h^n - n\,!\,h^n = 0.$

In particular, when $h = 1$, we get from (4), $\Delta^n \mathbf{x}^{(n)} = \mathbf{n}\,!$

Note: From the above results, we observe that if a polynomial can be expressed in factorial notation then its various differences can be evaluated by simple rule of term by term differentiation.

1.10.1 To Show that $\left[x^{(-n)} = \dfrac{1}{(x+n)^{(n)}}\right]$ is the Interval of Differencing Being Unity

From the definition of $x^{(n)}$, we have

$$x^{(n)} = (x - \overline{n-1}\,h)\, x^{(n-1)} \qquad \ldots(1)$$

when the interval of differencing is h.

$\therefore$ when $n = 0$, we have $x^{(0)} = (x + h)\, x^{(-1)}$

Again $x^{(0)} = 1$.* $\quad \therefore \quad x^{(-1)} = \dfrac{1}{(x+h)}$

when $n = -1$, $\quad x^{(-1)} = (x + 2h)\, x^{(-2)}$ from (1)

or $\dfrac{1}{(x+h)} = (x + 2h)\, x^{(-2)}$

or $x^{(-2)} = \dfrac{1}{(x+h)(x+2h)}$.

In general $\quad x^{-(n)} = \dfrac{1}{(x+h)(x+2h)\ldots(x+nh)} = \dfrac{1}{(x+nh)^{(n)}}$. $\qquad \ldots(2)$

Here $x^{(-n)}$ is known as reciprocal factorial where n is a positive integer.

Particular Case: If $h = 1$

$$x^{(-n)} = \frac{1}{(x+1)(x+2)(x+3)\ldots(x+n)} = \frac{1}{(x+n)^{(n)}}.$$

Differences of Reciprocal Factorial **[Garhwal 2004, 2007]**

Again, $\Delta x^{(-n)} = (x + h)^{(-n)} - x^{(-n)}$

$$= \frac{1}{(x+2h)(x+3h)\ldots(x+\overline{n+1}\,h)} - \frac{1}{(x+h)(x+2h)\ldots(x+nh)}$$

[from (2)]

$$= \frac{1}{(x+2h)(x+3h)\ldots(x+nh)}\left[\frac{1}{(x+\overline{n+1}\,h)} - \frac{1}{(x+h)}\right]$$

---

* Since $\quad \Delta x^{(n)} = nhx^{(n-1)}$.

$\therefore$ When $n = 1 \Rightarrow \Delta x^{(1)} = hx^{(0)}$

Again $\quad \Delta x^{(1)} = \Delta x = h$

$x^{(0)} = 1$.

$$= -nh \frac{1}{(x+h)(x+2h)\ldots(x+\overline{n+1}\,h)}$$

$$= -nhx^{-\overline{(n+1)}} \qquad \text{i.e.} \quad \Delta x^{(-n)} = (-n)\, hx^{-(n+1)}$$

or equivalently $\dfrac{\Delta x^{(-n)}}{\Delta x} = -nx^{-\overline{(n+1)}}$ $(\because\ \Delta x = x + h - x = h)$

Similarly, $\Delta^2 x^{(-n)} = -\Delta[\Delta x^{(-n)}]$

$$= \Delta[-nh\, x^{-\overline{(n+1)}}] = -nh\, \Delta x^{-\overline{(n+1)}}$$

$$= (-nh)(-\overline{n+1})\, hx^{-\overline{(n+2)}}$$

$$= n(n+1)\, h^2 x^{-\overline{(n+2)}}$$

and so on.

In case the interval of differencing is unity, we have

$$x^{(n)} = \frac{x\,!}{(x-n)\,!} = \frac{n\,!}{n\,!} \cdot \frac{x\,!}{(x-n)\,!} = n\,!\ {}^{x}C_n \qquad \ldots(3)$$

Now $\Delta^r x^{(n)} = n(n-1)\ldots(n-\overline{r-1})\, x^{(n-r)}$

$$= n(n-1)\ldots(n-\overline{r-1})\,(n-r)\,!\ {}^{x}C_{n-r} \qquad \text{[from (3)]}$$

$$= n(n-1)\ldots(n-\overline{r-1})\,(n-r)\ldots 1\ {}^{x}C_{n-r}$$

$$= n\,!\ {}^{x}C_{n-r},$$

or $\Delta^r \dfrac{x^{(n)}}{n\,!} = {}^{x}C_{n-r}$, or $\Delta^r \dfrac{n\,!\ {}^{x}C_n}{n\,!} = {}^{x}C_{n-r}$ from (3)

or $\Delta^r \,.\, {}^{x}C_n = {}^{x}C_{n-r}$

Obviously $\Delta^n\, {}^{x}C_n = 1.$

Again, $x^{(r)}(x - rh)^{(n)} = x^{(n+r)}$

$$x^{(r)}(x-rh)^{(n)} = x(x-h)\ldots(x-\overline{r-1}\,h)(x-rh)^{(n)}$$

$$= x(x-h)\ldots(x-\overline{r-1}\,h)(x-rh)(x-rh-h)\ldots(x-rh-\overline{n-1}\,h$$

$$= x(x-h)\ldots(x-\overline{r+n-1}\,h) = x^{(n+r)}$$

If $h = 1$, then $\mathbf{x}^{(r)}(\mathbf{x} - \mathbf{r})^{(n)} = \mathbf{x}^{(n+r)}$.

This relation is known as ***exponential law of pseudo exponents.***

Example 3: *If m is any integer and c is any constant, show that*

(a) $\frac{\Delta}{\Delta x}[cx^{(n)}] = c\frac{\Delta}{\Delta x}x^{(n)} = ncx^{(n-1)}$ *(b)* $\Delta[cx^{(n)}] = c\,\Delta x^{(n)} = nchx^{(n-1)}$

[Himachal 2006, 2007]

Solution: Since Δ and $\frac{\Delta}{\Delta x}$ are linear operators, we have

$$\frac{\Delta}{\Delta x}[cx^{(n)}] = c\frac{\Delta x^{(n)}}{\Delta x} \text{ and } \Delta[cx^{(n)}] = c\,\Delta x^{(n)}$$

The results are derived by **1.10** and **1.10.1**.

Example 4: *Find values of*

(a) $\frac{\Delta}{\Delta x}[2x^{(5)}]$ *(b)* $\Delta[9x^{(4)}]$ *(c)* $\frac{\Delta}{\Delta x}[3x^{(2)}]$ *(d)* $\Delta[-5x^{(-4)}]$,

the interval of differencing is h.

Solution:

(a) $\frac{\Delta}{\Delta x}[2x^{(5)}] = 5.2\,x^{(4)} = 10\,x^{(4)} = 10\,x\,(x-h)\,(x-2h)\,(x-3h)$

(b) $\Delta[9\,x^{(4)}] = 4.9\,.hx^{(3)} = 36\,hx^{(3)} = 36\,hx\,(x-h)\,(x-2h)$

(c) $\frac{\Delta}{\Delta x}[3x^{(-2)}] = (-2).3x^{(-3)} = -6x^{(-3)} = \frac{-6}{(x+h)\,(x+2h)\,(x+3h)}$

(d) $\Delta[-5x^{(-4)}] = (-4).(-5)\,hx^{(-5)} = 20\,hx^{(-5)}$

$$= \frac{20h}{(x+h)\,(x+2h)\,(x+3h)\,(x+4h)\,(x+5h)}$$

Example 5: *Find the value of*

(a) $\frac{\Delta}{\Delta x}[3x^{(4)} - 2x^{(3)} - 3x^{(2)} + x - 5]$ *(b)* $\Delta\,2x^{(-2)} - 3x^{(3)} - 4x^{(-1)}]$

(c) $\frac{\Delta^2}{\Delta x^2}[3x^{(4)} - 5x^{(-2)}]$

Solution: Since Δ and $\frac{\Delta}{\Delta x}$ are linear operators, we have

(a) $\frac{\Delta}{\Delta x}[3x^{(4)} - 2x^{(3)} - 3x^{(2)} + x - 5] = 12x^{(3)} - 6x^{(2)} - 6x^{(1)} + 1$

(b) $\Delta[2x^{(-2)} - 3x^{(3)} - 4x^{(-1)}] = [-4x^{(-3)} - 9x^{(2)} + 4x^{(-2)}]\,h$

(c) $\frac{\Delta^2}{\Delta x^2}[3x^{(4)} - 5x^{(-2)}] = \frac{\Delta}{\Delta x}\frac{\Delta}{\Delta x}[3x^{(4)} - 5x^{(-2)}]$

$$= \frac{\Delta}{\Delta x}[12x^{(3)} + 10x^{(-3)}] = 36x^{(2)} - 30x^{(-4)}$$

1.10.2 Generalised Factorial Functions

To generalised factorial function corresponding to any given function $f(x)$ is defined by

$$[f(x)]^{(n)} = f(x)\, f(x-h)\, f(x-2h)\,.\, f(x-\overline{n-1}h),\ n=1,2,3,...$$

and $$[f(x)]^{(-n)} = \frac{1}{f(x+h)\, f(x+2h)\ldots f(x+nh)},\ n=1,2,3,...$$

Also $$[f(x)]^{(0)} = 1.$$

Example 6: *Show that, if $n=1,2,3,...$*

$$(ax+b)^n = (ax+b)(ax+b-ah)(ax+b-2ah)\ldots\ldots(ax+b-nah+ah)$$

Solution: By **1.10.2**, we have

$$[f(x)]^{(n)} = f(x)\, f(x-h)\, f(x-2h)\ldots + f(x-\overline{n-1}h).$$

Here $$f(x) = ax+b,$$

$\Rightarrow$ $$f(x-h) = a(x-h)+b = ax+b-ah$$

$$f(x-2h) = a(x-2h)+b = ax+b-2ah$$

....

$$f(x-\overline{n-1}h) = a[x-(n-1)h]+b$$
$$= ax+b-nah+ah$$

Putting these values, we get the required result.

Example 7: *Prove that*

$$(ax+b)^{(-n)} = \frac{1}{(ax+b+ah)(ax+b+2ah)\ldots(ax+b+nah)}$$

Solution: Apply **1.10.2**

$$[f(x)]^{(-n)} = \frac{1}{f(x+h)\,.\,f(x+2h)\ldots f(x+nh)}.$$

Now proceed as in Ex. 6

1.11 Methods of Representing any Given Polynomial in Factorial Notation

Example 8: *Express $2x^3-3x^2+3x-10$ and its differences in factorial notation, the interval of differencing being unity.*

Solution: 1. ***Direct Method***: Let

$$2x^3-3x^2+3x-10 = Ax^{(3)}+Bx^{(2)}+Cx^{(1)}+D$$
$$= Ax(x-1)(x-2)+Bx(x-1)+Cx+D \quad ...(1)$$

where A, B, C and D are constants to be found.

Putting $x = 0$ on both sides of (1), we get

$$D = -10.$$

Now putting $x = 1$ on both sides of (1), we get

$$2 - 3 + 3 - 10 = C + D \quad \text{i.e.} \quad C = 2.$$

Again putting $x = 2$, we have

$$16 - 12 + 6 - 10 = 2B + 2C + D$$

or $$0 = 2B - 6 \quad \text{i.e.} \quad B = 3.$$

By equating the coefficients of x^2 on both sides of (1), we get

$$A = 2.$$

Hence the required polynomial in factorial notation will be

$$f(x) = 2x^{(3)} + 3x^{(2)} + 2x^{(1)} - 10.$$

Again by the rule of simple differentiation, we have

$$\Delta f(x) = 6x^{(2)} + 6x + 2$$

$$\Delta^2 f(x) = 12x + 6$$

and $$\Delta^3 f(x) = 12.$$

2. ***Method of Detached Coefficients or Synthetic Division.***

Represent $2x^3 - 3x^2 + 3x - 10$ in factorial notation

i.e. $$f(x) = 2x^3 - 3x^2 + 3x - 10 = Ax^{(3)} + Bx^{(2)} + Cx^{(1)} + D$$

$$= Ax(x-1)(x-2) + Bx(x-1) + Cx + D$$

In case we divide the function $f(x)$ by x. Then the remainder will be -10 and the quotient will be $2x^2 - 3x + 3$.

$$\therefore \quad D = -10.$$

Now divide the quotient by $(x - 1)$ *i.e.*

$$\begin{array}{r l} & \quad 2x - 1 \\ (x-1) \,) & \overline{2x^2 - 3x + 3} \\ & 2x^2 - 2x \\ \hline & \quad -x + 3 \\ & \quad -x + 1 \\ \hline & \qquad 2 \end{array}$$

In this case quotient is $(2x - 1)$ and remainder $2 = C$. Again divide $(2x - 1)$ *by* $(x - 2)$

$$\begin{array}{r l} & \qquad 2 \\ (x-2) \,) & \overline{2x - 1} \\ & 2x - 4 \\ \hline & \qquad 3 \end{array}$$

The quotient $2 = A$ and the remainder $3 = B$. Hence the required polynomial will be

$$2x^{(3)} + 3x^{(2)} + 2x - 10$$

We can simplify the above method by the procedure of detached coefficients in the following way:

Taking the coefficients of various powers of x in $f(x)$, we have

1	2	-3	3	$-10 = D$	...(*a*)
	0	2	-1		
2	2	-1	$2 = C$		...(*b*)
	0	4			
3	2	$3 = B$			...(*c*)
	0				
	$2 = A$				

The following steps are to be followed in the method of detached coefficients:

1. Put the coefficients of different powers of x in order beginning with the coefficients of higher power of x.
2. Put 1 in the left hand side column and write zero below the coefficients of highest power of x; in this case we have written 0 below 2 which is coefficient of x^3.
3. Now multiply 2 by 1 and 0 by 1, add them to get the sum 2, put 2 below -3 as given in (*a*). Now multiply -3 by 1 and 2 by 1 and add them to get the sum -1 which is to be written below 3. The remainder -10 is the value of D.
4. Add the terms of corresponding columns of (*a*) and get $2, -1$ and 2 of (*b*).
5. Now again apply the steps (1) and (3); in this way we get $(2 \times 2) + (0 \times 2) = 4$ which is to be written below -1. The remainder 2 of (*b*) is equal to C.
6. Apply step (4) on (b) and get 2 and 3 of (*c*).
7. Again apply the steps (2), (3) and (4) to get 2 which will be equal to A and remainder 3 of (*c*) which will be equal to B.

1.12 Differences of Zero

If n and m be positive integers we have in usual notation of finite difference calculus

$$\Delta^n x^m = (E-1)^n x^m$$

$$= E^n - {}^nc_1 E^{n-1} + {}^nc_2 E^{n-2} - \ldots + (-1)^{n-1} {}^nc_{n-1} E + (-1)^n] x^m$$

$$= (x+n)^m - {}^nc_1 (x+n-1)^m + {}^nc_2 (x+n-2)^m - \ldots$$

$$\ldots + {}^nc_{(n-1)} (-1)^{n-1} (x+1)^m + (-1)^n x^m$$

(Interval of differencing being unity)

Putting $x = 0$, we have

$$[\Delta^n x^m]_{x=0} = n^m - {}^nc_1 (n-1)^m + {}^nc_2 (n-2)^m - \ldots$$

$$\ldots + {}^nc_{n-1} (-1)^{n-1} \qquad \ldots(1)$$

The expression $[\Delta^n x^m]_{x=0}$ is written as $\Delta^n 0^m$. The quantities $\Delta^n 0^m$ are known as ***differences of zero*** because the leading term is always zero.

We can calculate the values of $\Delta^n 0^m$ for various integral values of n and m.

e. g. if $n = 3, m = 4$, we have from (1)

$$\Delta^3 0^4 = 3^4 - 3.2^4 + 3.1^4 = 36$$

If $\quad n = 1,\ m = 1, \quad \Delta 0^2 = 1^3 = 1$

$n = 2, m = 3, \quad \Delta^2 0^3 = 2^3 - 2.1^3 = 6$

$n = 3, m = 3, \quad \Delta^3 0^3 = 3^3 - 3.2^3 + 3.1^3 = 6$, etc.

We observe that $\quad \Delta^n 0^n = [\Delta^n x^n]_{x=0} = [n!]_{(x=0)} = n!$

Again $\quad \Delta^n x^m = 0$ for $n > m$, therefore

$$\Delta^n 0^m = [\Delta^n x^m]_{(x=0)} = \{0\}_{x=0} = 0, \quad \text{whenever } n > m.$$

1.12.1 Recurrence Relation between $\Delta^n 0^m, \Delta^{n-1} 0^{m-1}$ and $\Delta^n 0^{m-1}$ [Avadh 2004]

From (1) of 1.12, we have

$$\Delta^n 0^m = n^m - {}^nc_1 (n-1)^m + {}^nc_2 (n-2)^m - \ldots + {}^nc_{n-1} (-1)^{n-1}$$

$$= n^m - n(n-1)^m + \frac{n(n-1)}{2!}(n-2)^m - \ldots + n(-1)^{n-1}$$

$$= n\left[n^{m-1} - (n-1)^m + \frac{(n-1)(n-2)^m}{2!} - \ldots + (-1)^{n-1}\right]$$

$$= n\left[n^{m-1} - (n-1)(n-1)^{m-1} + \frac{(n-1)(n-2)}{2!}(n-2)^{m-1} - \ldots + (-1)^{n-1}\right]$$

$$= n[(1+n-1)^{m-1} - {}^{(n-1)}c_1 (n-1)^{m-1} + {}^{(n-1)}c_2 (n-2)^{m-1} - \ldots + (-1)^{n-1}]$$

$$= n[(1+n-1)^{m-1} - {}^{(n-1)}c_1 (1+n-2)^{m-1} + {}^{(n-1)}c_2 (1+n-3)^{n-1} - \ldots + (-1)^{n-1}]$$

$$= n\,[E^{n-1}\,(1)^{m-1} - {}^{(n-1)}c_1\, E^{n-2}\,(1)^{m-1} + {}^{(n-1)}c_2\, E^{n-3}\,(1)^{m-1} - \ldots + (-1)^{n-1}\,(1)^{m-1}]$$

$$= n\,[E-1]^{n-1}\,(1)^{m-1} = n\,\Delta^{n-1}\,(1)^{m-1} \qquad [\because\ (1)^{m-1} = 1]$$

$$= n\,\Delta^{n-1}\ E(0)^{m-1} \qquad [\because\ E(0) = 1]$$

$$= n\,\Delta^{n-1}\,(1+\Delta)\,0^{m-1} = n\,[\Delta^{n-1}\,0^{m-1} + \Delta^{n}\,0^{m-1}]$$

This is the required recurrence relation between differeces of zero for different values of n and m.

Example 9: *Prove that* $\Delta^n\,0^{n+1} = \dfrac{n\,(n+1)}{2}\,\Delta^n\,0^n$.

Solution: We know that $\Delta^n 0^m = n\,[\Delta^{n-1}\,0^{m-1} + \Delta^n 0^{m-1}]$,

$$\therefore \quad \Delta^n\,0^{n+1} = n\,[\Delta^{n-1}\,0^n + \Delta^n\,0^n]$$

$$\Rightarrow \quad \Delta^{n-1}\,0^n = (n-1)\,[\Delta^{n-2}\,0^{n-1} + \Delta^{n-1}\,0^{n-1}]$$

$$\Rightarrow \quad \Delta^{n-2}\,0^{n-1} = (n-2)\,[\Delta^{n-3}\,0^{n-2} + \Delta^{n-2}\,0^{n-2}]$$

$$\ldots \quad \ldots \quad \ldots \quad \ldots \quad \ldots \quad \ldots \quad \ldots \quad \ldots$$

$$\ldots \quad \ldots \quad \ldots \quad \ldots \quad \ldots \quad \ldots \quad \ldots \quad \ldots$$

$$\Rightarrow \quad \Delta^2\,0^3 = 2\,[\Delta\,0^2 + \Delta^2\,0^2]$$

$$\Rightarrow \quad \Delta\,0^2 = 1\,[\Delta^0\,0^1 + \Delta^1\,0^1].$$

By back substitution of these values, we immediately obtain,

$$\Delta^n 0^{n+1} = n\,\Delta^n\,0^n + n(n-1)\,\Delta^{n-1}0^{n-1} + n\,(n-1)\,(n-2)\,\Delta^{n-2}\,0^{n-2} + \ldots + n\,(n-1)\,(n-2)\ldots 2\,.1\,\Delta^1 0^1$$

$$= nn! + n\,(n-1)\,(n-1)\,! + n\,(n-1)\,(n-2)\,(n-2)\,! + \ldots\ldots + n\,(n-1)\,(n-2)\ldots 2\,.1.1!$$

$$= n\,!\,\{n + (n-1) + (n-2) + \ldots + 2 + 1\}$$

$$= n\,!\,.\frac{n\,(n+1)}{2} = \frac{n\,(n+1)}{2}\,.\,\Delta^n\,0^n. \qquad [\because\ \Delta^n\,0^n = n\,!]$$

1.13 Leibnitz's Rule

We have studied Leibnitz's rule for finding n^{th} derivative of the product of two functions u and v as

$$D^n\,(uv) = n\,D^n\,(v) + {}^nC_1\,(Du)\,D^{n-1}\,(v) + {}^nC_2\,(D^2\,u)\,D^{n-2}\,(v) + \ldots + {}^nC_n\,(D^n u)\,v\,.$$

An analogous formula exists for differences and is given by

$$\Delta^n(uv) = u\Delta^n\,(v) + {}^nC_1\,(\Delta u)\,(\Delta^{n-1}\,Ev) + {}^nC_2\,(\Delta^2 u)\,(\Delta^{n-2}\,E^2 v) + \ldots + {}^nC_n\,(\Delta^n\,u\,E^n v)$$

This rule is called ***Leibnitz's rule*** for differences.

Example 10: *Use Leibnitz's rule for finding $\Delta^3 (x^2\ a^x)$ if interval of differencing is h.*

Solution: Here $u = x^2$ and $v = a^x$, by Leibnitz's rule

$$\Delta^3 (x^2\ a^x) = x^2\ \Delta^3\ (a^x) + {}^3C_1\ (\Delta x^2)\ [(\Delta^3\ E\,a^x)]$$

$$+ {}^3C_2\ (\Delta^2\ x^2)\ [\Delta\ E^2\ (a^x)] + {}^3C_3\ (\Delta^3\ x^2)\ [(E^3\ (a^x))]$$

$$= x^2\ a^x\ (a^h - 1)^3\ + 3\ (2hx + h^2)\ a^{x+h}\ (a^h - 1)^2 + 3\ (2h^2)\ a^{x+2h}\ (a^h - 1).$$

1.14 Effect of an Error in a Tabular Value

Let $y_0, y_1, y_2, \ldots, y_n$ be the true values of any function y and let the value y_5 be affected with an error ε so that its erroneous value becomes $y_5 + \varepsilon$. Now the successive differences of y's are as given below.

Data showing the effect of an error in the tabular values

y	Δy	$\Delta^2 y$	$\Delta^3 y$	$\Delta^4 y$
y_0				
	Δy_0			
y_1		$\Delta^2 y_0$		
	Δy_1		$\Delta^3 y_0$	
y_2		$\Delta^2 y_1$		$\Delta^4 y_0$
	Δy_2		$\Delta^3 y_1$	
y_3		$\Delta^2 y_2$		$\Delta^4 y_1 + \varepsilon$
	Δy_3		$\Delta^3 y_2 + \varepsilon$	
y_4		$\Delta^2 y_3 + \varepsilon$		$\Delta^4 y_2 - 4\varepsilon$
	$\Delta y_4 + \varepsilon$		$\Delta^3 y_3 - 3\varepsilon$	
$y_5 + \varepsilon$		$\Delta^2 y_4 - 2\varepsilon$		$\Delta^4 y_3 + 6\varepsilon$
	$\Delta y_5 - \varepsilon$		$\Delta^3 y_4 + 3\varepsilon$	
y_6		$\Delta^2 y_5 + \varepsilon$		$\Delta^4 y_4 - 4\varepsilon$
	Δy_6		$\Delta^3 y_5 - \varepsilon$	
y_7		$\Delta^2 y_6$		$\Delta^4 y_5 + \varepsilon$
	Δy_7		$\Delta^3 y_6$	
y_8		$\Delta^2 y_7$		$\Delta^4 y_6$
	Δy_8		$\Delta^3 y_7$	
y_9		$\Delta^2 y_8$		
	Δy_9			
y_{10}				

From this table we see that the effect of an error increases with the successive differences; the coefficients of the ε's are the binomial coefficient with alternating signs; the algebraic sum of the errors in any difference column is zero and the maximum error in the differences is in the same horizontal line as the erroneous tabular value.

Example 11: *Find and correct by means of differences the error in the following table.*

$$20736, 28561, 38416, 50625, 65540, 83521, 104976, 130321, 160000.$$

Solution: **Difference table for the given data.**

y	Δy	$\Delta^2 y$	$\Delta^3 y$	$\Delta^4 y$	$\Delta^5 y$
20736					
	7825				
28561		2030			
	9855		324		
38416		2354		28	
	12209		352		−20
50625		2706		8	
	14915		360		40
65540		3066		48	
	17981		408		−40
83521		3474		8	
	21455		416		20
104976		3890		28	
	24345		444		
130321		4334			
	29679				
160000					

From here, it is obvious that the pattern of departure in third differences is quite irregular and the irregularity starts around the horizontal line corresponding to the value $y = 65540$. But we see that the algebraic sum of the fifth differences is 0, so the fifth differences found in this example are accumulated in errors.

$$\Rightarrow \qquad -5\varepsilon = -20 \quad \Rightarrow \varepsilon = 4.$$

$\Rightarrow$ true value of $y_5 = 65540 - 4 = 65536$.

Example 12: *Construct a forward difference table:*

x:	0	5	10	15	20	25
$f(x)$:	7	11	14	18	24	32

Solution:

x	$y = f(x)$	$\Delta f(x)$	$\Delta^2 f(x)$	$\Delta^3 f(x)$	$\Delta^4 f(x)$	$\Delta^5 f(x)$
0	7					
		4				
5	11		−1			
		3		2		
10	14		1		−1	
		4		1		0
15	18		2		−1	
		6		0		
20	24		2			
		8				
25	32					

Example 13: *Evaluate* **(a)** $\Delta^3 (1-x)(1-2x)(1-3x)$, **(b)** $\Delta^n (e^{ax+b})$, *the interval of differencing being unity.* **[Bangaluru 2002, 2005]**

Solution: (a) Here $f(x) = (1-x)(1-2x)(1-3x)$

$$= -6x^3 + 11x^2 - 6x + 1$$

i.e. $f(x)$ is a polynomial in x of degree of 3

$$\therefore \quad \Delta^3 f(x) = (-6)(3!) = -36$$

(b) $\Delta(e^{ax+b}) = f(x+1) - f(x)$ where $f(x) = e^{ax+b}$

$$= e^{a(x+1)+b} - e^{ax+b} = [e^{ax+b}(e^a - 1)],$$

$$\Delta^2 (e^{ax+b}) = \Delta(\Delta e^{ax+b}) = \Delta[e^{ax+b}(e^a - 1)],$$

$$= e^{a(x+1)+b}(e^a - 1) - e^{ax+b}(e^a - 1)$$

$$= e^{ax+b}(e^a - 1)^2.$$

Proceeding like this, we get $\Delta^n (e^{ax+b}) = e^{ax+b}(e^a - 1)^n$.

Example 14: *Prove that* $e^x = \left(\frac{\Delta^2}{E}\right) e^x \cdot \frac{Ee^x}{\Delta^2 e^x}$; *the interval of differencing being h.*

[Meerut 2003; Rajasthan 2002, 2009]

Solution: We know that $Ef(x) = f(x+h)$; $\therefore \quad Ee^x = e^{x+h}$.

Again $\quad \Delta e^x = e^{x+h} - e^x = e^x (e^h - 1), \Delta^2 e^x = e^x (e^h - 1)^2$,

$$\therefore \quad \left(\frac{\Delta^2}{E}\right) e^x = (\Delta^2 E^{-1}) e^x = \Delta^2 e^{x-h} = e^{-h} \Delta^2 e^x = e^{-h} \cdot e^x (e^h - 1)^2$$

$$\therefore \quad \text{R.H.S.} = e^{-h} \cdot e^x (e^h - 1)^2 \cdot \frac{e^{x+h}}{e^x (e^h - 1)^2} = e^x .$$

Example 15: *Evaluate* $\left(\frac{\Delta^2}{E}\right) x^3$.

[Meerut 2007]

Solution: $\left(\frac{\Delta^2}{E}\right) x^3 = \left[\frac{(E-1)^2}{E}\right] x^3 = \left(\frac{E^2 - 2E + 1}{E}\right) x^3$

$$= \left(E - 2 + \frac{1}{E}\right) x^3 = Ex^3 - 2x^3 + E^{-1} x^3$$

$$= (x+1)^3 - 2x^3 + (x-1)^3$$

$$= x^3 + 3x^2 + 3x + 1 - 2x^3 + x^3 - 3x^2 + 3x - 1 = 6x .$$

Example 16: *Evaluate* $\Delta^2 (\cos 2x)$.

[Meerut 2006; U.P.P.C.S. 2006]

Solution: $\Delta^2 \cos 2x = (E-1)^2 \cos 2x = (E^2 - 2E + 1) \cos 2x$

$$= E^2 \cos 2x - 2E \cos 2x + \cos 2x$$

$$= E \cos 2(x+h) - 2 \cos 2(x+h) + \cos 2x$$

$$= \cos \{2(x+2h)\} - 2 \cos \{2(x+h)\} + \cos 2x$$

$$= \cos (2x+4h) - \cos (2x+2h) - \cos (2x+2h) + \cos 2x$$

$$= 2 \sin (2x+3h) \sin (-h) + \{2 \sin (2x+h) \sin h\}$$

$$= 2 \sin h [\sin (2x+3h) - \sin (2x+h)]$$

$$= -2 \sin h [2 \cos (2x+2h) \sin h]$$

$$= -4 \sin^2 h \cos (2x+2h) .$$

Example 17: *Evaluate* $\Delta^2 (3e^x)$.

[U.P.P.C.S. 2004]

Solution: $\Delta (3e^x) = 3 (\Delta e^x) = 3 (e^{x+h} - e^x) = 3e^x (e^h - 1)$

$$\therefore \quad \Delta^2 (e^x) = \Delta \{3e^x (e^h - 1)\} = 3 (e^h - 1) (\Delta e^x)$$

$$= 3 (e^h - 1) (e^{x+h} - e^x) = 3 (e^h - 1)^2 e^x .$$

Example 18: *Evaluate* $\Delta (x + \cos x)$; *the interval of differencing is* α.

Solution: $\Delta (x + \cos x) = \Delta x + \Delta \cos x = (E - 1) x + (E - 1) \cos x$

$$= \{(x + \alpha) - x\} + \{\cos (x + \alpha) - \cos x\}$$

$$= \alpha + 2 \sin \left(\frac{2x + \alpha}{2}\right) \sin \left(-\frac{\alpha}{2}\right)$$

$$= \alpha - 2 \sin \left(x + \frac{\alpha}{2}\right) \sin \frac{\alpha}{2}.$$

Example 19: *Evaluate* $\Delta \tan^{-1} x.$,

[Patna 2006]

Solution: $\Delta \tan^{-1} x = \tan^{-1} (x + h) - \tan^{-1} x = \tan^{-1} \left\{\frac{(x + h) - x}{1 + (x + h) x}\right\} = \tan^{-1} \left[\frac{h}{1 + hx + x^2}\right].$

Example 20: *Show that* $\Delta \log f (x) = \log \left\{1 + \frac{\Delta f (x)}{f (x)}\right\}.$

[Rajasthan 2001, 2005; Bangaluru 2007]

Solution: $\Delta \log f (x) = \log f (x + h) - \log f (x)$

$$= \log \left[\frac{f (x + h)}{f (x)}\right] = \log \left[\frac{Ef (x)}{f (x)}\right]$$

$$= \log \left[\frac{(1 + \Delta) f (x)}{f (x)}\right] = \log \left[\frac{f (x) + \Delta f (x)}{f (x)}\right]$$

$$= \log \left[1 + \frac{\Delta f (x)}{f (x)}\right].$$

Example 21: *Evaluate* $\Delta^n [ax^n + bx^{n-1}]$.

Solution: $\Delta^n [ax^n + bx^{n-1}] = \Delta^n (ax^n) + b \Delta^n (x^{n-1})$

$$= a (n!) + b . 0$$

$$= a (n!).$$

Example 22: *Evaluate* $\Delta^{10}\,[(1-ax)(1-bx^2)(1-cx^3)(1-dx^4)]$.

Solution: By **1.4** for a polynomial of nth degree, $\Delta^r\, f(x)=0$ for $r>n$.

$$\therefore \quad \Delta^{10}\,[(1-ax)(1-bx^2)(1-cx^3)(1-dx^4)]=\Delta^{10}\,(abcd\; x^{10})$$

$$=abcd\;\Delta^{10}\,x^{10}=abcd\;(10\,!)$$

Example 23: *Evaluate*

(*a*) $\Delta\left(\dfrac{1}{1+x^2}\right)$ (*b*) $\Delta^2\left[\dfrac{5x+12}{x^2+5x+6}\right]$ **[Meerut 2001]**

(*c*) $\Delta^n\left(\dfrac{1}{x}\right)$ (*d*) $\Delta^n\,(ab^{cx})$.

Solution: (a) $\Delta\left(\dfrac{1}{1+x^2}\right)=\dfrac{1}{1+(x+1)^2}-\dfrac{1}{1+x^2}$ (taking $h=1$)

$$=\frac{(1+x^2)-\{1+(x+1)^2\}}{(1+x^2)\{1+(x+1)^2\}}=\frac{(1+x^2)-2-x^2-2x}{(1+x^2)\{1+(x+1)^2\}}=-\frac{(1+2x)}{(1+x^2)\{1+(x+1)^2\}}$$

(b) $$\Delta^2\left[\frac{5x+12}{x^2+5x+6}\right]=\Delta^2\left[\frac{2(x+3)+3(x+2)}{(x+2)(x+3)}\right]$$

$$=\Delta^2\left[\frac{2}{x+2}+\frac{3}{x+3}\right]=\Delta\,.\,\Delta\left[\frac{2}{x+2}+\frac{3}{x+3}\right] \quad ...(1)$$

Now $$\Delta\left[\frac{2}{x+2}+\frac{3}{x+3}\right]=\left[\frac{2}{x+3}-\frac{2}{x+2}\right]+\left[\frac{3}{x+4}-\frac{3}{x+3}\right]$$

$$=-\frac{2}{(x+2)(x+3)}-\frac{3}{(x+4)(x+3)}$$

$\therefore$ From (1),

$$\Delta^2\left[\frac{5x+12}{x^2+5x+6}\right]=\Delta\left[-\frac{2}{(x+2)(x+3)}-\frac{3}{(x+4)(x+3)}\right]$$

$$=-2\left[\frac{1}{(x+3)(x+4)}-\frac{1}{(x+2)(x+3)}\right]-3\left[\frac{1}{(x+5)(x+4)}-\frac{1}{(x+4)(x+3)}\right]$$

$$=-2\left[\frac{(x+2)-(x+4)}{(x+2)(x+3)(x+4)}\right]-3\left[\frac{(x+3)-(x+5)}{(x+3)(x+4)(x+5)}\right]$$

$$=\frac{4}{(x+2)(x+3)(x+4)}+\frac{6}{(x+3)(x+4)(x+5)}$$

(c) $\Delta^n\left(\frac{1}{x}\right) = \Delta^{n-1}\,\Delta\left(\frac{1}{x}\right)$

Now $\Delta\left(\frac{1}{x}\right) = \frac{1}{x+1} - \frac{1}{x} = -\frac{1}{x\,(x+1)}$

Again $\Delta^2\left(\frac{1}{x}\right) = \frac{(-1)^2\,2\,!}{x\,(x+1)\,(x+2)}$ and so on,

... ...

$\therefore$ $\Delta^n\left(\frac{1}{x}\right) = \frac{(-1)^n\,n\,!}{x\,(x+1)\,(x+2)\ldots(x+n)}$

(d) $\Delta^n\,(ab^{cx}) = \Delta^{n-1}\,\Delta\,(ab^{cx})$.

Now $\Delta\,(ab^{cx}) = ab^{c\,(x+1)} - ab^{cx} = ab^{cx}\,(b^c - 1)$

$\therefore$ $\Delta^2\,(ab^{cx}) = \Delta\,\{(ab^{cx})\,(b^c - 1)\}$

$= (b^c - 1)^2\,ab^{cx}$ and so on.

$\therefore$ $\Delta^n\,(ab^{cx}) = (b^c - 1)^n\,ab^{cx}$.

Example 24: *Evaluate* $\Delta^n \log ax$ **[Patna 2007, 2009]**

Solution: We have $\Delta \log ax = \log a\,(x+h) - \log ax$ ...(1)

$\therefore$ $\Delta^2 \log ax = \Delta\,[\Delta \log ax]$

$= \Delta\,[\log a\,(x+h) - \log ax]$

$= \Delta \log a\,(x+h) - \Delta \log ax$

$= \log\,[a\,(x+2h) - \log a\,(x+h)] - [\log a\,(x+h) - \log ax]$

$= \log a\,(x+2h) - 2\log a\,(x+h) + \log ax$ ...(2)

From (1) and (2), we observe that the relation

$\Delta^n \log ax = \log a\,(x+nh) - nC_1 \log a\,(x+\overline{n-1}\,h) + \ldots$ ...(3)

is true for $n = 1, 2$.

We shall prove that relation (3) is true for all positive integral values of *n*.

Now $\Delta^{n+1} \log ax = \Delta\,[\Delta^n \log ax]$

$= \Delta \log a\,(x+nh) - {}^nC_1\,\Delta \log a\,(x+\overline{n-1}\,h)$

$+ \ldots + (-1)^r\,{}^nC_r\,\Delta \log a\,(x+\overline{n-r}\,h) + \ldots + (-1)^n\,\Delta \log ax$

$$= \log [a(x + \overline{n+1}\,h) - \log a(x + nh)]$$
$$- {}^nC_1 [\log a(x + nh) - \log a(x + \overline{n-1}\,h)] + \ldots$$
$$+ (-1)^r\, {}^nC_r [\log a(x + \overline{n-r+1}\,h)$$
$$- \log a(x + \overline{n-r}\,h)]$$
$$+ \ldots + (-1)^n \log [a(x + h) - \log ax]$$

$$= \log a(x + \overline{n+1}\,h) - (1 + {}^nC_1) \log a(x + nh) + \ldots$$
$$+ (-1)^r [{}^nC_{r-1} + {}^nC_r] \log a(x + \overline{n-r+1}\,h) + \ldots$$
$$+ (-1)^{n+1} \log ax$$

$$= \log a(x + \overline{n+1}\,h) - {}^{(n+1)}C_1 \log a(x + nh) + \ldots$$
$$+ (-1)^r\, {}^{n+1}C_r \log a(x + \overline{n-r+1}\,h) + \ldots$$
$$+ (-1)^{n+1} \log ax \qquad \ldots(4)$$

$$(\because\ {}^nC_r + {}^nC_{r+1} = {}^{n+1}C_{r+1})$$

From (4), We observe that relation (3) is true for $n + 1$.

Since (3) is true for $n = 1, 2$, so it is true for all positive integral values of n.

Example 25: Evaluate ***(a)*** $\Delta(e^{ax} \log bx)$ ***(b)*** $\Delta\left(\frac{x^2}{\cos 2x}\right)$ ***(c)*** $\Delta\left[\frac{2^x}{(x+1)!}\right]; (h = 1)$

[Rajasthan 2002, 2007]

Solution: (a) Take $f(x) = e^{ax}$ and $g(x) = \log bx$

Now $\quad \Delta f(x) = f(x + h) - f(x)$

i.e., $\quad \Delta e^{ax} = e^{a(x+h)} - e^{ax} = e^{ax}(e^{ah} - 1)$

Also $\quad \Delta g(x) = g(x + h) - g(x) = \log b(x + h) - \log bx$

$$= \log\left(1 + \frac{h}{x}\right)$$

Again we know that

$$\Delta f(x)\, g(x) = f(x + h)\, \Delta g(x) + g(x)\, \Delta f(x)$$

On putting the values of $f(x)$ and $g(x)$, we have

$$\Delta(e^{ax} \log bx) = e^{a(x+h)} \log\left(1 + \frac{h}{x}\right) + (\log bx)\, e^{ax}(e^{ah} - 1)$$

$$= e^{ax}\left[e^{ah} \log\left(1 + \frac{h}{x}\right) + (e^{ah} - 1) \log bx\right]$$

(b) Take $f(x) = x^2$ and $g(x) = \cos 2x$

$$\therefore \quad \Delta f(x) = f(x+h) - f(x) = (x+h)^2 - x^2 = h(2x+h)$$

and
$$\Delta g(x) = g(x+h) - g(x) = \cos 2(x+h) - \cos 2x$$
$$= -2 \sin(2x+h) \sin h$$

We know that $\Delta\left[\frac{f(x)}{g(x)}\right] = \frac{g(x)\,\Delta f(x) - f(x)\,\Delta g(x)}{g(x+h)\,g(x)}$

Putting the values of $f(x)$ and $g(x)$, we have

$$\Delta\left[\frac{f(x)}{g(x)}\right] = \frac{(\cos 2x)\,h(2x+h) - x^2\,[-2\sin h \sin(2x+h)]}{\cos(2x+2h)\cos 2x}$$

$$= \frac{h(2x+h)\cos 2x + 2x^2 \sin h \sin(2x+h)}{\cos(2x+2h)\cos 2x}$$

(c) Take $f(x) = 2^x$ and $g(x) = (x+1)\,!$

$$\therefore \quad \Delta f(x) = 2^{x+1} - 2^x = 2^x(2-1) = 2^x \qquad \text{(taking } h = 1)$$

and
$$\Delta g(x) = (x+1+1)\,! - (x+1)\,! = (x+2)\,! - (x+1)\,!$$
$$= (x+1)\,!\,(x+2) - (x+1)\,!$$
$$= (x+1)\,!\,(x+1)$$

Again
$$\Delta\left[\frac{f(x)}{g(x)}\right] = \frac{g(x)\,\Delta f(x) - f(x)\,\Delta g(x)}{g(x+h)\,g(x)}$$
$$= \frac{(x+1)\,!\,2^x - (x+1)\,!\,2^x\,(x+1)}{(x+2)\,!\,(x+1)\,!}$$
$$= \frac{(x+1)\,!\,2^x\,\{1-(x+1)\}}{(x+2)\,!\,(x+1)\,!} = -\frac{x}{(x+2)\,!}\,2^x$$

Example 26: *Show that* $\sum_{k=0}^{n-1} \Delta^2 f_k = \Delta f_n - \Delta f_0$. **[Meerut 2003]**

Solution: We have L.H.S. $\sum_{k=0}^{n-1} \Delta^2 f_k = \sum_{k=0}^{n-1} (E-1)^2 f_k$

$$(\because \ \Delta \equiv E - 1)$$

$$= \sum_{k=0}^{n-1} (E^2 - 2E + 1)\,f_k = \sum_{k=0}^{n-1} (f_{k+2} - 2f_{k+1} + f_k)$$

$$= (f_2 - 2f_1 + f_0) + (f_3 - 2f_2 + f_1)$$
$$+ (f_4 - 2f_3 + f_2) + (f_5 - 2f_4 + f_3)$$
$$\ldots\ldots\ldots\ldots\ldots\ldots\ldots\ldots$$
$$+ (f_{n-1} - 2f_{n-2} + f_{n-3})$$
$$+ (f_n - 2f_{n-1} + f_{n-2}) + (f_{n+1} - 2f_n + f_{n-1})$$
$$= f_{n+1} - f_n + f_0 - f_1, \text{ adding and cancelling the diagonal terms}$$
$$= (f_{n+1} - f_n) - (f_1 - f_0) = \Delta f_n - \Delta f_0 = \text{R.H.S. } \textbf{Proved.}$$

Example 27: *Show that* $\Delta^r y_k = \nabla^r y_{k+r}$.

[Kurukshetra 2006]

Solution: $\nabla^r y_{k+r} = (1 - E^{-1})^r y_{k+r}$ $[\because \nabla \equiv 1 - E^{-1}]$

$$= \left(\frac{E-1}{E}\right)^r y_{k+r} \qquad (\because E^{-1} \equiv 1/E)$$
$$= (E-1)^r E^{-r} y_{k+r}$$
$$= (E-1)^r (E^{-r} y_{k+r})$$
$$= (E-1)^r y_{k+r-r}$$
$$= (E-1)^r y_k = \Delta^r y_k.$$

Example 28: *Use the method of separation of symbols to prove the following identities*

(a) $u_x = u_{x-1} + \Delta u_{x-2} + \Delta^2 u_{x-3} + \ldots + \Delta^{n-1} u_{x-n} + \Delta^n u_{x-n}$.

[Delhi (H) 2001, 2005, 2009]

(b) $u_0 + {}^xC_1 \Delta u_1 + {}^xC_2 \Delta^2 u_2 + \ldots$

$$= u_x + {}^xC_1 \Delta^2 u_{x-1} + {}^xC_2 \Delta^4 u_{x-2} + \ldots$$

(c) $u_1 x + u_2 x^2 + u_3 x^3 + \ldots$

$$= \frac{x}{1-x} u_1 + \frac{x^2}{(1-x)^2} \Delta u_1 + \frac{x^3}{(1-x)^3} \Delta^2 u_1 + \ldots$$

where $y = u_x$ *is any function of x and* $0 < x < 1$.

[Agra 2005; Rajasthan 2002, 2006]

Solution: (a) $u_x - \Delta^n u_{x-n} = u_x - \Delta^n E^{-n} u_x = (1 - \Delta^n E^{-n}) u_x$

$$= \left[1 - \frac{\Delta^n}{E^n}\right] u_x = \frac{E^n - \Delta^n}{E^n} u_x = \frac{1}{E^n}\left[\frac{E^n - \Delta^n}{E - \Delta}\right] u_x \qquad \left\{\begin{array}{l}\because E \equiv 1 + \Delta \\ \Rightarrow E - \Delta \equiv 1\end{array}\right\}$$
$$= E^{-n} [E^{n-1} + \Delta E^{n-2} + \Delta^2 E^{n-3} + \ldots + \Delta^{n-1}] u_x$$
$$= [E^{-1} + \Delta E^{-2} + \Delta^2 E^{-3} + \ldots + \Delta^{n-1} E^{-n}] u_x$$
$$= u_{x-1} + \Delta u_{x-2} + \Delta^2 u_{x-3} + \ldots + \Delta^{n-1} u_{x-n}.$$
$$\therefore \quad u_x = u_{x-1} + \Delta u_{x-2} + \Delta^2 u_{x-3} + \ldots + \Delta^{n-1} u_{x-n} + \Delta^n u_{x-n}$$

(b) $u_x + {}^xC_1\Delta^2 u_{x-1} + {}^xC_2\Delta^4 u_{x-2} + \ldots$

$$= [1 + {}^xC_1\Delta^2 E^{-1} + {}^xC_2\Delta^4 E^{-2} + \ldots]\, u_x$$

$$= (1 + \Delta^2 E^{-1})^x u_x = \left(\frac{E + \Delta^2}{E}\right)^x u_x = \left(\frac{E^2 - E + 1}{E}\right)^x u_x$$

$$= \frac{1}{E^x}[1 + E(E-1)]^x u_x = E^{-x}(1 + \Delta E)^x u_x$$

$$= (1 + \Delta E)^x u_0 = (1 + {}^xC_1\Delta E + {}^xC_2\Delta^2 E^2 + \ldots)\, u_0$$

$$= u_0 + {}^xC_1\Delta u_1 + {}^xC_2\Delta^2 u_2 + \ldots$$

(c) $\text{R.H.S.} = \frac{x}{1-x} u_1 + \frac{x^2}{(1-x)^2}(E-1)\, u_1 + \frac{x^3}{(1-x)^3}(E-1)^2 u_1 + \ldots$

$$= \left\{\frac{x}{1-x} - \frac{x^2}{(1-x)^2} + \frac{x^3}{(1-x)^3} + \ldots\right\} u_1$$

$$+ \left\{\frac{x^2}{(1-x)^2} - \frac{2x^3}{(1-x)^3} + \ldots\right\} Eu_1 + \left\{\frac{x^3}{(1-x)^3}\ldots\right\} E^2 u_1 + \ldots$$

$$= \frac{x}{1-x}\left(1 + \frac{x}{1-x}\right)^{-1} u_1 + \frac{x^2}{(1-x)^2}\left(1 + \frac{x}{1-x}\right)^{-2} u_2$$

$$+ \frac{x^3}{(1-x)^3}\left(1 + \frac{x}{1-x}\right)^{-3} u_3 + \ldots$$

$$= u_1 x + u_2 x^2 + u_3 x^3 + \ldots$$

Example 29: *Use the method of separation of symbols to prove the following identities:*

(a) $u_0 + u_1 + u_2 + \ldots + u_n = {}^{n+1}C_1 u_0 + {}^{n+1}C_2\,\Delta u_0 + {}^{n+1}C_3\,\Delta^2 u_0 + \ldots + \Delta^n u_0$.

[Karnataka 2004, 2006; Mysore 2007]

(b) $u_{x+n} = u_n + {}^xC_1\Delta\, u_{n-1} + {}^{x+1}C_2\Delta^2 u_{n-2} + {}^{x+2}C_3\Delta^3\, u_{n-3} + \ldots +$

[Bangaluru 2002, 2003, 2007]

(c) $\Delta^n u_{x-n} = u_x - {}^nC_1\, u_{x-1} + {}^nC_2\, u_{x-2} - {}^nC_3\, u_{x-3} + \ldots$

Solution: (a) $\text{L.H.S.} = u_0 + u_1 + u_2 + \ldots + u_n$

$$= u_0 + Eu_0 + E^2 u_0 + \ldots + E^n u_0$$

$$= (1 + E + E^2 + \ldots + E^n)\, u_0$$

$$= \frac{E^{n+1} - 1}{E - 1} u_0 \quad \text{(sum up to } n \text{ terms of G.P.)}$$

$$= \frac{(1+\Delta)^{n+1}-1}{\Delta} u_0 = \frac{1}{\Delta}[(1 + {}^{n+1}C_1 \Delta + {}^{n+1}C_2 \Delta^2 + {}^{n+1}C_3\Delta^3 + \ldots + \Delta^{n+1}) - 1] u_0$$

$$= \frac{1}{\Delta}[{}^{n+1}C_1\Delta u_0 + {}^{n+1}C_2\Delta^2 u_0 + {}^{n+1}C_3\Delta^3 u_0 + \ldots + \Delta^{n+1}u_0]$$

$$= {}^{n+1}C_1 u_0 + {}^{n+1}C_2\Delta u_0 + {}^{n+1}C_3\Delta^2 u_0 + \ldots + \Delta^n u_0 = \text{R. H. S.}$$

(b) $\text{R.H.S.} = u_n + {}^xC_1\Delta u_{n-1} + {}^{x+1}C_2\Delta^2 u_{n-2} + {}^{x+2}C_3\Delta^3 u_{n-3} + \ldots$

$$= u_n + {}^xC_1\Delta E^{-1}u_n + {}^{x+1}C_2\Delta^2 E^{-2}u_n + {}^{x+2}C_3\Delta^3 E^{-3}u_n + \ldots$$

$$= [1 + {}^xC_1 \Delta E^{-1} + {}^{x+1}C_2\Delta^2 E^{-2} + {}^{x+2}C_3\Delta^3 E^{-3} + \ldots] u_n$$

$$= [1 - \Delta E^{-1}]^{-x} u_n = \left[1 - \frac{\Delta}{E}\right]^{-x} u_n = \left[\frac{E-\Delta}{E}\right]^{-x} u_n$$

$$= \left(\frac{1}{E}\right)^{-x} u_n = E^x u_n = u_{n+x} = \text{L. H. S.}$$

(c) $\text{R.H.S.} = u_x - {}^nC_1 u_{x-1} + {}^nC_2 u_{x-2} - {}^nC_3 u_{x-3} + \ldots$

$$= u_x - {}^nC_1 E^{-1} u_x + {}^nC_2 E^{-2} u_x - {}^nC_3 E^{-3}u_x + \ldots$$

$$= (1 - {}^nC_1 E^{-1} + {}^nC_2 E^{-2} - {}^nC_3 E^{-3} + \ldots) u_x$$

$$= (1 - E^{-1})^n u_x = \left[1 - \frac{1}{E}\right]^n u_x = \left[\frac{E-1}{E}\right]^n u_x$$

$$= \left(\frac{\Delta}{E}\right)^n u_x = \Delta^n E^{-n} u_x = \Delta^n u_{x-n} = \text{L. H. S.}$$

Example 30: *Prove the following identities:*

(*a*) $u_0 + \frac{u_1 x}{1!} + \frac{u_2 x^2}{2!} + \frac{u_3 x^3}{3!} + \ldots = e^x \left[u_0 + x\Delta u_0 + \frac{x^2}{2!}\Delta^2 u_0 + \frac{x^3}{3!}\Delta^3 u_0 + \ldots\right]$

[Rajasthan 2008; Delhi (H) 2005, 2009]

(*b*) $u_x - \frac{1}{8}\Delta^2 u_{x-1} + \frac{1.3}{8.16}\Delta^4 u_{x-2} - \frac{1.3.5}{8.16.24}\Delta^6 u_{x-3} + \ldots$

$$= u_{x+(1/2)} - \frac{1}{2}\Delta u_{x+(1/2)} + \frac{1}{4}\Delta^2 u_{x+1/2} - \ldots$$

[Bhopal 2002, 2006]

(*c*) $u_{2n} - {}^nC_1\, 2\, u_{2n-1} + {}^nC_2\, 2^2\, u_{2n-2} + \ldots + (-2)^n u_n$

$= (-1)^n (c - 2an)$ *where* $u_n = an^2 + bn + c.$

Solution: (a) L.H.S. $= u_0 + \frac{u_1 x}{1!} + \frac{u_2 x^2}{2!} + \frac{u_3 x^3}{3!} + \ldots$

$$= \left[1 + \frac{Ex}{1!} + \frac{E^2 x^2}{2!} + \frac{E^3 x^3}{3!} + \ldots\right]$$

$$= (e^{xE})\, u_0 = \{e^{x(1+\Delta)}\}\, u_0 = e^x \,.\, e^{x\Delta}\, u_0$$

$$= e^x \left[1 + x\Delta + \frac{x^2\Delta^2}{2!} + \frac{x^3\Delta^3}{3!} + \ldots\right] u_0$$

$$= e^x \left[u_0 + x\Delta u_0 + \frac{x^2\Delta^2 u_0}{2!} + \frac{x^3\Delta^3 u_0}{3!} + \ldots\right] = \text{R. H. S.}$$

(b) To show $u_x - \frac{1}{8}\Delta^2 u_{x-1} + \frac{1.3}{8.16}\Delta^4 u_{x-2} - \frac{1.3.5}{8.16.24}\Delta^6 u_{x-3} + \ldots$

$$= u_{x+(1/2)} - \frac{1}{2}\Delta u_{x+(1/2)} + \frac{1}{4}\Delta^2 u_{x+(1/2)} + \ldots$$

$$\text{L.H.S.} = \left[1 - \frac{1}{8}\Delta^2 E^{-1} + \frac{1.3}{8.16}\Delta^4 E^{-2} - \frac{1.3.5}{8.16.24}\Delta^6 E^{-3} + \ldots\right] u_x$$

$$= \left[1 + \left(-\frac{1}{2}\right)\left(\frac{\Delta^2 E^{-1}}{4}\right) + \frac{\left(-\frac{1}{2}\right)\left(-\frac{3}{2}\right)}{2!}\left(\frac{\Delta^2 E^{-1}}{4}\right)^2 + \frac{\left(-\frac{1}{2}\right)\left(-\frac{3}{2}\right)\left(-\frac{5}{2}\right)}{3!}\left(\frac{\Delta^2 E^{-1}}{4}\right)^3 + \ldots\right] u_x$$

$$= \left[1 + \frac{\Delta^2 E^{-1}}{4}\right]^{-1/2} u_x = E^{1/2}\left[E + \frac{\Delta^2}{4}\right]^{-1/2} u_x$$

$$= E^{1/2}\left[1 + \Delta + \frac{\Delta^2}{4}\right]^{-1/2} u_x \qquad [\because\ E \equiv 1 + \Delta]$$

$$= E^{1/2}\left[\left(1 + \frac{\Delta}{2}\right)^2\right]^{-1/2} u_x = E^{1/2}\left(1 + \frac{\Delta}{2}\right)^{-1} u_x$$

$$= E^{1/2}\left[1 - \frac{\Delta}{2} + \frac{\Delta^2}{2^2} - \ldots\right] u_x$$

$$= u_{x+(1/2)} - \frac{1}{2}\Delta u_{x+(1/2)} + \frac{1}{4}\Delta^2 u_{x+(1/2)} - \ldots \qquad = \text{R. H. S.}$$

(c) L.H.S. $= u_{2n} - {}^nC_1\, 2\, u_{2n-1} + {}^nC_2\, 2^2\, u_{2n-2} + \ldots + (-2)^n u_n$

$$= E^n u_n - {}^nC_1\, 2E^{n-1} u_n + {}^nC_2\, 2^2 E^{n-2} u_n + \ldots + (-2)^n u_n$$

$$= (E-2)^n u_n = (\Delta - 1)^n u_n = (-1)^n (1 - \Delta)^n u_n$$

$$= (-1)^n \left[1 - n\Delta + \frac{n(n-1)}{2}\Delta^2\right] u_n$$

[We have neglected higher order differences as polynomial is of second degree]

$$= (-1)^n \left[1 - n\Delta + \frac{n^2 - n}{2}\Delta^2\right] (an^2 + bn + c)$$

$$= (-1)^n \left[(an^2 + bn + c) - n\{a\Delta n^2 + b\Delta n\} + \frac{n^2 - n}{2} . a\Delta^2 n^2\right]$$

$$= (-1)^n \left[(an^2 + bn + c) - n\{a(n+1)^2 - an^2\} - nb(n + 1 - n) + \frac{n^2 - n}{2} a\Delta\{(n+1)^2 - n^2\}\right]$$

$$= (-1)^n \left[(an^2 + bn + c) - n(2an + a + b) + \frac{n^2 - n}{2} . a\Delta(2n + 1)\right]$$

$$= (-1)^n \left[(an^2 + bn + c) - n(2an + a + b) + \frac{n^2 - n}{2} . a\Delta 2n\right]$$

$$= (-1)^n \left[(an^2 + bn + c) - n(2an + a + b) + \frac{n^2 - n}{2} . a\{2(n+1) - 2n\}\right]$$

$$= (-1)^n \left[(an^2 + bn + c - 2an^2 - an - bn + \frac{n^2 - n}{2} . 2a\right]$$

$$= (-1)^n (c - 2an).$$

Example 31: *Prove the following identities.*

(a) $u_x - u_{x+1} + u_{x+2} - u_{x+3} + \ldots$

$$= \frac{1}{2}\left[u_{x-1/2} - \frac{1}{8}\Delta^2 u_{x-3/2} + \frac{1.3}{2!}\left(\frac{1}{8}\right)^2 \Delta^4 u_{x-5/2} - \frac{1.3.5}{3!}\left(\frac{1}{8}\right)^3 \Delta^6 u_{x-7/2} + \ldots\right]$$

[Lucknow 2003; Agra 2005; Bhopal 2001]

(b) $u_0 + {}^nC_1 u_1 x + {}^nC_2 u_2 x^2 + {}^nC_3 u_3 x^3 + \ldots$

$$= (1+x)^n u_0 + {}^nC_1 (1+x)^{n-1} x\Delta u_0 + {}^nC_2 (1+x)^{n-2} x^2 \Delta^2 u_0 + \ldots$$

(c) $\Delta^n y_x = y_{x+n} - {}^nC_1 y_{x+n-1} + {}^nC_2 y_{x+n-2} - \ldots + (-1)^n y_x$

(d) $u_0 - u_1 + u_2 - \ldots = \frac{1}{2}u_0 - \frac{1}{4}\Delta u_0 + \frac{1}{8}\Delta^2 u_0 - \frac{1}{16}\Delta^3 u_0 + \ldots$

(e) $\sum_{x=0}^{\infty} u_{2x} = \frac{1}{2}\sum_{x=0}^{\infty} u_x + \frac{1}{4}\left(1 - \frac{\Delta}{2} + \frac{\Delta^2}{4} - \ldots\right) u_0$

(f) *If $\Delta^3 u_x = 0$, prove that*

$$u_{x+1/2} = \frac{1}{2}(u_x + u_{x+1}) - \frac{1}{16}(\Delta^2 u_{x+1} + \Delta^2 u_x).$$

[Agra 2006, 2009]

Solution: (a) R.H.S. $= \frac{1}{2}\left[u_{x-1/2} - \frac{1}{8}\Delta^2 u_{x-3/2} + \frac{1.3}{2!}\left(\frac{1}{8}\right)^2 \Delta^4 u_{x-5/2} - \frac{1.3.5}{3!}\left(\frac{1}{8}\right)^3 \Delta^6 u_{x-7/2} + \ldots\right]$

$$= \frac{1}{2}\left[E^{-1/2} u_x - \left(\frac{1}{2}\right)\left(\frac{1}{4}\right)\Delta^2 E^{-3/2} u_x + \frac{\left(\frac{1}{2}\right)\left(\frac{3}{2}\right)}{2!}\left(\frac{1}{4}\right)^2 \Delta^4 E^{-5/2} u_x - \frac{\left(\frac{1}{2}\right)\left(\frac{3}{2}\right)\left(\frac{5}{2}\right)}{3!}\left(\frac{1}{4}\right)^3 \Delta^6 E^{-7/2} u_x + \ldots\right]$$

$$= \frac{1}{2}E^{-1/2}\left[1 + \left(-\frac{1}{2}\right)\left(\frac{1}{4}\Delta^2 E^{-1}\right) + \frac{\left(-\frac{1}{2}\right)\left(-\frac{3}{2}\right)}{2!}\left(\frac{1}{4}\Delta^2 E^{-1}\right)^2 + \frac{\left(-\frac{1}{2}\right)\left(-\frac{3}{2}\right)\left(-\frac{5}{2}\right)}{3!}\left(\frac{1}{4}\Delta^2 E^{-1}\right)^3 + \ldots\right] u_x$$

$$= \frac{1}{2}E^{-1/2}\left[1 + \frac{1}{4}\Delta^2 E^{-1}\right]^{-1/2} u_x$$

$$= \frac{1}{2}E^{-1/2}\left[\frac{4E + \Delta^2}{4E}\right]^{-1/2} u_x = \frac{1}{2}E^{-1/2}\left[\frac{4 + 4\Delta + \Delta^2}{4E}\right]^{-1/2} u_x$$

$$= \frac{1}{2}E^{-1/2} . 2E^{1/2}\{(2 + \Delta)^2\}^{-1/2} u_x = (2 + \Delta)^{-1} u_x$$

$$= (1 + E)^{-1} u_x = [1 - E + E^2 - E^3 + E^4 - E^5 + \ldots] u_x$$

$$= u_x - u_{x+1} + u_{x+2} - u_{x+3} + u_{x+4} - u_{x+5} + \ldots = \text{L.H.S.}$$

(b) R.H.S. $= (1 + x)^n u_0 + {}^nC_1 (1 + x)^{n-1} x\Delta u_0 + {}^nC_2 (1 + x)^{n-2} x^2 \Delta^2 u_0 + \ldots$

$$= \{(1 + x) + x\Delta\}^n u_0 = \{1 + x(1 + \Delta)\}^n u_0$$

$$= (1 + xE)^n u_0 = [1 + {}^nC_1 xE + {}^nC_2 x^2 E^2 + {}^nC_3 x^3 E^3 + \ldots] u_0$$

$$= u_0 + {}^nC_1 x u_1 + {}^nC_2 x^2 u_2 + {}^nC_3 x^3 u_3 + \ldots = \text{L. H. S.}$$

(c) $\text{R.H.S.} = y_{x+n} - {}^nC_1 y_{x+n-1} + {}^nC_2 y_{x+n-2} - \ldots + (-1)^n\, y_x$

$= [E^n - {}^nC_1 E^{n-1} + {}^nC_2 E^{n-2} - \ldots + (-1)^n]\, y_x$

$= (E-1)^n\, y_x = \Delta^n y_x = \text{L. H. S.}$

(d) $\text{R.H.S.} = \frac{1}{2} u_0 - \frac{1}{4} \Delta u_0 + \frac{1}{8} \Delta^2 u_0 - \frac{1}{16} \Delta^3 u_0 + \ldots$

$= \frac{1}{2} \left[1 - \frac{1}{2}\Delta + \left(\frac{1}{2}\Delta\right)^2 - \left(\frac{1}{2}\Delta\right)^3 + \ldots\right] u_0$

$= \frac{1}{2} \left[\frac{1}{1 + \frac{1}{2}\Delta}\right] u_0 = \frac{1}{2} \left(1 + \frac{1}{2}\Delta\right)^{-1} u_0 = (2 + \Delta)^{-1} u_0$

$= (1 + E)^{-1} u_0 = (1 - E + E^2 - E^3 + \ldots)\, u_0$

$= u_0 - u_1 + u_2 - u_3 + \ldots = \text{L.H.S.}$

(e) $\text{R.H.S.} = \frac{1}{2} \sum_{x=0}^{\infty} u_x + \frac{1}{4} \left(1 - \frac{\Delta}{2} + \frac{\Delta^2}{4} - \ldots\right) u_0$

$= \frac{1}{2} [1 + E + E^2 + E^3 + \ldots]\, u_0 + \frac{1}{4} \left(1 + \frac{\Delta}{2}\right)^{-1} u_0$

$= \frac{1}{2} \left[\frac{1}{1 - E}\right] u_0 + \frac{1}{4} \left(1 + \frac{\Delta}{2}\right)^{-1} u_0$

$= \frac{1}{2} (1 - E)^{-1} u_0 + \frac{1}{2} (2 + \Delta)^{-1} u_0$

$= \frac{1}{2} (1 - E)^{-1} u_0 + \frac{1}{2} (1 + E)^{-1} u_0$

$= \frac{1}{2} [(1 - E)^{-1} + (1 + E)^{-1}]\, u_0$

$= \frac{1}{2} . 2\, [1 + E^2 + E^4 + E^6 + \ldots]\, u_0$

$= u_0 + u_2 + u_4 + u_6 + \ldots$

$= \sum_{x=0}^{\infty} u_{2x} = \text{L.H.S.}$

(f) $u_{x+1/2} = E^{1/2}\, u_x = (1 + \Delta)^{1/2}\, u_x$

$= \left(1 + \frac{1}{2}\Delta - \frac{1}{8}\Delta^2\right) u_x,$

(expanding upto Δ^2 only, since $\Delta^3 u_x = 0$, etc.)

$= u_x + \frac{1}{2} \Delta u_x - \frac{1}{8} \Delta^2 u_x .$

Again $\Delta^3 u_x = \Delta^2 u_{x+1} - \Delta^2 u_x = 0.$ ...(1)

$\therefore \quad \Delta^2 u_{x+1} = \Delta^2 u_x.$

Also $\Delta u_x = u_{x+1} - u_x.$

Putting these values in (1), we get

$$u_{x+1/2} = u_x - \frac{1}{2}(u_{x+1} - u_x) - \frac{1}{8}\left(\frac{\Delta^2 u_x}{2} + \frac{\Delta^2 u_{x+1}}{2}\right)$$

$$= \frac{1}{2}(u_x + u_{x+1}) - \frac{1}{16}(\Delta^2 u_x + \Delta^2 u_{x+1}).$$

Example 32: *Show that*

$$\Delta x^m - \frac{1}{2}\Delta^2 x_m + \frac{1.3}{2.4}\Delta^3 x^m - \frac{1.3.5}{2.4.6}\Delta^4 x_m + \ldots m \text{ terms}$$

$$= (x + \tfrac{1}{2})^m - (x - \tfrac{1}{2})^m.$$

[Gujarat 2008]

Solution: We know that $\Delta^r x^m = 0$ for $r > m$; thus the sum of m terms of the series will be same as the sum of infinite terms of the series.

Now $\text{L.H.S.} = \Delta x^m - \frac{1}{2}\Delta^2 x^m + \frac{1.3}{2.4}\Delta^3 x^m - \frac{1.3.5}{2.4.6}\Delta^4 x^m + \ldots.. m \text{ terms}$

$$= \Delta\left[1 - \frac{\Delta}{2} + \frac{1.3}{2.4}\Delta^2 - \frac{1.3.5}{2.4.6}\Delta^3 + \ldots m \text{ terms}\right]x^m$$

$$= \Delta\left[1 - \frac{1}{2}\Delta + \frac{1.3}{2.4}\Delta^2 - \frac{1.3.5}{2.4.6}\Delta^3 + \ldots + \text{ad infinitum}\right]x^m$$

$$= \Delta[1 + \Delta]^{-1/2} x^m = \Delta E^{-1/2} x^m$$

$$= \Delta\left(x - \frac{1}{2}\right)^m, \text{ the interval of differencing being unity.}$$

$$= \left(x + \frac{1}{2}\right)^m - \left(x - \frac{1}{2}\right)^m = \text{R.H.S.}$$

Example 33: *Evaluate* $\dfrac{\Delta^2}{E}\sin(x+h) + \dfrac{\Delta^2 \sin(x+h)}{E\sin(x+h)}.$

[Nagpur 2001, 2005]

Solution: $\dfrac{\Delta^2}{E}\sin(x+h) + \dfrac{\Delta^2 \sin(x+h)}{E\sin(x+h)}$

$$= \frac{(E-1)^2}{E}\sin(x+h) + \frac{(E-1)^2 \sin(x+h)}{E\sin(x+h)}$$

$$= (E - 2 + E^{-1})\sin(x+h) + \frac{(E^2 - 2E + 1)\sin(x+h)}{E\sin(x+h)}$$

$$= \sin(x+2h) - 2\sin(x+h) + \sin x + \frac{[\sin(x+3h) - 2\sin(x+2h) + \sin(x+h)]}{\sin(x+2h)}$$

$$= 2\sin(x+h)(\cos(h-1)) + \frac{2\sin(x+2h)(\cos(h-1))}{\sin(x+2h)}$$

$$= 2(\cos(h-1))\,[\sin(x+h)+1].$$

Example 34: *Sum to n terms of the series*

$$1.2\,\Delta x^n - 2.3\,\Delta^2 x^n + 3.4\,\Delta^3 x^n - 4.5\,\Delta^4 x^n + \ldots$$

Solution: Since $\Delta^{n+m} x^n = 0$ for $m \geq 1$, thus the sum of the above series to n terms is the same as upto ∞.

Let $\quad S = 1.2\,\Delta x^n - 2.3\,\Delta^2 x^n + 3.4\,\Delta^3 x^n - 4.5\,\Delta^4 x^n + \ldots$

$$\Delta S = 1.2\,\Delta^2 x^n - 2.3\,\Delta^3 x^n + 3.4\,\Delta^4 x^n + \ldots$$

$\therefore \quad (\Delta+1)\,S = [1.2\Delta x^n - 2.2\Delta^2 x^n + 2.3\Delta^3 x^n - 2.4\Delta^4 x^n + \ldots]$

$$= 2\Delta\,[1 - 2\Delta + 3\Delta^2 - 4\Delta^3 + \ldots]\,x^n. \qquad \ldots(1)$$

Again let $\quad S_1 = 1 - 2\Delta + 3\Delta^2 - 4\Delta^3 + \ldots$ upto ∞.

$\therefore \quad \Delta S_1 = 1\Delta + 2\Delta^2 + 3\Delta^3 + \ldots$ upto ∞.

Therefore $\quad (1+\Delta)\,S_1 = 1 - \Delta + \Delta^2 - \Delta^3 + \ldots$ upto ∞.

$$= \frac{1}{1+\Delta} \quad \text{or} \quad S_1 = \frac{1}{(1+\Delta)^2}.$$

Therefore, from (1) we have $(\Delta+1)\,S = \dfrac{2\Delta}{(1+\Delta)^2}\,x^n$.

or $\quad S = 2\Delta\,(1+\Delta)^{-3}\,x^n = 2\Delta E^{-3}\,x^n = 2\,(E-1)\,(x-3)^n$

$$= 2E\,(x-3)^n - 2\,(x-3)^n = 2\,(x-2)^n - 2\,(x-3)^n.$$

Example 35: *Prove that*

(a) $\quad f(4) = f(3) + \Delta f(2) + \Delta^2 f(1) + \Delta^3 f(1)$

(b) $\quad f(4) = f(0) + 4\Delta f(0) + 6\Delta^2 f(-1) + 10\Delta^3 f(-1)$ *as for as third differences.*

Solution: (a) $f(4) - f(3) = \Delta f(3)$

$$= \Delta\,[f(2) + \Delta f(2)] \qquad \{\because \Delta f(2) = f(3) - f(2)\}$$

$$= \Delta f(2) + \Delta^2 f(2)$$

$$= \Delta f(2) + \Delta^2 [f(1) + \Delta f(1)]$$

$$= \Delta f(2) + \Delta^2 f(1) + \Delta^3 f(1),$$

or $$f(4) = f(3) + \Delta f(2) + \Delta^2 f(1) + \Delta^3 f(1).$$

(b) $$f(4) = E^5 f(-1) = (1 + \Delta)^5 f(-1)$$

$$= (1 + 5\Delta + 10\Delta^2 + 10\Delta^3 + 5\Delta^4 + \Delta^5) f(-1)$$

$$= f(-1) + 5\Delta f(-1) + 10\Delta^2 f(-1) + 10\Delta^3 f(-1) + 5\Delta^4 f(-1) + \Delta^5 f(-1)$$

$$= \{f(-1) + \Delta f(-1)\} + 4\Delta\{f(-1) + \Delta f(-1)\} + 6\Delta^2 f(-1) + 10\Delta^3 f(-1)$$

(taking upto third differences only)

$$= f(0) + 4\Delta f(0) + 6\Delta^2 f(-1) + 10\Delta^3 f(-1)$$

as for the third differences only.

Example 36: *Obtain the estimate of the missing figures in the following table:*

x	1	2	3	4	5	6	7	8
$f(x)$	1	8	?	64	?	216	343	512

Solution: We are given six values, therefore fifth differences are constant and consequently sixth differences are zero *i.e.* $\Delta^6 f(x) = 0$ for all values of x or $(E-1)^6 f(x) = 0$ for all values of x

or $$(E^6 - 6E^5 + 15E^4 - 20E^3 + 15E^2 - 6E + 1) f(x) = 0$$

[here interval of differencing is unity]

or $$f(x+6) - 6f(x+5) + 15f(x+4) - 20f(x+3) + 15f(x+2) - 6f(x+1) + f(x) = 0$$

Putting $x = 1$ and 2, we get

$$f(7) - 6f(6) + 15f(5) - 20f(4) + 15f(3) - 6f(2) + f(1) = 0 \quad ...(1)$$

and $$f(8) - 6f(7) + 15f(6) - 20f(5) + 15f(4) - 6f(3) + f(2) = 0. \quad ...(2)$$

On putting the given values of $f(8), f(7), f(6), f(4), f(2)$, and $f(1)$ in (1) and (2), we get

$$15f(5)+15f(3)=2280 \quad i.e. \quad f(5)+f(3)=152 \qquad ...(3)$$

and $$10f(5)+3f(3)=1331. \qquad ...(4)$$

Solving (3) and (4), we get, $f(3)=27, f(5)=125$.

Example 37: *Obtain the missing terms in the following table:* **[Agra 2006]**

x	2.0	2.1	2.2	2.3	2.4	2.5	2.6
$f(x)$	0.135	?	0.111	0.100	?	0.080	0.074

Solution: We are given five values so $\Delta^5 f(x)=0, \forall\, x$

$$\Rightarrow \quad (E-1)^5 f(x)=0, \forall\, x$$

$$\Rightarrow \quad (E^5-5E^4+10E^3-10E^2+5E-1)f(x)=0, \forall\, x$$

$$\Rightarrow \quad E^5 f(x)-5E^4 f(x)+10E^3 f(x)-10E^2 f(x)+5Ef(x)-f(x)=0, \forall\, x$$

$$\Rightarrow \quad f(x+5\times.1)-5f(x+4\times.1)+10f(x+3\times.1)-10f(x+2\times.1)$$
$$+5f(x+.1)-f(x)=0, \forall\, x \qquad \text{[here interval of differencing is .1.]}$$

Hence, putting $x=2.0$ and 2.1, we get

$$f(2.5)-5f(2.4)+10f(2.3)-10f(2.2)+5f(2.1)-f(2.0)=0$$

and $$f(2.6)-5f(2.5)+10f(2.4)-10f(2.3)+5f(2.2)-f(2.1)=0$$

Now substituting the values of $f(2.0), f(2.2), f(2.3), f(2.4), f(2.5), f(2.6)$ and then solving the equations simultaneously, we obtain

$$f(2.1)=.123 \text{ and } f(2.4)=.090.$$

Example 38: *Estimate the missing term in the following table:*

x	0	1	2	3	4
$y=f(x)$	1	3	9	?	81

[Meerut 2004; Avadh 2005]

Solution: We are given 4 values, so have $\Delta^4 f(x)=0, \forall\, x$

$$\Rightarrow \quad (E-1)^4 f(x)=0, \forall\, x$$

$$\Rightarrow \quad (E^4-4E^3+6E^2-4E+1)f(x)=0 \;\forall\, x,$$

$\Rightarrow \quad E^4 f(x) - 4E^3 f(x) + 6E^2 f(x) - 4E\, f(x) + f(x) = 0, \forall\, x,$

$\Rightarrow \quad f(x+4) - 4f(x+3) + 6f(x+2) - 4f(x+1) + f(x) = 0, \forall\, x$

[where interval of differencing is 1.]

Now, putting $x = 0$, we obtain

$$f(4) - 4f(3) + 6f(2) - 4f(1) + f(0) = 0, \quad ...(1)$$

Again substituting the values of $f(0), f(1), f(2), f(4)$ in (1), we get,

$$81 - 4f(3) + 6 \times 9 - 4 \times 3 + 1 = 0$$

$$\Rightarrow \quad 4f(3) = 124 \Rightarrow f(3) = 31$$

Example 39: *Find the first term of the series whose second and subsequent terms are* $8, 3, 0, -1, 0$.

[Agra 2001, 2003; Avadh 2005]

Solution: We know that $f(1) = E^{-1} f(2)$, the interval of differencing being unity.

$$= (1 + \Delta)^{-1} f(2)$$

$$= (1 - \Delta + \Delta^2 - \Delta^3 \ldots) f(2).$$

Again five observations are given so that 4th difference will be constant and fifth difference will be zero.

Construct the following table:

x	$f(x)$	$\Delta f(x)$	$\Delta^2 f(x)$
2	8		
		-5	
3	3		2
		-3	
4	0		2
		-1	
5	-1		2
		1	
6	0		

$$f(1) = f(2) - \Delta f(2) + \Delta^2 f(2) \text{ (higher order differences are zero)}$$

$$= 8 - (-5) + 2 = 15.$$

Example 40: *Given* $u_0 = 3, u_1 = 12, u_2 = 81, u_3 = 200, u_4 = 100, u_5 = 8$; *find* $\Delta^5 u_0$.

[Agra 2009]

Solution: $\Delta^5 u_0 = (E - 1)^5 u_0 = (E^5 - 5E^4 + 10E^3 - 10E^2 + 5E - 1) u_0$

$$= u_5 - 5u_4 + 10u_3 - 10u_2 + 5u_1 - u_0$$

$$= 8 - 500 + 2000 - 810 + 60 - 3 = 755.$$

Example 41: *(a) Given* $u_0 = 1, u_1 = 11, u_2 = 21, u_3 = 28, u_4 = 29$; *find* $\Delta^4 u_0$.

(b) Given $u_0 = 580, u_1 = 556, u_2 = 520$ *and* $u_4 = 385$; *find* u_3.

Solution: (a) $\Delta^4 u_0 = (E-1)^4 u_0$

$$= (E^4 - 4c_1 E^3 + 4c_2 E^2 - 4c_3 E + 1)\, u_0$$

$$= u_4 - 4u_3 + 6u_2 - 4u_1 + u_0$$

$$= 29 - 112 + 126 - 44 + 1 = 0.$$

(b) In this case out of five observations at equal intervals of width unity, four of them are known and one unknown, for given four observations, so we can fit a polynomial of third degree and hence the fourth difference will be zero.

i.e. $\Delta^4 u_0 = 0$ or $(E-1)^4 u_0 = 0$

or $(E^4 - 4E^3 + 6E^2 - 4E + 1)\, u_0 = 1$

$$u_4 - 4u_3 + 6u_2 - 4u_1 + u_0 = 0.$$

Putting the given values, we get

$$385 - 4u_3 + 6 \times 520 - 4 \times 556 + 580 = 0 \text{ or } u_3 = 465.$$

Example 42: *Find* $f(6)$; *it is given* $f(0) = -3, f(1) = 6, f(2) = 8, f(3) = 12$, *the third difference being constant.* **[Bhopal 2006]**

Solution: Construct the following difference table:

x	$f(x)$	$\Delta f(x)$	$\Delta^2 f(x)$	$\Delta^3 f(x)$
0	−3			
		9		
1	6		−7	
		2		9
2	8		2	
		4		
3	12			

Again $f(0+6) = E^6 f(0) = (1+\Delta)^6 f(0) = (1 + 6\Delta + 15\Delta^2 + 20\Delta^3)\, f(0)$

higher differences being zero

or $f(6) = f(0) + 6\Delta f(0) + 15\Delta^2 f(0) + 20\Delta^3 f(0)$

$$= -3 + 6(9) + 15(-7) + 20(9) = 126.$$

Example 43: *Given* $u_0 + u_8 = 1.9243$, $u_1 + u_7 = 1.9590$, $u_2 + u_6 = 1.9823$, $u_3 + u_5 = 1.9956$ *Find* u_4.

[Delhi 2005, 2009]

Solution: Since 8 entries are given, we have $\Delta^8 u_0 = 0$

i.e. $(E-1)^8 u_0 = 0$

or $(E^8 - {}^8C_1 E^7 + {}^8C_2 E^6 - {}^8C_3 E^5 + {}^8C_4 E^4 - {}^8C_5 E^3 + {}^8C_6 E^2 - {}^8C_7 E + 1)\, u_0 = 0$

or $(E^8 - 8E^7 + 28E^6 - 56E^5 + 70E^4 - 56E^3 + 28E^2 - 8E + 1)\, u_0 = 0$

or $(u_8 + u_0) - 8(u_7 + u_1) + 28(u_6 + u_2) - 56(u_5 + u_3) + 70 u_4 = 0$

Putting for given values, we get

$$1.9243 - 8(1.9590) + 28(1.9823) - 56(1.9956) + 70 u_4 = 0$$

or $-69.9969 + 70 u_4 = 0$ or $u_4 = \dfrac{69.9969}{70} = 0.999955$.

Example 44: *Evaluate*

(a) $(2\Delta^2 + \Delta - 1)(x^2 + 2x + 1)$, *(b)* $(\Delta + 1)(2\Delta - 1)(x^2 + 2x + 1)$

(c) $(E-2)(E-1)(2^{x/h} + x)$, *(d)* $(E^2 - 3E + 2)(2^{x/h} + x)$.

Solution: (a) $(2\Delta^2 + \Delta - 1)(x^2 + 2x + 1)$

$$= 2\Delta^2 (x^2 + 2x + 1) + \Delta (x^2 + 2x + 1) - 1(x^2 + 2x + 1)$$

$$= 2\Delta [(x+h)^2 + 2(x+h) + 1 - \{x^2 + 2x + 1\}]$$

$$+ [\{(x+h)^2 + 2(x+h) + 1\} - (x^2 + 2x + 1)] - x^2 - 2x - 1$$

$$= 2\Delta (2hx + h^2 + 2h) + (2hx + h^2 + 2h) - x^2 - 2x - 1$$

$$= 2[\{2h(x+h) + h^2 + 2h\} - \{2hx + h^2 + 2h\}] + 2hx + h^2 + 2h - x^2 - 2x - 1$$

$$= 5h^2 + 2hx + 2h - x^2 - 2x - 1.$$

(b) $(\Delta + 1)(2\Delta - 1)(x^2 + 2x + 1)$

$$= (\Delta + 1)[2\Delta (x^2 + 2x + 1) - 1(x^2 + 2x + 1)]$$

$$= (\Delta + 1)[2\{(x+h)^2 + 2(x+h) + 1\} - 2(x^2 + 2x + 1) - 1(x^2 + 2x + 1)]$$

$$= (\Delta + 1)[2\{(x+h)^2 + 2(x+h) + 1\} - 3(x^2 + 2x + 1)]$$

$$= (\Delta + 1)[4hx + 2h^2 + 4h - x^2 - 2x - 1]$$

$$= \Delta [4hx + 2h^2 + 4h - x^2 - 2x - 1] + [4hx + 2h^2 + 4h - x^2 - 2x - 1]$$

$$= 4h\Delta x - \Delta x^2 - 2\Delta x + 4hx + 2h^2 + 4h - x^2 - 2x - 1$$

$$= 4h\{(x+h)-x\} - \{(x+h)^2 - x^2\} - 2\{(x+h)-x\} + 4hx + 2h^2 + 4h - x^2 - 2x - 1$$

$$= 4h^2 - 2hx - h^2 - 2h + 4hx + 2h^2 + 4h - x^2 - 2x - 1$$

$$= 5h^2 + 2hx + 2h - x^2 - 2x - 1.$$

(c) $(E-2)(E-1)(2^{x/h} + x) = (E-2)[E(2^{x/h} + x) - (2^{x/h} + x)]$

$$= (E-2)[(2^{(x+h)/h} + x + h) - (2^{x/h} + x)]$$

$$= (E-2)(2^{x/h} + h) \qquad [\because 2^{(x+h)/h} - 2^{x/h} = 2^{x/h}(2-1) = 2^{x/h}]$$

$$= E(2^{x/h} + h) - 2(2^{x/h} + h) = 2^{(x+h)/h} + h - 2^{(x+h)/h} - 2h = -h.$$

(d) $(E^2 - 3E + 2)(2^{x/h} + x)$

$$= E^2(2^{x/h} + x) - 3E(2^{x/h} + x) + 2(2^{x/h} + x)$$

$$= [2^{(x+2h)/h} + x + 2h) - 3(2^{(x+h)/h} + x + h) + 2^{(x+h)/h} + 2x$$

$$= (4.2^{x/h} + x + 2h) - 3(2.2^{x/h} + x + h) + 2.2^{x/h} + 2x = -h.$$

Example 45: *Represent the function*

$$f(x) = x^4 - 12x^3 + 24x^2 - 30x + 9$$

and its successive differences into factorial notation. **[Himachal 2006, 2010]**

Solution: $f(x) = x^4 - 12x^3 + 24x^2 - 30x + 9$

$$\equiv Ax(x-1)(x-2)(x-3) + Bx(x-1)(x-2) + Cx(x-1) + Dx + E$$

where A, B, C, D and E are constants to be determined.

Putting $x = 0$, we get, $9 = 0 + 0 + 0 + 0 + E$ or $E = 9$.

Putting $x = 1$, we get $-8 = 0 + 0 + 0 + D + E$ *or* $D = -8 - E = -8 - 9 = -17$.

Similarly by putting $x = 2$ and 3 in turn, we get $C = -5$ and $b = -6$.

Again on comparing the coefficients of x^4 on both sides, we get $A = 1$.

$$\therefore \quad f(x) = x^{(4)} - 6x^{(3)} - 5x^{(2)} - 17x^{(1)} + 9.$$

Hence $\Delta f(x) = 4x^{(3)} - 6 \times 3x^{(2)} - 5 \times 2x^{(1)} - 17 \times 1 = 4x^{(3)} - 18x^{(2)} - 10x^{(1)} - 17;$

$$\Delta^2 f(x) = 12x^{(2)} - 36x^{(1)} - 10, \Delta^3 f(x) = 24x^{(1)} - 36; \ \Delta^4 f(x) = 24; \ \Delta^5 f(x) = 0.$$

Method of detached coefficients. By **1.11**, we have A, B, C, D and E directly

1	1	-12	24	-30	$9 = E$
	0	1	-11	13	
2	1	-11	13	$-17 = D$	
	0	2	-18		
3	1	-9	$-5 = C$		
	0	3			
4	1	$-6 = B$			
	0				
	$1 = A$				

Example 46: *Find the function whose first difference is*

$$9x^2 + 11x + 5.$$ [Meerut 2002, 2004]

Solution: Let $f(x)$ be the required function

$$\therefore \quad \Delta f(x) = 9x^2 + 11x + 5 = 9x(x-1) + Ax + B.$$

Putting $x = 0$, we get $B = 5$; Putting $x = 1$, we get $A = 20$.

$$\therefore \quad \Delta f(x) = 9x(x-1) + 20x + 5 = 9x^{(2)} + 20x^{(1)} + 5$$

and summing it, we get

$$f(x) = \frac{9x^{(3)}}{3} + \frac{20x^{(2)}}{2} + 5x^{(1)} + C., \text{ where } C \text{ is constant}$$

or

$$f(x) = 3x^{(3)} + 10x^{(2)} + 5x^{(1)} + C. = 3x^3 + x^2 + x + C.$$

Example 47: *What is the lowest degree polynomial which takes the following values*

x	0	1	2	3	4	5
$f(x)$	0	3	8	15	24	35

Solution: We have

$$f(x) = f(0) + {}^xC_1 \Delta f(0) + {}^xC_2 \Delta^2 f(0) + \ldots$$ [Putting $a = 0, h = 1, n = x$]

$$= f(0) + x^{(1)} \Delta(0) + \frac{x^{(2)}}{2!} \Delta^2 f(0) + \ldots \quad \ldots(1)$$

Now prepare a difference table for the given data to find $\Delta f(0), \Delta^2 f(0)$ etc.

x	$f(x)$	$\Delta f(x)$	$\Delta^2 f(x)$	$\Delta^3 f(x)$
0	0			
		3		
1	3		2	
		5		0
2	8		2	
		7		0
3	15		2	
		9		0
4	24		2	
		11		
5	35			

Thus putting the values of $f(0), \Delta f(0), \Delta^2 f(0), \Delta^3 f(0)$ in (1), we get,

$$f(x) = 0 + 3x^{(1)} + \frac{2}{2!}x^{(2)} + 0 = x^{(2)} + 3x^{(1)} = x(x-1) + 3x = x^2 + 2x.$$

Example 48: *Write down the polynomial of lowest degree which satisfies the following set of numbers*

$$0, 7, 26, 63, 124, 215, 342, 511.$$

Solution: By the result of **1.5.2**, we have

$$f(x) = f(0) + x_{c_1}\,\Delta f(0) + x_{c_2}\,\Delta^2 f(0) + \ldots$$

[Putting $a = 0, h = 1, n = x$]

$$= f(0) + x^{(1)}\,\Delta f(0) + \frac{x^{(2)}}{2!}\Delta^2 f(0) + \ldots \quad \ldots(1)$$

Prepare the following difference table for the given data to find $\Delta f(0), \Delta^2 f(0)$ and $\Delta^3 f(0)$ etc.

x	$f(x)$	$\Delta f(x)$	$\Delta^2 f(x)$	$\Delta^3 f(x)$	$\Delta^4 f(x)$
0	0				
		7			
1	7		12		
		19		6	
2	26		18		0
		37		6	
3	63		24		0
		61		6	
4	124		30		0
		91		6	
5	215		36		0
		127		6	
6	342		42		
		169			
7	511				

Thus putting the values of $f(0), \Delta f(0), \Delta^2 f(0), \Delta^3 f(0)$ in (1), we get

$$f(x) = 0 + 7x^{(1)} + \frac{12}{2!}x^{(2)} + \frac{6}{3!}x^{(3)} \quad \text{(higher order differences being equal to zero)}$$

$$= 7x + 6x(x-1) + x(x-1)(x-2) = 7x + 6x^2 - 6x + x^3 - 3x^2 + 2x = x^3 + 3x^2 + 3x.$$

Example 49: *Obtain a function whose first difference is*

$$x^3 + 2x^2 + 5x + 12.$$

Solution: Proceed as in Ex. 45.

$$\textbf{Ans. } f(x) = \frac{x^{(4)^\circ}}{4} + \frac{6x^{(3)}}{3} + \frac{9x^{(2)}}{2} + 12x^{(1)} + C.$$

Example 50: *Prove that $\Delta^2 x^{(m)} = m(m-1)x^{(m-2)}$ where m is a positive integer and interval of differencing is* 1.

Solution: $x^{(m)} = x(x-1)\ldots(x-\overline{m-1})$.

$$\therefore \quad \Delta x^{(m)} = [(x+1)x\ldots(x+1-\overline{m-1})] - [x(x-1)\ldots(x-\overline{m-1})] = mx^{(m-1)}$$

$$\text{and} \quad \Delta^2 x^{(m)} = \Delta.\Delta x^{(m)} = m\,\Delta x^{(m-1)} = m(m-1)x^{(m-2)}.$$

Example 51: *Prove that $\Delta^2 x^{(-m)} = m(m+1)x^{(-m-2)}$.*

Solution: $x^{(-m)} = \dfrac{1}{(x+1)(x+2)\ldots(x+m)}$.

$$\therefore \quad \Delta x^{(-m)} = \frac{1}{(x+2)\ldots(x+m+1)} - \frac{1}{(x+1)(x+2)\ldots(x+m)}$$

$$= \frac{1}{(x+2)\ldots(x+m)}\left[\frac{1}{(x+m+1)} - \frac{1}{(x+1)}\right]$$

$$= -m.\frac{1}{(x+1)(x+2)\ldots(x+m+1)} = -m.x^{(-m-1)}$$

$$\Delta^2 x^{(-m)} = -\Delta m x^{(-m-1)} = m(m+1)x^{(-m-2)}.$$

Example 52: *Express $f(x) = \dfrac{x-1}{(x+1)(x+3)}$ in terms of negative factorial polynomials.*

Solution: We know that the negative factorial polynomial $x^{(-n)}$ is given by

$$x^{(-n)} = \frac{1}{(x+1)(x+2)\ldots(x+n)}.$$

$$\text{Now,} \quad f(x) = \frac{x-1}{(x+1)(x+3)} = \frac{(x-1)(x+2)}{(x+1)(x+2)(x+3)} = \frac{x^2+x-2}{(x+1)(x+2)(x+3)}$$

$$= \frac{x(x+3) - 2(x+3) + 4}{(x+1)(x+2)(x+3)}$$

$$= \frac{x-2}{(x+1)(x+2)} + \frac{4}{(x+1)(x+2)(x+3)}$$

$$= \frac{x+2-4}{(x+1)(x+2)} + \frac{4}{(x+1)(x+2)(x+3)}$$

$$= \frac{1}{x+1} - \frac{4}{(x+1)(x+2)} + \frac{4}{(x+1)(x+2)(x+3)} = x^{(-1)} - 4x^{(-2)} + 4x^{(-3)}.$$

Example 53: *Prove that* $(x\Delta)^{(n)} u_x = (x+n-1)^{(n)} \Delta^n u_x$. **[Patna 2003, 2008]**

Solution: We shall prove this result by the method of mathematical induction.

When $n = 1$, we have, $(x\Delta)\, u_x = x\Delta u_x$, which is clearly true.

Now when $n = 2$, the left side gives

$$(x\Delta)^{(2)} u_x = (x\Delta)(x\Delta - 1)\, u_x = (x\Delta)(x\Delta\, u_x) - x\Delta u_x$$

$$= x\Delta\,(x\Delta\, u_x) - x\Delta u_x = x\,[(x+1)\,\Delta^2 u_x + 1\,.\,\Delta u_x] - x\,\Delta u_x = (x+1)^{(2)}\,\Delta^2 u_x.$$

Thus the theorem is true for $n = 2$.

When $n = 3$, the left side gives,

$$(x\Delta)^{(3)} u_x = (x\Delta)(x\Delta - 1)(x\Delta - 2)\, u_x$$

$$= (x\Delta - 2)\, x\Delta\,(x\Delta - 1)\, u_x = (x\Delta - 2)(x+1)^{(2)}\,.\,\Delta^2 u_x$$

$$= x\Delta\,[(x+1)^{(n)}\,\Delta^2\, u_x] - n\,(x+1)^{(2)}\,\Delta^2\, u_x$$

$$= (x+2)^{(3)}\,\Delta^3\, u_x + 2x\,(x+1)\,\Delta^2\, u_x - 2\,(x+1)^{(2)}\,\Delta^2\, u_x = (x+2)^{(3)}\,\Delta^3\, u_x.$$

Hence the theorem is true for $n = 3$.

Let the theorem be true for n. We shall show that it is true for the index $n+1$.

$$(x\Delta)^{(n+1)} u_x = (x\Delta)(x\Delta - 1)\ldots(x\Delta n - \overline{n-1})(x\Delta - n)\, u_x$$

$$= (x\Delta - n)(x\Delta)^n\, u_x = (x\Delta - n)\,[(x+n-1)^{(n)}\,\Delta^n]\, u_x$$

$$= x\Delta\,[(x+n-1)^{(n)}\,\Delta^n u_x] - n\,(x+n-1)^{(n)}\,\Delta^n\, u_x$$

$$= x\,[(x+n)^{(n)}\,\Delta^{n+1}\, u_x + n\,(x+n-1)^{(n-1)}\,\Delta^n\, u_x]. - n\,(x+n-1)^{(n)}\,\Delta^n\, u_x$$

$$= (x+n)^{(n+1)}\,\Delta^{n+1}\, u_x + n\,(x+n-1)^{(n)}\,\Delta^n\, u_x - n\,(x+n-1)^{(n)}\,\Delta^n\, u_x$$

$$= (x+n)^{(n+1)}\,\Delta^{n+1}\, u_x$$

which is of the similar form as the theorem. Hence the result holds good universally.

Example 54: *Find the relation between α, β and γ in order that $\alpha + \beta x + \gamma x^2$ may be expressible in one term in the factorial notation.*

[I.A.S. 2004]

Solution: Let $f(x) = \alpha + \beta x + \gamma x^2 = (a + bx)^{(2)}$

where a and b are unknown constants.

Again $(a + bx)^{(2)} = (a + bx)[a + b(x - 1)]$ (By definition)

$$= (a + bx)(a - b + bx) = (a^2 - ab) + (2ab - b^2)x + b^2 x^2$$

Comparing with $\alpha + \beta x + \gamma x^2$, we get $\alpha = a^2 - ab, \beta = 2ab - b^2, \gamma = b^2$

Eliminating a, b from these relations, we get $\gamma^2 + 4\alpha\gamma = \beta^2$,

which is the required relation between α, β and γ.

Example 55: *Given* $\log 100 = 2, \log 101 = 2.0043, \log 103 = 2.0128, \log 104 = 2.0170$, *find* $\log 102$.

Solution: Since four values are given, so third difference will be constant and consequently fourth differences are *zero i.e.* $\Delta^4 f(x) = 0$ for all values of x. Let the missing value be y_2.

The difference table is as under:

x	$y = f(x)$	$\Delta f(x)$	$\Delta^2 f(x)$	$\Delta^3 f(x)$	$\Delta^4 f(x)$
100	2.0000				
		.0043			
101	2.0043		$y_2 - 2.0086$		
		$y_2 - 2.0043$		$6.0257 - 3y_2$	
102	y_2		$4.0171 - 2y_2$		$6y_2 - 12.0514$
		$2.0128 - y_2$		$3y_2 - 6.0257$	
103	2.0128		$y_2 - 2.0086$		
		.0042			
104	2.0170				

Since $\Delta^4 f(x) = 0$, $\therefore$ $6y_2 - 12.0514 = 0$ or $y_2 = 2.0086$.

Example 56: *Find the function whose first difference is e^x.*

Solution: We know that, $\Delta e^x = e^{x+h} - e^x = e^x (e^h - 1)$

where h is the interval of differencing

$$\text{or} \quad e^x = \frac{1}{e^h - 1} \Delta e^x \quad \text{or } \Delta\left[\frac{e^x}{e^h - 1}\right] = e^x \quad \text{or} \quad f(x) = \frac{e^x}{e^h - 1}.$$

Example 57: *Find a function u_x for which $\Delta u_x = x(x-1)$.*

Solution: $\Delta u_x = x(x-1) = x^{(2)}$.

$$\therefore \quad u_x = \frac{x^{(3)}}{3} + B = \frac{1}{3} x(x-1)(x-2) + B.$$

Example 58: *Find the function whose first difference is*

(a) a, *(b)* $x^{(2)} + 5x$, *(c)* e^{a+bx}.

Solution: (a) $\Delta f(x) = a$ or $f(x) = ax + c$.

(b) $\Delta f(x) = x^{(2)} + 5x = x^{(2)} + 5x^{(1)}$

$$\therefore \quad f(x) = \frac{x^{(3)}}{3} + \frac{5x^{(2)}}{2} + C.$$

(c) $\Delta e^{a+bx} = e^{a+b(x+h)} - e^{a+bx}$, h being the interval of differencing

$= e^{a+bx} (e^{bh-1})$.

$$\text{or} \quad \frac{1}{e^{bh} - 1} \Delta e^{a+bx} = e^{a+bx} \quad \text{or} \quad \Delta\left(\frac{e^{a+bx}}{e^{bh} - 1}\right) = e^{a+bx};$$

$$\therefore \quad f(x) = \frac{e^{a+bx}}{e^{bh} - 1}.$$

Example 59: *Denoting $\binom{x}{n} = \frac{x(x-1)\ldots(x-n+1)}{n!}$, prove that for any polynomial $\phi(x)$ of degree k, $\phi(x) = \sum_{i=0}^{k} \binom{x}{i} \Delta^i \phi(0)$.*

Solution: From 1.5.2 P.10, we have

$$E^n f(a) = f(a + nh) = f(a) + {}^nC_1 \Delta f(a) + {}^nC_2 \Delta^2 f(a) + \ldots + \Delta^n f(a) \quad \ldots(1)$$

If we put $a = 0$ and $n = x$ in (1), we get

$$f(x) = f(0) + {}^xC_1 \Delta f(0) + {}^xC_2 \Delta^2 f(0) + \ldots$$

Again $f(x) = \phi(x)$ is given of degree k therefore $\Delta^k \phi(x)$ will be constant and higher order differences will be zero, thus

$$\phi(x) = \phi(0) + {}^xC_1 \Delta \phi(0) + \ldots + {}^xC_k \Delta^k \phi(0)$$

$$= \sum_{i=0}^{k} \binom{x}{i} \Delta^i \phi(0).$$

Example 60: *Show that $B(m+1, n) = (-1)^m \Delta^m \left(\frac{1}{n}\right)$ where m is a positive integer.*

Solution: We know that, $\int_0^\infty e^{-nx}\, dx = \frac{1}{n}$

$$\therefore \quad \Delta^m \int_0^\infty e^{-nx}\, dx = \Delta^m \left(\frac{1}{n}\right)$$

or
$$\int_0^\infty \Delta^m e^{-nx}\, dx = \Delta^m \left(\frac{1}{n}\right).$$

Again
$$\Delta^m e^{-nx} = \Delta^{m-1} (e^{-(n+1)x} - e^{-nx})$$

$$= \Delta^{m-1} e^{-nx} (e^{-x} - 1) = \ldots$$

$$= e^{-nx} (e^{-x} - 1)^m.$$

$$\therefore \quad \int_0^\infty e^{-nx} (e^{-x} - 1)^m\, dx = \Delta^m \left(\frac{1}{n}\right)$$

Putting $z = e^{-x} \Rightarrow -e^{-x}\, dx = dz$ we get,

$$(-1)^m \int_0^\infty z^{n-1} (1-z)^m\, dz = \Delta^m \left(\frac{1}{n}\right).$$

or
$$B(m+1, n) = (-1)^m \Delta^m \left(\frac{1}{n}\right).$$

Example 61: *Prove that $\Delta^n 0^{n+1} = \frac{n(n+1)}{2} \Delta^n 0^n$.*

Solution: By **1.12.1**, we know that

$$\Delta^n 0^m = n[\Delta^{n-1} 0^{m-1} + \Delta^n 0^{m-1}]$$

using this recurrence relation, we get

$$\Delta^n 0^{n+1} = n[\Delta^{n-1} 0^n + \Delta^n 0^n]$$

$$\Delta^{n-1} 0^n = (n-1)[\Delta^{n-2} 0^{n-1} + \Delta^{n-1} 0^{n-1}]$$

$$\Delta^{n-2}0^{n-1} = (n-2)\,[\Delta^{n-3}0^{n-2} + \Delta^{n-2}0^{n-2}]$$

$$\ldots \quad \ldots \quad \ldots \quad \ldots \quad \ldots \quad \ldots$$

$$\ldots \quad \ldots \quad \ldots \quad \ldots \quad \ldots \quad \ldots$$

$$\Delta^2 0^3 = 2\,[\Delta^1 0^2 + \Delta^2 0^2]$$

$$\Delta 0^2 = 1\,[\Delta^0 0^1 + \Delta^1 0^1]$$

By back substitution of these values, we have

$$\Delta^n 0^{n+1} = n\Delta^n 0^n + n(n-1)\,\Delta^{n-1}0^{n-1} + n(n-1)(n-2)\,\Delta^{n-2}0^{n-2}$$

$$+ \ldots + n(n-1)(n-2)\ldots 2.1.\Delta^1 0^1$$

$$= n.n! + n(n-1)(n-1)! + n(n-1)(n-2)(n-2)! + \ldots + n(n-1)(n-2)\ldots 2.1.1!$$

$$(\because \Delta^n 0^n = n!)$$

$$= n!\,[n + (n-1) + (n-2) + \ldots + 2 + 1]$$

$$= n!\,\frac{n(n+1)}{2} = \frac{n(n+1)}{2}\,\Delta^n 0^n \qquad (\because n! = \Delta^n 0^n)$$

Example 62: *Sum the series (using differences of zero)*

$$n^2 + {}^n c_1\,(n-1)^2 + {}^n c_2\,(n-2)^2 + \ldots$$

n being a positive integer.

Solution: The given series is $n^2 + {}^n c_1\,(n-1)^2 + {}^n c_2\,(n-2)^2 + \ldots$

$$= [(x+n)^2 + {}^n c_1\,(x+n-1)^2 + {}^n c_2\,(x+n-2)^2 + \ldots]_{(x=0)}$$

$$= [E^n x^2 + {}^n c_1 E^{n-1} x^2 + {}^n c_2 E^{n-2} x^2 + \ldots]_{(x=0)}$$

$$= [(E^n + {}^n c_1 E^{n-1} + {}^n c_2 E^{n-2} + \ldots)\,x^2]_{(x=0)}$$

$$= [(E+1)^n\,x^2]_{(x=0)}$$

$$= [(2+\Delta)^n\,x^2]_{(x=0)} \qquad (\because E \equiv 1 + \Delta)$$

$$= [(2^n + {}^n c_1 2^{n-1}\,\Delta + {}^n c_2 2^{n-2}\,\Delta^2 + \ldots)\,x^2]_{(x=0)}$$

$$= [(2^n x^2 + {}^n c_1 2^{n-1}\,\Delta x^2 + {}^n c_2 2^{n-2}\,\Delta^2 x^2 + \ldots]_{(x=0)}$$

$$= 0 + {}^n c_1 2^{n-1}\,\Delta 0^2 + {}^n c_2 2^{n-2}\,\Delta^2 0^2 + {}^n c_3 2^{n-3}\,\Delta^3 0^2 + \ldots$$

$$= n.2^{n-1}.1 + \frac{n(n-1)}{1.2}\,2^{n-2}.2! + 0 + 0 + \ldots$$

$$[\because \Delta^n 0^n = [\Delta^n x^n]_{(x=0)} = (n!)_{(x=0)} = n!]$$

and $\quad \Delta^n x^m = 0$ whenever $n > m$

$\therefore \quad \Delta^n 0^m = [\Delta^n 0^m]_{(x=0)} = n.2^{n-2}\,[2 + n - 1] = n(n+1)\,2^{n-2}$.

1.15 Stirling Numbers

Stirling numbers $S_i^{(n)}$ of the first kind occur when the factorial polynomials are expressed into ordinary polynomials, *i.e.*

$$x^{(n)} = S_1^{(n)} x + S_2^{(n)} x^2 + \ldots + S_n^{(n)} x^n. \qquad \ldots(1)$$

For example, $x^{(4)} = x(x-1)(x-2)(x-3) = -6x + 11x^2 - 6x^3 + x^4$

$$S_1^{(4)} = -6, S_2^{(4)} = 11, S_3^{(4)} = -6 \quad \text{and} \quad S_4^{(4)} = 1.$$

Stirling numbers $s_i^{(n)}$ of the second kind occur when x^n is expressed as a linear combination of the factorial functions *i.e.*

$$x^n = s_1^{(n)} x^{(1)} + s_2^{(n)} x^{(2)} + \ldots + s_n^{(n)} x^{(n)}$$

$x^3 = x^{(1)} + 3x^{(2)} + x^{(3)}$. Then clearly

$$s_1^{(3)} = 1, s_2^{(3)} = 3 \quad \text{and} \quad s_3^{(3)} = 1.$$

***Recurrence Relations*:**

Following are the recurrence relations for the stirling numbers of first and second kind respectively.

(i) $s_i^{(x+1)} = s_{i-1}^{(n)} - ns_i^{(n)}$. (ii) $s_i^{(n+1)} = s_{i-1}^{(n)} + i s_i^{(n)}$.

✦✦ Problem Set ✦✦

1. (i) Define operator E and Δ and show that

(a) $E \equiv 1 + \Delta$. (b) $E\Delta \equiv \Delta E$. (c) $E^n \equiv (1+\Delta)^n$

(ii) Discuss, if operators E and Δ obey the distributive, commutative, associative and indices laws of algebra. **[Kanpur 2002, 2004]**

(iii) Prove the operators relation

$(I + \Delta)(I - \nabla) \equiv I$.

(iv) $\nabla = 1 - E^{-1}, \nabla \equiv \Delta E^{-1}$. **[Rohilkhand 2003]**

2. Evaluate

(i) $\Delta^2 (ab^{cx})$ (ii) $\Delta \cot 2^x$ (iii) $\dfrac{\Delta^2}{E} x^3$

(iv) $\dfrac{\Delta^2 x^3}{Ex^3}$ (v) $\Delta \sin h (a + bx)$ (vi) $\Delta \cos h (a + bx)$

3. Evaluate

(i) $\Delta^3\,[ax^3 + bx^2 + cx + d]$, h being the interval of differencing

(ii) $\Delta \tan ax$ (iii) $\Delta \tan^{-1} ax$ (iv) $\Delta^4\,(ae^x)$

(v) $\Delta^3\,[(1-x)(1-2x)(1-3x)]$.

4. Show that (i) $\sum_{k=0}^{n-1} \Delta^2 f_k = \Delta f_n - \Delta f_0$

(ii) $\Delta^2\left[\dfrac{a^{2x} + a^{4x}}{(a^2-1)^2}\right] = a^{2x} + (a^2+1)^2\,a^{4x}$.

(iii) $\Delta^n \sin(ax+b) = \left(2\sin\dfrac{ah}{2}\right)^n \sin\left[ax + b + n\left(\dfrac{ah+\pi}{2}\right)\right]$

(iv) $\Delta \cot(a+bx) = \dfrac{-\sin b}{\sin(a+bx)\sin(a+b+bx)}$ [Bangaluru 2003, 2006]

5. Prove that, if $f(x)$ and $g(x)$ are any functions of x, then

(i) $\Delta[f(x) + g(x)] = \Delta f(x) + \Delta g(x)$,

(ii) $\Delta[af(x)] = a\Delta f(x)$, where a is constant,

(iii) $\Delta[f(x)\,g(x)] = f(x+1)\,\Delta g(x) + g(x)\,\Delta f(x) = f(x)\,\Delta g(x) + g(x+1)\,\Delta f(x)$,

(iv) $\Delta\left[\dfrac{f(x)}{g(x)}\right] = \dfrac{g(x)\,\Delta f(x) - f(x)\,\Delta g(x)}{g(x)\,g(x+1)}$

6. A third degree polynomial passes through the points $(0,-1), (1,1), (2,1)$ and $(3,-2)$. Find the polynomial.

7. (i) Prove that $\Delta x^{(n)} = nx^{(n-1)}$ for all integers n.

(ii) Prove that if m is a positive integer, then

(a) $\dfrac{(x+1)^{(m)}}{m!} = \dfrac{x^{(m)}}{m!} + \dfrac{x^{(m-1)}}{(m-1)!}$. (b) $x^{(m+1)} + mx^{(m)} = x \,.\, x^{(m)}$.

8. Find by constructing the difference table:

(i) eighth term of the series

$1, 1.095, 1.179, 1.251, 1.310 \ldots$ [Agra 2000, 2001, 2003]

(ii) tenth term of the series

$3, 14, 39, 84, 155, 258, \ldots$

9. Prove that

(i) $f(4) = f(3) + \Delta f(2) + \Delta^2 f(1) + \Delta^3 f(1)$,

(ii) $f(4) = f(0) + 4\Delta f(0) + 6\Delta^2 f(-1) + 10\Delta^3\, f(-1)$ as far as third differences.

10. Obtain the estimate of the missing terms in the following table:

x	2.0	2.1	2.2	2.3	2.4	2.5	2.6
$f(x)$	0.135	–	0.111	0.100	–	0.082	0.024

11. Evaluate the missing term in the following

x	100	101	102	103	104
$\log x$	2.000	2.0043	–	2.0128	2.0170

12. Estimate the missing term in the following

x	1	2	3	4	5	6	7
y	2	4	8	–	32	64	128

Explain why the result differs from 16.

13. What is the difference between $\left(\frac{\Delta u_x}{E u_x}\right)^2$ and $\left(\frac{\Delta^2 u_x}{E^2 u_x}\right)$. If $u = x^3$ and interval of differencing is h, find out the expression for both.

[Gujarat 2004, 2008]

14. Show that

$$u_0 + {}^x c_1 \Delta u_1 + {}^x c_2 \Delta^2 u_2 + {}^x c_3 \Delta^3 u_3 + \ldots = u_x + {}^x c_1 \Delta^2 u_{x+1} + {}^x c_2 \Delta^4 u_{x+2}$$

15. Show that

$$u_x = u_{x-1} + \Delta u_{x-2} + \Delta^2 u_{x-3} + \ldots + \Delta^{n-1} u_{x-n} + \Delta^n u_{x-n}.$$

16. Find the successive differences of $x^4 - 12x^3 + 42x^2 - 30x + 9$ when the interval of differencing is unity.

17. If $u_x = x(x-1)(x-2)$, prove that $\Delta u_x = 3x(x-1)$.

18. Calculate the values of

(i) $\Delta^2 0^5$ (ii) $\Delta^3 0^6$ (iii) $\Delta^4 0^5$ (iv) $\Delta^5 0^5$ (v) $\Delta 0^n$

19. Prove that $\Delta^n 0^m = n^m - nc_1 (n-1)^m + nc_2 (n-2)^m \ldots$

and deduce that $n! = n^n - nc_1 (n-1)^n + nc_2 (n-2)^n$.

20. Prove that $\frac{\Delta^n 0^m}{n!} = \frac{n \Delta^n 0^{m-1}}{n!} + \frac{\Delta^{n-1} 0^{m-1}}{(n-1)!}$.

21. Show that $(n+1)\,\Delta^n 0^n = 2\,[\Delta^{n-1}\,0^n + \Delta^n 0^n]$.

22. Prove the identity

$$\Delta^m 0^n + nc_1\Delta^m 0^{n-1} + nc_2\Delta^m 0^{n-2} + \ldots + \frac{n\,!}{(n-m)\,!} = \frac{1}{m+1}\,\Delta^{m+1}\,0^{n+1}$$

23. Express $f(x) = 2x^3 - 3x^2 + 3x - 10$ and its differences in factorial notation, the interval of differencing being unity.

24. Find the values of

(i) $\dfrac{\Delta}{\Delta x}\,[x^{(-8)} - 6x^{(-2)}]$ (ii) $\dfrac{\Delta^2}{\Delta x^2}\,[x^4 - 2x^2 + 6x - 2]$.

25. Express each of the following as a product of suitable factors

(i) $(2x+5)^{(3)}$ if $h = 1$. (ii) $(3x-4)^{(-2)}$ if $h = 1$.

26. Find $\Delta^n\,(x^2 a^x)$.

27. Sum the series

$$(n-1)^2\,{}^nC_1 + (n-3)^2\,{}^nC_3 + (n-5)^2\,{}^nC_5 + \ldots$$

Hint: *The given expression*

$$= [({}^nC_1E^{-1} + {}^nC_3E^{-3} + \ldots)\,x^2]_{x=n}$$

$$= \left[\frac{1}{2}\,\{(1+E^{-1})^n - (1-E^{-1})^n\}\,x^2\right]_{x=n}$$

$$= \left[\frac{1}{2}\,\{(\Delta+2)^n - \Delta^n\}\,E^{-n}\,x^2\right]_{x=n}$$

$$= \left[\frac{1}{2}\,\{(\Delta+2)^n - \Delta^n\}\,(x-n)^2\right]_{x=n}$$

$$= \frac{1}{2}\,\{(\Delta+2)^n - \Delta^n\}\,0^2]$$

$$= \frac{1}{2}\,[2^n 0^2 + n2^{n-1}\,\Delta 0^2 - \frac{1}{2}\,n\,(n-1)\,2^{n-2}\,\Delta^2 0^2 + \ldots$$

$$= \frac{1}{2}\,[n2^{n-1} + n\,(n-1)\,2^{n-2}]\ \text{etc.}$$

28. (i) Express the following polynomials into factorial notations and find second differences, if $h = 1$

(a) $x^4 + x + 1$; (b) $2x^4 + 5x^2 + 4x + 6$

(ii) Express $y = 3x^3 + x^2 + x + 1$ into factorial notation and hence show that $\Delta^3 y = 18$.

29. Write x^4 as a sum of factorials and thus show that

$$\Delta^{-1} x^4 = \frac{x^{(5)}}{5} + \frac{3x^{(4)}}{2} + \frac{x^{(4)}}{3} + \frac{x^{(2)}}{2} + c$$

[Meerut 2005]

✦✦ Objective Type Question ✦✦

❖ Multiple Choice Questions

1. The nth forward difference is given by

(a) $\Delta^n f(x+h) - \Delta^{n-1} f(x)$ (b) $\Delta^{n+1} f(x+h) - \Delta^n f(x)$

(c) $\Delta^{n-1} f(x+h) - \Delta^n f(x)$ (d) $\Delta^{n-1} f(x) - \Delta^{n-1} f(x+h)$

2. The nth backward difference is given by

(a) $\Delta[\nabla^{n-1} f(x)]$ (b) $\nabla[\nabla^{n-1} f(x)]$

(c) $\nabla[\Delta^{n-1} f(x)]$ (d) $\nabla^{n-1} f(x) - \nabla^{n-1} f(x-h)$

3. The value of Δe^x is

(a) $e^x - e^{x+h}$ (b) $e^x - e^{x-h}$

(c) $e^{x+h} + e^x$ (d) $e^{x+h} - e^x$.

4. If $f(x)$ be a polynomial of nth degree then

(a) $\nabla^n f(x) = 0$ (b) $\Delta^{n-1} f(x) = \text{const.}$

(c) $\Delta^{n+1} f(x) = 0$ (d) $\Delta^{n+1} f(x) = \text{const.}$

5. If the nth differences of a tabulated function $f(x)$ are constant, the value of independent variables are taken at equal intervals, then

(a) $f(x)$ is a polynomial of degree n

(b) $f(x)$ is const.

(c) $f(x)$ is zero

(d) $f(x)$ is a polynomial of degree $n - 1$.

6. Which of the following statements is not correct regarding the tabulated differences:
   (a) The effect of an error goes on decreasing with the succession.
   (b) In various difference columns of the difference table, the algebraic sum of the errors is zero.
   (c) The maximum error occurs in the same line as the erroneous tabular value.
   (d) The coefficients of ε' s are the binomial coefficients with alternating signs.

7. Which of the following is not correct:
   (a) $E^m E^n f(x) = E^{m+n} f(x)$ (b) $E \nabla \equiv \nabla E \equiv \Delta$
   (c) $E^{-n} f(x) = f(x - nh)$ (d) $E^2 f(x) = [E f(x)]^2$

8. $\Delta^n x^{(n)}$, where $x^{(n)}$ denotes the factorial notation, stants for:
   (a) $n^2 h^2$ (b) $\lfloor n \, h^n$
   (c) nh (d) $\frac{h^n}{\lfloor n}$

9. The values of $\Delta^n [\alpha x^n + \beta x^{n-1}]$ is:
   (a) 0 (b) 1
   (c) $\alpha \lfloor n$ (d) $\beta \lfloor n$

10. $\Delta [f(x) g(x)]$ stands for:
   (a) $f(x+1) \Delta g(x) + g(x) \Delta f(x)$ (b) $f(x) \Delta g(x) + g(x+1) \Delta f(x)$
   (c) $\Delta f(x) + \Delta g(x)$ (d) $\Delta f(x+1) \Delta g(x-1) + \Delta g(x) . f(x)$

11. $(n+1) \Delta^n 0^n = ?$
   (a) $[\Delta^{n-1} 0^n + \Delta^n 0^n]$ (b) $2 [\Delta^{n-1} 0^n + \Delta^n 0^{n-1}]$
   (c) $2 [\Delta^{n-1} 0^n + \Delta^n 0^n]$ (d) $2 [\Delta^n 0^{n-1} + \Delta^n 0^n]$

12. The value of $\Delta^6 0^6$ is:
   (a) 1560 (b) 1680
   (c) 1450 (d) 1

13. If interval of differencing is unity, then the value of:
$$\Delta^4 (\alpha x^4 + \beta x^3 + \gamma x^2 + \delta x + \xi) \text{ is}$$
   (a) 24α (b) 6α
   (c) 16β (d) $4 \alpha + 3 \beta + 2 \alpha + \delta$

14. The value of $\frac{\Delta^2 x^3}{E x^3}$ is:
   (a) $\frac{5}{(x+1)^2}$ (b) $\frac{4}{(x+1)^3}$
   (c) $\frac{8}{(x+1)^4}$ (d) $\frac{6}{(x+1)^2}$

✦✦ Examination Questions ✦✦

1. Find $\Delta^{10}(1-ax)(1-bx^2)(1-cx^3)(1-dx^4)$ **[Agra 2004]**

2. Express $f(x)=x^4-12x^3+24x^2-30x+9$ and its successive differences in factorial notation. Hence show that $\Delta^5 f(x)=0$. **[Agra 2004, 2009]**

✦✦ Answers ✦✦

❖ Problem Set

2. (i) $a(b^c-1)^2 b^{cx}$ (ii) $-\operatorname{cosec} 2^{x+1}$ (iii) $6x$

(iv) $\dfrac{6}{(1+x)^2}$ (v) $2\sin h\dfrac{b}{2}\cos h\left(a+\dfrac{b}{2}+bx\right)$

(vi) $2\sin h\dfrac{b}{2}\sin h\left(a+\dfrac{b}{2}+cx\right)$

3. (i) $6ah^3$ (ii) $\dfrac{\sin a}{\cos ax\cos a(x+1)}$ (iii) $\tan^{-1}\left(\dfrac{a}{1+a^2x+a^2x^2}\right)$

(iv) $a(e-1)^4e^x$ (v) -36.

6. $-\dfrac{1}{6}(x^3+3x^2-16x+6)$

8. (i) 1.399 (ii) 1110

10. .132 ; 090

11. 2.0086

12. 17

13. $\left(\dfrac{\Delta}{E}\right)^2 u_x=6xh-6,\ \dfrac{\Delta^2 u_x}{E^2 u_x}=\dfrac{6xh^2+6h^3}{(x+2h)^3}$.

16. $\Delta f(x)=4x^3-30x^2+52x+1,\ \Delta^2 f(x)=12x^2-48x+26$

$\Delta^3 f(x)=24x-36$ *and* $\Delta^4 f(x)=24$.

23. $f(x)=2x^{(3)}+3x^{(2)}+2x-10,\ \Delta f(x)=6x^{(2)}+6x+2$

$\Delta^2 f(x)=12x+6,\ \Delta^3 f(x)=12$.

24.	(i) $-3x^{(-4)} + 12x^{(-3)}$ (ii) $12x^{(2)} + 36x^{(1)} + 10$
25.	(i) $(2x+5)(2x+3)(2x+1)$ (ii) $\dfrac{1}{(3x-1)(3x+2)}$.
26.	$a^x(a^h-1)^{n-2}[x^2(a^h-1)^2 + n(2hx+h^2)a^h(a^h-1) + n(n-1)h^2a^{2h}]$.
28.	(i) (a) $x^{(4)} + 6x^{(3)} + 7x^{(2)} + 2x^{(1)} + 1, 12x^2 + 24x + 14$.
	(b) $2x^{(4)} + 12x^{(3)} + 19x^{(2)} + 11x^{(1)} + 6, 24x^2 + 48x + 38$.

❖ Multiple Choice Questions

1.	(c)	**2.**	(b) & (d)	**3.**	(d)	**4.**	(c)	**5.**	(a)
6.	(a)	**7.**	(d)	**8.**	(b)	**9.**	(c)	**10.**	(a) & (b)
11.	(c)	**12.**	(b)	**13.**	(a)	**14.**	(d)		

❖ Examination Questions

1. $abcd\,(10\,!)$

2.

$$f(x) = x^{(4)} - 6x^{(3)} - 5x^{(2)} - 17x^{(1)} + 9$$

$$\Delta f(x) = 4x^{(3)} - 18x^{(2)} - 10\,x^{(1)} - 17$$

$$\Delta^2 f(x) = 12x^{(2)} - 36x^{(1)} - 10$$

$$\Delta^3 f(x) = 24x^{(1)} - 36$$

$$\Delta^4 f(x) = 24\,,\ \Delta^5 f(x) = 0$$

◆◆◆

Theory | Solved Examples | Problem Set

Chapter 2

Interpolation with Equal Intervals

Introduction, Interpolation methods, Use of Calculus of Finite Differences, Subdivision of Intervals.

2.1 Introduction

[Avadh 2003, 2004; Rohilkhand 2001, 2003, 2007, 2009]

Interpolation according to Theile is as "the art of reading between the lines of the table". It also means insertion of filling up intermediate terms of the series. It is the technique of obtaining the value of a function for any intermediate values of the Independent variable *i.e.* of argument when the values of the function corresponding to number of values of the argument are given. The process of computing the value of the function outside the range of given values of the variable is called ***extrapolation.*** All interpolation formulae are based on the hypothesis that the given function is polynomial or it can be represented by a polynomial with a good degree of approximation, *e.g.* the population of a town in the decennial census were as under:

Year	1891	1901	1911	1921	1931
Population (in thousands)	46	66	81	93	101

The process of finding population for the year say 1925 with the help of above data is called ***interpolation*** while the process to find the population for the year 1935 will be known as ***extrapolation.***

The following assumptions are to be kept in mind for interpolation:

[Rohilkhand 2005; Delhi (H) 2004, 2009]

1. The values of the function should be either in increasing or in decreasing order, *i.e.* in $y = f(x)$, y should either increase with increase in value of x or y should decrease with decrease in the value of x. We can say in other words that there are no sudden jumps or falls in the value of function during the period under consideration.
2. The rise or fall in the values should be uniform, *e.g.* if we are given data regarding the deaths in various years in a particular town and some of the observations are for the years in which epidemics or famine or war overtook the town, then interpolation methods are not applicable in such cases.

2.2 The Following Interpolation Methods are Used

1. Graphic method. 2. Method of curve fitting.
3. Application of the calculus of finite differences formulae.

2.2.1 Graphic Method

Let $y = f(x)$, then we can easily plot a graph between different values of x and corresponding values of y. From the graph so obtained, we can find out the value of y for given x, *e.g.* consider the data given in 2.1:

Year (x)	1891	1901	1911	1921	1931
Population (y) (in thousands)	46	66	81	93	101

Interpolate population for the year 1925.

The following steps are to be employed:

1. Take a suitable scale for x and y and plot the various points on the graph paper for given data.
2. Join the points by free hand curve.
3. Find the point on the curve corresponding to $x = 1925$ and find the corresponding value of y.

Drawbacks: This is simply an approximate method of estimating value of y and is not reliable in majority of the cases.

2.2.2 Methods of Curve Fitting

This method is applicable only in those cases in which the form of the function is known. In such cases by the method of least squares, we can fit the curve of known form to given set of observations, afterwards we can calculate the unknown value with the help of fitted curve.

Drawbacks in the Method **[C.S.I.R. (Net) 2007; Delhi (H) 2008]**

1. The method is not exact.
2. In case number of observations is sufficiently large, the method becomes complicated.
3. In this method form of the function for the given set of observations is assumed to be known. Consider the above example, in which population for the year 1925 is to be found. Let us assume that the function $y = f(x)$ be a first degree polynomial, and let it be $y = a + bx$. Now we will find values of a and b from the given data to get the fitted curve.

x	$x-1911$	$z=\frac{x-1911}{10}$	y	yz	z^2
1891	−20	−2	46	−92	4
1901	−10	−1	66	−66	1
1911	0	0	81	0	0
1921	10	1	93	93	1
1931	20	2	101	202	4
Total		0	387	137	10

By the method of least squares, it is required to minimise

$$S=\Sigma\,(y-a-bz)^2.\ \text{Now } (\partial S/\partial a)=\Sigma\,(y-a-bz)=0 \qquad ...(1)$$

$$S/\partial b=\Sigma\,(y-a-bz)\,z=0 \qquad ...(2)$$

i.e. $$\Sigma y=na+b\,\Sigma z \qquad ...(3)$$

and $$\Sigma zy=a\,\Sigma z+b\,\Sigma z^2 \qquad ...(4)$$

Putting the value of $\Sigma\, y, \Sigma\, z, \Sigma\, z\, y$ and Σz^2 in (3) and (4), we get

$$387=5a+0 \text{ or } a=77.4 \text{ and } 137=0+10b \text{ or } b=13.7.$$

$\therefore$ required fitted polynomial is $y=77.4+13.7z$.

We want to find population for the year 1925, so that put

$$z=\frac{1925-1911}{10}=1.4 \text{ in } (5)$$

i.e. $$y=77.4+(13.7)(1.4)=77.4+19.18=96.58 \text{ thousands.}$$

Hence, population for the year 1925 is estimated to be 96.58 thousands.

2.2.3 Use of Calculus of Finite Differences

(i) Newton-Gregory formula for Interpolation.

[Meerut 2007; Bhopal 2002; Av.dh 2004; Rohilkhand 2002, 2008]

Let $y=f(x)$ represent a function which assumes the values $f(a), f(a+h)$, $f(a+2h), ..., f(a+nh)$ for $(n+1)$ equidistant values $a, a+h, a+2h, ..., a+nh$ of the independent variable x and let $P_n(x)$ be a polynomial in x of degree n. This polynomial may be written in the form

$$P_n(x)=A_0+A_1(x-a)+A_2(x-a)(x-a-h)+A_3(x-a)(x-a-h)(x-a-2h)$$
$$+\ldots+A_n(x-a)(x-a-h)(x-a-2h)\ldots(x-a-\overline{n-1}\,h \qquad ...(1)$$

where $A_0, A_1, \ldots, A_n$ are constants and are chosen, such that

$$P_n(a) = f(a), P_n(a+h) = f(a+h), \ldots, P_n(a+nh) = f(a+nh).$$

Putting successively the values $a, a+h, a+2h, \ldots, a+nh$ in (1) and writing the values of $P_n(a), P_n(a+h), \ldots, P_n(a+nh)$, we have

$$f(a) = A_0 \quad \text{or} \quad A_0 = f(a) \qquad f(a+h) = A_0 + h A_1$$

$$\text{or} \quad A_1 = \frac{f(a+h) - f(a)}{h} = \frac{\Delta f(a)}{h}, \qquad f(a+2h) = A_0 + 2hA_1 + h.h.A_2$$

$$\text{or} \quad A_2 = [f(a+2h) - 2\{f(a+h) - f(a)\} - f(a)]/2h^2$$

$$= [f(a+2h) - 2f(a+h) + f(a)]/2h^2 = \frac{1}{2h^2}\Delta^2 f(a) = \frac{1}{2!h^2}\Delta^2 f(a).$$

Similarly, we get $A_3 = \dfrac{1}{3!h^3}\Delta^3 f(a), \ldots, A_n = \dfrac{1}{n!h^n}\Delta^n f(a)$.

Putting the values of $A_0, A_1, \ldots, A_n$ so obtained in (1), we get

$$P_n(x) = f(a) + \frac{\Delta f(a)}{h}(x-a) + \frac{\Delta^2 f(a)}{2!h^2}(x-a)(x-a-h)$$

$$+ \frac{\Delta^3 f(a)}{3!h^3}(x-a)(x-a-h)(x-a-2h) + \ldots + \frac{\Delta^n f(a)}{n!h^n}(x-a)(x-a-h)\ldots(x-a-\overline{n-1}\,h)$$

This is Newton-Gregory formula for forward interpolation.

Putting $(x-a)/h = u$ or $x = a + hu$, the formula takes the simple form

$$P_n(x) = P_n(a+hu) = f(a) + u\Delta f(a) + \frac{u(u-1)}{2!}\Delta^2 f(a)$$

$$+ \frac{u(u-1)(u-2)}{3!}\Delta^3 f(a) + \ldots + \frac{u(u-1)(u-2)\ldots(u-n+1)}{n!}\Delta^n f(a) \quad \ldots(2)$$

$$\text{or} \quad P_n(x) = f(a) + u^{(1)}\Delta f(a) + \frac{1}{2!}u^{(2)}\Delta^{(2)} f(a) \ldots \frac{1}{n!}u^{(n)} f(a),$$

$$\text{where} \quad u^{(n)} = u(u-1)\ldots(u-n+1) \quad \text{and} \quad P_n(x) \equiv f(x)$$

This is the form in which Newton-Gregory formula for forward interpolation is usually written.

Another form

Replacing a by x_0, u by $[(x-a)/h]$ *i.e.* $x = a + hu$; we get

$$P_n(a+hu) = f(x_0) + u\Delta f(x_0) + \frac{u(u-1)}{2!}\Delta^2 f(x_0) + \frac{u(u-1)(u-2)}{3!}\Delta^3 f(x_0)$$

$$+ \ldots + \frac{u(u-1)\ldots(u-\overline{n-1})}{n!}\Delta^n f(x_0)$$

or $$P_n(x) = f(x_0) + u\Delta f(x_0) + \frac{u(u-1)}{2!}\Delta^2 f(x_0)$$

$$+ \frac{u(u-1)(u-2)}{3!}\Delta^3 f(x_0) + \ldots + \frac{u(u-1)\ldots(u-\overline{n-1})}{n!}\Delta^n f(x_0)$$

or $$f(x) = f(x_0) + u\Delta f(x_0) + \frac{u(u-1)}{2!}\Delta^2 f(x_0) + \frac{u(u-1)(u-2)}{3!}\Delta^3 f(x_0)$$

$$+ \ldots + \frac{u(u-1)\ldots(u-\overline{n-1})}{n!}\Delta^n f(x_0)$$

or $$y = y_0 + u\Delta y_0 + \frac{u(u-1)}{2!}\Delta^2 y_0 + \ldots + \frac{u(u-1)\ldots(u-\overline{n-1})}{n!}\Delta^n y_0$$

Aliter: We have $y = f(x_0 + uh) = E^u f(x_0)\,(1+\Delta)^u\, y_0$ $\qquad (\because E \equiv 1 + \Delta)$

$$= \left\{1 + u\Delta + \frac{u(u-1)}{2!}\Delta^2 + \frac{u(u-1)(u-2)}{3!} + \ldots\right\} y_0$$

$$= y_0 + u\Delta y_0 + \frac{u(u-1)}{2!}\Delta^2 y_0 + \frac{u(u-1)(u-2)}{3!}\Delta^3 y_0 + \ldots$$

But $y = f(x) =$ polynomial of nth degree, so $\Delta^{n+1} y_0$ and all other higher differences are zero,

$$\Rightarrow \quad y = y_0 + u\Delta y_0 + \frac{u(u-1)}{2!}\Delta^2 y_0 + \ldots + \frac{u(u-1)\ldots(u-\overline{n-1})}{n!}\Delta^n y_0$$

Note: It is said to be "forward interpolation formula" due to the fact that formula contains values of the tabulated function from $f(a)$ onward to the right and none to the left of $f(a)$. This formula is used mainly for interpolating the values of y near the beginning $(x > a)$ of a set of tabulated values.

(ii) Newton-Gregory formula for Backward Interpolation.

[Meerut 2008; Avadh 2003]

In this case we write

$$P_n(x) = A_0 + A_1(x-a-nh) + A_2(x-a-nh)(x-a-nh+h) + A_3(x-a-nh)$$

$$(x-a-nh+h)(x-a-nh+2h) + \ldots + A_n(x-a-nh)(x-a-nh+h)\ldots(x-a-h) \quad \ldots(1)$$

where $A_0, A_1, \ldots, A_n$ are constants and are chosen such that

$$P_n(a+nh) = f(a+nh), \ldots, P_n(a) = f(a)$$

Putting in (1), $x = a + nh, a + nh - h, \ldots$ and also putting

$P_n(a+nh) = f(a+nh) \ldots,$ we have $\qquad f(a+nh) = A_0$

or $\qquad A_0 = f(a+nh) \;\Rightarrow\; f(a+nh-h) = A_0 + A_1(-h)$

or $$A_1 = \frac{f(a+nh) - f(a+nh-h)}{h} \quad \text{or} \quad A_1 = \frac{\nabla f(a+nh)}{h}$$

$$f(a+nh-2h) = A_0 + A_1(-2h) + A_2(-2h)(-h)$$

or $$A_2 = \frac{f(a+nh) - 2f(a+\overline{n-1}h) + f(a+\overline{n-2}\,h)}{2h^2} = 1/2!\,h^2\,\nabla^2 f(a+nh).$$

Similarly, we have

$$A_3 = 1/3!\,h^3\,\nabla^3 f(a+nh), \ldots, A_n = 1/n!\,h^h\,\nabla^n f(a+nh)$$

Putting these values of $A_0, A_1, A_2, \ldots, A_n$ in (1), we get

$$P_n(x) = f(a+nh) + \frac{\nabla f(a+nh)}{h}(x - \overline{a+nh}) + \nabla^2 f(a+nh)/2!\,h^2(x-\overline{a+nh})(x-\overline{a+nh-h})\ldots$$

$$\ldots + \frac{\nabla^n f(a+nh)}{n!\,h^n}(x-\overline{a+nh})(x-\overline{a+nh-h})\ldots(x-a-h) \qquad \ldots(2)$$

This is Newton-Gregory formula for ***backward interpolation.***

Putting $u = \dfrac{x-(a+nh)}{h}$ or $x = a + nh + hu$ in (2), the formula takes the form

$$P_n(x) = P_n(a+nh+hu)$$

$$= f(a+nh) + u\nabla f(a+nh) + \frac{u(u+1)}{2!}\nabla^2 f(a+nh) + \frac{u(u+1)(u+2)}{3!}\nabla^3 f(a+nh) + \ldots$$

$$+ \frac{u(u+1)(u+2)\ldots(u+n-1)}{n!}\nabla^n f(a+nh). \text{ Where } P_n(x) \equiv f(x)$$

Aliter:

Let the function $y = f(x)$ have the values $y_0, y_1, y_2, \ldots$ corresponding to $x_0, x_0 + h$, $x_0 + 2h, \ldots$ of x. Let it be required to evaluate $f(x)$ for $x = x_n + uh$, where u is any real number. Then we have

$$y = f(x_n + uh) = E^u f(x_n) = (1-\nabla)^{-u} y_n \qquad [\because E^{-1} = 1 - \nabla]$$

$$= \left[1 + u\nabla + \frac{u(u+1)}{2!}\nabla^2 + \frac{u(u+1)(u+2)}{3!}\nabla^3 + \ldots\right] y_n$$

using Binomial theorem.

$$\Rightarrow \quad y = y_n + u\nabla y_n + \frac{u(u+1)}{2!}\nabla^2 y_n + \frac{u(u+1)(u+2)}{3!}\nabla^3 y_n + \ldots \qquad \ldots(1)$$

Note: Here $x_0 = a$, $x_n = x_0 + nh$

Solved Examples

Example 1: *The following table gives the population of a town during the last six censuses. Estimate using any suitable interpolation formula, the increase in the population during the period from* 1946 *to* 1948:

Year:	1911	1921	1931	1941	1951	1961
Population: (*in thousands*)	12	15	20	27	39	52

Solution: The difference table is as under **[Bhopal 2007]**

year	Population	Differences				
x	y	Ist Δy	2nd $\Delta^2 y$	3rd $\Delta^3 y$	4th $\Delta^4 y$	5th $\Delta^5 y$
1911	12					
		3				
1921	15		2			
		5		0		
1931	20		2		3	
		7		3		−10
1941	27		5		−7	
		12		−4		
1951	39		1			
		13				
1961	52					

Here $u = \dfrac{1946 - 1911}{10} = 3.5$

Applying Newton's formula for forward differences, we have

$$y = y_0 + u(\Delta y_0) + \frac{u(u-1)}{2!}(\Delta^2 y_0) + \frac{u(u-1)(u-2)}{3!}(\Delta^3 y_0) + \ldots$$

$$= 12 + 3.5 \times 3 + \frac{(3.5)(2.5)}{2!} \times 2 + 0 + \frac{(3.5)(2.5)(1.5)(.5)}{4!} 3$$

$$+ \frac{(3.5)(2.5)(1.5)(.5)(-.5)}{5!}(-10)$$

$$= 12 + 10.5 + 8.75 + 0.8203 + .2734 = 32.3437.$$

Therefore increase in the population during the period from 1946 to 1948

$= 34.8732 - 32.3437 = 2.5295$ thousands $= 2.53$ thousands approximately.

Example 2: *From the following table find the number of students who obtained less than 46 marks.*

Marks	No. of Students
30 – 40	31
40 – 50	42
50 – 60	51
60 – 70	35
70 – 80	31

[U.P.P.C.S. 2006; Avadh 2005; Rohilkhand 2004]

Solution: The difference table is as under:

Marks x	*No. of Students* $f(x)$	*Ist difference* $\Delta f(x)$	*2nd difference* $\Delta^2 f(x)$	*3rd difference* $\Delta^3 f(x)$	*4th difference* $\Delta^4 f(x)$
Below 40	31				
		42			
" 50	73		9		
		51		−25	
" 60	124		−16		37
		35		12	
" 70	159		−4		
		31			
" 80	190				

Here, $h = 10, a = 40$

$$f(45) = f(40 + .5 \times 10) = E^{1/2} f(40) = (1 + \Delta)^{1/2} f(40)$$

$$= f(40) + \frac{1}{2}\Delta f(40) + \frac{\frac{1}{2}\left(-\frac{1}{2}\right)}{2\,!}\Delta^2 f(40) + \frac{\frac{1}{2}\left(1-\frac{1}{2}\right)\left(-\frac{3}{2}\right)}{3\,!}\Delta^3 f(40)$$

$$+ \frac{\frac{1}{2}\left(-\frac{1}{2}\right)\left(-\frac{3}{2}\right)\left(-\frac{5}{2}\right)}{4\,!}\Delta^4 f(40)$$

$$= 31 + \frac{1}{2}(42) - \frac{1}{8}(9) - \frac{1}{16}(-25) - \frac{5}{128}(37) = 47.868.$$

Example 3: *Given,* $\sin 45° = 0.7071, \sin 50° = 0.7660$ $\sin 55° = 0.8192$, $\sin 60° = 0.8660$

Find $\sin 52°$, *by using any method of interpolation.*

[U.P.P.C.S. 2004, 2008; Avadh 2004; U.P.T.U. 2004]

Solution: We have

x	45°	50°	52°	55°	60°
$f(x)$	0.7071	0.7660	?	0.8192	0.8660

The difference table is as under:

x	$f(x)$	$\Delta f(x)$	$\Delta^2 f(x)$	$\Delta^3 f(x)$
45	**0.7071**			
		0.0589		
50	0.7660		**−0.0057**	
		0.0532		**−0.0007**
55	0.8192		−0.0064	
		0.0468		
60	0.8660			

By Newton's interpolation formula, we have

$$f(a+uh) = f(a) + u\Delta f(a) + \frac{u(u-1)}{2!}\Delta^2 f(a) + \frac{u(u-1)(u-2)}{3!}\Delta^3 f(a) + \ldots$$

Here, $a = 45°,\ u = \frac{x-a}{h} = \frac{52-45}{5} = 1.4$

$$f(52°) = 0.7071 + 1.4 \times 0.0589 + \frac{(1.4)(0.4)}{2!} \times (-0.0057) + \frac{(1.4)(0.4)(-0.6)}{3!} \times (-0.0007)$$

$$= 0.7071 + 0.08246 - 0.001596 + 0.000032 = .7880032$$

$\Rightarrow \quad \sin 52° = 0.7880032 = 0.7880$ approx .

Example 4: *The area A of a circle of diameter d is given for the following values:*

d	80	85	90	95	100
A	5026	5674	6362	7088	7854

Find approximate values for the areas of circles of diameters 82 *and* 91 *respectively.*

[U.P.P.C.S. (M.P.) 2005, 2010; Ajmer 2002, 2005, 2008; Meerut 2002, 2006]

Solution: We shall find the value of A corresponding to $d = 82$.

Let $A = f(d)$. Now, the difference table is as given below:

d	$f(d)$	$\Delta f(d)$	$\Delta^2 f(d)$	$\Delta^3 f(d)$	$\Delta^4 f(d)$
80	**5026**				
		648			
85	5674		**40**		
		688		**−2**	
90	6362		38		**4**
		726		2	
95	7088		40		
		766			
100	7854				

$\Rightarrow \quad f(82) = \text{area of circle of diameter } 82 = f(a+uh).$

$\therefore \quad 82 = a + uh \quad \Rightarrow \quad 82 = 80 + u \times 5 \quad \Rightarrow \quad u = \frac{2}{5}.$

Hence by Newton's forward interpolation formula, we have

$$f(82) = f(80) + \frac{2}{5}\,\Delta f(80) + \frac{2}{5}\left(\frac{2}{5}-1\right)\frac{\Delta^2 f(80)}{2!}$$

$$+\frac{2}{5}\left(\frac{2}{5}-1\right)\left(\frac{2}{5}-2\right)\frac{\Delta^3 f(80)}{3!} + \frac{2}{5}\left(\frac{2}{5}-1\right)\left(\frac{2}{5}-2\right)\left(\frac{2}{5}-3\right)\frac{\Delta^4 f(80)}{4!}$$

$$= 5026 + \frac{2}{5} \times 648 + \frac{2}{5}\left(-\frac{3}{5}\right) \times \frac{40}{2} + \frac{2}{5}\left(-\frac{3}{5}\right)\left(-\frac{8}{5}\right)\frac{(-2)}{6} + \frac{2}{5}\left(-\frac{3}{5}\right)\left(-\frac{8}{5}\right)\left(-\frac{13}{5}\right).\frac{4}{24}$$

$$= 5026 + 259.2 - 4.8 - 0.128 - 0.1664 = 5280.1056 = 5280 \text{ approx.}$$

Similarly we can find $f(91)$ *i.e.* the area of circle of diameter 91, which we get as $f(91) = 6504$.

Example 5: *The population of a country in the decennial census were as under: Estimate the population for the year* 1925.

Year x	1891	1901	1911	1921	1931
Population y: (in thousands)	46	66	81	93	101

[Meerut 2005]

Solution: Let us introduce a new variable *u*, given by $u = \frac{x - 1891}{10}$.

$\therefore$ *u* takes the values $0, 1, 2, 3, 4$.

The difference table is as follows:

u	y	Δy	$\Delta^2 y$	$\Delta^3 y$	$\Delta^4 y$
0	46				
		20			
1	66		−5		
		15		2	
2	81		−3		−3
		12		−1	
3	93		−4		
		8			
4	101				

Here five values are given, so we must assume that fourth differences are constant. We want to entry for $x = 1925$ *i.e.*, for

$$u = \frac{1925 - 1891}{10} = 3.4.$$

Now, $y_{3.4} = E^{3.4}\ y_0 = (1+\Delta)^{3.4}\ y_0$

$$= y_0 + 3.4\,\Delta\, y_0 + \frac{3.4\times 2.4}{1\times 2}\Delta^2 y_0 + \frac{3.4\times 2.4\times 1.4}{1\times 2\times 3}\Delta^3 y_0 + \frac{3.4\times 2.4\times 1.4\times .4}{1\times 2\times 3\times 4}\Delta^4 y_0$$

$$= 46 + 3.4\times 20 + \frac{3.4\times 2.4}{2}(-5) + \frac{3.4\times 2.4\times 1.4}{6}\times 2 + \frac{3.4\times 2.4\times 1.4\times .4}{24}(-3)$$

$$= 46 + 68 - 20.4 + 3.808 - 0.5712 = 96.8368 \text{ thousands.}$$

Hence the population for 1925 is estimated as 96.8368 thousands.

Example 6: *Using Newton's formula for interpolation, estimate the population for the year* 1905:

Year	*Population*
1891	98,752
1901	132,285
1911	168,076
1921	195,690
1931	246,050

[Indore 2006, 2009]

Solution: The difference table is as under:

Year (x)	*Population* $f(x)$	$\Delta f(x)$	$\Delta^2 f(x)$	$\Delta^3 f(x)$	$\Delta^4 f(x)$
1891	**98752**				
		33533			
1901	132285		**2258**		
		35791		**– 10435**	
1911	168076		– 8177		**41358**
		27614		30923	
1921	195690		22746		
		50360			
1931	246050				

Here $\quad a = 1891,\ u = \dfrac{x-a}{h} = \dfrac{1905-1891}{10} = 1.4.$

By Newton's interpolation formula, we get

$$f(1905) = 98725 + (1.4)(33533) + \frac{(1.4)(0.4)}{2!}(2258)$$

$$+ \frac{(1.4)(0.4)(-0.6)}{3!}(-10435) + \frac{(1.4)(0.4)(-0.6)(-1.6)}{4!}(41358)$$

$$= 98752 + 46946.2 + 632.24 + 584.36 + 926.42 = 147841 \text{ approx.}$$

Example 7: *Find the number of men getting wages between Rs.* 10 *and Rs.* 15 *from the following table:*

Wages in Rs.	*Frequency*
0 – 10	9
10 – 20	30
20 – 30	35
30 – 40	42

Solution: The difference table is as under: **[Delhi (H) 2008; Avadh 2004]**

Wages in Rs. x	*Frequency* $f(x)$	$\Delta f(x)$	$\Delta^2 f(x)$	$\Delta^3 f(x)$
Under 10	9			
		30		
" 20	39		5	
		35		2
" 30	74		7	
		42		
" 40	116			

Here $a = 10, u = \frac{x-a}{h} = \frac{15-10}{10} = .5$

$$\therefore \quad f(15) = 9 + .5\,(30) + \frac{(.5)\,(-.5)}{2\,!}(5) + \frac{(.5)\,(-.5)\,(-1.5)}{3\,!}(2)$$

$$= 9 + 15 - .6 + .1 = 24 \text{ approx.}$$

Therefore no. of persons getting wages between Rs. 10 and Rs. 15 is $24 - 9 = 15$.

Example 8: *Given* $\log x$ *for* $x = 310, 320, 330, 340, 350$ *and* 360 *according to the following table. Find the value of* $\log 3375$.

Solution: The difference table is as under:

x	$\log x$	$\Delta \log x$	$\Delta^2 \log x$	$\Delta^3 \log x$	$\Delta^4 \log x$	$\Delta^5 \log x$
310	2.4913617					
		.0137883				
320	2.5051500		–.0004244			
		.0133639		.0000255		
330	2.5185139		–.0003989		–.0000025	
		.0129650		.0000230		–.000008
340	2.5314789		–.0003759		–.0000017	
		.0125891		.0000213		
350	2.5440680		–.0003546			
		.0122345				
360	2.5563025					

Here $a = 310, u = \frac{x-a}{h} = \frac{337.5-310}{10} = 2.75$

$$\therefore \quad \log 337.5 = \log 310 + (2.75)\,\Delta \log 310 + \frac{(2.75)(1.75)}{2!}\Delta^2 \log 310$$

$$+ \frac{(2.75)(1.75)(.75)}{3!}\Delta^3 \log 310 + \frac{(2.75)(1.75)(.75)(-.25)}{4!}\Delta^4 \log 310$$

$$= 2.49136 + 2.75\,(.01379) + \frac{(2.75)(1.75)}{2!}(-.00042)$$

$$+ \frac{(2.5)(1.75)(.75)}{3!}(.00003) \quad \text{(leaving further terms)}$$

$$= 2.49136 + .03792 - .00101 + .00002 = 2.52829$$

Now $\log 3375 = \log (10 \times 337.5) = \log 10 + \log 337.5$

$$= 1 + 2.52829 = 3.52829 \text{ approx.}$$

Example 9: *Use Newton's formula for interpolation to find the net premium at age 25 from the table given below:*

Age	20	24	28	32
Annual net premium	0.01427	0.01581	0.01772	0.01996

Solution: The difference table is as under:

Age (x)	Premium $f(x)$	$\Delta f(x)$	$\Delta^2 f(x)$	$\Delta^3 f(x)$
20	**0.01427**			
		0.00154		
24	0.01581		**0.00037**	
		0.00191		**– 0.00004**
28	0.01772		0.00033	
		0.00224		
32	0.01996			

Here $u = \frac{x-a}{h} = \frac{25-20}{4} = 1.25.$

By Newton's formula

$$f(25) = 0.01427 + 1.25\,(0.00154) + \frac{(1.25)(0.25)}{2!}(0.00037)$$

$$+ \frac{(1.25)(0.25)(-0.75)}{3!}(-0.00004)$$

$$= 0.01427 + 0.001925 + 0.0000578 + 0.0000015 = .0162543.$$

Example 10: *The following are the number of deaths in four successive ten year age groups. Find the number of deaths at* $45-50$ *and* $50-55$.

Age group :	25 – 35	35 – 45	45 – 55	55 – 65
Deaths :	13229	18139	24225	31496

Solution: The difference table is as under: **[Agra 2007]**

Age (x)	Deaths $f(x)$	$\Delta f(x)$	$\Delta^2 f(x)$	$\Delta^3 f(x)$
under 35 and above 25	**13229**			
		18139		
under 45 and above 25	31368		**6086**	
		24225		**1185**
under 55 and above 25	55593		7271	
		31496		
under 65 and above 25	87089			

We have to obtain $f(50)$ *i.e.* number of deaths above the age of 25 and below 50.

Here $$u=\frac{x-a}{h}=\frac{50-35}{10}=1.5$$

By Newton's formula, we have

$$f(50)=f(35)+1.5\,\Delta f(35)+\{(1.5)\,.\,(1.5-1)/2!\}\,\Delta^2 f(35)+\frac{(1.5)\,(1.5-1)}{3!}(1.5-2)\,\Delta^3 f(35)$$

$$\Rightarrow\quad f(50)=13229+(1.5)\,(18139)+\frac{(1.5)\,(0.5)}{2!}(6086)+\frac{(1.5)\,(0.5)\,(-0.5)}{3!}(1185)$$

$$=13229+27208.5+2282.25-74.0625=42646 \text{ approx.}$$

Therefore required number of deaths between 45 and 50

$$=42646-31368=11278$$

Hence the number of deaths between 50 and 55

$$=24225-11278=12947.$$

Example 11: *If l_x represents the numbers living at age x in a life table, find accurately as data will permit, l_x for values of $x = 35, 42$ and 47, given $l_{20} = 512, l_{30} = 439, l_{40} = 346$ and $l_{50} = 243$.*

[Rajasthan 2002, 2007]

Solution: The difference table is as under:

x	l_x	Δl_x	$\Delta^2 l_x$	$\Delta^3 l_x$
20	512			
		– 73		
30	439		– 20	
		–93		10
40	346		–10	
		–103		
50	243			

To find l_{35}: $l_{35} = l_{20+10\times 3/2} = E^{3/2}\, l_{20} = (1+\Delta)^{3/2}\, l_{20}$

$$= l_{20} + \frac{3}{2}\Delta l_{20} + \frac{\left(\frac{3}{2}\right)\left(\frac{1}{2}\right)}{2!}\Delta^2 l_{20} + \frac{\left(\frac{3}{2}\right)\left(\frac{1}{2}\right)\left(-\frac{1}{2}\right)}{3!}\Delta^3 l_{20}$$

$$= 512 - \frac{3}{2}(73) - \frac{3}{8}(20) - \frac{1}{16}(10)$$

$$= 512 - 109.5 - 7.5 - .625 = 394.375 = 394 \text{ nearly.}$$

Similarly, we can find l_{42} and l_{47} which are $325.88, 315.66$.

Example 12: *The following table is given*

x	0	1	2	3	4
$f(x)$	3	6	11	18	27

What is the form of the function $f(x)$

[Bangaluru 2008; Mysore 2002, 2006]

Solution: The difference table is as under:

x	$f(x)$	$\Delta f(x)$	$\Delta^2 f(x)$	$\Delta^3 f(x)$
0	3			
		3		
1	6		2	
		5		0
2	11		2	
		7		0
3	18		2	
		9		
4	27			

We know that $f(a + hu) = f(a) + {}^{u}c_1 \Delta f(a) + {}^{u}c_2 \Delta^2 f(a)$

Here $a = 0$ and $h = 1$. $\therefore$ $a + hu = x$ or $u = x$

$$\therefore \quad f(x) = f(0) + {}^{x}c_1 \Delta f(0) + {}^{x}c_2 \Delta^2 f(0) \qquad \text{(Third difference is zero)}$$

$$= 3 + x(3) + \frac{x(x-1)}{2!}(2)$$

$$= 3 + 3x + x(x-1) = 3 + 3x + x^2 - x = x^2 + 2x + 3.$$

Example 13: *Given*

x :	1	2	3	4	5	6	7	8
$f(x)$:	1	8	27	64	125	216	343	512

Find $f(7.5)$. **[Avadh 2004; M.K.U. (Tamil Nadu) 2005]**

Solution: Obviously, the value to be interpolated lies at the end of the given observations *i.e.* near $x = 8$. Hence, in this case Newton's backward formula gives

$$u = \frac{x - (a + nh)}{h} = \frac{7.5 - 8}{1} = -0.5.$$

To Calculate Backward Differences

x	$f(x)$	$\nabla f(x)$	$\nabla^2 f(x)$	$\nabla^3 f(x)$
1	1			
		7		
2	8		12	
		19		6
3	27		18	
		37		6
4	64		24	
		61		6
5	125		30	
		91		6
6	216		36	
		127		6
7	343		**42**	
		169		
8	**512**			

But $\nabla^3 f(x)$ is constant, so we can leave higher order difference

Now by Newton's backward interpolation formula, we have

$$f(a+nh+uh) = f(a+nh) + u\nabla f(a+nh) + \frac{u(u+1)}{2\,!}\nabla^2 f(a+nh) + \frac{u(u+1)(u+2)}{3\,!}\nabla^3 f(a+nh).$$

$$\Rightarrow \quad f(7.5) = f(8) + (-0.5)\nabla f(8) + \frac{(-0.5)(-0.5+1)}{2}\nabla^2 f(8) + \frac{(-0.5)(-0.5+1)(-0.5+2)}{6}\nabla^3 f(8)$$

$$= 512 + (-0.5)\times 169 + \frac{(-0.5)(0.5)}{2}\times 42 + \frac{(-0.5)(0.5)(1.5)}{6}\times 6$$

$$= 512 - 84.5 - 5.25 - .375 = 421.875.$$

Example 14: *A second degree polynomial passes through* $(0,1),(1,3),(2,7)$ *and* $(3,13)$. *Find the polynomial.* **[Rajasthan 2005, 2009; Meerut 2005, 2008]**

Solution: Since the given observations are at equal intervals of width unity. Construct the following difference table.

x	$f(x)$	$\Delta f(x)$	$\Delta^2 f(x)$	$\Delta^3 f(x)$
0	1			
		2		
1	3		2	
		4		0
2	7		2	
		6		
3	13			

We have $f(x) = f(0) + {}^xc_1\,\Delta f(0) + {}^xc_2\,\Delta^2 f(0) = 1 + x\times 2 + \dfrac{x(x-1)}{2\,!}\times 2 = x^2 + x + 1.$

Example 15: *If p, q, r, s be the successive entries corresponding to equidistant arguments in a table, show that when third differences are taken into account, the entry corresponding to the argument half-way between arguments of q and r is* $A + \dfrac{1}{24}B$, *where A is the arithmetic mean of q and r and B is the arithmetic mean of* $3q - 2p - s$ *and* $3r - 2s - p$.

[Nagpur 2006, 2009; Delhi (H) 2005, 2008; Venketeswara 2004, 2007, 2009; M.K.U. (Tamil Nadu) 2005, 2007]

Solution: Let the equidistant arguments be $a, a+h, a+2h$ and $a+3h$, h being the intervals and p, q, r, s be their respective entries.

x	$f(x)$	$\Delta f(x)$	$\Delta^2 f(x)$	$\Delta^3 f(x)$
a	p			
		$q-p$		
$a+h$	q		$r-2q+p$	
		$r-q$		$s-3r+3q-p$
$a+2h$	r		$s-2r+q$	
		$s-r$		
$a+3h$	s			

Now the argument half-way between the arguments of q and r is $\frac{1}{2}(a+h+a+2h)$ *i.e.* $a+\frac{3}{2}h$, thus the required entry is given by

$$f\left(a+\frac{3}{2}h\right)=E^{3/2}f(a)=(1+\Delta)^{3/2}f(a)$$

$$=f(a)+\frac{3}{2}\Delta f(a)+\frac{\left(\frac{3}{2}\right)\left(\frac{1}{2}\right)}{2!}\Delta^2 f(a)+\frac{\left(\frac{3}{2}\right)\left(\frac{1}{2}\right)\left(-\frac{1}{2}\right)}{3!}\Delta^3 f(a)$$

$$=p+\frac{3}{2}(q-p)+\frac{3}{8}(r-2q+p)-\frac{1}{16}(s-3r+3q-p)$$

$$=p\left(1-\frac{3}{2}+\frac{3}{8}+\frac{1}{16}\right)+q\left(\frac{3}{2}-\frac{3}{4}-\frac{3}{16}\right)+r\left(\frac{3}{8}+\frac{3}{16}\right)-\frac{1}{16}s$$

$$=-\frac{1}{16}p+\frac{9}{16}q+\frac{9}{16}r-\frac{1}{16}s$$

$$=\frac{1}{2}(q+r)+\frac{1}{16}(q+r-p-s) \qquad ...(1)$$

Now $\quad$ A = arithmetic mean of q and $r=\frac{q+r}{2}$

B = arithmetic mean of $3q-2p-s$ and $3r-2s-p$

$$=\frac{1}{2}[3q-2p-s+3r-2s-p]=\frac{3}{2}(q+r-p-s).$$

$$\therefore \qquad A+\frac{1}{24}B=\frac{1}{2}(q+r)+\frac{1}{16}(q+r-p-s).$$

Thus from (1), we get, $f\left(a+\frac{3}{2}h\right)=A+\frac{1}{24}B.$

Example 16: *Taking fifth order differences of U_x to be constant and given $U_0, U_1, \ldots, U_6$. Prove that* $U_{5/2}=\frac{1}{2}c+\frac{25(c-q)+3(a-c)}{256}$

where $\qquad a=U_0+U_5, b=U_1+U_4, c=U_2+U_3.$

[Meerut 2008; Kanpur 2003, 2004, 2006; I.A.S. 2003; U.P. P.C.S. 2003; Agra 2003, 2007]

Solution: $U_{5/2}=E^{5/2}U_0=(1+\Delta)^{5/2}U_0$

$$=U_0+\frac{5}{2}\Delta U_0+\frac{\frac{5}{2}\left(\frac{5}{2}-1\right)}{2!}\Delta^2U_0+\frac{\frac{5}{2}\left(\frac{5}{2}-1\right)\left(\frac{5}{2}-2\right)}{3!}\Delta^3U_0$$

$$+\frac{\frac{5}{2}\left(\frac{5}{2}-1\right)\left(\frac{5}{2}-2\right)\left(\frac{5}{2}-3\right)}{4!}\Delta^4U_0+\frac{\frac{5}{2}\left(\frac{5}{2}-1\right)\left(\frac{5}{2}-2\right)\left(\frac{5}{2}-3\right)\left(\frac{5}{2}-4\right)}{5!}\Delta^5U_0$$

$$= U_0 + \frac{5}{2}\Delta U_0 + \frac{15}{8}\Delta^2 U_0 + \frac{5}{16}\Delta^3 U_0 - \frac{5}{128}\Delta^4 U_0 + \frac{3}{256}\Delta^5 U_0$$

$$= U_0 + \frac{5}{2}(E-1)U_0 + \frac{15}{8}(E-1)^2 U_0 + \frac{5}{16}(E-1)^3 U_0$$

$$- \frac{5}{128}(E-1)^4 U_0 + \frac{3}{256}(E-1)^5 U_0$$

$$= U_0 + \frac{5}{2}(U_1 - U_0) + \frac{15}{8}(E^2 - 2E + 1)U_0 + \frac{5}{16}(E^3 - 3E^2 + 3E - 1)U_0$$

$$- \frac{5}{128}(E^4 - 4E^3 + 6E^2 - 4E + 1)U_0 + \frac{3}{256}[E^5 - 5E^4 + 10E^3 - 10E^2 + 5E - 1]U_0$$

$$= U_0 + \frac{5}{2}(U_4 - U_1) + \frac{15}{8}(U_2 - 2U_1 + U_0) + \frac{5}{16}(U_3 - 3U_2 + 3U_1 - U_0)$$

$$- \frac{5}{128}(U_4 - 4U_3 + 6U_2 - 4U_1 + U_0) + \frac{3}{256}(U_5 - 5U_4 + 10U_3 - 10U_2 + 5U_1 - U_0)$$

$$= U_0\left(1 - \frac{5}{2} + \frac{15}{8} - \frac{5}{16} - \frac{5}{128} - \frac{3}{256}\right) + U_1\left(\frac{5}{2} - \frac{15}{4} + \frac{15}{16} + \frac{5}{32} + \frac{15}{256}\right)$$

$$+ U_2\left(\frac{15}{8} - \frac{15}{16} - \frac{15}{64} - \frac{15}{128}\right) + U_3\left(\frac{5}{16} + \frac{5}{32} + \frac{15}{128}\right) + U_4\left(-\frac{5}{128} - \frac{15}{256}\right) + \frac{3}{256}U_5$$

$$= \frac{3}{256}U_0 - \frac{25}{256}U_1 + \frac{75}{128}U_2 + \frac{75}{128}U_3 - \frac{25}{256}U_4 + \frac{3}{256}U_5$$

$$= \frac{3}{256}(U_0 + U_5) - \frac{25}{256}(U_1 + U_4) + \frac{75}{128}(U_2 + U_3)$$

$$= \frac{3}{256}a - \frac{25}{256}b + \frac{75}{128}c = \frac{3a}{256} - \frac{25b}{256} + \left(\frac{1}{2} + \frac{11}{128}\right)c$$

$$= \frac{1}{2}c + \frac{3a - 25b + 22c}{256} = \frac{1}{2}c + \frac{3a - 25b + 25c - 3c}{256} = \frac{1}{2}c + \frac{3(a-c) + 25(c-b)}{256}$$

Example 17: *Show that Newton-Gregory interpolation formula can be put in the form,* $u_x = u_0 + x\Delta u_0 - xa\Delta^2 u_0 + xab\Delta^3 u_0 - xabc\,\Delta^4 u_0 + \ldots$

where $a = 1 - \frac{1}{2}(x+1), b = 1 - \frac{1}{3}(x+1), c = 1 - \frac{1}{4}(x+1)$ etc.

[Meerut 2006; Avadh 2005, 2007]

Solution: $a = 1 - \frac{1}{2}(x+1), \quad \therefore \quad -a = \frac{1}{2}(x+1) - 1 = \frac{1}{2}(x-1),$

$b = 1 - \frac{1}{3}(x+1). \quad \therefore \quad -b = \frac{1}{3}(x+1) - 1 = \frac{1}{3}(x-2),$

Similarly $\quad -c = \frac{1}{4}(x+1) - 1 = \frac{1}{4}(x-3), \quad -d = \frac{1}{5}(x+1) - 1 = \frac{1}{5}(x-4)$ etc.

Again $$u_x = u_0 + \frac{x}{1}\Delta u_0 + \frac{x(x-1)}{2.1}\Delta^2 u_0 + \frac{x(x-1)(x-2)}{1.2.3}\Delta^3 u_0 + \frac{x(x-1)(x-2)(x-3)}{2.3.4}\Delta^4 u_0 + \ldots$$

$$= u_0 + x\Delta u_0 + x\left(\frac{x-1}{2}\right)\Delta^2 u_0 + x\left(\frac{x-1}{2}\right)\left(\frac{x-2}{3}\right)\Delta^3 u_0 + x\left(\frac{x-1}{2}\right)\left(\frac{x-2}{3}\right)\left(\frac{x-3}{4}\right)\Delta^4 u_0 +$$

$$= u_0 + x\Delta u_0 + x(-a)\Delta^2 u_0 + x(-a)(-b)\Delta^3 u_0 + x(-a)(-b)(-c)\Delta^4 u_0 + \ldots$$

$$= u_0 + x\Delta u_0 - xa\Delta^2 u_0 + xab\Delta^3 u_0 - xabc\Delta^4 u_0 + \ldots$$

2.3 Sub-division of Intervals

In some cases observations are given at the intervals of width *e.g.* at 10, 20 and it is required to complete the series $f(0), f(1), f(2), \ldots$; then in usual way, we will interpolate the values for $x = 1$ and $x = 2$ and so on; in this way calculations become very tedious. In order to make the procedure simple, the following method is adopted which is known as ***sub-division of intervals.***

Let $\delta f(x)$ denote the difference for unit intervals of x and $\Delta f(x)$ denote the difference when interval of differencing is h.

Then,

$$E^h f(x) = ef(x) = f(x+h) \quad \ldots(1)$$

where E and e are operators for unit and h intervals respectively.

Now $E = 1 + \delta$ and $e = 1 + \Delta$. Putting these values in (1), we get

$$(1+\delta)^h f(x) = (1+\Delta) f(x)$$

or $$(1+\delta)^h \equiv (1+\Delta) \quad \text{or} \quad (1+\delta) \equiv (1+\Delta)^{1/h} \quad \ldots(2)$$

or $$(1+\delta) = 1 + \frac{1}{h}\Delta + \frac{\frac{1}{h}\left(\frac{1}{h}-1\right)}{2!}\Delta^2 + \ldots$$

or $$\delta = \frac{1}{h}\Delta + \frac{\frac{1}{h}\left(\frac{1}{h}-1\right)}{2!}\Delta^2 + \ldots \quad \ldots(3)$$

Equation (3) is a relation between δ and Δ, which can be used to determine $f(1), f(2)$, with the help of difference table.

Let $h = 4$; then, $$\delta = \frac{1}{4}\Delta + \frac{\frac{1}{4}\left(\frac{1}{4}-1\right)}{2!}\Delta^2 + \ldots$$

$$= 0.25\,\Delta + \frac{0.25\,(0.25-1)}{2!}\Delta^2 + \ldots = 0.25\,\Delta - 0.0937\,\Delta^2 + \ldots$$

Example 18: *Given* $u_1 = 1, u_2 + u_3 = 5.41, u_4 + u_5 + u_6 = 18.47,$

$u_7 + u_8 + u_9 + u_{10} + u_{11} + u_{12} = 90.36$. *Find the value of* u_x *for all values of x, for* $x = 1, 2, \ldots, 12$.

Solution: According to given data, we have

$$f(1) = \sum_{x=1}^{12} u_x = 115.24,\ f(4) = \sum_{x=4}^{12} u_x = 108.83,\ f(7) = \sum_{x=7}^{12} u_x = 90.36.$$

Above values are at intervals of 3 and with the help of method of sub-division, we can complete the series.

Difference table for Observations at Interval of 3

x	$f(x)$	$\Delta f(x)$	$\Delta^2 f(x)$
1	115.24		
		−6.41	
4	108.83		−12.06
		−18.47	
7	90.36		

Now if δ be the difference for interval of unity and Δ is the corresponding difference with interval 3, then from 2.3 equation (3), we get, $\delta = \left(\frac{1}{3}\Delta - \frac{1}{9}\Delta^2 + \ldots\right)$.

$$\therefore \quad \delta f(1) = \left(\frac{1}{3}\Delta - \frac{1}{9}\Delta^2 + \ldots\right) f(1)$$

$$= \frac{1}{3}\Delta f(1) - \frac{1}{9}\Delta^2 f(1) + \ldots = \frac{1}{3}(-6.41) - \frac{1}{9}(-12.06) = -0.80.$$

Again $\quad \delta^2 f(1) = \delta.\delta f(1) = \left(\frac{1}{3}\Delta - \frac{1}{9}\Delta^2 + \ldots\right)^2 f(1)$

$$= \frac{1}{9}\Delta^2 f(1) = \frac{1}{9}(-12.06) = -1.34,$$

$$\delta f(4) = \left(\frac{1}{3}\Delta - \frac{1}{9}\Delta^2 + \ldots\right) f(4) = \frac{1}{3}(-18.47) - \frac{1}{9}(-12.06) = -4.82,$$

$$\delta^2 f(4) = \frac{1}{9}\Delta^2 f(4) = \frac{1}{9}(-12.06) = -1.34.$$

Now we Construct the Difference Table for Intervals:

x	$f(x)=\sum_{x}^{12} u_x$	$\delta f(x)$	$\delta^2 f(x)$	$f(x)-f(x+1)$
1	**115.24**			1.00
2	114.24	**−0.80**	**−1.34**	2.14
3	112.10	−2.14	−1.34	3.27
4	**108.83**	−3.48	−1.34	4.82
5	104.01	−4.82	−1.34	6.16
6	97.85	−6.16	−1.34	7.50
7	**90.36**	−7.50	−1.34	8.84
8	81.52	−8.84	−1.34	10.18
9	71.34	−10.18	−1.34	11.52
10	59.82	−11.52	−1.34	12.86
11	**46.96**	−12.86	−1.34	14.20
12	32.76	−14.20	−1.34	**32.76**

Dark figures in the table are for three given observations:

Since given observations are three, so second differences will be constant, each being equal to -1.34. The other figures of the table are obtained by reading it in the reverse order *e.g.* $-2.14=-0.80+(-1.34)$ and $112.10=-2.14+114.24$ and so on.

Hence the values of u_x for all values of x from 1 to 12 will be $1.00, 2.14, 3.27, 4.82, 6.16, 7.50, 8.84, 10.18, 11.52, 12.86, 14.20, 32.76$.

Example 19: *Given* $\sum_{1}^{10} f(x)=500426, \sum_{4}^{10} f(x)=329240, \sum_{7}^{10} f(x)=175212$ *and* $f(10)=40365$. *Find* $f(1)$. **[Kanpur 2008]**

Solution: According to the given data, we have $u_1=f(10)=40365$,

$$u_4=\sum_{7}^{10} f(x)=175212,\ u_7=\sum_{4}^{10} f(x)=329240,\ u_{10}=\sum_{1}^{10} f(x)=500426.$$

It is required to find δu_0, since $f(1)=u_{10}-u_9=\delta u_9$.

Values of u_1, u_4, u_7 and u_{10} are given and it is required to complete the series $u_1, u_2, u_3, \ldots$

Construct the following difference table:

x	u_x	Δu_x	$\Delta^2 u_x$	$\Delta^3 u_x$
1	40365			
		134847		
4	175212		19181	
		154028		−2023
7	329240		17158	
		171186		
10	500426			

Now only four observations are given, third differences are constant.

Now from **2.3** equation **3**, putting $h = 3$, we get

$$\delta u_x = \frac{1}{3}\Delta u_x - \frac{1}{9}\Delta^2 u_x + \frac{5}{31}\Delta^3 u_x = \frac{1}{3}(134847) - \frac{1}{9}(19181) + \frac{5}{31}(-2023) = 42692.90,$$

$$\delta^2 u_x = \frac{1}{9}\Delta^2 u_x - \frac{2}{27}\Delta^3 u_x = 2281.07.$$

$$\delta^3 u_x = \frac{1}{27}\Delta^3 u_x = -74.92 \text{ (upto 2 places of decimals).}$$

Now construct the difference table for unit intervals:

x	u_x	δu_x	$\delta^2 u_x$	$\delta^3 u_x$
1	**40365**			
2		**42692.90**		
3		44973.97	**2281.07**	**−74.92**
4		47180.12	2206.15	−74.92
5		49311.35	2131.23	−74.92
6		51367.66	2056.31	−74.92
7		53349.05	1981.39	−74.92
8		55255.52	1906.47	−74.92
9		57087.07	1831.55	−74.92
10		58843.70	1756.63	−74.92

From the above table $f(1) = \delta u_9 = 58843.70$.

✦✦ Problem Set ✦✦

1. What do you understand by interpolation? What are the underlying assumptions for the validity of the various methods used for interpolation?

[Delhi (H) 2002, 2005, 2009; Agra 2008]

2. (i) Establish an interpolation formula for equal intervals.

[Delhi (H) 2003; Meerut 2003]

(ii) Prove the following interpolation formula due to Newton

$$f(x) = f(0) + x\Delta(-1) + x(x+1)/2!\,\Delta^2 f(-2)\ldots$$

given values of $f(x)$ *for* $x = 0, -1, -2, \ldots$ **[Agra 2005]**

3. Estimate the production of cotton in the year 1935 from the data given below:

Year :	1931	1932	1933	1934	1935	1936	1937
Production : (in millions of bales)	17.1	13.0	14.0	9.6	–	12.4	18.2

4. Find the values of sin 30° 15′ 30″ from the following table:

Angle $x°$:	30	31	32	33	34
sin $x°$:	.5000	.5150	.5299	.5446	.5592

5. Find (i) $\log_{10} 5.2374$, (ii) $\log_{10} 5.4933$ from the following table:

x :	0.00	0.25	0.50	0.75
erf (x) :	0.0000	0.27633	0.52049	0.71116

6. From the following table of yearly premiums for policies maturing at quinquennial ages, estimate the premiums for policies maturing at the ages of 46 years:

Age	x :	45	50	55	60	65
Premium	y_x :	2.871	2.404	2.083	1.862	1.712

[I.P.S. 2002]

7. By the method of interpolation, estimate the missing value in the following table of rice cultivation giving area in 10,00,000 hactares.

Year :	1911	1912	1913	1914	1915	1916	1917	1918	1919
Area :	76.6	78.7	?	77.7	78.7	79.5	80.6	77.6	78.7

[Avadh 2003]

8. In an examination the number of candidates who secured marks between certain limits were as follows:

Marks	No. of Candidates
0 – 19	41
20 – 39	62
40 – 59	65
60 – 79	50
80 – 99	17

Estimate the number of candidates getting marks less than 70.

9. The length of the day was 12 hours on March 19th, 14 hours on April 18th and 15th hours 40 minutes on May 18th. Estimate (i) the length of the day on May 3rd (ii) the mean length of the day during the period. March 19th to May 18th.

Hint: (i) $y_0 = 12, y_{30} = 14, y_{60} = 15\frac{40}{60} = \frac{47}{3}$

$$y_{45} = E^{3/2}\ y_0 = \frac{3}{2}\Delta y_0 + \frac{\frac{3}{2}\cdot\frac{1}{2}}{2!}\Delta^2 y_0 = 14\frac{7}{8} \text{ hours.}$$

(ii) We have $12 = \frac{\Sigma x_1}{30} \quad \Rightarrow \quad \Sigma x_1 = 360$

$$\Sigma x_2 = 30 \times 14 = 420, \Sigma x_3 = 30 \times \frac{47}{3} = 470$$

$$\text{Mean length} = \frac{360 + 420 + 470}{30 + 30 + 30} = 13\frac{8}{9} \text{ hours.}$$

10. The following table gives the amount of a chemical dissolved in water:

Temp :	10°	15°	20°	25°	30°	35°
Solubility :	19.97	21.51	22.47	23.52	24.65	25.89

Compute the amount dissolved at 22° and 8°.

11. Using Newton's backward interpolation formula, find the declinations at $2^h\ 35^m\ 15^s$ and 5^h respectively:

Hours :	0	1	2	3	4
Declinations :	8°20′53.7″	8°18′19.4″	8°6′43.5″	7°55′6.1″	7°43′27.2″

12. Apply Gregory-Newton backward formula to the following table to find sun's declination on Feb. 12 :

Date :	1	3	5	
Declination:	−17°0′19.0″	−16°25′22.9″	−15°49′18.8″	
Date :	7	9	11	13
Declination:	−15°12′09.8″	−14°33′59.1″	−13°54′49.8″	−13°14′45.0″

[Delhi (H) 2004]

13. From the following data, find the value of u_{47} (state explicitly the hypothesis you make)

$$u_{46} = 0.2884, u_{48} = 0.5356, u_{49} = 0.6513 \text{ and } u_{50} = 0.7620.$$

[Kurukshetra 2006]

14. By constructing a difference table, find the *7th* term as well as the general term of the sequence 0, 0, 2, 6, 12, 20.

15. Find polynomial which fits the data in the following table

x	3	5	7	9	11
y	6	24	58	108	174

16. Given the following table find (i) $e^{0.243}$ (ii) $e^{0.411}$

x	0.1	0.2	0.3	0.4	0.5
e^x	1.10517	1.2140	1.34986	1.49182	1.64872

17. The gamma function, $\Gamma(x)$ is tabulated for various values of x in the following table:

x	1.15	1.16	1.17	1.18	1.19
$\Gamma(x)$	0.93304	0.92980	0.92670	0.92373	0.92088

Find $\Gamma(1.1673)$.

18. What do you understand by interpolation? State the underlying assumption for the validity of various methods used for the interpolation.

[Avadh 2003]

✦✦ Objective Type Question ✦✦

❖ Multiple Choice Questions

1. If $f(x)$ is given at the points $a = x_0, x_1, x_2 \dots x_n = b$ of the interval $[a, b]$, where $x_0 < x_1 < x_2 \dots < x_n = b$, then the problem of finding $f(x)$ at a point lying in any of the sub-intervals $[x_{r-1}, x_r]$ is knowns as:

(a) extrapolation (b) interpolation

(c) correlation (d) estimation **[Rohilkhand 2009]**

2. The $(n+1)^{th}$ term in Newton-Gregory's forward interpolation formula is:

(a) $\dfrac{\Delta f(a)}{\underline{|n}\, h^n}(x-a)(x-a-h)\dots(x-a-nh+h)$

(b) $\dfrac{\Delta f(x)}{\underline{|n}\, h^n}(x-a)(x-a-h)\dots(x-a-nh-h)$

(c) $\dfrac{\Delta^{n+1} f(a)}{(n+1)!\, h^{n+1}}(x-a)(x-a-h)\dots(x-a-nh)$

(d) $\dfrac{\Delta f(a)}{n!\, h^n}(x-a)(x-a-h)\dots(x-a-nh)$

3. The $(n+1)^{th}$ term in Newton-Gregory's backward interpolation formula is

(a) $\dfrac{\nabla^{n+1} f(a+nh)}{(n+1)!\, h^{n+1}}(x-a-nh-h)\dots(n-a-h)$

(b) $\dfrac{\nabla^n f(a+nh)}{n!\, h^n}(x-a-nh-h)\dots(x-a-h)$

(c) $\dfrac{\nabla^n f(a+nh)}{n!\, h^n}(x-a-nh)\dots(x-a-h)$

(d) $\dfrac{\nabla^n f(a+nh)}{n!\, h^n}(x-a-nh+h)\dots(x-a-h)$

4. If $y_0 = 580, y_1 = 556, y_2 = 520, y_4 = 384$ value of y_3 is

(a) 1860 (b) 930

(c) 465 (d) 234

5. Newton-Gregory formula for forward interpolation is used for

(a) equal interval (b) unequal interval

(c) central difference (d) None of these **[Rohilkhand 2010]**

6. Value of $e^2 f(x)$, where e is the shift operator is:

(a) $f(x+2h)$ (b) $f(x-2h)$

(c) $f(x \pm 2h)$ (d) None of these

7. The value of y_{25} when $y_{20}=24$, $y_{24}=32$, $y_{28}=35$, $y_{32}=40$ is

(a) 32.926 (b) 20.453

(c) 18.524 (d) 1.000 **[Garhwal 2008]**

✦✦ Examination Questions ✦✦

1. The following are the measurements t made on a curve recorded by the oscillograph representing a change of current i due to a change in the conditions of an electric current:

t :	1.5	2.0	2.5	3.0
i :	1.36	0.58	0.34	0.20

Applying an appropriate formula interpolate for the value of i when $t=1.6$.

2. Find the cubic polynomial which takes the following values:

$$y_{(0)}=1,\ y_{(1)}=0,\ y_{(2)}=1 \quad \text{and} \quad y_{(3)}=10$$

Hence or otherwise, obtain $y(4)$. **[I.A.S. 2002; U.P.T.U. 2008]**

3. The following values of the function $f(x)=\sin x+\cos x$ are given:

x :	10°	20°	30°
$f(x)$:	1.1585	1.2817	1.3360

Construct the quadratic interpolating formula that fits the data. Hence calculate $f\left(\frac{\pi}{12}\right)$. Compare with exact value.

[I.A.S. 2008]

4. In the following table the values of x and y are given:

x :	0.00	0.250	0.50	0.75	1.00
y :	0.46	0.39	0.25	0.12	0.04

Use Newton-Gregory's interpolation formula to deduce the value of y when $x=0.1$.

5. Find the first and second derivatives at $x = 1.1$ for the function of the following table:

x :	1.0	1.2	1.4	1.6	1.8	2.00
y :	0	0.1280	0.5440	1.2960	2.4320	4.00

6. Find from the following table, the area bounded by the curve $y = f(x)$ and the x – axis from $x = 7.47$ to $x = 7.52$:

x :	7.47	7.48	7.49	7.50	7.51	7.52
$f(x)$:	1.93	1.95	1.98	2.01	2.03	2.06

7. Derive the difference formula for the second order differentiation of $f(x)$ using the backward difference operator. Also, find its order of error of approximation.

8. Find the derivative of $f(x)$ at $x = 0.4$ from the following table:

x	0.1	0.2	0.3	0.4
$f(x)$	1.10517	1.22140	1.34986	1.49182

9. Find the missing term in the table:

(i)

x :	2	3	4	5	6
$f(x)$:	45	49.2	54.1	–	67.4

[U.P.T.U. 2008]

(ii)

Year :	1961	1962	1963	1964	1965	1966	1967
Production :	200	220	260	–	350	–	430

[U.P.T.U. 2002]

(iii)

x :	1	2	3	4	5
$f(x)$:	7	–	13	21	37

[U.P.T.U. 2002]

(iv)

x :	2.0	2.1	2.2	2.3	2.4	2.5	2.6
y :	0.135	–	0.111	0.100	–	0.082	0.074

[Garhwal 2004, 2008; U.P.T.U. 2004]

10. Find the value at age of 46 from the given table:

Age :	45	50	55	60	65
Premium:	114.84	96.16	83.32	74.48	68.48

[U.P.T.U. 2004]

11. Find the cubic polynomial which takes the following values:

x :	0	1	2	3
$f(x)$:	1	2	1	10

[U.P.T.U. 2002, 2008]

12. Find the polynomial from the following data given the distances in nautical miles of the visible horizon for the given heights in feet above the earth's surface.

x :	100	150	200	250	300	350	400
y :	10.63	13.03	15.04	16.81	18.42	19.90	21.27

[U.P.T.U. 2009]

13. Find the polynomial of degree four which takes the following values:

x :	2	4	6	8	10
y :	0	0	1	0	0

[U.P.T.U. 2007]

14. Evaluate from the following table $f(3.8)$ to 3 significant figure using Newton-Gregory backward formula:

x :	0	1	2	3	4
$f(x)$:	1	1.5	2.2	3.1	4.6

[U.P.T.U. 2009]

✦✦ Answers ✦✦

❖ Problem Set

3.	6.60	**4.**	0.5039	**5.**	(i) 0.71911
	(ii) 0.73983	**6.**	(i) 0.30788		(ii) 0.62705
	(iii) 0.84270	**7.**	6.60	**8.**	194
9.	(i) $14\frac{7}{8}$ hours		(ii) $13\frac{8}{9}$ hours	**10.**	22.8616
	and 18.9158	**11.**	7°47′36.8″ and 7°31′46.9″		
12.	−13°33′40.7″	**13.**	$u_{47} = .4147$	**14.**	30; $r(r-1)$
15.	$2x^2 - 7x + 9$	**16.**	(i) 1.27507		(ii) 1.50833
17.	0.92723				

❖ Multiple Choice Questions

1.	(b)	**2.**	(a)	**3.**	(c)	**4.**	(c)	**5.**	(a)
6.	(a)	**7.**	(a)						

◆ Examination Questions

1.	0.76	2.	$y(x) = x^3 - 2x^2 + 1,\ y(4) = 33$
3.	$1.1585 + .1232\,u + .03445\,u(u-1),\ u = \dfrac{x-10}{10}$		
4.	0.43512	5.	$f'(1.1) = 0.63,\ f''(1.1) = 6.6$
6.	0.15	8.	1.49133
9.	(i) 48.8		(ii) $f(1964) = 304,\ f(1966) = 390$
	(iii) $f(2) = 9.5$		(iv) $f(2.1) = .123,\ f(2.4) = 0.090$
10.	$y(x) = 110.525632$	11.	$f(x) = 2x^3 - 7x^2 + 6x + 1$
12.	15.6993 nautical miles	13.	$y = \dfrac{1}{2}u(u-1)(u-2)(u-3),\ u = \dfrac{x-2}{2}$
14.	10.7204		

Theory | Solved Examples | Problem Set

Chapter 3

Interpolation with Unequal Intervals

Divided differences, Properties, Newton's formula for unequal intervals, Divided differences and ordinary differences, Sheppard's rule, Lagrange's interpolation formula for unequal intervals, Iterative method, Spline interpolation, Hermite interpolation formula.

3.1 Introduction

In chapter 2 all the interpolation formulae for the function $y = f(x)$ are applicable when the arguments are given at equal intervals. In such cases for finding the various differences we simply consider the differences between successive values of the entry and do not take into account the corresponding changes in the values of the argument. In case the values of the arguments are given at unequal intervals then the various differences will be effected with the change in values of the argument and consequently definition of various differences for equal intervals will not hold good. *The differences defined by taking into consideration the change in the values of the argument are called divided differences.*

3.2 Divided Differences

Let $f(x_0), f(x_1) \ldots, f(x_n)$ be the values of the function $y = f(x)$ corresponding to the values $x_0, x_1, \ldots, x_n$ of the arguments x, where $x_1 - x_0, x_2 - x_1, \ldots, x_n - x_{n-1}$, are not necessarily equal, *i.e.* when there is a case of unequal intervals.

The first divided differences of $f(x)$ for the arguments x_0, x_1 is defined as $\dfrac{f(x_1) - f(x_0)}{x_1 - x_0}$

and is denoted by $f(x_0, x_1)$ or by $\underset{x_1}{\Delta} f(x_0)$

Similarly the other divided differences of $f(x)$ for the arguments

$$x_1, x_2 ; x_2, x_3; \ldots, x_{n-1}, x_n; \text{ are } f(x_1, x_2) = \frac{f(x_2) - f(x_1)}{x_2 - x_1} = \underset{x_2}{\Delta} f(x_1)$$

$$f(x_2, x_3) = \frac{f(x_3) - f(x_2)}{x_3 - x_2} = \underset{x_3}{\Delta} f(x_2)$$

$$\ldots \quad \ldots \quad \ldots \quad \ldots \quad \ldots \quad \ldots \quad \ldots$$

$$f(x_{n-1}, x_n) = \frac{f(x_n) - f(x_{n-1})}{x_n - x_{n-1}} = \underset{x_n}{\Delta} f(x_{n-1})$$

Again the second and higher divided differences are defined in terms of lower divided differences, *e.g.* the second divided differences of $f(x)$, for the three arguments is given by $\frac{f(x_1, x_2) - f(x_0, x_1)}{x_2 - x_0}$ and is denoted by $f(x_0, x_1, x_2)$ or by $\underset{x_1, x_2}{\Delta^2} f(x_0)$. Similarly the nth divided difference is given by

$$\frac{f(x_1, x_2, \ldots, x_n) - f(x_0, x_1, \ldots, x_{n-1})}{x_n - x_0}$$

This is denoted by $f(x_0, x_1, \ldots, x_n)$ or by $\underset{x_1, x_2, \ldots, x_n}{\overset{n}{\Delta}} f(x_0)$.

Note: In case two arguments coincide, the divided differences can be given a meaning *e.g.*

$$f(x_0, x_0) = \lim_{\varepsilon \to 0} f(x_0 + \varepsilon, x_0) = \lim_{\varepsilon \to 0} \frac{f(x_0 + \varepsilon) - f(x_0)}{\varepsilon} = f'(x_0).$$

Similarly, we can show that

$$f(x_0, x_0, x_0) = \frac{1}{2!} f''(x) \text{ and finally}$$

$$f(x_0, x_1, x_2, \ldots, x_0) \text{ upto } (r+1) \text{ arguments} = \frac{1}{r!} f^r(x_0).$$

3.3 Properties of Divided Differences

***Theorem 1**: Divided differences are symmetric functions of their arguments, i.e. the value of any divided difference is independent of the order of the order of the argument.*

[Meerut 2002, 2003; I.A.S. 2005; Rohilkhand 2008]

Proof:

$$f(x_0, x_1) = \frac{f(x_1) - f(x_0)}{x_1 - x_0} = \frac{f(x_0) - f(x_1)}{x_0 - x_1} = f(x_1, x_0) = \underset{x_1}{\Delta} f(x_0).$$

Also

$$f(x_0, x_1) = \frac{f(x_1)}{x_1 - x_0} + \frac{f(x_0)}{x_0 - x_1} = \Sigma \frac{f(x_0)}{x_0 - x_1}$$

Again

$$f(x_0, x_1, x_2) = \frac{f(x_1, x_2) - f(x_0, x_1)}{x_2 - x_0}$$

$$= \frac{1}{x_2 - x_0}\left[\frac{f(x_2) - f(x_1)}{x_2 - x_1} - \frac{f(x_1) - f(x_0)}{x_1 - x_0}\right]$$

$$= \frac{f(x_2)}{(x_2 - x_0)(x_2 - x_1)} + \frac{f(x_1)}{(x_1 - x_0)(x_1 - x_2)} + \frac{f(x_0)}{(x_0 - x_1)(x_0 - x_2)}$$

$$= \Sigma \frac{f(x_0)}{(x_0 - x_1)(x_0 - x_2)},$$

which is a symmetric function $f(x)$ of the arguments x_0, x_1 and x_2.

Thus $\quad f(x_0, x_1, x_2) = f(x_2, x_1, x_0) = f(x_1, x_2, x_0)$ etc.,

i.e., we can choose any of the permutations of the arguments x_0, x_1 and x_2 for the notation. By mathematical induction, we can prove that

$$f(x_0, x_1, \ldots, x_n) = \frac{f(x_n)}{(x_n - x_0)(x_n - x_1)\ldots(x_n - x_{n-1})}$$

$$+ \frac{f(x_{n-1})}{(x_{n-1} - x_0)(x_{n-1} - x_1)\ldots(x_{n-1} - x_n)} + \ldots + \frac{f(x_0)}{(x_0 - x_1)(x_0 - x_2)\ldots(x_0 - x_n)}$$

$$= f \text{ (any one of the permutations of the arguments } x_0, x_1, \ldots, x_n).$$

Thus we observe that the value of a divided difference depends only on the values of the arguments involved and not on the order in which they involve.

***Theorem* 2**: *The nth divided differences of a polynomial of the nth degree are constant.*

[Lucknow 2006; Rohilkhand 2007; Bhopal 2002, 2008; Avadh 2004, 2010]

Proof: Consider a function $f(x) = x^n$.

The first divided differences of $f(x)$ for the arguments x_r, x_{r+1} are

$$f(x_r, x_{r+1}) = \frac{f(x_{r+1}) - f(x_r)}{x_{r+1} - x_r} = \frac{x_{r+1}^n - x_r^n}{x_{r+1} - x_r}$$

$$= x_{r+1}^{n-1} + x_r\, x_{r+1}^{n-2} + \ldots + x_r^{n-2}\, x_{r+1} + x_r^{n-1}.$$

This is a symmetric function of the $(n-1)^{th}$ degree in x_r, x_{r+1}.

The second divided difference of $f(x)$ for the arguments x_r, x_{r+1}, x_{r+2} is given by

$$f(x_r, x_{r+1}, x_{r+2}) = \frac{f(x_r, x_{r+1}) - f(x_{r+1}, x_{r+2})}{x_r - x_{r+2}}$$

$$= \frac{f(x_{r+1}, x_{r+2}) - f(x_r, x_{r+1})}{x_{r+2} - x_r}$$

$$= \Big[\left(x_{r+2}^{n-1} + x_{r+1}\, x_{r+2}^{n-2} + \ldots + x_{r+1}^{n-2}\, x_{r+2} + x_{r+1}^{n-1}\right)$$

$$- \left(x_{r+2}^{n-1} + x_r\, x_{r+1}^{n-2} + \ldots + x_r^{n-2}\, x_{r+1} + x_r^{n-1}\right)\Big] \Big/ (x_{r+2} - x_r)$$

$$= \frac{x_{r+2}^{n-1} - x_r^{n-1}}{x_{r+2} - x_r} + \frac{x_{r+1}\left(x_{r+2}^{n-2} - x_r^{n-2}\right)}{x_{r+2} - x_r} + \ldots + \frac{x_{r+1}^{n-2}\,(x_{r+2} - x_r)}{x_{r+2} - x_r}$$

$$= (x_{r+2}^{n-2} + \ldots + x_r^{n-2}) + x_{r+1}\,(x_{r+2}^{n-3} + \ldots + x_r^{n-3}) + \ldots + x_{r+1}^{n-2}.$$

This is a symmetric function of $(n-2)^{\text{th}}$ degree in x_r, x_{r+1} and x_{r+2}.

By induction it can be shown that $f(x_r, x_{r+1}, \ldots, x_{r+m})$ is a symmetric function of degree $n-m$. In particular, the nth divided difference of $f(x) = x^n$ is constant and therefore independent of the values of $x_r, x_{r+1}, x_{r+2}, \ldots, x_{r+n}$. If the coefficient of x^n is a_n then the nth divided difference of $f(x) = a_n x^n$ will be a_n.

***Theorem* 3:** *The nth divided difference can be expressed as the quotient of two determinants each of order $n+1$.* **[Rohilkhand 2002, 2006, 2008; Delhi (H) 2004, 2009]**

***Proof*:** Third divided difference is

$$f(x_0, x_1, x_2, x_3) = \Sigma \frac{f(x_0)}{(x_0 - x_1)(x_0 - x_2)(x_0 - x_3)}$$

or $$f(x_0, x_1, x_2, x_3) = \Sigma \left[\frac{f(x_0)\,(\text{difference product of } x_1, x_2, x_3)}{(\text{difference product of } x_0, x_1, x_2, x_3)} \right]$$

Again by the theorem of determinant due to the Vandermonde, we know that

$$\text{difference-product of } x_1, x_2, x_3 = \begin{vmatrix} x_1^2 & x_2^2 & x_3^2 \\ x_1 & x_2 & x_3 \\ 1 & 1 & 1 \end{vmatrix}. \text{ Hence}$$

$$f(x_0, x_1, x_2, x_3) = \Sigma \left\{ f(x_0) \begin{vmatrix} x_1^2 & x_2^2 & x_3^2 \\ x_1 & x_2 & x_3 \\ 1 & 1 & 1 \end{vmatrix} \div \begin{vmatrix} x_0^3 & x_1^3 & x_2^3 & x_3^3 \\ x_0^2 & x_1^2 & x_2^2 & x_3^2 \\ x_0 & x_1 & x_2 & x_3 \\ 1 & 1 & 1 & 1 \end{vmatrix} \right\}$$

or $$f(x_0, x_1, x_2, x_3) = \begin{vmatrix} f(x_0) & f(x_1) & f(x_2) & f(x_3) \\ x_0^2 & x_1^2 & x_2^2 & x_3^2 \\ x_0 & x_1 & x_2 & x_3 \\ 1 & 1 & 1 & 1 \end{vmatrix} \div \begin{vmatrix} x_0^3 & x_1^3 & x_2^3 & x_3^3 \\ x_0^2 & x_1^2 & x_2^2 & x_3^2 \\ x_0 & x_1 & x_2 & x_3 \\ 1 & 1 & 1 & 1 \end{vmatrix}$$

Proceeding in the similar manner, we can represent higher order differences as the quotient of two determinants each of order one more than the order of the difference.

***Theorem* 4:** *The nth divided difference can be expressed as the product of multiple integrals i.e.*

$$f(x_1, x_2, \ldots, x_n) = \int_0^1 dt_1 \int_0^{t_1} dt_2 \int_0^{t_2} dt_3 \ldots \int_0^{t_{n-2}} f^{n-1}(u_n)\, dt_{n-1}$$

where $$u_n = (1-t_1)\, x_1 + (t_1 - t_2)\, x_2 + \ldots + (t_{n-2} - t_{n-1})\, x_{n-1} + t_{n-1}\, x_n,$$

$t_1, t_2, t_3, \ldots, t_n$ *are independent variables, and* f^{n-1} *means the* $(n-1)^{th}$ *derivative of f.*

[Rohilkhand 2003]

***Proof*:** First of all, we shall prove the result for $n=2$ and $n=3$.

For $$n = 2,$$

$$\text{R.H.S.} = \int_0^1 f'(u_2)\, dt_1 = \int_0^1 f'\{(1-t_1)\, x_1 + t_1 x_2\}\, dt_1$$

$$= \frac{f(x_2) - f(x_1)}{x_2 - x_1} = f(x_1, x_2) = \text{L.H.S.}$$

For $n = 3$,

$$\text{R.H.S.} = \int_0^1 dt_1 \int_0^{t_1} f''(u_3)\, dt_2$$

$$= \int_0^1 dt_1 \int_0^{t_1} f''[(1-t_1)x_1 + (t_1 - t_2)x_2 + t_2 x_3]\, dt_2$$

$$= \int_0^1 dt_1 \left[f' \left\{ (1-t_1)x_1 + (t_1 - t_2)x_2 + t_2 x_3 \right\} \right]_0^{t_1} / (x_3 - x_2)$$

$$= \frac{1}{x_3 - x_2} \left[\int_0^1 f'\{(1-t_1)x_1 + t_1 x_3\}\, dt_1 - \int_0^1 f'\{(1-t_1)x_1 + t_1 x_2\}\, dt_1 \right]$$

$$= \frac{1}{(x_3 - x_2)} \cdot \frac{1}{(x_3 - x_1)} [f(x_3) - f(x_1)] \frac{1}{(x_3 - x_2)(x_2 - x_1)} [f(x_2) - f(x_1)]$$

$$= \frac{f(x_1)}{(x_1 - x_2)(x_1 - x_3)} + \frac{f(x_2)}{(x_2 - x_1)(x_2 - x_3)} + \frac{f(x_3)}{(x_3 - x_1)(x_3 - x_2)}$$

$$= f(x_1, x_2, x_3) = \text{L. H. S.}$$

Let the result be valid for n arguments. We shall show that it is valid for $n + 1$ arguments. Consider

$$\int_0^{t_{n-1}} f^n(u_{n+1})\, dt_n = \int_0^{t_{n-1}} f^n[(1-t_1)x_1 + (t_1 - t_2)x_2 + \ldots + (t_{n-1} - t_n)x_n + t_n x_{n+1}]\, dt_n$$

$$= \frac{1}{x_{n+1} - x_n} [f^{n-1}\{(1-t_1)x_1 + (t_1 - t_2)x_2 + \ldots + (t_{n-1} - t_n)x_n + t_n x_{n+1}\}]_0^{t_{n-1}}$$

$$= f^{n-1}[(1-t_1)x_1 + \ldots + (t_{n-2} - t_{n-1})x_{n-1} + t_{n-1} x_n]$$

$$- f^{n-1}[(1-t_1)x_1 + \ldots + (t_{n-2} - t_{n-1})x_{n-1} + t_{n-1} x_{n+1}] \div (x_n - x_{n+1})$$

$$\therefore \int_0^1 dt_1 \int_0^{t_1} dt_2 \ldots \int_0^{t_{n-1}} f^n(u_{n+1})\, dt_n = \frac{f(x_1, x_2, \ldots, x_n) - f(x_1, x_2, \ldots, x_{n-1}, x_{n+1})}{(x_n - x_{n+1})}$$

On interchanging x_1 and x_n,

$$= \frac{f(x_n, x_2, \ldots, x_1) - f(x_n, x_2, \ldots, x_{n-1}, x_{n+1})}{(x_1 - x_{n+1})}$$

$$= \frac{f(x_1, x_2, \ldots, x_n) - f(x_2, x_3, \ldots, x_n, x_{n+1})}{(x_1 - x_{n+1})} = f(x_1, x_2, \ldots, x_{n+1}).$$

Thus the result holds good for $n + 1$ arguments. The result holds goods for 2 and 3 arguments, so it holds for n arguments.

3.4 Newton's Formula for Unequal Intervals

[Avadh 2003; U.P.T.U. 2009]

Let $f(x_0), f(x_1), \ldots, f(x_n)$ be the values of $f(x)$ corresponding to the arguments $x_0, x_1, \ldots, x_n$ not necessarily spaced. From the definition of divided differences,

$$f(x, x_0) = \frac{f(x) - f(x_0)}{x - x_0} \quad \text{or} \quad f(x) = f(x_0) + (x - x_0) f(x, x_0). \qquad \ldots(1)$$

Again $f(x, x_0, x_1) = \dfrac{f(x, x_0) - f(x_0, x_1)}{x - x_1}$

or $$f(x, x_0) = f(x_0, x_1) + (x - x_1) f(x, x_0, x_1) \quad ...(2)$$

Similarly $$f(x, x_0, x_1) = f(x_0, x_1, x_2) + (x - x_2) f(x, x_0, x_1, x_2) \quad ...(3)$$

... ...

$$f(x, x_0, x_1, ..., x_{n-1}) = f(x_0, x_1, ..., x_n) + (x - x_n) f(x, x_0, x_1, ..., x_n). \quad ...(4)$$

Multiplying equation (2) by $(x - x_0)$, (3) by $(x - x_0)(x - x_1)$ and so on and finally equation (4) by $(x - x_0)(x - x_1)...(x - x_{n-1})$ and adding to equation (1), we have

$$f(x) = f(x_0) + (x - x_0) f(x_0, x_1) + (x - x_0)(x - x_1) f(x_0, x_1, x_2)$$
$$+ ... + (x - x_0)(x - x_1)...(x - x_{n-1}) f(x_0, x_1, ..., x_n) + R_n,$$

where the remainder R_n is given by

$$R_n = (x - x_0)(x - x_1)...(x - x_n) f(x, x_0, x_1, ..., x_n).$$

If our function $f(x)$ is a polynomial of nth degree, then $f(x, x_0, x_1, ..., x_n)$ vanishes, so that

$$f(x) = f(x_0) + (x - x_0) f(x_0, x_1) + (x - x_0)(x - x_1) f(x_0, x_1, x_2)$$
$$+ ... + (x - x_0)(x - x_1)...(x - x_{n-1}) f(x_0, x_1, ..., x_n) \quad ...(5)$$

This formula is called ***Newton's Divided Difference Interpolation Formula***.

3.5 Relation between Divided Differences and Ordinary Differences

In case the arguments $x_0, x_1, ..., x_n$ are equally spaced, *i.e.*

$$h = x_1 - x_0 = x_2 - x_1 = ... = x_n - x_{n-1}$$

and let $x = x_0 + nh$, then $f(x_0, x_1) = \dfrac{f(x_1) - f(x_0)}{x_1 - x_0} = \dfrac{1}{h} \Delta f(x_0)$.

$$f(x_0, x_1, x_2) = \frac{f(x_0, x_1) - f(x_1, x_2)}{x_0 - x_2} = \frac{\frac{1}{h} . \Delta f(x_0) - \frac{1}{h} \Delta f(x_1)}{-2h} = \frac{1}{2! h^2} . \Delta^2 f(x_0).$$

Similarly, we have $f(x_0, x_1, ..., x_n) = \dfrac{1}{(n!) h^n} \Delta^n f(x_0)$.

Putting the values of the divided differences in Newton's formula (5) of article **3.4**, we get $$f(x_0 + nh) = f(x_0) + \frac{nh}{1! h} \Delta f(x_0) + \frac{nh(nh - h)}{2! h^2} \Delta^2 f(x_0) + ...$$
$$+ \frac{nh(nh - h)(nh - 2h)...(nh - \overline{n-1}h)}{n! h^n} \Delta^n f(x_0)$$

$$= f(x_0) + {}^n c_1 \Delta f(x_0) + {}^n c_2 \Delta^2 f(x_0) + ... + {}^n c_n \Delta^n f(x_0),$$

which is ***Newton's formula for advancing differences***.

Solved Examples

Example 1: *If $f(x) = 1/x^2$ find the divided differences $f(a, b)$; $f(a, b, c)$ and $f(a, b, c, d)$.*

[Mysore 2005; Delhi (H) 2004, 2008; Rohilkhand 2007; Kurukshetra 2008; P.C.S. (M.P.) 2010]

Solution: $$f(a, b) = \frac{f(b) - f(a)}{b - a} = \frac{\frac{1}{b^2} - \frac{1}{a^2}}{b - a} = -\frac{(b^2 - a^2)}{(b - a)\, b^2 a^2} = -\frac{a + b}{a^2 b^2}$$

Similarly, we can show, $f(b, c) = -\dfrac{b + c}{b^2 c^2}$.

Again $$f(a, b, c) = \frac{f(b, c) - f(a, b)}{c - a} = -\frac{1}{(c - a)}\left[\frac{b + c}{b^2 c^2} - \frac{a + b}{a^2 b^2}\right]$$

$$= -\frac{1}{(c - a)}\left[\frac{a^2 (b + c) - c^2 (a + b)}{a^2 b^2 c^2}\right] = -\frac{1}{(c - a)}\left[\frac{a^2 b + a^2 c - c^2 a - c^2 b}{a^2 b^2 c^2}\right]$$

$$= -\left[\frac{b(a^2 - c^2) - ac(a - c)}{(c - a)\, a^2 b^2 c^2}\right] = -\left[\frac{(a - b)\{(a + c)\, b + ac\}}{(c - a)\, a^2 b^2 c^2}\right] = \frac{ab + bc + ca}{a^2 b^2 c^2}$$

By symmetry, we have $f(b, c, d) = \dfrac{bc + cd + db}{b^2 c^2 d^2}$

Again $$f(a, b, c, d) = \frac{f(b, c, d) - f(a, b, c)}{d - a}$$

$$= \frac{1}{(d - a)}\left[\frac{bc + cd + db}{b^2 c^2 d^2} - \frac{ab + bc + ca}{a^2 b^2 c^2}\right]$$

$$= \frac{1}{(d - a)}\left[\frac{a^2 (bc + cd + db) - d^2 (ab + bc + ca)}{a^2 b^2 c^2 d^2}\right]$$

$$= \frac{1}{(d - a)}\left[\frac{a^2 bc + a^2 cd + a^2 db - d^2 ab - d^2 bc - d^2 ca}{a^2 b^2 c^2 d^2}\right]$$

$$= \frac{1}{(d - a)}\left[\frac{bc(a^2 - d^2) + acd(a - d) + abd(a - d)}{a^2 b^2 c^2 d^2}\right]$$

$$= \frac{1}{(d - a)}\left[\frac{(a - d)(abc + bcd + acd + abd)}{a^2 b^2 c^2 d^2}\right]$$

$$= -\frac{abc + bcd + acd + abd}{a^2 b^2 c^2 d^2}.$$

Example 2: *Construct a divided difference table for the following:*

x	1	2	4	7	12
$f(x)$	22	30	82	106	216

Solution:

x	$f(x)$	$\Delta f(x)$	$\Delta^2 f(x)$	$\Delta^3 f(x)$	$\Delta^4 f(x)$
1	22				
		$\frac{30-22}{2-1}=8$			
2	30		$\frac{26-8}{4-1}=6$		
		$\frac{82-30}{4-2}=26$		$\frac{(-3.6)-6}{7-1}$	
4	82		$\frac{8-26}{7-2}=-3.6$	$=-1.6$	$\frac{0.535-(-1.6)}{12-1}$
		$\frac{106-82}{7-4}=8$		$\frac{(1.75)-(-3.6)}{12-2}$	$=0.194$
7	106		$\frac{22-8}{12-4}=1.75$	$=0.535$	
		$\frac{216-106}{12-7}=22$			
12	216				

Example 3: *Prove that* $\underset{bcd}{\Delta^3}\left(\frac{1}{a}\right)=-\frac{1}{abcd}$.

[Meerut 2005]

Solution: Construct the following divided difference table:

x	$f(x)$	$\Delta f(x)$	$\Delta^2 f(x)$	$\Delta^3 f(x)$
a	$\frac{1}{a}$	$\frac{\frac{1}{b}-\frac{1}{a}}{b-a}=-\frac{1}{ba}$	$(-1)\frac{\frac{1}{bc}-\frac{1}{ba}}{c-a}=(-1)^2\frac{1}{abc}$	
b	$\frac{1}{b}$	$\frac{\frac{1}{c}-\frac{1}{b}}{c-b}=-\frac{1}{bc}$	$(-1)\frac{\frac{1}{dc}-\frac{1}{bc}}{d-b}=(-1)^2\frac{1}{bcd}$	$(-1)^2\frac{\frac{1}{bcd}-\frac{1}{abc}}{d-a}$
c	$\frac{1}{c}$	$\frac{\frac{1}{d}-\frac{1}{c}}{d-c}=-\frac{1}{dc}$		$=(-1)^3\frac{1}{abcd}$
d	$\frac{1}{d}$			

From the table we observe $\underset{bcd}{\Delta^3}\frac{1}{a}=f(a,b,c,d)=-\frac{1}{abcd}$

Example 4: *Show that* n^{th} *order divided difference* $f(x_0, x_1, \ldots, x_n)$ *for the function* $u_x = \dfrac{1}{x}$ *is equal to* $\dfrac{(-1)^n}{x_0, x_1, \ldots, x_n}$

[Kurukshetra 2009; B.H.U. 2001, 2004; Avadh 2004; Bhopal 2002, 2008]

Solution: This is general case of above example 3; proceeding like Ex. 3, we get

$$\underset{x_1, x_2, \ldots, x_n}{\Delta^n} \frac{1}{x_0} = f(x_0, x_1, \ldots, x_n)$$

$$= (-1)^{n-1} \frac{\dfrac{1}{x_0 x_1 \ldots x_{n-1}} - \dfrac{1}{x_1 x_2 \ldots x_n}}{x_0 - x_n} = (-1)^n \frac{1}{x_0 x_1 \ldots x_n}.$$

Example 5: *Prove that* $\underset{yz}{\Delta^2} x^3 = x + y + z$.

[Indore 2007, 2009; Meerut 2001, 2004]

Solution: Construct the following divided difference table:

Argument	Entry	First divided difference $\Delta f(x)$	Second divided difference $\Delta^2 f(x)$
x	x^3		
		$\dfrac{y^3 - x^3}{y - x} = y^2 + x^2 + yx$	$\dfrac{(z^2 + y^2 + zy) - (y^2 + x^2 + yx)}{z - x}$
y	y^3		
		$\dfrac{z^3 - y^3}{z - y} = z^2 + y^2 + zy$	$= \dfrac{(z^2 - x^2) + y(z - x)}{z - x} = x + y + z$
z	z^3		

Example 6: *Find the third divided difference with arguments* 2, 4, 9, 10 *of the function* $f(x) = x^3 - 2x$.

Solution:

x	$f(x)$	$\Delta f(x)$	$\Delta^2 f(x)$	$\Delta^3 f(x)$
2	4			
		$\dfrac{56-4}{4-2} = 26$		
4	56		$\dfrac{131-26}{9-2} = 15$	
		$\dfrac{711-56}{9-4} = 131$		$\dfrac{23-15}{10-2} = 1$
9	711		$\dfrac{269-131}{10-4} = 23$	
		$\dfrac{980-711}{10-9} = 269$		
10	980			

Hence the third divided difference is 1.

Example 7: *By means of Newton's divided difference formula find the value of $f(8)$ and $f(15)$ from the following table:*

x	4	5	7	10	11	13
$f(x)$	48	100	294	900	1210	2028

[Rohilkhand 2007; Agra 2002, 2004; Delhi (H) 2008]

Solution: The divided difference table is as under:

x	$f(x)$	$\Delta f(x)$	$\Delta^2 f(x)$	$\Delta^3 f(x)$	$\Delta^4 f(x)$
4	48				
		$\frac{100-48}{5-4}=52$			
5	100		$\frac{97-52}{7-4}=15$		
		$\frac{294-100}{7-5}=97$		$\frac{21-15}{10-4}=1$	
7	294		$\frac{202-97}{10-5}=21$		0
		$\frac{900-294}{10-7}=202$		$\frac{27-21}{11-5}=1$	
10	900		$\frac{310-202}{11-7}=27$		0
		$\frac{1210-900}{11-10}=310$		$\frac{33-27}{13-7}=1$	
11	1210		$\frac{409-310}{13-10}=33$		
		$\frac{2028-1210}{13-11}=409$			
13	2028				

Now making use of Newton's interpolation formula for unequal intervals, we get

$$f(8) = 48 + (8-4)\,52 + (8-4)(8-5)\,15 + (8-4)(8-5)(8-7)\,1 = 448.$$

$$f(15) = 48 + (15-4)\,52 + (15-4)(15-5)\,15 + (15-4)(15-5)(15-7)\,1 = 3150.$$

Example 8: *Given that $f(0)=8$, $f(1)=68$ and $f(5)=123$, construct a divided difference table. Using the table, determine the value of $f(2)$.*

Solution: Divided difference table is as under:

x	$f(x)$	$\Delta f(x)$	$\Delta^2 f(x)$
0	8		
		$\frac{68-8}{1-0}=60$	
1	68		$\frac{13.75-60}{5-0}=-9.25$
		$\frac{123-68}{5-1}=13.75$	
5	123		

Now making use of Newton's interpolation formula, we get

$$f(2) = 8 + (2-0)\,60 + (2-0)(2-1)(-9.25) = 109.50.$$

Example 9: *Find the polynomial of the lowest possible degree which assumes the values* $3, 12, 15, -21$ *when* x *has the value* $3, 2, 1, -1$ *respectively.*

[M.D.U. (Rohtak) 2005, 2008; Avadh 2003]

Solution: Construct the following divided difference table:

x	$f(x)$	$\Delta f(x)$	$\Delta^2 f(x)$	$3\Delta^3 f(x)$
-1	-21			
		$\frac{15+21}{1+1} = 18$		
1	15		$\frac{-3-18}{2+1} = -7$	
		$\frac{12-15}{2-1} = -3$		$\frac{-3+7}{3+1} = 1$
2	12		$\frac{-9+3}{3-1} = -3$	
		$\frac{3-12}{3-2} = -9$		
3	3			

Now applying Newton's divided difference formula; we get

$$f(x) = -21 + \{x-(-1)\}(18) + \{x-(-1)\}(x-1)(-7) + \{x-(-1)\}(x-1)(x-2)\,(1)$$

$$= -21 + (x+1)(18) + (x+1)(x-1)(-7) + (x+1)(x-1)(x-2)$$

$$= x^3 - 9x^2 + 17x + 6.$$

Example 10: *In the following data, find $f(x)$ as a polynomial in powers of $(x-5)$ by extending table to include arguments $x=5$ repeated as many times as may be necessary.*

$$f(0)=4,\ f(2)=26,\ f(3)=58,\ f(4)=112,\ f(7)=466,\ f(9)=922.$$

Solution: The divided difference table is as under:

x	$f(x)$	$\Delta f(x)$	$\Delta^2 f(x)$	$\Delta^3 f(x)$
0	4			
		$\frac{26-4}{2-0}=11$		
2	26		$\frac{32-11}{3-0}=7$	
		$\frac{58-26}{3-2}=32$		$\frac{11-7}{4-0}=1$
3	58		$\frac{54-32}{4-2}=11$	
		$\frac{112-58}{4-3}=54$		$\frac{16-11}{7-2}=1$
4	112		$\frac{118-54}{7-3}=16$	
		$\frac{466-112}{7-4}=118$		$\frac{22-16}{9-3}=1$
7	466		$\frac{228-118}{9-4}=22$	
		$\frac{922-466}{9-7}=228$		$\frac{a-22}{5-4}=1$
9	922		$\frac{b-228}{5-7}=a$	
...	...	...	...	...
5	c			$\frac{a'-a}{5-7}=1$
		$\frac{c-922}{5-9}=b$	$\frac{b'-b}{5-9}=a'$	
5	c			
		b'		$\frac{a''-a'}{5-9}=1$
5	c	b''	a''	

Since the third differences are constant, $f(x)$ is a polynomial of third degree and hence the arguments should appear three times successively in the difference table. We have shown the extended table below the dotted line. Now from column V in the table

$$\frac{a-22}{5-4}=1 \quad \text{or } a=22, \text{ also } \frac{a'-a}{5-7}=1 \quad \text{or } a'-22=-2 \quad \text{or } a'=20$$

and $$\frac{a''=a'}{5-9}=1 \quad \text{or } a'-20=-4 \quad \text{or } a''=16$$

Again from column IV, $\dfrac{b-288}{5-7}=a$ or $\dfrac{b-228}{-2}=22$ or $b=228-44=184$.

Also $\dfrac{b'-b}{5-9}=a'$ or $\dfrac{b'-184}{-4}=20$ or $b'=184-80=104$

and from column III, we have

$$\frac{c-922}{5-9}=b \text{ or } \frac{c-922}{5-9}=184 \text{ or } c=922-4\,(184)=922-736=186$$

Newton's formula with arguments x_0, x_1, x_2, x_3 is

$$f(x)=f(x_0)+(x-x_0)\,f(x_0,x_1)+(x-x_0)(x-x_1)\,f(x_0,x_1,x_2)$$
$$+(x-x_0)(x-x_1)(x-x_2)\,f(x_0,x_1,x_2,x_3)$$

Putting $x_0=x_1=x_2=x_3=5$, we get

$$f(5)=f(x)+(x-5)\,b'+(x-5)^2\,a''+(x-5)^3\times 1$$
$$=186+104\,(x-5)+16\,(x-5)^2+(x-5)^3.$$

Example 11: *Using the following table, find $f(x)$ as a polynomial in powers of $(x-6)$.*

x	−1	0	2	3	7	10
$f(x)$	−11	1	1	1	141	561

Solution: Construct the following difference table:

x	$f(x)$	$\Delta f(x)$	$\Delta^2 f(x)$	$\Delta^3 f(x)$
−1	−11			
		$\frac{1+11}{0+1}=12$		
			$\frac{0-12}{2+1}=-4$	
0	1			
		$\frac{1-1}{2-0}=0$		$\frac{0+4}{3+1}=1$
			$\frac{0-0}{3-0}=0$	
2	1			
		$\frac{1-1}{3-2}=0$		$\frac{7-0}{7-0}=1$
			$\frac{35-0}{7-2}=7$	
3	1			
		$\frac{141-1}{7-3}=35$		$\frac{15-7}{10-2}=1$
			$\frac{140-35}{10-3}=15$	
7	141			
		$\frac{561-141}{10-7}=140$		$\frac{a-15}{6-3}=1$
			$\frac{b-140}{6-7}=a$	
10	561			
		$\frac{c-561}{6-10}=b$		$\frac{a'-a}{6-7}=1$
			$\frac{b'-b}{6-10}=a'$	
6	c			
		b'		$\frac{a''-a'}{6-10}=1$
6	c		a''	
		b''		
6	c			

Since the third differences are constants, $f(x)$ is a polynomial of degree three and hence the argument 6 should appear three times successively in the difference table.

We have shown the extended table below the dotted line.

Now from column V, $\frac{a-15}{6-3}=1$ or $a=15+3=18$

Also $\frac{a'-a}{6-7}=1$ or $a''=a-1=17$ and $\frac{a''-a'}{6-10}=1$ or $a''=a'-4=13$

From column IV, we have $\frac{b-140}{6-7}=a$ or $b=140-a=140-18=122$

$\frac{b'-b}{6-10}=a'$ or $b'=b-4a'=122-4\times17=54$.

Again from column III, we have $\frac{c-561}{6-10}=b$ or $c=561-4b=561-488=73$

Newton's formula with arguments x_0, x_1, x_2, x_3 is

$$f(x)=f(x_0)+(x-x_0)\,f(x_0,x_1)+(x-x_0)(x-x_1)\,f(x_0,x_1,x_2)$$

$$+(x-x_0)(x-x_1)(x-x_2)\,f(x_0,x_1,x_2,x_3).$$

On putting $x_0=x_1=x_2=x_3=6$, we get

$$f(x)=f(6)+(x-6)\,b'+(x-6)^2\,a''+(x-6)^3\times1$$

$$=73+54(x-6)+13(x-6)^2+(x-6)^3.$$

Example 12: *Using the following table find $f(x)$ as a polynomial in powers of $(x-3)$.*

x	5	11	27	34	42
$f(x)$	23	899	17315	35606	68510

Solution: Construct the following divided difference table:

x	$f(x)$	$\Delta f(x)$	$\Delta^2 f(x)$	$\Delta^3 f(x)$
5	23			
		$\frac{899-23}{11-5}=146$		
			$\frac{1026-146}{27-5}=40$	
11	899			
		$\frac{17315-899}{27-11}=1026$		$\frac{69-40}{34-5}=1$
			$\frac{2613-1026}{34-11}=69$	
27	17315			
		$\frac{35606-17315}{34-27}=2613$		$\frac{100-69}{42-11}=1$
			$\frac{4113-2613}{42-27}=100$	
34	35606			
		$\frac{68510-35606}{42-34}=4113$		$\frac{a-100}{3-27}=1$
			$\frac{b-4113}{3-34}=a$	
42	68510			
...	...	...	...	...
		$\frac{c-68510}{3-42}=b$		$\frac{a'-a}{3-34}=1$
3	c			
		b'	$\frac{b'-b}{3-42}=a'$	
3	c		a''	
		b''		$\frac{a''-a'}{3-42}=1$
3	c			

Giving the similar argument for the extended table below the dotted line, as in ***Ex.* 10** or in ***Ex.* 11**. Now from column V, we have $\frac{a-100}{3-27}=1$ or $a=100-24=76$, $\frac{a'-a}{3-34}=1$ or $a'=a-31=78-31=45$ and $\frac{a'-a'}{3-42}=1$ or $u''=a'-39=45-39=6$. From column IV, we have $\frac{b-4113}{3-34}=a$ or $b=4113-31a$ or $b=4113-31\times 76=1757$

$\frac{b'-b}{3-42}=a'$ or $b'=b-39a'$ or $b'=1757-39\times 45=2$.

From column III, we have $\frac{c-68510}{3-42}=b$ or $c=68510-39b=68510-68523=-13$

Newton's formula with arguments x_0, x_1, x_2, x_3 is

$$f(x)=f(x_0)+(x-x_0)\,f(x_0,x_1)+(x-x_0)(x-x_1)\,f(x_0,x_1,x_2)$$
$$+(x-x_0)(x-x_1)(x-x_2)\,f(x_0,x_1,x_2,x_3)$$

Putting $x_0=x_1=x_2=x_3=3$ we get

$$f(x)=f(3)+(x-3)\,b'+(x-3)^2\,a''+(x-3)^3\times 1$$
$$=-13+2(x-3)+6(x-3)^2+(x-3)^3.$$

Example 13: *Given* $\log_{10} 654 = 2.8156$, $\log_{10} 658 = 2.8182$, $\log_{10} 659 = 2.8189$, $\log_{10} 661 = 2.8202$ *find by divided difference formula* $\log_{10} 656$.

[Agra 2002, 2007; Lucknow 2005, 2009; Rohilkhand 2007]

Solution: Shift the origin to 654, then we can consider the data given for $x = 0, 4, 5$ and 7 and are required to find $f(x)$ at $x = 2$.

The divided difference table is as under:

x	$f(x)$	$\Delta f(x)$	$\Delta^2 f(x)$	$\Delta^3 f(x)$
0	2.8156			
		$\frac{2.8182 - 2.8156}{4-0} = .00065$		
4	2.8182		$\frac{.00070 - .00065}{5-0} = 0.00001$	
		$\frac{2.8189 - 2.8182}{5-4} = .00070$		$\frac{-.000017 - .00001}{7-0} = -0.000004$
5	2.8189		$\frac{.00065 - .00070}{7-4} = -.000017$	
		$\frac{2.8202 - 2.8189}{7-5} = .00065$		
7	2.8202			

$$\log_{10} 656 = 2.8156 + (2-0)(.00065) + (2-0)(2-4)(.00001)$$

$$+ (2-0)(2-4)(2-5)(-.000004)$$

$$= 2.8156 + 0.0013 - 0.00004 - .0000048 = \mathbf{2.8168 \text{ approx}}$$

Example 14: *If* $\log 2 = 0.30103$, $\log 3 = 0.47712$ $\log 5 = 0.69897$, $\log 7 = 0.84510$, *find the value of* $\log 4.7$ *to four places of decimal.*

Solution: Proceed as in Ex. 13.

Ans. 0.69110 approx.

Example 15: *Find the polynomial of the lowest possible degree which assumes the values* $1245, 33, 5, 9$ *and* 1335 *at* $x = -4, -1, 0, 2$ *and* 5 *respectively. Also find the value of the polynomial at the abscissa* 1.

Solution: The divided difference table is as under:

x	$f(x)$	$\Delta f(x)$	$\Delta^2 f(x)$	$\Delta^3 f(x)$	$\Delta^4 f(x)$
-4	1245				
		$\frac{33-1245}{-1-(-4)} = -404$			
-1	33		$\frac{-28-(-404)}{0-(-4)} = 94$		
		$\frac{5-33}{0-(-1)} = -28$		$\frac{10-94}{2-(-4)} = -14$	
0	5		$\frac{2-(-28)}{2-(-1)} = 10$		$\frac{13-(-14)}{5-(-4)} = 3$
		$\frac{9-5}{2-0} = 2$		$\frac{88-10}{5-(-1)} = 13$	
2	9		$\frac{442-2}{5-0} = 88$		
		$\frac{1335-9}{5-2} = 442$			
5	1335				

$$\therefore \quad f(x) = f(x_0) + (x - x_0)\, f(x_0, x_1) + (x - x_0)(x - x_1)\, f(x_0, x_1, x_2)$$

$$+ (x - x_0)(x - x_1)(x - x_2)\, f(x_0, x_1, x_2, x_3)$$

$$+ (x - x_0)(x - x_1)(x - x_2)(x - x_3)\, f(x_0, x_1, x_2, x_3, x_4)$$

$$= 1245 - (x+4)\,404 + (x+4)(x+1)\,94 - (x+4)(x+1)(x)\,14 + (x+4)(x+1)(x)(x-2)\,3$$

or $$f(x) = 5 - 14x + 6x^2 - 5x^3 + 3x^4$$

At $$x = 1,\ f(x) = 5 - 14 + 6 - 5 + 3 = -5.$$

Example 16: *The observed values of a function are respectively* 168, 120, 72 *and* 63 *at the four positions* 3, 7, 9 *and* 10 *of the independent variable. What is the best estimate you can give for the value of the function at the position* 6 *of the independent variable.*

[Bangaluru 2005, 2010; Delhi (H) 2002, 2003, 2007; U.P.P.C.S. 2008; Gujarat 2008]

Solution: The divided difference table is as under:

x	$f(x)$	$\Delta f(x)$	$\Delta^2 f(x)$	$\Delta^3 f(x)$
3	168			
		$\frac{120-168}{7-3}=-12$		
7	120		$\frac{-24-(-12)}{9-3}=-2$	
		$\frac{72-120}{9-7}=-24$		$\frac{5-(-2)}{10-3}=1$
9	72		$\frac{-9-(-24)}{10-7}=5$	
		$\frac{63-72}{10-9}=-9$		
10	63			

$$f(x) = 168 - (x-3)\,12 - (x-3)(x-7)\,2 + (x-3)(x-7)(x-9)\,1$$

$$= x^3 - 21x^2 + 119x - 27.$$

At $\quad x = 6,\ f(x) = 6^3 - 21.6^2 + 119\,(6) - 27 = 216 - 756 + 714 - 27 =$ **147.**

Example 17: *The following are the mean temperatures (Fahrenheit) on three days, 30 days apart round the periods of summer and winter. Estimate the approximate dates and values of the maximum and minimum temperature.* **[Meerut 2006 (B.P.); Delhi B.Sc. (H) 2004, 2006]**

Summer			Winter	
Day	***Date***	***Temperature***	***Date***	***Temperature***
0	15th *June*	58.8	16th *Dec.*	40.7
30	15th *July*	63.4	15th *Jan.*	38.1
60	14th *August*	62.5	14th *Feb.*	39.3

Solution: Let us choose unit $1 \equiv 30$ days, thus we are given the entries (temperatures) corresponding to equidistant arguments, the interval of differencing is unity. The divided difference table for summer is as under:

x	$f(x)$	$\Delta f(x)$	$\Delta^2 f(x)$
0	58.8		
		$\frac{63.4-58.8}{1-0}=4.6$	
1	63.4		$\frac{-0.9-4.6}{2-0}=-2.75$
		$\frac{62.5-63.3}{2-1}=-0.9$	
2	62.5		

$$\therefore \quad f(x) = 58.8 + (x-0)(4.6) + (x-0)(x-1)(-2.75)$$

$$= -2.75x^2 + 7.35x + 58.8 \qquad \text{...(1)}$$

Now for maximum or minimum of $f(x)$, we have

$$f'(x) = 0 \quad \Rightarrow \quad -5.5x + 7.35 = 0 \quad \Rightarrow \quad x = 1.342.$$

Again $\quad f''(x) = -5.5 < 0$. Thus $f(x)$ is maximum at $x = 1.342$

Since unit $1 \equiv 30$ days $\quad \therefore\ 1.342 \equiv 30 \times 1.342 = 40.26$ days.

Therefore maximum temperature was on 15th June + 40 days *i.e.* on 25th July and the value of maximum temperature is

$$\{f(x)\}_{max} = \{f(x)\}_{x=1.342}$$

$$= -2.75 \times (1.342)^2 + 7.35\,(1.342) + 58.8 \qquad \text{[From (1)]}$$

$$= 63.72°\ \text{F approximately.}$$

Divided difference table for winter is as under:

x	$f(x)$	$\Delta f(x)$	$\Delta^2 f(x)$
0	40.7		
		$\frac{38.1-40.7}{1-0}=-2.6$	
1	38.1		$\frac{1.2-(-2.6)}{2-0}=1.9$
		$\frac{39.3-38.1}{2-1}=1.2$	
2	39.3		

$$\therefore \quad f(x) = 40.7 + (x-0)(-2.6) + (x-0)(x-1)(1.9)$$

$$= 1.9x^2 - 4.5x + 40.7. \qquad \text{...(2)}$$

Now for $f(x)$ to be maximum or minimum, we have $f'(x) = 0$

i.e. $3.8x - 4.5 = 0 \Rightarrow x = 1.184.$

Again $f''(x) = 3.8 > 0.$

Hence $f(x)$ is minimum at $x = 1.184$.

Again unit $1 \equiv 30$ days.

$\therefore \quad 1.184 \equiv 30 \times 1.184 \text{ days} = 35.520 \text{ days}.$

Therefore minimum temperature was on 16th Dec. + 35.5 days

i.e. on the midnight of 20th January and its value can be obtained from (2).

3.6 Sheppard's Rule

We have seen that in Newton's divided difference formula, a function $f(x)$ is expressed in terms of the leading term and leading differences. Now we shall define here a rule known as ***Sheppard Rule*** by which divided difference formula can be written with any value of $f(x)$ as the initial.

Newton's divided difference formula for interpolation is $f(x) = P(x)$

$$= f(x_0) + (x - x_0) \underset{x_1}{\Delta} f(x_0) + (x - x_0)(x - x_1) \underset{x_1 x_2}{\Delta^2} f(x_0) \dots$$

$$+ (x - x_0)(x - x_1)\dots(x - x_{n-1}) \underset{x_1 \dots x_n}{\Delta^n} f(x_0) \qquad \dots(1)$$

Now in (1), put $x - x_0 = X_0, x - x_1 = X_1, \dots, x - x_{n-1} = X_{n-1}$.

Then, we have $f(x) = f(x_0) + X_0 \underset{x_1}{\Delta} f(x_0) + X_0 X_1 \underset{x_1 x_2}{\Delta^2} f(x_0)$

$$+ \dots + X_0 \dots X_{n-1} \underset{x_1 \dots x_n}{\Delta^n} f(x_0) \qquad \dots(2)$$

In (2) from R.H.S. we observe that coefficient of various terms are written in capital letters $X_0, X_1, \dots$ etc. 2nd the suffixes of operator and the operand are given in small letters, x_0, x_1 etc. Again in first term of R.H.S. of (2), the coefficient of $f(x_0)$ is one and suffix of the operand is x_0. In second term, coefficient is X_0 and there are two suffixes x_0 and x_1 in the operator and the operand. In the third term the coefficient consist of two letters X_0, X_1 and there are three suffixes x_0, x_1 and x_2 in the operator and operand and so on. We conclude from this that small letters in each term of R.H.S. of (2) are one more than the number of capital letters. Now we give the small and capital letters term by term.

Small letters	x_0	$x_0 x_1$	$x_0 x_1 x_2$	...	$x_0 x_1 \dots x_n$
Capital letters	1	X_0	$X_0 X_1$	...	$X_0 X_1 \dots X_{n-1}$

The characteristic of Newton's divided difference formula has given rise to a rule which is called ***Sheppard's Rule*** or ***Zigzag Rule***, which is as follows:

(i) Begin with any initial term.

(ii) In order to get second term, take any first order difference either moving upward or downward in the divided difference table which must contain the suffixes of initial term. Now multiply this difference table which must contain the suffixes of initial term. Now multiply this difference by the term equal to (x – the value of suffix of initial term).

(iii) In the same way find the third term, keeping in mind the suffixes of second term. In this way complete the formula.

By the following example application of the rule will be clear.

Example 18: *The following observations are given for the function* $y = f(x)$:

x	x_0	x_1	x_2	x_3	x_4	x_5
$f(x)$	$f(x_0)$	$f(x_1)$	$f(x_2)$	$f(x_3)$	$f(x_4)$	$f(x_5)$

Solution: Construct the following difference table for the given data.

x	$f(x)$	$\Delta f(x)$	$\Delta^2 f(x)$	$\Delta^3 f(x)$	$\Delta^4 f(x)$	$\Delta^5 f(x)$
x_0	$f(x_0)$					
		$\underset{x_1}{\Delta} f(x_0)$				
x_1	$f(x_1)$		$\underset{x_1 x_2}{\Delta^2} f(x_0)$			
		$\underset{x_2}{\Delta} f(x_1)$		$\underset{x_1 x_2 x_3}{\Delta^3} f(x_0)$		
x_2	$f(x_2)$		$\underset{x_2 x_3}{\Delta^2} f(x_1)$		$\underset{x_1 x_2 x_3 x_4}{\Delta^4} f(x_0)$	
		$\underset{x_3}{\Delta} f(x_2)$		$\underset{x_2 x_3 x_4}{\Delta^3} f(x_1)$		$\underset{x_1 x_2 x_3 x_4 x_5}{\Delta^5} f(x_0)$
x_3	$f(x_3)$		$\underset{x_3 x_4}{\Delta^2} f(x_2)$		$\underset{x_2 x_3 x_4 x_5}{\Delta^4} f(x_1)$	
		$\underset{x_4}{\Delta} f(x_3)$		$\underset{x_3 x_4 x_5}{\Delta^3} f(x_2)$		
x_4	$f(x_4)$		$\underset{x_4 x_5}{\Delta^2} f(x_3)$			
		$\underset{x_5}{\Delta} f(x_4)$				
x_5	$f(x_5)$					

Beginning with $f(x_2)$ as the initial term and moving one step upward and one step downward alternatively in the difference table, applying Sheppard's Rule, we get

$$f(x) = f(x_2) + X_2 \underset{x_2}{\Delta} f(x_1) + X_2\, X_1 \underset{x_2 x_3}{\Delta^2} f(x_1) + X_2\, X_1\, X_3 \underset{x_1 x_2 x_3}{\Delta^3} f(x_0)$$

$$+ X_2\, X_1\, X_3\, X_0 \underset{x_1 x_2 x_3 x_4}{\Delta^4} f(x_0) + X_2\, X_1\, X_3\, X_0\, X_4 \underset{x_1 x_2 x_3 x_4 x_5}{\Delta^5} f(x_0)$$

$$= f(x_2) + (x - x_2) \underset{x_2}{\Delta} f(x_1) + (x - x_2)(x - x_1) \underset{x_2 x_3}{\Delta^2} f(x_1)$$

$$+ (x - x_2)(x - x_1)(x - x_3) \underset{x_1 x_2 x_3}{\Delta^3} f(x_0) + \ldots$$

This is the required interpolation formula with $f(x_2)$ as the initial term. In case we take our step in downward direction of the difference table, then the formula will be

$$f(x) = f(x_2) + X_2 \underset{x_3}{\Delta} f(x_2) + X_2 X_3 \underset{x_2 x_3}{\Delta^2} f(x_1) + X_1 X_2 X_3 \underset{x_2 x_3 x_4}{\Delta^3} f(x_1)$$

$$+ X_1 X_2 X_3 X_4 \underset{x_1 x_2 x_3 x_4}{\Delta^4} f(x_0) + \ldots$$

$$= f(x_2) + (x - x_2) \underset{x_3}{\Delta} f(x_2) + (x - x_2)(x - x_3) \underset{x_2 x_3}{\Delta^2} f(x_1)$$

$$+ (x - x_1)(x - x_2)(x - x_3) \underset{x_2 x_3 x_4}{\Delta^3} f(x_1) + \ldots$$

Example 19: ***(a)*** *If the data are $u_0, u_3, u_4, u_7, u_{11}$ and the interpolation formula is*

$$u_x = u_4 + c_1 \underset{3}{\Delta} u_4 + c_2 \underset{4,7}{\Delta^2} u_3 + c_3 \underset{3,4,7}{\Delta^3} u_0 + c_4 \underset{3,4,7,11}{\Delta^4} u_0$$

find the values of c_1, c_2, c_3 and c_4. **[Agra 2010]**

(b) *If in the above data*

$$u_x = u_3 + (x - 3)\, \Delta u + (x - 3)(x - 4)\, \Delta^2 u + (x - 3)(x - 4)\, x\, \Delta^3 u$$

$$+ (x - 3)(x - 4)\, x\, (x - 7)\, \Delta^4\, u,$$

find the missing suffixes of the operators and the subscripts of the u's. **[C.S.I.R. (Net) 2005]**

Solution: (a) Newton's divided difference formula is

$$u_x = u(x_0) + (x - x_0)\, u(x_0 x_1) + (x - x_0)(x - x_1)\, u(x_0 x_1 x_2)$$

$$+ (x - x_0)(x - x_1)(x - x_2)\, u(x_0 x_1 x_2 x_3) + (x - x_0)(x - x_1)(x - x_2)(x - x_3)\, u(x_0 x_1 x_2 x_3 x_4)$$

$$\therefore \quad u_x = u_4 + (x - 4) \underset{3}{\Delta} u_4 + (x - 4)(x - 3) \underset{4,7}{\Delta^2} u_3 + (x - 7)(x - 4)(x - 3) \underset{3,4,7}{\Delta^3} u_0$$

$$+ (x - 0)(x - 7)(x - 4)(x - 3) \underset{3,4,7,11}{\Delta^4} u_0$$

On comparing with the given result, we get

$$c_1 = (x - 4),\ c_2 = (x - 4)(x - 3),\ c_3 = (x - 7)(x - 4)(x - 3),\ c_4 = x(x - 7)(x - 4)(x - 3).$$

(b) Again $u_x = u_3 + (x-3) \underset{4}{\Delta} u_3 + (x-3)(x-4) \underset{4,0}{\Delta^2} u_3$

$$+ (x-3)(x-4)(x-0) \underset{4,0,7}{\Delta^3} u_3 + (x-3)(x-4)(x-0)(x-7) \underset{4,0,7,11}{\Delta^4} u_3.$$

Arranging in standard form, according to (u), we have

$$u_x = u_3 + (x-3) \underset{3}{\Delta} u_4 + (x-3)(x-4) \underset{4,3}{\Delta^2} u_0$$

$$+ (x-3)(x-4)(x-0) \underset{0,4,3}{\Delta^3} u_7 + (x-3)(x-4)\, x\, (x-7) \underset{11,0,4,3}{\Delta^4} u_7.$$

Hence, the Δu's are $\underset{3}{\Delta} u_4, \underset{4,3}{\Delta^2} u_0, \underset{0,4,3}{\Delta^3} u_7$ and $\underset{11,0,4,3}{\Delta^4} u_7$

Note: Question can be done by Sheppard's rule as well.

3.7 Lagrange's Interpolation Formula for Unequal Intervals

[Kanpur 2008; Avadh 2003, 2005; M.K.U. (Tamil Nadu) 2005; Rohilkhand 2005, 2009]

Let $f(x_0), f(x_1), f(x_2), \ldots, f(x_n)$ be the $(n+1)$ values of the function $y = f(x)$ corresponding to the arguments $x_0, x_1, x_2, x_3 \ldots, x_n$ not necessarily equally spaced. It is assumed that the function $f(x)$ is a polynomial in x and since $(n+1)$, values of $f(x)$ are given so $(n+1)^{th}$ differences are zero. Thus $f(x)$ is supposed to the polynomial in x of degree n.

Writing $f(x)$ as $f(x) = A_0 (x - x_1)(x - x_2) \ldots (x - x_n)$

$$+ A_1 (x - x_0)(x - x_2) \ldots (x - x_n) + \ldots + A_n (x - x_0)(x - x_1) \ldots (x - x_{n-1}), \qquad \ldots(1)$$

where A's are constants. The relation (1) is true for all values of x. To determine A_0, put $x = x_0$.

$$\therefore \qquad f(x_0) = A_0 (x_0 - x_1)(x_0 - x_2) \ldots (x_0 - x_n)$$

or $$A_0 = \frac{f(x_0)}{(x_0 - x_1)(x_0 - x_2) \ldots (x_0 - x_n)}$$

Similarly $$A_1 = \frac{f(x_1)}{(x_1 - x_0)(x_1 - x_2) \ldots (x_1 - x_n)}$$

$$\ldots \qquad \ldots \qquad \ldots \qquad \ldots$$

$$A_n = \frac{f(x_n)}{(x_n - x_0)(x_n - x_1) \ldots (x_n - x_{n-1})}$$

Putting these values of A's in (1), we get

$$f(x)=\frac{(x-x_1)(x-x_2)\dots(x-x_n)}{(x_0-x_1)(x_0-x_2)\dots(x_0-x_n)}f(x_0)+\frac{(x-x_0)(x-x_2)\dots(x-x_n)}{(x_1-x_0)(x_1-x_2)\dots(x_1-x_n)}f(x_1)+$$

$$\dots+\frac{(x-x_0)(x-x_1)\dots(x-x_{n-1})}{(x_n-x_0)(x_n-x_1)\dots(x_n-x_{n-1})}f(x_n)+ \quad \text{...(2)}$$

which is Lagrange's interpolation formula.

3.8 Iterative Method

Newton's forward difference formula is given by

$$y_u=y_0+u\Delta y_0+\frac{u(u-1)}{2!}\Delta^2 y_0+\frac{u(u-1)(u-2)}{3!}\Delta^3 y_0+\dots$$

$$\Rightarrow \quad u=\frac{1}{\Delta y_0}\left[y_u-y_0-\frac{u(u-1)}{2!}\Delta^2 y_0-\frac{u(u-1)(u-2)}{3!}\Delta^3 y_0-\dots\right] \quad \text{...(1)}$$

If we neglect the second and higher differences, we obtain the first approximation to u as $u_1=(y_u-y_0)/\Delta y_0$ ...(2)

To find the second approximation, we retain the terms up to second differences

$$\Rightarrow \quad u_2=\frac{1}{\Delta y_0}\left[y_u-y_0-\frac{u_1(u_1-1)}{2!}\Delta^2 y_0\right] \quad \text{...(3)}$$

Further, to find the third approximation, we again retain the terms with third differences in (1) and get

$$u_3=\frac{1}{\Delta y_0}\left[y_u-y_0-\frac{u_2(u_2-1)}{2!}\Delta^2 y_0-\frac{u_2(u_2-1)(u_2-2)}{3!}\Delta^3 y_0\right] \text{ etc.}$$

This process is continued till two successive approximations agree with each other.

Example 19: (c) *The following values of $y=f(x)$ are given*

x	10	15	20
y	1754	2648	3564

Find the values of x for $y=3000$ by iterative method.

Solution: Taking $x_0=10$ and $h=5$, the difference table is as follows:

x	y	Δy	$\Delta^2 y$
10	1754		
		894	
15	2648		22
		916	
20	3564		

Now $\quad y_u=3000,\ y_0=1754,\ \Delta y_0=894$ and $\Delta^2 y_0=22$.

Hence the successive approximations of u are

$$u_1 = \frac{1}{894}(3000 - 1754) = 1.39$$

$$u_2 = \frac{1}{894}\left[3000 - 1754 - \frac{1.39\,(1.39 - 1)}{2} \times 22\right] = 1.387$$

$$u_3 = \frac{1}{894}\left[3000 - 1754 - \frac{1.387\,(1.387 - 1)}{2} \times 22\right] = 1.3871$$

Thus we take $u = 1.387$ correct to three decimal places.

Hence the value of x (corresponding to $y = 3000$) $= x_0 + uh = 10 + 1.387 \times 5 = 16.935$.

Example 19: **(d)** *Using inverse interpolation, find the real root of the equation* $x^3 + x - 3 = 0$, *which is close to* 1.2. **[Avadh 2000]**

Solution: The difference table is as follows:

x	u	$y\ (= x^3 + x - 3)$	Δy	$\Delta^2 y$	$\Delta^3 y$	$\Delta^4 y$
1	−0.2	−1				
			0.431			
1.1	−0.1	−0.569		0.066		
			0.497		0.006	
1.2	0	−0.072		0.072		0
			0.569		0.006	
1.3	0.1	0.497		0.78		
			0.647			
1.4	0.2	1.144				

The root of the given equation lies between 1.2 and 1.3. Then assuming the origin at $x = 1.2$ and using Stirling's formula; we readily get.

$$y = y_0 + x\frac{\Delta y_0 + \Delta y_{-1}}{2} + \frac{x^2}{2}\Delta^2 y_{-1} + \frac{x(x^2 - 1)(\Delta^3 y_{-1} + \Delta^3 y_{-2})}{12}$$

$$\Rightarrow \quad 0 = -.072 + x.\frac{0.569 + 0.467}{2} + \frac{x^2}{2}(0.072)$$

$$+ \frac{x(x^2 - 1)}{6}\,\frac{0.006 + 0.006}{2} \quad (\because y = 0)$$

$$\Rightarrow \quad 0 = -.072 + 0.532x + 0.036x^2 + 0.001x^3$$

$$\Rightarrow \quad x = \frac{0.072}{0.532} - \frac{0.036}{0.532}x^2 - \frac{0.001}{0.532}x^3 \quad ...(1)$$

Now first approximation, $x^{(1)} = \dfrac{0.072}{0.532} = 0.1353$

Then putting $x = x^{(1)}$ on R.H.S. of (1), we get

Second approximation $x^{(2)}$

$$= 0.1353 - 0.067\,(0.1353)^2 - 1.8797\,(0.1353)^3 = 0.134$$

Hence the desired root $= 1.2 + 0.1 \times 0.134 = 1.2134$.

Example 19: **(e)** *Obtain the value of t when $A = 85$ from the following table, using Lagrange's method:*

t	2	5	8	14
A	94.8	87.9	81.3	68.7

Solution: Proceed as in Exp 19(c). **Ans:** 6.5928

(f) Apply Lagrange's formula inversely to obtain the root of the equation $f(x) = 0$, given that

$$f(30) = -30,\ f(34) = -13,\ f(38) = 3 \ \text{ and } \ f(42) = 18.$$

Solution: Proceed as in Exp 19(d). **Ans:** 37.23

3.9 Hermite Interpolation Formula

[Rohilkhand 2010; Meerut 2004]

In various interpolation formulae discussed earlier, one chooses a function $y(x)$ for a given function $f(x)$ such that $y(x)$ agrees with $f(x)$ at certain values of x, often referred to as "*interpolation points*". Sometimes to have a more closer approximation one may also specify that certain derivatives of $y(x)$ agree with corresponding derivatives of $f(x)$ at some interpolation points. Here $y(x)$ is considered to be the sum of $(n+1)$ terms of the Taylor's series for $f(x)$ at the point $x = a$ and is considered as an interpolating polynomial for $f(x)$ of degree n or less such that $y^{(k)}(a) = f^{(k)}(a)$ for $k = 0, 1, 2, \ldots, n$ ...(1)

As a matter of fact Hermite interpolation formula is based on the above assumption and is similar to Lagranges method of interpolation.

In Lagranges method, the interpolating polynomial $y(x)$ agrees with $f(x)$ at the interpolation points $x_0, x_1, \ldots, x_n$ whereas in Hermite interpolation method $y(x)$ and $f(x)$ as well as $y'(x)$ and $f'(x)$, coincide at $(n+1)$ points *i.e.*

$$y(x_k) = f(x_k) \quad \text{and} \quad y'(x_k) = f'(x_k) \quad (k = 0, 1, n) \qquad \ldots(2)$$

More precisely, we choose non-negative integers $r_0, r_1, r_2, \ldots, r_n$ and requires that for each $k = 0, 1, \ldots, n$; $y(x)$ and all its derivatives upto and including the $r_k{}^{th}$ agree with $f(x)$ and the corresponding derivatives.

Let $f(x)$ be the unknown polynomial approximated by another polynomial $y(x)$ of degree N such that $y(x_k) = f(x_k)$

$$y^{(k)}(x_i) = f^{(k)}(x_i), \quad k = 0, 1, \ldots, r_i \quad \text{for } i = 1, 2, \ldots, n.$$

where r_i is given by $\sum_{i=0}^{n} (r_i + 1) = N + 1, i = 0, 1, \ldots, n.$ ...(3)

Hence there exist $(N + 1)$ arbitrary constants in $y(x)$ and $f(x) - y(x)$ must have zero's of order at least $r_i + 1$ at $x = x_i$.

We now consider the case where r_i is either 0 or 1; for all i. Evidently here $N = 2n + 1$ and the polynomial $y(x)$ has zeroes of multiplicity two at each of the x_i.

Hence using the idealogy of Lagranges method, we take $y(x)$ to be the form

$$y(x) = \sum_{i=0}^{n} L(x_i) \prod_{\substack{j=0 \\ j \neq i}}^{n} \left(\frac{x - x_j}{x_i - x_j} \right)^2 \quad \text{...(4)}$$

This expanded form can be written as

$$y(x) = L(x_0) \left[\frac{(x - x_1)(x - x_2) \ldots (x - x_n)}{(x_0 - x_1)(x_0 - x_2) \ldots (x_0 - x_n)} \right]^2 + L(x_1) \left[\frac{(x - x_0)(x - x_2)(x - x_3) \ldots (x - x_n)}{(x_1 - x_0)(x_1 - x_2) \ldots (x_1 - x_n)} \right]^2$$

$$+ \ldots + L(x_n) \left[\frac{(x - x_0)(x - x_1) \ldots (x - x_{n-1})}{(x_n - x_0)(x_n - x_1) \ldots (x_n - x_{n-1})} \right]^2 \quad \text{...(5)}$$

Here each of the repeated product in (5) is a polynomial of degree $2n$. So for $y(x)$ to be of degree $(2n + 1)$, each $L(x_i)$ should be a first degree polynomial with two undetermined co-efficients. Now $L(x_i)$ can be determined by using condition (2) *i.e.*

$$y(x_k) = f(x_k) \quad \text{and} \quad y'(x_k) = f'(x_k)$$

Putting $y(x_k) = f(x_k)$ in (5), we get

$$y(x) = \sum_{i=0}^{n} L(x_k) \prod_{\substack{j=0 \\ j \neq i}}^{n} \left(\frac{x_k - x_j}{x_i - x_j} \right)^2 \quad \text{...(6)}$$

i.e. $$y(x_k) = f(x_k) = L_k(x_k) \quad \text{...(7)}$$

Now differentiating (5), we obtain

$$y(x_k) = \sum_{i=0}^{n} L_i'(x) = \prod_{\substack{j=0 \\ j \neq i}}^{n} \left(\frac{x - x_i}{x_i - x_j} \right)^2 + \sum_{i=0}^{n} L_i(x) \sum_{\substack{r=0 \\ r \neq i}}^{n} \frac{2(x - x_r)}{(x_i - x_r)^2} \times \prod_{\substack{j=0 \\ j \neq i}}^{n} \left(\frac{x - x_j}{x_i - x_j} \right)^2 \quad \text{...(8)}$$

Putting $x = x_k$, eqn. (8) $\Rightarrow$

$$y'(x_k) = f'(x_k) = L'(x_k) + L(x_k) \sum_{\substack{j=0 \\ j \neq i}}^{n} \left(\frac{2}{x_k - x_j} \right) \quad \text{...(9)}$$

Substituting (9) in (7), we readily get

$$L(x_i) = f(x_i) + (x - x_i) \left\{ f'(x_i) - f(x_i) \sum_{\substack{j=0 \\ j \neq i}}^{n} \frac{2}{(x_i - x_j)} \right\} \quad \text{...(10)}$$

Again putting the value of $L(x_i)$ from (10) in (4), we have the required Hermite-interpolation formula as

$$y(x) = \sum_{i=1}^{n} [1 - 2\, L'(x_i)\,(x - x_i)]\,[L(x_i)]^2\, f(x_i)$$

$$+ \sum_{i=1}^{n} (x - x_i)\,[L(x_i)]^2\, f'(x_i) \quad \text{...(11)}$$

For two interpolation points $x = x_0$ and $x = x_1$; the relation (11) can be put as

$$y(x) = \frac{(x - x_1)^2}{(x_1 - x_2)^2} \left\{ \left[1 - (x - x_0) \frac{2\,(x_0 - x_1)}{(x_0 - x_1)^2} \right] f(x_0) + (x - x_0)\, f'(x_0) \right\}$$

$$+ \frac{(x - x_1)^2}{(x_1 - x_0)^2} \left\{ \left[1 - (x - x_1) \frac{2\,(x_1 - x_0)}{(x_1 - x_0)^2} \right] f(x_1) + (x - x_1)\, f'(x_1) \right\} \quad \text{...(12)}$$

In the case of three interpolating points x_0, x_1 and x_2 where $r_0 = r_2 = 1$ and $r_1 = 1$, we have

$$y(x) = \frac{(x - x_1)^2\,(x - x_2)}{(x_0 - x_1)^2\,(x_0 - x_2)}\, f(x_0)$$

$$+ \frac{(x - x_0)\,(x - x_2)}{(x_1 - x_0)\,(x_1 - x_2)} \times \left\{ \left[1 - (x - x_1) \left(\frac{1}{x_1 - x_0} + \frac{1}{x_1 - x_2} \right) \right] f(x_1) + (x - x_1)\, f(x_1) \right\}$$

$$+ \frac{(x - x_0)\,(x - x_1)^2}{(x_2 - x_0)\,(x_2 - x_1)^2}\, f(x_2) \quad \text{...(13)}$$

The method of Hermite interpolation is also known as ***Osculating interpolation.***

It can be seen that in comparison to Lagranges interpolation formula, the Hermite interpolation formula is computationally uneconomical.

3.10 Spline Interpolation

[I.A.S. 2002, 2004]

In all the interpolation methods so far discussed; a single polynomial has been fitted with the given data. If the set of points belong to the polynomial, then this method works well, otherwise the results become rough approximations. When, we draw lines through every two close points, the graph will not be smooth and similarly if we draw a quadratic curve through the points A_i, A_{i+1} and another quadratic curve through A_{i+1}, A_{i+2}, in such a way that the slopes of the two quadratic curves are the same at A_{i+1}. Then the final curve looks better but is again not smooth. It can be ensured by drawing a cubic curve through A_i, A_{i+1} and another cubic through A_{i+1}, A_{i+2} in such a way that the slopes and curvatures of the two curves are equal at A_{i+1}; this type of curve is called a ***Cubic Spline***.

We can use polynomials of higher order but the resulting graph is not better. For this very reason, cubic splines are usually used. This technique of '***spline-fitting***' is of recent origin. It has wider applications.

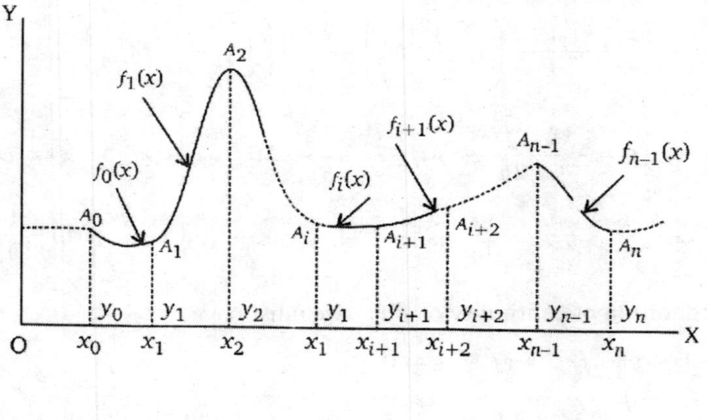

3.10.1 Cubic Spline

[I.A.S. 2003]

Let us consider the problem of interpolating between the data points (x_0, y_0), $(x_1, y_1), .. (x_n, y_n)$ with the help of spline fitting. Here the cubic spline $f(x)$ must exist in such a way that

(i) $f(x)$ is a linear polynomial outside the interval (x_0, x_n),

(ii) $f(x)$ is a cubic polynomial in each of the sub-intervals,

(iii) $f'(x)$ and $f''(x)$ are continuous at each point.

Now $f(x)$ is cubic in each of the sub-intervals so $f''(x)$ must be linear. Then taking equally-spaced values of x so that $x_{i+1} - x_i = h$, we have

$$f''(x) = \frac{1}{h}[(x_{i+1} - x)\, f''(x_i) + (x - x_i)\, f''(x_{i+1})]$$

Integrating the above two times, we get

$$f(x) = \frac{1}{h}\left[\frac{(x_{i+1} - x)^3}{3\,!} f''(x_i) + \frac{(x - x_i)^3}{3\,!} f''(x_{i+1})\right]$$

$$+ a_i (x_{i+1} - x) + b_i (x - x_i) \quad ...(1)$$

The constants a_i, b_i can be determined by substituting the values of $y = f(x)$ at x_i and x_{i+1}.

$$\Rightarrow \quad a_i = \frac{1}{h}\left[y_i - \frac{h^2}{3\,!} f''(x_i)\right] \text{ and } b_i = \frac{1}{h}\left[y_{i+1} - \frac{h^2}{3\,!} f'' e(x_{i+1})\right]$$

Hence substituting the values of a_i, b_i and writing $f''(x_i) = M_i$ relation (1) takes the following form:

$$f(x) = \frac{(x_{i+1} - x)^3}{6h} M_i + \frac{(x - x_i)^3}{6h} M_{i+1}$$

$$+ \frac{x_{i+1} - x}{h}\left(y_i - \frac{h^2}{6} M_i\right) + \frac{x - x_i}{h}\left(y_{i+1} - \frac{h^2}{6} M_{i+1}\right) \quad ...(2)$$

$$\Rightarrow \quad f'(x) = -\frac{(x_{i+1} - x)^2}{2h} M_i + \frac{(x - x_i)^2}{2h} M_{i+1}$$

$$- \frac{h}{6}(M_{i+1} - M_i) + \frac{1}{h}(y_{i+1} - y_i)$$

Then for the condition of continuity of $f'(x)$, we must have

$$f'(x - \varepsilon) = f'(x + \varepsilon) \text{ as } \varepsilon \to 0.$$

$$\Rightarrow \quad \frac{h}{6}(2M_i + M_{i-1}) + \frac{1}{h}(y_i - y_{i-1}) = -\frac{h}{6}(2M_i + M_{i+1}) + \frac{1}{h}(y_{i+1} - y_i)$$

$$\Rightarrow \quad M_{i-1} + 4M_i + M_{i+1} = \frac{6}{h^2}(y_{i-1} - 2y_i + y_{i+1}), i = 1 \text{ to } n-1 \quad ...(3)$$

But the graph is linear for $x < x_0$ and $x > x_n$. So, we have

$$M_0 = 0, M_n = 0 \quad ...(4)$$

Thus (3) and (4) give $(n + 1)$ equations in $(n + 1)$ unknowns M_i $(i = 0, 1, ..., n)$. This can be solved. Then putting the value of M_i in (2), we get the required cubic spline.

Example 19: (g) *The following values of x and y are given*:

x	1	2	3	4
y	1	2	5	11

the cubic splines and evaluate $y(1.5)$ *and* $y'(3)$. **[I.A.S. 2000, 2005]**

Solution: The points are equispaced with $h=1$ and $n=3$. Then from (3) above; we readily obtain

$$M_{i-1}+4M_i+M_{i+1}=6\,(y_{i-1}-2y_i+y_{i+1}),\quad i=1,2.$$

$$\Rightarrow \qquad M_0+4M_1+M_2=6\,(y_0-2y_1+y_2)=12$$

$$M_1+4M_2+M_3=6\,(y_1-2y_2+y_3)=18$$

Putting $M_0=0$ and $M_3=0$ in the above relations, we get

$$4M_1+M_2=12 \quad \text{and} \quad M_1+4M_2=18 \Rightarrow M_1=2, M_2=4.$$

Thus the cubic splines are:

$$f(x)=\begin{cases}\frac{1}{3}(x^3-3x^2+5x), & 1\le x\le 2\\ \frac{1}{3}(x^3-3x^2+5x), & 2\le x\le 3\\ \frac{1}{3}(-2x^3+24x^2-76x+81), & 3\le x\le 4\end{cases}$$

Further $y(1.5)=f(1.5)=(11/8)$. Also $y'(3)=(14/3)$.

Example 20: *Apply Hermite's formula to interpolate for* sin (1.5) *from the following data:*

x	sin x	cos x
1.00	0.84147	0.54030
1.10	0.89121	0.45360

[Rohilkhand 2001, 2007]

Solution: Here $f(x)=\sin x$ and $f'(x)=\cos x$. Also

$$L(x_1)=\frac{x-x_2}{x_1-x_2}=\frac{x-1.10}{1.00-1.10}=-10x+11,\ L'(x_1)=-10$$

$$L(x_2)=\frac{x-x_1}{x_2-x_1}=\frac{x-1.0}{1.1-1.0}=10x-10,\ L'(x_2)=10$$

$$f(x_1)=0.84147 \qquad f'(x_1)=0.54030.$$

$$f(x_2)=0.89121 \qquad f'(x_2)=0.45360.$$

Hence the Hermite-interpolation in this case is given by

$$y(x)=[1-2L'(x_1)][L(x_1)]^2 f(x_1)+(x-x_1)[L(x_1)]^2 f'(x_1)+[1-2L'(x_2)(x-x_2)]$$

$$\times[L(x_2)]^2 f(x_2)+(x-x_2)[L(x_2)]^2 f'(x_2)$$

$$=[1-2(-10)(x-10)][-10x+11]^2(0.84147)+(x-1.0)(-10x+11)^2(.54030)$$

$$+[1-2(10)(x-1.1)]\times[10x-10]^2(0.89121)+(x-1.1)(10x-10)^2(.45360)$$

Putting $x = 1.05$ in $y(x)$, we get

$$\sin(1.05) = [1 - 2(10)(1.05 - 1.0)][-10(1.05) + 11]^2 (0.84147)$$
$$+ (1.05 - 1.0)[-10(1.05) + 11]^2 (0.54030)$$
$$+ [1 - 2(10)(1.05 - 1.1)[10(1.05) - 10]^2 (0.89121)$$
$$+ (1.05 - 1.1)[10(1.05) - 10]^2 (0.45360) = 0.86742375.$$

Example 21: *Apply Hermite's formula to find a polynomial which meets the following specifications.*

x	$f(x)$	$f'(x)$
0	0	0
1	1	0
2	0	0

Solution: Hermite formula is $y(x) = [1 - 2L_0'(x_0)(x - x_0)][L_0(x)]^2 f(x_0)$

$$+ (x - x_0)[L(x_0)]^2 f'(x_0) + [1 - 2L_1'(x)(x - x_1)][L_1(x)]^2 f(x_1)$$
$$+ (x - x_1)[L_1(x)]^2 f'(x_1) + [1 - 2L_2'(x_2)(x - x_2)]$$
$$[L_2(x)]^2 f(x_2) + (x - x_2)[L_2(x)]^2 f'(x_2)$$

Here $x_0 = 0, x_1 = 1, x_2 = 2, f(x_0) = 0, f(x_1) = 1, f(x_2) = 0$

and $f'(x_0) = f'(x_1) = f'(x_2) = 0$. Putting these values in $y(x)$, we get

$$y(x) = [1 - 2L'(x_1)(x - 1)][L_1(x)]^2.$$

Now $$L_1(x) = \frac{(x - x_0)(x - x_2)}{(x_1 - x_0)(x_1 - x_2)} = \frac{(x - 0)(x - 2)}{(1 - 0)(1 - 2)} = -x(x - 2) = -x^2 + 2x$$

$$L_1'(x_1) = (-2x + 2)_{x=1} = 0.$$

$\Rightarrow$ $$y(x) = [L_1(x)]^2 = (-x^2 + 2x)^2 = (x^2 - 2x)^2.$$

Example 22: *A switching path between parallel railroad tracks is to be a cubic polynomial joining positions* $(0, 0)$ *and* $(4, 2)$ *and tangents to the lines* $y = 0$ *and* $y = 2$. *Apply Hermite method to find the polynomial, given*

	x	y	y'
x_1	0	0	0
x_2	4	2	0

Solution: Proceed as in Exp 21. **Ans.** $\frac{x^2(6 - x)}{16}$

Illustration: *From Hermite's formula for point oscillation, derive the important formula*

$$y\left(\frac{1}{2}\right)=\frac{1}{2}(y_0+y_1)+\frac{1}{3}L(y_0'-y_1'),\qquad \text{where } L=(x_1-x_0).$$

Example 23: *The value of x and y are given as below:*

x	5	6	9	11
y	12	13	14	16

Find the value of y when $x=10$. **[Meerut 2004 (B.P.)]**

Solution: Here $x_0=5, x_1=6, x_2=9, x_3=11$.

$$\therefore\quad y_{10}=\frac{(10-6)(10-9)(10-11)}{(5-6)(5-9)(5-11)}\times 12+\frac{(10-5)(10-9)(10-1)}{(6-5)(6-9)(6-11)}\times 13$$

$$+\frac{(10-5)(10-6)(10-11)}{(9-5)(9-6)(9-11)}\times 14+\frac{(10-5)(10-6)(10-9)}{(11-5)(11-6)(11-9)}\times 16$$

$$=2-4.33+11.66+5.33=14.66.$$

Example 24: *Deduce Lagrange's formula for interpolation. The observed values of a function are respectively* 168, 120, 72 *and* 63 *at the four positions* 3, 7, 9 *and* 10 *of the independent variable. What is the best estimate you can give for the value of the function at the position* 6 *of the independent variable?* **[Agra 2000, 2001]**

Solution: For first part See Article 3.7.

Put the data in the following tabular form:

x	3	6	7	9	10
y	168	?	120	72	63

Here $x_0=3, x_1=7, x_2=9, x_3=10$

$$\therefore\quad y_6=168\frac{(6-7)(6-9)(6-10)}{(3-7)(3-9)(3-10)}+120\frac{(6-3)(6-9)(6-10)}{(7-3)(7-9)(7-10)}$$

$$+72\frac{(6-3)(6-7)(6-10)}{(9-3)(9-7)(9-10)}+63\frac{(6-3)(6-7)(6-9)}{(10-3)(10-7)(10-9)}$$

$$=168\times\frac{1}{14}+120\times\frac{3}{2}+72\times(-1)+63\times\frac{3}{7}=12+180-72+27=147.$$

Therefore, the best estimate that can be given for the value of the function at the position 6 of the independent variable is 147.

Example 25: *The following table gives the normal weights of babies during the first 12 months of life:*

Age in months	0	2	5	8	10	12
Weights in lbs	$7\frac{1}{2}$	$10\frac{1}{4}$	15	16	18	21

Estimate the weight of the baby at the age of 7 months. **[M.K.U. (Tamil Nadu) 2005, 2008]**

Solution: Here $x_0 = 0, x_1 = 2, x_2 = 5, x_3 = 8, x_4 = 10, x_5 = 12$;

$$\therefore y_7 = \frac{(7-2)(7-5)(7-8)(7-10)(7-12)}{(0-2)(0-5)(0-8)(0-10)(0-12)} \times \frac{15}{2} + \frac{(7-0)(7-5)(7-8)(7-10)(7-12)}{(2-0)(2-5)(2-8)(2-10)(2-12)} \times \frac{41}{4}$$

$$+ \frac{(7-0)(7-2)(7-8)(7-10)(7-12)}{(5-0)(5-2)(5-8)(5-10)(5-12)} \times 15 + \frac{(7-0)(7-2)(7-5)(7-10)(7-12)}{(8-0)(8-2)(8-5)(8-10)(8-12)} \times 16$$

$$+ \frac{(7-0)(7-2)(7-5)(7-8)(7-12)}{(10-0)(10-2)(10-5)(10-8)(10-12)} \times 18$$

$$+ \frac{(7-0)(7-2)(7-5)(7-8)(7-10)}{(12-0)(12-2)(12-5)(12-8)(12-10)} \times 21$$

$$= \frac{15}{128} - \frac{287}{384} + 5 + \frac{175}{13} - \frac{63}{16} + \frac{21}{32} = \frac{15}{128} - \frac{287}{384} + 5 + \frac{175}{13} - \frac{63}{16} + \frac{21}{32}$$

$$= .11718 - .7473 + 5 + 14.583 - 3.937 + .6562 = 15.67 \text{ lbs.}$$

Example 26: *Determine by Lagrange's formula the percentage number of criminals under 35 years:*

Age	*% number of Criminals*
Under 25 years	52.0
" 30 "	67.3
" 40 "	84.1
" 50 "	94.4

Solution: The above data can be put in the following tabular form:

x	25	30	40	50
y	52	67.3	84.1	94.4

Hence $x_0 = 25, x_1 = 30, x_2 = 40, x_3 = 50$

$$\therefore \quad y_{35} = \frac{(35-30)(35-40)(35-50)}{(25-30)(25-40)(25-50)} \times 52 + \frac{(35-25)(35-40)(35-50)}{(30-25)(30-40)(30-50)} \times 67.3$$

$$+ \frac{(35-25)(35-30)(35-50)}{(40-25)(40-30)(40-50)} \times 84.1 + \frac{(35-25)(35-30)(35-40)}{(50-25)(50-30)(50-40)} \times 94.4$$

$$= -10.4 + 50.475 + 42.05 - 4.72 = 77.405.$$

Thus the criminals under 35 years are 77%.

Example 27: *Given*

$$\log_{10} 654 = 2.8156, \log_{10} 658 = 2.8182, \log_{10} 659 = 2.8189,$$

$$\log_{10} 661 = 2.8202; \textit{ find } \log_{10} 656.$$

[Agra 2007; Bangaluru 2008; M.D.U. (Rohtak) 2006, 2010]

Solution: Here

$$f(x) = \log_{10} 656, x_0 = 654, x_1 = 658, x_2 = 659, x_3 = 661.$$

Thus by Lagrange's formula, we have

$$\log_{10} 656 = \frac{(656-658)(656-659)(656-661)}{(654-658)(654-659)(654-661)} \times (2.8156)$$

$$+ \frac{(656-654)(656-659)(656-661)}{(658-654)(658-659)(658-661)} \times (2.8182)$$

$$+ \frac{(656-654)(656-658)(656-661)}{(659-654)(659-658)(659-661)} \times (2.8189)$$

$$+ \frac{(656-654)(656-658)(656-659)}{(661-654)(661-658)(661-659)} \times (2.8202)$$

$$= \frac{3}{14}(2.8156) + \frac{5}{2}(2.8182) - 2(2.8189) + \frac{2}{7}(2.8202)$$

$$= .6033 + 7.045 - 5.6378 + .8057 = 2.8170.$$

Example 28: *Find the form of the function given by*

x	3	2	1	−1
$f(x)$	3	12	15	−21

Solution: In this case $x_0 = 3, x_1 = 2, x_2 = 1, x_3 = -1$. **[Kurukshetra 2008]**

∴ By Lagrange's formula, we have

$$f(x) = \frac{(x-2)(x-1)(x+1)}{(3-2)(3-1)(3+1)} \times 3 + \frac{(x-3)(x-1)(x+1)}{(2-3)(2-1)(2+1)} \times 12$$

$$+ \frac{(x-3)(x-2)(x+1)}{(1-3)(1-2)(1+1)} \times 15 + \frac{(x-3)(x-2)(x-1)}{(-1-3)(-1-2)(-1-1)} \times (-21)$$

On solving this, we get $f(x) = x^3 - 9x^2 + 17x + 6$.

Example 29: *Find the form of the function, given:*

x	0	1	2	3	4
$f(x)$	3	6	11	18	27

Solution: Here $x_0 = 0, x_1 = 1, x_2 = 2, x_3 = 3, x_4 = 4$.

Thus from Lagrange's formula, we have

$$f(x) = \frac{(x-1)(x-2)(x-3)(x-4)}{(0-1)(0-2)(0-3)(0-4)} \times 3 + \frac{(x-0)(x-2)(x-3)(x-4)}{(1-0)(1-2)(1-3)(1-4)} \times 6$$

$$+ \frac{(x-0)(x-1)(x-3)(x-4)}{(2-0)(2-1)(2-3)(2-4)} \times 11 + \frac{(x-0)(x-1)(x-2)(x-4)}{(3-0)(3-1)(3-2)(3-4)} \times 18$$

$$+ \frac{(x-0)(x-1)(x-2)(x-3)}{(4-0)(4-1)(4-2)(4-3)} \times 27$$

$$= \frac{1}{8}(x-1)(x-2)(x-3)(x-4) - x(x-2)(x-3)(x-4)$$

$$+ \frac{11}{4} x(x-1)(x-3)(x-4) - 3x(x-1)(x-2)(x-4) + \frac{27}{24} x(x-1)(x-2)(x-3)$$

or $$\frac{f(x)}{x(x-1)(x-2)(x-3)(x-4)} = \frac{1}{8x} - \frac{1}{x-1} + \frac{11}{4(x-2)} - \frac{3}{x-3} + \frac{9}{8(x-4)}$$

$$= \frac{x^2 + 2x + 3}{x(x-1)(x-2)(x-3)(x-4)}$$

$\therefore \; f(x) = x^2 + 2x + 3$.

Example 30: *The following table is given:*

x	0	1	2	5
$f(x)$	2	3	12	147

What is the form of $f(x)$? **[Avadh 2004, 2009]**

Solution: Here $x_0 = 0, x_1 = 1, x_2 = 2, x_3 = 5$.

Now, Lagrange's formula gives

$$f(x) = \frac{(x-x_1)(x-x_2)(x-x_3)}{(x_0-x_1)(x_0-x_2)(x_0-x_3)} f(x_0) + \frac{(x-x_0)(x-x_2)(x-x_3)}{(x_1-x_0)(x_1-x_2)(x_1-x_3)} f(x_1)$$

$$+ \frac{(x-x_0)(x-x_1)(x-x_3)}{(x_2-x_0)(x_2-x_1)(x_2-x_3)} f(x_2) + \frac{(x-x_0)(x-x_1)(x-x_2)}{(x_3-x_0)(x_3-x_1)(x_3-x_2)} f(x_3).$$

Hence substituting the values of x_0, x_1, x_2, x_3 in this, we get

$$f(x) = \frac{(x-1)(x-2)(x-5)}{(0-1)(0-2)(0-5)} \times 2 + \frac{(x-0)(x-2)(x-5)}{(1-0)(1-2)(1-5)} \times 3$$

$$+ \frac{(x-0)(x-1)(x-5)}{(2-0)(2-1)(2-5)} \times 12 + \frac{(x-0)(x-1)(x-2)}{(5-0)(5-1)(5-2)} \times 147$$

$$\Rightarrow \quad \frac{f(x)}{x(x-1)(x-2)(x-5)} = -\frac{1}{5x} + \frac{3}{4(x-1)} - \frac{2}{x-2} + \frac{49}{20(x-5)}$$

$$= \frac{20x^3 + 20x^2 - 20x + 40}{20x(x-1)(x-2)(x-5)} \quad \Rightarrow \quad f(x) = x^3 + x^2 - x + 2.$$

Example 31: *Find the form of the function $f(x)$ for the following table:*

x	0	1	4	5
$f(x)$	8	11	68	123

Solution: Proceed as in ***Ex***. **31**. **Ans:** $f(x) = x^3 - x^2 + 3x + 8.$

Example 32: *By means of Lagrange's formula, prove that*

(a) $y_1 = y_3 - .3(y_5 - y_{-3}) + .2(y_{-3} - y_{-5})$ *approx.* **[Avadh 2007; U.P.P.C.S. 2006]**

(b) $y_0 = \frac{1}{2}(y_1 + y_{-1}) - \frac{1}{8}\left[\frac{1}{2}(y_3 - y_1) - \frac{1}{2}(y_{-1} - y_{-3})\right]$ *approx.*

[Agra 2004, 2006]

Solution: (a) In this case, y_1 is to be obtained while y_{-5}, y_{-3}, y_3, y_5 are given

Now

$$y_1 = \frac{(1+3)(1-3)(1-5)}{(-5+3)(-5-3)(-5-5)} y_{-5} + \frac{(1+5)(1-3)(1-5)}{(-3+5)(-3-3)(-3-5)} y_{-3}$$

$$+ \frac{(1+5)(1+3)(1-5)}{(3+5)(3+3)(3-5)} y_3 + \frac{(1+5)(1+3)(1-3)}{(5+5)(5+3)(5-3)} y_5$$

$$= \frac{(4)(-2)(-4)}{(-2)(-8)(-10)} y_{-5} + \frac{(6)(-2)(-4)}{(2)(-6)(-8)} y_{-3} + \frac{(6)(4)(-4)}{(8)(6)(-2)} y_3 + \frac{(6)(4)(-2)}{(10)(8)(2)} y_5$$

$$= -\frac{1}{5} y_{-5} + \frac{1}{2} y_{-3} + y_3 - \frac{3}{10} \cdot y_5 \quad = .2\, y_{-5} + .5\, y_{-3} + y_3 - .3\, y_5$$

$$= y_3 - .3(y_5 - y_{-3}) + .2(y_{-3} - y_{-5}).$$

(b) In this case y_{-3}, y_{-1}, y_1 and y_3 are given: to find y_0.

$$y_0 = \frac{(0+1)(0-1)(0-3)}{(-3+1)(-3-1)(-3-3)} y_{-3} + \frac{(0+3)(0-1)(0-3)}{(-1+3)(-1-1)(-1-3)} y_{-1}$$

$$+ \frac{(0+3)(0+1)(0-3)}{(1+3)(1+1)(1-3)} y_1 + \frac{(0+3)(0+1)(0-1)}{(3+3)(3+1)(3-1)} y_3$$

$$= -\frac{1}{16} y_{-3} + \frac{9}{16} y_{-1} + \frac{9}{16} y_1 - \frac{1}{16} y_3$$

$$= \frac{1}{2}(y_1 + y_{-1}) - \frac{1}{16}[(y_3 - y_1) - (y_{-1} - y_{-3})]$$

$$= \frac{1}{2}(y_1 + y_{-1}) - \frac{1}{8}\left[\frac{1}{2}(y_3 - y_1) - \frac{1}{2}(y_{-1} + y_{-3})\right].$$

Example 33: *Four equidistant values u_{-1}, u_0, u_1 and u_2 being given, a value is interpolated by Lagrange's formula; show that it may be written in the form*

$$u_x = yu_0 + xu_1 + \frac{y(y^2-1)}{3!}\Delta^2 u_{-1} + \frac{x(x^2-1)}{3!}\Delta^2 u_0$$

where $x + y = 1$.

[Baroda 2004; Nagpur 2006, 2009; Bangaluru 2005, 2008; Lucknow 2005; Delhi (H) 2008; Kurukshetra 2006, 2010; Rohilkhand 2006, 2009]

Solution: $u_x = yu_0 + xu_1 + \frac{y(y^2-1)}{3!}\Delta^2 u_{-1} + \frac{x(x^2-1)}{3!}\Delta^2 u_0$

$$= (1-x)u_0 + xu_1 + \frac{(1-x)\{(1-x^2)-1\}}{6}(u_2 - 2u_0 + u_{-1}) + \frac{x(x^2-1)}{6}(u_2 - 2u_1 + u_0)$$

$$= (1-x)u_0 + xu_1 + \frac{(1-x)x(x-2)}{6}(u_1 + 2u_0 + u_{-1}) + \frac{x(x^2-1)}{6}(u_2 - 2u_1 + u_0)$$

$$= u_{-1}\left\{\frac{(1-x)x(x-2)}{6}\right\} + u_0\left\{(1-x) - \frac{(1-x)x(x-2)}{3} + \frac{x(x-1)(x+1)}{6}\right\}$$

$$+ u_1\left\{x + \frac{(1-x)x(x-2)}{6} - \frac{x(x^2-1)}{3}\right\} + u_2\left\{\frac{x(x-1)(x+1)}{6}\right\}$$

$$= -\frac{x(x-1)(x-2)}{6}u_{-1} + \frac{(x-1)}{6}\{-6 + 2x(x-2) + x(x+1)\}u_0$$

$$+ \frac{1}{6}x\{6 + (1-x)(x-2) - 2(x^2-1)\}u_1 + \frac{(x+1)x(x-1)}{6}u_2$$

$$= -\frac{x(x-1)(x-2)}{6}u_{-1} + \frac{(x+1)(x-1)(x-2)}{2}u_0 - \frac{(x+1)x(x-2)}{2}u_1 + \frac{(x+1)x(x-1)}{6}u_2 \quad ...(1)$$

Again taking u_{-1}, u_0, u_1, u_2 as known values, we have by Lagrange's formula

$$u_x = \frac{(x-0)(x-1)(x-2)}{(-1-0)(-1-1)(-1-2)}u_{-1} + \frac{(x+1)(x-1)(x-2)}{(0+1)(0-1)(0-2)}u_0$$

$$+ \frac{(x+1)(x-0)(x-2)}{(1+1)(1-0)(1-2)}u_1 + \frac{(x+1)(x-0)(x-1)}{(2+1)(2-0)(2-1)}u_2$$

$$= -\frac{x(x-1)(x-2)}{6}u_{-1} + \frac{(x+1)(x-1)(x-2)}{2}u_0$$

$$-\frac{(x+1)x(x-2)}{2}u_1 + \frac{(x+1)x(x-1)}{6}u_2 \qquad \ldots(2)$$

Thus we observe that (1) and (2) are the same.

Example 34: *Given* $f(0) = -18, f(1) = 0, f(3) = 0, f(5) = -248,$

$$f(6) = 0, f(9) = 13104, \textit{ find } f(x).$$

Solution: $f(x) = \frac{(x-1)(x-3)(x-5)(x-6)(x-9)}{(0-1)(0-3)(0-5)(0-6)(0-9)}(-18)$

$$+\frac{(x-0)(x-3)(x-5)(x-6)(x-9)}{(1-0)(1-3)(1-5)(1-6)(1-9)}(0) + \frac{(x-0)(x-1)(x-5)(x-6)(x-9)}{(3-0)(3-1)(3-5)(3-6)(3-9)}(0)$$

$$+\frac{(x-0)(x-1)(x-3)(x-6)(x-9)}{(5-0)(5-1)(5-3)(5-6)(5-9)}(-248) + \frac{(x-0)(x-1)(x-3)(x-5)(x-9)}{(6-0)(6-1)(6-3)(6-5)(6-9)}(0)$$

$$+\frac{(x-0)(x-1)(x-3)(x-5)(x-6)}{(9-0)(9-1)(9-3)(9-5)(9-6)}(13104)$$

$$= (x-1)(x-3)(x-6)\left[\frac{(x-5)(x-9)}{45} - x(x-9)\frac{31}{20} + x(x-5)\frac{91}{36}\right]$$

$$= (x-1)(x-3)(x-6)\left[\frac{(x-9)}{180}.\{4(x-5) - 279x\} + \frac{91}{36}x(x-5)\right]$$

$$= (x-1)(x-3)(x-6)\left[-\frac{(x-9)(55x+4)}{36} + \frac{91}{36}x(x-5)\right]$$

$$= (x+1)(x-3)(x-6)\left[\frac{36x^2+36x+36}{36}\right] = (x+1)(x-3)(x-6)(x^2+x+1).$$

Example 35: *The following values of the function $f(x)$ for values of x are given:*

$$f(1) = 4, f(2) = 5, f(7) = 5, f(8) = 4.$$

Find the value of $f(6)$ and also the value of x for which $f(x)$ is maximum or minimum.

Solution: By Lagrange's formula, we have

$$f(x) = \frac{(x-2)(x-7)(x-8)}{(1-2)(1-7)(1-8)}(4) + \frac{(x-1)(x-7)(x-8)}{(2-1)(2-7)(2-8)}(5)$$

$$+\frac{(x-1)(x-2)(x-8)}{(7-1)(7-2)(7-8)}(5) + \frac{(x-1)(x-2)(x-7)}{(8-1)(8-2)(8-7)}(4)$$

$$=\left[-\frac{4}{42}(x-2)(x-7)(x-8)+\frac{5}{30}(x-1)(x-7)(x-8)\right.$$

$$\left.-\frac{5}{30}(x-1)(x-2)(x-8)+\frac{4}{42}(x-1)(x-2)(x-7)\right]$$

$$=\left[\frac{4}{42}(x-2)(x-7)\{(x-1)-(x-8)\}+\frac{5}{30}(x-1)(x-8)\{(x-7)-(x-2)\}\right]$$

$$=\left[\frac{2}{3}(x-2)(x-7)-\frac{5}{6}(x-1)(x-8)\right]$$

$$=\frac{1}{6}[4(x^2-9x+14)-5(x^2-9x+8)]=\frac{1}{6}[-x^2+9x+16]$$

$$\therefore\ f(6)=\frac{1}{6}[-36+54+16]=\frac{34}{6}=5.66.$$

Again for maximum or minimum of $f(x)$, we have

$$f'(x)=0 \quad i.e.\ -2x+9=0 \quad or\ x=4.5.$$

Again $f''(x)=-2$. Hence $f(x)$ is maximum at point $x=4.5$.

Example 36: *The mode of certain frequency curve $y=f(x)$ is very near $x=9$ and the values of the frequency density $f(x)$ for $x=8.9, 9.0$ and 9.3 are respectively equal to $0.30, 0.35$ and 0.25. Calculate the approximate value of mode.*

[M.D.U. (Rohtak) 2004, 2006, 2009; Delhi (H) 2005, 2008, 2010]

Solution: In this case

$$f(8.9)=0.30,\ f(9.0)=0.35,\ f(9.3)=0.25$$

$$\therefore\quad f(x)=\frac{(x-9)(x-9.3)}{(8.9-9)(8.9-9.3)}(0.30)+\frac{(x-8.9)(x-9.3)}{(9.0-8.9)(9.0-9.3)}(0.35)$$

$$+\frac{(x-8.9)(x-9.0)}{(9.3-8.9)(9.3-9.0)}(0.25)$$

$$=\frac{(x^2-18.3x+83.7)(0.30)}{(0.04)}+\frac{(x^2-18.2x+82.77)(0.35)}{-(0.03)}+\frac{(x^2-17.9x+80.1)(0.25)}{(0.12)}$$

$$=\frac{1}{12}[(x^2-18.3x-83.7)(90)-(x^2-18.2x+82.77)(140)+(x^2-17.9x+80.1)25]$$

$$=\frac{1}{12}[90x^2-1647.0x+7533.0-140x^2+2848.0x-12587.8+25x^2-447.5x+2022.5]$$

$$=-\frac{25}{12}x^2+\frac{453.5}{12}x-\frac{3032.3}{12}.$$

For modal value $f'(x)=0$.

i.e. $$-\frac{25}{6}x+\frac{453.5}{12}=0 \quad \text{or} \quad x=\frac{453.5}{12}\times\frac{6}{25}=9.07.$$

Thus mode of the frequency $=9.07$.

Example 37: *From the following data estimate the number of persons having incomes between Rs.* 1000 *and Rs.* 1500.

Income	Below 400	500-1000	1000-2000	2000-3000	3000-4000
No. of persons	6000	4250	3600	1500	650

Solution: First of all we put all the frequencies in the form of cumulative frequencies and form the following table:

Income less than	500	1000	2000	3000	4000
No. of persons	6000	10250	13850	15350	16000

Now shift the origin to 500; and divide the scale by 500. In this way, we have known $f(x)$ for $x = 0, 1, 3, 5$ and 7.

Now, we shall find number of persons whose income is less than Rs. 1500 *i.e.* $f(x)$ for $x = \frac{1500 - 500}{500} = 2$.

By Lagrange's formula,

$$f(2) = \frac{(2-1)(2-3)(2-5)(2-7)}{(0-1)(0-3)(0-5)(0-7)} \times 6000 + \frac{(2-0)(2-3)(2-5)(2-7)}{(1-0)(1-3)(1-5)(1-7)} \times 10250$$

$$+ \frac{(2-0)(2-1)(2-5)(2-7)}{(3-0)(3-1)(3-5)(3-7)} \times 13850 + \frac{(2-0)(2-1)(2-3)(2-7)}{(5-0)(5-1)(5-3)(5-7)} \times 15350$$

$$+ \frac{(2-0)(2-1)(2-3)(2-5)}{(7-0)(7-1)(7-3)(7-5)} \times 16000$$

$$= -\frac{1}{7} \times 6000 + \frac{5}{8} \times 10250 + \frac{5}{8} \times 13850 - \frac{1}{8} \times 15350 + \frac{1}{56} \times 16000$$

$$= -857.14 + 6406.25 + 8656.25 - 1918.75 + 285.71 = 12572 \text{ approx.}$$

i.e., number of persons having income less than Rs. $1500 = 12572$. But number of persons having income less than Rs. $1000 = 10250$. Therefore persons having income between Rs. 1000 and Rs. 1500 are 2322.

Example 38: *The values of $f(x)$ are given at a, b and c. Show that the maximum is obtained by*

$$x = \frac{f(a)(b^2 - c^2) + f(b)(c^2 - a^2) + f(c)(a^2 - b^2)}{[f(a)(b-c) + f(b)(c-a) + f(c)(a-b)]}$$

[Calicut 2006; I.A.S. 2006; U.P.P.C.S. 2005, 2007; Nagpur 2005, 2008, 2010; Sri Venketeswara 2006; Delhi (H) 2009, 2010]

Solution: By Lagrange's formula, $f(x)$ for the arguments a, b and c is given by

$$f(x) = \frac{(x-b)(x-c)}{(a-b)(a-c)} f(a) + \frac{(x-a)(x-c)}{(b-a)(b-c)} f(b) + \frac{(x-a)(x-b)}{(c-a)(c-b)} f(c)$$

$$= \frac{x^2 - (b+c)x + bc}{(a-b)(a-c)} f(a) + \frac{x^2 - (a+c)x + ac}{(b-a)(b-c)} f(b) + \frac{x^2 - (a+b)x + ab}{(c-a)(c-b)} f(c).$$

For maximum or minimum of $f(x)$, we have $f'(x)=0$

$$\text{i.e.}\quad \frac{2x-(b+c)}{(a-b)(a-c)}f(a)+\frac{2x-(a+c)}{(b-a)(b-c)}f(b)+\frac{2x-(a+b)}{(c-a)(c-b)}f(c)=0,$$

$$\text{or}\quad [2x\{(b-c)\,f(a)+(c-a)\,f(b)+(a-b)\,f(c)\}$$
$$-\{(b^2-c^2)\,f(a)+(c^2-a^2)\,f(b)+(a^2-b^2)\,f(c)\}=0$$

$$\text{or}\quad x=\frac{f(a)\,(b^2-c^2)+f(b)\,(c^2-a^2)+f(c)\,(a^2-b^2)}{2\,[f(a)\,(b-c)+f(b)\,(c-a)+f(c)\,(a-b)]}.$$

Example 39: *Values of y_x are given for all integral values of x from 0 to $n-1$. Show that y_x is capable of expression in the form*

$$\frac{x\,!}{(x-n)\,!\,(n-1)\,!}\left[\frac{y_{n-1}}{x-n+1}-{}^{n-1}C_1\frac{y_{n-2}}{x-n+2}+{}^{n-1}C_2\frac{y_{n-1}}{x-n+3}+(-1)^{n-1.\,n-1}C_{n-1}\frac{y_0}{x_0}\right].$$

[Bangaluru 2004, 2008; Patna 2006, 2008; Meerut 2003; Delhi (H) 2004, 2007]

Solution: With n values of $y_x, (y_0, y_1, \dots, y_{n-1})$, the Lagrange's formula is

$$y=\frac{(x-0)\,(x-1)\,(x-2)\dots(x-\overline{n-2})}{(\overline{n-1}-0)\,(\overline{n-1}-1)\,(\overline{n-1}-2)\dots(\overline{n-1}-\overline{n-2})}\,y_{n-1}$$

$$+\frac{(x-0)\,(x-1)\dots(x-\overline{n-3})\,(x-\overline{n-1})}{(\overline{n-2}-0)\,(\overline{n-2}-1)\dots(\overline{n-2}-\overline{n-3})\,(\overline{n-2}-\overline{n-1})}\,y_{n-2}$$

$$+\frac{(x-0)\,(x-1)\dots(x-\overline{n-4})\,(x-\overline{n-2})\,(x-\overline{n-1})}{(\overline{n-3}-0)\,(\overline{n-3}-1)\dots(\overline{n-3}-\overline{n-4})\,(\overline{n-3}-\overline{n-2})\,(\overline{n-3}-\overline{n-1})}\,y_{n-3}$$

$$+\dots+\frac{(x-1)\,(x-2)\dots(x-\overline{n-1})}{(0-1)\,(0-2)\dots(0-\overline{n-1})}\,y_0$$

(we have taken last term as first)

$$\text{or}\quad y_x=\frac{x\,(x-1)\,(x-2)\dots(x-n+2)}{(n-1)\,!}\,y_{n-1}+\frac{x\,(x-1)\dots(x-n+3)\,(x-n+1)}{(n-2)\,!\,(-1)}\,y_{n-2}$$

$$+\frac{x\,(x-1)\dots(x-n+4)\,(x-n+2)\,(x-n+1)}{(n-3)\,!\,(-1)\,(-2)}\,y_{n-3}+\dots+\frac{(x-1)\,(x-2)\dots(x-n+1)}{(-1)\,(-2)\dots(-\overline{n-1})}\,y_0$$

$$\text{or}\quad y_x=\frac{x\,(x-1)\dots(x-n+2)\,(x-n+1)}{(n-1)\,!}\cdot\frac{y_{n-1}}{x-n+1}$$

$$+\frac{x\,(x-1)\dots(x-n+3)\,(x-n+2)\,(x-n+1)}{(n-2)\,!\,(-1)}\cdot\frac{y_{n-2}}{x-n+2}$$

$$+\frac{x\,(x-1)\dots(x-n+1)}{(n-3)\,!\,(-1)\,(-2)}\cdot\frac{y_{n-3}}{x-n+3}+\dots+\frac{x\,(x-1)\,(x-2)\dots(x-n+1)}{(-1)\,(-2)\dots(-\overline{n-1})}\cdot\frac{y_0}{x}$$

$$= \frac{x!}{(x-n)!} \cdot \frac{1}{(n-1)!} \cdot \frac{y_{n-1}}{x-n+1} + (-1) \frac{x!}{(x-n)!} \cdot \frac{1}{(n-2)!} \cdot \frac{1}{1!} \cdot \frac{y_{n-2}}{x-n+2}$$

$$+ (-1)^2 \frac{x!}{(x-n)!} \cdot \frac{1}{(n-3)!} \cdot \frac{1}{2!} \cdot \frac{y_{n-3}}{x-n+3}$$

$$+ \ldots (-1)^{n-1} \frac{x!}{(x-n)!} \cdot \frac{1}{0!} \cdot \frac{1}{(n-1)!} \cdot \frac{y_0}{x}$$

$$= \frac{x!}{(x-n)!} \frac{1}{(n-1)!} \frac{y_{n-1}}{x-n+1} + (-1) \frac{x!}{(x-n)!} \frac{1}{(n-1)!} \, {}^{n-1}C_1 \frac{y_{n-2}}{x-n+2}$$

$$+ (-1)^2 \frac{x!}{(x-n)!} \cdot \frac{1}{(n-1)!} \, {}^{n-1}C_2 \cdot \frac{y_{n-3}}{x-n+3} + \ldots + (-1)^{n-1} \frac{x!}{(x-n)!} \cdot \frac{1}{(n-1)!} \cdot {}^{n-1}C_{n-1} \frac{y_0}{x}$$

$$= \frac{x!}{(x-n)!(n-1)!} \left[\frac{y_{n-1}}{x-n+1} + (-1) \, {}^{n-1}C_1 \frac{y_{n-2}}{x-n+2} \right.$$

$$\left. + (-1)^2 . {}^{n-1}C_2 \frac{y_{n-3}}{x-n+3} + \ldots + (-1)^{n-1} . {}^{n-1}C_{n-1} \frac{y_0}{x_0} \right]$$

Example 40: *If $y_0, y_1, y_2, \ldots, y_6$ are the consecutive terms of a series, then prove that*

$$y_3 = 0.05 (y_0 + y_6) - 0.3 (y_1 + y_5) + 0.75 (y_2 + y_4).$$

[Meerut 2001; Avadh 2005]

Solution: Lagrange's formula is

$$f(x) = \frac{(x-x_1)(x-x_2)\ldots(x-x_n)}{(x_0-x_1)(x_0-x_2)\ldots(x_0-x_n)} f(x_0) + \frac{(x-x_0)(x-x_2)\ldots(x-x_n)}{(x_1-x_0)(x_1-x_2)\ldots(x_1-x_n)} f(x_1)$$

$$+ \ldots + \frac{(x-x_0)(x-x_1)\ldots(x-x_{n-1})}{(x_n-x_0)(x_n-x_1)\ldots(x_n-x_{n-1})} f(x_n)$$

or

$$\frac{f(x)}{(x-x_0)(x-x_1)\ldots(x-x_n)} = \frac{1}{(x-x_0)(x_0-x_1)(x_0-x_2)\ldots(x_0-x_n)} f(x_0)$$

$$+ \frac{1}{(x-x_1)(x_1-x_0)(x_1-x_2)\ldots(x_1-x_n)} f(x_1) + \ldots$$

$$+ \frac{1}{(x-x_n)(x_n-x_0)(x_n-x_1)\ldots(x_n-x_{n-1})} f(x_n). \qquad \ldots(1)$$

Putting

$$x = 3, x_0 = 0, x_1 = 1, x_2 = 2, x_3 = 4, x_4 = 5, x_5 = 6,$$

$f(0) = y_0, f(1) = y_1, f(2) = y_2, f(4) = y_4, f(5) = y_5, f(6) = y_6$ and $f(3) = y_3$, in (1) we get $\dfrac{y_3}{(3-0)(3-1)(3-2)(3-4)(3-5)(3-6)}=\dfrac{y_0}{(3-0)(-1)(-2)(-4)(-5)(-6)}$

$$+\frac{y_1}{(3-1)(1)(-1)(-3)(-4)(-5)}+\frac{y_2}{(3-2)(2)(1)(-2)(-3)(-4)}+\frac{y_4}{(3-4)(4)(3)(2)(-1)(-2)}$$

$$+\frac{y_5}{(3-5)(5)(4)(3)(1)(-1)}+\frac{y_6}{(3-6)(6)(5)(4)(2)(1)}$$

or $-\dfrac{y_3}{1.2.3.1.2.3}=-\dfrac{y_0}{1.2.3.4.5.6}+\dfrac{y_1}{1.2.3.4.5}-\dfrac{y_2}{2.1.2.3.4}$

$$-\frac{y_4}{2.1.2.3.4}+\frac{y_5}{1.2.3.4.5}-\frac{y_6}{1.2.3.4.5.6}$$

$$=-\frac{y_0+y_6}{1.2.3.4.5.6}+\frac{y_1+y_5}{1.2.3.4.5}-\frac{y_2+y_4}{2.1.2.3.4}$$

or $y_3=\dfrac{6(y_0+y_6)}{4.5.6}-\dfrac{6(y_1+y_5)}{4.5}+\dfrac{6(y_2+y_4)}{2.4}$

$$=0.05(y_0+y_6)-0.3(y_1+y_5)+0.75(y_2+y_4).$$

Example 41: *If all terms except y_5 of the sequence $y_1, y_2, y_3, \ldots, y_9$ be given, show that the value of y_5 is*

$$\left[\frac{56(y_4+y_6)-28(y_3+y_7)+8(y_2+y_8)-(y_1+y_9)}{70}\right]$$

[Meerut 2007]

Solution: Lagrange's formula gives

$$f(x)=\frac{(x-x_1)(x-x_2)\ldots(x-x_n)}{(x_0-x_1)(x_0-x_2)\ldots(x_0-x_n)}f(x_0)+\frac{(x-x_0)(x-x_2)\ldots(x-x_n)}{(x_1-x_0)(x_1-x_2)\ldots(x_1-x_n)}f(x_1)$$

$$+\ldots+\frac{(x-x_0)(x-x_1)\ldots(x-x_{n-1})}{(x_n-x_0)(x_n-x_1)\ldots(x_n-x_{n-1})}f(x_n)$$

$$\Rightarrow \quad \frac{f(x)}{(x-x_0)(x-x_1)\ldots(x-x_n)}=\frac{f(x_0)}{(x-x_0)(x_0-x_1)(x_0-x_2)\ldots(x_0-x_n)}$$

$$+\frac{f(x_1)}{(x-x_1)(x_1-x_0)(x_1-x_2)\ldots(x_1-x_n)}$$

$$+\ldots+\frac{f(x_n)}{(x-x_n)(x_n-x_0)(x_n-x_1)\ldots(x_n-x_{n-1})}$$

Now putting

$x_0=1, x_1=2, x_2=3, x_3=4, x_4=6, x_5=7, x_6=8, x_7=9, x=5,$

$f(1)=y_1, f(2)=y_2, f(3)=y_3, f(4)=y_4, f(5)=y_5, f(6)=y_6, f(7)=y_7,$

$f(8)=y_8, f(9)=y_9$, we get

$$\frac{y_5}{(5-1)(5-2)(5-3)(5-4)(5-6)(5-7)(5-8)(5-9)}$$

$$= \frac{y_1}{(5-1)(1-2)(1-3)(1-4)(1-6)(1-7)(1-8)(1-9)}$$

$$+ \frac{y_2}{(5-2)(2-1)(2-3)(2-4)(2-6)(2-7)(2-8)(2-9)}$$

$$+ \frac{y_3}{(5-3)(3-1)(3-2)(3-4)(3-6)(3-7)(3-8)(3-9)}$$

$$+ \frac{y_4}{(5-4)(4-1)(4-2)(4-3)(4-6)(4-7)(4-8)(4-9)}$$

$$+ \frac{y_6}{(5-6)(6-1)(6-2)(6-3)(6-4)(6-7)(6-8)(6-9)}$$

$$+ \frac{y_7}{(5-7)(7-1)(7-2)(7-3)(7-4)(7-6)(7-8)(7-9)}$$

$$+ \frac{y_8}{(5-8)(8-1)(8-2)(8-3)(8-4)(8-6)(8-7)(8-9)}$$

$$+ \frac{y_9}{(5-9)(9-1)(9-2)(9-3)(9-4)(9-6)(9-7)(9-8)}$$

$$\Rightarrow \quad \frac{y_5}{1.2.3.4..1.2.3.4} = \frac{-y_1}{1.2.3.4.5.6.7.8} + \frac{y_2}{1.2.3.4.5.6.7}$$

$$- \frac{y_3}{2.1.2.3.4.5.6} + \frac{y_4}{6.1.2.3.4.5} + \frac{y_6}{6.1.2.3.4.5}$$

$$- \frac{y_7}{2.1.2.3.4.5.6} + \frac{y_8}{1.2.3.4.5.6.7} - \frac{y_9}{1.2.3.4.5.6.7.8}$$

$$\Rightarrow \quad \frac{y_5}{24} = -\frac{y_1}{1680} + \frac{y_2}{210} - \frac{y_3}{60} + \frac{y_4}{30} + \frac{y_6}{30} + \frac{y_7}{60} + \frac{y_8}{210} - \frac{y_9}{1680}$$

$$= \frac{1}{30}(y_4 + y_6) - \frac{1}{60}(y_3 + y_7) + \frac{1}{210}(y_2 + y_8) - \frac{1}{1680}(y_1 + y_9)$$

$$\Rightarrow \quad y_5 = \frac{4}{5}(y_4 + y_6) - \frac{2}{5}(y_3 + y_7) + \frac{8}{70}(y_2 + y_8) - \frac{1}{70}(y_1 + y_9)$$

$$= \frac{56(y_4 + y_6) - 28(y_3 + y_7) + 8(y_2 + y_8) - (y_1 + y_9)}{70}$$

Example 42: *Prove that the Lagrange's formula can be put in the form*

$$P_n(x) = \sum_{r=1}^{n} \frac{\phi(x)\, f(x_r)}{(x - x_r)\,\phi'(x_r)}$$

where $\phi(x) = \prod_{r=0}^{n} (x - x_r)$.

[Rohilkhand 2005; Garhwal 2006; M.D.U. (Rohtak) 2008]

Solution: Lagrange's formula can be written as

$$P_n(x) = \sum_{r=0}^{n} \frac{(x - x_0)(x - x_1)\ldots(x - x_n)}{(x_r - x_0)(x_r - x_1)\ldots(x_r - x_n)} f(x_r)$$

$$= \sum_{r=0}^{n} \left[\frac{\phi(x)\, f(x_r)}{(x - x_r)}\right]\left[\frac{1}{(x_r - x_0)(x_r - x_1)\ldots(x_r - x_n)}\right]$$

Again $\phi(x) = \prod_{r=0}^{n} (x - x_r)$. $\therefore \phi'(x_r) = \left[\frac{d}{dx}\phi(x)\right]_{x = x_r} = (x_r - x_0)(x_r - x_1)\ldots(x_r - x_n)$

Therefore, $$P_n(x) = \sum_{r=0}^{n} \frac{\phi(x)\, f(x_r)}{(x - x_r)\,\phi'(x_r)}.$$

Example 43: *Find the polynomial of fifth degree from the following data* $u_0 = -18, u_1 = 0, u_3 = 0, u_5 = -248, u_6 = 0, u_9 = 13104$.

Solution: From the given data, it is obvious that the value of the function is zero at $x = 1, 3, 6$. Let the function $f(x)$ be a polynomial in x. Then $(x-1)$, $(x-3)$ and $(x-6)$ will be factors of $f(x)$.

Now, let $$f(x) = (x-1)(x-3)(x-6)P(x). \quad \ldots(1)$$

But we are given 6 values, so we can fit a polynomial of fifth degree, as such $P(x)$ will be a polynomial of second degree in x.

Now (1) $\Rightarrow P(x) = \dfrac{f(x)}{(x-1)(x-3)(x-6)}$.

$$\Rightarrow P(0) = \frac{f(0)}{(0-1)(0-3)(0-6)} = \frac{-18}{-18} = 1;$$

$$P(5) = \frac{f(5)}{(5-1)(5-3)(5-6)} = \frac{-248}{-8} = 31;$$

and $$P(9) = \frac{f(9)}{(9-1)(9-3)(9-6)} = \frac{13104}{144} = 91.$$

To find $P(x)$, we proceed as follows:

x	P	$\Delta P(x)$	$\Delta^2 P(x)$
0	1		
		6	
5	31		1
		15	
9	91		

By Newton's divided difference formula, we have

$$P(x) = P(0) + (x-0)\,\Delta\, P(0) + (x-0)(x-5)\,\Delta^2\, P(0)$$

$$\Rightarrow \quad P(x) = 1 + x.6 + x(x-5).1 = x^2 + x + 1.$$

$$\Rightarrow \quad f(x) = (x-1)(x-3)(x-6)(x^2 + x + 1).$$

✦✦ Problem Set ✦✦

1. Find out the divided differences of y_x, given that

x	1	2	4	7	12
y_x	22	30	82	106	216

2. $y_{35.0} = 1175$, $y_{35.5} = 1280$, $y_{39.5} = 2180$, $y_{40.5} = 2420$. Find y_{40} by divided differences.

3. If $\log 2 = 0.30103$, $\log 3 = 0.47712$, $\log 5 = 0.62897$, $\log 7 = 0.84510$. Find the value of $\log 4.7$ to four places of decimal. **[Lucknow 2004, 2008]**

4. From the following table find $f(x)$ in powers of $(x-3)$:

x	5	11	27	34	42
$f(x)$	23	899	17315	35606	68510

5. Find the form of the function $y = u_x$ given that $u_0 = 8, u_1 = 11, u_4 = 68, u_5 = 123$.

6. By means of Lagrange's formula prove that approximately

$$y_0 = \frac{1}{2}(y_1 + y_{-1}) - \frac{1}{8}\left[\frac{1}{2}(y_3 - y_1) - \frac{1}{2}(y_{-1} - y_{-3})\right].$$

[Kanpur 2004, 2007]

7. Apply Lagrange's formula to find $f(1.50)$, using the following values of the function $f(x)$:

x	1.00	1.20	1.40	1.60	1.80	2.00
$f(x)$	0.2420	0.1942	0.1497	0.1109	0.0790	0.0540

8. Prove that if y_x be a polynomial for the nth degree in x, and if values y_a, y_b of y_c be given, then the expression for y_x in terms of its divided differences are identically equal whatever be the order of the argument of the y's.

9. Apply Lagrange's formula to find the cubic polynomial which includes the following values of x and y_x:

x	0	1	4	6
y_x	1	−1	1	−1

10. In the following table, h is the height above the sea-level and p the barometric pressure, calculate p when $h = 5280$.

h	0	4763	6942	10594
p	27	25	23	20

11. The function $y = \int_x^{\infty} \frac{e^{-t}}{t} dt$ is given in the table below. Find y for $x = 0.0378$:

x	0.00	0.01	0.02	0.03	0.04	0.05	0.06
y	∞	4.0379	3.3547	2.9591	2.6813	2.4679	2.2953

12. The following data are given for certain function

x	$f(x)$	$f'(x)$
0.4	1.554284	0.243031
0.5	1.561136	−0.089618

In the interval $0.4 < x < 0.5$, $f(x)$ has a maximum at $x = a$. Find $[a, f(a)]$.

[Delhi (H) 2001, 2004, 2010]

[**Hint:** By Lagrange's formula, we have

$$f'(a) = \frac{(a - .5)}{(.4 - .5)} \times .243031 + \frac{(a - .4)}{(.5 - .4)} \times (-0.089618).$$

Since $f'(a) = 0$ as $f(x)$ is maximum at $x = a$, thus we have $a = .47305$.

Again $$f(a) = \frac{.47305 - .5}{.4 - .5} \times 1.554284 + \frac{.47305 - .4}{.5 - .4} \times 1.561136]$$

13. Find a polynomial satisfied by $(-4, 1245), (-1, 33), (0, 5), (2, 9)$ and $(5, 1335)$, by the use of Newton's interpolation formula with divided differences.

14. Show that $f(x_2, x_1, x_0) = f(x_{\alpha_0}, x_{\alpha_1}, x_{\alpha_2})$

where $\alpha_0, \alpha_1, \alpha_2$ is any permutation of intergers $2, 1, 0$ and $f(x_2, x_1, x_0)$ is finite divided difference of order 2.

15. Finite the polynomial of fifth degree from the following data

$u_0 = -18, u_1 = 0, u_3 = 0, u_5 = -248, u_6 = 0, u_9 = 3104.$

16. Find approximately the real root of the equation

$$y^3 - 2y - 5 = 0.$$

[**Hint: Put** $x = y^3 - 2y - 5$ *i.e.* $y = f(x)$, find $f(0)$ take $y = 1.9, 2.0, 2.1, 2.2$ and 2.3; form difference table, apply Newton's divided difference formula.]

17. Assuming that the third divided differences of $f(x)$ is constant for all x, fill in the spaces in the following divided difference table, from right, and hence evaluate.

(i) $f'(8)$ and $f''(8)$, (ii) $f'(6)$ and $f''(10)$

(i)

x	$f(x)$	1st	2nd	3rd
0	8			
		1		
1	4		4	
		13		1
3	30		10	
		63		1
6	219		17	
		148		-
8	515		-	
		-		-
8	515			

(ii)

x	$f(x)$	1st	2nd	3rd
0	−1			
		1		
2	1		14	
		71		2
5	-		26	
		-		2
6	-		-	
		-		-
6	-		-	
		-		-
10	-		-	
		-		
10	-			

18. State Two important properties of divided differences and prove one of them.

19. Apply Lagrange's formula to find $f(5)$ given that $f(1)=2, f(2)=4, f(3)=8, f(4)=16$, $f(7)=128$ and explain why the result differs from 2^5.

20. Derive Lagrange's formula for interpolation and discuss its merits and demerits. **[Avadh 2003, 2008]**

21. State Newton's divided difference formula for interpolation. **[U.P. (P.C.S.) 2008]**

✦✦ Objective Type Question ✦✦

❖ Multiple Choice Questions

1. Which of the following statement is correct:
   (a) Divided differences are skew symmetric functions of their arguments
   (b) The value of any divided difference is independent of the order of the argument
   (c) The value of any divided difference is dependent at the order of the argument
   (d) The divided difference is independent of the values of arguments involved.

2. Which of the following statement is incorrect:
   (a) The nth divided difference can be expressed as the quotient of two determinants each of order $n+1$
   (b) The nth divided differences of a polynomial of the nth degree are constant
   (c) The nth divided difference of $a_n x^n$ is a_n
   (d) The nth divided difference of x^n is zero.

3. If $f(x) = \frac{1}{x^2}$, then the divided differences $f(a, b)$ is:
   (a) $\frac{a+b}{a^2 b^2}$ (b) $\frac{a-b}{a^2 b}$ (c) $-\frac{(a+b)}{a^2 b^2}$ (d) $\frac{a+b}{ab}$

4. The nth order divided difference $f(x_0, x_1, \ldots, x_n)$ for the function $u_n = \frac{1}{x}$ is equal to:
   (a) $\frac{(-1)^{n+1}}{x_0, x_1, \ldots x_{n+1}}$ (b) $\frac{(-1)^n}{x_0, x_1, \ldots, x_n}$ (c) $\frac{n}{x_0, x_1, \ldots x_n}$ (d) $\frac{\lfloor n}{x_0, x_1, \ldots, x_n}$.

5. The third divided difference with arguments 2, 4, 9, 10 of the function $f(x) = x^3 - 2x$ is:
   (a) 2 (b) 0 (c) -1 (d) 1

6. The Lagrange's formula can be put in the form $P_n(x) = \sum_{r=0}^{n} \frac{\phi(x)\, f(x_r)}{(x - x_r)\, \phi'(x_r)}$ where:
   (a) $\phi(x) = \prod_{r=0}^{n-1} (x - x_r)$ (b) $\phi(x) = \prod_{r=0}^{n} (x_r - x_{r-1})$
   (c) $\phi(x) = \prod_{r=1}^{n} (x - x_r)$ (d) $\phi(x) = \prod_{r=0}^{n} (x - x_r)$.

✦✦ Examination Questions ✦✦

1. Certain corresponding values of x and $\log_{10} x$ are as follows:

$\log_{10} x$	300	304	305	307
x	2.4771	2.4829	2.4843	2.4871

Find $\log_{10} 301$, using Lagrange's interpolation formula.

2. Apply Lagrange's formula to find a root of the equation $f(x)=0$ given that $f(30)=-30, f(34)=-13, f(38)=3$ and $f(42)=18$.

3. Find the unique polynomial $P(x)$ of degree 2 or less such that $P(1)=1, P(3)=27, P(4)=64$. Using the Lagrange interpolation formula and the Newton's divided difference formula, evaluate $P(1.5)$. **[I.A.S. 2005]**

4. From the following data

x	1	8	27	64
y	1	2	3	4

calculate $y(20)$, using Lagrangion interpolation technique. Use four decimal points for computations. **[I.F.S. 2008]**

5. Define interpolation. Find the polynomial $P_2(x)$ which satisfies

$f(-1)=P_2(-1)=2, f(1)=P_2(1)=1$

$f(2)=P_2(2)=1$. Find $f(1.5)$. **[I.F.S. 2000]**

6. Find Lagrange's interpolation polynomial $P_2(x)$ which satisfies

$f(0)=P_2(0)=1; f(-1)=P_2(-1)=2$

$f(1)=P_2(1)=3$. Find $f(0.5)$. **[I.F.S. 2001]**

7. From the data given below

x	0	1	2	4	5	6
$f(x)$	1	14	15	5	6	19

using Lagrange's interpolation formula calculate $f(3)$. **[I.F.S. 2002]**

8. Derive the Lagrange's interpolation formula with a remainder term.

9. From the following data, find $f'(10)$

x	3	5	11	27	34
$f(x)$	–13	23	899	17315	35606

10. Given that $f(0) = 8$, $f(1) = 68$ and $f(5) = 123$, construct a table of divided differences. Using the table find the value of $f(2)$ and also determine the form of the function.

11. Find an interpolating polynomial with the help of the following data:

x	3	4	6	9	10	12
$f(x)$	38	90	284	890	1200	2018

12. Given the following data, find $f(8)$:

x	0	2	3	4	7	9
$f(x)$	10	32	64	118	472	928

13. **Drive the expression for error of approximation of an interpolating polynomial of nth order for unequal subintervals.**

14. **State Lagrange's interpolation formula and using this find x if**

$$y_1 = 4,\ y_3 = 12,\ y_4 = 19 \ \text{and} \ y_x = 7.$$

15. **Fit the natural cubic spline for the data:**

x	0	1	2	3	4
y	0	0	1	0	0

16. Fit the following four points by the cubic splines:

i	0	1	2	3
x_i	1	2	3	4
y_i	1	5	11	8

Use the end conditions $y''_0 = y''_3 = 0$

Hence compute

(i) $y(1.5)$

(ii) $y'(3)$.

[I.A.S. 2004; Agra 2002, 2008]

17. Using Lagrange's interpolation formula find $y(10)$ from the following table:

x	5	6	9	11
y	12	13	14	16

[U.P.T.U. 2003, 2005, 2009]

18. Find the cubic Lagrange's interpolating polynomial from the following data:

x	0	1	2	5
$f(x)$	2	3	12	147

[U.P.T.U. 2004]

19. Using Lagrange's interpolation formula calculate $f(3)$ from the following table:

x	0	1	2	4	5	6
$f(x)$	1	14	15	5	6	19

[U.P.T.U. 2006]

20. Find $f(x)$ as a polynomial in x from the data:

x	−1	0	3	6	7
$f(x)$	3	−6	39	822	1611

[U.P.T.U. 2009]

21. Using Newton's divided difference formula, find a polynomial function satisfying the following data:

x	−4	−1	0	2	5
$f(x)$	1245	33	5	9	1335

[U.P.T.U. 2004]

22. Find the value of $f(8)$ and $f(15)$ from the following data:

x	4	5	7	10	11	13
$f(x)$	48	100	294	900	1210	2028

[U.P.T.U. 2004]

23. Find the value of $f(6)$ from the table:

x	3	7	9	10
$f(x)$	168	120	72	63

[U.P.T.U. 2007]

24. Using the Newton's divided differences formula, find a polynomial which takes the values $3, 12, 15, -21$ when x has the values $3, 2, 1, -1$ respectively.

[U.P.T.U. 2008]

Answers

Problem Set

1.	2300	3.	0.69110 approx.
4.	$(x-3)^3+6(x-3)^2+2(x-3)-13$		
5.	$u_x=x^3-x^2+3x+8$	7.	$f(1.50)=0.1295$
9.	$\frac{(x-1)(x-4)(x-6)}{-24}-\frac{x(x-4)(x-6)}{-15}+\frac{x(x-1)(x-6)}{-24}-\frac{x(x-1)(x-4)}{60}$		
10.	24.8	11.	2.7357
13.	$3x^4-5x^3+6x^2-14x+5$		
15.	$-18+18x+x(x-1)(-6)+x(x-1)(x-3)(-3)$ $+x(x-1)(x-3)(x-5)6+x(x-1)(3-x)(x-5)(x-6).1$		
16.	2.09454		

Multiple Choice Questions

1.	(b)	2.	(d)	3.	(c)	4.	(b)	5.	(d)	6.	(d)

Examination Questions

1.	2.4786	2.	37.23
3.	$P(x)=8x^2-19x+12,\ P(1.5)=1.5$		
4.	$y(20)=37158$	5.	$f(1.5)=3.95$
6.	$f(0.5)=1.625$	7.	$f(3)=9$
9.	$f(10)=233$	10.	$f(2)=109.50$
11.	$f(x)=x^3+2x^2+x-10$	12.	647.1566
14.	1.86	15.	$y=\frac{1}{2}u(u-1)(u-2)(u-3),\ u=\frac{x-2}{2}$
16.	$\begin{cases} y(1.5)=2.576 \\ y(3)=2.067 \end{cases}$	17.	$y(10)=14.67$
18.	$f(x)=x^3+x^2-x+2$	19.	5.6
20.	$f(x)=x^4-3x^3+5x^2-6$	21.	$f(x)=3x^4-5x^3+6x^2-14x+5$
22.	$f(8)=448,\ f(15)=3150$	23.	$f(6)=147$
24.	$f(x)=x^3-9x^2+17x+6$		

Theory | Solved Examples | Problem Set

Chapter 4

Central Difference Interpolation Formulae

Central difference operator, Average operator, Gauss interpolation formulae, Stirling's formula, Bessel's formula, Laplace-Everett formula, Fraser or Lozenge diagram.

4.1 Introduction

Newton's formulae which have been already discussed are fundamental and are applicable to nearly all cases of interpolation, but they do not converge as rapidly as the central difference formulae. These formulae are based on differences obtained from the values of $f(x)$ on either side of the origin.

The ***central difference operator*** (δ) is defined by the operator equation

$$\delta = E^{1/2} - E^{-1/2}.$$

$\therefore$ the first central difference $\delta f(x) = f\left(x + \frac{h}{2}\right) - f\left(x - \frac{h}{2}\right)$

$$= (E^{1/2} - E^{-1/2})\, f(x) \text{ where } E \equiv 1 + \Delta.$$

$\therefore$ $$\delta = E^{1/2} - E^{-1/2} = E^{-1/2}(E - 1) = E^{-1/2}\,\Delta. \qquad ...(1)$$

Again the first backward or ascending difference $\nabla f(x)$ of $f(x)$ is defined as

$$\nabla f(x) = f(x) - f(x - h) = (1 - E^{-1})\, f(x).$$

i.e. $$\nabla \equiv (1 - E^{-1}) \text{ or } \nabla E^{1/2} \equiv E^{1/2} - E^{-1/2} = \delta. \qquad ...(2)$$

Thus from (1) and (2), we have $\delta = \Delta E^{-1/2} = \nabla E^{1/2}$. ...(3)

The nth power of these operators applied to y_x gives

$$\delta^n y_x = \Delta^n E^{-n/2} y_x = \nabla^n E^{n/2} y_x$$

or $$\delta^n y_x = \Delta^n y_{x-n/2} = \nabla^n y_{x+n/2}.$$ **[Avadh 2005, 2010]**

The average operator μ is defined by $\mu = \frac{1}{2}[E^{1/2} + E^{-1/2}]$.

[Avadh 2005, 2010]

$\therefore$ $$\mu\, y_x = \frac{1}{2}[y_{x+1/2} + y_{x-1/2}] \text{ and } \mu\,\delta^n y_x = \frac{1}{2}[\delta^n y_{x+1/2} + \delta^n y_{x-1/2}].$$

Again $$\mu^2\, y_x = \frac{1}{4}[E^{1/2} + E^{-1/2}]^2\, y_x = \frac{1}{4}[(E^{1/2} - E^{-1/2})^2 + 4]\, y_x$$

$$= \frac{1}{4}(\delta^2 + 4)\, y_x = \left(1 + \frac{1}{4}\delta^2\right) y_x. \quad \therefore \quad \mu^2 \equiv 1 + \frac{1}{4}\delta^2. \qquad \text{...(4)}$$

Again $$\delta\, y_x = y_{x+1/2} - y_{x-1/2} \text{ and } \mu\, y_x = \frac{1}{2}(y_{x+1/2} + y_{x-1/2})$$

$\therefore$ $$2\mu\, y_x + \delta\, y_x = 2\, y_{x+1/2} \text{ or } (2\mu + \delta)\, y_x = 2\, E^{1/2}\, y_x$$

$\therefore$ $$2\mu + \delta = 2E^{1/2} \quad \text{or} \quad E^{1/2} = \mu + \frac{1}{2}\delta. \qquad \text{...(5)}$$

The operator inverse to δ is called the *central sum operator* and is denoted by $\sigma\,(= \delta^{-1})$. It is defined by

$$\sigma\, f(x) = \sigma\, f(x - h) + f\left(x - \frac{1}{2}h\right) \text{ or } f(x) = \sigma\, f\left(x + \frac{1}{2}h\right) - \sigma\, f\left(x - \frac{1}{2}h\right)$$

Also $$(\sigma - \sigma E^{-1})\, f(x) = E^{-1/2}\, f(x) \Rightarrow \sigma = \frac{E^{1/2}}{E - 1}.$$

[Avadh 2005]

Note: $\Delta^2 y_0 - \Delta^2 y_{-1} = \Delta^3 y_{-1}$ and $\Delta^2 y_0 = \Delta^2 y_{-1} + \Delta^3 y_{-1}$

Similarly $\Delta^3 y_0 = \Delta^3 y_{-1} + \Delta^4 y_{-1}$, $\Delta^4 y_0 = \Delta^4 y_{-1} + \Delta^5 y_{-1}$ etc.

$\Delta^3 y_{-1} - \Delta^3 y_{-2} = \Delta^4 y_{-2}$, $\Delta^3 y_{-1} = \Delta^3 y_{-2} + \Delta^4 y_{-2}$

and also $\Delta^4 y_{-1} = \Delta^4 y_{-2} + \Delta^5 y_{-2}$ etc.

The appearance of a central difference table is as under:

x	y_x	$\delta\, y_x$	$\delta^2\, y_x$	$\delta^3\, y_x$	$\delta^4\, y_x$
-2	y_{-2}	$\Delta\, y_{-2} =$			
		$\delta\, y_{-3/2}$	$\Delta^2\, y_{-2} =$		
-1	y_{-1}	$\Delta\, y_{-1} =$	$\delta^2\, y_{-1}$	$\Delta^3\, y_{-2} =$	
		$\delta\, y_{-1/2}$	$\Delta^2\, y_{-1} =$	$\delta^3\, y_{-1/2}$	$\Delta^4\, y_{-2} =$
0	y_0	$\Delta\, y_0 =$	$\delta^2\, y_0$	$\Delta^3\, y_{-1} =$	$\delta^4\, y_0$
		$\delta\, y_{1/2}$	$\Delta^2\, y_0$	$\delta^3\, y_{1/2}$	
1	y_1	$\Delta\, y_1 =$	$\delta^2\, y_1$		
		$\delta\, y_{3/2}$			
2	y_2				

4.2 Gauss's Interpolation Formulae

[Avadh 2003]

(i) The general Newton formula gives

$$y = f(x) = f(x_0) + (x - x_0)\, f(x_0, x_1) + (x - x_0)(x - x_1)\, f(x_0, x_1, x_2)$$
$$+ (x - x_0)(x - x_1)(x - x_2)\, f(x_0, x_1, x_2, x_3)$$
$$+ (x - x_0)(x - x_1)(x - x_2)(x - x_3)\, f(x_0, x_1, x_2, x_3, x_4)$$
$$+ (x - x_0)(x - x_1)(x - x_2)(x - x_3)(x - x_4)\, f(x_0, x_1, x_2, x_3, x_4, x_5)$$
$$+ (x - x_0)(x - x_1) \ldots (x - x_5)\, f(x_0, x_1, x_2, x_3, x_4, x_5, x_6) + \ldots$$

Now putting $x_0 = x_0, x_1 = x_0 + h, x_2 = x_0 - h, x_3 = x_0 + 2h,$
$x_4 = x_0 - 2h, x_5 = x_0 + 3h, x_6 = x_0 - 3h$ etc., we immediately get

$$f(x) = f(x_0) + (x - x_0)\, f(x_0, x_0 + h)$$
$$+ (x - x_0)(x - x_0 - h)\, f(x_0, x_0 + h, x_0 - h)$$
$$+ (x - x_0)(x - x_0 - h)(x - x_0 + h)\, f(x_0, x_0 + h, x_0 - h, x_0 + 2h)$$
$$+ (x - x_0)(x - x_0 - h)(x - x_0 + h)(x - x_0 + 2h)$$
$$\times f(x_0, x_0 + h, x_0 - h, x_0 + 2h, x_0 - 2h)$$
$$+ (x - x_0)(x - x_0 - h)(x - x_0 + h)(x - x_0 - 2h)(x - x_0 + 2h)$$
$$\times f(x_0, x_0 + h, x_0 - h, x_0 + 2h, x_0 - 2h, x_0 + 3h) + \ldots$$

Further, let $u = (x - x_0)/h \Rightarrow x - x_0 = hu$.

$$\Rightarrow \quad f(x) = f(x_0) + hu\, f(x_0, x_0 + h) + hu\,(hu - h)\, f(x_0 - h, x_0, x_0 + h)$$
$$+ hu\,(hu - h)(hu + h)\, f(x_0 - h, x_0, x_0 + h, x_0 + 2h)$$
$$+ hu\,(hu - h)(hu + h)(hu - 2h)\, f(x_0 - 2h, x_0 - h, x_0, x_0 + h, x_0 + 2h)$$
$$+ hu\,(hu - h)(hu + h)(hu - 2h)(hu + 2h)$$
$$\times f(x_0 - 2h, x_0 - h, x_0, x_0 + h, x_0 + 2h, x_0 + 3h) + \ldots \qquad \ldots(A)$$

But, we also know that

$$f(x_0, x_0 + h) = \frac{\Delta y_0}{h}, \quad f(x_0 - h, x_0, x_0 + h) = \frac{\Delta^2 y_{-1}}{2!h^2},$$

$$f(x_0 - h, x_0, x_0 + h, x_0 + 2h) = \frac{\Delta^3 y_{-1}}{3!h^3},$$

$$f(x_0 - 2h, x_0 - h, x_0, x_0 + h, x_0 + 2h) = \frac{\Delta^4 y_{-2}}{4!h^4},$$

$$f(x_0 - 2h, x_0 - h, x_0, x_0 + h, x_0 + 2h, x_0 + 3h) = \frac{\Delta^5 y_{-2}}{5!h^5}, \text{etc.}$$

Now, substituting these values in (A), we readily obtain

$$y = y_0 + hu\frac{\Delta y_0}{h} + h^2 u(u-1)\frac{\Delta^2 y_{-1}}{2!h^2} + h^3 u(u-1)(u+1)\frac{\Delta^3 y_{-1}}{3!h^3}$$

$$+ h^4 u(u-1)(u+1)(u-2)\frac{\Delta^4 y_{-2}}{4!h^4}$$

$$+ h^5 u(u-1)(u+1)(u-2)(u+2)\{\Delta^5 y_{-2}/\{5!h^5\} + \ldots$$

$$\Rightarrow \quad y = y_0 + u\Delta y_0 + u(u-1)\frac{\Delta^2 y_{-1}}{2!} + u(u^2-1)\frac{\Delta^3 y_{-1}}{3!}$$

$$+ u(u^2-1)(u-2)\frac{\Delta^4 y_{-2}}{4!} + u(u^2-1)(u^2-2^2)\frac{\Delta^5 y_{-2}}{5!} + \ldots$$

$$\Rightarrow \quad y = y_0 + u_{c_1}\Delta y_0 + u_{c_2}\Delta^2 y_{-1} + (u+1)_{c_3}\Delta^3 y_{-1} + (u+1)_{c_4}\Delta^4 y_{-2} + \ldots \quad \ldots(1)$$

This result is known as ***Gauss's forward formula for equal intervals***. In the central difference notation, the formula reduces to

$$y = y_0 + u_{c_1}\delta y_{1/2} + u_{c_2}\delta^2 y_0 + (u+1)_{c_3}\delta^3 y_{1/2} + (u+1)_{c_4}\delta^4 y_0 + \ldots$$

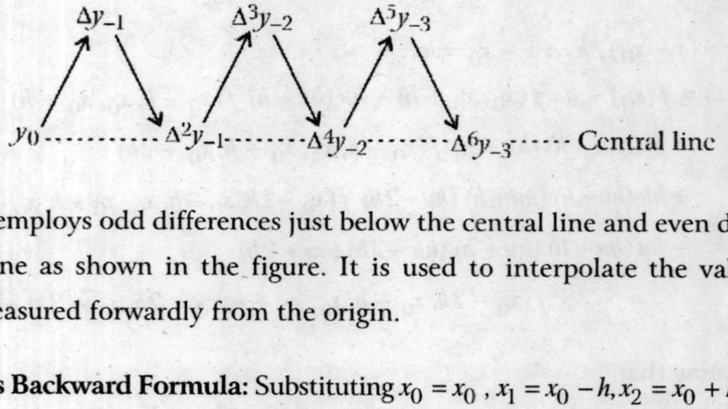

The formula employs odd differences just below the central line and even differences on the central line as shown in the figure. It is used to interpolate the values of y for $u: 0 < u < 1$ measured forwardly from the origin.

(ii) Gauss's Backward Formula: Substituting $x_0 = x_0$, $x_1 = x_0 - h, x_2 = x_0 + h, x_3 = x_0 - 2h$, $x_4 = x_0 + 2h, x_5 = x_0 - 3h, x_6 = x_0 + 3h$ etc. in general Newton formula, we get

$$y = y_0 + (x - x_0)\, f(x_0, x_0 - h) + (x - x_0)(x - x_0 + h)\, f(x_0, x_0 - h, x_0 + h)$$

$$+ (x - x_0)(x - x_0 + h)(x - x_0 - h)\, f(x_0, x_0 - h, x_0 + h, x_0 - 2h)$$

$$+ (x - x_0)(x - x_0 + h)(x - x_0 - h)(x - x_0 - 2h) \times$$

$$f(x_0, x_0 - h, x_0 + h, x_0 - 2h, x_0 + 2h)$$

$$+ (x - x_0)(x - x_0 + h)(x - x_0 - h)(x - x_0 + 2h)(x - x_0 - 2h)$$

$$\times f(x_0, x_0 - h, x_0 + h, x_0 - 2h, x_0 + 2h, x_0 - 3h) + \ldots$$

Further, putting $u = \dfrac{x - x_0}{h}$ *i.e.*, $x - x_0 = uh$; we get

$$y_u = y_0 + hu\, f(x_0 - h, x_0) + hu\,(hu + h)\, f(x_0 - h, x_0, x_0 + h)$$
$$+ hu\,(hu + h)\,(hu - h)\, f(x_0 - 2h, x_0 - h, x_0, x_0 + h)$$
$$+ hu\,(hu + h)\,(hu - h)\,(hu + 2h)\, f(x_0 - 2h, x_0 - h, x_0, x_0 + h, x_0 + 2h)$$
$$+ hu\,(hu + h)\,(hu - h)\,(hu + 2h)\,(hu - 2h)$$
$$\times f(x_0 - 3h, x_0 - 2h, x_0 - h, x_0, x_0 + h, x_0 + 2h) + \ldots$$

Again we know that

$$f(x_0 - h, x_0) = \frac{\Delta y_{-1}}{h},\; f(x_0 - h, x_0, x_0 + h) = \frac{\Delta^2 y_{-1}}{2!\,h^2}$$

$$f(x_0 - 2h, x_0 - h, x_0, x_0 + h) = \frac{\Delta^3 y_{-2}}{3!\,h^3},$$

$$f(x_0 - 2h, x_0 - h, x_0, x_0 + h, x_0 + 2h) = \frac{\Delta^4 y_{-2}}{4!\,h^4},$$

$$f(x_0 - 3h, x_0 - 2h, x_0 - h, x_0, x_0 + h, x_0 + 2h) = \frac{\Delta^5 y_{-3}}{5!\,h^5} \text{ etc.}$$

$$\Rightarrow \quad y_u = y_0 + u\,\Delta y_{-1} + u\,(u+1)\,\frac{\Delta^2 y_{-1}}{2!} + u\,(u^2 - 1)\,\frac{\Delta^3 y_{-2}}{3!}$$
$$+ u\,(u^2 - 1)\,(u + 2)\,\frac{\Delta^4 y_{-2}}{4!} + u\,(u^2 - 1)\,(u^2 - 2^2)\,\frac{\Delta^5 y_{-3}}{5!} + \ldots$$

$$\Rightarrow \quad y_u = y_0 + {}^{u}C_1\,\Delta y_{-1} + {}^{(u+1)}C_2\,\Delta^2 y_{-1} + {}^{(u+1)}C_3\,\Delta^3 y_{-2}$$
$$+ {}^{(u+2)}C_4\,\Delta^4 y_{-2} + \ldots + {}^{(u+k-1)}C_{2k-1}\,\Delta^{2k-1} y_{-k} \qquad \ldots(1)$$

This result is known as ***Gauss's Backward Formula.***

Another formula called ***Gauss Backward Formula*** for equal intervals may be derived in a similar way; we have

$$\Delta y_0 = \Delta y_{-1} + \Delta^2 y_{-1};\; \Delta^3 y_{-1} = \Delta^3 y_{-2} + \Delta^4 y_{-2}, \text{ and so on.}$$

Putting these values in (1) and grouping the terms in a slightly different way, we have

$$y_u = y_0 + {}^{u}C_1 \Delta y_{-1} + {}^{u+1}C_2 \Delta^2 y_{-1} + {}^{u+1}C_3 \Delta^3 y_{-2}$$
$$+ {}^{u+2}C_4 \Delta^4 y_{-2} + \ldots + {}^{u+k-1}C_{2k-1}\, \Delta^{2k-1} y_{-k}$$
$$+ {}^{u+k}C_{2k}\, \Delta^{2k} y_{-k} + \ldots \qquad \ldots(2)$$

We observe that this formula *employs the odd differences just above the central line through* y_0 *and even differences on the central line.*

In the central differences notation, this formula reduces to

$$y_u = y_0 + u\delta\, y_{-1/2} + \frac{(u-1)\,u}{2\,!}\,\delta^2\, y_0 + \frac{(u+1)\,u\,(u-1)}{3\,!}\,\delta^3\, y_{-1/2} + \frac{(u+2)\,(u+1)\,u\,(u-1)}{4\,!}\,\delta^4\, y_0 + \ldots$$

The formula contains odd differences above the central line and even differences on the central line:

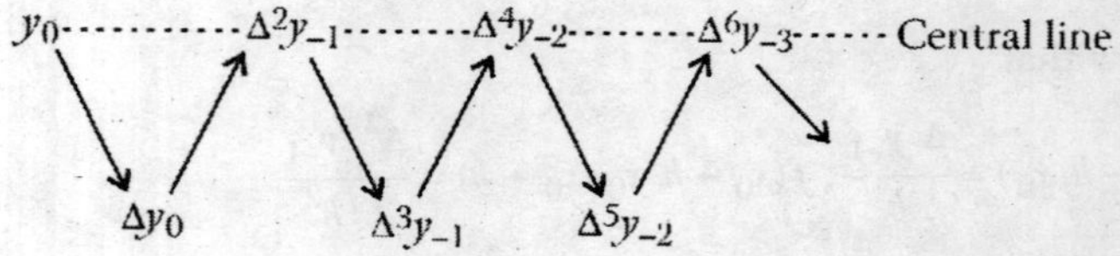

This formula is used to interpolate the values of y for a negative value of $u : -1 < u < 0$.

Gauss's forward and backward formulae are not of much practical importance. However, these serve as intermediate steps for obtaining some important formulae.

Aliter. (i) Gauss Forward Formula.

Let $f(x_0), f(x_1), f(x_2), f(x_3)$, and $f(x_4)$ be the values of the function $y = f(x)$ corresponding to the arguments x_0, x_1, x_2, x_3 and x_4 respectively. Suppose we want to deduce the formula for $f(x)$ in terms of say $f(x)$. The divided difference table with the given values is of the following form:

Table 1

x	$f(x)$	$\Delta f(x)$	$\Delta^2 f(x)$	$\Delta^3 f(x)$	$\Delta^4 f(x)$
x_0,	$f(x_0)$				
		$\underset{x_1}{\Delta} f(x_0)$			
x_1,	$f(x_1)$		$\underset{x_1 x_2}{\Delta^2} f(x_0)$		
		$\underset{x_2}{\Delta} f(x_1)$		$\underset{x_1 x_2 x_3}{\Delta^3} f(x_0)$	
x_2,	$f(x_2)$		$\underset{x_2 x_3}{\Delta^2} f(x_1)$		$\underset{x_1 x_2 x_3 x_4}{\Delta^4} f(x_0)$
		$\underset{x_3}{\Delta} f(x_2)$		$\underset{x_2 x_3 x_4}{\Delta^3} f(x_1)$	
x_3,	$f(x_3)$		$\underset{x_3 x_4}{\Delta^2} f(x_2)$		
		$\underset{x_4}{\Delta} f(x_3)$			
x_4,	$f(x_4)$				

From the above table we see that there are two alternative ways for the second term *i.e.* we can take either $\underset{x_2}{\Delta} f(x_1)$ or $\underset{x_3}{\Delta} f(x_2)$ since both these differences contain x_2 ***as one of their suffixes, where*** x_2 ***is the suffix of leading term*** $f(x_2)$. ***Again*** x_1, x_2 or x_2, x_3 ***are the suffixes of second terms, thus the difference taken in third term can be only*** $\underset{x_2\,x_3}{\Delta^2} f(x_1)$. For the fourth term we have again two choices *viz.*

$$\underset{x_1\,x_2\,x_3}{\Delta^3} f(x_0) \quad \text{or} \quad \underset{x_2\,x_3\,x_4}{\Delta^3} f(x_1) \text{ and so on}$$

If we simply take the differences just lying below or on the horizontal line through $x = x_2$, then expression so obtained is called ***Gauss Forward Formula.*** This formula will contain the following values in succession.

$$f(x_2),\ \underset{x_3}{\Delta} f(x_2),\ \underset{x_2\,x_3}{\Delta^2} f(x_1),\ \underset{x_2\,x_3\,x_4}{\Delta^3} f(x_1),\ \underset{x_1\,x_2\,x_3\,x_4}{\Delta^4} f(x_0) \qquad ...(1)$$

Again by Shepard's rule, using the terms given in (1), the formula will be

$$f(x) = f(x_2) + X_2 \underset{x_3}{\Delta} f(x_2) + X_2 X_3 \underset{x_2\,x_3}{\Delta^2} f(x_1) + X_1 X_2 X_3 \underset{x_2\,x_3\,x_4}{\Delta^3} f(x_1) + X_1 X_2 X_3 X_4 \underset{x_1\,x_2\,x_3\,x_4}{\Delta^4} f(x_0) + \ldots$$

$$= f(x_2) + (x - x_2) \underset{x_2}{\Delta} f(x_2) + (x - x_2)(x - x_3) \underset{x_2\,x_3}{\Delta^2} f(x_1) + (x - x_1)(x - x_2)(x - x_3) \underset{x_2\,x_3\,x_4}{\Delta^3} f(x_1)$$
$$+ (x - x_1)(x - x_2)(x - x_3)(x - x_4) \underset{x_1\,x_2\,x_3\,x_4}{\Delta^4} f(x_0) + \ldots \qquad ...(2)$$

In case the values of the argument be given at equal intervals of unit length and if the origin be at point x_2, then the table already deduced will transform to the following table:

Table 2

x	$f(x)$	$\Delta f(x)$	$\Delta^2 f(x)$	$\Delta^3 f(x)$	$\Delta^4 f(x)$
-2	$f(-2)$				
		$\underset{-1}{\Delta} f(-2)$			
-1	$f(-1)$		$\underset{-1,0}{\Delta^2} f(-2)$		
		$\underset{0}{\Delta} f(-1)$		$\underset{-1,0,1}{\Delta^3} f(-2)$	
0	$f(0)$		$\underset{0,1}{\Delta^2} f(-1)$		$\underset{-1,0,1,2}{\Delta^4} f(-2)$
		$\underset{1}{\Delta} f(0)$		$\underset{0,1,2}{\Delta^3} f(-1)$	
1	$f(1)$		$\underset{1,2}{\Delta^2} f(0)$		
		$\underset{2}{\Delta} f(1)$			
2	$f(2)$				

Again, we know that $\underset{-1}{\Delta} f(0) = \Delta f(0)$; $\quad \underset{0,1}{\Delta^2} f(-1) = \dfrac{\Delta^2 f(-1)}{2!}$; $\quad \underset{0,1,2}{\Delta^3} f(-1) = \dfrac{\Delta^3 f(-1)}{3!}$

and $\quad \underset{-1,0,1,2}{\Delta^4} f(-2) = \dfrac{\Delta^4 f(-2)}{4!}$

Thus from (2), we have

$$f(x) = f(0) + x\Delta f(0) + \frac{x(x-1)}{2!}\Delta^2 f(-1) + \frac{(x+1)x(x-1)}{3!}\Delta^3 f(-1)$$

$$+ \frac{(x+1)x(x-1)(x-2)}{4!}\Delta^4 f(-2) + \ldots$$

or on further simplification, we get

$$f(x) = f(0) + {}^xC_1 \Delta f(0) + {}^xC_2 \Delta^2 f(-1) + {}^{x+1}C_2 \Delta^3 f(-1) + \ldots$$

This expression is called ***Gauss forward formula.*** In this formula only odd order differences lying just below and the even order differences lying on the horizontal line through $x = 0$ are taken.

(ii) Gauss Backward Formula.

In case, we take the differences just above and those lying on the horizontal line through $x = x_2$ ***(refer table* 1)** *i.e.*

$f(x_2), \underset{x_2}{\Delta} f(x_1), \underset{x_2\,x_3}{\Delta^2} f(x_1), \underset{x_1\,x_2\,x_3}{\Delta^3} f(x_0)$ and $\underset{x_1\,x_2\,x_3\,x_4}{\Delta^4} f(x_0)$ and so on then by Shepard's rule, we have

$$f(x) = f(x_2) + (x - x_2)\underset{x_2}{\Delta} f(x_1), + (x - x_2)(x - x_1)\underset{x_2\,x_3}{\Delta^2} f(x_1)$$

$$+ (x - x_2)(x - x_1)(x - x_3)\underset{x_1\,x_2\,x_3}{\Delta^3} f(x_0) + (x - x_2)(x - x_1)(x - x_3)(x - x_0)\underset{x_1\,x_2\,x_3\,x_4}{\Delta^4} f(x_0) + \ldots$$

Putting $x_0 = -2, x_1 = -1, x_2 = 0, x_3 = 1, x_4 = 2$ and various divided differences in terms of ordinary differences, we get

$$f(x) = f(0) + x\Delta f(-1) + \frac{x(x+1)}{2!}\Delta^2 f(-1) + \frac{(x+1)x(x-1)}{3!}\Delta^3 f(-2)$$

$$+ \frac{(x+2)(x+1)x(x-1)}{4!}\Delta^4 f(-2) + \ldots$$

On further simplification, we get

$$f(x) = f(0) + {}^xC_1 \Delta f(-1) + {}^{x+1}C_2 \Delta^2 f(-1) + {}^{x+1}C_3 \Delta^3 f(-2) + {}^{x+2}C_4 \Delta^4 f(-2) + \ldots \quad \ldots(3)$$

This is called ***Gauss backward formula.***

(iii) Third formula due to Gauss.

This formula starts with y_1 and runs parallel to the backward formula

We have $u = \dfrac{x - x_0}{h} \Rightarrow \dfrac{x - x_k}{h} = \dfrac{x - (x_0 + kh)}{h} = u - k.$

To obtain the formula, we increase the subscripts of x only in backward formula by one unit and change the u's by putting $k = 1$ in the formula $u - k = \dfrac{x - x_k}{h}$.

We thus get $x - x_1 = hu - h$ *i.e.* we have to put $u - 1$ for u.

Hence equation (2) P. 157

$$\Rightarrow \quad y_u = y_1 + (u-1)\,\Delta y_0 + u(u-1)\frac{\Delta^2 y_0}{2!} + u(u-1)(u-2)\frac{\Delta^3 y_{-2}}{3!}$$

$$+ u(u^2-1)(u-2)\frac{\Delta^4 y_{-1}}{4!} + u(u^2-1)(u-2)(u-3)\frac{\Delta^5 y_{-2}}{5!} + \ldots \quad \ldots(1)$$

Aliter

Taking $f(1)$ as the initial term and proceding as in Gauss backward formula, taking the successive differences in the following order:

$$f(x_3),\ \underset{x_3}{\Delta} f(x_2),\ \underset{x_3\,x_4}{\Delta^2} f(x_2),\ \underset{x_2\,x_3\,x_4}{\Delta^3} f(x_1),\ \underset{x_1\,x_2\,x_3\,x_4}{\Delta^4} f(x_0)$$

and so on, we get

$$f(x) = f(x_3) + (x - x_3)\underset{x_3}{\Delta} f(x_2) + (x - x_3)(x - x_2)\underset{x_3\,x_4}{\Delta^2} f(x_2)$$

$$+ (x - x_3)(x - x_2)(x - x_4)\underset{x_2\,x_3\,x_4}{\Delta^3} f(x_1) + (x - x_3)(x - x_2)(x - x_4)(x - x_1)\underset{x_1\,x_2\,x_3\,x_4}{\Delta^4} f(x_0) + \ldots \quad \ldots(1)$$

Putting $x_0 = -2, x_1 = -1, x_2 = 0, x_3 = 1, x_4 = 2$ and replacing the various divided differences in terms of ordinary differences in (1), we get

$$f(x) = f(1) + (x-1)\,\Delta f(0) + \frac{(x-1)\,x}{2!}\Delta^2 f(0) + \frac{(x-1)\,x\,(x-2)}{3!}\Delta^3 f(-1)$$

$$+ \frac{(x-2)(x+1)\,x\,(x-1)}{4!}\Delta^4 f(-2) + \ldots \quad \ldots(2)$$

On further simplication, we get

$$f(x) = f(1) + {}^{x-1}C_1 \Delta f(0) + {}^{x}C_2 \Delta^2 f(0) + {}^{x}C_3 \Delta^3 f(-1) + {}^{x+1}C_4 \Delta^4 f(-2) + \ldots \quad \ldots(3)$$

This is known as ***third formula due to Gauss.***

In the following difference table the paths of the three Gauss formulae have been shown. The designations P, Q, R correspond to [eqn. (1) eqn. (2) eqn. (2)]. Now refer table.

x	y	Δy	$\Delta^2 y$	$\Delta^3 y$	$\Delta^4 y$	$\Delta^5 y$	$\Delta^6 y$
x_{-6}	y_{-6}						
		Δy_{-6}					
x_{-5}	y_{-5}		$\Delta^2 y_{-6}$				
		Δy_{-5}		$\Delta^3 y_{-6}$			
x_{-4}	y_{-4}		$\Delta^2 y_{-5}$		$\Delta^4 y_{-6}$		
		Δy_{-4}		$\Delta^3 y_{-5}$		$\Delta^5 y_{-6}$	
x_{-3}	y_{-3}		$\Delta^2 y_{-4}$		$\Delta^4 y_{-5}$		$\Delta^6 y_{-6}$
		Δy_{-3}		$\Delta^3 y_{-4}$		$\Delta^5 y_{-5}$	
x_{-2}	y_{-2}		$\Delta^2 y_{-3}$		$\Delta^4 y_{-4}$		$\Delta^6 y_{-5}$
		Δy_{-2}		$\Delta^3 y_{-3}$		$\Delta^5 y_{-4}$	
x_{-1}	y_{-1}		$\Delta^2 y_{-2}$		$\Delta^4 y_{-3}$		$\Delta^6 y_{-4}$
		Δy_{-1}		$\Delta^3 y_{-2}$		$\Delta^5 y_{-3}$ **P**	
x_0	y_0		$\Delta^2 y_{-1}$		$\Delta^4 y_{-2}$		$\Delta^6 y_{-3}$
		Δy_0		$\Delta^3 y_{-1}$		$\Delta^5 y_{-2}$ **Q**	
x_1	y_1		$\Delta^2 y_0$		$\Delta^4 y_{-1}$	**R**	$\Delta^6 y_{-2}$
		Δy_1		$\Delta^3 y_0$		$\Delta^5 y_{-1}$	
x_2	y_2		$\Delta^2 y_1$		$\Delta^4 y_0$		$\Delta^6 y_{-1}$
		Δy_2		$\Delta^3 y_1$		$\Delta^5 y_0$	
x_3	y_3		$\Delta^2 y_2$		$\Delta^4 y_1$		$\Delta^6 y_0$
		Δy_3		$\Delta^3 y_2$		$\Delta^5 y_1$	
x_4	y_4		$\Delta^2 y_3$		$\Delta^4 y_2$		
		Δy_4		$\Delta^3 y_3$			
x_5	y_5		$\Delta^2 y_4$				
		Δy_5					
x_6	y_6						

4.3 Stirling's Formula

[Avadh 2004; Bhopal 2002]

Taking the mean of the Gauss's formulae, we have

$$y_u = y_0 + u\frac{\Delta y_0 + \Delta y_{-1}}{2} + \frac{u^2}{2!}\Delta^2 y_{-1} + \frac{u(u^2-1^2)}{3!}\cdot\frac{\Delta^3 y_{-1} + \Delta^3 y_{-2}}{2}$$

$$+\frac{u^2(u^2-1^2)}{4!}\Delta^4 y_{-2} + \frac{u(u^2-1^2)(u^2-2^2)}{5!}\cdot\frac{\Delta^5 y_{-3} + \Delta^5 y_{-2}}{2} + \dots$$

where $u = (x - x_0)/h$.

This formula is known as stirling's formula. It employs the mean of the odd differences just above and just below the central line and even differences on the central line. The following difference table gives the position of the differences used in the formula:

	Δy_{-1}		$\Delta^3 y_{-2}$		$\Delta^5 y_{-3}$		$\Delta^7 y_{-4}$	
y_0		$\Delta^2 y_{-1}$		$\Delta^4 y_{-2}$		$\Delta^6 y_{-3}$		$\Delta^8 y_{-4}$
	Δy_0		$\Delta^3 y_{-1}$		$\Delta^5 y_{-2}$		$\Delta^7 y_{-3}$	

The most general formula is as follows:

$$y_u = y_0 + u\frac{\Delta y_{-1} + \Delta y_0}{2} + \frac{u^2}{2!}\Delta^2 y_{-1} + \frac{u(u^2-1^2)}{3!}\cdot\frac{\Delta^3 y_{-1} + \Delta^3 y_{-2}}{2} + \frac{u^2(u^2-1^2)}{4!}\Delta^4 y_{-2} + \dots$$

$$+\frac{u(u^2-1^2)(u^2-2^2)\dots[u^2-(k-1)^2]}{(2k-1)!}\cdot\frac{\Delta^{2k-1} y_{-(k-1)} + \Delta^{2k-1} y_{-k}}{2}$$

$$+\frac{u^2(u^2-1^2)(u^2-2^2)\dots[u^2-(k-1)^2]}{(2k)!}\Delta^{2k} y_{-k} + \dots \qquad \dots[A]$$

In central differences notation, [A] takes the form

$$y_u = y_0 + u\mu\delta y_0 + \frac{u^2}{2!}\delta^2 y_0 + \frac{u(u^2-1^2)}{3!}\mu\delta^3 y_0 + \frac{u^2(u^2-1^2)}{4!}\delta^4 y_0 + \dots \qquad \dots[B]$$

$$\left[\because \frac{1}{2}(\Delta y_0 + \Delta y_{-1}) = \frac{1}{2}(\delta y_{1/2} + \delta y_{-1/2}) = \mu\delta y_0,\right.$$

$$\left.\frac{1}{2}(\Delta^3 y_{-1} + \Delta^3 y_{-2}) = \frac{1}{2}(\delta^3 y_{1/2} + \delta^3 y_{-1/2}) = \mu\delta^3 y_0 \text{ etc}\right]$$

This formula has means of the odd differences just below and above the central line and even differences on this line.

$$-\,y_0\begin{pmatrix}\Delta y_{-1}\\ \Delta y_0\end{pmatrix}\dots\Delta^2 y_{-1}\dots\begin{pmatrix}\Delta^3 y_{-2}\\ \Delta^3 y_{-1}\end{pmatrix}\dots\Delta^4 y_{-2}\dots\begin{pmatrix}\Delta^5 y_{-3}\\ \Delta^5 y_{-2}\end{pmatrix}\Delta^6 y_{-3}\quad \text{central line}$$

4.4 Bessel's Formula

[Avadh 2005]

Bessel's Interpolation Formula: Taking the means of Gauss's forward formula and the third formula due to Gauss's we obtain

$$y_u = \frac{y_0 + y_1}{2} + \left(u - \frac{1}{2}\right) \Delta y_0 + \frac{u(u-1)}{2} \frac{(\Delta^2 y_{-1} + \Delta^2 y_0)}{2} + \frac{u\left(u - \frac{1}{2}\right)(u-1)}{3!} \Delta^3 y_{-1}$$

$$+ \frac{u(u^2-1)(u-2)}{4!} \frac{(\Delta^4 y_{-2} + \Delta^4 y_{-1})}{2} + \frac{u\left(u - \frac{1}{2}\right)(u^2-1)(u-2)}{5!} \Delta^5 y_{-2} + \ldots \qquad \ldots(1)$$

This is Bessel's formula and can be written in a slightly different form by transforming the first two terms to $y_0 + u\,\Delta y_0$ $[\because \quad \Delta y_0 = y_1 - y_0]$.

Then equation (1)

$$\Rightarrow \qquad y_u = y_0 + u\Delta y_0 + \frac{u(u-1)}{2} \frac{(\Delta^2 y_{-1} + \Delta^2 y_0)}{2} + \frac{u\left(u - \frac{1}{2}\right)(u-1)}{3!} \Delta^3 y_{-1}$$

$$+ \frac{u(u^2-1)(u-2)}{4!} \frac{(\Delta^4 y_{-2} + \Delta^4 y_{-1})}{2} + \ldots \qquad \ldots(2)$$

Hence the more general form of Bessel's formula is given by

$$y_u = y_0 + u\Delta y_0 + \frac{u(u-1)}{2} \frac{(\Delta^2 y_{-1} + \Delta^2 y_0)}{2} + \frac{u\left(u - \frac{1}{2}\right)(u-1)}{3!} \Delta^3 y_{-1}$$

$$+ \frac{(u+1)u(u-1)(u-2)}{4!} \frac{(\Delta^4 y_{-1} + \Delta^4 y_{-2})}{2} + \frac{u\left(u - \frac{1}{2}\right)(u^2-1)(u-2)}{5!} \Delta^5 y_{-2}$$

$$+ \frac{u(u^2-1)(u^2-4)(u-3)}{6!} \frac{(\Delta^6 y_{-3} + \Delta^6 y_{-2})}{2} + \ldots$$

$$+ \frac{u(u^2-1)(u^2-4)\ldots(u-n)(u+n-1)}{(2n)!} \frac{(\Delta^{2n} y_{-n} + \Delta^{2n} y_{-n+1})}{2}$$

$$+ \frac{u\left(u - \frac{1}{2}\right)(u^2-1)(u^2-4)\ldots(u-n)(u+n-1)}{(2n+1)!} \Delta^{2n+1} y_{-n}. \qquad \ldots(3)$$

Now substituting $u = \frac{1}{2}$ in (3), we obtain **[Bessel's Formula]**

$$y_u = \frac{y_0 + y_1}{2} - \left(\frac{1}{8}\right) \frac{\Delta^2 y_{-1} + \Delta^2 y_0}{2} + \left(\frac{3}{128}\right) \frac{\Delta^4 y_{-2} + \Delta^4 y_{-1}}{2} - \left(\frac{5}{1024}\right) \frac{\Delta^6 y_{-3} + \Delta^6 y_{-2}}{2} + \ldots$$

$$+ (-1)^n \frac{[1.3.5\ldots(2n-1)]^2}{2^{2n}(2n)!} \frac{\Delta^{2n} y_{-n} + \Delta^{2n} y_{-n+1}}{2} \qquad \ldots(4)$$

This is the special case of Bessel's formula and is called the formula for interpolating to halves. It is used for computing the values of the function mid-way between any two given values.

Further, putting $u - \frac{1}{2} = v$ or $u = v + \frac{1}{2}$ in (3), we get a more convenient form of Bessel's formula [symmetrical, too]

$$y_u = \frac{y_0 + y_1}{2} + v\Delta y_0 + \frac{\left(v^2 - \frac{1}{4}\right)}{2!} \cdot \frac{\Delta^2 y_{-1} + \Delta^2 y_0}{2} + \frac{v\left(v^2 - \frac{1}{4}\right)}{3!} \Delta^3 y_{-1}$$

$$+ \frac{\left(v^2 - \frac{1}{4}\right)\left(v^2 - \frac{9}{4}\right)}{4!} \cdot \frac{\Delta^4 y_{-2} + \Delta^4 y_{-1}}{2} + \frac{v\left(v^2 - \frac{1}{4}\right)\left(v^2 - \frac{9}{4}\right)}{5!} \Delta^5 y_{-2}$$

$$+ \dots + \frac{\left(v^2 - \frac{1}{4}\right)\left(v^2 - \frac{9}{4}\right) \dots \left\{v^2 - \frac{(2n-1)^2}{4}\right\}}{(2n)!} \times \frac{\Delta^{2n} y_{-n} + \Delta^{2n} y_{-n+1}}{2}$$

$$+ \frac{v\left(v^2 - \frac{1}{4}\right)\left(v^2 - \frac{9}{4}\right) \dots \left\{v^2 - \frac{(2n-1)^2}{4}\right\}}{(2n+1)!} \Delta^{2n+1} y_{-n}.$$

The quantities that occur in Stirling's formula are shown in the following difference table:

y_0		$\Delta^2 y_{-1}$		$\Delta^4 y_{-2}$		$\Delta^6 y_{-3}$		$\Delta^8 y_{-4}$
	Δy_0		$\Delta^3 y_{-1}$		$\Delta^5 y_{-2}$		$\Delta^7 y_{-3}$	
y_1		$\Delta^2 y_0$		$\Delta^4 y_{-1}$		$\Delta^6 y_{-2}$		$\Delta^8 y_{-3}$

Now in the central differences notation, (3) takes the form

$$y_u = y_0 + u\delta\, y_{1/2} + \frac{u(u-1)}{2!} \mu\delta^2 y_{1/2} + \frac{\left(u - \frac{1}{2}\right) u(u-1)}{3!} \delta^3 y_{1/2}$$

$$+ \frac{(u+1)(u-1)(u-2)}{4!} \mu\delta^4 y_{1/2} + \dots \qquad \dots(5)$$

$$\left[\because \frac{1}{2}(\Delta^2 y_{-1} + \Delta^2 y_0) = \mu\delta^2 y_{1/2}, \frac{1}{2}(\Delta^4 y_{-2} + \Delta^4 y_{-1}) = \mu\delta^4 y_{1/2} \text{ etc}\right]$$

Above is a very useful formula for practical purposes. It has odd differences below the central line and means of even differences on and below this line:

$$y_0 \cdots\cdots \left\{\begin{matrix} \Delta^2 y_{-1} \\ \\ \Delta^2 y_0 \end{matrix}\right\} \cdots\cdots \left\{\begin{matrix} \Delta^4 y_{-2} \\ \\ \Delta^4 y_{-1} \end{matrix}\right\} \cdots\cdots \left\{\begin{matrix} \Delta^6 y_{-3} \\ \\ \Delta^6 y_{-2} \end{matrix}\right\} \dots \text{ central line}$$

$$\Delta y_0 \qquad \Delta^3 y_{-1} \qquad \Delta^5 y_{-2}$$

4.5 Laplace-Everett Formula

The Gauss forward formula is

$$y_u = y_0 + u\Delta y_0 + u(u-1)\frac{\Delta^2 y_{-1}}{2!} + u(u^2-1)\frac{\Delta^3 y_{-1}}{3!}$$

$$+ u(u^2-1)(u-2)\frac{\Delta^4 y_{-2}}{4!} + u(u^2-1)(u^2-2^2)\frac{\Delta^5 y_{-2}}{5!} + \ldots \quad \ldots(1)$$

But, we have

$$\Delta^{2k+1} y_{-k} = \Delta^{2k}(\Delta y_{-k}) = \Delta^{2k}(y_{-k+1} - y_{-k}) = \Delta^{2k} y_{1-k} - \Delta^{2k} y_{-k} \quad \ldots(2)$$

Now, putting the values of odd differences in (1) in terms of even difference by (2), we get

$$y_u = y_0 + u(y_1 - y_0) + \frac{u^{(2)}}{2!}\Delta^2 y_{-1} + \frac{(u+1)^{(3)}}{3!}(\Delta^2 y_0 - \Delta^2 y_{-1}) + \frac{(u+1)^{(4)}}{4!}\Delta^4 y_{-2}$$

$$+ \ldots + \frac{(u+k-1)^{(2k)}}{(2k)!}\Delta^{2k} y_{-k} + \frac{(u+k)^{(2k+1)}}{(2k+1)!}(\Delta^{2k} y_{1-k} - \Delta^{2k} y_{-k} + \ldots$$

[in terms of factorial notation]

$$= (1-u)y_0 + uy_1 + \left\{\frac{u^{(2)}}{2!} - \frac{(u+1)^{(3)}}{3!}\right\}\Delta^2 y_{-1} + \frac{(u+1)^{(3)}}{3!}\Delta^2 y_0 + \ldots$$

$$+ \left\{\frac{(u+1)^{(4)}}{4!} - \frac{(u+2)^{(5)}}{5!}\right\}\Delta^4 y_{-2} + \frac{(u+2)^{(5)}}{5!}\Delta^4 y_{-1} + \ldots$$

$$+ \left\{\frac{(u+k-1)^{(2k)}}{(2k)!} - \frac{(u+k)^{(2k+1)}}{(2k+1)!}\right\}\Delta^{2k} y_{-k} + \frac{(u+k)^{(2k+1)}}{(2k+1)!}\Delta^{2k} y_{1-k} + \ldots \quad \ldots(3)$$

But

$$\frac{(u+k-1)^{(2k)}}{(2k)!} - \frac{(u+k)^{(2k+1)}}{(2k+1)!} = \frac{(u+k-1)^{(2k)}}{(2k+1)!}\{(2k+1) - (u+k)\}$$

$$= \frac{(k+1-u)(u+k-1)^{(2k)}}{(2k+1)!} = -\frac{(u-k-1)(u+k-1)^{(2k)}}{(2k+1)!}$$

$$= -\frac{(u+k-1)^{(2k+1)}}{(2k+1)!} = -\frac{(k-v)^{(2k+1)}}{(2k+1)!} \quad \text{[Putting } v = 1-u\text{]}$$

$$= -\frac{(v+k)^{(2k+1)}}{(2k+1)!} = \frac{v(v^2-1)(v^2-4)\ldots(v^2-k^2)}{(2k+1)!}.$$

Now, introducing the variable v, the equation (3) yields

$$y_u = vy_0 + \frac{v(v^2-1)}{3!}\Delta^2 y_{-1} + \frac{v(v^2-1)(v^2-4)}{5!}\Delta^4 y_{-2} + \dots$$

$$+ \frac{(v^2-1)(v^2-4)\dots(v^2-k^2)}{(2k+1)!}\Delta^{2k} y_{-k} + \dots$$

$$+ uy_1 + \frac{u(u^2-1)}{3!}\Delta^2 y_0 + \frac{u(u^2-1)(u^2-4)}{5!}\Delta^4 y_{-1} + \dots$$

$$+ \frac{u(u^2-1)(u^2-4)\dots(u^2-k^2)}{(2k+1)!}\Delta^{2k} y_{1-k} + \dots \quad \dots(4)$$

This formula is extensively used and involves only even differences on and below the central line:

y_0 .... $\Delta^2 y_{-1}$ .... $\Delta^4 y_{-2}$ .... $\Delta^6 y_{-3}$ .... central line

....

y_1 $\Delta^2 y_0$ $\Delta^4 y_{-1}$ $\Delta^6 y_{-2}$

This is ***Laplace-Everett's formula*** in the most common form. This formula is convenient especially when using tables in which only even order differences are tabulated.

Table representing the zigzag paths for various formulae.

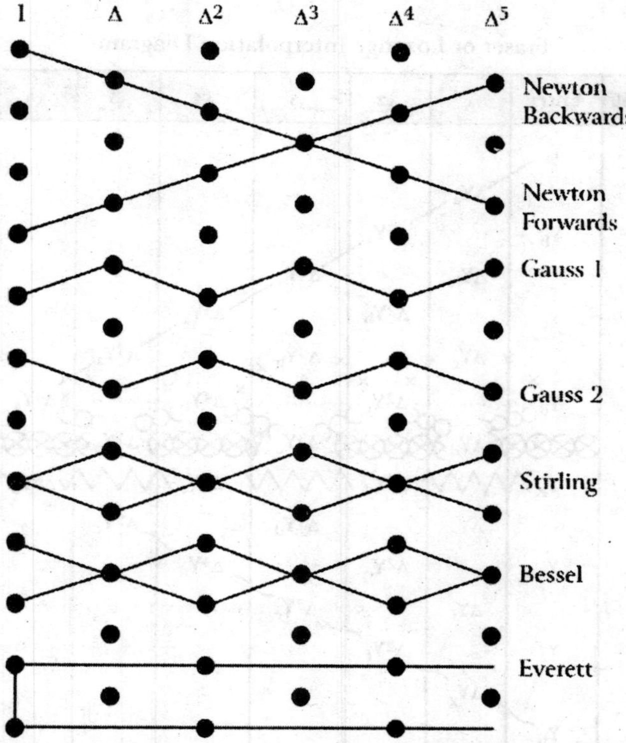

Note: Fraser or Lozenge Diagram: The above figure shows the path followed by various interpolation formulae. It is known as lozenge diagram because of its diamond pattern. Different paths can be used to write various interpolation polynomials. The following rules could be used to generate various interpolation results:

(i) Start with the entry in the first (functional value) column and proceed along the path in the Lozenge diagram. The path can be chosen according to the position of the unknown value and could be terminated at any difference.

(ii) Choosing a particular path, one proceeds to the right, either diagonally upward or downward to the next column or alternatively horizontally. One term is added for each column traversed in the chosen path consisting of the difference on which the segment terminates multiplied by a suitable binomial coefficient.

Actually, the added term is the entry multiplied by the entry above if the last step was diagonally downward; by the entry below if the last step was diagonally upward; and by the average of entries above and below if it was horizontal. The terms below or above are well explained by the diagram given below:

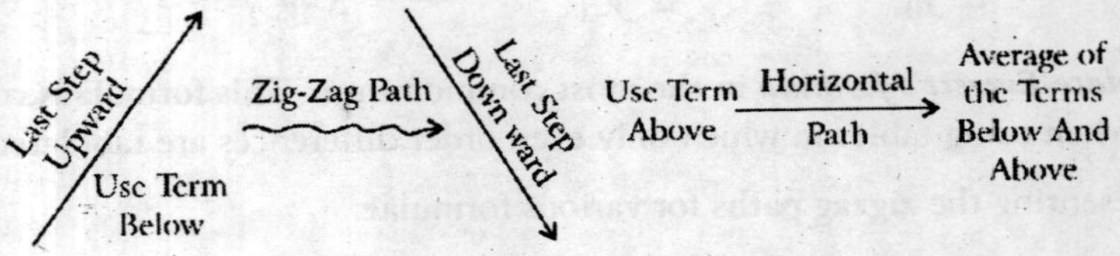

Fraser or Lozenge Interpolation Diagram

Argument	Entry	Δ	Δ^2	Δ^3	Δ^4	Δ^5	Δ^6	Δ^7
a	Y_a							
		ΔY_a						
b	Y_b		$\Delta^2 Y_a$					
		ΔY_b		$\Delta^3 Y_a$				
c	Y_c		$\Delta^2 Y_b$		$\Delta^4 Y_a$			
		ΔY_c		$\Delta^3 Y_b$		$\Delta^5 Y_a$		
d	Y_d		$\Delta^2 Y_c$		$\Delta^4 Y_b$		$\Delta^6 Y_a$	
		ΔY_d		$\Delta^3 Y_c$		$\Delta^5 Y_b$		$\Delta^7 Y_a$
e	Y_e		$\Delta^2 Y_d$		$\Delta^4 Y_c$		$\Delta^6 Y_b$	
		ΔY_e		$\Delta^3 Y_d$		$\Delta^5 Y_c$		
f	Y_f		$\Delta^2 Y_e$		$\Delta^4 Y_d$			
		ΔY_f		$\Delta^3 Y_e$				
g	Y_g		$\Delta^2 Y_f$					
		ΔY_g						
h	Y_h							

Paths for Various Interpolation Formulae

First Path-Newton's-Gregory forward: It is diagonally downward from Y_a as origin.

Second Path-Newton's backward: It is diagonally upward from Y_h, as origin.

Third Path-Gauss forward zig-zag: (Y_d as origin) first step downward.

Fourth Path-Gauss backward-zig-zag: (Y_d as origin) first step is upward.

Fifth Path-Stirling's formula: It is along the horizontal line from Y_d as origin, with alternative odd order difference terms as average of the two differences lying just above and below the horizontal line *e.g.* we have

$$\frac{\Delta Y_c + \Delta Y_d}{2}, \frac{\Delta^3 Y_b + \Delta^3 Y_c}{2}, \ldots$$

First Path		Fifth Path	————————
Second Path		Sixth Path	⊗⊗⊗⊗⊗
Third Path	o o o o o o	Seventh Path	ΛΛΛΛΛΛΛΛΛΛΛΛ
Fourth Path	+ + + + +		

Sixth Path-Bessel's formula: It is along the horizontal line from some point lying between Y_d and Y_e with the starting. The alternate terms are the average of the values lying just above and below the horizontal line *e.g.*

$$\frac{Y_d + Y_e}{2}, \frac{\Delta^2 Y_c + \Delta^2 Y_d}{2}, \ldots$$

Seventh Path-Everett's formula: It is along the horizontal line from Y_e as origin. It considers only even order differences lying along this line *e.g.*

$$\Delta^2 Y_d, \Delta^4 Y_c, \Delta^6 Y_b, \ldots$$

Note:

1. In order to find a tabulated value near the beginning of the table, the use of Newton's forward formula is must.
2. To find the tabulated value near the end of the table, the use of Newton's backward formula is must.
3. To find the interpolated value near the centre of the table, use any of the given formulae-Stirling/Bessel/Everett.

   Further, if interpolation is required for u:

   $-(1/4) < u < (1/4)$; then prefer stirling method otherwise Bessel/Everett if $(1/4) < u < (3/4)$.

Solved Examples

Example 1: *Prove that*

(*a*) $\Delta \equiv \frac{1}{2}\delta^2 + \delta\left(1+\frac{\delta^2}{4}\right)^{\frac{1}{2}}$ (*b*) $\delta^3 y_{1/2} = y_2 - 3y_1 + 3y_0 - y_{-1}$,

[Rohilkhand 2005, 2008; Meerut 2002, 2005, 2007]

(*c*) $\Delta\nabla \equiv \nabla\Delta \equiv \Delta - \nabla \equiv \delta^2$, (*d*) $\delta^n y_x \equiv \Delta^n y_{x-(n/2)}$.

[Rohilkhand 2010; Meerut 2003] **[Avadh 2004, 2005, 2009]**

Solution: (a) $\Delta \equiv \frac{1}{2}\delta^2 + \delta\left(1+\frac{\delta^2}{4}\right)^{\frac{1}{2}}$

$$= \frac{(E^{1/2} - E^{-1/2})^2}{2} + (E^{1/2} - E^{-1/2})\left(1 + \frac{(E^{1/2} - E^{-1/2})^2}{4}\right)^{\frac{1}{2}}$$

$$= \frac{(E^{1/2} - E^{-1/2})^2}{2} + (E^{1/2} - E^{-1/2})\left\{\frac{4 + (E^{1/2} - E^{-1/2})^2}{4}\right\}^{\frac{1}{2}}$$

$$= \frac{E + E^{-1}}{2} - 1 + \frac{(E - E^{-1})}{2} = E - 1 = \Delta.$$

(b) $\delta^3 y_{1/2} = (\Delta E^{-1/2})^3 y_{1/2}$ $[\because \delta \equiv \Delta E^{-1/2}]$

$= \Delta^3 E^{-3/2} E^{1/2} y_0 = \Delta^3 E^{-1} y_0 = (E-1)^3 E^{-1} y_0$ $[\because \Delta \equiv E - 1]$

$= (E^3 - 3E^2 + 3E - 1) E^{-1} y_0 = (E^2 - 3E + 3 - E^{-1}) y_0 = y_2 - 3y_1 + 3y_0 - y_{-1}$.

(c) $\Delta\nabla = (\delta E^{1/2})(\delta E^{-1/2}) = \delta^2$, $\nabla\Delta = (\delta E^{-1/2})(\delta E^{1/2}) = \delta^2$,

and $\Delta - \nabla = \delta E^{1/2} - \delta E^{-1/2} = \delta(E^{1/2} - E^{-1/2}) = \delta.\delta = \delta^2$.

$$\Delta\nabla \equiv \nabla\Delta \equiv \Delta - \nabla \equiv \delta^2$$

(d) $\delta^n y_x = (\Delta E^{-1/2})^n y_x = (\Delta^n E^{-n/2}) y_x = \Delta^n (E^{-n/2} y_x) = \Delta^n y_{x-(n/2)}$.

Example 2: *Use Gauss's forward formula to find the value of* y *when* $y = 3.75$ *from the following table:*

x	2.5	3.0	3.5	4.0	4.5	5.0
y	24.145	22.043	20.225	18.644	17.262	16.047

[M.K.U. (Tamil Nadu) 2001, 2005, 2006]

Solution: Taking 3.5 as the origin and 0.5 as the unit, the value of y required will be value for $u = \frac{3.75 - 3.5}{0.5} = 0.5$.

Difference table is:

x	u	y_u	Δy_u	$\Delta^2 y_u$	$\Delta^3 y_u$	$\Delta^4 y_u$	$\Delta^5 y_u$
2.5	−2	24.145					
			−2.102				
3.0	−1	22.043		.284			
			−1.818		−.047		
3.5	0	20.225		.237		.009	
			−1.581		−.038		−.003
4.0	1	18.644		.199		.006	
			−1.382		−.032		
4.5	2	17.262		.167			
			−1.215				
5.0	3	16.047					

Again Gauss's forward formula is

$$y_u = y_0 + u\Delta y_0 + \frac{u(u-1)}{2}\Delta^2 y_{-1} + \frac{(u+1)u(u-1)}{6}\Delta^3 y_{-1}$$

$$+ \frac{(u+1)u(u-1)(u-2)}{24}\Delta^4 y_{-2} + \frac{(u+2)(u+1)(u-1)u(u-2)}{120}\Delta^5 y_{-2}$$

$$\therefore \quad y_{.5} = 20.225 + .5(-1.581) + \frac{(.5)(.5-1)}{2}(.237)$$

$$+ \frac{(.5+1)(.5)(.5-1)}{6}\times(-.038) + \frac{(.5+1)(.5)(.5-1)(.5-2)}{24}\times(.009)$$

$$+ \frac{(.5+2)(.5+1)(.5)(.5-1)(0.5-2)}{120}\times(-.003)$$

$$= 20.225 - 0.7905 - 0.029625 + .00238 + 0.0023750 + 0.0002106$$

$$= 19.40 \text{ approx.}$$

Thus value of y for $x = 3.75$ is 19.40 approximately.

Example 3: *Use Gauss's forward formula to find y_{30} given that*

$$y_{21} = 18.4708;\ y_{25} = 17.8144;\ y_{29} = 17.1070;\ y_{33} = 16.3432;\ y_{37} = 15.5154.$$

[Meerut 2004, 2006; Avadh 2003; I.A.S. 2006]

Solution: Arrange the above data in the following form:

x	21	25	29	33	37
y	18.4708	17.8144	17.1070	16.3432	15.5154

Take the origin at $x = 29$ and $h = 4$ as the unit; then the value of y for $u = \frac{30 - 29}{4} = 0.25$ is to be found. Construct the following difference table:

x	$u = \frac{x-29}{4}$	y_u	Δy_u	$\Delta^2 y_u$	$\Delta^3 y_u$	$\Delta^4 y_u$
21	−2	18.4708				
			−0.6564			
25	−1	17.8144		−0.0510		
			−0.7074		−0.0054	
29	0	17.1070		−0.0564		−0.0022
			−0.7638		−0.0076	
33	1	16.3432		−0.640		
			−0.8278			
37	2	15.5154				

Now applying the Gauss forward interpolation formula, we get

$$y_{0.25} = 17.1070 + (0.25)(-0.7638) + \frac{(0.25)(-0.75)}{2}(-0.0564)$$

$$+ \frac{(1.25)(0.25)(-0.75)}{6}(-0.0076) + \frac{(1.25)(0.25)(-0.75)(-1.75)}{24}(-0.0022)$$

$$= 17.1070 - .19095 + .0052875 + .00002968 - .00000375 = 16.9216 \text{ approx.}$$

Example 4: *Given that*

$\sqrt{(12500)} = 111.803399$; $\sqrt{(12510)} = 111.848111$;

$\sqrt{(12520)} = 111.892806$; $\sqrt{(12530)} = 111.937483$.

Show by Gauss's backward formula that $\sqrt{(12516)} = 111.874930$. **[Rajasthan 2008]**

Solution: Taking 12520 as the origin and $h = 10$ as the unit, the value of y required is for $u = \frac{12516 - 12520}{10} = -0.4$.

x	u	y_u	Δy_u	$\Delta^2 y_u$	$\Delta^3 y_u$
12500	−2	111.803399			
			0.044712		
12510	−1	111.848111		−0.000017	
			0.044695		−0.000001
12520	0	111.892806		−0.000018	
			0.044677		
12530	1	111.937483			

Now by Gauss's backward formula, we have

$$y_u = y_0 + {}^uC_1 \Delta y_{-1} + {}^{u+1}C_2 \Delta^2 y_{-1} + {}^{u+1}C_3 \Delta^3 y_{-2} + \dots$$

$$\therefore \quad y_{-0.4} = 111.8928 + (-0.4)(0.044695) + \frac{(0.6)(-0.4)}{2!}(-0.000018) + \frac{(0.6)(-0.4)(-1.4)}{3!}(-0.000008)$$

$$= 111.8928 - 0.017878 + \text{negligible quantities} = 111.874930.$$

i.e. $\sqrt{(12516)} = 111.874930.$

Example 5: *Find by Gauss's backward formula the sales by a concern for the year* 1936, *given*

Year	1901	1911	1921	1931	1941	1951
Sale (in thousands)	12	15	20	27	39	52

[Meerut 2003, 2006]

Solution: Taking 1931 as the origin and $h = 10$ years as the unit, then sale of the concern is to be found for $u = \frac{1936 - 1931}{10} = .5$

The difference table is as under:

x	$u = \frac{x - 1931}{10}$	y_u	Δy_u	$\Delta^2 y_u$	$\Delta^3 y_u$	$\Delta^4 y_u$	$\Delta^5 y_u$
1901	−3	12					
			3				
1911	−2	15		2			
			5		0		
1921	−1	20		2		3	
			7		3		−10
1931	0	27		5		−7	
			12		−4		
1941	1	39		1			
			13				
1951	2	52					

Again Gauss backward formula is

$$y_u = y_0 + {}^uC_1 \Delta y_{-1} + {}^{u+1}C_2 \Delta^2 y_{-1} + {}^{u+1}C_3 \Delta^3 y_{-2} + \dots$$

or

$$y_u = y_0 + u\Delta y_{-1} + \frac{(u+1)\,u}{2}\Delta^2 y_{-1} + \frac{(u+1)\,u\,(u-1)}{6}\Delta^3 y_{-2} + \frac{(u+2)(u+1)\,u\,(u-1)}{24}\Delta^4 y_{-2} + \dots$$

or $$y_0 = 27 + 0.5 \times 7 + \frac{(1.5)\times(.5)}{2}\times 5 + \frac{(1.5)(0.5)(-0.5)}{6}\times 3$$
$$+ \frac{(2.5)(1.5)(0.5)(-0.5)}{24}\times(-7) + \frac{(2.5)(1.5)(0.5)(-0.5)}{120}\times(-10)$$
$$= 27 + 3.5 + 1.875 - 0.1875 + 0.2734 - 0.11718$$
$$= 32.6484 - 0.30468 = 32.3437 \text{ thousands.}$$

Example 6: *Use Stirling's formula to find* y_{28}, *given*

$$y_{20} = 49225,\ y_{25} = 48316,\ y_{30} = 47236,\ y_{35} = 45926,\ y_{40} = 44306.$$

[Rohilkhand 2004, 2008; Agra 2006; Bhopal 2002; Avadh 2005, 2008]

Solution: Taking $x = 30$ as the origin and $h = 5$ as the unit, we have to find the value of y for $u = \frac{28-30}{5} = -0.4$.

Construct the following difference table:

x	$u = \frac{x-30}{5}$	y_u	Δy_u	$\Delta^2 y_u$	$\Delta^3 y_u$	$\Delta^4 y_u$
20	−2	49225				
			−909			
25	−1	48316		−171		
			−1080		−59	
30	0	47236		−230		−21
			−1310		−80	
35	1	45926		−310		
			−1620			
40	2	44306				

The Striling's formula is

$$y_u = y_0 + u\frac{\Delta y_0 + \Delta y_{-1}}{2} + \frac{u^2}{2}\Delta^2 y_{-1} + \frac{u(u^2-1)}{6}\cdot\frac{\Delta^3 y_{-1} + \Delta^3 y_{-2}}{2} + \frac{u^2(u^2-1)}{24}\Delta^4 y_{-2}.$$

Putting $u = -0.4$ and the values of various differences from the table, we get

$$y_{-0.4} = 47236 + (-0.4)\frac{-1310-1080}{2} + \frac{(0.16)}{2}(-230)$$
$$+ \frac{(-0.4)(0.16-1)}{6}\cdot\frac{(-80-59)}{2} + \frac{(0.16)(0.16-1)}{24}(-21)$$
$$= 47236 + 478 - 18.4 - 3.8920 + .1176 \qquad \textit{i.e. } y_{28} = 47692.$$

Example 7: *Apply Bessel's formula to obtain y_{25}, given*

$$y_{20} = 2854,\ y_{24} = 3162,\ y_{28} = 3544,\ y_{32} = 3992.$$

[Delhi (H) 2004, 2008; Meerut 2005]

Solution: Take 24 as the origin and 4 as the unit. We have to find y_u for value of $u = \dfrac{25-24}{4} = \dfrac{1}{4}$ or 0.25.

The difference table is:

x	$u = \dfrac{x-24}{4}$	y_u	Δy_u	$\Delta^2 y_u$	$\Delta^3 y_u$
20	−1	2854			
			308		
24	0	3162		74	
			382		−8
28	1	3544		66	
			448		
32	2	3992			

Bessel's formula is

$$y_u = \frac{1}{2}(y_0 + y_1) + \left(u - \frac{1}{2}\right)\Delta y_0 + \frac{u(u-1)}{2!}\left(\frac{\Delta^2 y_{-1} + \Delta^2 y_0}{2}\right) + \frac{\left(u-\frac{1}{2}\right)u(u-1)}{3!}\Delta^3 y_{-1} + \ldots$$

$$\therefore y_{1/4} = \frac{1}{2}(3162 + 3544) + \left(\frac{1}{4} - \frac{1}{2}\right)382 + \frac{\left(\frac{1}{4}\right)\left(\frac{1}{4}-1\right)}{2!}\cdot\left(\frac{74+66}{2}\right) + \frac{\left(\frac{1}{4}-\frac{1}{2}\right)\left(\frac{1}{4}\right)\left(\frac{1}{4}-1\right)}{3!}(-8)$$

$$= 3353 - 95.5 - 6.5625 - 0.0625 = 3250.875.$$

Example 8: *Given $y_{20} = 24$, $y_{24} = 32$, $y_{28} = 35$, $y_{32} = 40$, find y_{25} by Bessel's formula.*

[Meerut 2003; Agra 2006]

Solution: Take origin at $x = 24$ and 4 as the unit, we have to find y_u for $u = \dfrac{25-24}{4} = \dfrac{1}{4}$.

The difference table is as under:

x	$u = \dfrac{x-24}{4}$	y_u	Δy_u	$\Delta^2 y_u$	$\Delta^3 y_u$
20	−1	24			
			8		
24	0	32		−5	
			3		7
28	1	35		2	
			5		
32	2	40			

The Bessel's formula is

$$x_0 = \frac{y_0 + y_{-1}}{2} + \left(u - \frac{1}{2}\right)\Delta y_0 + \frac{u(u-1)}{2} \cdot \frac{\Delta^2 y_{-1} + \Delta^2 y_0}{2} + \frac{\left(u - \frac{1}{2}\right) u (u-1)}{3!} \Delta^3 y_{-1}$$

Putting the values of various differences so obtained and $u = \frac{1}{4}$ we get

$$y_{1/4} = \frac{32 + 34}{2} + \left(\frac{1}{4} - \frac{1}{2}\right) 3 + \frac{\frac{1}{4}\left(\frac{1}{4} - 1\right)}{2} \cdot \left(\frac{-5+2}{2}\right) + \frac{\left(\frac{1}{4} - \frac{1}{2}\right)\frac{1}{4}\left(\frac{1}{4} - 1\right)}{6} (7)$$

$$= 33.5 - 0.75 + 0.1406 + 0.054687 = 32.945287.$$

Example 9: *Apply Everett's formula to obtain y_{25}, given*

$$y_{20} = 2854,\ y_{24} = 3162,\ y_{28} = 3544,\ y_{32} = 3992.$$

[Kanpur 2004; Bangaluru 2008; Meerut 2000, 2001]

Solution: Take $x = 24$ as the origin and $h = 4$ as the unit, we have to find y_u for $u = \frac{25 - 24}{4} = \frac{1}{4}$ or 0.25.

The difference table is as under:

x	u	y_u	Δy_u	$\Delta^2 y_u$	$\Delta^3 y_u$
20	−1	2854			
			308		
24	0	3162		74	
			382		−8
28	1	3544		66	
			448		
32	2	3992			

The Everett's formula is

$$y_u = u y_1 + \frac{u(u^2-1)}{3!}\Delta^2 y_0 + \frac{u(u^2-1)(u^2-4)}{5!}\Delta^4 y_{-1} + \ldots$$

$$+ v y_0 + \frac{v(v^2-1)}{3!}\Delta^2 y_{-1} + \ldots \quad \text{where } v = 1 - u$$ [Refer 4.5]

$$= \frac{1}{4}(3544) + \frac{\frac{1}{4}\left(\frac{1}{16} - 1\right)}{6} \times 66 + \frac{3}{4}(3162) \times \frac{\frac{3}{4}\left(\frac{9}{16} - 1\right)}{6} \times 74$$

$$= 886 - 2.5781 + 2371.5 - 4.0469 = 3250.875.$$

Example 10: *From the following table, find the value of* log 337.5 *by Gauss, Stirling, Bessel and Everett formulae.*

x	310	320	330	340	350	360
$\log_{10} x$	2.4913617	2.5051500	2.5185139	2.5314789	2.5440680	2.5563025

[Avadh 2003, 2010]

Solution: Taking 330 as the origin and 10 as the unit, the value of $\log_{10}$ 337.5 required will be for $u = \dfrac{337.5 - 330}{10} = .75$.

The difference table is as under:

x	u	y_u	Δy_u	$\Delta^2 y_u$	$\Delta^3 y_u$	$\Delta^4 y_u$	$\Delta^5 y_u$
310	−2	2.4913617					
			.0137883				
320	−1	2.5051500		−.0004244			
			.0133639		.0000255		
330	0	2.5185139		−.0003989		-25×10^{-7}	
			.0129650		.0000230		8×10^{-7}
340	1	2.5314789		−.0003759		-17×10^{-7}	
			.0125891		.0000213		
350	2	2.5440680		−.0003546			
			.0122345				
360	3	2.5563025					

(i) Gauss's forward formula is

$$y_u = y_0 + {}^uC_1\Delta y_0 + {}^uC_2\Delta^2 y_{-1} + {}^{u+1}C_3\Delta^3 y_{-1} + {}^{u+1}C_4\Delta^4 y_{-2} + {}^{u+2}C_5\Delta^5 y_{-2} + \ldots$$

$$\therefore \quad y_{.75} = 2.5185139 + \frac{3}{4}(.0129650) + \frac{\frac{3}{4}\cdot\left(-\frac{1}{4}\right)}{2}(-.0003989)$$

$$+ \frac{\frac{7}{4}\cdot\frac{3}{4}\left(-\frac{1}{4}\right)}{6}(.0000230) + \frac{\frac{7}{4}\cdot\frac{3}{4}\left(-\frac{1}{4}\right)\left(-\frac{5}{4}\right)}{24}(-.0000025)$$

$$+ \frac{\frac{11}{4}\cdot\frac{7}{4}\cdot\frac{3}{4}\left(-\frac{1}{4}\right)\left(-\frac{5}{4}\right)}{120}(.0000008) = 2.52827374.$$

(ii) Gauss's backward formula is

$$y_u = y_0 + {}^uC_1\Delta y_{-1} + {}^{u+1}C_2\Delta^2 y_{-1} + {}^{u+1}C_3\Delta^3 y_{-2} + {}^{u+1}C_4\Delta^4 y_{-2} + \dots$$

$$= 2.5185139 + \frac{3}{4}(.0133639) + \frac{\frac{7}{4}\cdot\frac{3}{4}}{2}(.0003989)$$

$$+ \frac{\frac{7}{4}\cdot\frac{3}{4}\left(-\frac{1}{4}\right)}{6}(.0000255) + \frac{\frac{11}{4}\cdot\frac{7}{4}\cdot\frac{3}{4}\cdot\left(-\frac{1}{4}\right)}{24}(.0000025) = 2.52827375.$$

(iii) Stirling's formula is $y_u = y_0 + u\cdot\frac{1}{2}[\Delta y_0 + \Delta y_{-1}] + \frac{u^2}{2}\Delta^2 y_{-1}$

$$+ \frac{u(u^2-1)}{(3)!}\frac{1}{2}[\Delta^3 y_{-1} + \Delta^3 y_{-2}] + \frac{u^2(u^2-1)}{(4)!}\Delta^4 y_{-2} + \dots$$

$$= 2.5185139 + \frac{3}{4}\cdot\frac{1}{2}[.0129650 + .0133639] + \frac{\left(\frac{3}{4}\right)^2}{2}(.0003989)$$

$$+ \frac{\frac{3}{4}\left(\frac{9}{16}-1\right)}{6}\frac{1}{2}\cdot[.0000230 + .000255] + \frac{\frac{9}{16}\left(\frac{9}{16}-1\right)}{24}(.0000025) = 2.52827374.$$

(iv) Bassel's formula is $y_u = \frac{1}{2}[y_0 + y_1] + \left(u - \frac{1}{2}\right)\Delta y_0$

$$+ \frac{u(u-1)}{(2)!}\frac{1}{2}[\Delta^2 y_{-1} + \Delta^2 y_0] + \frac{\left(u-\frac{1}{2}\right)u(u-1)}{3!}\Delta^3 y_{-1}$$

$$+ \frac{(u+1)u(u-1)(u-2)}{4!}\frac{1}{2}[\Delta^4 y_{-1} + \Delta^4 y_{-2}]$$

$$+ \frac{\left(u-\frac{1}{2}\right)(u+1)u(u-1)(u-2)}{5!}\Delta^5 y_{-2} + \dots$$

$$= \frac{1}{2}[0.5185139 - 2.5314789] + \frac{1}{4}(.0129650)$$

$$+ \frac{\frac{3}{4}\left(-\frac{1}{4}\right)}{2}\frac{1}{2}[-.0003989 - .0003759] + \frac{\left(\frac{1}{4}\right)\left(\frac{3}{4}\right)\left(-\frac{1}{4}\right)}{6}(.0000230)$$

$$+ \frac{\frac{7}{4}\cdot\frac{3}{4}\left(-\frac{1}{4}\right)\left(-\frac{5}{4}\right)}{24}\frac{1}{2}[-.0000017 - .0000025]$$

$$+ \left(\frac{11}{4}\right)\left(\frac{7}{4}\right)\left(\frac{3}{4}\right)\left(-\frac{1}{4}\right)\left(-\frac{5}{4}\right)(.0000008) = 2.52827374.$$

(v) **Everett's formula is**

[Agra 2003; Avadh 2003]

$$y_u = uy_1 + \frac{u(u^2-1)}{3!}\Delta^2 y_0 + \frac{u(u^2-1)(u^2-4)}{5!}\Delta^4 y_{-1} + \ldots$$

$$+ vy_0 + \frac{v(v^2-1)}{(3)!}\Delta^2 y_{-1} + \frac{v(v^2-1)(v^2-4)}{5!}\Delta^4 y_{-2} + \ldots$$

where $v = 1 - u$

$$= \frac{3}{4}(2.5314789) + \frac{\frac{3}{4}\left(\frac{9}{16}-1\right)}{6}(-.0003759)$$

$$+ \frac{\frac{3}{4}\left(\frac{9}{16}-1\right)\left(\frac{9}{16}-4\right)}{120}(-.0000017) + \frac{1}{4}(2.5185139)$$

$$+ \frac{\frac{3}{4}\left(\frac{1}{16}-1\right)}{6}(-.0003989) + \frac{\frac{1}{4}\left(\frac{1}{16}-1\right)\left(\frac{1}{16}-4\right)}{120}(.0000025)$$

$$= 2.52827374.$$

Thus we see that the value of log 337.5 calculated from different formula is nearly the same.

Example 11: *Given*

θ	0°	5°	10°	15°	20°	25°	30°
tan θ	0.0000	0.0875	0.1763	0.2679	0.3640	0.4663	0.5774

Show that tan 16° = 0.2867 (*use Stirling's formula*).

[M.K.U. (Tamil Nadu) 2008]

Solution: Taking 15° as the origin and 5° as the unit, the value (of tan 16°) required will be for $u = \frac{16° - 15°}{5°} = .2°$.

The difference table is as under:

θ	u	y_u	Δy_u	$\Delta^2 y_u$	$\Delta^3 y_u$	$\Delta^4 y_u$	$\Delta^5 y_u$	$\Delta^6 y_u$
0°	−3	0.0000						
			.0875					
5°	−2	0.0875		.0013				
			.0888		.0015			
10°	−1	0.1763		.0028		.0002		
			.0916		.0017		−.0002	
15°	0	0.2679		.0045		.0000		.0011
			.0961		.0017		.0009	
20°	1	0.3640		.0062		.0009		
			.1023		.0026			
25°	2	0.4663		.0088				
			.1111					
30°	3	0.5774						

Stirling's formula is

$$y_u = y_0 + u\frac{1}{2}[\Delta y_0 + \Delta y_{-1}] + \frac{u^2}{2}\Delta^2 y_{-1} + \frac{u(u^2-1)}{3!}\frac{1}{2}[\Delta^3 y_{-1} + \Delta^3 y_{-2}]$$

$$+ \frac{u^2(u^2-1)}{(4)!}\Delta^4 y_{-2} + \frac{u(u^2-1)(u^2-4)}{(5)!}\frac{1}{2}[\Delta^5 y_{-2} + \Delta^5 y_{-3}]$$

$$+ \frac{u^2(u^2-1)(u^2-4)}{(6)!}\Delta^6 y_{-3}$$

Now putting the necessary values from the difference table, we have

$$\tan 16° = y_{.2} = 0.2679 + \frac{.2}{2}[.0961 + .0916] + \frac{.04}{2}(.0045)$$

$$+ \frac{.2(.04-1)}{6}\frac{1}{2}(.0017 + .0017) + \frac{.04(.04-1)}{24}.0000$$

$$+ \frac{.2(.04-1)(.04-4)}{120}\frac{1}{2}[-.0002 + .0009] + \frac{.2(.04-1)(.04-4)}{720}(.0011)$$

$$= .2679 + .01877 + .00009 + \text{negligible quantities} = 0.2867.$$

Example 12: *If third differences are constant, prove that*

$$y_{x+1/2} = \frac{1}{2}(y_x + y_{x+1}) - \frac{1}{16}(\Delta^2 y_{x-1} + \Delta^2 y_x).$$

[Avadh 2004]

Solution: Bessel's formula is

$$y_x = \frac{y_0 + y_1}{2} + \left(x - \frac{1}{2}\right)\Delta y_0 + \frac{x(x-1)}{2!} \cdot \frac{\Delta^2 y_{-1} + \Delta^2 y_0}{2} + \frac{\left(x - \frac{1}{2}\right) x (x-1)}{3!} \Delta^3 y_{-1}. \quad ...(1)$$

Formula is taken upto third differences since third differences are constant.

Putting $x = \frac{1}{2}$ in (i), we get

$$y_{1/2} = \frac{y_0 + y_1}{2} - \frac{1}{16}(\Delta^2 y_{-1} + \Delta^2 y_0) \quad ...(2)$$

Now shift the origin to x; thus (2) reduces to

$$y_{x+1/2} = \frac{1}{2}(y_x + y_{x+1}) - \frac{1}{16}(\Delta^2 y_{x+1} + \Delta^2 y_x).$$

Example 13: *Given $y_0, y_1, y_2, y_3, y_4, y_5$ (Fifth differences constant). Prove that*

$$y_{\left(2\frac{1}{2}\right)} = \frac{1}{2}c + \frac{25(c-b) + 3(a-c)}{256}$$

where $a = y_0 + y_5; b = y_1 + y_4; c = y_2 + y_3$.

[Agra 2001, 2004; Rohilkhand 2010; Patna 2006, 2008]

Solution: Putting $x = \frac{1}{2}$ in the Bessel's formula, we get

$$y_{1/2} = \frac{1}{2}(y_0 + y_1) - \frac{1}{8}\left(\frac{\Delta^2 y_{-1} + \Delta^2 y_0}{2}\right) + \frac{3}{128}\left(\frac{\Delta^4 y_{-2} + \Delta^4 y_{-1}}{2}\right) \quad ...(1)$$

We have written the formula upto fifth differences, since it is given that fifth differences are constant.

Now shift the origin to 2; so (1) reduces to

$$y_{\left(2\frac{1}{2}\right)} = \frac{1}{2}(y_2 + y_3) - \frac{1}{16}(\Delta^2 y_1 + \Delta^2 y_2) + \frac{3}{256}(\Delta^4 y_0 + \Delta^4 y_1) \quad ...(2)$$

Now consider the following difference table:

y_u	Δy_u	$\Delta^2 y_u$	$\Delta^3 y_u$	$\Delta^4 y_u$
y_0				
	$y_1 - y_0$			
y_1		$y_2 - 2y_1 + y_0$		
	$y_2 - y_1$		$y_3 - 3y_2 + 3y_1 - y_0$	
y_2		$y_3 - 2y_2 + y_1$		$y_4 - 4y_3 + 6y_2 - 4y_1 - y_0$
	$y_3 - y_2$		$y_4 - 3y_3 + 3y_2 - y_1$	
y_3		$y_4 - 2y_3 + y_2$		$y_5 - 4y_4 + 6y_3 - 4y_2 - y_1$
	$y_4 - y_3$		$y_5 - 3y_4 + 3y_3 - y_2$	
y_4		$y_5 - 2y_4 + y_3$		
	$y_5 - y_4$			
y_5				

Now putting the values of various differences from the table in (2),

we get $$y_{\left(2\frac{1}{2}\right)} = \frac{1}{2}(y_2 + y_3) - \frac{1}{16}(y_4 - y_3 - y_2 + y_1)$$

$$+ \frac{3}{256}(y_5 - 3y_4 + 2y_3 + 2y_2 - 3y_1 + y_0)$$

or $$y_{\left(2\frac{1}{2}\right)} = \frac{1}{2}c - \frac{1}{16}(b - c) + \frac{3}{256}(a - 3b + 2c)$$

$$= \frac{1}{2}c + \frac{1}{256}[16(c - b) + 3\{(a - c) + 3(c - b)\}]$$

$$= \frac{1}{2}c + \frac{1}{256}[3(a - c) + 25(c - b)].$$

Example 14: *Apply* **(a)** *Stirling's formula,* **(b)** *Bessel's formula* **(c)** *Gauss forward formula,* **(d)** *Laplace-Everett's formula to find the value of $f(0.44)$ from the following table which gives the values of*

$$f(t)=\frac{1}{\sqrt{(2\pi)}}\int_0^t e^{-\frac{1}{2}t^2}\,dt$$

at intervals of $t = 0.5$ from $t = 0$ to $t = 3$.

t	*f*(*t*)
0.00	0.000
0.50	0.191
1.00	0.341
1.50	0.433
2.00	0.477
2.50	0.494
3.00	0.499

[Avadh 2005]

Solution: Take 1.00 as the origin and .5 as the unit, thus the new values of t are $-2, -1, 0, 1, 2, 3, 4$.

t	$f(t)$	$\Delta f(t)$	$\Delta^2 f(t)$	$\Delta^3 f(t)$	$\Delta^4 f(t)$	$\Delta^5 f(t)$	$\Delta^6 f(t)$
−2	0.000						
		0.191					
−1	0.191		−0.041				
		0.150		−0.017			
0	0.341		−0.058		0.027		
		0.092		0.010		−0.016	
1	0.433		−0.048		0.011		−0.001
		0.044		0.021		−0.017	
2	0.477		−0.027		−0.006		
		0.017		0.015			
3	0.494		−0.012				
		0.005					
4	0.499						

(a) The Stirling's formula in this case is

$$f(t) = f(0) + \frac{t}{1!}\frac{\Delta f(0) + \Delta f(-1)}{2} + \frac{t^2}{2!}\Delta f(-1)$$

$$+ \frac{t(t^2 - 1^2)}{3!}\frac{\Delta^3 f(-1) + \Delta^3 f(-2)}{2} + \frac{t^2(t^2 - 1^2)}{4!}\Delta^4 f(-2).$$

$$\therefore \quad f(t) = 0.341 + \frac{.44}{1!}\left(\frac{0.150 + 0.092}{2}\right) + \frac{(.44)^2}{2!}(-0.058)$$

$$+ \frac{.44\,(.44^2 - 1)}{3!}\cdot\frac{-0.017 + 0.010}{2} + \frac{(.44)^2\,(.44^2 - 1)}{4!}(0.027)$$

$$= 0.341 + .44\,(0.121) - (.1936)\,(0.029) + \frac{(.44)\,(.8064)\,(.027)}{12} - \frac{(.1936)\,(.8064)\,(0.027)}{24}$$

$$= 0.341 + .44\,(0.121) - (.1936)\,(0.029) + (.44)\,(.0672)\,(.007)$$

$$- (.0968)\,(.0672)\,(.0027)$$

$$= 0.341 + .0532 - .0056 + .0002 - .00018 = 0.3886 \text{ approx.}$$

(b) The Bessel's formula is

$$f(t) = \frac{1}{2}[f(0) + f(1)] + \left(t - \frac{1}{2}\right)\Delta f(0) - \frac{t(t-1)}{2!}\frac{\Delta^2 f(0) + \Delta^2 f(-1)}{2}$$

$$+ \frac{\left(t - \frac{1}{2}\right)t(t-1)}{3!}\Delta^3 f(-1) + \frac{t(t+1)\,t(t-1)(t-2)}{4!} \times \frac{\Delta^4 f(-1) + \Delta^4 f(-2)}{2}$$

$$+ \frac{\left(t - \frac{1}{2}\right)(t+1)\,t(t-1)(t-2)}{5!}\Delta^5 f(-2)$$

$$\therefore \quad f(t) = \frac{1}{2}[0.341 + 0.433] + \left[.44 - \frac{1}{2}\right](0.092) + \frac{.44\,(.44 - 1)}{2!} \times \frac{-0.058 - 0.048}{2}$$

$$+ \frac{\left(.44 - \frac{1}{2}\right)(.44)(.44 - 1)}{3!}(0.010) + \frac{(.44 + 1)(.44)(.44 - 1)(.44 - 2)}{4!} \times \frac{0.027 + 0.011}{2}$$

$$+ \frac{\left(.44 - \frac{1}{2}\right)(.44 + 1)(.44)(.44 - 1)(.44 - 2)}{5!}(-0.016)$$

$$= 0.387 - (.06)\,(0.092) + (.22)\,(.28)\,(.160) + (.01)\,(.44)\,(.58)\,(0.010)$$

$$+ (.06)\,(.44)\,(.56)\,(1.56) + (0.019) + (.06)\,(.44)\,(.56)\,(1.56)\,(0.0032)$$

$$= 0.388 \text{ approx.}$$

(c) The Gauss's formula is

$$f(t)=f(0)+{}^{t}C_1\Delta f(0)+{}^{t}C_2\Delta^2 f(-1)+{}^{t+1}C_3\Delta^3 f(-1)+{}^{t+1}C_4\Delta^4 f(-2)+{}^{t+1}C_5\,\Delta^5(-2),$$

$$\therefore\quad f(.44)=0.341+(.44)(0.092)+\frac{(.44)(.44-1)}{2\,!}(-0.058)+\frac{(1.44)(.44)(.44-1)}{3\,!}(0.010)$$

$$+\frac{(1.44)(.44)(.44-1)(.44-2)}{4\,!}(0.027)+\frac{(2.44)(1.44)(.44)(.44-1)(.44-2)}{5\,!}(-0.016)$$

$$=0.341+(.44)(0.092)+(.22)(.56)(0.058)$$

$$-(.24)(.44)(.56)(0.010)+(.06)(.44)(.56)(0.027)-(2.44)(.06)(.44)(.56)(1.56)(.0032)$$

$$=.389 \text{ approx.}$$

(d) The Laplace-Everett's formula is

$$f(t)=\left\{uf(0)+\frac{u(u^2-1)}{3\,!}\Delta^2 f(-1)+\frac{u(u^2-1)(u^2-4)}{5\,!}\Delta^4 f(-2)\right\}$$

$$+\left\{tf(1)+\frac{t(t^2-1)}{3\,!}\Delta^2 f(0)+\frac{t(t^2-1)(t^2-4)}{5\,!}\Delta^4 f(-1)\right\}$$

where $u=(1-t)$

$$\therefore\quad f(t)=\left[.56\times 0.341+\frac{(.56)(.56^2-1)}{6}(-0.058)+\frac{(.56)(.56^2-1).(.56^2-4)}{5\,!}(0.027)\right]$$

$$+\left[.44\times 0.433+\frac{(.44)(.44^2-1)}{3\,!}(-0.048)+\frac{(.44)(.44^2-1)(.44^2-4)}{5\,!}(.011)\right]$$

$$=[.56\times 0.341+(.56)(.1144)(0.058)+(.56)(.1144)(3.1144)(0.0054)]$$

$$+[.44\times 0.43+(.44)(.1344)(0.048)+(.44)(.1344)(3.1344)(.0022)]$$

$$=0.389 \text{ approximately.}$$

Example 15: *Employ Stirling's formula to compute $y_{12.2}$ from the following table ($y_x = 1+\log_{10}\sin x$):*

x	10	11	12	13	14
$10^5 u_x$	23,967	28,060	31,788	35,209	38,368

Solution: Taking the origin at $x=12$, $h=1$ and $u=\dfrac{x-12}{1}$, we have the following central table:

x	u	y_u	Δy_u	$\Delta^2 y_u$	$\Delta^3 y_u$	$\Delta^4 y_u$
10	−2	.23967				
			.04093			
11	−1	.28060		−.00365		
			.3728		**.00058**	
12	0	**.31788**		**−.00307**		**−.00013**
			.03421		**−0.00045**	
13	1	.35209		−.00062		
			.03159			
14	2	.38368				

At $x=12.2$, $u=0.2$. [$\because$ u lies between $-\dfrac{1}{4}$ and $\dfrac{1}{4}$, the use of Stirling's formula is suitable.]

Now Stirling's formula is given by

$$y_u = y_0 + \frac{u}{1}\cdot\frac{\Delta y_{-1} + \Delta y_{-0}}{2} + \frac{u^2}{2!}\Delta^2 y_{-1} + \frac{u(u^2-1)}{3!}\times\frac{\Delta^3 y_{-1} + \Delta^3 y_{-2}}{2}$$

$$\times\frac{u^2(u^2-1)}{4!}\Delta^4 y_{-2} + \ldots$$

When $u=0.2$, we readily get

$$\therefore \quad y_{0.2} = 0.31788 + 0.2\left(\frac{0.03728+0.03421}{2}\right) + \frac{(0.2)^2}{2}(-0.00307)$$

$$+\frac{(0.2)\,[(0.2)^2-1]}{6}\left(\frac{0.00058-0.00045}{2}\right)$$

$$+\frac{(0.2)^2\,[(0.2)^2-1]}{24}(-0.00013)$$

$$=0.31788+0.00715-0.00006-0.000002+0.0000002$$

$$=0.32497.$$

4.6 Use of Various Interpolation Formulae [Avadh 2003]

Lagrange's formula for interpolation is applicable for any type of observation but when the observations are given at equi-spaced values of argument, the formulae using various order differences are found to be more convenient and easy to apply rather than Lagrange's interpolation formula.

Newton's forward formula is appropriate to apply only when the unknown value lies near the beginning of the table while Newton's backward formula is usually applied when the unknown value to be interpolated lies near the end of the table.

The central difference formulae must be used when the value of the argument for unknown entry lies somewhere in the middle of the difference table. The reason is that central difference formulae converge more rapidly than others. Out of these; Gauss's forward or backward formulae are applicable when the interpolated value lies near to the right or left of the central values in the table, While Stirling's formula is applicable when the value of u in the expression $x = a + uh$ is very near to zero. Bessel's formula gives the best result when we interpolate the middle of an interval.

✦✦ Problem Set ✦✦

1. Use Gauss's interpolation formula to find y_{41} with the help of following data:

$$y_{30} = 3678.2;\ y_{35} = 2995.1;\ y_{40} = 2400.1;\ y_{45} = 1876.2;\ y_{50} = 1416.3.$$

[Meerut 2008]

2. Apply a central difference formula to obtain y_{22}, given that $y_{25} = 0.2707$; $y_{30} = 0.3027$; $y_{35} = 0.3386$; $y_{40} = 0.3794$.

3. Given $y_2 = 10$; $y_1 = 8$; $y_0 = 5$; $y_{-1} = 10$; find $y_{1/2}$ by Gauss's forward formula table.
Find the value of e^{-x} when $x = 1.7489$ by Gauss, Strilling, Bessel and Everett formulae.

x	e^{-x}
1.72	.179066
1.73	.177284
1.74	.175520
1.75	.173774
1.76	.172045
1.77	.170333
1.78	.168638

[Agra 2003]

4. The mean atmospheric refraction R for a start at various altitudes $h°$ above the horizon is given in the table below. Using Bessel's formula for interpolation to halves, find the refraction for a star at an altitude of 27° above the horizon,

h	22°	24°	26°	28°	30°	32°
R	2′23.3″	2′10.2″	1′58.9″	1′49.2″	1′40.6″	1′33.0″

5. Prove that if third differences are assumed to be constant

$$y_x = xy_1 + \frac{x(x^2-1)}{3!}\Delta^2 y_0 + uy_0 + \frac{u(u^2-1)}{3!}\Delta^2 y_{-1}$$

where $u = 1 - x$.

Apply this formula to find the value of y_{25} and y_{10} given that $y_0 = 3010$, $y_5 = 2710$, $y_{10} = 2285$, $y_{15} = 1860$, $y_{20} = 1560$, $y_{25} = 1510$ and $y_{30} = 1885$.

[**Hint:** This formula can be easily proved with the help of Everett's formula.]

6. Use Stirling's formula to find $f(35)$ given

$$f(20) = 512,\ f(30) = 439,\ f(40) = 346 \text{ and } f(53) = 243$$

[Agra 2003]

7. Use Stirling's formula to find $f(1.22)$ from the following data:

x	1.0	1.1	1.2	1.3	1.4
$f(x)$	0.84147	0.89121	0.93204	0.96356	0.98545
x	1.5	1.6	1.7	1.8	
$f(x)$	0.99749	0.99957	0.97385	0.97385	

8. From the following table find the value of $f(.5437)$ by Gauss, Stirling, Bessel and Everett formula:

x	$f(x)$
.51	.529244
.52	.537895
.53	.546464
.54	.554939
.55	.563323
.56	.571616
.57	.579816

9. The value of elliptic integral

$$k(m) = \int_0^{\pi/2} (1 - m^2 \sin^2 \theta)^{-1/2}\, d\theta$$

for certain equidistant values of m are given below, use Everett's or Bessel's formula to determine $k(0.25)$

m	0.20	0.22	0.24	0.26	0.28	0.30
$k(m)$	1.659624	1.669850	1.680373	1.691208	1.702374	1.713889

10. **(a)** Prove that (i) $\delta = \Delta E^{-1/2} = \nabla E^{1/2}$

(ii) $\mu^2 = 1 + \frac{1}{4}\delta^2$

[Meerut 2006]

(iii) $E^{\pm 1/2} = \mu \pm \frac{1}{2}\delta$

[Meerut 2005]

(iv) $\Delta = \frac{1}{2}\delta^2 + \delta\sqrt{1 + \frac{\delta^2}{4}}$

[U.P.T.U. 2009]

(v) $\sqrt{(1 + \delta^2 \mu^2)} = 1 + \frac{1}{2}\delta^2$

(b) Establish the following relations,

(i) $\Delta \nabla \equiv \nabla \Delta \equiv \Delta - \nabla \equiv \delta^2$ (ii) $\mu\delta \equiv \frac{1}{2}(\nabla + \Delta) \equiv \frac{1}{2}\Delta E^{-1} + \frac{1}{2}\Delta$

(iii) $\Delta + \nabla \equiv \Delta/\nabla - \nabla/\Delta$.

[U.P.T.U. 2008]

11. Prove that (i) $\delta^2 y_0 = y_1 - 2y_0 + y_{-1}$

(ii) $\delta^3 y_{1/2} = y_2 - 3y_1 + 3y_0 - y_{-1}$, and in general

$$\delta^n y_x = \sum_{k=0}^{n} (-1)^k \frac{n!}{k!(n-k)!} y_{x+1/2n-k}$$

[**Hint:** $\delta^n = E^{-n/2}(E-1)^n \quad \therefore \delta^n y_x = E^{-n/2}(E-1)^n y_x = (E-1)^n y_{x-n/2}$ etc.]

12. Define the operator E, Δ, μ and δ used in the calculus of finite differences and prove the following relations:

(i) $\delta^n y_x = \Delta^n y_{x-n/2}$ (ii) $\mu^2 y_x = y_x + \frac{1}{4}\delta^2 y_x$ (iii) $E^{1/2} y_x = \mu y_x + \frac{1}{2}\delta y_x$.

13. If D, E, δ and μ be the operators with usual meanings and if $hD \equiv U$, where h is the interval of differencing prove the following relations between the operator.

(i) $E = e^U$ (ii) $\delta = 2 \sin h(U/2)$

(iii) $\mu = \cos h(U/2)$ (iv) $e^{-U} = 1 - \nabla$

(v) $(E+1)\delta = 2(E-1)\mu$.

14. What are the practical advantages arising from the use of the central differences in interpolation.

15. Derive Gauss's interpolation formula for central differences.

16. Eliminate odd differences from the Gauss's forward formula to derive Everett's formula.

$$y_\alpha = (1-\alpha)\, f_0 + \alpha f_1 - \frac{\alpha\,(\alpha-1)\,(\alpha-2)}{3\,!}\,\delta^2 f_0 + \frac{(\alpha+1)\,\alpha\,(\alpha-1)}{3\,!}\,\delta^2 f_1 + \dots$$

where $\quad y = f(x_0 + \alpha h), \alpha = \dfrac{x - x_0}{h}.$

17. The function $\int_x^\infty \frac{e^{-1}}{t}\,dt$ is given in the table below.

Find y for $x = 0.0378$ by using Stirling's formula.

x	0.00	0.01	0.02	0.03	0.04	0.05	0.06
y	∞	4.0379	3.3547	3.9591	2.6813	2.4679	2.5953

18. Apply (i) Stirling's formula, (ii) Bessel's formula to find the value of $f(0.44)$ from the following table which gives the values of $f(t) = \frac{1}{\sqrt{(2\pi)}} \int_0^t \exp\left(-\frac{t^2}{2}\right) dt$ at intervals of $t = 0.5$ from $t = 0$ to $t = 3$.

t	$f(t)$
0	0
0.5	0.19146
1.0	0.34134
1.5	0.43319
2.0	0.47725
2.5	0.49379
3.0	0.49865

Show also that Newton's forward formula gives $f(0.44) = 0.38867$. Find also the error in each case when the true value of $f(0.44) = 0.38867$.

19. Define the operators δ and μ and prove that

$$\delta\,[f(x)\,g(x)] = \mu\, f(x)\,\delta\, g(x) + \mu\, g(x)\,\delta\, f(x)$$

✦✦ Objective Type Question ✦✦

❖ Multiple Choice Questions

1. Which of the following statement is correct:

(a) Newton's formula of interpolation is more convergent than central difference formula

(b) Newton's formula do not converge as rapidly as the central difference formulae

(c) Central difference formulae are not convergent

(d) Newton's formula is divergent.

2. The ascending central difference formula is defined as:

(a) $\delta^n y_x = \Delta^{n-1} y_{x-n}$ (b) $\delta^n y_x = \Delta^n y_{\left(\frac{x}{2}-n\right)}$

(c) $\delta^n y_x = \Delta^n y_{(x-n/2)}$ (d) $\delta^n y_x = \nabla^n y_{(x+n/2)}$.

3. The average operator (μ) is defined as:

(a) $\mu = \frac{1}{4}[E^{1/2} - E^{-1/2}]$ (b) $\mu = \frac{1}{2}[E^{-1/2} + E^{1/2}]$

(c) $\mu = \frac{1}{4}[E^{-1/2} - E^{1/2}]$ (d) $\mu = \frac{1}{2}[E^{1/2} - E^{-1/2}]$.

4. Which of the following relation is valid:

(a) $E^{1/2} = \frac{1}{2}\mu + \delta$ (b) $E^2 = \mu + \frac{1}{2}\delta$

(c) $E^{1/2} = \mu + \frac{1}{2}\delta$ (d) $E = \mu + \delta$.

5. $y = y_0 + u_{c_1} \Delta y_0 + u_{c_2} \Delta^2 y_{-1} + (u+1)_{c_3} \Delta^3 y_{-1} + (u+1)_{c_4} \Delta^4 y_{-2} + \ldots$ is a formula known as:

(a) Newton's formula

(b) Gauss's forward formula for equal intervals

(c) Lagrange's divided difference formula

(d) Gauss's backward formula.

6. Which formula is more conveniently applicable to a tabulated value near the beginning of the table:

(a) Newton's forward formula (b) Stirling formula

(c) Newton's backward formula (d) Bessel formula.

7. To find the interpolated value near the centre of the table, which one of the formulae should be used:

(a) Gauss's backward formula (b) Stirling formula

(c) Lagrange's formula (d) Newton's forward formula.

8. Which of the following relation is correct:

(a) $\mu\,\delta = \frac{1}{2}(\nabla + \Delta)$ (b) $\mu\,\delta = (\nabla + \Delta)$

(c) $\mu\,\delta = (\nabla + \Delta)^2$ (d) $\mu\,\delta = \frac{1}{2}(\nabla - \Delta)$.

9. Which of the following is true:

(a) $\mu^2 = 1 + \delta^2$ (b) $E^{1/2} = \mu - \frac{1}{2}\delta$

(c) $\delta = \Delta E^{1/2}$ (d) $E^{-1/2} = \mu - \frac{1}{2}\delta$.

10. $\Delta + \nabla$ gives the value:

(a) $\frac{\nabla}{\Delta} + \frac{\Delta}{\nabla}$ (b) $\nabla/\Delta - \Delta/\nabla$

(c) $\Delta/\nabla - \nabla/\Delta$ (d) $\Delta/\nabla + \nabla/\Delta$.

11. Stirling's interpolation formula is the average of:

(a) Newton's forward formula and Newton's backward formula

(b) Bessel's interpolation formula and Laplace-Everett's interpolation formula

(c) Gauss's forward formula and Gauss's backward formula

(d) None of the above. **[Bhopal 2008]**

12. Which of the following is not applicable to find the value near the centre of table:

(a) Bessel's formula (b) Everett's formula

(c) Stirling's formula (d) Newton's formula.

[Rohilkhand 2009]

✦✦ Examination Questions ✦✦

1. Prove that

$hD = -\log(1 - \nabla) = \sin h^{-1}(\mu\,\delta)$ **[U.P.T.U. 2006]**

2. Prove that

$(E^{1/2} + E^{-1/2})(1 + \Delta)^{1/2} = 2 + \Delta$ **[U.P.T.U. 2004]**

✦✦ Answers ✦✦

❖ Problem Set

1.	$y_{41} = 2290.1$	2.	.3165
3.	$y_{1/2} = 6$	4.	1′52.4″
5.	$y_{11} = 2196$, $y_{16} = 1786$	6.	395
7.	.93258	8.	.558052
9.	1.685750	17.	3.0689
18.	(i) 0.38891; (ii) 0.38873.		

❖ Multiple Choice Questions

1.	(b)	2.	(c) & (d)	3.	(d)	4.	(c)	5.	(b)
6.	(a)	7.	(b)	8.	(a)	9.	(d)	10.	(c)
11.	(c)	12.	(d)						

◆◆◆

Theory | Solved Examples | Problem Set

Chapter 5

Numerical Differentiation

Derivatives using forward and backward difference formulae, Derivatives using central difference formulae, Maxima and minima of a tabulated function.

5.1 Introduction

Numerical differentiation is the process by which we can find the derivative or derivatives of a function at some values of the independent variable when we are given a set of values of that function. The problem of differentiation is solved by first approximating the function by an interpolation formula and then differentiating this formula as many times as desired. In case the values of the argument are equally spaced, we represent the function by Newton-Gregory formula. If we desire to find the derivative of the function at a point near the beginning (end) of a set of tabular values, we use Newton-Gregory forward (backward) formula. To find the derivative at a point near the middle of the table, we should use a central difference formula. In case the values of the argument are unequally spaced, we should use ***Newton's divided difference*** formula to represent the function.

Solved Examples

Example 1: *Find the first and second derivatives of the function tabulated below at the point* $x = 3.0$: **[Rajasthan 2004, 2006; P.C.S. 2007; Bhopal 2009]**

x	$f(x)$	Δ	Δ^2	Δ^3	Δ^4
3.0	−14.000				
		3.968			
3.2	−10.032		.768		
		4.736		.048	
3.4	−5.296		.816		0
		5.552		.048	
3.6	0.256		.864		0
		6.416		.048	
3.8	6.672		.912		
		7.328			
4.0	14.000				

Solution: Newton-Gregory formula is

$$f(a+xh) = f(a) + {}^xC_1\Delta f(a) + {}^xC_2\Delta^2 f(a) + {}^xC_3\Delta^3 f(a)$$

$$= f(a) + x\Delta f(a) + \frac{x^2 - x}{2}\Delta^2 f(a) + \frac{(x^3 - 3x^2 + 2x)}{6}\Delta^3 f(a)$$

Differentiating *w.r.t.* x twice and then putting $x = 0$ in the equations obtained, we get

$$hf'(a) = \Delta f(a) - \frac{1}{2}\Delta^2 f(a) + \frac{1}{3}\Delta^3 f(a)$$

$$h^2 f''(a) = \Delta^2 f(a) - \Delta^3 f(a).$$ Here $a = 3, h = 0.2$.

$\therefore$ $0.2 f'(3) = 3.968 - \frac{1}{2}(.768) + \frac{1}{5}(.048) = 3.6.$ $\therefore$ $f'(3) = 18.$

Again $(0.2)^2\ f''(3) = .768 - .048 = .72$

$\therefore$ $f''(3) = 18,$ $\therefore$ $\frac{dy}{dx}$ and $\frac{d^2y}{dx^2}$ at $x = 3$ are 18.

Note: The function which is tabulated above is

$y = x^3 - 9x - 14$ $\qquad \frac{dy}{dx} = 3x^2 - 9;\ \frac{d^2y}{dx^2} = 6x$

On putting x = 3, we get $\left(\frac{dy}{dx}\right)_{x=3} = 18;\ \left(\frac{d^2y}{dx^2}\right)_{x=3} = 18.$

These values are the same as obtained by numerical differentiation.

Example 2: *Find the first, second and third derivatives of the function tabulated below, at the point* $x = 1.5$ **[Raipur 2009]**

x	1.5	2.0	2.5	3.0	3.5	4.0
$f(x)$	3.375	7.000	13.625	24.000	38.875	59.000

Solution: Since required derivatives are at a point near the beginning of the table, therefore we shall use Newton-Gregory forward formula. The difference table is as follows:

x	$f(x)$	$\Delta f(x)$	$\Delta^2 f(x)$	$\Delta^3 f(x)$	$\Delta^4 f(x)$
1.5	3.375				
		3.625			
2.0	7.000		3.000		
		6.625		.750	
2.5	13.625		3.750		0
		10.375		.750	
3.0	24.000		4.500		0
		14.875		.750	
3.5	38.875		5.250		
		20.125			
4.0	59.000				

Newton-Gregory formula is

$$f(a+xh) = f(a) + {}^xC_1\Delta f(a) + {}^xC_2\Delta^2 f(a) + {}^xC_3\Delta^3 f(a) \qquad \text{upto 3rd differences}$$

$$= f(a) + x\Delta f(a) + \frac{x^2 - x}{2}\Delta^2 f(a) + \frac{(x^3 - 3x^2 + 2x)}{6}\Delta^3 f(a)$$

Differentiating *w.r.t.* x thrice and then putting $x = 0$ in the equations obtained, we get

$$hf'(a) = \Delta f(a) - \frac{1}{2}\Delta^2 f(a) + \frac{1}{3}\Delta^3 f(a)$$

$$h^2 f''(a) = \Delta^2 f(a) - \Delta^3 f(a), h^3 f'''(a) = \Delta^3 f(a). \quad [a = 1.5, h = .5]$$

$$\therefore \qquad f'(1.5) = \frac{1}{.5}\left[3.625 - \frac{1}{2}(3.000) + \frac{1}{3}(.750)\right] = 4.750$$

$$f''(1.5) = \frac{1}{.25}[3.000 - .750] = 9.000.\ f'''(1.5) = \frac{1}{.5^3}[.750] = 6.000.$$

Note: The function which is tabulated above is $y = x^3 - 2x + 3$.

Clearly $\quad (dy/dx)_{1.5} = (3x^2 - 2)$ at $1.5 = 4.750$

$(d^2y/dx^2)_{1.5} = [6x]$ at $1.5 = 9.000$. $\quad (d^3y/dx^3)_{1.5} = 6.000$.

These values are exactly the same as obtained by numerical differentiation.

Example 3: *Find the first and second derivatives of the function tabulated below at the point* $x = 1.1$:

[Bhopal 2007; Indore 2010]

x	$f(x)$	$\Delta f(x)$	$\Delta^2 f(x)$	$\Delta^3 f(x)$	$\Delta^4 f(x)$
1.0	0				
		.1280			
1.2	.1280		.2880		
		.4160		.0480	
1.4	.5440		.3360		0
		.7520		.0480	
1.6	1.2960		.3840		0
		1.1360		.0480	
1.8	2.4320		.4320		
		1.5680			
2.0	4.0000				

Solution: Newton's-Gregory formula is

$$f(a+xh) = f(a) + {}^xC_1\Delta f(a) + {}^xC_2\Delta^2 f(a) + {}^xC_3\Delta^3 f(a)\ldots$$

$$= f(a) + x\,\Delta\, f(a) + \frac{x^2 - x}{2}\Delta^2 f(a) + \frac{(x^3 - 3x^2 + 2x)}{6}\Delta^3 f(a) + \ldots \quad \ldots(1)$$

Differentiating (1) *w.r.t.* *x* twice, we get

$$hf'(a+xh) = \Delta f(a) + \frac{(2x-1)}{2}\Delta^2 f(a) + \frac{(3x^2-6x+2)}{6}\Delta^3 f(a) + \ldots \quad \ldots(2)$$

and $$h^2 f''(a+xh) = \Delta^2 f(a) + (x-1)\Delta^3 f(a) + \ldots \quad \ldots(3)$$

Putting $x = \frac{1}{2}$ and the values of all differences in (2) and (3), we have

$$(.2)\ f'(1.1) = 0.1280 + \frac{\left(2.\frac{1}{2}-1\right)}{2}(.2880) + \frac{\left(3.\frac{1}{4}-6.\frac{1}{2}+2\right)}{6}(.0480) + 0$$

$$= .1280 + 0 - .002 + 0 \text{ or } f'(1.1) = .630$$

and $(.2)^2 f''(1.1) = .2880 + \left(\frac{1}{2}-1\right)(.0480) + 0 = .2880 - .024 = .264$ or $f''(1.1) = 6.60$.

> **Note: The function, which is tabulated above, is**
>
> $y = x^3 - 3x + 2, \quad \therefore \frac{dy}{dx} = 3x^2 - 3$ and $\frac{d^2y}{dx^2} = 6x.$
>
> Hence the actual values of derivatives are .630 and 6.60 respectively, which are same as obtained by Numerical differentiation.

Example 4: *Find the derivative of* $f(x)$ *at* $x = 1.4$ *from the following table:*

x	.1	.2	.3	.4
$y = f(x)$	1.10517	1.22140	1.34986	1.49182

[U.P.P.C.S. 2008]

Solution: Since $x = .4$ lies near the end of the table therefore in this case we shall use Newton's Backward formula. The difference table is as below:

x	y	Δy	$\Delta^2 y$	$\Delta^3 y$
.1	1.10517			
		.11623		
.2	1.22140		.01223	
		.12846		.00127
.3	1.34986		.01350	
		.14196		
.4	1.49182			

Newton's Backward formula is $f(a+nh+xh) = f(a+nh) + x\Delta f(a+nh) + \frac{x^2+x}{2!}\Delta^2 f(a+nh)$

$$+\frac{x^3+3x^2+2x}{3!}\Delta^3 f(a+nh) \qquad ...(1)$$

Here $f(a+nh)$ is the last term and h is the differencing interval.

Differentiating (1) w.r.t. x, we get

$$hf'(a+nh+xh) = \Delta f(a+nh) + \frac{2x+1}{2}\Delta^2 f(a+nh) + \frac{3x^2+6x+2}{6}\Delta^3 f(a+nh). \qquad ...(2)$$

On putting $x = 0$ in (2), we have

$$(.1)\, f'(.4) = .14196 + \frac{1}{2}(.01350) + \frac{1}{3}(.00127) \Rightarrow f'(.4) = 1.4913$$

5.2 Direct Methods (using formula)

[A] Derivatives using forward difference formula

By Newton's forward interpolation formula, we have

$$y = y_0 + u\,\Delta y_0 + \frac{u(u-1)}{2!}\Delta^2 y_0 + \frac{u(u-1)(u-2)}{3!}\Delta^3 y_0 + \ldots$$

where the function $y = f(x)$ is tabulated for $x_i\ (= x_0 + ih), i = 0, 1, 2, \ldots n$

Differentiating both sides w.r.t. u, we have

$$\frac{dy}{du} = \Delta y_0 + \frac{2u-1}{2!}\Delta^2 y_0 + \frac{3u^2-6u+2}{3!}\Delta^3 y_0 + \ldots$$

But $\quad x = x_0 + uh \Rightarrow u = \frac{(x-x_0)}{h}, \Rightarrow \frac{du}{dx} = \frac{1}{h}.$

Now $\quad \frac{dy}{dx} = \frac{dy}{du}\cdot\frac{du}{dx} = \frac{1}{h}\left[\Delta y_0 + \frac{2u-1}{2!}\Delta^2 y_0 + \frac{3u^2-6u+2}{3!}\times\Delta^3 y_0\right.$

$$\left. + \frac{4u^3-18u^2+22u-6}{4!}\Delta^4 y_0 + \ldots\right] \qquad ...(1)$$

When $\quad x = x_0, u = 0.$

$$\Rightarrow \left(\frac{dy}{dx}\right)_{x_0} = \frac{1}{h}\left[\Delta y_0 - \frac{1}{2}\Delta^2 y_0 + \frac{1}{3}\Delta^3 y_0 - \frac{1}{4}\Delta^4 y_0 + \frac{1}{5}\Delta^5 y_0 - \frac{1}{6}\Delta^6 y_0 + \ldots\right] \qquad ...(2)$$

Further differentiating (1) w.r.t. x, we get

$$\frac{d^2y}{dx^2} = \frac{d}{du}\left(\frac{dy}{du}\right)\frac{du}{dx} = \frac{1}{h}\left[\frac{2}{2!}\Delta^2 y_0 + \frac{6u-6}{3!}\Delta^3 y_0 + \frac{12u^2-36u+22}{4!}\Delta^4 y_0 + \ldots\right]\frac{1}{h}$$

Putting $u = 0$, we obtain

$$\left(\frac{d^2 y}{dx^2}\right)_{x_0} = \frac{1}{h^2}\left[\Delta^2 y_0 - \Delta^3 y_0 + \frac{11}{12}\Delta^4 y_0 - \frac{5}{6}\Delta^5 y_0 + \frac{137}{180}\Delta^6 y_0 + \ldots\right] \quad \ldots(3)$$

and similarly $$\left(\frac{d^3 y}{dx^3}\right)_{x_0} = \frac{1}{h^3}\left[\Delta^3 y_0 - \frac{3}{2}\Delta^4 y_0 + \ldots\right] \quad \ldots(4)$$

Aliter: We know that $1 + \Delta \equiv E \equiv e^{hD}$

$$\Rightarrow \quad hD = \log(1+\Delta) = \Delta - \frac{1}{2}\Delta^2 + \frac{1}{3}\Delta^3 - \frac{1}{4}\Delta^4 + \ldots$$

$$\Rightarrow \quad D \equiv \frac{1}{h}\left[\Delta - \frac{1}{2}\Delta^2 + \frac{1}{3}\Delta^3 - \frac{1}{4}\Delta^4 + \ldots\right]$$

$$\Rightarrow \quad D^2 \equiv \frac{1}{h^2}\left[\Delta - \frac{1}{2}\Delta^2 + \frac{1}{3}\Delta^3 - \frac{1}{4}\Delta^4 + \ldots\right]^2$$

$$= \frac{1}{h^2}\left[\Delta^2 - \Delta^3 + \frac{11}{12}\Delta^4 + \ldots\right] \text{ and } D^3 \equiv \frac{1}{h^3}\left[\Delta^3 - \frac{3}{2}\Delta^4 + \ldots\right]$$

Then Dy_0 *i.e.* $$\left(\frac{dy}{dx}\right)_{x_0} = \frac{1}{h}\left[\Delta y_0 - \frac{1}{2}\Delta^2 y_0 + \frac{1}{3}\Delta^3 y_0 - \frac{1}{4}\Delta^4 y_0 + \frac{1}{5}\Delta^5 y_0 - \frac{1}{6}\Delta^6 y_0 + \ldots\right]$$

$$D^2 y_0 = D(Dy_0) = \left(\frac{d^2 y}{dx^2}\right)_{x_0} = \frac{1}{h^2}\left[\Delta^2 y_0 - \Delta^3 y_0 + \frac{11}{12}\Delta^4 y_0 - \frac{5}{6}\Delta^5 y_0 + \frac{137}{180}\Delta^6 y_0 - \ldots\right]$$

and $$\left(\frac{d^3 y}{dx^3}\right)_{x_0} = \frac{1}{h^3}\left[\Delta^3 y_0 - \frac{3}{2}\Delta^4 y_0 + \ldots\right]$$

These are the same as obtained above.

[B] Derivatives using backward difference formula

$$y = y_n + u\nabla y_n + \frac{u(u+1)}{2!}\nabla^2 y_n + \frac{u(u+1)(u+2)}{3!}\nabla^2 y_n + \ldots$$

Then differentiating both sides w.r.t. u, we get

$$\frac{dy}{dx} = \nabla y_n + \frac{2u+1}{2!}\nabla^2 y_n + \frac{3u^2+6u+2}{3!}\nabla^3 y_n + \ldots$$

But $$u = \frac{x - x_n}{h}, \Rightarrow \frac{du}{dx} = \frac{1}{h}.$$

Now $$\frac{dy}{dx} = \frac{dy}{du}\cdot\frac{du}{dx} = \frac{1}{h}\left[\nabla y_n + \frac{2u+1}{2!}\nabla^2 y_n + \frac{3u^3+6u+2}{3!}\nabla^2 y_n + \ldots\right] \quad \ldots(5)$$

But at $x = x_n$ $u = 0$. Hence keeping $u = 0$, we get

$$\left(\frac{dy}{dx}\right)_{x_n} = \frac{1}{h}\left[\nabla y_n + \frac{1}{2}\nabla^2 y_n + \frac{1}{3}\nabla^3 y_n + \frac{1}{4}\nabla^4 y_n + \frac{1}{5}\nabla^5 y_n + \frac{1}{6}\nabla^6 y_n + \ldots\right] \quad \ldots(6)$$

and $$\frac{d^2 y}{dx^2} = \frac{d}{du}\left(\frac{dy}{dx}\right)\frac{du}{dx} = \frac{1}{h}\left[\nabla^2 y_n + \frac{6u+6}{3!}\nabla^3 y_n + \frac{6u^2 + 18u + 11}{12}\nabla^4 y_n + \ldots\right]$$

Then putting $u = 0$, we get

$$\left(\frac{d^2 y}{dx^2}\right)_{x_n} = \frac{1}{h^2}\left[\nabla^2 y_n + \nabla^3 y_n + \frac{11}{12}\nabla^4 y_n + \frac{5}{6}\nabla^5 y_n + \frac{137}{180}\nabla^6 y_n + \ldots\right] \quad \ldots(7)$$

on the same lines, we get

$$\left(\frac{d^3 y}{dx^3}\right)_{x_n} = \frac{1}{h^3}\left[\nabla^3 y_n + \frac{3}{2}\nabla^4 y_n + \ldots\right] \quad \ldots(8)$$

Aliter. $1 - \nabla \equiv E^{-1} \equiv e^{-hD}$, Taking log on both sides

$$\Rightarrow \quad -hD = \log(1 - \nabla) = -[\nabla + \frac{1}{2}\nabla^2 + \frac{1}{3}\nabla^3 + \frac{1}{4}\nabla^4 + \ldots]$$

$$\Rightarrow \quad D \equiv \frac{1}{h}\left[\nabla + \frac{1}{2}\nabla^2 + \frac{1}{3}\nabla^3 + \frac{1}{4}\nabla^4 + \ldots\right]$$

$$\Rightarrow \quad D^2 \equiv \frac{1}{h^2}\left[\nabla + \frac{1}{2}\nabla^2 + \frac{1}{3}\nabla^4 + \ldots\right]^2$$

$$\equiv \frac{1}{h^2}\left[\nabla^2 + \nabla^3 + \frac{11}{12}\nabla^4 + \ldots\right] \Rightarrow D^3 \equiv \frac{1}{h^3}\left[\nabla^3 + \frac{3}{2}\nabla^4 + \ldots\right]$$

Then Dy_n *i.e.* $$\left(\frac{dy}{dx}\right)_{x_n} = \frac{1}{h}\left[\nabla y_n + \frac{1}{2}\nabla^2 y_n + \frac{1}{3}\nabla^3 y_n + \frac{1}{4}\nabla^4 y_n + \frac{1}{5}\nabla^5 y_n + \frac{1}{6}\nabla^6 y_n + \ldots\right]$$

$$\Rightarrow \quad \left(\frac{d^2 y}{dx^2}\right)_{x_n} = \frac{1}{h^2}\left[\nabla^2 y_n + \nabla^3 y_n + \frac{11}{12}\nabla^4 y_n + \frac{5}{6}\nabla^5 y_n + \frac{137}{180}\nabla^6 y_n + \ldots\right]$$

and $$\left(\frac{d^3 y}{dx^3}\right)_{x_n} = \frac{1}{h^3}\left[\nabla^3 y_n + \frac{3}{2}\nabla^4 y_n + \ldots\right]$$

There are again the same as (6), (7) and (8).

[C] Derivatives using central difference formulae

By Stirling's formula, we have

$$y_u = y_0 + \frac{u}{1!}\left(\frac{\Delta y_0 + \Delta y_{-1}}{2}\right) + \frac{u^2}{2!}\Delta^2 y_{-1}$$

$$+ \frac{u(u^2 - 1^2)}{3!}\left(\frac{\Delta^3 y_{-1} + \Delta^3 y_{-2}}{2}\right) + \frac{u^2(u^2 - 1^2)}{4!}\Delta^4 y_{-2} + \ldots$$

$$\Rightarrow \frac{dy}{du} = \left(\frac{\Delta y_0 + \Delta y_{-1}}{2}\right) + \frac{2u}{2!}\Delta^2 y_{-1} + \frac{3u^2-1}{3!}\left(\frac{\Delta^3 y_{-1} + \Delta^3 y_{-2}}{2}\right) + \frac{4u^3-2u}{4!}\Delta^4 y_{-2} + \ldots$$

But $u = \frac{x - x_0}{h}, \Rightarrow \frac{du}{dx} = \frac{1}{h}.$

$$\Rightarrow \quad \frac{dy}{dx} = \frac{dy}{du}\cdot\frac{du}{dx} = \frac{1}{h}\left[\left(\frac{\Delta y_0 + \Delta y_{-1}}{2}\right) + u\Delta^2 y_{-1}\right.$$

$$\left. + \frac{3u^2-1}{6}\times\left(\frac{\Delta^3 y_{-1} + \Delta^3 y_{-2}}{2}\right) + \frac{2u^3-u}{12}\Delta^4 y_{-2} + \ldots\right]$$

But at $x = x_0, u = 0$. Hence putting $u = 0$, we have

$$\left(\frac{dy}{dx}\right)_{x_0} = \frac{1}{h}\left[\frac{\Delta y_0 + \Delta y_{-1}}{2} - \frac{1}{6}\frac{\Delta^3 y_{-1} + \Delta^3 y_{-2}}{2} + \frac{1}{30}\frac{\Delta^5 y_{-2} + \Delta^5 y_{-3}}{2} + \ldots\right] \quad \ldots(9)$$

and similarly $\left(\frac{d^2 y}{dx^2}\right)_{x_n} = \frac{1}{h^2}\left[\Delta^2 y_{-1} - \frac{1}{12}\Delta^4 y_{-2} + \frac{1}{90}\Delta^6 y_{-3} - \ldots\right]$ ...(10)

Example 5: *Given that*

x	1.0	1.1	1.2	1.3	1.4	1.5	1.6
y	7.989	8.403	8.781	9.129	9.451	9.750	10.031

find $\frac{dy}{dx}$ *and* $\frac{d^2 y}{dx^2}$ *at* (***a***) $x = 1.1$ (***b***) $x = 1.6$

[Delhi (H) 2005, 2007, 2010]

Solution: (a) The difference table is as under

x	y	Δy	$\Delta^2 y$	$\Delta^3 y$	$\Delta^4 y$	$\Delta^5 y$	$\Delta^6 y$
1.0	7.989						
		.414					
1.1	8.403		−.036				
		.378		.006			
1.2	8.781		−.030		−.002		
		.348		.004		.002	
1.3	9.129		−.026		.000		−.003
		.322		.004		−.001	
1.4	9.451		−.023		−.001		
		.299		.005			
1.5	9.750		−.018				
		.281					
1.6	10.031						

By the standard formula, we have

$$\left(\frac{dy}{dx}\right)_{x_0} = \frac{1}{h}\left[\Delta y_0 - \frac{1}{2}\Delta^2 y_0 + \frac{1}{3}\Delta^3 y_0 - \frac{1}{4}\Delta^4 y_0 + \frac{1}{5}\Delta^5 y_0 - \frac{1}{6}\Delta^6 y_0 + \ldots\right] \quad \ldots(1)$$

and $$\left(\frac{d^2 y}{dx^2}\right)_{x_0} = \frac{1}{h^2}\left[\Delta^2 y_0 - \Delta^3 y_0 + \frac{11}{12}\Delta^4 y_0 - \frac{5}{6}\Delta^5 y_0 + \frac{37}{180}\Delta^6 y_0 - \ldots\right] \quad \ldots(2)$$

Here $h = 0.1, x_0 = 1.1, \Delta y_0 = 0.378, \Delta^2 y_0 = -0.03$ etc.

The putting these values in (1) and (2), we get

$$\left(\frac{dy}{dx}\right)_{1.1} = \frac{1}{.1}\left[0.378 - \frac{1}{2}(-0.03) + \frac{1}{3}(0.004) - \frac{1}{4}(0) + \frac{1}{5}(-0.001) - \frac{1}{6}(-0.003)\right] = 3.946$$

and $$\left(\frac{d^2 y}{dx^2}\right)_{1.1} = \frac{1}{(.1)^2}\left[-0.03 - (0.004) + \frac{11}{12}(0) - \frac{5}{6}(-0.001) + \frac{137}{180}(-0.003)\right] = -3.545.$$

(b) Using the above difference table and the backward difference operator ∇ instead of Δ; we get

$$\left(\frac{dy}{dx}\right)_{x_n} = \frac{1}{h}\left[\nabla y_n + \frac{1}{2}\nabla^2 y_n + \frac{1}{3}\nabla^3 y_n + \frac{1}{4}\nabla^4 y_n + \frac{1}{5}\nabla^5 y_n + \frac{1}{6}\nabla^6 y_n + \ldots\right] \quad \ldots(3)$$

and $$\left(\frac{d^2 y}{dx^2}\right)_{x_n} = \frac{1}{h^2}\left[\nabla^2 y_n + \nabla^3 y_n + \frac{11}{12}\nabla^4 y_n + \frac{5}{6}\nabla^5 y_n + \frac{137}{180}\nabla^6 y_n + \ldots\right] \quad \ldots(4)$$

Here $h = 0.1, x_n = 1.6, \nabla y_n = 0.281, \nabla^2 y_n = -0.018$ etc.

Then putting these values in (3) and (4), we get

$$\left(\frac{dy}{dx}\right)_{1.6} = \frac{1}{0.1}\left[0.281 + \frac{1}{2}(-0.018) + \frac{1}{3}(0.005)\right.$$
$$\left. + \frac{1}{4}(-0.001) + \frac{1}{5}(-0.001) + \frac{1}{6}(-0.003)\right] = 2.727$$

$$\left(\frac{d^2 y}{dx^2}\right)_{1.6} = \frac{1}{(0.1)^2}\left[-0.018 + 0.005 + \frac{11}{12}(-0.001) + \frac{5}{6}(-0.001) + \frac{137}{180}(-0.003) = -1.703.\right.$$

5.3 Maxima and Minima of a Tabulated Function

Newton's forward interpolation formula yields:

$$y = y_0 + u\Delta y_0 + \frac{u(u-1)}{2!}\Delta^2 y_0 + \frac{u(u-1)(u-2)}{3!}\Delta^3 y_0 + \ldots$$

Then differentiating it w.r.t. u, we have

$$\frac{dy}{du} = \Delta y_0 + \frac{2u-1}{2}\Delta^2 y_0 + \frac{3u^2 - 6u + 2}{6}\Delta^3 y_0 + \ldots \quad \ldots(1)$$

But for maxima, or minima, $dy/du = 0$.

$$\therefore \qquad \Delta y_0 + \frac{2u-1}{2}\Delta^2 y_0 + \frac{3u^2-6u+2}{6}\Delta^3 y_0 = 0 \quad \text{[retaining up to 3rd diff.]}$$

$$\Rightarrow \qquad \left(\frac{1}{2}\Delta^3 y_0\right)u^2 + (\Delta^2 y_0 - \Delta^3 y_0)\,u + \left(\Delta y_0 - \frac{1}{2}\Delta^2 y_0 + \frac{1}{3}\Delta^3 y_0\right) = 0.$$

Then putting the values of $\Delta y_0, \Delta^2 y_0, \Delta^3 y_0$ from the difference table,

we can solve this quadratic in *u*. *The corresponding values of* x are given by $x = x_0 + uh$.

Example 6: *From the table given below, for what values of x ; y is minimum? Also find this value of y .*

x	3	4	5	6	7	8
y	0.205	0.240	0.259	0.262	0,250	0.224

[Madurai 2008]

Solution: The difference table is given as under:

x	*y*	Δ	Δ^2	Δ^3
3	0.205			
		0.035		
4	0.240		−0.016	
		0.019		0.000
5	0.259		−0.016	
		0.003		0.001
6	0.262		−0.015	
		−0.012		0.001
7	0.250		−0.014	
		−0.026		
8	0.224			

Assuming $x_0 = 3$, we get

$$y_0 = 0.205, \Delta y_0 = 0.035, \Delta^2 y_0 = -0.016 \text{ and } \Delta^3 y_0 = 0.$$

Then using Newton's forward difference formula, we get

$$y = 0.205 + u(0.035) + \frac{u(u-1)}{2}(-0.016) \qquad \text{...(1)}$$

Differentiating it w.r.t. *u*, we have

$$\frac{dy}{du} = 0.035 + \frac{2u-1}{2}(-0.016). \text{ For } y \text{ to be minimum, } dy/du = 0$$

$$\Rightarrow \qquad 0.035 - 0.008(2u-1) = 0 \quad \Rightarrow u = 2.6875$$

and $\qquad x = x_0 + uh = 3 + 2.6875 \times 1 = 5.6875.$

Thus y is minimum at $x = 5.6875$.

$$\therefore \qquad y_{\min} = 0.205 + 2.6875 \times 0.035 + \frac{1}{2}(2.6875 \times 1.6875)(-0.016) = 0.2628.$$

Example 7: *Find the value of $f'(x)$ at $x = .04$ from the following table:*

x	.01	.02	.03	.04	.05	.06
$f(x)$	.1023	.1047	.1071	.1096	.1122	.1148

Solution: Since we want to find the derivative at a pont near the middle of the table, we may use any central difference formula. In the case we have used Bessel's formula. Here $x = .01$ and $h = .01$.

Consider a new variate $u = \dfrac{x - .04}{h}$

We want $f'(x)$ at $x = .04$. Again for $x = .04, u = 0$

and $$\frac{d}{dx} f(u) = \frac{d\,du}{du\,dx} f(u) = \frac{d}{du} f(u) \frac{.1}{h} = \frac{f'(u)}{h}$$

The difference table is as under:

u	x	$f(x)$	$\Delta f(x)$	$\Delta^2 f(x)$	$\Delta^3 f(x)$	$\Delta^4 f(x)$
−3	.01	.1023				
			.0024			
−2	.02	.1047		.0000		
			.0024		.0001	
−1	.03	.1071		.0001		−.0001
			.0025		0.000	
0	.04	.1096		.0001		−.0001
			.0026		−.0001	
1	.05	.1122		.0000		
			.0026			
2	.06	.1148				

Bessel's formula is

$$f(u)=\frac{1}{2}[f(0)+f(1)]+\left(u-\frac{1}{2}\right)\Delta f(0)+\frac{u(u-1)}{2!}\frac{1}{2}[\Delta^2 f(-1)+\Delta^2 f(0)]$$

$$+\frac{\left(u-\frac{1}{2}\right)u(u-1)}{3!}\Delta^3 f(-1)+\frac{(u+1)u(u-1)(u-2)}{4!}\frac{1}{2}[\Delta^4 f(-1)+\Delta^4 f(-2)]$$

upto fourth differences.

Differentiating *w.r.t.* u and putting $u=0$, we have

$$f'(0)=\Delta f(0)-\frac{1}{4}[\Delta^2 f(-1)+\Delta^2 f(0)]+\frac{1}{12}\Delta^3 f(-1)+\frac{1}{24}[\Delta^4 f(-1)+\Delta^4 f(-2)]$$

$$=.0026-\frac{1}{4}[.0001+.0000]+\frac{1}{12}[-.0001]+\frac{1}{24}[-.0001-.0001]$$

$$=.0026-\frac{.0001}{4}-\frac{.0001}{12}-\frac{.0002}{24}=\frac{.03075}{12}$$

$$\therefore\quad f'(0)=\frac{f'(0)}{h}=\frac{.03075}{12\times .01}=\frac{3.075}{12}=.2561.$$

Example 8: *Find* $f'(7.50)$ *from the following table:*

x	7.47	7.48	7.49	7.50	7.51	7.52	7.53
$y=f(x)$	.193	.195	.198	.201	.203	.206	.208

[Rajasthan 2005, 2007; M.D.U. (Rohtak) 2005, 2010; Rohilkhand 2004, 2006, 2010]

Solution: Since we want to find the derivative near the middle of the table, we shall use one of the central difference formulae.

The Bessel's formula with a new variable u, given by $u=\dfrac{x-7.50}{h}$, is

$$f(u)=\frac{1}{2}[f(0)+f(1)]+\left(u-\frac{1}{2}\right)\Delta f(0)+\frac{u(u-1)}{2!}\frac{[\Delta^2 f(-1)+\Delta^2 f(0)]}{2}$$

$$+\frac{\left(u-\frac{1}{2}\right)u(u-1)}{3!}\Delta^3 f(-1)+\frac{(u+1)u(u-1)(u-2)}{4!}\cdot\frac{[\Delta^4 f(-1)+\Delta^4 f(-2)]}{2}$$

$$+\frac{\left(u-\frac{1}{2}\right)(u+1)u(u-1)(u-2)}{5!}\Delta^5 f(-2)$$

$$+\frac{(u+2)(u+1)u(u-1)(u-2)(u-3)}{6!}\cdot\frac{[\Delta^6 f(-3)+\Delta^6 f(-2)]}{2}+\ldots\quad\ldots(1)$$

	x	$f(x)$	$\Delta f(x)$	$\Delta^2 f(x)$	$\Delta^3 f(x)$	$\Delta^4 f(x)$	$\Delta^5 f(x)$	$\Delta^6 f(x)$
−3	7.47	.193						
			.002					
−2	7.48	.195		.001				
			.003		−.001			
−1	7.49	.198		.000		.000		
			.003		−.001		.003	
0	7.50	.201		−.001		.003		−.010
			.002		.002		−.007	
1	7.51	.203		.001		−.004		
			.003		−.002			
2	7.52	.206		−.001				
			.002					
3	7.53	.208						

Since $u = \dfrac{x - 7.50}{h}, \dfrac{du}{dx} = \dfrac{1}{h}$, $\quad \therefore \quad \dfrac{d}{dx}\{f(x)\} = \dfrac{d}{du} f(x) \cdot \dfrac{du}{dx} = \dfrac{1}{h} f'(u)$

Now differentiating (1) w.r.t. u and putting $u = 0$, we get

$$f'(0) = .002 - \frac{1}{4}[-.001 + .001] + \frac{1}{12}(.002) + \frac{1}{24}[-.004 + .003] - \frac{1}{120}(-.007) - \frac{1}{120}(-.010)$$

$$= .002 + 0 + .0001666 - .0000416 + .0000583 + .0000833$$

$$= 0.0022666 \text{ (on simplification)}$$

$$\therefore \quad f'(7.50) = \frac{1}{h} f'(0) = \frac{1}{.01}(.0022666) = .22666.$$

Example 9: *Given the values of an emperical function $f(x)$ for certain values of x. Find* **(a)** $f'(93)$, **(b)** *the value of x for which $f(x)$ is a maximum,* **(c)** *the maximum value of $f(x)$ in the range of x.*

x	60	75	90	105	120
$f(x)$	28.2	38.2	43.2	40.9	37.7

Solution: (a) Since we require the derivative at a point near the middle of the table, so we shall use one of the central difference formulae. In this case, we have used Stirling's formula; The difference table is as under:

u	x	$f(x)$	$\Delta f(x)$	$\Delta^2 f(x)$	$\Delta^3 f(x)$	$\Delta^4 f(x)$
−2	60	28.2				
			10.0			
−1	75	38.2		−5.0		
			5.0		−2.3	
0	90	43.2		−7.3		8.7
			−2.3		6.4	
1	105	40.9		−.9		
			−3.2			
2	120	37.7				

where a new variate $u = \dfrac{x-90}{15}$, for $x = 93, u = 1/5 = 0.2$.

Now $\dfrac{d}{dx} f(u) = \dfrac{1}{h}\dfrac{d}{du} f(u) = \dfrac{1}{h} f'(u)$.

$$f(u) = f(0) + u\frac{\Delta f(0) + \Delta f(-1)}{2} + \frac{u^2}{2!}\Delta^2 f(-1) + \frac{u(u^2-1^2)}{3!} \times \frac{1}{2}[\Delta^3 f(-1)$$

$$+ \Delta^3 f(-2)] + \frac{u^2(u^2-1^2)}{4!}\Delta^4 f(-2) + \ldots \qquad \ldots(1)$$

Differentiating w.r.t. u and putting $u = 0.2$; we get

$$f'(u) = \frac{\Delta f(0) + \Delta f(-1)}{2} + \frac{2(.2)}{2!}\Delta^2 f(-1)$$

$$+ \frac{3(.2)^2 - 1}{3!}\frac{1}{2}[\Delta^3 f(-1) + \Delta^3 f(-2)] + \frac{4(.2)^3 - 2(.2)}{4!}\Delta^4 f(-2)$$

$$= \frac{-2.3 + (5.0)}{2} + .2(-7.3) + \frac{.12 - 1}{12}[6.4 - 2.3] + \frac{.032 - .4}{24}(8.7)$$

$$= \frac{2.7}{2} - 1.46 - \frac{.22(4.1)}{3} - \frac{.368(8.7)}{24}$$

$$= 1.35 - 1.46 - .30067 - .1334 = -.54407.$$

Now $f'(x) = \dfrac{1}{h} f'(u) = \dfrac{1}{15}(-.54407) = -.036271.$

(b) In order to have $f(x)$ maximum, solve the equation

$$f'(x) = 0 \quad \text{or} \quad f'(u) = 0$$

i.e. $$\frac{\Delta f(0) + \Delta f(-1)}{2} + \frac{2u}{2!}\Delta^2 f(-1) + \frac{3u^2 - 1}{3!} \times \frac{1}{2}[\Delta^3 f(-1) + \Delta^3 f(-2)] + \frac{4u^3 - 2u}{4!}\Delta^4 f(-2) = 0$$

or $$1.35 + u(-7.3) + \frac{3u^2 - 1}{12}[4.1] + \frac{4u^3 - 2u}{24}(8.7) = 0$$

or $$16.20 - 87.6u + (3u^2 - 1)(4.1) + (2u^3 - u)\,8.7 = 0.$$

$$17.4u^3 + 12.3u^2 - 96.3u + 12.10 = 0$$

Solving this equation by Newton-Rephson method, we have

$$u = .128126. \quad \therefore \quad x = 90 + 15u = 90 + 15\,(0.128126) = 91.92189.$$

(c) The value of $f(x)$ at this point is obtained by putting

$u = .128126$ in Stirling's formula (1) : $f(91.92189) = 43.2641.$

Example 10: *Compute $f'''(15)$ given*

x	2	4	9	13	16	21	29
$f(x)$	57	1345	66340	402052	1118209	4287844	21242820

[I.F.S. 2007; Lucknow 2008]

Solution: In this case the values of the argument are unequally spaced, so we may use Newton's divided difference formula.

The divided difference table is as under:

x	$f(x)$	$\Delta f(x)$	$\Delta^2 f(x)$	$\Delta^3 f(x)$	$\Delta^4 f(x)$	$\Delta^5 f(x)$
2	57					
		644				
4	1345		1765			
		12999		556		
9	66340		7881		45	
		83928		1186		1
13	402052		22113		64	
		238719		2274		1
16	1118209		49401		89	
		633927		4054		
21	4287844		114265			
		2119372				
29	21242820					

Since the fifth divided differences are constant, Newton's divided difference formula is

$$f(x) = f(a) + f(x-a) + \Delta f(a) + (x-a)(x-b)\Delta^2 f(a) + (x-a)(x-b)(x-c)\Delta^3 f(a)$$

$$+ (x-a)(x-b)(x-c)(x-d)\Delta^4 f(a) + (x-a)(x-b)(x-c)(x-d)(x-e)\Delta^5 f(a) + \ldots$$

Differentiating *w.r.t.* x thrice, we get

$$f'''(x) = 6\Delta^3 f(a) + [24x - 6(a+b+c+d)]\Delta^4 f(a)$$

$$[60x^2 - 24x(a+b+c+d) + 6(ab+cd) + (a+b)(c+d)$$

$$- e(24x - 6(a+b+c+d)]\Delta^5 f(a).$$

Putting $a = 2, b = 4, c = 9, d = 13, e = 16, x = 5$ we get

$$f'''(5) = 6 \times 556 + [120 - 168]\, 45 + [1500 - 3360 + 750 + 792 - 16(120 - 168)]$$

$$= 3336 - 2160 + 450 = 1626.$$

Example 11: *Find the first three derivatives of the function tabulated below at the point $x = 2.5$:*

x	1.5	1.9	2.5	3.2	4.3	5.9
$f(x)$	3.375	6.059	13.625	29.368	73.907	196.579

[Allahabad 2008]

Solution: In this case the values of the argument are unequally spaced, we may use here Newton's divided difference formula.

The divided difference table is as under:

x	$f(x)$	Δ	Δ^2	Δ^3
1.5	3.375			
		6.71		
1.9	6.059		5.90	
		12.61		1
2.5	13.625		7.60	
		22.49		1
3.2	29.368		10.00	
		40.49		1
4.3	73.907		13.40	
		76.67		
5.9	196.579			

We observe that the third divided differences are constant.

Again Newton's divided difference formula is given by

$$f(x) = f(a) + (x-a)\Delta f(a) + (x-a)(x-b)\Delta^2 f(a) + (x-a)(x-b)(x-c)\Delta^3 f(a)$$

taking upto third differences.

On differentiating w.r.t. x thrice, we get

$$f'(x) = \Delta f(a) + [2x - a - b]\,\Delta^2 f(a) + [3x^2 - 2x(a + b + c) + ab + ac + bc]\,\Delta^3 f(a)$$

$$f''(x) = 2\,\Delta^2 f(a) + [6x - 2(a + b + c)]\,\Delta^3 f(a)$$

$$f'''(x) = 6\,\Delta^3 f(a)$$

Here $a = 1.5, b = 1.9, c = 2.5$ On putting $x = 2.5$, we get

$$f'(2.5) = 6.710 + [5 - 3.4]\,5.9 + [3 \times 6.25 - 5\,(1.5 + 1.9 + 2.5) + 11.35]\,.1$$

$$= 6.710 + 9.44 + .600 = 16.750$$

$$f''(2.5) = 2\,[5.9] + [15.00 - 2 \times 5.9]\,1 = 15.00,$$

$$f'''(2.5) = 6 \times 1 = 6.00.$$

Example 12: *Using divided difference, find the value of* $f(8)$, *given that* $f(6) = 1.556$, $f(7) = 1.690$, $f(9) = 1.908$, $f(12) = 2.158$ **[Rajasthan 2006, 2010]**

Solution: Divided difference formula is given by

$$f(x) = f(x_0) + (x - x_0)\,\Delta f(x_0) + (x - x_0)(x - x_1)\,\Delta^2 f(x_0) + (x - x_0)(x - x_1)(x - x_2)\,\Delta^3 f(x_0)$$
$$+ (x - x_0)(x - x_1)(x - x_2)(x - x_3)\,\Delta^4 f(x_0)$$
$$+ (x - x_0)(x - x_1)(x - x_2)(x - x_3)(x - x_4)\,\Delta^5 f(x_0) \ldots \qquad \ldots(1)$$

The divided difference table is given by:

x	$f(x)$	Δ	Δ^2	Δ^3
6	1.556			
		.134		
7	1.690		−.0083	
		.109		.00051
9	1.908		−.0052	
		.083		
12	2.158			

Differentiating (1) w.r.t. to x; we get

$$f'(x) = \Delta f(x_0) + [2x - x_0 - x_1]\,\Delta^2 f(x_0)$$
$$+ [3x^2 - 2x(x_0 + x_1 + x_2) + x_0x_1 + x_1x_2 + x_0x_2]\,\Delta^3 f(x_0)$$

Putting $x_0 = 6, x_1 = 7, x_2 = 9, x_3 = 12, x = 8$ and the values of the divided differences from the table, we get

$$f'(8) = .134 + [2 \times 8 - 6 - 7](-.0083)$$
$$+ [3 \times 64 - 2 \times 8(6 + 7 + 9) + 6 \times 7 + 7 \times 9 + 6 \times 9](.00051)$$
$$= .134 - .0249 + (192 - 352 + 159)(.00051)$$
$$= .134 - .0249 - .00051 = .134 - .0254 = .10859$$

Example 13: *Given the following pairs of values of x and* $y = f(x)$:

x	1	2	4	8	10
$y = f(x)$	0	1	5	21	27

Determine numerically the first derivative at $x = 4$.

[Meerut 2005; Allahabad 2008]

Solution: In this case the value of the argument are not equally spaced, so we shall use Newton's divided difference formula. The divided difference formula table is:

x	y	Δ	Δ^2	Δ^3	Δ^4
1	0				
		1			
2	1		$\frac{1}{3}$		
		2		0	
4	5		$\frac{1}{3}$		$-\frac{1}{144}$
		4		$-\frac{1}{16}$	
8	21		$-\frac{1}{6}$		
		3			
10	27				

Newton's divided difference formula is

$$f(x) = f(a) + (x-a)\,\Delta f(a) + (x-a)(x-b)\,\Delta^2 f(a) + (x-a)(x-b)(x-c)\,\Delta^3 f(a)$$

$$+ (x-a)(x-b)(x-c)(x-d)\,\Delta^4 f(a) + \ldots$$

Differentiating this *w.r.t.* x and putting $x = c$, we have

$$f'(c) = \Delta f(a) + (2c - a - b)\,\Delta^2 f(a) + (c-a)(c-b)\,\Delta^3 f(a) + (c-a)(c-b)(c-d)\,\Delta^4 f(a).$$

Putting $a = 1, b = 2, c = 4, d = 8, e = 10$ and the values of differences from the table, we get

$$f'(4) = 1 + 5 \times \frac{1}{2} + 3 \times 2 \times 0 + 3 \times 0 + 3 \times 2 \times (-4) \times \left(-\frac{1}{144}\right)$$

$$= 1 + 1.666 + .1666 = 2.833.$$

Example 14: *Find $f'(5)$ from the following table:*

x	0	2	3	4	7	9
$f(x)$	4	26	58	112	466	922

[I.F.S. 2009]

Solution: The value of the argument are not equally spaced, so we shall use Newton's divided difference formula. The divided difference table is given below:

x	$f(x)$	$\Delta f(x)$	$\Delta^2 f(x)$	$\Delta^3 f(x)$
0	4			
		11		
2	26		7	
		32		1
3	58		11	
		54		1
4	112		16	
		118		1
7	466		22	
		228		
9	922			

Newton's divided difference formula, if third differences are constant is given by

$$f(x) = f(x_0) + (x - x_0)\, f(x_0, x_1) + (x - x_0)(x - x_1)\, f(x_0, x_1, x_2)$$

$$+ (x - x_0)(x - x_1)(x - x_2)\, f(x_0, x_1, x_2, x_3).$$

Now differentiating this *w.r.t.* x, we get

$$f'(x) = f(x_0, x_1) + \{(x - x_1) + (x - x_0)\}\, f(x_0, x_1, x_2)$$

$$+ \{(x - x_1)(x - x_2) + (x - x_0)(x - x_2) + (x - x_0)(x - x_1)\}\, f(x_0, x_1, x_2, x_3).$$

Hence putting $x = 5, x_0 = 0, x_1 = 2, x_2 = 3, x_3 = 4$ and the values of various divided differences, we get

$$f'(5) = 11 + \{(5 - 2)(5 - 0)\} \times 7 + \{(5 - 2)(5 - 3) + (5 - 0)(5 - 3) + (5 - 0)(5 - 2)\} \times 1$$

$$= 11 + 56 + 31 = 98$$

Example 15: *Assuming Stirling's formula, obtain the following approximation*:

$$\frac{d}{dx} f(x) = \frac{2}{3}\,[f(x+1) - f(x-1)] - \frac{1}{12}\,[f(x+2) - f(x-2)] \text{ upto third differences.}$$

[Delhi (H) 2007]

Solution: The Stirling's formula is

$$f(x) = f(0) + x\,\frac{\Delta f(0) + \Delta f(-1)}{2} + \frac{x^2}{2\,!}\,\Delta^2 f(-1) + \frac{x\,(x^2-1)}{3\,!}\cdot\frac{\Delta^3 f(-1) + \Delta^3 f(-2)}{2} + \ldots$$

Differentiating *w.r.t.* x, we get

$$\frac{d}{dx} f(x) = \frac{\Delta f(0) + \Delta f(-1)}{2} + \frac{2x}{2\,!}\,\Delta^2 f(-1) + \frac{(3x^2-1)}{3\,!}\cdot\frac{\Delta^3 f(-1) + \Delta^3 f(-2)}{2}$$

(taking upto third differences only)

Putting $x = 0$, we get

$$\frac{d}{dx} f(0) = \frac{\Delta f(0) + \Delta f(-1)}{2} - \frac{1}{12}\,[\Delta^3 f(-1) + \Delta^3 f(-2)]$$

Now putting $\Delta f(0) = f(1) - f(0), \Delta f(-1) = f(0) - f(-1)$

$$\Delta^3 f(-1) = f(1) - 3f(1) + 3f(0) - f(-1),\ \Delta^3 f(-2) = f(1) - 3f(0) + 3f(-1) - f(-2)$$

and then simplifying, we get

$$\frac{d}{dx} f(0) = \frac{2}{3}\,[f(1) - f(-1)] - \frac{1}{12}\,[f(2) - f(-2)]$$

Shifting the origin to x, we have

$$\frac{d}{dx} f(x) = \frac{2}{3}\,[f(x+1) - f(x-1)] - \frac{1}{12}\,[f(x+2) - f(x-2)].$$

Example 16: *Assuming Bessel's Interpolation formula, prove that*

$$\frac{d}{dx}(y_x) = \Delta y_{x-1/2} - \frac{1}{24}\,\Delta^3 y_{x-3/2} + \ldots$$

[Avadh 2004]

Solution: The Bessel's formula is

$$y_x = \frac{y_0 + y_1}{2} + \left(x - \frac{1}{2}\right)\Delta y_0 + \frac{x\,(x-1)}{2\,!}\,\frac{\Delta^2 y_{-1} + \Delta^2 y_0}{2} + \frac{\left(x - \frac{1}{2}\right)x\,(x-1)}{3\,!}\,\Delta^3 y_{-1} + \ldots \quad \ldots(1)$$

Changing x to $x + \frac{1}{2}$, we get

$$y_{x+1/2} = \frac{y_0 + y_1}{2} + x\,\Delta y_0 + \frac{\left(x+\frac{1}{2}\right)\left(x-\frac{1}{2}\right)}{2\,!} \cdot \frac{\Delta^2 y_{-1} + \Delta^2 y_0}{2}$$

$$+ \frac{x\left(x+\frac{1}{2}\right)\left(x-\frac{1}{2}\right)}{3}\,\Delta^3 y_{-1} + \ldots \qquad \ldots(2)$$

Differentiating (2) *w.r.t.* x, we get

$$\frac{d}{dx}(y_{x+1/2}) = \Delta\,y_0 + \frac{2\,x}{2\,!}\,\frac{\Delta^2 y_{-1} + \Delta^2 y_0}{2} + \frac{\left(x^2 - \frac{1}{4}\right)}{3\,!}\,\Delta^3 y_{-1} + \ldots$$

Putting $x = 0$, we get

$$\frac{d}{dx}(y_{x+1/2}) = \Delta\,y_0 - \frac{1}{24}\,\Delta^3 y_{-1} + \ldots$$

Now shifting the origin from $x = 0$ to $x - \frac{1}{2}$, we get

$$\frac{d}{dx}(y_x) = \Delta\,y_{x-1/2} - \frac{1}{24}\,\Delta^3 y_{x-3/2} + \ldots$$

Example 17: *Prove that*

$$y' = \frac{1}{h}\left(\delta\,y - \frac{1}{24}\,\delta^3 y + \frac{3}{640}\,\delta^5 y + \ldots\right) \qquad \textbf{[Avadh 2004]}$$

and $$y'' = \frac{1}{h^2}\left(\delta^2 y - \frac{1}{12}\,\delta^4 y + \frac{1}{90}\,\delta^6 y - \ldots\right)$$

Solution: We know that

$$\delta = E^{1/2} - E^{-1/2} = e^{hD/2} - e^{-hD/2} \qquad (\because \quad E \equiv e^{hD})$$

$$= 2\sin h\,\frac{hD}{2}$$

or $$\frac{hD}{2} = \sin h^{-1}\,\frac{\delta}{2} \qquad \ldots(1)$$

by Taylor's expansion, we have from (1)

$$\sin h^{-1}\,x = x - \frac{x^3}{6} + \frac{3}{40}\,x^5 - \ldots$$

Therefore by this expression, we have

$$\frac{hD}{2} = \frac{\delta}{2} - \frac{\delta^3}{6 \times 8} + \frac{3}{40 \times 32}\,\delta^5 - \ldots$$

or $$D = \frac{1}{h}\left[\delta - \frac{1}{24}\,\delta^3 + \frac{3}{640}\,\delta^5 - \ldots\right] \qquad \ldots(2)$$

Again operating these operators on y, we get

$$D\,y = y' = \frac{1}{h}\left[\delta\,y - \frac{1}{24}\delta^3\,y + \frac{3}{640}\delta^5\,y - \ldots\right] \quad \ldots(3)$$

From (2), we have $D^2 = \dfrac{1}{h^2}\left[\delta^2 - \dfrac{1}{12}\delta^4 + \dfrac{1}{90}\delta^6 - \ldots\right]$

Operating these operators on y, we get

$$D^2\,y = y'' = \frac{1}{h^2}\left[\delta^2\,y - \frac{1}{12}\delta^4\,y + \frac{1}{90}\delta^6\,y - \ldots\right]$$

Example 18: *Show that* $y' = \dfrac{\mu}{h}\left(\delta y - \dfrac{1}{6}\delta^3\,y + \dfrac{1}{30}\delta^5\,y - \ldots\right)$ *and*

$$y_0' = \frac{1}{2\,h}\left[(y_1 - y_{-1}) - \frac{1}{6}(\delta^2\,y_1 - \delta^2\,y_{-1}) + \frac{1}{30}(\delta^4\,y_1 - \delta^4\,y_{-1})\ldots\right]$$

[B.H.U. 2006, 2009]

Solution: We know that $\mu^2 = 1 + \dfrac{\delta^2}{4}$.

$$\Rightarrow \qquad \mu^{-1} = \left(1 + \frac{\delta^2}{4}\right)^{-1/2} = 1 - \frac{\delta^2}{8} + \frac{3}{128}\delta^4 - \ldots$$

Also from equation (2) of Ex. 14, we have

$$\frac{hD}{\delta} = 1 - \frac{\delta^2}{24} + \frac{3}{640}\delta^4 - \ldots$$

Now $\quad \dfrac{hD}{\delta\mu} = \dfrac{hD}{\delta}\mu^{-1} = \left[1 - \dfrac{\delta^2}{24} + \dfrac{3}{640}\delta^4 - \ldots\right] \times \left[1 - \dfrac{\delta^2}{8} + \dfrac{3}{128}\delta^4 - \ldots\right]$

$$= 1 - \frac{\delta^2}{6} + \frac{1}{30}\delta^4 - \ldots$$

$$\Rightarrow \qquad D = \frac{\delta\mu}{h}\left[1 - \frac{\delta^2}{6} + \frac{1}{30}\delta^4 - \ldots\right] = \frac{\mu}{h}\left[\delta - \frac{\delta^3}{6} + \frac{\delta^5}{30} - \ldots\right]$$

Again, operating these operators on y, we obtain

$$Dy = \frac{\mu}{h}\left[\delta - \frac{\delta^3}{6} + \frac{\delta^5}{30} - \ldots\right]y \quad \text{or} \quad y' = \frac{\mu}{h}\left[\delta y - \frac{\delta^3\,y}{6} + \frac{\delta^5\,y}{30} - \ldots\right] \ldots(1)$$

But by definition, we have

$$\delta = E^{1/2} - E^{-1/2} \quad \text{and} \quad \mu = \frac{1}{2}(E^{1/2} + E^{-1/2}).$$

$$\Rightarrow \qquad \delta\,\mu = \frac{1}{2}(E - E^{-1}) = \mu\,\delta$$

$$\Rightarrow \qquad (\delta\,\mu)\;y_0 = \frac{1}{2}(E - E^{-1})\;y_0 = \frac{1}{2}(y_1 - y_{-1}) = \mu\,\delta\;y_0 \quad \ldots(2)$$

Hence from (1), we get

$$y'_0 = \frac{1}{h}\left[\mu\,\delta y_0 - \frac{\mu\,\delta^3}{6}\,y_0 + \mu\,\frac{\delta^5}{30}\,y_0 - \ldots\right]$$

$$= \frac{1}{2h}\left[(y_1 - y_{-1}) - \frac{1}{6}(\delta^2 y_1 - \delta^2 y_{-1}) + \frac{1}{30}(\delta^4 y_1 - \delta^4 y_{-1}) - \ldots\right]$$

Example 19: *Prove that* $y' = \frac{1}{h}\left(\Delta y - \frac{1}{2}\Delta^2 y + \frac{1}{3}\Delta^3 y - \frac{1}{4}\Delta^4 y + \ldots\right)$

and $$y'' = \frac{1}{h^2}\left(\nabla^2 y + \nabla^3 y + \frac{11}{12}\nabla^4 y + \ldots\right).$$

Solution: We have $E \equiv e^{hD}$.

$$\Rightarrow \qquad 1 + \Delta \equiv e^{hD}.$$

$$\Rightarrow \qquad hD \equiv \log(1 + \Delta)$$

$$\Rightarrow \qquad D \equiv \frac{1}{h}\log(1 + \Delta)$$

$$\Rightarrow \qquad Dy \equiv \frac{1}{h}\log(1 + \Delta)\;y$$

$$\equiv \frac{1}{h}\left\{\Delta - \frac{\Delta^2}{2} + \frac{\Delta^3}{3} - \frac{\Delta^3}{4} + \ldots\right\} y.$$

$$\Rightarrow \qquad y' \equiv \frac{1}{h}\left\{\Delta y - \frac{\Delta^2 y}{2} + \frac{\Delta^3 y}{3} - \frac{\Delta^4 y}{4} + \ldots\right\}$$

Again $\quad e^{-hD} \equiv 1 - \nabla. \qquad \Rightarrow \quad D \equiv -\frac{1}{h}\log(1 - \nabla).$

Now, $$y'' = D^2 y = \left\{-\frac{1}{h}\log(1 - \nabla)\right\}^2 y = \frac{1}{h^2}\{\log(1 - \nabla)\}^2 y$$

$$= \frac{1}{h^2}\left\{\nabla + \frac{1}{2}\nabla^2 + \frac{1}{3}\nabla^3 + \ldots\right\}^2 y = \frac{1}{h^2}\left\{\nabla^2 + \nabla^3 + \frac{11}{12}\nabla^4 + \ldots\right\} y$$

$$= \frac{1}{h^2}\left\{\nabla^2 y + \nabla^3 y + \frac{11}{12}\nabla^4 y + \ldots\right\}$$

Example 20: *Prove that*

$$\frac{d}{dx}(y_x) = \frac{1}{h}(y_{x+h} - y_{x-h}) - \frac{1}{2h}(y_{x+2h} - y_{x-2h}) + \frac{1}{3h}(y_{x+3h} - y_{x-3h})$$

[Lucknow 2006]

Solution: R.H.S. $= \frac{1}{h}\{y_{x+h} - \frac{1}{2} y_{x+2h} + \frac{1}{3} y_{x+3h} - \ldots\}$

$$- \frac{1}{h}\left\{y_{x-h} - \frac{1}{2} y_{x-2h} + \frac{1}{3} y_{x-3h} - \ldots\right\}$$

$$= \frac{1}{h}[\{Ey_x - \frac{1}{2} E^2 y_x + \frac{1}{3} E^3 y_x - \ldots\} - \{E^{-1} y_x - \frac{1}{2} E^{-2} y_x + \frac{1}{3} E^{-3} y_x - \ldots\}]$$

$$= \frac{1}{h}[\{\log(1+E)\} y_x - \{\log(1+E^{-1})\} y_x]..$$

$$= \frac{1}{h}\log\left(\frac{1+E}{1+E^{-1}}\right) y_x = \left\{\frac{1}{h}\log E\right\} y_x = \left(\frac{1}{h}\log e^{hD}\right) y_x \left(\because \quad E \equiv e^{hD}\right)$$

$$= Dy_x = \frac{d}{dx}(y_x) = \textbf{L.H.S.}$$

✦✦ Problem Set ✦✦

1. Find $\frac{dy}{dx}$ at $x = 1$ from the following table:

x	.7	.8	.9	1.0	1.1	1.2	1.3
y	0.644218	0.717356	0.783327	0.841471	0.891207	0.932039	0.963558

2. Find the first two derivatives of $f(x)$ at $x = 1$ from the following table:

x	−2	−1	0	1	2	3	4
$f(x)$	104	17	0	−1	8	69	272

3. Find $f'(6)$ from the following table:

x	0	1	3	4	5	7	9
$f(x)$	150	108	0	−54	−100	−144	−84

4. Show that the expressions given below are approximations to the third derivatives of y_x:

(i) $\Delta^3 y_0 + \left(x - \frac{3}{2}\right) \Delta^4 y_0$,

(ii) $\Delta^3 y_{-1} + \left(x - \frac{1}{2}\right) \cdot \frac{1}{2} (\Delta^4 y_{-2} + \Delta^4 y_{-1})$.

5. Using divided differences, find the value of $f'(8)$, given that $f(6) = 1.556$, $f(7) = 1.690$, $f(9) = 1.908$, $f(12) = 2.158$.

6. Use the following data to find $f(1)$

x	3	5	11	27	34
$f(x)$	−13	23	899	17315	35606

7. Find $\frac{dy}{dx}$ and $\frac{d^2y}{dx^2}$ of $y = x^{1/3}$ at $x = 50$, from the following table:

x	$y = x^{1/3}$
50	3.6840
51	3.7084
52	3.7325
53	3.7563
54	3.7798
55	3.8030
56	3.8259

8. For what value of x is the following tabulated function minimum:

x	0.2	0.3	0.4	0.5	0.6	0.7
y	.9182	.8975	.8873	.8862	.8935	.9086

9. Assuming Bessel's interpolation formula, deduce the following approximations:

$$\frac{d}{dx} y_x = \Delta\, y_{x-1/2} - \frac{1}{24}\Delta^3 y_{x-3/2}$$

$$\frac{d^2}{dx^2}(y_x) = \frac{1}{2}[\Delta^2 y_{x-3/2} + \Delta^2 y_{x-1/3}] + \ldots$$

$$\frac{d^3}{dx^3}(y_x) = \Delta^2 y_{x-3/2} + \ldots$$

$$\frac{d^4}{dx^4}(y_x) = \Delta^3 y_{-1} + \left(x - \frac{1}{2}\right) \cdot \frac{1}{2}(\Delta^4 y_{-2} + \Delta^4 y_{-1}) + \ldots$$

10. By using Stirling formula of degree six, shown that

(i) $y'(x_0) = \frac{1}{h}\left(\delta\mu\, y_0 - \frac{1}{6}\delta^3\mu\, y_0 + \frac{1}{30}\delta^5\mu\, y_0 + \ldots\right)$

(ii) $y''(x_0) = \frac{1}{h}\left[\delta^2 f_0 - \frac{1}{12}\delta^4 f_0 + \ldots\right]$

11. Prove the following formula

$$y' = \frac{1}{h}\left(\Delta y - \frac{1}{2}\Delta^2 y + \frac{1}{3}\Delta^3 y - \frac{1}{4}\Delta^4 y + \ldots\right)$$

and
$$y'' = \frac{1}{h}\left(\nabla^2 y + \nabla^3 y + \frac{11}{12}\nabla^4 y + \ldots\right)$$

12. Use Stirling formula to find the first derivative of the function $y = 2e^x - x - 1$ tabulated below at the point $x = 0.6$

x	y
0.4	1.5836494
0.5	1.7974426
0.6	2.0442376
0.7	2.3275054
0.8	2.6510818

Compare with the true value which is 2.044238. **[Rajasthan 2004, 2006]**

13. Find $f'(1)$ for $f(x) = \frac{1}{(1+x^2)}$ using the following data:

x	1.0	1.1	1.2	1.3	1.4
$f(x)$	.2500	.2268	.2066	.1890	.1736

[Meerut 2002, 2004]

14. The function $y = \sin x$ is tabulated in the scheme below. Find the derivative at the point $x = 1$.

x	0.7	0.8	0.9	1.0	1.1	1.2	1.3
y	.644218	.717356	.783327	.841471	.891207	.932039	.963558

15. A slider in a machine moves along a fixed straight rod. Its distance x cm. along the rod is given below for various values for the time t seconds. Find the velocity and acceleration of the slider, when $t = 0.3$ second

t	0	0.1	0.2	0.3	0.4	0.5	0.6
x	30.13	31.62	32.87	33.64	33.95	33.81	33.24

[Agra 2003]

✦✦ Answers ✦✦

❖ Problem Set

1.	0.54030	2.	1, 6
3.	−23	5.	0.109
6.	233	7.	.02455, −.0003
8.	0.4623	12.	2.644225
13.	−0.5031	14.	0.54030
15.	Velocity = 5.34 cm/sec. Acceleration = −45.6 cm/sec^2.		

◆◆◆

Theory | Solved Examples | Problem Set

Chapter 6

Numerical Integration

Introduction, General quadrature formula for equidistant ordinates, Trapezoidal rule, Simpson's 1/3 rule, Simpson's 3/8 rule, Weddle's rule, Boole's rule, Errors in quadrature formulae, Cote's method and numbers, Euler Maclaurin's summation formula, Stirling formula for approximations to factorials, Method of undetermined coefficients, Differentiation and integration formulae, Quadrature formulae having central differences, Lozenge diagrams, Romberg integration, Hardy's formula, Gaussian integration.

6.1 Introduction

It is the process of finding or evaluating a definite integral $I = \int_a^b f(x)\,dx$ from a set of numerical values of the integrand $f(x)$. If it is applied to the integration of function of a single variable the process is known as ***quadrature***. The problem of numerical integration is solved by first approximating the integrand by a polynomial with the help of an interpolation formula and then integrating this expression between the desired limits. Thus to evaluate the definite integral $\int_a^b f(x)\,dx$, first express the function $f(x)$ by an interpolation formula say $p(x)$ and then integrate $f(x)$ between the limits a and b

i.e. $$\int_a^b f(x)\,dx \sim \int_a^b p(x)\,dx$$

The error in E in such type of approximation is given by

$$\int_a^b f(x)\,dx - \int_a^b p(x)\,dx = \int_a^b [f(x) - p(x)]\,dx.$$

6.2 A General Quadrature Formula for Equidistant Ordinates

[Meerut 2000, 2002, 2003, 2005; Avadh 2003, 2004, 2005; Bhopal 2002; Agra 2003; Pune 2008]

Let $I = \int_a^b y\,dx$ where $y = f(x)$. Let $f(x)$ be given for certain equally distant values of arguments, say $x_0, x_0 + h, x_0 + 2h, \ldots\ldots$ Let the range $(b - a)$ be divided into n equal parts, each of which is of width h, *i.e.* $b - a = nh$.

Let $x_0 = a, x_1 = x_0 + h = a + h, x_2 = a + 2h, \ldots, x_n = a + nh = b,$

we have assumed that the $(n+1)$ ordinates $y_0, y_1, \ldots, y_n$ are at equal intervals.

$$\therefore \quad I = \int_a^b y\,dx = \int_{x_0}^{x_0+nh} y_x\,dx = \int_0^n y_{x_0+uh}\,h\,du.$$

where new variate $u = \dfrac{x - x_0}{h}$; $dx = h\,du$

or
$$I = h\int_0^n \left[y_0 + u\Delta y_0 + \frac{u(u-1)}{2!}\Delta^2 y_0 + \frac{u(u-1)(u-2)}{3!}\Delta^3 y_0 + \ldots + \frac{u(u-1)\ldots(u-n+1)}{n!}\Delta^n y_0 \right] du$$

$$= h\left[ny_0 + \frac{n^2}{2}\Delta y_0 + \left(\frac{n^3}{3} - \frac{n^2}{2}\right)\frac{\Delta^2 y_0}{2!} + \left(\frac{n^4}{4} - n^3 + n^2\right)\frac{\Delta^3 y_0}{3!} + \ldots \text{ up to } (n+1) \text{ terms}\right]. \quad \ldots(1)$$

$$= nh\left[y_0 + \frac{n}{2}\Delta y_0 + \frac{n(2n-3)}{12}\Delta^2 y_0 + \frac{n(n-2)^2}{24}\Delta^3 y_0 + \left(\frac{n^4}{5} - \frac{3n^3}{2} + \frac{11n^2}{3} - 3n\right)\frac{\Delta^4 y_0}{4!} \right.$$
$$+ \left(\frac{n^5}{6} - 2n^4 + \frac{35n^3}{4} - \frac{50n^2}{3} + 12n\right)\frac{\Delta^5 y_0}{5!}$$
$$\left. + \left(\frac{n^6}{7} - \frac{15n^5}{6} + 17n^4 - \frac{225n^3}{4} + \frac{274n^2}{3} - 60n\right)\frac{\Delta^6 y_0}{6!} + \ldots \right] \quad \ldots(1')$$

This is known as ***Newton-Cote's quadrature*** formula and is a general formula. We deduce the following important quadrature rules by taking $n = 1, 2, 3, \ldots$

6.3 The Trapezoidal Rule

Put $n = 1$ in (1) and neglect second and higher differences when $n = 1$, the interval of integration will be from x_0 to $x_0 + h$, and there are only two functional values y_0 and y_1 in this interval, with only two values, there can be no differences higher than the first. Thus we have

$$\int_{x_0}^{x_0+h} y\,dx = h\,[y_0 + \frac{1}{2}\Delta y_0] = h\left[y_0 + \frac{y_1 - y_0}{2}\right] = h\left[\frac{y_0 + y_1}{2}\right]$$

Similarly $\displaystyle\int_{x_0+h}^{x_0+2h} y\,dx = h\left(\frac{y_1 + y_2}{2}\right)$

... ...

$$\int_{x_0+(n-1)h}^{x_0+nh} y\,dx = h\left(\frac{y_{n-1} + y_n}{2}\right)$$

Adding these n integrals, we get

$$\int_{x_0}^{x_0+nh} y\,dx = h.[\frac{1}{2}(y_0 + y_n) + (y_1 + y_2 + \dots + y_{n-1})]$$

= distance between two consecutive ordinates

× [mean on the first and the last ordinates + sum of all the intermediate ordinates]

This rule is called the ***Trapezoidal Rule.*** ...(2)

Note: Here we have taken y, a polynomial of the first degree in x or a straight line.

6.4 Simpson's One-Third Rule

[Bhopal 2002; Avadh 2005]

Put $n = 2$ in (1) of **6.2** and neglect third and higher differences. [In this case interval of integration will be from x_0 to $x_0 + 2h$ and there will be only three functional values y_0, y_1 and y_2: this with these values, there will be no differences higher than the second].

$$\therefore \qquad \int_{x_0}^{x_0+nh} y\,dx = h\left[2y_0 + 2(y_1 - y_0) + \frac{\left(\frac{8}{3}-2\right)}{2}(y_2 - 2y_1 + y_0)\right]$$

$$= \frac{h}{3}(y_0 + 4y_1 + y_2)$$

Similarly,
$$\int_{x_0+2h}^{x_0+4h} y\,dx = \frac{h}{3}(y_2 + 4y_3 + y_4)$$

... ...

$$\int_{x_0+(n-2)h}^{x_0+nh} y\,dx = \frac{h}{3}(y_{n-2} + 4y_{n-1} + y_n) \qquad (n \text{ is even});$$

on adding all these integrals, we get

$$\int_{x_0}^{x_0+nh} y\,dx = \frac{h}{3}[(y_0 + y_n) + 4(y_1 + y_3 + \dots + y_{n-1}) + 2(y_2 + y_4 + \dots + y_{n-2})]$$

= (One third of the distance between two consecutive ordinates) × [(Sum of the extreme ordinates) + 4 (Sum of the odd ordinates) + 2 (Sum of even ordinates)] ...(3)

This formula is known as ***Simpson's one-third rule.*** It is also called as ***parabolic formula.***

Note: In this case, we have neglected all differences above the second; so y will be polynomial of second degree only

i.e. $y = ax^2 + bx + c$

6.5 Simpson's Three-Eighth's Rule

[Meerut 2007; U.P.P.C.S. 2005, 2008; Bhopal 2002; Avadh 2005]

Put $n = 3$ in (1) of **6.2** and neglect all differences above the third. In this case only four functional values will exist and consequently there will be no differences higher than the third. Thus we get

$$\int_{x_0}^{x_0+3h} y\,dx = h\left[3y_0 + \frac{9}{2}(y_1 - y_0) + \frac{9}{4}(y_2 - 2y_1 + y_0)\right.$$

$$\left. + \frac{3}{8}(y_3 - 3y_2 + 3y_1 - y_0)\right]$$

$$= \frac{3h}{8}[y_0 + 3y_1 + 3y_2 + y_3].$$

Similarly, $$\int_{x_0+3h}^{x_0+6h} y\,dx = \frac{3h}{8}[(y_3 + 3y_4 + 3y_5 + y_6)]$$

... ...

$$\int_{x_0+(n-3)h}^{x_0+nh} y\,dx = \frac{3h}{8}[y_{n-3} + 3y_{n-2} + 3y_{n-1} + y_n],$$

Where n is multiple of 3.

Adding all these integrals, we have, when n is a multiple of 3,

$$\int_{x_0}^{x_0+nh} y\,dx = \frac{3h}{8}[(y_0 + y_n) + 3(y_1 + y_2 + y_4 + y_5 + \ldots + y_{n-1})$$

$$+ 2(y_3 + y_6 + \ldots + y_{n-3})]. \qquad \ldots(4)$$

This formula is known as ***Simpson's three-eighth's rule.*** *Applying this rule, the number of sub-intervals should be taken as multiple of three.*

> **Note:** Since we have neglected all differences above the third so y will be polynomial of the third degree.
>
> i.e. $$y = ax^3 + bx^2 + cx + d$$

6.6 Boole's Rule

Putting $n = 4$ in (l) of **6.2** and neglecting all differences above the fourth, we get

$$\int_{x_0}^{x_0+4h} f(x)\,dx = 4h\left(y_0 + 2\Delta y_0 + \frac{5}{3}\Delta^2 y_0 + \frac{2}{3}\Delta^3 y_0 + \frac{7}{90}\Delta^4 y_0\right)$$

$$= \frac{2h}{45}(7y_0 + 32y_1 + 12y_2 + 32y_3 + 7y_4)$$

and $$\int_{x_0+4h}^{x_0+8h} f(x)\,dx = \frac{2h}{45}(7y_4 + 32y_5 + 12y_6 + 32y_7 + 7y_8) \text{ etc.}$$

Adding such integrals from x_0 to $x_0 + nh$, where n is a multiple of 4, we readily obtain

$$\int_{x_0}^{x_0+nh} f(x)\,dx = \frac{2h}{45}(7y_0 + 32y_1 + 12y_2 + 32y_3 + 14y_4$$

$$+ 32y_5 + 12y_6 + 32y_7 + 14y_8 + \ldots) \qquad \ldots(5)$$

This rule is known as ***Boole's rule.***

6.7 Weddle's Rule

Put $n=6$ in (1) of **6.2** and neglect the seventh and higher differences. [In this case interval of integration will be from x_0 to $x_0 + 6h$, and there will be only seven functional values; so there can be no differences higher than the sixth]. Thus we get

$$\int_{x_0}^{x_0+6h} y\,dx = h\left[6y_0 + 18\Delta y_0 + 27\Delta^2 y_0 + 24\Delta^3 y_0 + \frac{123}{10}\Delta^4 y_0 + \frac{33}{10}\Delta^5 y_0 + \frac{41}{140}\Delta^6 y_0\right].$$

Now replace $\frac{41}{140}\Delta^6 y_0$ by $\frac{3}{10}\Delta^6 y_0$ since the error involved is negligible *. Thus the above result can be put as

$$\int_{x_0}^{x_0+6h} y\,dx = h\left[6y_0 + 18\Delta y_0 + 27\Delta^2 y_0 + 24\Delta^3 y_0 + \frac{123}{10}\Delta^4 y_0 + \frac{33}{10}\Delta^5 y_0 + \frac{41}{140}\Delta^6 y_0\right]$$

$$= \frac{3h}{10}[6y_0 + 5y_1 + y_2 + 6y_3 + y_4 + 5y_5 + y_6]$$

Similarly, $$\int_{x_0}^{x_0+12h} y\,dx = \frac{3h}{10}[y_6 + 5y_7 + y_8 + 6y_9 + y_{10} + 5y_{11} + y_{12}]$$

$$\int_{x_0+(n-6)h}^{x_0+nh} y\,dx = \frac{3h}{10}[y_{n-6} + 5y_{n-5} + y_{n-4} + 6y_{n-3} + y_{n-2} + 5y_{n-1} + y_n]$$

If n is multiple of 6, adding all these integrals, we have

$$\int_{x_0}^{x_0+nh} y\,dx = \frac{3h}{10}[y_0 + 5y_1 + y_2 + 6y_3 + y_4 + 5y_5 + 2y_6 + 5y_7 + y_8 + \ldots]. \qquad \ldots(6)$$

This formula is known as ***Weddle's Rule*** and is more accurate than the Simpson's Rule, but it requires at least seven consecutive values of the function. Also the method is applicable, when n is a multiple of six.

Note: In this case we have assumed that y is of the form

$$y = ax^6 + bx^5 + cx^4 + dx^3 + ex^2 + fx + g.$$

6.8 Error in Quadrature Formulae

The error in the quadrature formulae is given by $E = \int_a^b y\,dx - \int_a^b P(x)\,dx$

where $P(x)$ is the polynomial representing the function $y = f(x)$, in the interval $[a, b]$.

[A] Error in Trapezoidal Rule: Expanding $y = f(x)$, about $x = x_0$ by Taylor's series, we obtain

$$y = y_0 + (x - x_0)\,y_0' + \frac{(x - x_0)^2}{2!}\,y_0'' + \ldots \qquad \ldots(1)$$

$$\Rightarrow \quad \int_{x_0}^{x_0+h} y\,dx = \int_{x_0}^{x_0+h} \left[y_0 + (x - x_0)\,y_0' + \frac{(x - x_0)^2}{2!}\,y_0'' + \ldots\right] dx$$

$$= y_0 h + \frac{h^2}{2!}\,y_0' + \frac{h^3}{3!}\,y_0'' + \ldots \qquad \ldots(2)$$

But area of the first trapezium in the interval $[x_0, x_1]$

$$= \frac{1}{2}\,h\,(y_0 + y_1) = A_1 \text{ say} \qquad \ldots(3)$$

Then putting $x = x_0 + h$ and $y = y_1$ in (1), we obtain

$$y_1 = y_0 + h y_0' + \frac{h^2}{2!}\,y_0'' + \ldots$$

Putting this value of y_1 in (3), we have

$$A_1 = \frac{1}{2}\,h\left[y_0 + y_0 + h y_0' + \frac{h^2}{2!}\,y_0'' + \ldots\right]$$

$$= h y_0 + \frac{h^2}{2}\,y_0' + \frac{h^3}{2.2!}\,y_0'' + \ldots \qquad \ldots(4)$$

Whence the error in the interval $[x_0, x_1]$

$$= \int_{x_0}^{x_1} y\,dx - A_1 = \left(\frac{1}{3!} - \frac{1}{2.2!}\right) h^3\,y_0'' + \ldots = -\frac{h^3}{12}\,y_0'' + \ldots$$

$\Rightarrow$ Principal part of the error in $[x_0, x_1] = -\dfrac{h^3}{12}\,y_0''$

And similarly principal part of the error in $[x_1, x_2] = -\dfrac{h^3}{12}\,y_1''$ etc.

Thus the total error $= -\dfrac{h^3}{12}\,[y_0'' + y_1'' + \ldots + y_{n-1}''] = E$, say.

Then assuming that $y''(X)$ is the largest of the n quantities $y_0'', y_1'', \ldots, y_{n-1}''$, we can say that

$$E < -\frac{nh^3}{12} y''(X) = -\frac{(b-a)\,h^2}{12} y''(X) \quad \text{as } b - a = nh \qquad \ldots(5)$$

Thus the error in the trapezoidal rule is of the order h^2

[B] Error in Simpson's $\frac{1}{3}$ Rule: Expanding $y = f(x)$ about $x = x_0$ by Taylor's series, we have $y = y_0 + (x - x_0)\, y_0' + \frac{(x - x_0)^2}{2\,!} y_0'' + \ldots$ ...(1)

$$\Rightarrow \quad \int_{x_0}^{x_2} y\,dx = \int_{x_0}^{x_0+2h} \left[y_0 + (x - x_0)\, y_0' + \frac{(x - x_0)^2}{2\,!} y_0'' + \ldots \right] dx$$

$$= 2hy_0 + \frac{4h^2}{2\,!} y_0' + \frac{8h^3}{3\,!} y_0'' + \frac{16h^4}{4\,!} y_0''' + \frac{32h^5}{5\,!} y_0^{iv} + \ldots \qquad \ldots(2)$$

and area over the first double strip by Simpson's 1/3 rule

$$= \frac{1}{3} h\,(y_0 + 4\,y_1 + y_2) = A_1 \text{ say} \qquad \ldots(3)$$

Then putting $x = x_0 + h$ and $y = y_1$ in (1), we have

$$y_1 = y_0 + hy_0' + \frac{h^2}{2\,!} y_0'' + \frac{h^3}{3\,!} y_0''' + \ldots$$

Further putting $x = x_0 + 2h$ and $y = y_2$ in (1), we get

$$y_2 = y_0 + 2hy_0' + \frac{4h^2}{2\,!} y_0'' + \frac{8h^3}{3\,!} y_0''' + \ldots$$

$$\therefore \quad (3) \Rightarrow A_1 = \frac{h}{3} \left[y_0 + 4\left(y_0 + hy_0' + \frac{h^2}{2\,!} y_0'' + \ldots \right) + \left(y_0 + 2hy_0' + \frac{4h^2}{2\,!} y_0'' + \frac{8h^3}{3\,!} y_0''' + \ldots \right) \right]$$

$$= 2hy_0 + 2h^2 y_0' + \frac{4h^3}{3} y_0'' + \frac{2h^2}{8} y_0''' + \frac{5h^5}{18} y_0^{iv} + \ldots \qquad \ldots(4)$$

Whence the error in the interval $[x_0, x_2] = \int_{x_0}^{x_2} y\,dx - A_1$

$$= \left(\frac{4}{15} - \frac{5}{18} \right) h^5\, y_0^{iv} + \ldots \qquad \ldots(5)$$

and the **Principal** part of the error in $[x_0, x_2]$

$$= \left(\frac{4}{15} - \frac{5}{18} \right) h^5\, y_0^{iv} = -\frac{h^5}{90} y_0^{iv}$$

On the same lines principal part of the error in $[x_2, x_4] = -\dfrac{h^5}{90} y_2^{iv}$, etc.

$$\Rightarrow \quad \text{total error} = -\frac{h^5}{90}[y_0^{iv} + y_2^{iv} + \ldots + y_{2(n-1)}^{iv}] = E, \text{say} \quad \ldots(6)$$

Then assuming $y_{iv}(X)$ as the largest of $y_0^{iv}, y_2^{iv}, \ldots, y_{2n-2}^{iv}$, we readily obtain

$$E < -\frac{nh^5}{90} y_0^{iv}(X) = -\frac{(b-a)\,h^4}{180} y^{iv}(X) \quad \ldots(7)$$

$[\because\ 2nh = b - a]$

[C] Error in Simpson's 3/8 -rule: Proceeding as above, we have the principal part of the error in the interval $[x_0, x_3]$ as

$$= -\frac{3h^5}{80} y^{iv} \quad \ldots(1)$$

[D] Error in Boole's Rule: The principal part of the error in the interval $[x_0, x_4]$ in this case is $= -\dfrac{8h^7}{945} y^{vi}$ ...(1)

[E] Error in Weddle's Rule: Principal part of the error into the interval $[x_0, x_6] = -(h^7/140)\, y_0^{vi}$ ...(1)

6.9 Cote's Method

[Delhi (H) 2006, 2010; Meerut 2000, 2001, 2003; Agra 2003, 2004]

As the Lagrange's formula is based on the same assumption as an approximate integration formula, viz., $f(x)$ is a polynomial, it can be used in finding an approximate formula.

Let $y_0, \ldots, y_n$ can be values of the function $y = f(x)$ corresponding to the argument $x_0, x_1, \ldots, x_n$. Let the values of the arguments be at equal intervals say h, *i.e.* $x_i = x_0 + ih$

$$x_1 = x_0 + h, x_2 = x_0 + 2h, \ldots, \quad i.e.\ x_n = x_0 + nh.$$

Now by Lagrange's formula

$$f(x) \approx p(x) = \sum_{k=1}^{n} L_k(x)\, y_k$$

where $$L_k(x) = \frac{(x - x_0)(x - x_1)\ldots(x - x_{k-1})(x - x_{k+1})(x - x_n)}{(x_k - x_0)(x_k - x_1)\ldots(x_k - x_{k-1})(x_k - x_{k+1})(x_k - x_n)}$$

Thus $$I = \int_{x_0}^{x_0+nh} f(x)\,dx = \int_{x_0}^{x_0+nh} P(x)\,dx$$

$$= \int_{x_0}^{x_0+nh} \sum_{k=0}^{n} L_k(x)\, y_k\, dx$$

$$= \int_{x_0}^{x_0+nh} \{L_0(x)\, y_0 + \ldots + L_n(x)\, y_n\, dx\}$$

$$= y_0 \int_{x_0}^{x_0+nh} L_0(x)\,dx + \ldots + y_n \int_{x_0}^{x_0+nh} L_n(x)\,dx$$

$$= \sum_{k=0}^{n} y_k \int_{x_0}^{x_0+nh} L_k(x)\,dx.$$

Substituting $x = x_0 + uh \Rightarrow dx = h\,du$, we get

$$I = h \sum_{k=0}^{n} y_k \int_0^n L_k\,du = nh \sum_{k=0}^{n} y_k \frac{1}{n}\int_0^n L_k\,du \qquad \ldots(1)$$

Where $L_k = L_k(x_0 + uh)$

$$= \frac{(x_0 + hu - x_0)\ldots\{x_0 + hu - x_0 - (k-1)h\}\{x_0 + hu - x_0 - (k+1)h\}\ldots\{x_0 + hu - x_0 - nh\}}{(x_0 + kh - x_0)\ldots\{x_0 + kh - x_0 - (k-1)h\}\{x_0 + kh - x_0 - (k+1)h\}\ldots\{x_0 + kh - x_0 - nh\}}$$

$$= \frac{u(u-1)\ldots(u-k+1)(u-k-1)\ldots(u-n)}{k(k-1)\ldots(+1)(-1)\ldots(k-n)} \qquad \ldots(2)$$

Now putting $\frac{1}{n}\int_0^n L_k\,du = C_k^n$, We get

$$I = nh \sum_{k=0}^{n} y_k C_k^n \qquad \ldots(3)$$

is the required formula, it is known as ***Cote's Formula.***

The numbers C_k^n $(0) \le k \le n$ are called ***Cote's Numbers.*** We can evaluate I from (3) in case we know the values of Cote's numbers.

Properties of Cote's Numbers.

(i) $C_k^n = C_{n-k}^n$; **[Meerut 2001, 2003, 2005; Agra 2002]**

(ii) $\sum_{k=0}^{n} C_k^n = 1$ **[Meerut 2002, 2004; Agra 2002; Avadh 2003]**

Proof: We have shown that

$$C_k^n = \frac{1}{n}\int_0^n L_k\,du = \frac{1}{n}\int_0^n \frac{u(u-1)\ldots\{u-(k-1)\}\{u-(k+1)\}\ldots(u-n)}{k(k-1)\ldots(+1).(-1)(k-n)}\,du$$

$$= \frac{1}{n}\int_0^n \frac{u(u-1)\ldots\{u-(k-1)\}\{u-(k+1)\}\ldots(u-n)}{k!.(-1)^{n-k}(n-k)!}\,du \qquad \ldots(4)$$

Again,

$$C_{n-k}^n = \frac{1}{n}\int_0^n \frac{u(u-1)\ldots\{u-(n-k-1)\}\{u-(n-k+1)\} - (u-n)}{(n-k)!\,k!\,(-1)^k}\,du$$

Putting $u-n=-t$ or $u=n-t, du=-dt$, we get

$$C_k^n=\frac{1}{n}\int_0^n \frac{(n-t)(n-t-1)\dots(-t+k-1)(-t+k-1).(-t)}{k!(n-k)!(-1)^k}(-dt)$$

$$=\frac{1}{n}\int_0^n \frac{(-1)^n t(t-1)\dots(t-k+1).(t-k-1)\dots(t-n)}{k!(n-k)!(-1)^k}dt$$

$$=\frac{1}{n}\int_0^n \frac{(-1)^{n-k} t(t-1)\dots\{t-(k-1)\}\{t-(k+1)\}\dots(t-n)}{k!(n-k)!}dt$$

$$=\frac{1}{n}\int_0^n \frac{t(t-1)\dots\{t-(k-1)\}\{t-(k+1)\}\dots(t-n)}{k!(n-k)!(-1)^{n-k}}dt=C_{n-k}^n.$$

{multiplying Nr. and Dr. by $(-1)^{n-k}$}

$\left\{\because \int_a^b f(x)\,dx=\int_a^b f(t)\,dt, \text{ by the properties of definite integrals}\right\}$

Some Deduction From Cote's Formula **[Meerut 2006]**

On putting $n=1$ in (3), we get

$$I=\int_{x_0}^{x_1} f(x)\,dx=1.h\sum_{k=0}^{n} C_k^1 y_k=h[C_0^1 y_0+C_1^1 y_1]$$

Again by $C_k^n=\frac{1}{n}\int_0^n L_k\,du$, we have

$$C_0^1=\frac{1}{1}\int_0^1 L_0\,du=\int_0^1\frac{(u-1)}{(0-1)}du$$

$$=(-)\int_0^1(u-1)\,du=(-1)\left(\frac{u^2}{2}-u\right)_0^1=\frac{1}{2}$$

and $C_1^1=\frac{1}{1}\int_0^1 L_1\,du=\int_0^1\frac{(u-0)}{(1-0)}du=\int_0^1 u\,du=\frac{1}{2}.$

Thus $I=\frac{h}{2}(y_0+y_1)$. This is the Trapezoidal rule.

Again putting $n=2$ in (3), we get

$$I=\int_{x_0}^{x_0+nh} f(x)\,dx=2h\sum_{k=0}^{2} C_k^2\,y_k$$

$$=2h(y_0C_0^2+y_1\,C_1^2+y_2\,C_2^2).$$

Now, $C_0^2=\frac{1}{2}\int_0^2 L_0du=\frac{1}{2}\int_0^2\frac{(u-1)(u-2)}{(0-1)(0-2)}du=\frac{1}{6}$

$$C_1^2=\frac{1}{2}\int_0^2 L_1du=\frac{1}{2}\int_0^2\frac{u(u-2)}{(1-0)(1-2)}du=\frac{2}{3}$$

and $C_2^2 = \frac{1}{6}$ by using $(C^n{}_k = C^n{}_{n-k})$.

Hence $I = 2h(\frac{1}{6}y_0 + \frac{2}{3}y_1 + \frac{1}{6}y_2) = \frac{h}{3}(y_0 + 4y_1 + y_2)$.

This is the Simpson's '$\frac{1}{3}$' Rule. **[Agra 2002; Puruanchal 2008]**

Similarly putting $n = 3$ in (3), we can find the Simpson's '$\frac{3}{8}$', rule.

Below we give the ***Cote's Numbers*** for some values on n.

	C_0^n	C_1^n	C_2^n	C_3^n	C_4^n	C_5^n	C_6^n
$n=1$	1/2	1/2					
$n=2$	1/6	4/6	1/6				
$n=3$	1/8	3/8	3/8	1/8			
$n=4$	7/90	32/90	12/90	32/90	7/90		
$n=5$	19/288	75/288	50/288	50/288	75/288	19/288	
$n=6$	41/840	216/840	27/840	272/840	27/840	216/840	41/840

6.10 The Euler-Maclaurin's Summation Formula

The formula is derived by the method stated below:

If $\Delta F(x) = f(x)$ then we have an operator Δ^{-1} known as inverse operator, which is defined by $F(x) = \Delta^{-1} f(x)$

Again, we have $\Delta F(x) = f(x_0)$

$$\Rightarrow \quad F(x_1) - F(x_0) = f(x_0)$$

$$F(x_2) - F(x_1) = f(x_1),$$

$$\cdots \quad \cdots \quad \cdots \quad \cdots$$

$$F(x_n) - F(x_{n-1}) = f(x_{n-1})$$

Now adding all these equations, we get

$$F(x_n) - F(x_0) = \sum_{i=0}^{n-1} f(x_i) \qquad ...(1)$$

where $x_0, \ldots, x_n$ are the $(n+1)$ equidistant values of x with width h.

Also, we have shown above that

$$F(x) = \Delta^{-1} f(x) = (E-1)^{-1} f(x)$$

$$= (e^{hD} - 1)^{-1} f(x) \qquad [\because E \equiv e^{hD}]$$

$$= \left\{\left(1 + hD + \frac{h^2D^2}{2!} + \frac{h^3D^3}{3!} + \dots\right) - 1\right\}^{-1} f(x)$$

$$= \left(hD + \frac{h^2D^2}{2!} + \frac{h^3D^3}{3!} + \dots\right)^{-1} f(x)$$

$$= (hD)^{-1} \left\{1 + \left(\frac{hD}{2!} + \frac{h^2D^2}{3!} + \dots\right)\right\}^{-1} f(x)$$

$$= \frac{1}{h} . D^{-1} \left\{1 - \left(\frac{hD}{2!} + \frac{h^2D^2}{3!} + \dots\right) + \frac{(-1)(-2)}{2!}\left(\frac{hD}{2!} + \frac{h^2D^2}{3!} + \dots\right)^2 \dots\right\} f(x)$$

$$= \frac{1}{h} . D^{-1} \left(1 - \frac{hD}{2!} + \frac{h^2D^2}{12} - \frac{h^4D^4}{720} + \dots\right) f(x)$$

$$= \frac{1}{h} \int f(x)\, dx - \frac{1}{2} f(x) + \frac{h}{12} f'(x) - \frac{h^3}{720} f'''(x) \qquad \dots(2)$$

[D^{-1} is integral operator]

Between limits $x = x_0$ and $x = x_n$, from (2), we have

$$F(x_n) - F(x_0) = \frac{1}{h} \int_{x_0}^{x_n} f(x)\, ax - \frac{1}{2} [f(x_n) - f(x_0)].$$

$$+ \frac{h}{12} [f'(x_n) - f'(x_0)] - \frac{h^3}{720} [f'''(x_n) - f'''(x_0)] + \qquad \dots(3)$$

Now from (1) and (3), we have

$$\sum_{i=0}^{n-1} f(x_i) = \frac{1}{h} \int_{x_0}^{x_n} f(x)\, dx - \frac{1}{2} [f(x_n) - f(x_0)]$$

$$+ \frac{h}{12} [f'(x_n) - f'(x_0)] - \frac{h^3}{720} [f'''(x_n) - f'''(x_0)] + \dots$$

$$\Rightarrow \quad \frac{1}{h} \int_{x_0}^{x_n} f(x)\, dx = \sum_{i=0}^{n-1} f(x_i) + \frac{1}{2} [f(x_n) - f(x_0)] - \frac{h}{12} [f'(x_n) - f'(x_0)]$$

$$+ \frac{h^3}{720} [f'''(x_n) - f'''(x_0)] - \dots$$

But $\sum_{i=0}^{n-1} f(x_i) = \sum_{i=0}^{n} f(x_i) - f(x_n)$ and $x_n = x_0 + nh$, thus the above relation reduces to

$$\frac{1}{h}\int_{x_0}^{x_0+nh} f(x)\,dx = \sum_{i=0}^{n} f(x_i) - \frac{1}{2}[f(x_n) + f(x_0)] - \frac{h}{12}[f'(x_0+nh) - f'(x)]$$

$$+\frac{h^3}{720}[f'''(x_0+nh) - f'''(x_0)] - \dots \qquad \dots(4)$$

This is called Euler-Maclaurin's summation formula

$$\Rightarrow \quad \frac{1}{h}\int_{x_0}^{x_n} f(x)\,dx = \frac{1}{2}[f(x_0) + 2f(x_1) + 2f(x_2) + \dots + 2f(x_{n-1}) + f(x_n)]$$

$$-\frac{h}{12}[f'(x_n) - f'(x_0)] + \frac{h^3}{720}[f''(x_n) - f'''(x_0)] + \dots$$

$$\Rightarrow \quad \int_{x_0}^{x_n} f(x)\,dx = \frac{h}{2}\left[f(x_0) + 2f(x_1) + 2f(x_2) + \dots + 2f(x_{n-1}) + f(x_n)\right]$$

$$-\frac{h^2}{12}[f'(x_n) - f'(x_0)] + \frac{h^4}{720}[f''(x_n) - f'''(x_0)] + \dots$$

$$\Rightarrow \quad \int_{x_0}^{x_n} y\,dx = \frac{h}{2}\left[y_0 + 2y_1 + 2y_2 + \dots + 2y_{n-1} + y_n\right]$$

$$-\frac{h^2}{12}(y'_n - y'_0) + \frac{h^4}{720}(y'''_n - y'''_0) + \dots$$

This is another form of Euler Maclaurian's summation formula.

Solved Examples

Example 1: *Using Euler-Maclaurin formula, obtain the value of* $\log_e 2$ *from* $\int_0^1 \frac{dx}{1+x}$.

Solution: $y = (1/1+x),\ x_0 = 0,\ n = 10,\ h = .1,\ x_n = 1$

$$y' = -\frac{1}{(1+x)^2},\ y'' = \frac{2}{(1+x)^3},\ y''' = \frac{-6}{(1+x)^4}.$$

Then by Euler-Maclaurin's formula, we have

$$\int_0^1 y\,dx = \frac{.1}{2}\left[\frac{1}{1+0} + \frac{2}{1+0.1} + \frac{2}{1+0.2} + \frac{2}{1+0.3} + \frac{2}{1+0.4} + \frac{2}{1+0.5} + \frac{2}{1+0.6} + \frac{2}{1+0.7}\right.$$

$$\left. + \frac{2}{1+0.8} + \frac{2}{1+0.9} + \frac{1}{1+1}\right] - \frac{(0.1)^2}{12}\left[\frac{-1}{(1+1)^2} - \frac{-1}{(1+0)^2}\right] + \frac{(0.1)^4}{720}\left[\frac{-6}{(1+1)^4} - \frac{-6}{(1+0)^4}\right]$$

$$= 0.693773 - 0.000625 + 0.000001 = 0.693149$$

Also $\quad \int_0^1 \frac{dx}{1+x} = \left[\log(1+x)\right]_0^1 = \log_e 2$ and hence $\log_e 2 = 0.693149$

6.11 Stirling's Formula for Approximation to Factorials

Putting $x_0 = 1; h = 1: n-1$ for n;

$$f(x) = \log_e x,\ f'(x) = \frac{1}{x},\ f''(x) = \frac{-1}{x^2},\ f'''(x) = \frac{2}{x^3}, \ldots, \text{ in (4), we get}$$

$$\int_1^n \log x\,dx = \frac{1}{2}\log 1 + \log 2 + \log 3 + \ldots + \log(n-1) + \frac{1}{2}\log n - \frac{1}{12}\left(\frac{1}{n} - \frac{1}{1}\right) + \frac{1}{720}\left(\frac{2}{n^3} - \frac{2}{1^3}\right) - \ldots$$

$$\Rightarrow \quad \left[x \log x - x\right]_1^n = \log(n!) - \frac{1}{2}\log n - \frac{1}{12n} + \frac{1}{360n^3} - \ldots$$

$$\Rightarrow \quad \log(n!) = (n + \tfrac{1}{2})\log n - n + \frac{1}{12n} - \frac{1}{360n^3} + \ldots + c \qquad \ldots(1)$$

where c is a constant independent of n.

To evaluate c, we make use of Walli's formula in Trigonometry, *viz,* we have

$$\frac{\pi}{2} = \lim_{n\to\infty}\left[\frac{2.2}{1.3}\cdot\frac{4.4}{3.5}\cdot\frac{6.6}{5.7}\cdot\frac{2n.2n}{(2n-1)(2n+1)}\right] = \lim_{n\to\infty}\frac{2^{4n}(n!)^4}{[(2n)!]^2\,(2n+1)}.$$

$$\Rightarrow \quad \log\frac{\pi}{2} = \lim_{n\to\infty}\left[4n\log 2 + 4\log(n!) - 2\log[(2n)!] - \log(2n+1)\right]. \qquad \ldots(2)$$

Whence substituting the values of $\log(n!)$ and $\log[(2n)!]$ from (1), in (2), we get

$$\log\frac{\phi}{2} = \lim_{n\to\infty}\left[4n\log 2 + 4\{(n+\tfrac{1}{2})\log n - n + c\} - 2\{(2n+\tfrac{1}{2})\log(2n) - 2n + c\} - \log(2n+1)\right]$$

$$= \lim_{n\to\infty}\left(2c + 2\log n - \log(2n) - (2n-1)\right]$$

$$= \lim_{n\to\infty}\left[2c + \log\frac{n^2}{4n^2 + 2n}\right] = 2c + \log\frac{1}{4} = 2c - \log 4.$$

$$\Rightarrow \quad c = \frac{1}{2}\log(2\pi) = \log\sqrt{(2\pi)}.$$

Whence substituting the value of c in (1), we readily obtain

$$\log(n!) = (n + \tfrac{1}{2})\log n + \log\sqrt{(2\pi)} - n + \frac{1}{12n} - \frac{1}{360n^3} + \ldots$$

$$= \log\left\{\sqrt{(2\pi)}\,.\,n^{n+\frac{1}{2}}\right\} + \log\exp\left\{-n\left(1 - \frac{1}{12n^2} + \frac{1}{360\,n^4} - \ldots\right)\right\}$$

$$\Rightarrow \quad n! = \sqrt{(2\pi)}\,.\,n^{n+\frac{1}{2}}\exp\left\{-n\left(1 - \frac{1}{12n^2} + \frac{1}{360n^4} + \ldots\right)\right\}$$

$$\Rightarrow \quad n! = \sqrt{(2\pi)}\,.\,n^{n+\frac{1}{2}}\,e^{-n}.$$

This is called ***Stirling's formula*** for factorial n, when n is very large.

6.12 Method of Undetermined Coefficients

So far, we have discussed formulae for numerical differentiation and integration by replacing the actual function with some interpolation polynomial that agrees with the actual function at certain number of points. "*The method of undetermined coefficients*" is an alternative and very convenient approach to develop a wide variety of differentiation and integration formulae. Here, we impose certain restrictions on a formula of presumed form involving certain unknown coefficients. Then we use these conditions to determine the unknown coefficients, termed as weights. If a formula is to be obtained involving $(n+1)$ functional values say $f(x_0),\ldots, f(x_n)$, then the unknown coefficients can be evaluated by assuming that the formula is exact for all polynomials of degree less than or equal to n. Thus we assume that the presumed formula is exact for the polynomials, 1, x, $x^2,\ldots, x^n$. To simplify the notations we shall denote $f(x_i)$ by f_i etc.

Differentiation Formulae

To derive a formula for the value of the derivative, we try to approximate a derivative by a linear combination of values of the function at certain points. For illustration if we want to write the derivative in terms of only two functional values *i.e.* f_0 and f_1, then we write

$$f_0' = a_0 f_0 + a_1 f_1 \qquad \ldots(1)$$

where a_0, a_1 are unknown constant coefficients to be determined in order to get a formula for $f'(x_0)$. We shall obtain a_0 and a_1 by making this formula exact for $f(x)=1$ and x *i.e.* x° and x respectively.

Putting $f(x) = x^\circ = 1$ and x respectively in (1), we obtain

$$0 = a_0 .1 + d' .1 \quad \text{and} \quad 1 = a_0 x_0 + a_1 (x_0 + h)$$

$$\Rightarrow \quad a_0 = -(1/h),\ a_1 = (1/h). \quad \Rightarrow \quad f_0' = \frac{f_1 - f_0}{h}$$

Similarly, to get a three term formula for f_0' we can proceed by assuming

$$f_0' = a_0 f_0 + a_1 f_1 + a_2 f_2 .$$

Making it exact for $f(x) = x^\circ$, x and x^2, we obtain

$$0 = a_0 .1 + a_1 .1 + a_2 .1$$

$$1 = a_0 . x_0 + a_1 (x_0 + h) + a_2 (x_0 + 2h)$$

$$2x_0 = a_0 . x_0^2 + a_1 (x_0 + h)^2 + a_2 (x_0 + 2h)^2 .$$

To simplify the evaluation of a_0, a_1, a_2, we try to shift the origin to x_0 *i.e.* let $x_0 = 0$. The value of f_0' will not change because f_0' denotes the slope of the curve $y = f(x)$ at $x = x_0$.

Thus putting $x_0 = 0$, above simultaneous equations are reduced to

$$0 = a_0 + a_1 + a_2,$$

$$1 = a_1 h + a_2 .2h,$$

$$0 = a_1 h^2 + a_2 .4h^2,$$

$$\Rightarrow \qquad a_0 = -(3/2h), a_1 = (2/h), \quad a_2 = -(1/2h),$$

$$\Rightarrow \qquad f_0' = \frac{-3 f_0 + 4 f_1 - f_2}{2h} \qquad ...(2)$$

Thus as approximation to $f'(x_0)$ can be found in any number of functional values.

In a similar manner we can extend the formulae involving functional values on both the sides.

Let us write $\qquad f_0' = a_{-1} f_{-1} + a_0 f_0 + a_1 f_1 \qquad ...(3)$

Making it exact for $f(x) = x^\circ, x,$ and x^2 and letting $x_0 = 0$, we get

$$0 = a_{-1}(-h)^2 + a_0 .0 + a_2 h^2$$

$$1 = a_{-1}(-h) + a_0 .0 + a_1 (h)$$

$$0 = a_{-1}(1) + a_0 (1) + a_1 (1).$$

$$\Rightarrow \qquad a_{-1} = -(1/2h), a_0 = 0, a_1 = (1/2h).$$

$$\Rightarrow \qquad f_0' = \frac{f_1 - f_{-1}}{2h} \qquad ...(4)$$

For the second order derivative, let us further assume

$$f_0'' = a_{-1} f_{-1} + a_0 f_0 + a_1 f_1$$

Again making it exact for $f(x) = 1, x, x^2$ and putting $x_0 = 0$, we get

$$f_0'' = \frac{f_{-1} - 2 f_0 + f_1}{h^2} \qquad ...(5)$$

Similarly it can be extented further to show that

$$f_0''' = \frac{-f_{-2} + 2 f_{-1} - 2 f_1 + f_2}{-2h^3} \qquad ...(6)$$

and $\qquad f_0^{(iv)} = \dfrac{f_{-2} + 4 f_{-1} + 6 f_0 - 4 f_1 + f_2}{h^4} \qquad ...(7)$

6.13 Integration Formula

Here also we approximate

$$\int_a^b f(x)\, dx = a_0 f_0 + a_1 f_1 + \ldots + a_n f_n$$

where a_i's are the coefficients to be determined. The coefficient a_i's are to be determined making this equation exact for $f(x) = 1 x, \ldots, x^{n-1}$. The 2-*term formula* is derived by taking

$$\int_{x_0}^{x_0 + h} f\, dx = a_0 y_0 + a_1 y_1 \qquad ...(1)$$

and the unknowns a_0, a_1 are to be determined by making (6) exact for $y(x) = 1, x$ respectively.

Hence putting $y(x) = 1, x$ successively in (1), we get

$$a_0 + a_1 = \int_{x_0}^{x_0+h} 1\,dx = h$$

and
$$a_0 x_0 + a_1 (x_0 + h) = \int_{x_0}^{x_0+h} x\,.dx = \frac{1}{2}[(x_0 + h)^2 - x_0^2]$$

Solving these, we obtain $a_0 = a_1 = \dfrac{h}{2}$.

$$\Rightarrow \qquad \int_{x_0}^{x_0+h} y\,dx = \frac{h}{2}(y_0 + y_1) \qquad \text{...(2)}$$

This is *trapezoidal rule.*

Further *the* 3-*term formula* is derived by taking

$$\int_{x_0-h}^{x_0+h} y\,dx = a_{-1}y_{-1} + a_0 y_0 + a_1 y_1 \qquad \text{...(3)}$$

where the unknowns a_{-1}, a_0, a_1 are obtained by making (3) exact for $y(x) = 1$, x, x^2 respectively.

Then putting $y = 1, x, x^2$ successively in (3), we readily get

$$a_{-1} + a_0 + a_1 = \int_{x_0-h}^{x_0+h} 1.dx = 2h$$

$$a_{-1}(x_0 - h) + a_0 x_0 + a_1 (x_0 + h) = \int_{x_0-h}^{x_0+h} x\,dx = \frac{1}{2}[(x_0 + h)^2 - (x_0 - h)^2]$$

$$a_{-1}(x_0 - h)^2 + a_0 x_0^2 + a_1 (x_0 + h)^2 = \int_{x_0-h}^{x_0+h} x^2\,dx = \frac{1}{3}[(x_0 + h)^3 - (x_0 - h)^3]$$

Solving these we get $a_{-1} = \dfrac{h}{3}, a_0 = (4h/3), a_1 = (h/3)$.

$$\Rightarrow \qquad \int_{x_0-h}^{x_0+h} y\,dx = \frac{h}{3}(y_{-1} + 4y_0 + y_1) \qquad \text{...(4)}$$

This is ***Simpson's rule***.

6.14 Quadrature Formulae Based on Central Differences

Here we try to develop rapidly converging quadrature formula by integrating Stirling's and Bessel's interpolation formulas.

Integrating Stirling's formula from $x_0 - h$ to $x_0 + h$ [*i.e.* $u = -1$ to $u = 1$], we obtain

$$\int_{x_0-h}^{x_0+h} y_x\, dx = h\int_{-1}^{1} y_u\, du, \text{ where } u = (x - x_0)/h.$$

$$= h\int_{-1}^{1} [y_0 + u.\left(\frac{\Delta y_{-1} + \Delta y_0}{2}\right) + \frac{u^2}{2}\Delta^2 y_{-1} + \frac{u(u^2-1)}{3!}.\left(\frac{\Delta^3 y_{-2} + \Delta^3 y_{-1}}{2}\right) + \frac{u^2(u^2-1)}{4!}\Delta^4 y_{-2}$$

$$+ \frac{u(u^2-1)(u^2-2^2)}{5!}.\left(\frac{\Delta^5 y_{-3} + \Delta^5 y_{-2}}{2}\right) + \frac{u(u^2-1)(u^2-2^2)}{6!}.\Delta^6 y_{-3} + \ldots]\, du$$

$$= h\left[2y_0 + \frac{1}{3}\Delta^2 y_{-1} - \frac{1}{90}\Delta^4 y_{-2} + \frac{1}{756}\Delta^6 y_{-3} \ldots\right] \quad \ldots(1)$$

It gives the approximate value of the integral from $x = x_0 - h$ to $x = x_0 + h$. As we can take x_0 at any interior point of a central difference table, the value of the integral from $x = x_0$ to $x = x_0 + 2h$, is also given by [advancing the subscripts of the y's only by one unit.]

$$\Rightarrow \quad \int_{x_0}^{x_0+2h} y_x\, dx = h\left[2y_1 + \frac{1}{3}\Delta^2 y_0 - \frac{1}{90}\Delta^4 y_{-1} + \frac{1}{756}\Delta^6 y_{-2} \ldots\right] \quad \ldots(2)$$

Similarly, we may obtain

$$\int_{x_0+2h}^{x_0+4h} y_x\, dx = h\left[2y_3 + \frac{1}{3}\Delta^2 y_2 - \frac{1}{90}\Delta^4 y_1 + \frac{1}{756}\Delta^6 y_0 \ldots\right], \ldots \text{etc.}$$

and $$\int_{x_0+(n-2)h}^{x_0+nh} y_x\, dx = h\left[2y_{n-1} + \frac{1}{3}\Delta y_{n-2}^2 - \frac{1}{90}\Delta^4 y_{n-3} + \frac{1}{756}\Delta^6 y_{n-4} \ldots\right]$$

Whence adding, the composite formula for numerical integration is given by

$$\int_a^b y_x\, dx = \int_{x_0}^{x_0+nh} y_x\, dx$$

$$= h\,[2\,y_1 + y_3 + \ldots + y_{n-1}] + (1/3)\,(\Delta^2 y_0 + \Delta^2 y_2 + \ldots + \Delta^2 y_{n-2})$$

$$- (1/90)\,(\Delta^4 y_{-1} + \Delta^4 y_1 + \Delta^4 y_3 + \ldots + \Delta^4 y_{n-2})$$

$$+ (1/756)\,(\Delta^6 y_{-2} + \Delta^6 y_0 + \Delta^6 y_2 + \ldots + \Delta^6 y_{n-4}) + \ldots] \quad \ldots(3)$$

Where $a = x_0$, $b = x_0 + nh$ and n being even. On the same lines integrating Bessel's formula for interpolation from $x = x_0$ to $x = x_0 + h$ *i.e.* from $v = -\frac{1}{2}$ to $v = \frac{1}{2}$, or $u = 0$ to $u = 1$, one may obtain

$$\int_{x_0}^{x_0+h} y_x\,dx = h\left[\frac{y_0+y_1}{2} - \frac{1}{12}\frac{\Delta^2 y_1+\Delta^2 y_0}{2} + \frac{11}{720}\cdot\frac{\Delta^4 y_{-2}+\Delta^4 y_{-1}}{2} - \frac{191}{60480}\cdot\frac{\Delta^6 y_{-2}+\Delta^6 y_{-1}}{2}\cdots\right] \quad ...(4)$$

Likewise, we have

$$\int_{x_0+h}^{x_0+2h} y_x dx = h\left[\frac{y_1+y_2}{2} - \frac{1}{12}\frac{\Delta^2 y_0+\Delta^2 y_1}{2} + \frac{11}{20}\frac{\Delta^4 y_{-1}+\Delta^4 y_0}{2} - \frac{191}{60480}\frac{\Delta^6 y_{-2}+\Delta^6 y_{-1}}{2}\cdots\right]$$

and

$$\int_{x_0+(n-1)h}^{x_0+nh} y_x\,dx = h\left[\frac{y_{n-1}+y_n}{2} - \frac{1}{12}\cdot\frac{\Delta^2 y_{n-2}+\Delta^2 y_{n-1}}{2} + \frac{11}{720}\frac{\Delta^4 y_{n-3}+\Delta^4 y_{n-2}}{2} - \frac{191}{60480}\cdot\frac{\Delta^6 y_{n-4}+\Delta^6 y_{n-3}}{2}\cdots\right]$$

Whence adding all these, one may obtain the composite formula for integration as given under:

$$\int_{x_0}^{x_0+nh} y_x\,dx = h\left[\left(\frac{y_0}{2} + y_1 + y_2 \ldots + y_{n-1} + \frac{y_n}{2}\right) - \frac{1}{12}\left(\frac{\Delta^2 y_{-1}}{2} + \Delta^2 y_0 + \Delta^2 y_1 + \ldots + \Delta^2 y_{n-2} + \frac{\Delta^2 y_{n-1}}{2}\right) + \frac{11}{720}\left(\frac{\Delta^2 y_{-2}}{2} + \Delta^4 y_{-1} + \Delta^4 y_0 + \ldots + \Delta^4 y_{n-2} + \frac{\Delta^4 y_{n-2}}{2}\right) - \frac{191}{60480}\left(\frac{\Delta^6 y_{-3}}{2} + \Delta^6 y_{-2} + \ldots + \Delta^6 y_{n-4} + \frac{\Delta^6 y_{n-3}}{2}\right) + \ldots\right] \quad ...(5)$$

where n is either even or odd.

Here *we may off at 6th order differences in both the above* formulae. If we off at the second order differences in (3), we get the Simpson's rule. If we off before the second order differences in (3), the formula reduces to usual Trapezoidal rule and is also known as Trapezoidal rule with correction terms.

The truncation errors of the formulae (3) and (4) are $-23h^9\,(y_0^{(8)}/113400)$ and $.0007h^9\,y_0^{(8)}$ respectively.

Alternative form of formula **(4)**

The formula (4) as such is much complicated for practical use. To simplify it, reducing the even-order differences to the next lower odd-order differences, we obtain

$$\Delta^2 y_{-1} = \Delta y_0 - \Delta y_{-1}, \Delta^2 y_0 = \Delta y_1 - \Delta y_0, \ldots$$

$$\Delta^2 y_{n-1} = \Delta y_n - \Delta y_{n-1};$$

$$\Delta^4 y_{-2} = \Delta^3 y_{-1} - \Delta^3 y_{-2}, \Delta^4 y_{-1} = \Delta^3 y_0 - \Delta^3 y_{-1}, \ldots,$$

$$\Delta^4 y_{n-2} = \Delta^3 y_{n-1} - \Delta^3 y_{n-2};$$

$$\Delta^6 y_{-3} = \Delta^5 y_{-2} - \Delta^5 y_{-3}, \Delta^6 y_{-2} = \Delta^5 y_{-1} - \Delta^5 y_{-2}, \ldots,$$

$$\Delta^6 y_{n-3} = \Delta^5 y_{n-2} - \Delta^5 y_{n-3} \text{ etc.}$$

Putting these values in (4) and then simplifying, we obtain

$$\int_{x_0}^{x_0+nh} y_x\,dx = h\,[(y_0/2) + y_1 + \ldots + y_{n-1} + (y_n/2)$$

$$+\frac{1}{12}\left(\frac{\Delta y_{-1} + \Delta y_0}{2}\right) - \frac{11}{720}\left(\frac{\Delta^3 y_{-2} + \Delta^3 y_{-1}}{2}\right) + \frac{191}{60480}\left(\frac{\Delta^5 y_{-3} + \Delta^5 y_{-2}}{2}\right)$$

$$-\frac{1}{12}\left(\frac{\Delta y_{n-1} + \Delta y_n}{2}\right) + \frac{11}{720}\left(\frac{\Delta^3 y_{n-2} + \Delta^3 y_{n-1}}{2}\right) - \frac{191}{60480}\left(\frac{\Delta^5 y_{n-3} + \Delta^5 y_{n-2}}{2}\right)\Bigg].$$

$$\Rightarrow \quad \int_{x_0}^{x_0+nh} y_x\,dx = h\,[(y_0/2) + y_1 + y_2 + \ldots + y_{n-1} + (y_n/2)$$

$$-\frac{1}{12}\left(\frac{\Delta y_{n-1} + \Delta y_n}{2} - \frac{\Delta y_{-1} + \Delta y_0}{2}\right) + \frac{11}{720}\left(\frac{\Delta^2 y_{n-2} + \Delta^2 y_{n-1}}{2} - \frac{\Delta^3 y_{-2} + \Delta^3 y_{-1}}{2}\right)$$

$$-\frac{191}{60480}\left(\frac{\Delta^5 y_{n-3} + \Delta^5 y_{n-2}}{2} - \frac{\Delta^5 y_{-3} + \Delta^5 y_{-2}}{2}\right)\Bigg] \qquad \ldots(6)$$

As a matter of fact we say that geometrically (3) replaces the graph of the given function by $(n/2)$ arcs of polynomials of sixth degree and (5) replaces the graph by n such arcs.

6.15 Lozenge Diagrams For Quadrature Formulae

So far, we obtained quadrature formulae by integrating the interpolation polynomials, then similar to derivatives, we can construct the Lozenge diagrams for quadrature formulae, integrating over 1 panel or 2 panels or 3 panels etc. The forming of the Lozenge diagrams and the method of constructing the quadrature formulae is similar as in the case of derivatives. The one line of constants can be had by putting $n = 1, 2$ in the general quadrature formula for equidistant ordinate for various Lozenge diagrams.

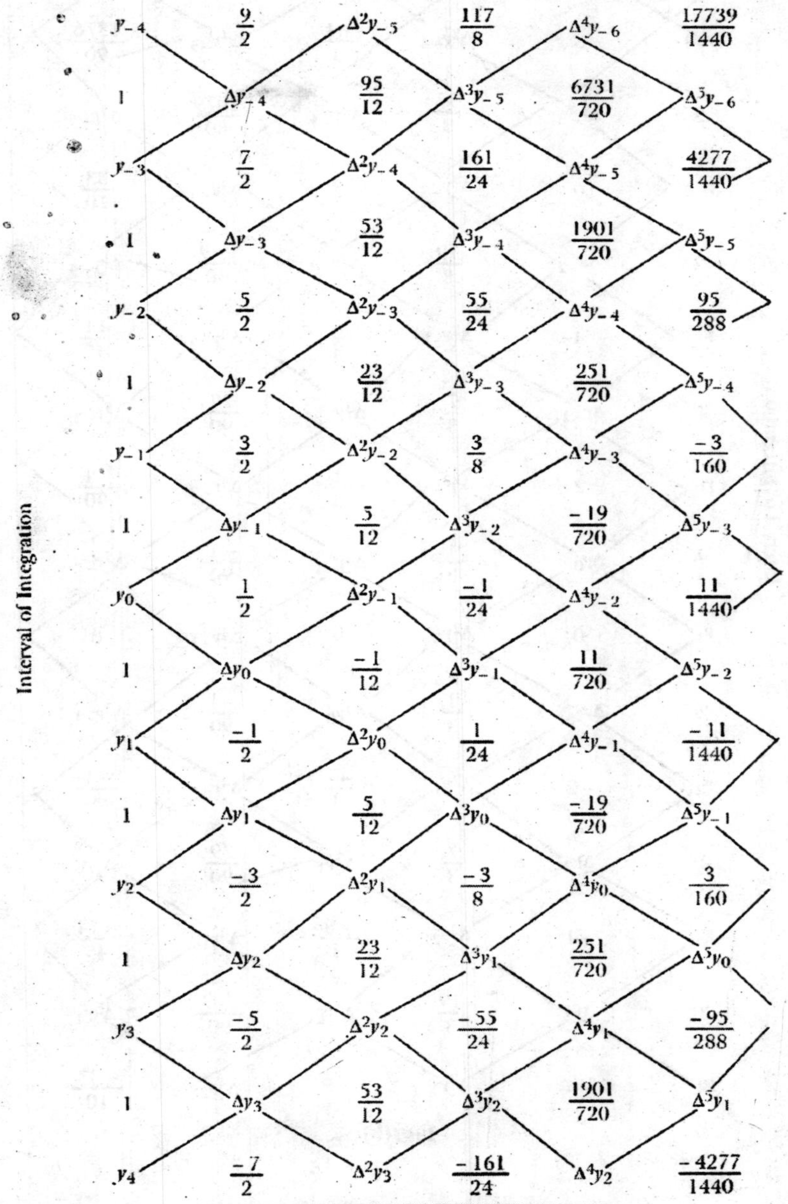

Fig. (a)

Since $x = x_0 + hu$, $\int_{x_0}^{x_1} f(x)\,dx = h\int_{u=0}^{1} \phi(u)\,du$. So all the formulae obtained from Fig. (a) and Fig. (b) must be multiplied by h.

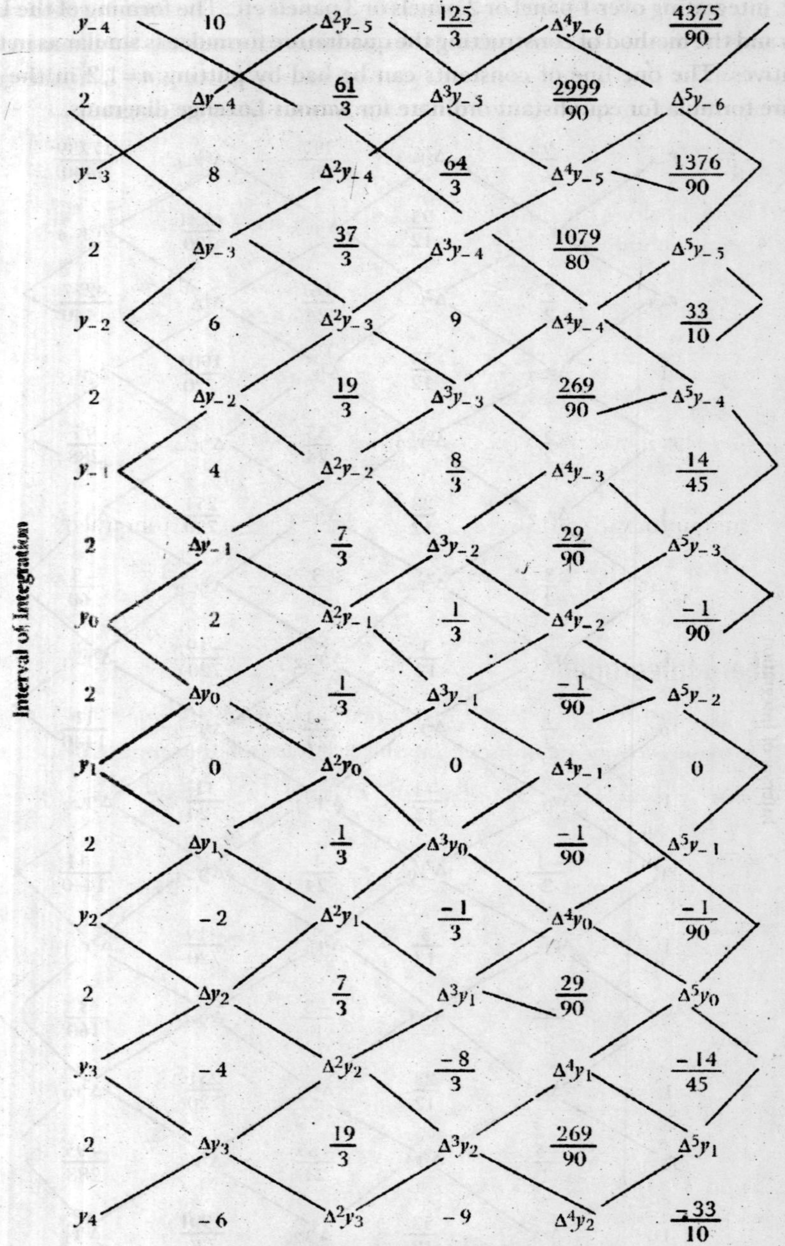

Fig. (b)

An Important observation makes the Lozenge diagrams more useful. Let a quadrature formula be written from the Lozenge diagram by terminating just after the term of ***m*th** differences *i.e.* including only upto $\Delta^m y_r$. Then *its local error term* (as discussed in the chapter 10 on errors) can be obtained just by writing one more term (next to $\Delta^m y_r$) in the formula to the right by the Lozenge diagram and then replacing the difference part of the term [it is immaterial that there exists a single difference $\Delta^{m+1} y_r$ or mean like

$(\Delta^m y_{r-1} + \Delta^m y_{r-1})/2$ by $h^{m+1} f^{m+1}(\xi)$, where ξ is some value of x in the interval (x_0, x_1)].

Let us start from y_0 along the downward diagonal in Fig. (b) and truncate the terms after 2nd term, then we obtain

$$\int_{x_0}^{x_1} y\,dx = h[y_0 + \frac{1}{2}\Delta y_0] \approx h[y_0 + \frac{1}{2}(y_1 - y_0)] = \frac{h}{2}[y_0 + y_1]$$

This is well known ***trapezoidal rule.***

It is interesting to note that the next term of the formula is $-\left(\frac{1}{12}\right)\Delta^2 y_0$. Here $m = 1$ as we have considered upto Δy_0; so its local error is $-(1/12)\,h^2 f^{(2)}(\xi)$, [obtained by replacing $h^2 f^{(2)}(\xi)$, where $y = f(x)$, where ξ is a point in the interval (x_0, x_1).

6.16 Romberg Integration

This method is due to L.F. Richardson (termed as *Richardson's deffered approach to the limit*), and provides a way to improve on the accuracy of the approximate values of definite integrals, obtained by finite-difference method. It is explained below in one case of Trapezoidal rule.

Let $I = \int_a^b y\,dx$, where $y = f(x)$ and let I_1 and I_2 be its values tabulated by Trapezoidal rule with h_1 and h_2 as width of sub-intervals. If E_1 and E_2 are the corresponding error then we have

$$I = I_1 + E_1 = I_2 + E_2.$$

where $\quad E_1 \approx -\frac{(b-a)}{12} h_1^2 f''(x_{k_1})$ and $E_2 \approx -\frac{(b-a)}{12} h_2^2 f''(x_{k_2})$

But $f''(x_{k_1})$ and $f''(x_{k_2})$, are both the largest values of $f''(x_{k_2})$.

$$\Rightarrow \quad \frac{E_2}{E_1} = \frac{h_2^2}{h_1^2} \quad \Rightarrow \quad \frac{E_1}{E_2 - E_1} = \frac{h_1^2}{h_2^2 - h_1^2} \qquad \text{...(1)}$$

But $\quad I = I_1 + E_1 = I_2 + E_2, \Rightarrow \quad E_2 - E_1 = I_1 - I_2 \qquad$ ...(2)

using (1) and (2), we obtain $E_1 = \dfrac{h_1^2}{h_2^2 - h_1^2}(I_1 - I_2)$

$$\Rightarrow \quad I = I_1 + E_1 = I_1 + \frac{h_1^2}{h_2^2 - h_1^2}(I_1 - I_2) \Rightarrow I = \frac{I_1 h_2^2 - I_2 h_1^2}{h_2^2 - h_1^2} \quad \text{...(3)}$$

This is the better approcimation of I.

Then to evaluate I systematically, we proceed by assuming

$$h_1 = h \quad \text{and} \quad h_2 = \frac{1}{2}h$$

Hence (3) implies $I = \dfrac{I_1 (h/2)^2 - I_2 h^2}{(h/2)^2 - h^2} = \dfrac{4I_2 - I_1}{3}$

$$\Rightarrow \quad I(h, h/2) = \frac{1}{3}[4I(h/2) - I(h)] \quad \text{...(4)}$$

Then we make use of trapezoidal rule again and again halving h and applying (4) to each pair of values following scheme.

$I(h)$			
	$I(h, h/2)$		
$I(h/2)$		$I(h, h/2, h/4)$	
	$I(h/2, h/4)$		$I(h, h/2, h/4, h/8)$
$I(h/4)$		$I(h/2, h/4, h/8)$	
	$I(h/4, h/8)$		
$I(h/8)$			

This computation is carried out till successive values are very close to each other.

Example 2: *Use Romberg's method of compute* $\int_0^1 \dfrac{dx}{1+x^2}$ *correct to 4 decimal places.*

Solution: Taking $h = 0.5, 0.25$ and 0.125 successively and then evaluating the given integral (using Trapezoidal rule], we readily obtain

(a) Taking $h = 0.5$, the values of $y = (1 + x^2)^{-1}$ are

x	0	0.5	1.0
y	1	0.8	0.5

$$\Rightarrow \quad I = (.5/2)[1 + 2 \times .8 + 0.5) = 0.775$$

(b) Taking $h = 0.25$, the values of $y = (1 + x^2)^{-1}$ are

x	0	0.25	0.5	0.75	1.0
y	1	0.9412	0.8	0.64	0.5

$$\Rightarrow \quad I = (0.25/2)[1 + 2(0.9412 + 0.8 + 0.64) + 0.5] = 0.7828$$

(c) Taking $h = 0.125$, and proceeding as above, we get $I = 0.7848$

$$\Rightarrow \quad I(h) = 0.7750, I(h/2) = 0.7828, I(h/4) = 0.7848$$

Whence using (4) above, we get

$$I(h, h/2) = \frac{1}{3}[4I(h/2) - I(h)] = \frac{1}{3}(3.1312 - 0.775) = 0.7854$$

$$I(h/2, h/4) = \frac{1}{3}[(4I(h/4) - I(h/2)] = \frac{1}{3}(3.1392 - 0.7828) = 0.7855$$

and $I(h, h/2, h/4) = \frac{1}{3}[4I(h/2, h/4) - I(h, h/2)]$

$$= \frac{1}{3}(3.142 - 0.7854 = 0.7855$$

Then the table of these values is as follows:

0.7750		
	0.7854	
0.7828		0.7855
	0.7855	
0.7848		

This implies that the value of the integral $= 0.7855$

Romberg Integration means the recursive systematic computation of the definite integral of a known function by using the extrapolation technique and involves the following steps:

(i) Choose an arbitrary value of h say h_1 and then compute the value of integral by trapezoidal rule *i.e.* compute $I(h_1)$.

(ii) Compute $I(h_1/2)$ by trapezoidal rule by halving the width.

(iii) Use relation 2 to obtain the first order extrapolated value.

(iv) To get second order extrapolated values compute

$$I(h_1/4), I[(h_1/4), (h_1/2)] \text{ and the } I[(h_1/4), (h_1/2), h_1].$$

Example 3: *Using Romberg's method, compute*

$$I = \int_0^{1.2} [(1/(1+x)] \, dx.$$

Solution: Here $f(x) = 1/(1+x)$. Assume $h = .6, .3, .15$.

x :	0	.15	.30	.45	.60	.75
$f(x)$:	1	.8695	.7692	.6896	.625	.5714
x :	.90		1.05		1.2	
$f(x)$:	.5263		.4878		.4545	

Using trapezoidal rule, (taking $h = .6$), we have

$$I(.6) = (.6)\,[\{(1 + .4545/2\} + .625]$$

$$= .8113$$

Now halving the width (*i.e.* taking $h = .3$), we have

$$I(.3) = (.3)\,[\{(1 + .4545)/2\} + .7692 + .625 + .5263\}]$$

$$= (.3)\,[.72725 + 1.2955] = .7943.$$

Again halving the width *i.e.* $h = .15$

We get $\quad I(.15) = (.15)\,[\{(1 + 4545/2\} + (.8695 + .7692 + .6896$

$$.625 + .5714 + .5263 + .4878)]$$

$$= (.15)\,[.72725 + 4.5388] = .7899$$

Then by extrapolation rule, we obtain

$$I(.3, .6) = (1/3)\,[4 \times I(.3) - I(.6)]$$

$$= (1/3)\,[4 \times .7943 - .8113] = .7886$$

and $\quad I(.15, .3) = (1/3)\,[4 \times I(.15) - I(.3)]$

$$= (1/3)\,[4 \times .7899 - .7943] = .7884$$

Further making use of extrapolation, the better approximation is as under:

$$I(.15, .3, .6) = (1/3)\,[4 \times I(.15, .3) - I(.3, .6)]$$

$$= (1/3)\,[4 \times .7884 - .7886] = .7883$$

But the actual values of the integral is

$$I = \left[\log_e (1 + x)\right]_0^{1.2} = \log_e 2.2 = .7884, \text{ up to 4 places of decimal.}$$

6.17 Hardy's Formula

Let $\qquad y_x = a + bx + cx^2 + dx^3 + ex^4 + fx^5$

so that $\qquad \int_{-3}^{3} y_x\, dx = 6a + 18c + \dfrac{486}{5} e.$

Let the values of y_x be given as follows:

$$x = 0, 1, 2, 3, 4, 5 \text{ and } 6, \quad y_0 = -3, -2, -1, 0, 1, 2 \text{ and } 3.$$

Then $\qquad y_0 = a, \; y_{-2} + y_2 = 2a + 8c + 32e$

and $\qquad y_{-3} + y_3 = 2a + 18c + 162e$

Solving for *a*, *c* and *e*, substituting, we get

$$\int_{-3}^{3} y_x \, dx = 2.2\, y_0 + 1.62\,(y_{-2} + y_2) + .28\,(y_{-3} + y_3)$$

or $$\int_0^6 y_x \, dx = 2.2\, y_3 + 1.62\,(y_1 + y_5) + .28\,(y_0 + y_6)$$

$$= .28\,(y_0 + y_6) + 1.62\,(y_1 + y_5) + 2.2\, y_3$$

This formula is called ***Hardy's formula.***

Extension

If the interval of differencing is *h*, then we have

$$\int_0^{6h} y_x \, dx = h\,\{0.28\,(y_0 + y_{6h}) + 1.62\,(y_h + y_{5h}) + 2.2\, y_{3h}$$

Similarly

$$\int_{6h}^{12h} y_x \, dx = h\,\{0\,28\,(y_{6h} + y_{12h}) + 1.62\,(y_{7h} + y_{11h}) + 2\,2\, y_{9h}$$

Again

$$\int_0^{\infty} y_x \, dx = \int_0^{6h} y_x \, dx + \int_{6h}^{12h} y_x \, dx + \ldots$$

$$\Rightarrow \quad \int_0^{\infty} y_x \, dx = h\,\{0.28\,(y_0 + 2\, y_{6h} + 2\, y_{12h} + \ldots)$$

$$+ 1.62\,(y_h + y_{5h} + y_{7h} + \ldots) + 2.2\,(y_{3h} + y_{9h} + \ldots)\}$$

This is the general form of ***Hardy's formula.***

6.18 Numerical Double Integration

Let us consider a double integral

$$I = \int_a^b \int_c^d f(x, y)\, dy\, dx = \int_a^b \int_c^d z\, dy\, dx, \text{ where } z = f(x, y)$$

Let the values of the function be given for equidistant values of variables *i.e.* $a = x_0$, $x_1 = x_0 + h, \ldots, x_n = x_0 + nh = b$.

and $$c = y_0,\ y_1 = y_0 + k, \ldots, y_n = y_0 + mk = d.$$

In the form of rectangular array, the above values can be written as follows:

$x \backslash y$	y_0	y_1	–	–	–	y_m
x_0	z_{00}	z_{01}	–	–	–	z_{0m}
x_1	z_{10}	z_{11}	–	–	–	z_{1m}
:	–	–	–	–	–	–
:	–	–	–	–	–	–
x_n	z_{n0}	z_{n1}	–	–	–	z_{nm}

where $\qquad z_{ij} = f(x_i, y_j)$.

The above process of evaluating the integral (with the help of given numerical data) is reffered as "*Numerical double integration*" or "*Mechanical Cubature*" and involves the following steps:

Step **1**: Apply any quadrature formula using equidistant ordinates, such as Simpson's and Weddle's formula to each horizontal row (or to each vertical column).

Step **2**: A similar formula is employed for the results obtained in step 1.

In this way, the value of the double integral can be evaluated by applying the Simpson's or Weddle's rule or any other quadrature formula repeatedly. In particular: by the repeated application of trapezoidal rule, we obtain the formulas follows:

$$I = \int_{x_0}^{x_1} \int_{y_0}^{y_1} (x, y)\, dy\, dx,$$

where $\qquad z = f(x, y) \quad$ and $\quad x_1 = x_0 + h, y_1 = y_0 + k$

$$= \frac{k}{2} \int_{x_0}^{x_1} [f(x, y_0) + f(x, y_1)]\, dx$$

$$= \frac{k}{2} \int^{0} \frac{h}{2} \{f(x_0, y_0) + f(x_1, y_0)\} + \frac{h}{2} \{f(x_0, y_1) + f(x_1, y_1)\} \Big]$$

$$= (hk/4)\, [z_{00} + z_{10} + z_{01} + z_{11}].$$

Similarly applying Simpson's rule repeatedly, we can get

$$I = \int_{x_0}^{x_2} \int_{y_0}^{y_2} f(x, y)\, dy\, dx, x_2 = x_0 + 2h, y_2 = y_0 + 2k$$

$$= \frac{k}{3} \int_{x_0}^{x_2} [f(x, y_0) + 4f(x, y_1) + f(x, y_2)]\, dx, y_1 = y_0 + h$$

$$= \frac{k}{3}\left[\int_{x_0}^{x_2} [f(x, y_0) + 4\int_{x_0}^{x_2} f(x, y_1) + \int_{x_0}^{x_2} f(x, y_2)\, dx\right]$$

$$= (k/3)\,[(h/3)\,\{f(x_0, y_0) + 4f(x_1, y_0) + f(x_2, y_0)\}$$

$$+ 4(h/3)\{f(x_0, y_1) + 4f(x_1, y_1) + f(x_2, y_1)\} + (h/3)\{f(x_0, y_2) + 4f(x_1, y_2) + f(x_2, y_2)\}]$$

$$= (hk/9)\,[(z_{00} + z_{02} + z_{20} + z_{22}) + 4(z_{01} + z_{10} + z_{12} + z_{21}) + 16z_{11}] \quad ...(1)$$

Example 4: *Find the value of the double integral*

$$I = \int_2^{3.2} \int_1^{2.8} [1/(x + y)]\, dy\, dx.$$

Solution: The values of x and y are in the intervals [2, 3.2] and [1, 2.6] respectively.

we have $z = 1/(x + y)$, taking $h = .2$ and $k = .3$.

Then applying Simpson's $\frac{1}{3}$ -rule to each row, we get the corresponding integral A_x as follows:

$$A_{2.0} = (k/3)\,[(y_0 + y_6) + 4(y_1 + y_3 + y_5) + 2(y_2 + y_4)]$$

$$= (.3/3)\,[(.3333 + .2083) + 4(.3030 + .2564 + .2222) + 2(.2777 + 2380)]$$

$$= (.1)\,[.5416 + 3.1264 + 1.0314] = .46994$$

y / x	$y_0 = 1.0$	$y_1 = 1.3$	$y_2 = 1.6$	$y_3 = 1.9$	$y_4 = 2.2$	$y_5 = 2.5$	$y_6 = 2.8$	A_x
2.0	.3333	.3030	.2777	.2564	.2380	.2222	.2083	0.46994
2.2	.3125	.2857	.2631	.2439	.2325	.2127	.2000	0.44729
2.4	.2941	.2702	.2500	.2325	.2173	.2040	.1923	0.42478
2.6	.2777	.2564	.2380	.2222	.2083	.1960	.1851	0.40538
2.8	.2631	.2439	.2325	.2127	.2000	.1886	.1785	0.38874
3.0	.2500	.2325	.2173	.2040	.1923	.1818	.1724	0.37148
3.2	.2380	.2222	.2083	.1960	.1851	.1754	.1666	0.35658

Also, Similarly, $A_{2.2} = 0.44729$, $A_{2.4} = 0.40538$.

$A_{2.8} = 0.38874$, $A_{3.0} = 0.37148$, $A_{3.2} = 0.35658$.

Thus we get 7 values of A_x for 7 equidistant values of x.

Applying the Weddle's rule to these values, we obtain (here $h = .2$)

$$\int_2^{3.2}\int_1^{2.8} 1/(x+y)]\, dy\, dx = \frac{3h}{10}[(A_2 + A_{3.2}) + 5(A_{2.2} + A_3) + (A_{2.4} + A_{2.8}) + 6A_{2.6}]$$

$$= (.3 \times .2)[(.46994 + .35658) + 5(.44729 + .37148) + (.42478 + .38874) + 6(.40538\})]$$

$$= .48997$$

But, the true value of the integral

$$= \left[(x+2.8)\log_e(2.8+x) - x\right]_2^{3.2} - \left[(x+1)\log_e(x+1) - x\right]_2^{3.2}$$

$$= [6\log_e 6 - 4.8\log_e 4.8 - 1.2] - [4.2\log 4.2 - 3\log 3 - 1.2]$$

$$= 6\log_e 6 - 4.8\log_e 4.8 - 4.2\log_e 4.2 + 3\log_e 3$$

$$= [3\log_{10} 36 - 4.8\log_{10} 4.8 - 4.2\log_{10} 4.2 + \log_{10} 3] \times \log_{10} e$$

$$= [3\log_{10} 108 - 4.8\log_{10} 4.8 - 4.2\log_{10} 4.2]$$

$$= [3 \times 2.0334 - 4.8 \times 0.6812 - 4.2 \times 0.6232] \times 2.3025 = .4904.$$

Example 5: *Using trapezoidal rule evaluate*

$$I = \int_1^2 \int_1^2 \frac{dxdy}{x+y}, \text{ taking four sub-intervals.}$$

Solution: Taking $h = k = 0.25$ so that $m = n = 4$, we have

$$I = \frac{1}{64}[f_{(1,1)} + f_{(1,2)} + 2(f_{(1,1.25)} + f_{(1,1.75)}) + f_{(2,1)} + f_{(2,2)} + 2(f_{(2,1.25)} + f_{(2,1.5)} + f_{(2,1.75)})$$

$$+ 2\{f_{(1.25,1)} + f_{(1.25,2)} + 2f_{(1.25,1.25)} + f_{(1.25,1.5)} + f_{(1.25,1.75)})$$

$$+ f_{(1.5,1)} + f_{(1.5,2)} + 2f_{(1.5,1.25)} + f_{(1.5,1.5)} + f_{(1.5,1.75)})$$

$$+ f_{(1.75,1)} + f_{(1.75,2)} + 2(f_{(1.75,1.25)} + f_{(1.75,1.5)} + f_{(1.75,1.75)})\}]$$

$$= 0.3407. \qquad \left(\because f(x,y) = \frac{1}{x+y}\right)$$

Example 6: *Apply Simpson's rule to evaluate the integral*

$$I = \int_2^{2.6}\int_4^{4.4} \frac{dxdy}{xy}$$

Solution: Let us take $h = 0.2$ and $k = 0.3$ so that $m = n = 2$.

Then, $I = \frac{hk}{9}[f(4,2) + 4f(4,2.3) + f(4,2.6) + 4\{f(4.2,2) + 4f(4.2,2.3) + f(4.2,2.6)\}$

$$+ f(4.4,2) + 4f(4.4,2.3) + f(4.4,2.6)]$$

$$= \frac{0.06}{9}[0.6559 + 4(0.6246) + 0.5962] = \frac{0.02}{3} \times 3.7505 = 0.025.$$

Example 7: *Apply Trapezoidal rule to evaluate*

$$\int_1^5 \int_1^5 \frac{dxdy}{\sqrt{(x^2+y^2)}}, \text{ taking two sub-intervals.}$$

Solution: Proceed as example 6. **Ans. 4.134**

Example 8: *Using Trapezoidal and Simpson's rules, evaluate*

$$\int_0^1 \int_0^1 e^{x+y}\, dxdy, \text{ taking two rules, evaluate}$$

Solution: Proceed as example 6. **Ans. 3.076, 2.955**

6.19 Gaussian Integration

Earlier, some integration formula were derived to evaluate the integral $I = \int_a^b f(x)\,dx$ when values of the function were known at equi-spaced points of the intervals. Gauss derived a formula which uses the same number of functional values but with different spacing and yields better results. This formula is expressed in form

$$\int_{-1}^{1} F(u)\,du = w_1 F(u_1) + w_2 F(u_2) + \ldots + w_n F(u_n) = \sum_{i=0}^{n} w_i F(u_i), \quad \ldots(1)$$

where w_i and u_i are called the ***weights*** and ***abscissae*** respectively. It is to be noted that the abscissae and weights are symmetrical with respect to the middle point of the interval. In relation (1) there exist $2n$ unknowns.

Thus $2n$ relations between them are necessary which can be obtained such that the formula is exact for all polynomials of degree not exceeding $(2n-1)$.

Thus, we may consider

$$F(u) = c_0 + c_1 u + c_2 u^2 + c_3 u^3 + \ldots + c_{2n-1} u^{2n-1} \quad \ldots(2)$$

Now, from the left hand side of (1), we readily get

$$\int_{-1}^{1} F(u)\,du = \int_{-1}^{1}\left[c_0 + c_1 u + c_2 u^2 + c_3 u^3 + \ldots + c_{2n-1} u^{2n-1}\right]du = 2c_0 + \frac{2}{3}c_2 + \frac{2}{5}c_3 + \ldots \quad \ldots(3)$$

Whence putting $u = u_i$ in (2), we obtain

$$F(u_i) = c_0 + c_1 u_i + c_2 u_i^2 + c_3 u_i^3 + \ldots + c_{2n-1} u_i^{2n-1} \quad \ldots(4)$$

Now, substituting these values on the right hand side of (1), we get

$$\int_{-1}^{1} F(u_1)\,du = w_1\left[c_0 + c_1 u_i + c_2 u_1^2 + c_3 u_1^3 + \ldots + c_{2n-1} u_1^{2n-1}\right]$$

$$+ w_2\left[c_0 + c_1 u_2 + c_2 u_2^2 + c_3 u_2^3 + \ldots + c_{2n-1} u_2^{2n-1}\right]$$

$$+ w_3 \left[c_0 + c_1 u_3 + c_2 u_3^3 + c_3 u_3^3 + \ldots + c_{2n-1} u_3^{2n-1}\right]$$

$$+ \quad \ldots\ldots \quad \ldots\ldots \quad \ldots\ldots \quad \ldots\ldots \quad \ldots\ldots$$

$$+ w_n \left[c_0 + c_1 u_n + c_2 u_n^2 + c_3 u_n^3 + \ldots + c_{2n-1} u_n^{2n-1}\right]$$

$$\Rightarrow \int_{-1}^{1} F(u_i)\, du = c_0 \left[w_1 + w_2 + w_3 + \ldots + w_n\right]$$

$$+ c_1 \left[w_1 u_1 + w_2 u_2 + w_3 u_3 + \ldots + w_n u_n\right]$$

$$+ c_2 \left[w_1 u_1^2 + w_2 u_2^2 + w_3 u_3^2 + \ldots + w_n u_n^2\right]$$

$$+ \quad \ldots \quad \ldots \quad \ldots \quad \ldots \quad \ldots$$

$$+ c_{2n-1} \left[w_1 u_1^{2n-1} + w_2 u_2^{2n-1} + w_3 u_3^{2n-1} + \ldots + w_n u_n^{2n-1}\right] \quad \ldots(5)$$

But the equations (3) and (5) are identical for all values of c_i hence comparing coefficients of c_i, we obtain $2n$ equations in $2n$ unknows w_i and

$u_i\ (i = 1, 2, \ldots, n)$; yielding $w_1 + w_2 + w_3 + \ldots + w_n = 2$

$$w_1 u_1 + w_2 u_2 + w_3 u_3 + \ldots + w_n u_n = 0$$

$$w_1 u_1^2 + w_2 u_2^2 + w_3 u_3^2 + \ldots + w_n u_n^2 = \frac{2}{3}$$

$$\ldots \quad \ldots \quad \ldots \quad \ldots \quad \ldots \quad \ldots \quad \ldots \quad \ldots \quad \ldots \quad \ldots$$

$$w_1 u_1^{2n-1} + w_2 u_2^{2n-1} + w_3 u_3^{2n-1} + \ldots + w_n u_n^{2n-1} = 0.$$

Theoretically, we can obtain n unknows w_i's and u_i's by solving the above of non-liner equations by the usual algebraic methods but partically it is very difficult to solve even for small values of n. In case, we know $u_1, u_2, \ldots, u_n$; the above system can be reduced to a system of linear equations.

It can be shown easily that u_i are the zeros of a set of Legendres polynomials. Here we tabulate the abscissae u_i and the weights w_i for different values of n $(n = 2, 3, 4, 5, 6)$.

Abscissae and Weights for Gaussian Integration (n = 2, 3,..., 6)

n	$\pm u_i$	w_i
2	0.5773502692	1.0000000000
3	0.0000000000	0.8888888889
	0.7745966692	0.5555555556
4	0.3399810436	0.6521451549
	0.8611363116	0.3478548451
5	0.000000000	0.5688888889
	0.5384693101	0.4786286705
	0.9061798459	0.2369268851
6	0.2386191861	0.4679139346
	0.6612093865	0.3607615730
	0.9324695142	0.1713244924

In general, the limits of the integral $\int_a^b f(x)\,dx$ are to be convert to those in (1) with the help of the transformation $x = \frac{1}{2} u(b-a) + \frac{1}{2}(a+b)$.

Example 9: *Compute the value of the definite integral*

$$\int_{.2}^{1.4} (\sin x - \log_e x + e^x)\,dx$$

by **(a)** *the Trapezoidal rule,* **(b)** *Simpson's one-third rule,* **(c)** *Simpson's three-eighth rule,* **(d)** *Weddle's rule. After finding the true value of the integral, compare the errors in the four cases.*

[I.A.S. 2009; Kurukshetra 2005, 2007]

Solution: In this case divide the range of integration into twelve equal parts by taking $h = .1$ and then the values of the function $y = \sin x - \log_e x + e^x$ are computed for each point of sub-division which are as under:

	x	$\sin x$	$\log_e x = \log_{10} x \times 2.30258$	e^x	$y = \sin x - \log_e x + e^x$
x_0	0.2	.19867	−1.60943	1.22140	3.02950
$x_0 + h$	0.3	.29552	−1.20397	1.34986	2.84935
$x_0 + 2h$	0.4	.38942	−.91629	1.49182	2.79753
$x_0 + 3h$	0.5	.47943	−.69315	1.64872	2.82130
$x_0 + 4h$	0.6	.56464	−.51083	1.82212	2.89759
$x_0 + 5h$	0.7	.64422	−.35667	2.01375	3.01464
$x_0 + 6h$	0.8	.71736	−.22314	2.22554	3.16604
$x_0 + 7h$	0.9	.78333	−.10537	2.45960	3.34830
$x_0 + 8h$	1.0	.84147	+.00000	2.71828	3.55975
$x_0 + 9h$	1.1	.89121	.09530	3.00417	3.80008
$x_0 + 10h$	1.2	.93204	.18232	3.32012	4.06984
$x_0 + 11h$	1.3	.96356	.26236	3.66930	4.37050
$x_0 + 12h$	1.4	.98545	.33647	4.05520	4.70418

(a) By Trapezoidal Rule, we have

$$\int_{.2}^{1.4} (\sin x - \log_e x + e^x)\, dx = \int_{.2}^{.2+12\times.1} y\, dx$$

Here $n = 12, h = .1, x_0 = .2, y = \sin x - \log_e x + e^x$.

Again we know that

$$\int_{x_0}^{x_0+nh} = \frac{h}{2}[y_0 + y_n + 2(y_1 + y_2 + \ldots + y_{n-1})].$$

Substituting the values of $h, y_0, y_n, \ldots$, in the above formula, we get

$$\int_{.2}^{1.4} (\sin x - \log_e x + e^x)\, dx = \frac{.1}{2}[3.02950 + 4.70418 + 2(2.8493 + \ldots + 4.37050)]$$

$$= \frac{1}{20}[7.73368 + 2(36.69492)] = 4.05617.$$

(b) By Simpson's '$\frac{1}{3}$' Rule, we have

$$\int_{x_0}^{x_0+nh} y\, dx = \frac{h}{3}[y_0 + y_n + 4(y_1 + y_3 + \ldots) + 2(y_2 + y_4 + \ldots)].$$

$$= \frac{.1}{3}(7.73368 + 4(20.20417) + 3(16.49075))] = \frac{1}{20}[121.53186] = 4.05106.$$

(c) By Simpson's '$\frac{3}{8}$' Rule, we have

$$\int_{x_0}^{x_0+nh} y\,dx = \frac{3h}{8}[y_0 + y_n + 3(y_1 + y_2 + y_4 + y_5 + \ldots) + 2(y_3 + y_6 + \ldots)]$$

$$= \frac{3(.1)}{8}[7.73368 + (26.90750) + 2(9.78742)] = 4.05116.$$

(d) By Weddlle's Rule, we have

$$\int_{x_0}^{x_0+nh} y\,dx = \frac{3h}{10}[y_0 + y_n + 5(y_1 + y_5 + y_7 + y_{11} + \ldots)$$

$$+ y_2 + y_4 + y_8 + y_{10} + 2y_6 + 6(y_3 + y_9)]$$

$$= \frac{3(.1)}{10}[7.73360 + 5(13.58879) + 13.32471 + 2(3.16604) - 6(6.62138)]$$

$$= 4.05098.$$

Again the value of the integral is

$$I = \int_{.2}^{1.4} (\sin x - \log_e x + e^x)\,dx$$

$$= \left[-\cos x - x(\log_e x - 1) + e^x\right]_{.2}^{1.4} = 4.05095.$$

Therefore the errors are:

due to Trapezoidal Rule	−.00522
due to Simpson's '$\frac{1}{3}$' Rule	−.00011
due to Simpson's '$\frac{3}{8}$' Rule	−.00021
due to Weddle's Rule	−.00003

We observe that Weddle's rule is more accurate than other rules.

Example 10: *A curve is drawn to pass through the points given by the following table:*

x :	1	1.5	2	2.5	3	3.5	4
y :	2	2.4	2.7	2.8	3	2.6	2.1

Estimate the area bounded by the curve, the x-axis and the lines $x = 1$, $x = 4$.

Solution: By Simpson's (1/3) Rule, we have required area

$$= \frac{h}{3}[y_0 + 4y_1 + 2y_2 + 4y_3 + \ldots + 4y_{n-1} + y_n]$$

$$= \frac{0.5}{3}[2 + 9.6 + 5.4 + 11.2 + 10.4 + 2.1]$$

$$= \frac{5}{30} \times 46.7 = \frac{23.35}{3} = 7.783 \text{ units of area}$$

By Weddle's Rule, we have required area

$$= \frac{3h}{10}[y_0 + 5y_1 + y_2 + 6y_3 + y_4 + 5y_5 + y_6]$$

$$= \frac{3 \times 0.5}{10}[2 + 12.0 + 2.7 + 16.8 + 3 + 13.0 + 2.1] = 7.74 \text{ units of area}$$

Example 11: *Calculate by Simpson's rule an approximate value of $\int_{-3}^{3} x^4\,dx$ by taking seven equidistant ordinates. Compare it with the exact value and the value obtained by using the Trapezoidal rule.*

[U.P.P.C.S. 2004, 2008; I.A.S. 2008; Indore 2006, 2010; Meerut 2002, 2005]

Solution: Let us divide the range of integration $(-3, 3)$ into six equal parts each of width $= \frac{3-(-3)}{6} = 1$ unit. Hence $h = 1$, value of the function for each point of sub- division are as given below:

x	$y = x^4$
$x_0 = -3$	$(-3)^4 = 81$
$x_0 + h = -2$	$(-2)^4 = 16$
$x_0 + 2h = -1$	$(-1)^4 = 1$
$x_0 + 3h = 0$	$0^4 = 0$
$x_0 + 4h = 1$	$1^4 = 1$
$x_0 + 5h = 2$	$2^4 = 16$
$x_0 + 6h = 3$	$3^4 = 81$

Now, by Simpson's rule, we obtain

$$\int_{-3}^{3} x^4\,dx = \frac{h}{3}[y_0 + y_6 + 4(y_1 + y_3 + y_5) + 2(y_2 + y_4)]$$

$$= \frac{1}{3}[162 + 4 \times 32 + 2 \times 2] = \frac{1}{3} \times 294 = 98.$$

But the exact value of

$$\int_{-3}^{3} x^4\,dx = \left[\frac{x^5}{5}\right]_{-3}^{3} = \frac{1}{5}\left[(3)^5 - (-3)^5\right] = \frac{1}{5} \times 486 = 97.2$$

Also by Trapezoidal rule, we have

$$\int_{-3}^{3} x^4\,dx = \frac{h}{2}\left[y_0 + y_6 + 2(y_1 + y_2 + y_3 + y_4 + y_5)\right]$$

$$= \frac{1}{2}\left[162 + 2 \times 34\right] = 115.$$

Thus it is obvious that the Trapezoidal rule does not give an accurate result. In general Simpson's rule give a better result than Trapezoidal rule.

Example 12: *Evaluate* $\int_0^1 \frac{dx}{1+x^2}$ *by using Simpson's* '$\frac{1}{3}$' *and* '$\frac{3}{8}$' *rule. Hence obtain the approximate value of* π *in each ease.*

[Delhi (H) 2010; Meerut 2001, 2003; I.A.S. 2000, 2006; Avadh 2004, 2010]

Solution: Divide the range into six equal parts each of with $h = \frac{1}{6}$ and compute the value of $y = \frac{1}{1+x^2}$ at each point of sub-division.

These values are given below:

x		$y_x = 1/(1+x^2)$
0	x_0	$(1/1) = 1.0000$
1/6	$x_0 + h$	$36/37 = 0.97297$
2/6	$x_0 + 2h$	$36/40 = 0.90000$
3/6	$x_0 + 3h$	$36/45 = .80000$
4/6	$x_0 + 4h$	$36/52 = .69231$
5/6	$x_0 + 5h$	$36/61 = .59016$
1	$x_0 + 6h$	$1/2 = .50000$

By Simpson's '$\frac{1}{3}$' rule, we have

$$\int_{x_0}^{x_0+6h} y\,dx = \frac{h}{3}[y_0 + y_6 + 4(y_1 + y_3 + y_5) + 2(y_2 + y_4)]$$

$$= \frac{1}{18}[1.00 + .500 + 4(.97297 + .80000 + .59016)] + 2(.900 + .69231)] \quad ...(1)$$

$$= .785395 \text{ (on simplification).}$$

By Simpson's '$\frac{3}{8}$' rule, we have

$$\int_{x_0}^{x_0+6h} y\,dx = \frac{3h}{8}[y_0 + y_6 + 3(y_1 + y_2 + y_4 + y_5) + 2(y_3)]$$

$$= \frac{1}{16}(1.5000 + 3(.97297 + .900 + .69231 + .59016 + 2 \times (.800)]$$

$$= .785395. \quad ...(2)$$

Again, $$\int_0^1 \frac{dx}{1+x^2} = \left[\tan^{-1} x\right]_0^1 = \frac{\pi}{4} \quad ...(3)$$

From (1) and (2), we get $\pi = 3.14188$ and from (2) and (3), we get $\pi = 3.141580$.

Example 13: *Evaluate* $\int_0^6 \frac{dx}{1+x^2}$ *by using* **(a)** *Trapezoidal rule*

(b) *Simpson's '$\frac{1}{3}$' rule* **(c)** *Simpson's '$\frac{3}{8}$' rule, and* **(d)** *Weddle's rule*

[Kurukshetra 2004, 2007; Rohilkhand 2008, 2010; Bhopal 2005, 2009]

Solution: We divide the range (0, 6) into six equal parts each of width $h = 1$ and compute the values of $y = \frac{1}{1+x^2}$ at each point of sub-division.

The computed values are as follows:

	x_0	x_0+h	x_0+2h	x_0+3h	x_0+4h	x_0+5h	x_0+6h
x:	0	1	2	3	4	5	6
y_x:	1.00	.500	.200	.100	.058824	.038462	.027027

(a) Trapezoidal rule,

$$\int_0^6 \frac{dx}{1+x^2} = \frac{h}{2}[(y_0+y_6)+2(y_1+y_2+y_3+y_4+y_5)]$$

$$= \frac{1}{2}[(1+.027)+2(.5+.2+.1+.0588+.0385)] = 1.4108.$$

(b) Simpson's (1/3) rule,

$$\int_0^6 \frac{dx}{1+x^2} = \frac{h}{3}[(y_0+y_6)+4(y_1+y_3+y_5)+2(y_2+y_4)]$$

$$= \frac{1}{3}[(1+0.027)+4(0.5+0.1+0.0385)+2(0.2+0.0588)] = 1.3662.$$

(c) Simpson's 3/8 rule,

$$\int_0^6 \frac{dx}{1+x^2} = \frac{3h}{8}[(y_0+y_6)+3(y_1+y_2+y_4+y_5)+2y_3]$$

$$= \frac{3}{8}[(1+0.027)+3(0.5+0.2+0.0588+0.0385)+2(0.1)] = 1.3571.$$

(d) Weddle's rule,

$$\int_0^6 \frac{dxc}{1+x^2} = \frac{3h}{10}[y_0+5y_1+y_2+6y_3+y_4+5y_5+y_6]$$

$$= 0.3[1+5(0.5)+0.2+6(0.1)+0.0588+5(0.0385)+0.027] = 1.3735$$

Also $\int_0^6 \frac{dx}{1+x^2} = [\tan^{-1} x]_0^6 = \tan^{-1} 6 = 1.4056$

Hence the value of the integral found by Weddle's rule is the nearest to the actual value followed by its value given by Simpson's 1/3 rule.

Example 14: *Calculate (up to 3 places of decimal)* $\int_2^{10} \frac{dx}{1+x}$ *by dividing the range into eight equal parts.* **[Meerut 2001, 2007; Rajasthan 2008, 2010]**

Solution: Dividing the whole range of integration *i.e.* (2, 10) into eight equal parts each of width $h = 1$, *computed values of* $y = \frac{1}{1+x}$ *at each point of subdivision; the computed values are as follows*:

x :	$x_0 = 2$	3	4	5	6	7	8	9	$10 = x_0 + 8h$
$y_x = \frac{1}{1+x}$	$\frac{1}{3}$	$\frac{1}{4}$	$\frac{1}{5}$	$\frac{1}{6}$	$\frac{1}{7}$	$\frac{1}{8}$	$\frac{1}{9}$	$\frac{1}{10}$	$\frac{1}{11}$

By Simpson's '$\frac{1}{3}$' rule, we get

$$\int_{x_0}^{x_0+8h} y\,dx = \frac{h}{3}[y_{x_0} + y_{x_0+8h} + 4(y_{x_0+h} \ldots + y_{x_0+7h})] + 2(y_{x_0+2h} + \ldots + y_{x_0+6h})]$$

$$= \frac{1}{3}\left[\frac{1}{3} + \frac{1}{11} + 4\left\{\frac{1}{4} + \frac{1}{6} + \frac{1}{8} + \frac{1}{10}\right\} + 2\left\{\frac{1}{5} + \frac{1}{7} + \frac{1}{9}\right\}\right]$$

$$= 1.2996$$

Example 15: *Show that* $\int_0^1 \frac{dx}{1+x} = \log 2 = 0.69315$.

Solution: Dividing the whole range (0, 1) into 10 equal parts making use of Simpson's '$\frac{1}{3}$' rule, we have

$$\int_0^1 \frac{dx}{1+x} = \int_{x_0}^{x_0+10h} y\,dx = \frac{h}{3}[y_0 + y_{10} + 4(y_1 + \ldots + y_9) + 2(y_2 + \ldots + y_8)]$$

$$= \frac{1}{3}\left[1 + \frac{1}{2} + 4\left(\frac{1}{1.1} + \frac{1}{1.3} + \frac{1}{1.5} + \frac{1}{1.7} + \frac{1}{1.9}\right) + 2\left(\frac{1}{1.2} + \frac{1}{1.4} + \frac{1}{1.6} + \frac{1}{1.8}\right)\right]$$

$$= \frac{1}{30}[1.5 + 4 \times 3.45955 + 2 \times 2.72818]$$

$$= \frac{1}{18}[20.79456] = .693152 = .69315 \quad \text{upto five decimal places.}$$

Again $\int_0^1 \frac{1}{1+x}\,dx = [\log(1+x)]_0^1 = \log 2$.

Hence $\log 2 = \int_0^1 \frac{1}{1+x}\,dx = .69315$.

Example 16: *Calculate* $\int_0^{\pi/2} e^{\sin x}\, dx$ *correct to four decimal places.*

Solution: Divide the range $(0, \pi/2)$ into three equal parts taking $h = \pi/6$, and compute the values of the function at each points of sub-division.

The values of the function are given below:

x :	0	$\pi/6$	$\pi/3$	$\pi/2$
$y_x = e^{\sin x}$:	1	1.64872	2.45960	2.71828

By Simpson's '$\frac{3}{8}$' rule, we have

$$\int_0^{\pi/2} e^{\sin x}\, dx = \frac{3h}{8}[y_0 + y_3 + 3(y_1 + y_2)]$$

$$= \frac{3}{8} \cdot \frac{\pi}{6}[1 + 2.71828 + 3(1.64872 + 2.45960)]$$

$$= \frac{\pi}{16}[3.71828 + 12.32496] = \frac{\pi}{16}[16.04324] = 3.150722930.$$

Example 17: *Find the value of* $\log 3$ *from* $\int_0^1 \frac{x^2}{1+x^3}\, dx$*, using Simpson's '*$\frac{1}{3}$*' rule, by dividing the range into four equal parts.*

Also find the error. **[Agra 2003; Avadh 2003]**

Solution: Divide the whole range (0, 1) into four equal parts taking $h = .25$. The values of the function $y = \frac{x^2}{1+x^3}$ at the point of sub-division are given below:

x :	0	.25	.50	.75	1.000
y_x :	0	.06153	.22222	.39560	.5000

By Simpson's '$\frac{1}{3}$' rule, we have

$$\int_0^1 \frac{x^2}{1+x^3}\, dx = \int_{x_0}^{x_0+4h} y\, dx = \frac{h}{3}[y_0 + y_4 + 4(y_1 + y_3) + 2y_2]$$

$$= \frac{.25}{3}[0 + .500 + 4(.06153 + .39560) + 2(.22222)]$$

$$= \frac{.25}{3}[.500 + 1.82852 + .4444] = .23108.$$

Again actual value of the integral is

$$\int_0^1 \frac{x^2}{1+x^2}\,dx = \frac{1}{3}\left[\log(1+x^3)\right]_0^1 = \frac{1}{3}\log 2 = \frac{1}{3}(.69315) = .23105$$

Therefore the error $= .23105 - .23108 = -.00003$.

Example 18: *Evaluate* $\int_0^4 e^x\,dx$, *by Simpson's rule, using the data* $e = 2.72$, $e^2 = 7.39$, $e^3 = 20.09$, $e^4 = 54.60$ *and compare it with the actual value.* **[Lucknow 2009; Avadh 2005]**

Solution: Divide the whole range (0, 4) into four equal parts by taking $h = 1$. By Simpson's '$\frac{1}{3}$' rule, we have

$$\int_0^4 e^x\,dx = \int_{x_0}^{x_0+4h} y\,dx = \frac{h}{3}[y_0 + y_4 + 4(y_1 + y_3) + 2y_2]$$

$$= \frac{1}{3}[1 + 54.60 + 4(2.72 + 20.09) + 2(7.39)]$$

$$= \frac{1}{3}[55.60 + 91.24 + 14.78] = \frac{1}{3}[161.62] = 53.873.$$

The actual value of the integral is

$$\int_0^4 e^x\,dx = e^4 - e^0 = 54.60 - 1.00 = 53.60.$$

Example 19: *Evaluate* $\int_4^{5.2} \log_e x\,dx$ *by* **(a)** *Simpson's '*$\frac{1}{3}$*'* **(b)** *'*$\frac{3}{8}$*' rule.* **(c)** *Weddle's rule.*

After finding the true value of the integral, compare the errors in three cases.

[Lucknow 2008; Bhopal 2002]

Solution: Divide the whole range of integration *i.e.* (4, 5.2) into six equal parts taking $h = .2$ and then compute the values of the function $f(x) = \log_e x$ for each of sub-division. These computed values are as follows:

x	$y = \log_e x$	x	$y = \log_e x$
$x_0 = 4.0$	1.38629436	$x_0 + 4h = 4.8$	1.56861592
$x_0 + h = 4.2$	1.43508453	$x_0 + 5h = 5.0$	1.60943791
$x_0 + 2h = 4.4$	1.48160454	$x_0 + 6h = 5.2$	1.64865863
$x_0 + 3h = 4.6$	1.52605630		

(a) By Simpson's '$\frac{1}{3}$' rule, we have

$$\int_4^{5.2} \log_e x\,dx = \frac{h}{3}[y_0 + y_6 + 4(y_1 + y_3 + y_5) + 2(y_2 + y_4)]$$

$$= \frac{.2}{8}[3.03495299 + 4(4.57056874) + 2(3.05022046)] = 1.82784726.$$

(b) By Simpson's '$\frac{3}{8}$' rule, we have

$$\int_4^{5.2} \log_e x\,dx = \frac{3h}{8}[y_0 + y_2 + 3(y_1 + y_2 + y_4 + y_5) + 2y_3]$$

$$= \frac{3(.2)}{8}[3.03495299 + 3(6.09424290) + 2(1.52605630)]$$

$$= \frac{.3}{4}[24.37129429l] = 1.82784707.$$

(c) By Weddle's rule, we have

$$\int_4^{5.2} \log_e x\,dx = \frac{3h}{10}[y_0 + y_6 + 5(y_1 + y_5) + y_2 + y_4 + 6y_3]$$

$$= \frac{3(.2)}{10}[3.03495299 + 5(3.04452244) + 3.05022046 + 5(1.52605630)]$$

$$= 1.82784741.$$

Again exact value of the integral is

$$\int_{4.0}^{5.2} \log_e x\,dx = \Big[x(\log_e x - 1)\Big]_{4.0}^{5.2} = 1.82784741$$

Hence the errors are

(a) Due to Sympson's '$\frac{1}{3}$' rule = .00000015.

(b) Due to Simpson's '$\frac{3}{8}$' rule = .00000034.

(c) Due to Weddle's rule = zero.

Therefore, we conclude that in this case Weddle's rule is more accurate than Simpson's '$\frac{1}{3}$' and '$\frac{3}{8}$' rule.

Example 20: *Calculate an approximate value of* $\int_0^{\pi/2} \sin x \, dx$ *by* **(a)** *the Trapezoidal rule,* **(b)** *Simpson's rule, using* 11 *ordinates.*

Solution: Divide the range of integration into ten equal parts taking $h = \pi/20$ and then compute the values of the function $f(x) = \sin x$ for each point of sub-division. These computed values are as follows:

x	$y = \sin x$	x	$y = \sin x$
$x_0 = 0$	.00000		
$x_0 + h = \pi/20$	.15663	$x_0 + 6h = 6\pi/20$	.80900
$x_0 + 2h = 2\pi/20$	.30902	$x_0 + 7h = 7\pi/20$	.89101
$x_0 + 3h = 3\pi/20$	.45399	$x_0 + 8h = 8\pi/20$	.95106
$x_0 + 4h = 4\pi/20$	.58778	$x_0 + 9h = 9\pi/20$	.98769
$x_0 + 5h = 5\pi/20$	.70711	$x_0 + 10h = 10\pi/20$	1.00000

(a) By the Trapezoidal rule, we have

$$\int_0^{\pi/2} \sin x \, dx = \frac{h}{2}[y_0 + y_{10} + 2(y_1 + y_2 + \ldots + y_9)]$$

$$= \frac{(\pi/20)}{2}[1.00000 + 2(5.85311)] = \frac{\pi}{40}[12.70622] = .9981.$$

(b) By Simpson's '$\frac{1}{3}$' Rule, we have

$$\int_0^{\pi/2} \sin x \, dx = \frac{h}{3}[y_0 + y_{10} + 4(y_1 + y_3 + \ldots + y_9) + 2(y_2 + y_4 + \ldots + y_8)]$$

$$= \frac{\pi}{60}[1.00000 + 4(3.19623) + 2(2.65688)]$$

$$= \frac{\pi}{60}[1.00000 + 12.78492 + 5.31376] = \frac{\pi}{60}[19.09868] = 1.0006.$$

Again the exact value of the integral

$$\int_0^{\pi/2} \sin x \, dx = \left[-\cos x\right]_0^{\pi/2} = 1.0000$$

Therefore the error

(a) Due to Simpson's '$\frac{1}{3}$' rule $= -.0006$.

(b) Due to Trapezoidal rule $= .0019$.

Example 21: *Use Simpson's rule to prove that* $\log_e 7$ *is approximately* 1.9587 *using* $\int_1^7 \frac{dx}{x}$.

[U.P.P.C.S. 2006; I.A.S. 2003; Lucknow 2005, 2009; Allahabad 2003, 2007; Bangaluru 2008]

Solution: Let us divide the range (1, 7) into six equal parts, each of width 1 unit. Hence $h = 1$. The values of y for each point of sub-division are as given below:

x :	$x_0 = 1$	$x_1 = 2$	$x_2 = 3$	$x_3 = 4$	$x_4 = 5$	$x_5 = 6$	$x_6 = 7$
y :	$y_0 = 1$	$y_1 = 1/2$	$y_2 = 1/3$	$y_3 = 1/4$	$y_4 = 1/5$	$y_5 = 1/5$	$y_6 = 1/7$

Whence using Simpson's '1/3' rule, we obtain

$$\int_1^7 \frac{dx}{x} = \frac{h}{3}\left[y_0 + y_6 + 4(y_1 + y_3 + y_5) + 2(y_2 + y_4)\right]$$

$$= \frac{1}{3}\left[1.1428571 + 3.6666665 + 1.0666667\right] = \frac{1}{3} \times 5.8761905$$

$$= 1.9587302 = 1.9587.$$

Also, the exact value of $\int_1^7 \frac{dx}{x} = \left[\log x\right]_0^7 = \log_e 7$.

$\therefore \qquad \log_e 7 = 1.9587.$

Example 22: *The velocity* v (km / min) *of a moped which starts from rest, is given at fixed intervals of time* t *(min) as follows:*

t	2	4	6	8	10	12	14	16	18	20
v	10	18	25	29	31	20	11	5	2	0

Estimate approximately the distance covered in 20 *minutes.*

Solution: If s (km) be the distance covered in t (min), then we have

$$\frac{ds}{dt} = v$$

$$\Rightarrow \quad [s]_0^{20} = \int_0^{20} v\,dt = \frac{h}{3}[X + 4.\rho + 2.E], \text{ by Simpson's rule}$$

Here $\qquad h = 2, v_0 = 0, v_1 = 10, v_2 = 18, v_3 = 25$ etc.

$\Rightarrow \qquad X = v_0 + v_{10} = 0 + 0 = 0$

$$\rho = v_1 + v_3 + v_5 + v_7 + v_9 = 10 + 25 + 32 + 11 + 2 = 80$$

$$E = v_2 + v_4 + v_6 + v_8 = 18 + 29 + 20 + 5 = 72$$

Hence the required distance

$$= [s]_0^{20} = \frac{2}{3}(0 + 4 \times 80 + 2 \times 72) = 309.33 \text{ km}.$$

Example 23: *A solid of revolution is formed by rotating about the x-axis, the area between the x-axis, the lines $x = 0$ and a curve through the points with the following co-ordinates:*

x	0.00	0.25	0.50	0.75	1.00
y	1.0000	0.9896	0.9589	0.9089	0.8415

Estimate the volume of the solid formed using Simpson's rule.

[Calicut B.Tech. 2003, 2007; I.A.S. 2007]

Solution: Here $h = 0.25$, $y_0 = 1$, $y_1 = 0.9896$, $y_2 = 0.9589$ etc.

Then the required of the solid generated

$$= \int_0^1 \pi y^2 \, dx = \pi \cdot \frac{h}{3} [(y_0^2 + y_4^2) + 4(y_1^2 + y_3^2) + 2y_2^2]$$

$$= \frac{0.25\pi}{3} [\{1 + (0.8415)^2\} + 4\{(0.9896)^2 + (0.9089)^2\} + 2(0.9589)^2]$$

$$= 0.2618 (10.7687) = 2.8192.$$

Example 24: *Evaluate $\int_{0.5}^{0.7} x^{1/2} e^{-x} \, dx$ approximately by using a suitable formula.*

[M.D.U. (Rohtak) 2003, 2007; Rohilkhand 2001, 2004, 2009]

Solution: Let us divide the range of integration (.5, .7) into 4 equal parts each of width $\frac{.7 - .5}{4} = .05; h = .05$. The values of y for each point of sub-division are as given below:

x	$y = x^{1/2} e^{-x}$
$x_0 = .50$	.4288818
$x_0 + h = .55$	.4278774
$x_0 + 2h = .60$	.4251076
$x_0 + 3h = .65$	.4208867
$x_0 + 4h = .70$	.4154730

Whence using Simpson's '1/3' rule, we obtain

$$\int_{.5}^{.7} x^{1/2} e^{-x} \, dx = \frac{h}{3} [y_0 + y_4 + 4(y_1 + y_3) + 2y_2]$$

$$= \frac{.05}{3} [.8443548 + 3.3950564 + .8502152] = .0848271.$$

Example 25: *If the third order differences are constant, prove that*

$$\int_0^2 U_x\,dx = \frac{1}{24}\left[U_{-1/2} + 23U_{1/2} + 23U_{3/2} + U_{5/2}\right].$$

Solution: The third order differences are given to be constant, so we may take U_x as a polynomial of degree 3. *i.e.*

$$U_x = a + bx + cx^2 + dx^3 \qquad ...(1)$$

Now, changing the scale to two times, we have to prove that

$$\int_0^4 U_x\,dx = \frac{1}{12}[U_{-1} + 23\,U_1 + 23\,U_3 + U_5].$$

Shifting the origin to -2, we have to prove that

$$\int_{-2}^{2} U_x\,dx = \frac{1}{12}[U_{-3} + 23\,U_{-1} + 23\,U_1 + U_3]. \qquad ...(2)$$

Now, L.H.S. of (2) $= \int_{-2}^{2} U_x\,dx = \int_{-2}^{2}(a + bx + cx^2 + dx^3)\,dx$

$$= \left[ax + \frac{bx^2}{2} + \frac{cx^3}{3} + \frac{dx^4}{4}\right]_{-2}^{2} = 2\left(2a + \frac{8c}{3}\right) = 4a + \frac{16c}{3}$$

and R.H.S. of (2) $= \frac{1}{12}[(U_{-3} + U_3) + 23\,(U_{-1} + U_1)]$

$$= \frac{1}{12}[2\,(a + 9c) + 232\,(a + c)] = \frac{1}{6}(24a + 32c) = 4a + \frac{16c}{3} = \textbf{L.H.S.}$$

Example 26: *If third differences are constant, prove that*

$$\int_{-1}^{1} f(x)\,dx = \frac{2}{3}[f(0) + f(1/\sqrt{2}) + f(-1/\sqrt{2})].$$

[Bhopal 2010; Avadh 2004, 2010; Allahabad 2010]

Solution: The third differences are given to be constant, so we consider $f(x)$ as a polynomial of degree 3

$$\Rightarrow \qquad f(x) = a + bx + cx^2 + dx^3 \qquad ...(1)$$

Now $\qquad$ L.H.S. $= \int_{-1}^{1} f(x)\,dx = \int_{-1}^{1}(a + bx + cx^2 + dx^3)\,dx$

$$= \left[ax + \frac{bx^2}{2} + \frac{cx^3}{3} + \frac{dx^4}{4}\right]_{-1}^{1} = 2\left(a + \frac{c}{3}\right)$$

and R.H.S. $= \frac{2}{3}\left[a + \left(a + \frac{b}{\sqrt{2}} + \frac{c}{2} + \frac{d}{2\sqrt{2}}\right) + \left(a - \frac{b}{\sqrt{2}} + \frac{c}{2} - \frac{d}{2\sqrt{2}}\right)\right]$, with the help of (1)

$$= \frac{2}{3}(3a + c) = 2\left(a + \frac{c}{3}\right) = \textbf{L.H.S.}$$

Example 27: *Use Euler-Maclaurin's formula to prove that*

$$\sum_{1}^{n} x^2 = \frac{n(n+1)(2n+1)}{6}.$$

Solution: Euler-Maclaurin formula is given by

$$\frac{1}{h}\int_{x_0}^{x_0+nh} f(x)\,dx = \sum_{i=0}^{n} f(x_i) - \frac{1}{2}[f(x_n) + f(x_0)]$$

$$-\frac{h}{12}[f'(x_0+nh) - f'(x_0)] + \frac{h^3}{720}[f'''(x_0+nh) - f'''(x_0)] - \ldots$$

Now, putting $f(x) = x^2$, $f'(x) = 2x$, $x_0 = 0$, $h = 1$, $x_0 + nh = n$, $x_i = x_0 + ih = i$; we easily obtain

$$\int_0^n x^2\,dx = \sum_{i=0}^{n} i^2 - \frac{1}{2}[n^2 + 0] - \frac{1}{12}[2n - 0],$$

[∵ third and higher order derivatives of x^2 are zero.]

$$\Rightarrow \qquad \frac{n^3}{3} = \sum_{i=0}^{n} i^2 - \frac{1}{2}n^2 - \frac{n}{6}.$$

$$\Rightarrow \qquad \sum_{i=0}^{n} i^2 = \frac{n^3}{3} + \frac{n^2}{2} + \frac{n}{6} = \frac{2n^3 + 3n^2 + n}{6} = \frac{n(2n^2 + 3n + 1)}{6} = \frac{n(n+1)(2n+1)}{6}$$

$$\Rightarrow \qquad \sum_{i=1}^{n} x^2 = \frac{n(n+1)(2n+1)}{6}.$$

Example 28: *Prove Simpson's formula*

$$\int_a^b f(x)\,dx = \frac{b-a}{6n}[f(x_0) + 4f(x_1) + 2f(x_2) + \ldots + f(x_{2n})],$$

where $x_0 = a$, $x_{2n} = b$ *and use it to evaluate*

$\int_0^2 \frac{dx}{x}$ *and give estimates of error for* $n = 1$ *and* 2 *given that* $\log_e 2 = 0.69315$.

Solution: We know that Simpson's '$\frac{1}{3}$' rule is

$$\int_{x_0}^{x_0+nh} f(x)\,dx = \frac{h}{3}[f(x_0) + f(x_0+nh) + 4\{f(x_0+h) + f(x_0+3h) + \ldots\}$$

$$+ 2\{f(x_0+2h) + f(x_0+4h) + \ldots\}].$$

Now putting $x_0 = a$, $n = 2n$, $x_0 + 2nh = x_{2n} = b$ and $h = \frac{b-a}{2n}$, we get the required form of Simpson's rule.

When $n=1$, the whole range $(1,2)$, is divided into two equal parts by three ordinates x_0, x_1, x_2. Thus the above formula reduces to

$$\int_1^2 \frac{dx}{x} = \int_{x_0}^{x_2} f(x)\, dx, \quad \text{where } f(x) = \frac{1}{x}, x_2 = 2, x_0 = 1$$

$$= \frac{b-a}{6n}[f(x_0) + 4f(x_1) + f(x_2)]$$

$$= \frac{2-1}{6\times 1}\left\{\frac{1}{1} + \frac{4}{(3/2)} + \frac{1}{2}\right\} = \frac{1}{6}\times\frac{25}{6} = \frac{25}{36} = .69444.$$

Again, when $n=2$, divide the whole range $(1,2)$ into four equal parts by the ordinates $x_0 = 1, x_1, x_2, x_3, x_4 = 2$. Thus we have

$$\int_1^2 \frac{dx}{x} = \int_{x_0}^{x_4} f(x)\, dx = \frac{b-a}{6n}[f(x_0) + 4f(x_1) + 2f(x_2) + 4f(x_3) + f(x_4)]$$

$$= \left[\frac{1}{12} + 4\frac{1}{(5/4)} + 2.\frac{1}{(3/2)} + 4.\frac{1}{(7/4)} + \frac{1}{2}\right]$$

$$= \frac{1}{12}\left[1 + \frac{16}{5} + \frac{4}{3} + \frac{16}{7} + \frac{1}{2}\right]$$

$$= \frac{1}{12}\left[\frac{210 + 672 + 280 + 480 + 105}{210}\right] = \frac{1}{12}\left(\frac{1347}{210}\right) = .69325.$$

The exact value is $\int_1^2 \frac{dx}{x} = [\log x]_1^2 = \log 2 = .69315$.

Therefore the error when $n=1$ is $.69315 - .69444 = -.00129$ and when $n=2$ is $.69315 - .69325 = -.0001$.

Example 29: *If $f(x)$ is a polynomial in x of the third degree, find an expression for $\int_0^1 f(x)\, dx$ in term of $f(0)$, $f(1)$, $f(2)$ and $f(3)$.*

Use this result to show that $\int_1^2 f(x)\, dx = \frac{1}{24}[-f(0) + 13f(1) + 13f(2) - f(3)]$

Solution: By Lagrange's formula, we know that

$$f(x) = \frac{(x-1)(x-2)(x-3)}{(-1)(-2)(-3)} f(0) + \frac{(x-0)(x-2)(x-3)}{(1)(-1)(-2)} f(1)$$

$$+ \frac{x(x-1)(x-3)}{(2)(1)(-1)} f(2) + \frac{x(x-1)(x-2)}{(3)(2)(1)} f(3)$$

$$= -\frac{1}{6}[x^3 - 6x^2 + 11x - 6]\, f(0) + \frac{1}{2}(x^3 - 5x^2 + 6x)\, f(1) - \frac{1}{2}x^3 - 4x^2 + 3x)\, f(2)$$

$$+ \frac{1}{6}(x^3 - 3x^2 + 2x)\, f(3)$$

$$\therefore \int_0^1 f(x)\,dx = \left[-\frac{1}{6}\left(\frac{x^4}{4} - \frac{6x^3}{3} + \frac{11x^2}{3} - 6x\right) f(0) + \frac{1}{2}\left(\frac{x^4}{4} - \frac{5x^3}{3} + \frac{6x^2}{2}\right) f(1)\right.$$

$$\left. - \frac{1}{2}\left[\left(\frac{x^4}{6} - \frac{4x^3}{3} + \frac{3x^2}{2}\right) f(2) + \frac{1}{6}\left(\frac{x^4}{4} - \frac{3x^3}{3} + \frac{2x^2}{2}\right) f(3)\right]\right]_0^t$$

$$= -\frac{1}{6}\left(\frac{t^4}{6} - \frac{6t^3}{3} + \frac{11t^2}{3} - 6t\right) f(0) + \frac{1}{2}\left(\frac{t^4}{4} - \frac{5t^3}{3} + \frac{6t^2}{2}\right) f(1)$$

$$- \frac{1}{2}\left(\frac{t^4}{4} - \frac{4t^3}{3} + \frac{3t^2}{2}\right) f(2) + \frac{1}{6}\left(\frac{t^4}{4} - t^3 + t^2\right) f(3). \quad ...(1)$$

Now putting $t = 2$ in (1), we get

$$\int_1^2 f(x)\,dx = \frac{1}{3} f(0) + \frac{4}{3} f(1) + \frac{1}{3} f(2) \quad ...(2)$$

and putting $t = 1$ in (1), we get

$$\int_0^1 f(x)\,dx = \frac{3}{8} f(0) + \frac{19}{24} f(1) - \frac{5}{24} f(2) + \frac{1}{24} f(3). \quad ...(3)$$

Subtracting (3) from (2), we have

$$\int_1^2 f(x)\,dx = -\frac{1}{24} f(0) + \frac{13}{24} f(1) + \frac{13}{24} f(2) + \frac{1}{24} f(3)].$$

$$= \frac{1}{24}[-f(0) + 13 f(1) + 13 f(2) - f(3)].$$

Example 30: *If $f(x) = a + bx + cx^2$ prove that*

$$\int_1^2 f(x)\,dx = \frac{1}{12}[f(0) + 22 f(2) + f(4)].$$

Solution: Since $f(x)$ is a polynomial of second degree in x, so that in this case third and higher differences are zero, also here we have $h = 2$.

Again $\quad f(x) = f\left(\frac{x}{2} 2\right) = f\left(\frac{x}{2} . h\right) = E^{x/2} f(0)$

$$= (1 + \Delta)^{x/2} f(0) = f(0) + \frac{x}{2}\Delta f(0) + \frac{\frac{x}{2}\left(\frac{x}{2} - 1\right)}{2}\Delta^2 f(0) \text{ (other terms vanish)}$$

$$\therefore \quad \int_1^3 f(x)\,dx = \int_1^3 \left[f(0) + \frac{x}{2}\Delta f(0) + \frac{\frac{x^2}{4} - \frac{x}{2}}{2}\Delta^2 f(0) \right] dx$$

$$= \left[xf(0) \frac{+x^2}{4} \Delta f(0) + \frac{\frac{x^3}{12} - \frac{x^3}{4}}{2} \Delta^2 f(0) \right]_1^3$$

$$= 2f(0) + 2\Delta f(0) + \frac{1}{12}\Delta^2 f(0)$$

$$= 2f(0) + 2[f(2) - f(0)] + \frac{1}{12}[f(4) - 2f(2) + f(0)]$$

$$= \frac{1}{12}[f(0) + 22f(2) + f(4)].$$

Example 31: *If* $U_x = a + bx + cx^2$, *prove that*

$$\int_1^3 U_x\,dx = 2U_2 + \frac{1}{12}(U_0 - 2U_2 + U_4)$$

and find approximation to $\int_{-1/2}^{1/2} e^{-(x^2/10)}\,dx$.

[Bhopal 2002, 2007]

Solution: Shifting the origin to -2, we have to prove that

$$\int_{-1}^{1} U_x\,dx = 2U_0 + \frac{1}{12}(U_{-2} - 2U_0 + U_2). \quad \text{...(1)}$$

Now L.H.S. of (1)

$$\int_{-1}^{1} U_x\,dx = \int_{-1}^{1}(a + bx + cx^2)\,dx = \left[ax + \frac{bx^2}{2} + \frac{cx^3}{3}\right]_{-1}^{1} = 2\left(a + \frac{c}{3}\right).$$

Again $\quad U_x = a + bx + cx^2$

$$\therefore \quad U_0 = a; U_{-2} = a - 2b + 4c; U_2 = a + 2b + 4c$$

$\therefore$ R.H.S. of (1) $= 2U_0 + \frac{1}{12}(U_{-2} - 2U_0 + U_2) = 2a + \frac{1}{12}(2a + 8c - 2a) = 2\left(a + \frac{c}{3}\right) =$ L.H.S.

Now changing the scale to $\frac{1}{2}$ in (1), we get

$$\int_{-1/2}^{1/2} U_x\,dx = \frac{1}{2}\left[2U_0 + \frac{1}{12}(U_{-1} - 2U_0 + U_1)\right] = U_0 + \frac{1}{24}(U_{-1} - 2U_0 + U_1).$$

Now putting $U_x = e^{-(x^2/10)}$, we get

$$\int_{-1/2}^{1/2} e^{-(x^2/10)}\,dx = 1 + \frac{1}{24}\left(e^{-(1/10)} + e^{-(1/10)} - 2\right) = 1 + \frac{1}{12}\left(e^{-(1/10)} - 1\right)$$

Example 32: *Obtain the approximate quadrature formula.*

(a) $\int_{-1/2}^{3/2} f(x)\,dx = \frac{1}{24}[27f(0) + 17f(1) + 5f(2) - f(3)]$

(b) $\int_{-1}^{1} f(x)\,dx = \frac{1}{12}[13\{f(1) + f(-1)\} - \{f(3) + f(-3)\}]$

(c) $\int_{0}^{2} f(x)\,dx = \frac{1}{24}[f(-\frac{1}{2}) + 23f(\frac{1}{2}) + 23f(\frac{3}{2}) + f(\frac{5}{2})]$, *if third differences are constant.*

(d) $\int_{-1/2}^{1/2} f(x)\,dx = \frac{1}{2}\{f(-\frac{1}{2}) + f(\frac{1}{2})\} - \frac{1}{24}\{\Delta f(-\frac{3}{2}) - \Delta f(\frac{1}{2})\}$.

Solution: (a) Here we are to obtain a formula in terms of $f(0), f(1), f(2), f(3)$ so the third differences are considered to be constant.

$$\therefore \int_{-1/2}^{3/2} f(x)\,dx = \int_{-1/2}^{3/2}\left[f(0) + x\Delta f(0) + \frac{x(x-1)}{2!}\Delta^2 f(0) + \frac{x(x-1)(x-2)}{3!}\Delta^3 f(0)\right]dx$$

$$= \left[x f(0) + \frac{x^2}{2}\Delta f(0) + \frac{1}{2}\left(\frac{x^3}{3} - \frac{x^2}{2}\right)\Delta^2 f(0) + \frac{1}{6}\left(x^4 - x^3 + x^2\right)\Delta^3 f(0)\right]_{-1/2}^{3/2}$$

$$= 2f(0) + \Delta f(0) + \frac{1}{12}\Delta^2 f(0) + \frac{1}{6}\left(-\frac{1}{4}\right)\Delta^3 f(0)$$

$$= 2f(0) + f(1) - f(0) + \frac{1}{12}[f(2) - 2f(1) + f(0)] - \frac{1}{24}[f(3) - 3f(2) + 3f(1) - f(0)]$$

$$= \frac{1}{24}[27f(0) + 17f(1) + 5f(2) - f(3)].$$

(b) In this case we have to derive a formula in terms of $f(-3), f(-1), f(1), f(3)$; obviously $x_0 = -3$ and $h = 2$.

Now $\quad f(x) = f(-3+3+x) = f\left(-3 + \frac{3+x}{2}.2\right)$

$$= f\left(-3 + \frac{3+x}{2}h\right) \text{ [form } f(a+nh)]$$

$$\therefore\ f(x) = E^{(3+x)/2}\, f(-3) = \left[f(-3) + \frac{x+3}{2}\Delta f(-3) + \frac{\frac{x+3}{2}\cdot\left(\frac{x+3}{2}-1\right)}{2}\Delta^2 f(-3)\right.$$

$$\left. + \frac{\frac{x+3}{2}\left(\frac{x+3}{2}-1\right)\left(\frac{x+3}{2}-2\right)}{6}\Delta^3 f(-3)\right]$$

considering upto third differences.

$$\therefore\ \int_{-1}^{1} f(x)\,dx = \int_{-1}^{1}\left[f(-3) + \frac{x+3}{2}\Delta f(-3) + \frac{\frac{x+3}{2}\cdot\left(\frac{x+3}{2}-1\right)}{2}\Delta^2 f(-3)\right.$$

$$\left. + \frac{\frac{x+3}{2}\left(\frac{x+3}{2}-1\right)\left(\frac{x+3}{2}-2\right)}{6}\Delta^3 f(-3)\right] dx$$

$$= \left[x\, f(-3) + \frac{1}{2}\left(\frac{x^3}{2-} + 3x\right)\Delta f(-3) + \frac{1}{2}\left\{\frac{\frac{x^3}{3} + \frac{6x^2}{2} + 9x}{4} - \frac{\frac{x^2}{2} + 3x}{2}\right\}\Delta^2 f(-3)\right.$$

$$\left. + \frac{1}{6}\left\{\frac{\frac{x^4}{4}\cdot\frac{9x^3}{3} + 27\frac{x^2}{2} + 27x}{8} - \frac{3}{4}\left(\frac{x^3}{3} + 6x^2 + 9x\right) + \frac{3}{2}\left(\frac{x^3}{2} + 3x\right)\right\}\Delta^3 f(-3)\right]_{-1}^{1}$$

$$= 2f(-3) + \frac{1}{2}6\Delta f(-3) + \frac{1}{2}\left(\frac{5}{3}\right)\Delta^2 f(-3) + \frac{1}{6}\left(-\frac{1}{2}\right)\Delta^3 f(-3)$$

$$= 2f(-3) + 3[f(-1) - f(-3)] + \frac{5}{6}[f(1) - 2f(-1) + f(-3)] - \frac{1}{12}[f(3) - 3f(1) + 3f(-1) - f(-3)]$$

$$= \frac{1}{12}[-f(-3) + 13f(-1) + 13f(1) - f(3)]$$

$$= \frac{1}{12}[13\{f(-1) + f(1)\} - \{f(3) + f(-3)\}].$$

(c) In this case $x_0 = \frac{1}{2}$ and $h = 1$.

$$\therefore\ f(x) = f\left(-\frac{1}{2} + x + \frac{1}{2}\right) \quad [\text{from } f(x_0 + nh)]$$

$$= E^{x+(1/2)} f\left(-\frac{1}{2}\right) = (1+\Delta)^{x+(1/2)} f\left(-\frac{1}{2}\right)$$

$$= f\left(-\frac{1}{2}\right) + \left(x+\frac{1}{2}\right)\Delta f\left(-\frac{1}{2}\right) + \frac{\left(x+\frac{1}{2}\right)\left(x-\frac{1}{2}\right)}{2}\Delta^2 f\left(-\frac{1}{2}\right)$$

$$+ \frac{\left(x+\frac{1}{2}\right)\left(x-\frac{1}{2}\right)\left(x-\frac{3}{2}\right)}{2}\Delta^3 f\left(-\frac{1}{2}\right)$$ considering upto third differences.

$$\therefore \quad \int_0^2 f(x)\,dx = \int_0^2 \left[f\left(-\frac{1}{2}\right) + \left(x+\frac{1}{2}\right)\Delta f\left(-\frac{1}{4}\right) + \left(\frac{x^2-\frac{1}{4}}{2}\right)\Delta^2 f\left(-\frac{1}{2}\right)\right.$$

$$\left. + \frac{1}{6}\left(x^3 - \frac{x}{4} - \frac{3x^2}{2} + \frac{3}{8}\right)\Delta^3 f\left(-\frac{1}{2}\right)\right] dx$$

$$= \left[xf\left(-\frac{1}{2}\right)\left(x^2 + \frac{1}{2}x)\right)\Delta f\left(-\frac{1}{2}\right) + \frac{1}{3}\left(\frac{x^3}{3} - \frac{1}{4}x\right)\Delta^2 f\left(-\frac{1}{2}\right)\right.$$

$$\left. + \frac{1}{6}\left(\frac{x^4}{2} - \frac{x^2}{8} - \frac{3x^3}{8} + \frac{3x}{8}\right)\Delta^3 f\left(-\frac{1}{2}\right)\right]_0^2$$

$$= 2f\left(-\frac{1}{2}\right) + 3\Delta f\left(-\frac{1}{2}\right) + \frac{1}{2}\left(\frac{13}{6}\right)\Delta^2 f\left(-\frac{1}{2}\right) + \frac{1}{8}\left(\frac{1}{4}\right)\Delta^3 f\left(-\frac{1}{2}\right)$$

$$= 2f\left(-\frac{1}{2}\right) + 3\left[f\left(\frac{1}{2}\right) - f\left(-\frac{1}{2}\right)\right] + \frac{13}{12}\left[f\left(\frac{1}{2}\right) - 2f\left(\frac{1}{2}\right) + f\left(-\frac{1}{2}\right)\right]$$

$$+ \frac{1}{24}\left[f\left(\frac{5}{2}\right) - 3f\left(\frac{3}{2}\right) - 3f\left(\frac{1}{2}\right) - f\left(-\frac{1}{2}\right)\right]$$

$$= \frac{1}{24} f\left(-\frac{1}{2}\right) + 23f\left(\frac{1}{2}\right) + 23f\left(\frac{3}{2}\right) + f\left(\frac{5}{2}\right)\Bigg]$$

$$\int_{-1/2}^{1/2} f(x)\,dx = \frac{1}{2}\left\{f\left(-\frac{1}{2}\right) + f\left(\frac{1}{2}\right)\right\} + \frac{1}{24}\left\{f\left(-\frac{1}{2}\right) - f\left(-\frac{3}{2}\right) - f\left(\frac{3}{2}\right) + f\left(\frac{1}{2}\right)\right\}$$

$$= \frac{1}{24}\left[13f\left(-\frac{1}{2}\right) + 13f\left(\frac{1}{2}\right) - f\left(-\frac{3}{2}\right) - f\left(\frac{3}{2}\right)\right].$$

In this case $h = 1, x_0 = -\frac{3}{2}$.

Now $\quad f(x) = f\left(-\frac{3}{2} + x + \frac{3}{2}\right)\Bigg]$ [From $f(x_0 + nh)$].

$$\therefore \quad \int_{-1/2}^{1/2} f(x)\,dx = \int_{-1/2}^{1/2} \left[f\left(-\frac{3}{2}\right) + \left(x+\frac{3}{2}\right) \Delta f\left(-\frac{3}{2}\right) \right.$$

$$\left. + \frac{\left(x+\frac{3}{2}\right)\left(x+\frac{1}{2}\right)}{2!} \Delta^2 f\left(-\frac{3}{2}\right) \frac{\left(x+\frac{3}{2}\right)\left(x+\frac{1}{2}\right)\left(x-\frac{1}{2}\right)}{3!} \Delta^3 f\left(-\frac{3}{2}\right) \right] dx$$

$$= \left[xf\left(-\frac{3}{2}\right) + \left(\frac{x^2}{2} + \frac{3x}{2}\right) \Delta f\left(-\frac{3}{2}\right) + \frac{1}{2}\left(\frac{x^3}{3} + \frac{2x^2}{2} + \frac{3x}{4}\right) \Delta^2 f\left(-\frac{3}{2}\right) \right.$$

$$\left. + \frac{1}{6}\left(\frac{x^4}{4} - \frac{x^2}{8} + \frac{3}{2} . \frac{x^3}{3} - \frac{3x}{8}\right) \Delta^3 f\left(-\frac{3}{2}\right) \right]_{-1/2}^{1/2}$$

$$= f\left(\frac{3}{2}\right) + \frac{3}{2} \Delta f\left(-\frac{3}{2}\right) + \frac{1}{2}\left[\frac{10}{12}\right] \Delta^2 f\left(-\frac{3}{2}\right) + \frac{1}{6}\left(-\frac{1}{4}\right) \Delta^3 f\left(-\frac{3}{2}\right)$$

$$= f\left(-\frac{3}{2}\right) + \frac{3}{2}\left[f\left(-\frac{1}{2}\right) - f\left(-\frac{3}{2}\right)\right] + \frac{5}{12}\left[f\left(\frac{1}{2}\right) - 2f\left(-\frac{1}{2}\right) + f\left(-\frac{3}{2}\right)\right]$$

$$- \frac{1}{24}\left[f\left(\frac{3}{2}\right) - 3f\left(\frac{1}{2}\right) + 3f\left(-\frac{1}{2}\right) - f\left(-\frac{3}{2}\right)\right]$$

$$= \frac{1}{24}\left[-f\left(-\frac{3}{2}\right) + 13f\left(-\frac{1}{2}\right) + 13f\left(\frac{1}{2}\right) - f\left(\frac{3}{2}\right)\right].$$

Example 33: *Find the sum of the fourth powers of the first n natural numbers by means of the Euler-Maclaurin formula.* **[Meerut 2000, 2001, 2003, 2005]**

Solution: The general form of the Euler-Maclaurin formula is

$$\frac{1}{h}\int_{x_0}^{x_0+nh} f(x)\,dx = \sum_0^n f(x+nh) - \frac{1}{2}[f(x_0+nh) + f(x_0)]$$

$$- \frac{h}{12}[f'(x_0+nh) - f'(x_0)] + \frac{h^3}{720}[f'''(x_0+nh) - f'''(x_0)] \ldots$$

Putting $x_0 = 0, h = 1, f(x) = x^4$, we get

$$\int_0^n x^4\,dx = \sum_0^n x^4 - \frac{1}{2}[n^4 + 0^4] - \frac{1}{12}[5n^3 - 4(0)^3] + \frac{1}{720}[24n - 24(0)]$$

or $$\frac{n^5}{5} = \sum_0^n x^4 - \frac{1}{2}n^4 - \frac{1}{3}n^3 + \frac{n}{30}.$$

or $$\sum_0^n x^4 = \frac{n^5}{5} + \frac{1}{2}n^4 + \frac{1}{3}n^3 - \frac{n}{30}.$$

Example 34: *Find the sum of* $\frac{1}{51^2}+\frac{1}{53^2}+\frac{1}{55^2}+\ldots+\frac{1}{99^2}$.

Solution: Putting $f(x)=\frac{1}{x^2}$, $x_0=51, h=2, n=24$ in Euler-Maclaurin formula, we get

$$\frac{1}{2}\int_{51}^{51+2\times 24}\frac{1}{x^2}\,dx=\sum_{0}^{24} f(x_0+nh)-\frac{1}{2}[f(x_0+nh)+f(x_0)]$$

$$-\frac{h}{12}[f'(x_0+nh)-f'(x_0)]+\frac{h^3}{720}[f'''(x_0+nh)-f'''(x_0)].$$

$$f(x)=\frac{1}{x^2},\ f'(x)=\frac{-2}{x^3},\ f'(x_0)=\frac{-2}{(51)^3},\ f'(x_0+nh)=\frac{-2}{(99)^3}$$

$$f'''(x)=\frac{-24}{x^5},\ f'''(x_0)=\frac{-24}{51^5},\ f'''(x_0+nh)=\frac{-24}{(99)^5}$$

Now $\frac{1}{2}\int_{51}^{99}\frac{1}{x^2}\,dx=\sum_{0}^{24} f(51+2n)-\frac{1}{2}\left[\frac{1}{99^2}+\frac{1}{51^2}\right]-\frac{1}{6}\left[\frac{-2}{99^3}+\frac{2}{51^3}\right]+\frac{1}{90}\left[\frac{-24}{99^5}+\frac{24}{51^5}\right]$

or $\frac{1}{2}\left[\frac{-1}{x}\right]_{51}^{99}=\left\{\frac{1}{51^2}+\frac{1}{53^2}+\ldots+\frac{1}{99^2}\right\}-\frac{1}{2}\left[\frac{1}{99^2}+\frac{1}{51^2}\right]-\frac{1}{6}\left[\frac{-2}{99^3}+\frac{2}{51^3}\right]+\frac{1}{90}\left[\frac{-24}{99^5}+\frac{24}{51^5}\right]$

or $\sum_{51}^{99}\frac{1}{x}=\frac{1}{2}\left[-\frac{1}{99}+\frac{1}{51}\right]+\frac{1}{2}\left[\frac{1}{99^2}+\frac{1}{51^2}\right]+\frac{1}{6}\left[\frac{2}{51^3}-\frac{2}{99^3}\right]-\frac{1}{90}\left[\frac{24}{51^5}-\frac{24}{99^5}\right]$

$=\frac{1}{2}[-.010101+.019608]+\frac{1}{2}\left[\frac{1}{9801}+\frac{1}{2601}\right]+\frac{1}{3}\left[\frac{1}{132651}-\frac{1}{970299}\right]-\frac{4}{15}\left[\frac{1}{51^5}-\frac{1}{99^5}\right]$

$=\frac{1}{2}[.009507]+\frac{1}{2}[.00010203+.00038446]+\frac{1}{3}[0.000007538-.0000010306]+\text{zero}$

$=\frac{1}{2}[.00999349]+\frac{1}{2}[.0000065074]=.004998914.$

Example 35: *Evaluate* $\sum_{m=0}^{n}\frac{1}{(10+m)^2}$.

Solution: Put $f(x)=\frac{1}{(a+x)^2}$

$\therefore\quad \int_0^\infty f(x)\,dx=\frac{1}{a},\ f'(0)=\frac{2}{a^3},\ f'''(0)=-\frac{24}{a^5},\ f^{v}(0)=\frac{720}{a^7}$ Put $a=10$

$\therefore\quad \sum_{m=0}^{\infty}\frac{1}{(10+m)^2}=\frac{1}{10}+\frac{1}{2}\cdot\frac{1}{10^2}+\frac{1}{12}\cdot\frac{2}{10^3}-\frac{1}{720}\cdot\frac{24}{10^5}$

$=.1+.005+.000167-.0000003=.1051664.$

Example 36: *Find $I = \int_0^1 x\,dx$, by Gauss's formula, with $n = 4$, upto 5 decimal places.*

Solution: First we change the limits of integration with the help of $x = \frac{1}{2}(u + 1)$.

This gives: $$I = \frac{1}{4}\int_{-1}^{1} (u+1)\,du = \frac{1}{4}\sum_{i=1}^{n} w_i\, F(u_i) \quad \text{where } F(u_i) = u_i + 1.$$

Now, we choose $n = 4$ and use the abscissae and weights corresponding to $n = 4$ in standard table and obtain

$$I \approx \frac{1}{4}[(-0.86114 + 1)(0.34785) + (-0.33998 + 1)(0.65214)$$

$$+ (0.33998 + 1)(0.65214) + (0.86114 + 1)(0.34785)]$$

$$= \frac{1}{4}[0.483024 + .4304254 + .8738545 + .6473975] = .49999.$$

Example 37: *If U_x is a function whose fifth differences are constant and if $\int_{-1}^{1} U_x\,dx$ can be expressed in the form $pU_{-\alpha} + qU_0 + pU_\alpha$. Find p, q and α. Use the formula to find $\log_e 2$ to four decimal places from the integral $\int_0^1 \frac{dx}{1+x}$.*

Solution: Here fifth differences of U_x are given to be constant, so we assume

$$U_x = a + bx + cx^2 + dx^3 + ex^4 + fx^5 \qquad ...(1)$$

Now, let $$\int_{-1}^{1} U_x\,dx = pU_{-\alpha} + qU_0 + pU_\alpha = p(U_{-\alpha} + U_\alpha) + qU_0.$$

$$\Rightarrow \quad \int_{-1}^{1} (a + bx + cx^2 + dx^3 + ex^4 + fx^5)\,dx = p[2(a + c\alpha^2 + e\alpha^4)] + qa$$

$$\Rightarrow \quad \left[ax + \frac{bx^2}{2} + \frac{cx^3}{3} + \frac{dx^4}{4} + \frac{ex^5}{5} + \frac{fx^6}{6}\right]_{-1}^{1} = (2p + q)^3\, a + 2pc\alpha^2 + 2pe\alpha^4$$

$$\Rightarrow \quad 2\left(a + \frac{c}{3} + \frac{e}{5}\right) = (2p + q)\,a + 2pc\alpha^2 + 2pe\alpha^4.$$

Whence comparing coefficients of a, c and e on both sides, we obtain

$$2p + q = 2 \qquad ...(2)$$

$$2p\alpha^2 = 2/3 \qquad ...(3)$$

$$2p\alpha^4 = 2/5 \qquad ...(4)$$

From here dividing (4) by (3), we get

$$\alpha^2 = 3/5 = 0.6 \Rightarrow \alpha = \pm\sqrt{(0.6)}.$$

Now Substituting in (3), we readily obtain

$$2p \cdot \frac{3}{5} = \frac{2}{3} \Rightarrow p = \frac{5}{9}.$$

Whence from (2), $q = 2 - 2p = \frac{8}{9}$.

$$\Rightarrow \quad \int_{-1}^{1} U_x \, dx = \frac{5}{9}\left[U(\sqrt{0.6}) + U(-\sqrt{0.6})\right] + \frac{8}{9} U_0 \qquad \text{...(5)}$$

Further, changing the origin to $x = -1$, we obtain

$$\int_{0}^{2} U_x \, dx = \frac{5}{9}\left(U_{1+\sqrt{(0.6)}} + U_{1-\sqrt{(0.6)}}\right) + \frac{8}{9} U_1 \qquad \text{...(6)}$$

Now, reducing the scale to $\frac{1}{2}$, we get

$$\int_{0}^{1} U_x \, dx = \frac{1}{2}\left[\frac{5}{9}\left\{U_{(1+\sqrt{(0.6)}/2} + U_{(1-\sqrt{(0.6)}/2}\right\} + \frac{8}{9} U_{1/2}\right] \qquad \text{...(7)}$$

But $$\int_{0}^{1} \frac{dx}{1+x} = \left[\log_e (1+x)\right]_0^1 = \log_e 2$$

Further, putting $U_x = \dfrac{1}{1+x}$ in (7) and simplifying, we obtain

$$\log_e 2 = \int_{0}^{1} \frac{dx}{1+x} = \frac{4}{9} U_{0.5} + \frac{5}{18}\left(U_{(1+\sqrt{(0.6)})/2} + U_{(1-\sqrt{(0.6)})/2}\right) = 0.694 \text{ (approx.)}$$

✦✦ Problem Set ✦✦

1. Calculate the approximate value of $\int_{-3}^{3} x^4\, dx$ by using (i) Trapezoidal rule, (ii) Simpson's rule, by dividing the range in six equal parts.

2. Use Simpson's rule dividing the range into ten equal parts, to show that $\int_0^1 \frac{\log(1+x^3)}{(1+x^2)} = 0.1730$.

3. Use Simpson's '$\frac{1}{3}$' rule to find $\int_0^6 \frac{dx}{(1+x)^2}$.

4. Evaluate $\int_3^5 \frac{4}{(2+x^2)}\, dx$ by dividing the range into eight equal parts.

5. Evaluate $\int_5^{12} \frac{dx}{x}$ by numerical methods.

6. Use Simpson's rule to prove that $\log_e 7$ is approximately 1.958 using $\int_0^7 \frac{dx}{x}$.

7. Evaluate $\int_0^1 x^2\, dx$ by Simpson's '$\frac{1}{3}$' rule.

8. Find approximate value of $\int_0^2 \frac{dx}{x}$ by using Simpson's Rule.

9. Use Simpson's '$\frac{1}{3}$' rule to find value of $\int_1^5 f(x)\, dx$ given

x :	1	2	3	4	5
$f(x)$:	10	50	70	80	100

10. Evaluate $\int_{0.7}^{0.6} x^{1/2} e^{-x}\, dx$ approximately by using a suitable formula.

[Rohilkhand 2010]

11. Evaluate $\int_0^1 \frac{dx}{1+x}$ correct to five places of decimal by using Euler-Maclaurin's formula.

12. Use Simpson's '$\frac{1}{3}$' rule to find the approximate area of the cross-section of a river 80 metres wide, the depth y (in metres) at a distance x from one bank being given by the following table:

x:	0	10	20	30	40	50	60	70	80
y:	0	4	7	9	12	15	14	8	3

[Rajasthan 2000, 2001, 2004]

[**Hint:** Area $= \frac{h}{3}[(y_0 + y_8) + 4(y_1 + y_3 + y_5 + y_7) + 2(y_2 + y_4 + y_6)]$

$= \frac{10}{3}[3 + 4(36) + 2(33)] = 710$ *sq.* metre]

13. Prove that if $f(x)$ is continuous function whose fifth differences are constant, then

$$\int_{-1}^{+1} f(x)\,dx = \frac{8}{9} f(0) + \frac{5}{9}[f\sqrt{(0.6)} + f\{-\sqrt{(0.6)}\}].$$

14. Obtain the approximate quadrature formula

$$\int_0^n f(x)\,dx = n\left[\frac{3}{8} f(0) + \frac{1}{24}\{19 f(n) - 5 f(2n) + f(3n)\}\right].$$

15. Evaluate $\int_{100}^{200} \frac{dx}{\log x}$ and compare with the exact value.

16. (i) If $f(x)$ is a polynomial of degree 2, prove that

$$\int_0^1 f(x)\,dx = \frac{1}{12}[5 f(0) + 8 f(1) - f(2)].$$

(ii) Prove that $\int_0^1 f(x)\,dx = \frac{1}{12}[5 f(1) + 8 f(0) - f(-1)]$.

17. Sum of series

(i) $\frac{1}{400} + \frac{1}{402} + \ldots + \frac{1}{498} + \frac{1}{505}$ (ii) $\frac{1}{100} + \frac{1}{101} + \frac{1}{102} + \frac{1}{103} + \frac{1}{104}$

(iii) $\frac{1}{201^2} + \frac{1}{203^2} + \ldots + \frac{1}{299^2}$

by using Euler-Maclaurin summation formula

18. Find the sum of the fifth powers of the first n natural numbers by means of Euler-Maclaurin formula.

19. If $f(x)$ and its derivative $f'(x)$ are continuously increasing in the range $0 < x < n$, show that

$$\int_0^n f(x)\,dx < \frac{1}{2}[f(0)+f(n)] + \sum_{x=0}^{n-1} f(x)$$

[**Hint:** In Euler-Maclaurin formula put $a = 0, h = 1$.]

20. Obtain the approximate quadrature formula

$$\int_0^1 \frac{dx}{1+x^2} = \frac{1}{4a}\left(1+\frac{1}{6a}\right) + \sum_{x=1}^{a} \frac{a}{a^2+x^2}$$

[**Hint:** Use Euler-Maclaurin formula with $f(x) = \dfrac{a}{a^2+x^2}$ and range $(0, a)$,

$$\int_0^a \frac{a}{a^2+x^2}\,dx = \sum_{x=0}^{a} \frac{a}{a^2+x^2} - \frac{1}{2}\left(\frac{1}{a}+\frac{1}{2a}\right) + \frac{1}{2a}\cdot\frac{1}{2a^2}.$$ Put $x = ay$ in the integral.]

21. Use Simpson's rule with two, four and ten intervals to evaluate $\int_1^2 \frac{1}{x}\,dx = \log 2$ and compare with $\log 2 = 0.693147$.

22. Find by Weddle's rule the value of the integral

$$I = \int_{0.4}^{1.6} \frac{x}{\sin h\, x}\,dx$$ by taking 12 sub-intervals.

23. In an experiment, a quantity G was measured as follows:

$G(20) = 95.90$ $\qquad$ $G(24) = 99.56$

$G(21) = 96.85$ $\qquad$ $G(25) = 100.41$

$G(22) = 97.77$ $\qquad$ $G(26) = 101.24$

$G(23) = 98.68$

Compute $\int_{20}^{26} G(x)$ by both Simpson's and Weddle's rule respectively.

24. A rocket is launched from the ground, its acceleration is registered during the first 80 second and is given in the table below:

t (sec):	0	10	20	30	40	50	60	70	80
n (m/sec):	30.00	31.63	33.44	35.47	37.75	40.33	43.25	46.69	50.67

Find the velocity and height of the rocket at time $t = 80$.

[**Hint:** For velocity apply Simpson's one third rule.]

25. Obtain the approximate quadrature formula

$$\int_{-1/2}^{3/2} y_x\,dx = \frac{1}{24}(27y_0 + 17y_1 + 5y_2 - y_3).$$

26. Derive the following quadrature formula

$$\int_{-a}^{b} f(x)\,dx = \frac{a+b}{6ab}\,[b\,(2a-b)\,f(-a) + (a-b^2)\,f(0) + a\,(2b-a)\,f(b)]$$

applicable when the intervals in a table are unequal.

[**Hint:** Let $f(x) = Ax^2 + Bx + C$.

Find the values of A, B and C in terms of $f(-a)$, $f(0)$ and $f(b)$.]

27. Show that if $y_x = a + bx + cx^2 + dx^3 + ex^4 + f\,x^5$,

then $\int_{-3}^{3} y_x\,dx = 2.2\,y_0 + 1.62\,(y_{-2} + y_2) + 0.28\,(y_{-3} + y_3)$.

Note: This is known as Hardly's formula.

28. A function $y = y(x)$ is known as equidistant point $0, \pm h, \pm 2h$. Find an approximate formula for

$\int_{-2h}^{2h} y\,dx$ which contains y_{-1}, y_0, y_1.

29. A function $f(x)$ is known experimentally for four values $a, a+h, a+2h, a+3h$. Making a suitable assumption concerning the form of $f(x)$.

Prove that

$$\int_{a}^{a+2h} f(x)\,dx = \frac{3h}{8}\left[f(a) + 3f(a+h) + 3f(a+2h) + f(a+3h)\right]$$

30. State and prove Simpson's one-third rule. What is the effect of

(i) Change of origin and (ii) Change of scale in this rule.

31. Using the data of the following table, compute the integral

$\int_{0.5}^{1.1} xy\,dx$ by Simpson's rule.

x:	0.5	0.6	0.7	0.8	0.9	1.0	1.1
y:	0.4804	0.5669	0.6490	0.7262	0.7985	0.8658	0.9281

32. Using the following table of values, approximate by Simpson's rule the arc length of the graph $y = 1/x$ between the points (1, 1) and $\left(5, \frac{1}{5}\right)$.

x:	1	2	3	4	5
$\left(\frac{1+x^4}{x^2}\right)^{1/2}$	1.414	1.031	1.007	1.002	1.001

[**Hint:** Arc length $s = \int_1^5 \left\{1 + \left(\frac{dy}{dx}\right)^2\right\}^{1/2} dx = \int_1^5 \left(\frac{1+x^4}{x^2}\right)^{1/2} dx$]

33. The integral $I = \int_a^b f(x)\,dx$ is to be estimated by Trapezoidal type rule using two base points x_1 and x_2, that do not necessarily coincide with integration limits a and b.

Show that the required approximation is

$$I = \frac{(b-a)}{(x_2 - x_1)}\left[x_2 f(x_1) - x_1 f(x_2) + \frac{b+a}{2}\{f(x_2) - f(x_1)\}\right].$$

✦✦ Objective Type Question ✦✦

❖ Multiple Choice Questions

1. The Trapezoidal rule is applicable to the polynomial of the .... or ....
   (a) Second degree, curve (b) First degree, circle
   (c) First degree, straight line (d) n^{th} degree, ellipse.

2. The formula $\int_{x_0}^{x_0+nh} y\,dx = h\left[\frac{1}{2}(y_0 + y_n) + (y_1 + y_2 + 2\,y_{n-1})\right]$ is known as:
   (a) Trapezoidal rule (b) Quadrature formula
   (c) Simpson's '$\frac{1}{3}$' rule (d) Weddle's rule

3. Simpson's three-eighth's rule is:
   (a) $$\int_{x_0}^{x_0+nh} y\,dx = \frac{3}{8}h\left[(y_0 + y_{n-1}) + 3\,(y_1 + y_2 + y_4 + y_5 + \ldots + y_n) + 2\,(y_3 + y_6 + \ldots + y_{n-3})\right]$$
   (b) $$\int_{x_0}^{x_0+nh} y\,dx = \frac{3}{8}h\left[(y_0 + y_n) + 3\,(y_1 + y_2 + y_4 + y_5 + \ldots + y_n) + 2\,(y_3 + y_6 + \ldots + y_{n-3})\right]$$
   (c) $$\int_{x_0}^{x_0+nh} y\,dx = \frac{3}{8}h\left[(y_0 + y_n) + 2\,(y_1 + y_2 + y_4 + y_5 + \ldots + y_n) + 3\,(y_3 + y_6 + \ldots + y_{n-3})\right]$$
   (d) None of these

4. Which of the following is not correct:
   (a) Weddle's rule is more accurate than the Simpson's rule
   (b) Weddle's rule requires at least seven consecutive values of y
   (c) In Weddle's rule y is of the form $y = ax^6 + bx^5 + cx^4 + dx^3 + ex^2 + fx + g$
   (d) None of these.

5. Simpson's one-third rule is:

(a) $\int_{x_0}^{x_0+nh} y\,dx = \frac{h}{3}[(y_0 + y_n) + 4(y_1 + y_3 + \ldots + y_{n-1})$
$+ 2(y_2 + y_4 + \ldots + y_{n-2})$

(b) $\int_{x_0}^{x_0+nh} y\,dx = \frac{h}{3}[(y_0 + y_{n-1}) + 4(y_1 + y_3 + \ldots + y_n)$
$+ 2(y_2 + y_4 + \ldots + y_{n-2})]$

(c) $\int_{x_0}^{x_0+nh} y\,dx = \frac{h}{3}[(y_0 + y_n) + 2(y_1 + y_3 + \ldots + y_{n-1})$
$+ 4(y_2 + y_4 + \ldots + y_{n-2})]$

(d) None of these

6. Simpson's one-third rule is called:

(a) Straight line formula (b) Hyperabolic formula
(c) Parabolic formula (d) None of these

7. The error in the Trapezoidal rule is of the order of

(a) h (b) h^2
(c) h^3 (d) 1

8. A formula which is applicable to any number of sub-intervals whether even or odd is:

(a) Weddle's formula (b) General quadrature rule
(c) Trapezoidal formula (d) All of the above.

9. In general quadrature formula we integrate............

(a) Newton's formula for backward interpolation
(b) Gauss formula for forward interpolation
(c) Newton's formula for forward interpolation
(d) Gauss formula for backward interpolation.

10. In Cote's method we integrate:

(a) Newton's interpolation formula
(b) Lagrange's interpolation formula
(c) Gauss interpolation formula
(d) None of these.

11. Which one of the following is not correct:

(a) Weddle's rule is obtained by putting $n = 5$ in the general quadrature formula
(b) In Trapezoidal rule we have assumed that y is a polynomial in x of degree one
(c) In Simpson's one-third rule, y is assumed as a polynomial of degree two
(d) In Simpson's three-eighth rule, y is assumed as a polynomial of degree three.

✦✦ Examination Questions ✦✦

1. Drive composite $\frac{1}{3}$rd Simpson's rule. Hence evaluate $\int_0^{0.6} e^{-x^2} dx$ by taking seven ordinates. Tabulate the integrand for these ordinates to four decimal places. **[I.F.S. 2008]**

2. Find the value of $\int_{1.6}^{3.4} f(x)\, dx$ from the following data using Simpson's $\frac{3}{8}$th rule for the interval (1.6, 2.2) and $\frac{1}{3}$rd rule for (2.2, 3.4):

x:	1.6	1.8	2.0	2.2	2.4	2.6	2.8	3.0	3.2	3.4
$f(x)$:	4.953	6.050	7.389	9.025	11.023	13.464	16.445	20.086	24.533	29.964

3. Evaluate $\int_1^2 \frac{dx}{x}$ by Simpson's rule with 4 strips. Determine the error by direct integration.

4. Obtain the Simpson's rule for the integral

$$I = \int_a^b f(x)\, dx$$

and show that this rule is exact for polynomials of degree $n \le 3$. In general show that the error of approximation for Simpson's rule is given by

$$R = -\frac{(b-a)^5}{2880} f^{iv}(n),\ n \in (0, 2)$$

Apply this rule to integral

$\int_0^1 \frac{dx}{1+x}$ and show that $|R| \le 0.008333$.

5. Evaluate $\int_0^1 e^{-x^2} dx$; employing three point Gaussian quadrature formula, finding the required weights and residues. Use five decimal places for computation. **[I.A.S. 2003]**

6. The velocity of a particle at distance S from a point on its path is given by the following table:

S (meters)	0	10	20	30	40	50	60
V (m/sec)	47	58	64	65	61	52	38

Estimate the time taken to travel the first 60 meters using Simpson's $\frac{1}{3}$ rd rule. Compare the result with Simpson's $\frac{3}{8}$ rule. **[I.A.S. 2004]**

7. Use appropriate quadrature formula out of the Trapezoidal and Simpson's rules to numerically integrate $\int_0^1 \frac{dx}{1+x^2}$ with $h = 0.2$. Hence obtain an appropriate value of π.

Justify the use of a particular quadrature formula. **[I.A.S. 2005]**

8. Find from the following table, the area bounded by the x-axis and the curve $y = f(x)$ between $x = 5.34$ and $x = 5.40$ using the Trapezoidal rule:

x:	5.34	5.35	5.36	5.37	5.38	5.39	5.40
$f(x)$:	1.82	1.85	1.86	1.90	1.95	1.97	2.00

[I.A.S. 2007]

9. Discuss Simpson's $\frac{1}{3}$rd rule of integration. Use it to find the value of $\int_1^2 x\,dx$.

[I.F.S. 2000]

10. Applying Simpson's $\frac{1}{3}$rd rule compute the value of the definite integral

$\int_4^{5.2} \log x\,dx$, with $h = 0.2$ and estimate the error.

[I.F.S. 2001]

11. A train is moving at the speed of 30 m/sec. Suddenly brakes are applied. The speed of train per second after t seconds is given by

Time (t):	0	5	10	15	20	25	30	35	40	45
Speed (v):	30	34	19	16	13	11	10	8	7	5

Apply Simpson's 3/8 rule to determine the distance moved by the train in 45 seconds.

[U.P.T.U. 2003]

12. Find the value of $\int_0^{\pi/2} \sin x\,dx$ by Simpson's 3/8 rule, $h = \pi/18$. **[U.P.T.U. 2007]**

13. (i) Evaluate $\int_0^8 x \sec x\,dx$ using eight intervals by Trapezoidal rule.

[U.P.T.U. 2009]

(ii) Evaluate $\int_0^4 e^{x^2}\,dx$ using 10 intervals by Trapezoidal rule. **[U.P.T.U. 2008]**

14. Drive an expression for error estimation in Simpson's 1/3 rule. **[U.P.T.U. 2008]**

15. Evaluate $\int_0^6 \frac{dx}{1+x^2}$ by using:

(i) Simpson's 1/3 rule. **[U.P.T.U. 2002]**

(ii) Simpson's 3/8 rule. **[U.P.T.U. 2004]**

Answers

Problem Set

1.	(i) 115 (ii) 98		
3.	.8946	**4.**	26.716
5.	0.87546854	**7.**	34598
8.	.6932	**9.**	256.66
10.	0.84827	**11.**	0.69315
17.	(i) 0.11382114 (ii) 0.0490291 (iii) 0.0008333290		
18.	$(n^6/6)+(n^5/2)+(5n^4/12)-(n^2/12)$		
22.	1.010784		
23.	(i) 591.853 (ii) 591.855		
24.	Velocity 30.87 m/sec; height 112.75 km.		
31.	0.358487	**32.**	4.187

Multiple Choice Questions

1.	(c)	**2.**	(b)	**3.**	(b)	**4.**	(d)	**5.**	(a)
6.	(c)	**7.**	(b)	**8.**	(c)	**9.**	(c)	**10.**	(b)
11.	(a)								

Examination Questions

1.	0.746832	**2.**	10.4572
3.	0.6932	**6.**	1.063, 1.064
7.	0.785397, $\pi=3.14158$	**8.**	.09964
10.	1.8278	**11.**	624.375
12.	0.96013	**13.**	(ii) 53.87
15.	(i) 1.3662 (ii) 1.3571		

Theory | Solved Examples | Problem Set

Chapter 7

Inverse Interpolation

Introduction, Lagrange's method, Iteration method, Reversion series method.

7.1 Introduction

Consider the function $y = f(x)$, where y is the dependent variable and x is the independent variable. The technique of determining y for x lying between two tabulated values of argument, is known as ***intropolation*** whereas the technique of determining the value x corresponding to the value of y is known as ***inverse interpolation***. In other words, we may define inverse interpolation as follows. ***The technique of determining the value of the argument corresponding to the given value of the function when the function lies between two tabulated values, is known as inverse intropolation.*** For example, if $y = \tan x$, then $x = \tan^{-1} y$; if $y = \cot x$, then $x = \cot^{-1} y$, which shows that the values of x can be calculated by substituting the value of y.

But many times, when the numerical value of x and y are given, the technique of determining the inverse interpolation offers difficulty and then we usually follow the following important method:

(1) Lagrange's method

(2) Iteration of successive approximation method

(3) Reversion of series method

7.1.1 Lagrange's Method

This method resembles to the method of direct interpolation as discussed earlier (Chapter 3). The main difference is that here we assume x to be a polynomial in $y[= f(x)]$, viz.

$$\begin{aligned} x = {} & A_0 [f(x) - f(x_1)] [f(x) - f(x_2)] \dots [f(x) - f(x_n)] \\ & + A_1 [f(x) - f(x_0)] [f(x) - f(x_2)] \dots [f(x) - f(x_n)] \\ & + A_2 [f(x) - f(x_0)] [f(x) - f(x_1)] [f(x) - f(x_3)] \dots [f(x) - f(x_n)] \\ & + \dots \quad \dots \quad \dots \quad \dots \quad \dots \quad \dots \quad \dots \quad \dots \quad \dots \\ & + A_n [f(x) - f(x_0)] [f(x) - f(x_1)] \dots [f(x) - f(x_{n-1})] \qquad \dots(1) \end{aligned}$$

where we are given n values of x and $y[= f(x)]$, *namely*

$$[x_0, f(x_0)], \ldots, [x_{n-1}, f(x_{n-1})].$$

In equation (1), there are $(n+1)$ *terms and n* factors in each term. The $(n+1)$ arbitrary constants $A_0, A_1 \ldots, A_n$ are evaluated as follows:

Putting $x = x_0$ in (1), we get

$$x_0 = A_0\,[f(x_0) - f(x_1)]\,[f(x_0) - f(x_2)] \ldots [f(x_0) - f(x_n)]$$

$$\Rightarrow \quad A_0 = \frac{x_0}{[f(x_0) - f(x_1)]\,[f(x_0) - f(x_2)] \ldots [f(x_0) - f(x_n)]}$$

$$= \frac{x_0}{(y_0 - y_1)(y_0 - y_2) \ldots (y_0 - y_n)} \qquad [\because\ y = f(x)]$$

Similarly other constants can be determined. This implies

$$x = \frac{(y - y_1)(y - y_2) \ldots (y - y_n)}{(y_0 - y_1)(y_0 - y_2) \ldots (y_0 - y_n)}\, x_n$$

$$+ \frac{(y - y_0)(y - y_2) \ldots (y - y_n)}{(y_1 - y_0)(y_1 - y_2) \ldots (y_1 - y_n)}\, x_1$$

$$+ \quad \ldots \quad \ldots \quad \ldots \quad \ldots$$

$$+ \quad \ldots \quad \ldots \quad \ldots \quad \ldots$$

$$+ \frac{(y - y_0)(y - y_1) \ldots (y - y_{n-1})}{(y_n - y_0)(y_n - y_1)(y_n - y_{n-1})}\, x_n \qquad \ldots(2)$$

This formula gives the value of x, when $y[= f(x)]$ is known.

Solved Examples

Example 1: *Apply Lagrange's formula inversely to find, to two decimal places, the value of x when $y = f(x) = 19$, given the following table.*

x	0	1	2
$y = f(x)$	0	1	20

Solution: We have $x_0 = 0, x_1 = 1, x_2 = 2;\ y_0 = 0, y_1 = 1, y_2 = 20.$

$$x = \frac{0\,(19-1)\,(19-20)}{(0-1)\,(0-20)} + \frac{1(19-0)\,(19-20)}{(1-0)\,(1-20)} + \frac{2\,(19-0)\,(19-1)}{(20-0)\,(20-1)}$$

$$= \frac{19}{19} + \frac{2 \times 19 \times 18}{20 \times 19} = 1 + 1.8 = 2.8$$

Example 2: *If $y_1 = 4$, $y_3 = 12$, $y_4 = 19$ and $y_x = 7$, find x.*

Solution: Applying Lagrange's formula expressing x as a function of y, we readily obtain

$$x = \frac{(7-12)(7-19)}{(4-12)(4-19)}(1) + \frac{(7-4)(7-19)}{(12-4)(12-19)}(3) + \frac{(7-4)(7-12)}{(19-4)(19-12)}(4)$$

$$= \frac{(-5)(-12)}{(-8)(-15)} + \frac{(3)(-12)}{(8)(-7)}(3) + \frac{(3)(-5)}{(15)(7)}(4)$$

$$= \frac{1}{2} + \frac{27}{14} - \frac{4}{7} = \frac{34}{14} - \frac{4}{7} = \frac{26}{14} = 1.86.$$

Example 3: *Applying Lagrang's formula inversely to find, to one decimal place, the value of x when $y = f(x) = 13.6$, given the following table:*

x	$f(x)$
30	15.9
35	14.9
40	14.1
45	13.3
50	12.5

Solution: Here, we have $x_0 = 30, x_1 = 35, x_2 = 40, x_3 = 45, x_4 = 50$; $y_0 = 15.9$, $y_1 = 14.9$, $y_2 = 14.1$, $y_3 = 13.3$, $y_4 = 12.5$ and $y = 13.6$;

whence using relation (2) of Lagranges method, we get

$$x = \frac{(13.6-14.9)(13.6-14.1)(13.6-13.3)(13.6-12.5)}{(15.9-14.9)(15.9-14.1)(15.9-13.3)(15.9-12.5)}30$$

$$+\frac{(13.6-15.9)(13.6-14.1)(13.6-13.3)(13.6-12.5)}{(14.9-15.9)(14.9-14.1)(14.9-13.3)(14.9-12.5)}35$$

$$+\frac{(13.6-15.9)(13.6-14.9)(13.6-13.3)(13.6-12.5)}{(14.1-15.9)(14.1-14.9)(14.1-13.3)(14.1-12.5)}40$$

$$+\frac{(13.6-15.9)(13.6-14.9)(13.6-14.1)(13.6-12.5)}{(13.3-15.9)(13.3-14.9)(13.3-14.1)(13.3-12.5)}45$$

$$+\frac{(13.6-15.9)(13.6-14.9)(13.6-14.1)(13.6-13.3)}{(12.5-15.9)(12.5-14.9)(12.5-14.1)(12.5-13.3)}50$$

$$= .04044117 - 4.3237305 + 21.41276 + 27.79541 - 2.1470014 = 43.1$$

7.1.2 Iteration or Successive Approximation Method

Let $y = f(x)$ be the polynomial of nth degree; then to find the value of x corresponding to the given value of y we make use of any of the interpolation formula discussed in earlier chapters.

By Newton's formula, we have

$$y = y_0 + x\Delta y_0 + \frac{x(x-1)}{2!}\Delta^2 y_0 + \frac{x(x-1)(x-2)}{3!}\Delta^3 y_0 + \frac{x(x-1)(x-2)(x-3)}{4!} + \Delta^4 y_0 \dots \quad \dots(1)$$

$$\Rightarrow x\Delta y_0 = y - y_0 - \frac{x(x-1)}{2!}\Delta^2 y_0 - \frac{x(x-1)(x-2)}{3!}\Delta^3 y_0 - \frac{x(x-1)(x-2)(x-3)}{4!}\Delta^4 y_0 \dots \dots(2)$$

$$\Rightarrow x = \frac{y-y_0}{\Delta y_0} - \frac{x(x-1)}{2!}\frac{\Delta^2 y_0}{\Delta y_0} - \frac{x(x-1)(x-2)}{3!}\frac{\Delta^3 y_0}{\Delta y_0} - \frac{x(x-1)(x-2)(x-3)}{4!}\frac{\Delta^4 y_0}{\Delta y_0} - \dots \quad \dots(3)$$

neglecting fifth and higher order differences.

For the first approximation, we suppose the polynomial to be of first degree only, so that second and higher order differences are neglected, implying $x^{(1)}$ = first approximate value of $x = \frac{y-y_0}{\Delta y_0}$.

For the second approximation, we put $x = x^{(1)}$ in the right side of (3) implying

$$x^{(2)} = \frac{y-y_0}{\Delta y_0} - \frac{x^{(1)}(x^{(1)}-1)}{2!}\frac{\Delta^2 y_0}{\Delta y_0} - \frac{x^{(1)}(x^{(1)}-1)(x^{(1)}-2)}{3!}\frac{\Delta^3 y_0}{\Delta y_0}$$
$$- \frac{x^{(1)}(x^{(1)}-1)(x^{(2)}-2)(x^{(3)}-3)}{4!}\frac{\Delta^4 y_0}{\Delta y_0} \quad \dots(4)$$

For the third approximation, we put $x = x^{(2)}$ in the right side of (3) implying third approximate value of x is

$$x^{(3)} = \frac{y-y_0}{\Delta y_0} - \frac{x^{(2)}(x^{(2)}-1)}{2!}\frac{\Delta^2 y_0}{\Delta y_0} - \frac{x^{(2)}(x^{(2)}-1)(x^{(2)}-2)}{3!}\frac{\Delta^3 y_0}{\Delta y_0}$$
$$- \frac{x^{(2)}(x^{(2)}-1)(x^{(2)}-2)(x^{(2)}-3)}{4!}\frac{{}^4 y_0}{\Delta y_0} \quad \dots(5)$$

Similarly, further approximations can be determined. The process can be continued till we obtain two successive approximations to be equal.

Example 4: *Obtain the value of x using data in second and third column of difference table, by inverse interpolation when* $y = \cos h\, x = 1.285$.

Solution: The difference table is given by

v	x	y	Δy	$\Delta^2 y$	$\Delta^3 y$	$\Delta^4 y$	$\Delta^5 y$
– 2	0.736	1.2832974					
			8049				
– 1	0.737	1.2841023		13			
			8062		– 1		
0	0.738	1.2849085		12		3	
			8074		2		– 6
1	0.739	1.2857159		14		– 3	
			8088		– 1		
2	0.740	1.2865247		13			
			8101				
3	0.741	1.2873348					

Inspection of this difference table shows that the desired value of x lies in the interval 0.738 and 0.739. Now assuming $x_0 = 0.738, h = .001, y = 1.285$ and using *Bessel's formula, we obtain

$$* \ y = \frac{y_0 + y_1}{2} + u\Delta y_0 + \frac{(u^2 - \frac{1}{4})}{2!} \frac{\Delta^2 y_{-1} + \Delta^2 y_0}{2} + \frac{u(u^2 + \frac{1}{4})}{3!} \Delta^3 y_{-1} + \ldots \qquad \ldots(1)$$

$$\Rightarrow 1.285 = 1.2853122 + u \times 0.0008074 + \frac{u^2 - 0.25}{2} \times .0000013 + \frac{u(u^2 - 0.25)}{6} (.0000002)$$

Dividing throughtout by 0.0008074, we obtain

$$u = -0.3866732 - (u^2 - 0.25)(0.0008051) - u(u^2 - 0.25)\,0.0000413 \qquad \ldots(2)$$

Neglecting all the terms beyond first power in u, we obtain first approximation is u as

$$u^{(1)} = -.3866732$$

Putting this value [of $u^{(1)} = u$] in the right side of (2), we get $u^{(2)} = -.3865939$

Proceeding in this manner, we readily obtain $u^{(3)} = -.3865939$. ...(3)

As $u^{(2)}$ and $u^{(3)}$ are nearly equal, so we do not make further approximations. Now $v = u + \frac{1}{2}, x = x_0 + hv \quad \Rightarrow \quad v = 0.1134061$ and $x = 0.7381134$.

Example 5: *Solve the equation* $x = 10 \log_{10} x$ *given the following data:*

x	1.35	1.36	1.37	1.38
$\log_{10} x$	0.1303	0.1335	0.1367	0.1399

Solution: The difference table is given by

x	v	$y = 10 \log_{10} x$	Δy	$\Delta^2 y$
1.35	– 2	1.303		
			0.32	
1.36	– 1	1.335		0
			0.32	
1.37	0	1.367		0
			0.32	
1.38	1	1.399		

From here it is obvious that all differences except Δy are zero. For $x = 1.37, x$ and $10(\log_{10} x)$ are nearest to each other, so we take $x_0 = 1.37$; also $h = .01$. Then applying Stirling's formula, we immediately get

$$y = y_0 + x \frac{\Delta y_0 + \Delta y_{-1}}{3} + \ldots \text{ up to 1st differences.}$$

$$\Rightarrow \quad 1.37 = 1.367 + x\frac{(.032 + .032)}{2} \quad \Rightarrow \quad x = \frac{.033}{.032} = .09375$$

$\Rightarrow$ required root $= x_0 + hx = 1.37 + .01 \times .09375 = 1.3709.$

Example 6: *The following values of $y = f(x)$ are given*

x	10	15	20
v	0	1	2
$y = f(x)$	1754	2648	3564

Find the value of x for $y = f(x) = 3000$ by successive approximation method.

Solution: The difference table is given by

x	y	Δy	$\Delta^2 y$
10	1754		
		894	
15	2648		22
		916	
20	3564		

Now $$x = \frac{y - y_0}{\Delta y_0} - \frac{x(x-1)}{2!} - \frac{\Delta^2 y_0}{\Delta y_0} + \ldots \quad \ldots(1)$$

where $y_0 = 1.54,\ \Delta y_0 = 894,\ \Delta^2 y_0 = 22$ and $y = 3000.$

But higher order differences are assumed to be zero, so we take the terms upto $\Delta^2 y_0$.

Now $$x^{(1)} = \frac{y - y_0}{\Delta y_0} = \frac{3000 - 1764}{894} = 1.39$$

Putting $x = 1.39$ and $\Delta^2 y_0$ etc. in right hand side of (1), we obtain

$$x^{(2)} = 1.39 - \frac{1.39(1.39 - 1)}{3} \times \frac{22}{894} = 1.3792$$

$\Rightarrow$ required value of $x = 10 + 5 \times 1.3792 = 16.896$ $\quad [\because h = 5 \text{ and } x_0 = 10]$

Example 7: *Find the real root of the equation $x^3 + x - 3 = 0$, which lies between* 1.2 *and* 1.3.

[Bhopal 2002]

Solution: The difference table is given by

x	v	$y(= x^3 + x - 3)$	Δy	$\Delta^2 y$	$\Delta^3 y$	$\Delta^4 y$
1	– 2	– 1				
			.431			
1.1	– 1	– 0.569		.066		
			.497		.006	
1.2	0	– 0.072		.072		0
			.569		.006	
1.3	1	+ 0.497		.078		
			.647			
1.4	2	+ 1.144				

From the table it is obvious that $f(x)$ changes sign between $x = 1.2$ and $x = 1.3$. Hence the root of the equation must lie in between $(1.2, 1.3)$. Let the origin be at $x = 1.2$.

The required root of the equation is $1.2 + 0.1x^{(2)}$ where $x^{(2)}$ is to be obtained.

Now assuming the origin at 1.2, and using Stirling's formula

$$y = y_0 + x\frac{\Delta y_0 + \Delta y_{-1}}{2} + \frac{x^2}{2}\Delta^2 y_{-1} + \frac{x(x^2-1)}{6}\cdot\frac{(\Delta^3 y_{-1} + \Delta^3 y_{-2})}{2}$$

$$\text{we get } 0 = -.0720 + x\frac{569 + .497}{2} + \frac{x^2}{2}(.072) + \frac{x(x^2-1)}{6}\cdot\frac{.006 + .006}{2} \qquad [\because y = 0]$$

$$= -.072 + .532x + .036x^2 + .001x^3 \qquad ...(1)$$

Equation (1) can be written as

$$x = \frac{.072}{.532} - \frac{.0036}{0.532}x^2 - \frac{.001}{.532}x^3. \qquad ...(2)$$

$\therefore$ First approximation, viz. $x^{(1)}$ is given by $x^{(1)} = \frac{.072}{.532} = 0.1353$.

For second approximation, we put $x = x^{(1)}$ in the right side of (2),

Implying $\quad x^{(2)} = .1353 - .067\,(.1353)^2 - \frac{.001}{.532}(.1353)^3$

$= .1353 - .001211075 - .0003428675 = .1438592425 = .1341$ Approx.

$\therefore$ Desired root = 1.2 + .1 × .134 = 1.2134.

7.1.3 Method of Reversion of Series

This method is based on the assumption that the given set of observations can be expressed in terms of power series in x, so that

$$y = a_0 + a_1 x + a_2 x^2 + a_3 x^3 + a_4 x^4 + \ldots \quad \ldots(1)$$

Putting $w = \dfrac{y - a_0}{a_1}$, we obtain

$$w = x + a_2 x^2 + a_3 x^3 + a_4 x^4 + \ldots \quad \ldots(2)$$

For the first approximation, we have $w = x$ or $\dfrac{y - a_0}{a_1} = x$.

Now let the inverse of the function $y = f(x)$ be expressed as a power series in $\dfrac{y - a_0}{a_1}$, in the form.

$$x = c_1 w + c_2 w^2 + c_3 w^3 + c_4 w^4 + \ldots \quad \ldots(3)$$

Putting the value of w in (3) and then equating the coefficients of like powers of x.

We obtain

$$c_1 = 1, c_2 = -(a_2 / a_1), c_3 = -(a_3 / a_1) + 2(a_2 / a_1)^2$$

and $$c_4 = -(a_4 / a_1) + 5(a_2 a_3 / a_1^2) - 5(a_2 / a_1)^3 \text{ etc.}$$

Note 1: If we use Gregory-Newton's formula assuming fourth differences as constant, then we have

$$y = y_0 + x\Delta y_0 + \frac{x(x-1)}{2!}\Delta^2 y_0 - \frac{x(x-1)(x-2)}{3!}\Delta^3 y_0 - \frac{x(x-1)(x-2)(x-3)}{4!}\Delta^4 y_0 \quad \ldots(4)$$

This is of the form $y = a_0 + a_1 x + a_2 x^2 + a_3 x^3 + a_4 x^4$. ...(5)

$$\left.\begin{aligned} a_0 &= y_0, a_1 = \Delta y_0 - (\Delta^2 y_0 / 2) + (\Delta^3 y_0 / 3) - (\Delta^4 y_0 / 4) \\ a_2 &= (\Delta^2 y_0 / 1) - (\Delta^3 y_0 / 2) + (11\Delta^4 y_0 / 24) \\ a_3 &= (\Delta^3 y_0 / 6) - (\Delta^4 y_0 / 4) \end{aligned}\right\} \quad (A)$$

and $$a_4 = (\Delta^4 y_0 / 24).$$

Having determined a_0, a_1, a_2, a_3, a_4 we can obtain c_1, c_2, c_3, c_4 and further gives the value of x from (3).

Note 2: If we use Stirling's formula, neglecting Δ^5 and higher order differences, then we have

$$y = y_0 + x\left(\frac{\Delta y_0 + \Delta y_{-1}}{2}\right) + \frac{x^2}{2!}\Delta^2 y_{-1} + \frac{x(x^2-1)}{3!}\left(\frac{\Delta^3 y_{-1} + \Delta^3 y_{-2}}{2}\right) + \frac{x^2(x^2-1)}{4!}\Delta^4 y_{-2}$$

$$= y_0 + \left(\frac{\Delta y_0 + \Delta y_{-1}}{2} - \frac{\Delta^3 y_{-1} + \Delta^3 y_{-2}}{12}\right)x + \left(\frac{\Delta^2 y_{-1}}{2} - \frac{\Delta^4 y_{-2}}{24}\right)x^2$$

$$+ \frac{\Delta^3 y_{-1} + \Delta^3 y_{-2}}{12} x^3 + \frac{\Delta^4 y_{-2}}{24} x^4 \quad ...(6)$$

This is of the form $y = a_0 + a_1 x + a_2 x^2 + a_3 x^3 + a_4 x^4$. ...(7)

Comparing (6) and (7), we get

$$\left.\begin{aligned} a_0 &= y_0, \; a_1 = \frac{\Delta y_0 + \Delta y_{-1}}{2} - \frac{\Delta^3 y_{-1} + \Delta^3 y_{-2}}{12} \\ a_2 &= \frac{\Delta^2 y_{-1}}{2} - \frac{\Delta^4 y_{-2}}{24}, \; a_3 = \frac{\Delta^3 y_{-1} + \Delta^3 y_{-2}}{12}, \; a_4 = \frac{\Delta^4 y_{-2}}{24} \end{aligned}\right] \quad ...(B)$$

Having determined a_0, a_1, a_2, a_3 we can easily obtain c_1, c_2, c_3, c_4 and hence x can be evaluated.

Note 3: If we use Bessel's formula with fourth differences regarded as constant, then we have

$$y = \frac{y_0 + y_1}{2} + x\Delta y_0 + \frac{x^2 - \frac{1}{4}}{2} \cdot \frac{\Delta^2 y_{-1} + \Delta^2 y_0}{2} + \frac{x(x^2 + \frac{1}{4})}{6}\Delta^3 y_{-1}$$

$$+ \frac{(x^2 - \frac{1}{4})(x^2 - \frac{9}{4})}{24} \cdot \frac{\Delta^4 y_{-2} + \Delta^4 y_{-1}}{2}$$

$$= \frac{1}{2}(y_0 + y_1) - \frac{1}{16}(\Delta^2 y_{-1} + \Delta^2 y_0) + \frac{3}{256}(\Delta^4 y_{-2} + \Delta^4 y_{-1})$$

$$+ \left(\Delta y_0 - \frac{1}{24}\Delta^3 y_{-1}\right)x + \left[\frac{1}{4}(\Delta^2 y_{-1} + \Delta^2 y_0) - \frac{5}{96}(\Delta^4 y_{-2} + \Delta^4 y_{-1})\right]x^2$$

$$+ \frac{1}{6}\Delta^2 y_{-1} x^3 + \frac{1}{48}(\Delta^4 y_{-2} - \Delta^4 y_{-1})x^4$$

$$\equiv a_0 + a_1 x + a_2 x^2 + a_3 x^3 + a_4 x^4$$

Whence equating coefficients of like powers of x, we obtain

$$a_0 = \frac{1}{2}(y_0 + y_1) - \frac{1}{16}(\Delta^2 y_{-1} + \Delta^2 y_0) + \frac{3}{256}(\Delta^4 y_{-2} + \Delta^4 y_{-1}).$$

$$a_1 = \Delta y_0 - \frac{1}{24}\Delta^3 y_{-1} \; a_2 = \frac{1}{4}(\Delta^2 y_{-1} + \Delta^2 y_0) - \frac{5}{96}(\Delta^4 y_{-2} + \Delta^4 y_{-1}),$$

$$a_3 = \frac{1}{6}\Delta^3 y_{-1}, a_4 = \frac{1}{48}(\Delta^4 y_{-2} + \Delta^4 y_{-1}).$$

Example 8: *Find the root of the equation $x^3 - 6x - 11 = 0$ which lies between 3 and 4.*

[Patna 2004, 2007]

Solution: Let $y = x^3 - 6x - 11$, then obtain the following difference table:

x	v	y	Δy	$\Delta^2 y$	$\Delta^3 y$
1	−2	−16			
			1		
2	−1	−15		12	
			13		6
3	0	−2		18	
			31		
4	1	29			

Any central difference formula can be used to find the value of x such as that $y = 0$, since the root lies between 3 and 4. Assuming the origin at $x = 3$, we have the other values of x as − 2, − 1, 0 and + 1.

Now using relations **(B) Note 2** we get

$$a_0 = y_0 = -2, a_1 = \frac{\Delta y_0 + \Delta y_{-1}}{2} - \frac{\Delta^3 y_{-1} + \Delta^3 y_{-2}}{12} = \frac{13+31}{2} - \frac{6+6}{12} = 21$$

$$a_2 = \frac{\Delta^2 y_{-1}}{2} - \frac{\Delta^4 y_{-1}}{24} = \frac{\Delta^2 y_{-1}}{2} = \frac{18}{2} = 9; \text{ as } \Delta^4 y_{-1} \text{ does not exist}$$

$$a_3 = \frac{\Delta^3 y_{-1} + \Delta^3 y_{-2}}{12} = \frac{6+6}{12} = 1 \text{ and } a_4 = \frac{\Delta^4 y_{-2}}{24} = 0.$$

Hence $\quad c_1 = 1 . c_2 = -\frac{a_2}{a_1} = -\frac{9}{21} = -\frac{3}{7};$

$$c_3 = (a_3 / a_1) + 2(a_2 / a_1)^2 = (47/147)$$

$$\Rightarrow \quad x = c_1 w + c_2 w^2 + c_3 w^3 \text{ where } w = (y - a_0)/a_1$$

$$\Rightarrow \quad x = c_1(-a_0/a_1) + c_2(-a_0/a_1)^2 + c_3(-a_0/a_1)^3 = 0.092 \text{ approx}$$

But the origin is at $x = 3$; hence the required root will be equal to 3 + 0.092 = 3.092.

Example 9: *The following table gives the value of $y = \sinh x$ for certain equidistant values of x. If $y = 62$ find x.*

x	v	y	Δy	$\Delta^2 y$	$\Delta^3 y$
4.80	– 2	60.7511			
			.6106		
4.81	– 1	61.3617		.0062	
			.6168		0
4.82	0	61.9785		.0062	
			.6230		0
4.83	1	62.6015		.0062	
			.6292		
4.84	2	63.2307			

Solution: We observe that all differences above the second are zero. The required value of x lies between 4.82 and 4.83. So we choose $x_0 = 4.82$.

Assuming the origin at $x_0 = 4.82$, we have the other values of x as $-2, -1, 0, 1$ and 2. Now using relations **B Note 2**, we get

$$a_0 = y_0 = 61.3785. \quad a_1 = \frac{\Delta y_0 + \Delta y_{-1}}{2} - \frac{\Delta^2 y_{-1} + \Delta^2 y_{-2}}{12} = 0.6199.$$

$$a_2 = \frac{\Delta^2 y_{-1}}{2} = 0.0031. \quad a_3 = \frac{\Delta^3 y_{-1} + \Delta^3 y_{-2}}{12} = 0. \; a_4 = 0.$$

Hence $\quad c_1 = 1, c_2 = -\frac{a_2}{a_1} = -0.005001.$

$$c_3 = (a_3 / a_1) + 2(a_2 / a_1)^2 = 0 + 2(0.005001)^2 = 0.00005002 \text{ and } c_4 = 0.$$

Also $\quad w = \{(y - a_0)/a_1\} = \{(62 - 61.9785)/.06199\} = 0.034683.$

This implies $x = c_1 w + c_2 w^2 \;\; c_3 w^3 + c_4 w^4$

$\Rightarrow \quad x = .034683 - .00501(0.34683)^2 + .00005002\,(.034683)^3 = .0347$ approx.

But the origin is assumed to be at $x = 4.82$, hence the desired value of x is

$$4.82 + .01 \times .0347 = 4.8203.$$

Example 10: *The following table gives the values of y for certain equidistant values of x. If $y = 3000$, find x*

x	v	y	Δy	$\Delta^2 y$
10	0	1754		
			894	
15	1	2648		22
			916	
20	2	3564		

Solution: Applying Gregory Newton's formula, we have

$$a_0 = y_0 = 1754;\ a_1 = \Delta y_0 - (\Delta^2 y_0 / 2) = 894 - 11 = 883;\ a_2 = (\Delta^2 y_0 / 2) = 11$$

$$\Rightarrow \quad c_1 = 1, c_2 = -(a_2 / a_1) = -(11/883) \text{ Also } w = (y - a_0) / a_1 = \frac{3000 - 1754}{883} = 1.4$$

$$\therefore \quad x = c_1 w + c_2 w^2 = w - \frac{11}{883} w^2 = 1.4 - \frac{11}{883}(1.4)^2 = 1.37 \text{ approx.}$$

But the origin is assumed at $x = 10$, hence the desired value of x is $10 + 1.37 \times 5 = 16.85$.

Example 11: *Find by the method of iterarion a real root of* $2x - \log_{10} x = 7$.

Solution: By plotting the graphs of the equations

$$y = 2x - 7 \text{ and } y = \log_{10} x:$$

one can easily find as approximate value of the root of the given equation. The graphs intersect at $x = 3.8$. So an appoximate value of the root is 3.8. Now, from the given equation,

$$x = \frac{1}{2}(\log_{10} x + 7) \qquad ...(1)$$

Whence putting $x = 3.8$ in the R.H.S of (1), we get first approximation

$$x^{(1)} = \frac{1}{2}(\log_{10} 3.8 + 7) = 3.7899.$$

Again substituting this for x in the R.H.S of (1), we get second approximation $x^{(2)} = 3.7893$.

And similarly third approximation $x^{(3)} = 3.7893$.

Here $x^{(2)}$ and $x^{(3)}$ are equal so we stop the process. The correct value of the root to four places of decimals is 3.7893.

✦✦ Problem Set ✦✦

1. Write a short note on inverse interpolation and convergence of iterative process.

2. Explain how Newton-Gregory formula can be used to carry out inverse interpolation of second order. Show that a good approximation to the interpolation factor x will be given by

$$x = \frac{f_x - f_0}{\Delta f}\left[1 - \left\{\frac{f_x - f_0}{2\,(\Delta f_0)^2}\right\}\Delta^2 f_0\right]$$

3. The equation $x^3 - 15x + 4 = 0$ has a root close to 0.3: obtain this root upto 6 decimal places, using inverse interpolation with Bessel's interpolation formula.

4. Find the value of x to five decimal accuracy lying between 15 and 20 satisfying the equation $x^2 + 250 \log_{10} x = 635$.

5. Find the root of the equation $x^3 - 9x - 14 = 0$ which lies between 3 and 4.

6. Find the two places of decimals the smallest positive root of the equation $x^3 - 5x + 3 = 0$ by making a difference table $x = 0, 1, 2$ and 3.

7. Solve the equations:

   (i) $x + \log_{10} x = 0.5$,

   (ii) $2 + \log_{10} x = 2e^{-x}$ by the method of iteration.

8. Find the real root of the equation $x^4 + 4 \sin x = 0$ correct to four places of decimals by any method that you consider suitable.

9. Find he value of x for which y is 18,600: given

x	52	53	54	55	56
y	19.231	18,868	18,519	18,182	17,835

10. $f(44) = 13.4$, $f(45) = 13.16$, $f(46) = 12.93$, $f(47) = 12.68$, find x when $f(x) = 13.00$.

11. Find x when y_x is 0.163: when

x	80	82	84	86	88
y	0.134	0.154	0.176	0.200	0.227

12. Given a table of values of the probability integral $(2/\sqrt{\pi})\int_0^x e^{-x}\,dx$. For what value of x is this integral is equal to $\frac{1}{2}$?

x	0.45	0.46	0.47	0.48	0.49	0.50
$f(x)$	4754818	0.4846555	0.4937452	0.5027498	0.5116683	0.5204994

13. Find the value of x to five decimal accuracy lying between 15 and 20 satisfying the equation $x^2 + 250 \log_{10} x = 635$.

14. Find the root of the equation $10x^3 - 15x + 3 = 0$ which lies between 1 and 2.

✦✦ Answers ✦✦

❖ Problem Set

3.	0.267949	4.	17.68	5.	3.5914
6.	0.66	9.	53.7646	10.	45.70
11.	82.8	12.	0.47693612	13.	17.68
14.	1.109				

Chapter 8

Summation of Series

Introduction, Sum up to *n* terms of a series, Illustrative examples.

8.1 Introduction

One of the very important applications of the calculus of finite differences is to obtain a formula for summing the series upto n terms. Just like the differentiation and integration the two inverse operations, there also extist summation differencing in theory of the summation of series. A problem of summation is nothing but the problem of finite integration.

8.2 To Find the Sum to *n* Terms of a Series Whose General Term is the First Difference of Another Function

Let the series whose sum to "n" terms is to be obtained be $u_1, u_2, u_3, \ldots, u_x, \ldots u_n$ where u_x is the first difference of the function $f(x)$ *i.e.*, $u_x = \Delta f(x) \Rightarrow \Delta^{-1} u_x = f(x)$.

We want to find $u_1 + u_2 + \ldots + u_n = \sum_{x=1}^{n} u_x$,

Now $$u_x = \Delta f(x) = f(x+h) - f(x),$$

If the interval of differencing be unity, then we have $h = 1$

$$\Rightarrow \qquad u_x = f(x+1) - f(x) \qquad \ldots(1)$$

$$\therefore \qquad u_1 = f(2) - f(1),$$

$$u_2 = f(3) - f(2),$$

$$\ldots \quad \ldots \quad \ldots \quad \ldots \quad \ldots$$

$$u_n = f(n+1) - f(n).$$

Adding, we obtain $\sum_{x=1}^{n} u_x = f(n+1) - f(1) = \left[f(x)\right]_1^{n+1}$ ...(2)

where $\left[f(x)\right]_1^{n+1}$ means the difference between the values of $f(x)$ at the upper and lower limits. The above discussion shows that obtain $\Sigma\, u_x$ we have to find a function $f(x)$, such that $\Delta f(x) = u_x$. Here $f(x) = \Delta^{-1}(u_x)$ is called the indefinite integral of u_x. In case limits exists, then it is termed as definite integral of u_x. Thus $\Delta^{-1}(u_x) = f(x) + c$ is an indefinite integral, but $\sum_a^b u_x = \left[f(x)\right]_a^{b+1}$ is a definite integral.

Note: If m is a positive integer, then it can be proved easily that.

(i) $\Delta\left[\dfrac{a^x}{(a^h - 1)}\right] = a^x$, interval of differencing is h,

(ii) $\Delta\left[\dfrac{(ax+b)^{(m)}}{h}\right] = am\,(ax+b)^{(m-1)}$, interval of differencing is h,

(iii) $\Delta[-\frac{1}{h}(ax+b)^{(-m)}] = am(ax+b)^{(-m-1)}$, interval of differencing is h,

(iv) $\Delta\left[\begin{pmatrix} x \\ m \end{pmatrix}\right] = \begin{pmatrix} x \\ m-1 \end{pmatrix}$, interval of differencing is unity, where $\begin{pmatrix} x \\ m \end{pmatrix} + {}^xC_m$,

(v) $\Delta\left[\dfrac{-\cos\left(\dfrac{ax+b-a}{2}\right)}{2\sin(a/2)}\right] = \sin(ax+b)$, interval of differencing is unity, $[a \neq 0]$,

(vi) $\Delta\left[\dfrac{\sin\left(\dfrac{ax+b-a}{2}\right)}{2\sin(a/2)}\right] = \cos(ax+b)$, interval of differencing is unity, $[a \neq 0]$,

(vii) $\Delta\left[\dfrac{a^{x+1}\sin b(x-1) - a^x \sin bx}{a^2 - 2a\cos b + 1}\right] = a^x \sin bx$, interval of differencing is unity,

(viii) The formula (2) can be used to obtain the sum to n terms of the series whose xth term can be put as

$$ca^x,\ x^{(m-1)}\ c,\ cx^{(-m-1)}.\ c\begin{pmatrix} x \\ m-1 \end{pmatrix} \text{ or a polynomial in } x.$$

(ix) The difference operator "Δ" converts:

(a) Exponential functions into exponential functions,

(b) Trigonometrical functions into trigonometrical functions,

(c) Polynomials into polynomials.

8.3 A Series with General Term of the Form $u_x = \phi(x) + cr^x$, where $\phi(x)$ is Some Rational Integral Function of x of Degree n

From the above series, we obtain successive differences. Each term in any of the successive differences consists of two parts, one arising due to the presence of $\phi(x)$ and the other from the terms of the type ar^x. But it has been given that $\phi(x)$ will be zero in the $(n+1)^{th}$, $(n+2)^{th}$, $(n+3)^{th}$ etc., differences with the result that the these differences from G.P. with common ratio "r". For example, *if we take $\phi(x) = c + bx$, then the second and higher order differences arising due to the presence of $\phi(x)$ will be zero consequently the second and higher order differences of u_x form G.P. with common ratio r.*

$$u_x = c + bx + ar^x$$

$$\Rightarrow \quad \Delta u_x = b + a(r-1)r^x, \Delta^2 u_x = a(r-1)^2 r^x$$

$$\Delta^3 u_x = a(r-1)^3 r^x, \Delta^4 u^x = a(r-1)^4 r^x,$$

$$\dots \quad \dots \quad \dots \quad \dots \quad \dots \quad \dots$$

$$\dots \quad \dots \quad \dots \quad \dots \quad \dots \quad \dots$$

$$\Delta^n u_x = a(r-1)^n r^x.$$

From the above discussion we arrive at the following conclusion

If first few terms of a series are given, and if the nth *differences of these terms form a G.P. with common ratio "r", then the general term of the series can be taken as $f(x) + ar^x$, where $f(x)$ is a rational integral function of degree $(n-1)$.*

Having determined the general term, the sum to n terms can be obtained easily.

Solved Examples

Example 1: *Sum to n terms the series whose xth term is*

(*a*) $x(x-1)(x-2)$, **[M.D.U. (Rohtak) 2005, 2008]**

(*b*) $\dfrac{1}{(x+1)(x+2)(x+3)}$, **[Baroda 2004, 2008]**

(*c*) $x(x+2)(x+4)$,

(*d*) $(x+3)(x+4)(x+5)$, **[Agra 2008]**

(*e*) $(3x-2)(3x+1)(3x+4)$. **[Andhra 2005, 2009]**

Solution: (a) we have $u_x = x(x-1)(x-2) \; x^{(3)} = \Delta f(x)$, say

$$\therefore \quad f(x) = \frac{x^{(4)}}{4} \qquad \left[\because \Delta \frac{x^{(4)}}{4} = x^{(3)}\right]$$

$$\Rightarrow \quad \sum_{x=1}^{n} u_x = \left[f(x)\right]_1^{n+1} = \tfrac{1}{4}\left[x^{(4)}\right]_1^{n+1} \quad \text{where } f(x) = \Delta^{-1} u_x$$

$$\Rightarrow \quad \sum_{x=1}^{n} u_x = \tfrac{1}{4}\left[x(x-1)(x-2)(x-3)\right]_1^{n+1} = \tfrac{1}{4}\left[n(n+1)(n-1)(n-2)\right].$$

(b) we have $u_x = \dfrac{1}{(x+1)(x+2)(x+3)} = x^{(-3)} = \Delta f(x)$, say

$$\Rightarrow \quad f(x) = \frac{x^{(-3+1)}}{-3+1} = -\frac{x^{(-2)}}{2} \quad \left[\because \Delta\left(-\frac{x^{(-2)}}{2}\right) = x^{(-3)}\right]$$

Thus $$\sum_{x=1}^{n} u_x = \left[f(x)\right]_1^{n+1} = \left[\frac{-x^{(-2)}}{2}\right]_1^{n+1} = \left[-\frac{1}{2(x+1)(x+2)}\right]_1^{n+1}$$

i.e. we have $\displaystyle\sum_{x=1}^{n} u_x = -\tfrac{1}{2}\left[\frac{1}{(n+2)(n+3)} - \frac{1}{2\,3}\right]$

(c) we have $u_x = x(x+2)(x+4) = x^3 + 6x^2 + 8x$

$$\Rightarrow \quad u_x = x^{(3)} + 9x^{(2)} + 15x^{(1)} \quad \text{[after converting into factorial notation]}$$

$$\Rightarrow \quad \sum_{x=1}^{n} u_x = \sum_{x=1}^{n} x^{(3)} + 9\sum_{x=1}^{n} x^{(2)} + 15\sum_{x=1}^{n} x^{(1)}$$

$$= \left[\frac{1}{4}x^{(4)}\right]_1^{n+1} + 9\left[\frac{1}{3}x^{(3)}\right]_1^{n+1} + 15\left[\frac{1}{2}x^{(2)}\right]_1^{n+1}$$

$$= \left[\frac{1}{4}(n+1)^{(4)} + \frac{9}{3}(n+1)^{(3)} + \frac{15}{2}(n+1)^{(2)}\right] - 0$$

$$= \frac{1}{4}(n+1)\,n(n-1)(n-2) + \frac{9}{3}(n+1)\,n(n-1) + \frac{15}{2}(n+1)\,n - 0$$

$$= \frac{n(n+1)}{12}\left[3(n-1)(n-2) + 36(n-1) + 90\right] = \frac{1}{4}n(n+1)(n+4)(n+5).$$

(d) we have $u_x = (x+5)(x+4)(x+3) = (x+5)^{(3)}$

$$\Rightarrow \quad \sum_{x=1}^{n} u_x = \sum_{x=1}^{n} (x+5)^{(3)} = \left[\frac{1}{4}(x+5)^{(4)}\right]_1^{n+1}$$

$$\sum_{x=1}^{n} u_x = \frac{1}{4}\left[(n+6)^{(4)} - 6^{(4)}\right] = \frac{1}{4}\left[(n+6)(n+5)(n+4)(n+3) - 360\right].$$

(e) We have $u_x = (3x+4)(3x+1)(3x-2) = (3x+4)^{(3)}$

$$\Rightarrow \sum_{x=1}^{n} u_x = \sum_{x=1}^{n} (3x+4)^{(3)} = \left[\frac{(3x+4)^{(4)}}{3\times 4}\right]_1^{n+1} \qquad \therefore \sum_{x=1}^{n} u_x = [f(x)]_1^{n+1}$$

$$= \frac{1}{12}[(3n+7)^{(4)}] - (7)^{(4)}] = \frac{1}{12}[(3n+7)(3n+4)(3n+1)(3n-2) - 840].$$

Example 2: *Sum to n terms the series whose xth term is*

$$(a)\ \frac{1}{(x+3)(x+4)} \qquad (b)\ \frac{1}{(x+1)(x+2)(x+3)} \qquad (c)\ \frac{x+3}{x(x+1)(x+2)}.$$

Solution: (a) we have $u_x = \dfrac{1}{(x+3)(x+4)} = (x+2)^{(-2)}$

$$\Rightarrow \sum_{x=1}^{n} u_x = \sum_{x=1}^{n} (x+2)^{(-2)} = \left[\frac{(x+2)^{(-1)}}{-1}\right]_1^{n+1}$$

$$= -\left[(n+3)^{(-1)} - 3^{(-1)}\right] = \frac{n}{4(n+4)}.$$

(b) we have $u_x = \dfrac{1}{(x+1)(x+2)(x+3)} = x^{(-3)}$

$$\Rightarrow f(x) = \frac{-x^{(-2)}}{2} \qquad \left[\because \Delta\left\{\frac{-x^{(-2)}}{2}\right\} = x^{(-3)}\right]$$

$$\Rightarrow \sum_{x=1}^{n} u_x = [f(x)]_1^{n+1} = \left[\frac{-x^{(-2)}}{2}\right]_1^{n+1} = -\left[\frac{1}{2(x+1)(x+2)}\right]_1^{n+1} = -\frac{1}{2}\left[\frac{1}{(n+2)(n+3)} - \frac{1}{6}\right].$$

(c) we have $u_x = \dfrac{1}{(x+1)(x+2)} + \dfrac{3}{x(x+1)(x+2)}$

$$\therefore \quad u_x = x^{(-2)} + 3(x-1)^{(-3)}$$

$$\Rightarrow \sum_{1}^{n} u_x = \left[\frac{x^{(-1)}}{-1}\right]_1^{n+1} + 3\left[\frac{(x-1)^{(-2)}}{-2}\right]_1^{n+1} = \left[-\frac{(n+1)^{-1}}{1} - \frac{3}{2}n^{(-2)}\right] - \left[\frac{1^{(1)}}{-1} - \frac{3}{2}.0^{(-2)}\right]$$

$$= -\left[\frac{1}{n+1} + \frac{3}{2(n+2)(n+1)}\right] + \left[\frac{1}{2} + \frac{3}{2\times 2\times 1}\right] = \frac{5n^2 + 11n}{4(4n+1)(n+2)}.$$

Example 3: *Sum the following series to n terms*

2, 12, 36, 80, 150, 252,... . **[Bhopal 2007]**

Solution: In the problem of this nature, we write u_x as the polynomial of lowest degree satisfying the given terms. Let the given series be $u_0, u_1, u_2, u_3, \ldots, u_{n-1}$. Then we want to find $\sum_{x=0}^{n-1} u_x$

x	u_x	Δu_x	$\Delta^2 u_x$	$\Delta^3 u_x$
0	2			
		10		
1	12		14	
		24		6
2	36		20	
		44		6
3	80		26	
		70		6
4	150		32	
		102		
5	252			

Third differences are constant, so we have

$$u_x = u_0 + (x)^{(1)}\,\Delta u_0 + \frac{x^{(2)}}{2\,!}\,\Delta^2 u_0 + \frac{x^{(3)}}{3\,!}\,\Delta^3 u_0, \quad \text{where } x^{(r)} \text{ means } {}^xC_r$$

$$\therefore \quad u_x = 2 + 10x^{(1)} + \frac{14x^{(2)}}{2!} + \frac{6x^{(3)}}{3!} = \Delta f(x), \text{ say}$$

$$\Rightarrow \quad \sum_{x=0}^{n-1} u_x = \left[f(x)\right]_0^n = \sum_0^{n-1}\left[2 + 10x^{(1)} + \frac{14x^{(2)}}{2\,!} + 6\,\frac{x^{(3)}}{3\,!}\right]$$

$$= \left[2x^{(1)} + \frac{10x^{(2)}}{2} + \frac{14x^{(3)}}{3!} + \frac{6x^{(4)}}{4!}\right]_0^n$$

$$= 2n^{(1)} + \frac{10n^{(2)}}{2} + \frac{14n^{(3)}}{6} + \frac{6n^{(4)}}{24}$$

$$= 2n + 10\,\frac{n(n-1)}{2} + 14\,\frac{n(n-1)(n-2)}{6} + 6\,\frac{n(n-1)(n-2)(n-3)}{24}$$

Simplifying, we obtain $\sum_{x=0}^{n-1} u_x = (n/12)(n+1)(n+2)(3n+1)$.

Example 4: *Use the method of finite differences to sum the series*

$$1^3 + 2^3 + 3^3 + \ldots + n^3.$$

[Bangaluru 2006, 2008]

Solution: We have $u_x = x^3 = x^{(3)} + 3x^{(2)} + x^{(1)} = \Delta f(x)$, say

$$\Rightarrow \quad \sum_{x=1}^{n} u_x = \left[f(x)\right]_1^{n+1} = \left[\frac{x^{(4)}}{4} + x^{(3)} + \frac{x^{(2)}}{2}\right]_1^{n+1}$$

$$= \frac{1}{4}(n+1)^{(4)} + (n+1)^{(3)} + \frac{1}{2}(n+1)^{(2)}$$

$$= \frac{1}{4}(n+1)\,n\,(n-1)\,(n-2) + (n+1)\,n\,(n-1) + \frac{1}{2}n\,(n+1)$$

$$= \frac{1}{4}n\,(n+1)\,[n^2+n] = \frac{1}{4}[n\,(n+1)]^2 = [n\,(n+1)/2]^2.$$

Example 5: *Sum the series*

5, 10, 17, 28, 47, 82,... to n terms. **[Delhi (H) 2006, 2009]**

Solution: The difference table is given by

x	u_x	Δu_x	$\Delta^2 u_x$
1	5		
		5	
2	10		2
		7	
3	17		4
		11	
4	28		8
		19	
5	47		16
		35	
6	82		

From here, it is obvious that the second differences are in G.P., with common ratio 2, so we can say that $f(x)$ is a rational integral function of x of degree 2 and consequently we have $u_x = a + bx^{(1)} + c.2^x \quad \Rightarrow \quad \Delta u_x = b + c\,(2-1)\,2^x \Rightarrow \Delta^2 u_x = c\,(2-1)^2\,2^x$

whence putting $x = 1$ in these results, we get $2 = c.2\,, 5 = b + 2c$

and $\qquad 5 = a + b + 2c \Rightarrow c = 1, b = 3, a = 0 \Rightarrow u_x = 3x^{(1)} + b^x = \Delta f(x)$ say

$$\Rightarrow \quad \sum_{x=1}^{n} u_x = \sum_{x=1}^{n}[3x^{(1)} + 2^x] = 3\sum_{x=1}^{n} x^{(1)} + \sum_{x=1}^{n} 2^x$$

$$\Rightarrow \quad \sum_{x=1}^{n} u_x = 3\left[\frac{x^{(2)}}{2}\right]_1^{n+1} + \left[\frac{2^x}{2-1}\right]_1^{n+1} = \frac{3}{2}[(n+1)\,n] + 2^{n+1} - 2$$

i.e., $\qquad u_1 + u_2 + \ldots + u_n = \frac{3}{2}n\,(n+1) + 2^{n+1} - 2$

Example 6: *Find the general term and the sum to n terms of the series.*

1, 2, 4, 8, 17, 40, 104 ,.... . **[Delhi (H) 2004]**

Solution: The difference table is given by

x	u_x	Δu_x	$\Delta^2 u_x$	$\Delta^3 u_x$
1	1			
		1		
2	2		1	
		2		1
3	4		2	
		4		3
4	8		5	
		9		9
5	17		14	
		23		27
6	40		41	
		64		
7	104			

From the above table, it is obvious that third differences are in G with common ratio 3; so we can assume that

$$u_x = a.3^x + x^{(2)} + cx^{(1)} + d,$$

$$\Rightarrow \quad \Delta u_x = a.(3-1))\,3^x + 2bx^{(1)} + c = 2a3^x + 2bx^{(1)} + c.$$

$$\Delta^2 u_x = 2a.(3-1)\,3^x + 2b = 4a.3^x + 2b. \qquad \text{and } \Delta^3 u^x = 8a.3^x,$$

Now putting $x = 1$ in the above results, we obtain

$$3a + c + d = 1 \qquad ...(1)$$

$$6a + 2b + c = 1 \qquad ...(2)$$

$$12a + 2b = 1 \qquad ...(3)$$

$$24a = 1 \qquad ...(4)$$

These imply $a = \frac{1}{24}, b = \frac{1}{4}, c = \frac{1}{4}, d = \frac{5}{8}$

$$\therefore \quad u_x = \frac{1}{24}3^x + \frac{1}{4}x^{(2)} + \frac{1}{4}x^{(1)} + \frac{5}{8} = \Delta f(x)$$

$$\Rightarrow \quad f(x)=\sum_{1}^{n} u_x=\left[\frac{1}{24}\cdot\frac{3^x}{3-1}+\frac{1}{4\times 3}x^{(2)}+\frac{1}{4\times 2}x^{(2)}+\frac{5}{8}x^{(1)}\right]_1^{n+1}$$

$$=\left[\frac{1}{48}3^{n+1}+\frac{(n+1)^{(3)}}{12}+\frac{(n+1)^{(2)}}{8}+\frac{5}{8}(n+1)^{(1)}\right]-\left[\frac{1}{24}\times\frac{3}{2}+0-0+\frac{5}{8}\right]$$

$$=\frac{1}{8}\left[\frac{3^n}{2}+\frac{2}{3}(n+1)\,n(n-1)+(n+1)\,n+5\,(n+1)-\frac{1}{2}-5\right]$$

$$=\frac{1}{8}\left[\frac{1}{2}(3^n-1)+5n+\frac{1}{3}n\,(n+1)\,(2n+1)\right].$$

8.4 Summation by Parts

Consider the series such that its general term is the product of two functions, *viz.*

$$u_x=f_1(x)\,g_2(x). \text{ Now, we have}$$

$$\Delta\{f_1(x)\,g_2(x)\}=f_1(x+1)\,g_2(x+1)-f_1(x)\,g_2(x)$$

where we assume $\Delta\, g_2(x)=f_2(x)$ and $\Delta\, g_1(x)=f_1(x)$

This implies

$$\Delta\{f_1(x)\,g_2(x)\}=f_1(x+1)\,g_2(x+1)-f_1(x)\,g_2(x+1)$$
$$+f_1(x)\,g_2(x+1)-f_1(x)\,g_2(x)$$
$$=g_2(x+1)\{f_1(x+1)-f_1(x)\}+f_1(x)\{g_2(x+1)-g_2(x)\}$$
$$=g_2(x+1)\,\Delta f_1(x)+f_1(x).\,\Delta g_2(x)$$
$$=g_2(x+1)\,\Delta f_1(x)+f_1(x)\,f_2(x)$$

$$\Rightarrow \quad f_1(x)\,f_2(x)=\Delta\{f_1(x).\,g_2(x)\}-g_2(x+1)\,\Delta f_1(x)$$

$$\Rightarrow \quad \sum_{x=1}^{n} f_1(x)\,f_2(x)=\left[f_1(x).\,g_2(x)\right]_1^{n+1}-\sum_{x=1}^{n} g_2(x+1).\,\Delta f_1(x)$$

$$\Rightarrow \sum_{x=1}^{n} f_1(x)\,\Delta g_2(x)=\left[f_1(x).\,g_2(x)\right]_1^{n+1}-\sum_{x=1}^{n} g_2(x+1).\,\Delta f_1(x) \qquad \text{...(A)}$$

This formula has a close analogy with the rule of integration by parts and is termed as summation by parts.

8.5 To Prove that $\sum_{x=1}^{n} u_x=\left[\Delta^{-1}u_x\right]_1^{n+1}$ where $\Delta^{-1}\equiv\frac{1}{\Delta}$

$$\sum_{x=1}^{n} u_x=u_1+u_2+\ldots+u_n=u_1+Eu_1+E^2u_1+\ldots+E^{n-1}u_1$$

$$=(1+E+E^2+\ldots+E^{n-1})\,u_1.=\frac{E^n-1}{E-1}u_1 \qquad (\because Eu_1=u_2 \text{ etc.})$$

If $Ef(x) = u_x$ and in particular $u_1 = \Delta f(1) = (E-1) f(1)$, then we have

$$= \frac{E^n - 1}{E - 1} u_1 = \frac{E^n - 1}{E - 1} (E-1)(1) = (E^n - 1) f(1)$$

$$= E^n f(1) - f(1) = f(n+1) - f(1) = \left[f(x)\right]_1^{n+1} = \left[\Delta^{-1} u_x\right]_1^{n+1}$$

$$\Rightarrow \quad \sum_{x=1}^{n} u_x = u_1 + u_2 + \ldots + u_n = \left[\Delta^{-1} u_x\right]_1^{n+1} = \frac{1}{\Delta}(u_{n+1} - u_1).$$

8.6 Relationship in between Δ and Σ

If $\Delta f(x) = u_x$, then we know that $f(x) = f(0) + \sum_{0}^{x-1} u_x$

or $\quad f(x) = k + \sum_{x=0}^{x-1} u_x$, provided k is constant ...(1)

This implies $\Delta f(x) = \Delta(k) + \Delta \sum_{x=0}^{x-1} u_x$

$$\Rightarrow \quad u_x = \Delta \sum_{x=0}^{x-1} u_x = \Delta \Sigma u_x \qquad (\because \Delta f(x) = u_x, \Delta k = 0)$$

$$\Rightarrow \quad \Delta \Sigma u_x = u_x, \qquad \Rightarrow \quad \Delta \Sigma \equiv 1$$

i.e., operator $\Delta \Sigma$ is equivalent to 1 *i.e.*, Σ is equivalent to $1/\Delta \equiv \Delta^{-1}$ which means that Σ can be replaced by $1/\Delta$.

But Δ cannot be replaced by $(1/\Sigma)$.

Further also, we have $\quad \Delta f(x) = u_x, \quad \therefore \quad \Sigma \Delta f(x) = \Sigma u_x$ ...(2)

But we have $\quad f(x) = f(0) + \sum_{x=0}^{x-1} u_x \quad \Rightarrow \quad f\{x\} - f(0) = \Sigma u_x$ ...(3)

Equations (2) and (3) give $\Sigma \Delta f(x) = f(x) - f(0)$

$$\Rightarrow \quad \Sigma \Delta \neq 1 \Rightarrow \Delta \text{ and } \Sigma \text{ are not commutative operators.}$$

8.7 If $\psi(x) = \frac{\Gamma'(x)}{\Gamma(x)} = \frac{d}{dx}[\log \Gamma(x)]$

Prove that $\Delta^{-1}[(x-b)^{-n}] = \frac{(-1)^{1-n}}{(n-1)!} \psi^{n-1}(x-b)$.

Proof: First we shall prove the result

$$\Delta^{-1}[x^{-n}] = \frac{(-1)^{1-n}}{(n-1)!} \psi^{n-1}(x), \quad \text{we have } \Gamma(x+1) = x\Gamma(x)$$

Taking log and then differentiating, we get

$$\frac{\Gamma'(x+1)}{\Gamma(x+1)} = \frac{1}{x} + \frac{\Gamma'(x)}{\Gamma(x)} \Rightarrow \psi(x+1) = \frac{1}{x} + \psi(x)$$

$$\Rightarrow \quad \psi(x+1) - \psi(x) = \frac{1}{x}, \quad \Rightarrow \Delta\psi(x) = \frac{1}{x} \Rightarrow \psi(x) = \Delta^{-1}\left(\frac{1}{x}\right) \qquad ...(1)$$

Further, also $\psi(x+1) - \psi(x) = 1/x$

$$\Rightarrow \quad \psi'(x+1) - \psi' = -\frac{1}{x^2} \Rightarrow \Delta\psi'(x) = -\frac{1}{x^2}$$

$$\Rightarrow \quad \Delta^{-1}\left(\frac{1}{x^2}\right) = -\psi'(x) \qquad ...(2)$$

Thus from above, we see that

$$\Delta^{-1}(1/x) = \Delta^{-1}[x^{-1}] = \psi(x), \Delta^{-1}(x^{-2}) = -\psi'(x)$$

and $$\Delta^{-1}(x^{-3}) = \frac{1}{2!}\psi''(x)$$

i.e., we have $\Delta^{-1}(x^{-2}) = \dfrac{(-1)^{1-2}}{(2-1)!}\psi'(x)$

and $$\Delta^{-1}(x^{-3}) = \frac{(-1)^{1-3}}{(3-1)!}\psi''(x)$$

We shall prove the above theorem by induction method *i.e.*, first assume that theorem is true for $n = m$ implying

$$\Delta^{-1}[x^m] = \frac{(-1)^{1-m}}{(m-1)!}\psi^{m-1}(x) \Rightarrow x^{-m} = \frac{(-1)^{1-m}}{(m-1)!}\Delta\psi^{m-1}(x) \qquad ...(G)$$

$$\Rightarrow \quad x^{-m} = \frac{(-1)^{1-m}}{(m-1)!}[\psi^{m-1}(x+1) - \psi^{m-1}(x)] \qquad ...(3)$$

Differentiating both the sides w.r.t "x", we get

$$-mx^{-m-1} = \frac{(-1)^{1-m}}{(m-1)!}[\psi^m(x+1) - \psi^m(x)]$$

$$\Rightarrow \quad x^{-m-1} = \frac{(-1)^{1-m}}{(-1)(m)!}[\Delta\psi^m(x)] \Rightarrow x^{-(m+1)} = \frac{(-1)^{1-(m+1)}}{m!}\Delta\psi^m(x)$$

i.e., the theorem is true for the next higher integer $n = m + 1$. But it is also true for $n = 1$, hence it will be true for $n = 2$ etc. *viz.* the theorem is true for all n.

Putting $x - b$ for x in (G), we obtain

$$\Delta^{-1}[(x-b)^{-m}] = \frac{(-1)^{1-m}}{(m-1)!}\psi^{m-1}(x-b),$$

which after replacing m by n proves the required proposition.

Cor: $\Delta \log \Gamma(x) = \log \Gamma\,(x+1) - \log \Gamma(x) = \log x$

$$[\because \Gamma(x+1) = (x)\,!, \Gamma(x) = (x-1)\,!]$$

$$\left\{\frac{\Gamma(x+1)}{\Gamma(x)} = \frac{(x)\,!}{(x-1)\,!} = x\right\}$$

$$\Rightarrow \qquad \Delta^{-1}(\log x) = \log \Gamma(x)\,\Gamma\,\Sigma_1^n \log x = [\log \Gamma(x)]_1^{n+1}$$

$$= \log\,[\Gamma(n+1)] - \log \Gamma(1)$$

$$= \log \Gamma(n+1)\,. \qquad [\because \Gamma(1) = 1 \text{ and } \log 1 = 0]$$

8.8 If $f(x)$ is Some Function of x and $\phi(E)$ is a Polynomial in E then Prove that $\phi(E)\,[a^x f(x)] = a^x\,\phi\,(aE)\,[f(x)]$

Proof: Let $\phi\,(E) = c_0 + c_1\,E + c_2\,E^2 + \ldots + c_r\,E^r + \ldots$, where c's are constants.

We have $c_r E^r\,[a^x f(x)] = c_r\,a^{r+x}\,E_r f(x) = c_r\,a^x a^r f(x+r)$

$$= a^x\,c_r\,a^r f(x+r) = a^x\,c_r\,a^r\,E^r f(x) = a^x c_r\,(aE)^r f(x) \qquad \ldots(1)$$

$$\therefore \qquad \phi\,(E)\,[a^x f(x)] = \sum\,[c_r E^r\{a^x f(x)\}]$$

$$= \sum_{r=0} [a^x c_r\,(aE)^r f(x)] \qquad [\text{using } (1)]$$

$$= a^x \sum_{r=0} c_r (aE)^r f(x) = a^x \phi\,(aE)\,[f(x)]$$

Cor: $(E-a)^n\,a^x\,f(x) = a^x\,(aE-a)^n\,f(x) = a^x a^n\,(E-1)^n\,f(x) = a^x a^n\,\Delta^n\,f(x)$.

Example 7: *Sum to n terms the series whose xth term is* $4^x\left\{\dfrac{x^2}{(x+1)\,(x+2)}\right\}$.

[Baroda 2004; Agra 2005, 2007]

Solution: We have $\displaystyle\sum_1^n u_x = \sum_1^n \left[4^x\left\{1 + \frac{1}{x+1} - \frac{4}{x+2}\right\}\right] = \sum_1^n 4^x + \sum_1^n 4^x\,[(x+1)^{-1} - 4\,(x+2)^{-1}]$

But $\displaystyle \Delta\left(\frac{4^x}{x+1}\right) = \frac{4^{x+1}}{x+2} - \frac{4^x}{x+1} = -4^x\left[\frac{1}{x+1} - \frac{4}{x+2}\right]$

$$\Rightarrow \qquad \sum_{x=1}^n u_x = \sum_{x=1}^n 4^x - \sum_{x=1}^n \Delta\,\{4^x/(x+1)\} \qquad \ldots(1)$$

So we have $\displaystyle \sum_{x=1}^n u_x = \left[4^x/(4-1)\right]_1^{n+1} + \left[4^x/(x+1)\right]_1^{n+1}$

$$= \frac{1}{3}\,[4^{n+1} - 4] - [\{4^{n+1}/(n+2)\} - (4/2)] = (2/3) + (4^{n+1}/3)\,[1 - (3/(n+2)].$$

Example 8: *Sum to n terms the series whose xth term is* $2^x(x^3+x)$. **[Agra M.A. 2006, 2008]**

Solution: $u_x = \text{General term} = (x^3+x).2^x$ ...(1)

But $\Delta(2^x) = 2^{x+1} - 2^x = 2^x(2-1) \Rightarrow \Delta\left(\dfrac{2^x}{2-1}\right) = 2^x \Rightarrow \Delta(2^x) = 2^x$

$\therefore$ (1) can be written as $u_x = (x^3+x)\,\Delta(2^x) = f_1(x)\,\Delta g_2(x)$, say

$$\Rightarrow \sum_{x=1}^{n} u_x = \left[(x^3+x)\,2^x\right]_1^{n+1} - \sum_{x=1}^{n}[2^{x+1}\,\Delta(x^3+x)]$$

$$= \left[2^x(x^3+x)\right]_1^{n+1} - \sum_{x=1}^{n} 2^{x+1}(3x^2+3x+2)$$

$\because$ $[\Delta(x^3+x) = 3x^2+3x+2]$ ...(2)

Further let $v_x = 2^{x+1}(3x^2+3x+2) = (3x^2+3x+2).\Delta(2^{x+1})$

$$\Rightarrow \sum_{x=1}^{n} v_x = \left[(3x^2+3x+2)\,2^{x+1}\right]_1^{n+1} - \sum_{x=1}^{n}[2^{x+2}\,\Delta(3x^2+3x+2)]$$

$$\Rightarrow \sum_{x=1}^{n} v_x = \left[(3x^2+3x+2)\,2^{x+1}\right]_1^{n+1} - \sum_{1}^{n}[2^{x+2}(6x+6)]$$

$$= \left[(3x^2+3x+2)\,2^{x+1}\right]_1^{n+1} - \left[\{2x^2(6x+6)\}_1^{n+1} - \sum_1^n 2^{x+3}.6\right]$$

whence using (3), equation (2)

$$\Rightarrow \sum_{x=1}^{n} u_x = 2^{n+1}(n^3-3n^2+10n-14)+28.$$

Example 9: *Find the sum up to n terms of the series*

$$\frac{3}{2.5.8} + \frac{5}{5.8.11} + \frac{7}{8.11.14} + \ldots$$

and hence evaluate the sum upto infinity. **[M.K.U. (Tamil Nadu) 2006]**

Solution: General term is given by

$$u_x = \frac{2x+1}{(3x-1)(3x+2)(2x+5)} = (2x+1)(3x-4)^{(-3)}$$

Now $f_1(x) = (2x+1) \Rightarrow \Delta f_1(x) = 2$

and $\Delta g_2(x) = (3x-4)^{(-3)} \Rightarrow g_2(x) = \dfrac{(3x-4)^{(-2)}}{-2\times 3}$

$$\therefore \sum_{1}^{n} f_1(x)\,\Delta g_2(x) = \left[f_1(x)\,g_2(x)\right]_1^{n+1} - \sum_{1}^{n}\left[\frac{(3x-1)^{(-2)}}{-6}\times 2\right]$$

$$= \sum_{1}^{n} u_x = \left[(2x+1).\frac{(3x-4)^{(-2)}}{-6}\right]_1^{n+1} - \left[\frac{(3x-1)^{(-1)}}{(-6)\times(-2)\times(-1)}\times 2\right]_1^{n+1}$$

$$= \left[\frac{-2n-3}{6(3n+2)(3n+5)} + \frac{1}{2.2.5}\right] - \left[(3n+2)^{(-1)} - \frac{2^{(-1)}}{9}\right]$$

$$= \frac{-2n-3}{6(3n+2)(3n+5)} - \frac{1}{9(3n+5)} + \frac{1}{20} + \frac{1}{45}$$

$$= \frac{13}{180} - \frac{12n+13}{18(3n+2)(3n+5)} \qquad ...(1)$$

when $n \to \infty$, $\Rightarrow u_1 + u_2 + ... = (13/180)$ expression B tends to zero and A remains constant, implying

Example 10: *Sum to n terms the series whose xth term is* $[x.2^x/(x+2)!]$.

Solution: Let $u_x = \dfrac{x.2^x}{(x+2)!} = \dfrac{x+2-2}{(x+2)!}2^x = \dfrac{2^x}{(x+1)!} - \dfrac{2^{x+1}}{(x+2)!} \equiv \Delta\left(\dfrac{-2^x}{(x+1)!}\right)$ ...(1)

$$\Rightarrow \sum_{x=1}^{n} u_x = \left[\frac{-2^x}{(x+1)!}\right]_1^{n+1} = 1 - \frac{2^{n+1}}{(n+2)!} \qquad ...(2)$$

Aliter: $u_x = \dfrac{x.2^x}{(x+2)!}\Delta v_x$ say. Let us assume $v_x = \dfrac{2^x f(x)}{(x+1)!}$ ...(3)

$$\Delta v_x = \frac{2^{x+1} f(x+1)}{(x+2)1} - \frac{2^x f(x)}{(x+1)!} = \frac{x.2^x}{(x+2)!} \text{ (given)}$$

$$\Rightarrow \frac{x.2^x}{(x+2)!} = \frac{2^x}{(1+x)!}\left[\frac{2f(x+1)}{(x+2)} - f(x)\right] \qquad ...(4)$$

$\to$ First degree $\to$ $\leftarrow$ Should be of first degree $\to$

Inspection of equation (3) implies that $f(x)$ reduces to some constant, say c.

$\therefore$ $f(x+1) = c$ ($\because$ $f(x)$ is constant function) ...(5)

$\Rightarrow$ $x = 2c - (x+2)c$ [putting the value of $f(x)$ in (4)]

$\Rightarrow$ $c = -1, \Rightarrow f(x) = -1$. Thus $v(x) = \dfrac{-2^x}{(x+1)!}$

Implying that the sum upto n terms $= \displaystyle\sum_{1}^{n} \frac{x2^x}{(x+2)!} = \left[\frac{-2^x}{(x+1)!}\right]_1^{n+1} = 1 - \frac{2^{n+1}}{(n+2)!}$.

Example 11: *Sum the series*

$$a^{n+1} - n(a+b)^{n+1} + \frac{n(n-1)}{2!}(a+2b)^{n+1} - \frac{n(n-1)(n-2)}{3!}(a+3b)^{n+1} + \ldots .$$

Solution: Let the interval of differencing be b, then the series may be written as

$$(1 - {}^nC_1 E + {}^nC_2 E^2 - \ldots)\, a^{n+1} = (1-E)^n\, a^{n+1} = (-1)^n \Delta^n a^{n+1}$$

$$\therefore \quad \Delta^n a^{n+1} = \frac{1}{2} b^n (n+1)!\,(2a+nb)$$

Thus sum of the series $= \frac{1}{2}(-b)^n (n+1)!\,(2a+nb) = \frac{1}{2}(-b)^n (n+1)!\,(2a+nb)$

Example 12: *Sum the series*

$$\frac{1}{x+1} - \frac{n}{(x+1)(x+2)} + \frac{n(n-1)}{(x+1)(x+2)(x+3)} - \ldots \text{ to } n \text{ terms.}$$

Solution: The given series can be written as

$$x^{(-1)} - nx^{(-2)} + n(n-1)\, x^{(-3)} - \ldots + (-1)^n n!\, x^{(-n-1)}$$

$$= x^{(-1)} + \frac{n}{1!}\Delta x^{(-1)} + \frac{n(n-1)}{2!}\Delta^2 x^{(-1)} + \frac{n!}{n!}\Delta^n x^{(-1)}$$

$$= [1 + {}^nC_1\, \Delta + {}^nC_2 + \ldots + \Delta^n]\, x^{(-1)} = (1+\Delta)^n (x^{(-1)})$$

$$= E^n x^{(-1)} = (x+n)^{(-1)} = 1/(x+n+1).$$

Example 13: *If fourth and higher differences are ignored, prove that the sum of successive terms of a function, of which u_0 is the central term is sum of successive terms of a function, of which u_0 is the central term is*

$$nu_0 + (1/24)(n^3 - n)\,\Delta^2 u_{-1}, \text{ where } n \text{ is odd.}$$

Solution: As a matter of fact u_0 is the central term, so any central difference formula can be used, *viz.* Gauss's forward formula implies.

$$u_x = u_0 + {}^xC_1 \Delta u_0 + {}^xC_2 \Delta^2 u_{-1} + {}^{x+1}C_3 \Delta^3 u_{-1} + \ldots$$

$$= u_0 + x^{(1)}\,\Delta u_0 + \frac{1}{2} x^{(2)} \Delta u_{-1} + \frac{1}{6}(x+1)^{(3)} \Delta^3 u_{-1} + \ldots$$

$$\Rightarrow \quad \Sigma u_x = c + xu_0 + \frac{1}{2} x^{(2)}\,\Delta u_0 + \frac{1}{6} x^{(3)} \Delta^3 u_{-1} + \frac{1}{24}(x+1)^{(4)}\,\Delta^3 u_{-1} - \frac{1}{2}(n-1)$$

$$\Rightarrow \quad \Sigma u_x = \left[c + xu_0 + \frac{1}{2} x^{(2)} \Delta u_0 + \frac{1}{6} x^{(3)} \Delta u_{-1} - \frac{1}{2}(n-1) + \frac{1}{24}(x+1)^{(4)}\,\Delta^3 u_{-1}\right]_{-\frac{1}{2}(n-1)}^{\frac{1}{2}(n-1)}$$

$$\Rightarrow \quad a^{n+1} = a^{(n+1)} + \frac{n(n+1)}{2} ba^{(n)} + \text{terms of } a^{(r)}, \text{ where } r < n$$

$$\Rightarrow \qquad \Delta^n a^{n+2} = \Delta^n \left[a^{(n+2)} + \frac{n(n+1)}{2} a^{(n)} b + \text{terms of } a^{(r)} \right]$$

$$= (n+1)!\, b^n a^{(1)} + \frac{n(n+1)}{2} . (n)!\, b^{n+1}$$

$$= \frac{b^n}{2} (n+1)!\,(2a + nb). \qquad [b \text{ is the interval of differencing.}]$$

$$= \left[\frac{n+1}{2} - \left(\frac{-n+1}{2} \right) u_0 + \frac{1}{6} \left[\frac{n+1}{2} . \frac{n-1}{2} . \frac{n-3}{2} \right] - \left(\frac{-n-1}{2} . \frac{n+1}{2} . \frac{n+3}{2} \right) \right] \Delta^2 u_{-1}$$

$$= nu_0 + \frac{1}{24} (n^3 - n)\, \Delta^2 u_{-1} \qquad [\text{coefficients of } \Delta u_0 \text{ and } \Delta u_{-1} \text{ cancel.}]$$

Example 14: *Evaluate*

(a) $\sum_0^\infty a^x f(x)$

(b) 2.2 + 7.4 + 14.8 + 23.16 + 34.32 + ... n terms.

Solution: (a) We have $\sum_0^\infty [a^x f(x)] = \Delta^{-1} [a^x f(x)] = (E-1)^{-1} a^x f(x)$ where $\phi(E) = (E-1)^{-1}$

$$\Rightarrow \qquad \sum_{n=0}^\infty a^x f(x) = a^x (aE - 1)^{-1} f(x) = a^x (a + a\Delta - 1)^{-1} f(x)$$

$$= a^x (a-1)^{-1} \left[1 + \frac{a\Delta}{a-1} \right]^{-1} f(x) = \frac{a^x}{a-1} \left[1 - \frac{a\Delta}{a-1} + \frac{a^2 \Delta^2}{(a-1)^2} \cdots \right] f(x) + c.$$

Thus we get process to obtain $\Sigma a^x f(x)$, where c is any constant.

(b) First of all, we shall obtain the general term of the given series. To find this, we proceed as follows:

The difference table is given by

S.N.	$f(x)$	$\Delta f(x)$	$\Delta^2 f(x)$
1	2		
		5	
2	7		2
		7	
3	14		2
		9	
4	23		2
		11	
5	34		

$$\therefore \qquad f(x) = f(1 + \overline{x-1}) = f(1) + (x-1)\,\Delta f(1) + \frac{(x-1)(x-2)}{2\,!}\Delta^2 f(1)$$

$$= 2 + (x-1)\,5 + \frac{1}{2}(x-1)(x-2)\,.\,2 = x^2 + 2x - 1.$$

Thus the general term of the given series by $2^x(x^2 + 2x - 1)$

$$\Rightarrow \qquad \sum_{x=1}^{n} 2^x (x^2 + 2x - 1) = \left[\frac{2^x}{2-1}(1 - 2\Delta + 4\Delta^2)(x^2 + 2 - 1)\right]_{x=1}^{n+1}$$

using (i) again, we have $\Delta(x^2 + 2x - 1) = 3x + 3, \Delta^2(x^2 + 2x - 1) = 2$. Hence the sum upto n terms is given by

$$\left[2^x (x^2 + 2x - 1) - 2^{x+1}(2x + 3) + 2^{x+2} \times 2\right]_1^{n+1}$$

$$= 2^{n+1}[(n+1)^2 + 2(n+1) - 1] - 2^{n+2}[2(n+1) + 3] - 2^2(2+3) + 2 \times 2^{n+3} - 2^3 \times 2$$

$$= n^2 . 2^{n+1}$$

Example 15: *Sum the series* $1^3 + 2^3 + 3^3 + \ldots + n^3$.

Solution: Denoting $1^3, 2^3, 3^3, \ldots$ by $u_0, u_1, u_2, \ldots$ respectively, the required sum as given below:

$$S = u_0 + u_1 + u_2 + \ldots + u_{n-1}$$

$$= (1 + E + E^2 + \ldots + E^{n-1})\,u_0 \qquad [\because u_1 = Eu_0, u_2 = E^2 u_0 \text{ etc.}]$$

$$= \frac{E^n - 1}{E - 1}u_0 = \frac{(1+\Delta)^n - 1}{\Delta}u_0$$

$$= \frac{1}{\Delta}\left[1 + n\Delta + \frac{n(n-1)}{2\,!}\Delta^2 + \frac{n(n-1)(n-2)}{3\,!}\Delta^3 + \ldots + \Delta^n - 1\right]u_0$$

$$= n + \frac{n(n-1)}{2\,!}\Delta u_0 + \frac{n(n-1)(n-2)}{31}\Delta^2 u_0 + \ldots$$

Now $\qquad \Delta u_0 = u_1 - u_0 = 2^3 - 1^3 = 7,$

$$\Delta^2 u_0 = u_2 - 2u_1 + u_0 = 3^3 - 2.2^3 + 1^3 = 12,$$

$$\Delta^3 u_0 = u_3 - 3u_2 + 3u_1 - u_0 = 4^3 - 3.3^3 + 3.2^3 - 1^3 = 6$$

and $\Delta^4 u_0, \Delta^5 u_0, \ldots$ are all zero as $u_r = r^3$ is a polynomial of third degree.

$$\Rightarrow \qquad S = n + \frac{n(n-1)}{2}.7 + \frac{n(n-1)(n-2)}{6}.12 + \frac{n(n-1)(n-2)(n-3)}{24}.6$$

$$= \frac{n^2}{4}(n^2 + 2n + 1) = \left[\frac{n(n+1)}{2}\right]^2.$$

Example 16: *Prove that*

$$u_0 + u_1 x + u_2 x^2 + \ldots \infty = \frac{u_0}{1-x} + \frac{x \Delta u_0}{(1-x)^2} + \frac{x^2 \Delta^2 u_0}{(1-x)^3} + \ldots \infty$$

Hence find the sum of the series $1.2 + 2.3x + 3.4x^2 + \ldots \infty$.

Solution: $u_0 + u_1 x + u_2 x^2 + \ldots \infty = (1 + xE + x^2 E^2 + x^3 E^3 + \ldots \infty)\, u_0$

$$= \frac{1}{1-xE} u_0 = \frac{1}{1 - x(1+\Delta)} u_0$$

$$= \frac{1}{(1-x) - x\Delta} u_0 = \frac{1}{1-x}\left(1 - \frac{x}{1-x}\Delta\right)^{-1} u_0$$

$$= \frac{1}{1-x}\left\{1 + \frac{x\Delta}{1-x} + \frac{x^2 \Delta^2}{(1-x)^2} + \ldots\right\} u_0$$

$$= \frac{u_0}{1-x} + \frac{x}{(1-x)^2}\Delta u_0 + \frac{x^2}{(1-x)^3}\Delta^2 u_0 + \ldots \infty$$

We now construct the difference table for the coefficients of the given series

u	Δu	$\Delta^2 u$	$\Delta^3 u$
$u_0 = 2$			
	4		
$u_1 = 6$		2	
	6		0
$u_2 = 12$		2	
	8		0
$u_3 = 20$		2	
	10		
$u_4 = 30$			

Thus, we have $u_0 = 2, \Delta u_0 = 4, \Delta^2 u_0 = 2, \Delta^3 u_0 = \Delta^4 u_0$ etc. all $= 0$.

$$\Rightarrow \quad 1.2 + 2.3x + 3.4x^2 + \ldots \infty = u_0 + u_1 x + {}_2 x^2 + \ldots \infty$$

$$= \frac{u_0}{1-x} + \frac{x}{(1-x)^2}\Delta u_0 + \frac{x^2}{(1-x)^3}\Delta^2 u_0 + \ldots \infty$$

$$= \frac{2}{1-x} + \frac{4x}{(1-x)^2} + \frac{2x^2}{(1-x)^3} = \frac{2}{(1-x)^3}.$$

✦✦ Problem Set ✦✦

1. Sum the following series to n terms.

$$1.3.5 + 3.5.7 + 5.7.9 + \dots .$$

[Patna 2004]

2. Sum the following series to n terms.

(i) $1^4 + 2^4 + \dots + n^4$,

(ii) $\dfrac{4}{1.2.3} + \dfrac{5}{2.3.4} + \dfrac{6}{3.4.5} + \dots$,

(iii) 5, 10, 17, 28, 47, 82, ... ,

(iv) 1, 0, 1, 8, 29, 80, 193, ... ,

(v) 5, 10, 23, 60, 169, 494, 1467, ..., **[Agra 2005]**

(vi) $1^2 + \dfrac{3^2}{2} + \dfrac{5^2}{2^2} + \dfrac{7^2}{2^3} + \dots$,

(vii) Show that $\Delta(x!) = x(x!)$ and hence sum to n terms the series

$(1 + 3)(2!) + 7(3!) + 13(4!) + 21(5!) + \dots$, **[Himachal 2008, 2010]**

(viii) $2.2 + 6.4 + 12.8 + 20.16 + 30.32 + \dots$,

(ix) $\dfrac{5.1}{1.2.3} + \dfrac{7}{2.3} \cdot \dfrac{1}{3^2} + \dfrac{9}{3.4} \cdot \dfrac{1}{3^2} + \dfrac{11}{4.5} \cdot \dfrac{1}{3^3} + \dots .$

3. Sum to n terms the series whose xth terms is

(i) $x(x-1)(x-2)$, (ii) $x(x+2)(x+5)$,

(iii) $\dfrac{1}{(x+1)(x+3)}$, (iv) $x(x+1)(x+3)$.

4. Prove that $\sum_{0}^{n-1} y_r x^r = \dfrac{y_0 - x^r y_n}{1-x} + \dfrac{x}{(1-x)^2}(\Delta y_0 - x^n \Delta y_n)$

$$+ \frac{x^2}{(1-x)^2}(\Delta^3 y_0 - x^n \Delta y_n) + \dots$$

Use it to obtain $\sum_{r=1}^{n} r(r+1)x^{r-1}$. **[Andhra 2001, 2004]**

5. Show that $\Delta^{-1}(u_x v_x) = u_x \Delta^{-1} v_x - \Delta^{-1}(\Delta u_x \Delta^{-1} v_{x+1})$.

6. Prove that $\Delta^{-1}\left[2^x . x . \dfrac{x!}{(2x+1)!}\right] = c + 2^{x-2} \dfrac{(x-1)!}{(2x-1)!}$ c being a constant.

7. Prove that $\Delta^{-1} \dfrac{1}{x(x+1)} = c - \dfrac{1}{x}$.

[Kurukshetra 2008]

8. Prove that $\sum_{x=1}^{n} (x^2 + 1)(x!) = n[(n+1)!]$. **[Ajmer 2006; Lucknow 2008]**

9. If u_n is the nth term of the series 1, 2, 3, 5, 8, 13 in which each term after the second is the sum of the two preceding terms, prove that

$$u_n^2 - u_{n-1} u_{n+1} = (-1)^n.$$

Solution: We shall prove the result by mathematical induction

If $n = 2$, then we have $u_2^2 - u_1 . u_3 = u_2^2 - u_1 (u_1 + u_2)$

$$= 2^2 - 1.(1+2) = 4 - 3 \times 1 = (-1)^2 \qquad ...(i)$$

Now, let the theorem be true for $n = m$, then we have

$$u_m^2 - u_{m-1} u_{m+1} = (-1)^m$$

$$\therefore \quad u_{m+1} - u_m u_{m+2} = u_{m+1} . u_{m+1} - u_m (u_m + u_{m+1})$$

$$= u_{m+1} . (u_m + u_{m-1}) - \left[u_m^2 + u_m . u_{m+1}\right]$$

$$= u_{m+1} . u_{m-1} - u_m^2 = -\left[u_m^2 - u_{m-1} . u_{m+1}\right]$$

$$= (-1)(-1)^m = (-1)^{m+1}$$

$\Rightarrow$ the result is true for $n = m + 1$

But it was true for $n = 2$, hence it will also be true for $n = 3$ *i.e.*, true for all n.

10. Show that

$$\Delta^{-1}(u_x v_x) = u_x \Delta^{-1} v_x - \Delta^{-1}(\Delta u_x \Delta^{-1} v_{x+1}).$$

[Allahabad 2008]

11. Derive the formula

$$\sum_{n=1}^{\infty} \left(\frac{-m}{n}\right) = \frac{1}{(m-1)[(m-1)]!}$$

where $(n-1)^{(-m)} = 1 - n(n+1)(n+2) \dots (n+m-1)$ and m is positive integer other than 1. **[Baroda 2004, 2006; Lucknow 2008]**

12. Evaluate

$$\Delta^{-1}\left\{\frac{x+4}{(x+2)(x+3)(x+5)(x+6)}\right\}.$$

13. Sum the series to n terms

(i) 4, 13, 35, 94, 262, 755, ...,

(ii) 5, 10, 23, 60, 169, 494, 1467, ...

[B.H.U. 2005, 2009]

[Hint: (ii) $u_x = a.3^x + bx^{(3)} + cx^{(2)} + dx^{(1)} + e$**]**.

14. Show that $\Delta(x!) = x(x!)$.

15. Sum the following series

$$\frac{1}{x+1} - \frac{n}{(x+1)(x+2)} + \frac{n(n-1)}{(x+1)(x+2)(x+3)} - \ldots + \frac{(-1)^n n!}{(x+1)(x+2)\ldots(x+n+1)}.$$

[Agra 2001, 2002; Patna 2002, 2008]

Hint: The given series can be written as

$$\left[x^{(-1)} + {}^nC_1 \Delta x^{(-1)} + {}^nC_2 \Delta^2 x^{(-1)} + \ldots + {}^nC_n \Delta^n x^{(-1)}\right] = [(1+\Delta)^n x^{(-1)} = \text{etc.}]$$

16. Evaluate the sum of the double series

$$\sum_{y=1}^{n} \sum_{x<y}^{n} y(y+2)\, x(x+1).$$

[Allahabad 2006, 2010]

[**Hint:** The given expression can be written as

$$= \sum_{y=1}^{n} y(y+2) \sum_{x=0}^{y=1} x(x+1) = \sum_{y=1}^{n} y(y+2) \sum_{x=1}^{y=1} x(x+1)$$

$$= \sum_{y=1}^{n} y(y+2) \frac{1}{3}(y-1)\, y(y+1) = \frac{1}{3} \sum_{1}^{n} (y+2)^{(4)} [(y+3)-3]$$

$$= \frac{1}{3} \sum_{1^n} (y+3)^{(5)} - \sum_{1}^{n} (y+2)^{(4)} \text{ etc.}]$$

Answers

Problem Set

1. $\frac{1}{8}[(2n-1)(2n+1)(2n+3)(2n+5)+15]$

2. (i) $\frac{1}{5}n^5+\frac{1}{2}n^4+\frac{1}{3}n^3-\frac{1}{39}n$

(ii) $\sum_{i=1}^{n} u_x=\frac{5}{4}-\frac{2n+5}{2(n+1)(n+2)}$

(iii) $2^{n+1}-2+\frac{3}{2}n(n+1)$

(iv) $2^{n+2}-4-\frac{1}{6}n(n+1)(2n+7)$

(v) $u_x=a.3^x+bx^{(3)}+cx^{(2)}+dx^{(1)}+e$, and then proceed

(vi) $34-(4n^2+12n+17).\frac{1}{2^n-1}$

(vii) $1-3\ [3(n+1)!+(n+2)!]$

(viii) $u_x=(x^2+x)2^x;\ S_n=(n^2-n+1)2^{n+1}-4$

(ix) $u_x=\frac{2x+3}{x(x+1)}\frac{1}{3^x},\ S_n=1-\frac{1}{n+1}.\frac{1}{3^n}.$

3. (i) $\frac{1}{4}(n+1)n(n-1)(n-2)$

(ii) $\frac{1}{12}n(n+1)(3n^2+31n+74)$

(iii) $\frac{n(5n+13)}{12(n+2).(n+3)}$

(iv) $\frac{1}{12}n(n+1)(n+2)(3n+13).$

13. (i) $\frac{1}{2}(3^{n+1}-3)+\frac{n}{6}(n^2+6n-11)$

Theory | Solved Examples | Problem Set

Chapter 9

Difference Equations

Introduction, Definitions, Various Types of Difference Equations, Existence and Uniqueness Theorems, Rules for Finding Complementary Solutions, Rule for Finding Particular Solutions, Method of Variation of Parameter, Generating Function Technique, Applications of Difference Equation in Social Science, Matrix Method, Cobweb Phenomenon, Application to the Deflection of a Loaded String.

9.1 Introduction

There exists a close analogy in between the differences and sum calculus and the differential and integral calculus respectively.

Hence there should be no surprise that corresponding to the theory of differential equations there exists the theory of difference equations. In order to develop this analogy, we recall that a differential equation is relationship of the type

$$F\left[x, y, \left(\frac{dy}{dx}\right), \left(\frac{d^2 y}{dx^2}\right), \ldots, \left(\frac{d^n y}{dx^n}\right)\right] = 0 \qquad \ldots(1)$$

between x and the derivative of an unknown function $y = f(x)$. If it is possible to solve for $\left(\frac{d^n y}{dx^n}\right)$ in (1) then equation (1) implies

$$\left(\frac{d^n y}{dx^n}\right) = G\left[x, y, \left(\frac{dy}{dx}\right), \ldots, \left(\frac{d^{n-1} y}{dx^{n-1}}\right)\right] \qquad \ldots(2)$$

Order of this highest derivative *viz.* n is known as the *order of the differential equation. A solution* of a differential equation is any function which satisfies the equation. *A general solution* is one which involves exactly n arbitrary independent constants. *A particular solution* is a solution obtained form the general solution by giving particular values to these constants.

For example, the equation $\left(\frac{d^2 y}{dx^2}\right) - 3\left(\frac{dy}{dx}\right) + 2y = 4x^2$ is a differential equation of order two. Its general solution is $y = k_1 e^x + k_2 e^{2x} + 2x^2 + 6x + 7$ and a particular solution is $y = 6e^x + 4e^{2x} + 6x + 7$.

9.2 Definition of a Difference Equation

[Garhwal 2001, 2002, 2008, 2010; Agra 2004]

By analogy with differential equations, we define a *difference equation* as a relationship of the form $F[x, y, (\Delta y/\Delta x), (\Delta^2 y/\Delta x^2), \ldots, (\Delta^n y/\Delta x^n)] = 0$ ...(1)

Let $y = f(x)$; then

$$(\Delta y/\Delta x) = \frac{f(x+h) - f(x)}{h}, (\Delta^2 y/\Delta x^2) = \frac{f(x+2h) - 2f(x+h) + f(x)}{h^2}$$

$$(\Delta^n y/\Delta x^n) = \frac{f(x+nh)}{h^n} \ldots,$$ where h is the interval of differencing.

Hence equation (1) can be re-written as

$$\phi[x, f(x), f(x+h), f(x+2h), \ldots, f(x+nh)] = 0 \quad \ldots(2)$$

where $f(x) = y$ is an unknown function. By the analogy with differential equations it might be suspected that the *order of the difference equation is the order of the highest difference present in it.* But this leads to some difficulties and so we difine it as the *difference between the largest and smallest arguments for the function involved divided by h e.g.*, in (2) if both $f(x)$ and $f(x+nh)$ appear explicitly, then the order of the difference equation is $\frac{x+nh-x}{h} = n.$

However, if $f(x)$ does not appear but $f(x+h)$ and $f(x+nh)$ both appear, then the order is $[(x+nh)-(x+h)]/h = (n-1)$

Solution of the Difference Equation

A ***Solution*** *of the difference equation is any function which satisfies the given equation.*

A *particular solution* is a solution obtained from the general solution by assigning particular periodic constants.

For example: consider the difference equation $\frac{\Delta^2 y}{\Delta x^2} - 3\frac{\Delta y}{\Delta x} + 2y = 4x^{(2)}$ which be re-written as $f(x+2h) - (3h+2)f(x+h) + (2h^2+3h+1)f(x) = 4h^2 x^{(2)}$, where $f(x) = y$, is a difference equation of order 2.Its general solution is given by

$y - f(x) = k_1 x[1+2h]^{(x/h)} + k_2(x)[1+h]^{(x/h)} + 2x^2 + (6-2h)x + 7$ putting

$^*k_1(x) = 2 + 4h\sin(2\pi x/h)$ and $^*k_2(x) = 5 + h^2[1 - \cos(2\pi x/h)]$. we get the particular solution as $y = [2 + 4h\sin(2\pi x/h)][1+2h]^{(x/h)}$

$$+ [5 + h^2\{1 - \cos(2\pi x/h)\}][1+h]^{(x/h)} + 2x^2 + (6-2h)x + 7.$$

Use of Subscript Notation

If the subscript notation is used, the difference equation

$$\phi[x, f(x), f(x+h), f(x+2h), \ldots, f(x+nh)] = 0,$$

$$\Rightarrow \quad G[k, y_k, y_{k+1}, \ldots, y_{k+n}] = 0, \text{where } y_{k+n} = f(x+nh) \text{ etc} \quad \ldots(3)$$

---

*Both have periods h.

If we are given the n values $y_0, y_1, y_2, \ldots, y_{n-1}$ then we can determine y_k for $k - n + 1, \ldots$ For example: the difference equation

$$f(x+3h) - 5f(x+2h) + 6f(x+h) + 3f(x) = 0 \qquad \ldots(4)$$

can be written $y_{k+3} - 5y_{k+2} + 6y_{k+1} + 3y_k = 0$ ...(5)

If, now we have

$y_0 = 1, y_1 = -2, y_2 = 0$, then putting $k = 0, 1, \ldots$ we easily obtain $y_3 = 9, y_4 = 51, \ldots$. Above difference equation (3) can be written as $\phi[k, y_k, Ey_k, E^2 y_k, \ldots, E^n y_k] = 0$, where E denotes the operator. Hence in terms of the operator E, the difference equation (3) can be put as

$$[E^3 - 5E^2 + 6E + 3] y_k = 0.$$

9.3 Various Types of Linear Difference Equations

A linear difference equation of order n is a difference equation having the form

$$a_0(k) E^n y_k + a_1(k) E^{n-1} y_k + \ldots + a_n(k) y_k = R(k) \qquad \ldots(1)$$

where $a_0(k) \neq 0$. This equation can be re-written as

$$[a_0(k) E^n + a_1(k) E^{n-1} + \ldots + a_n(k)] y_k = R(k) \qquad \ldots(2)$$

or simply $\phi(E) y_k = R(k)$ ...(3)

where the linear operator ϕ *(E)* is given by

$$\phi(E) \equiv a_0(k) E^n + a_1(k) E^{n-1} + \ldots + a_n(k) \qquad \ldots(4)$$

If $a_0(k), a_1(k), \ldots, a_n(k)$ are all constants *i.e.* independent of k, then above difference equation is termed as a *linear difference equation of order n with constant coefficients.* Further also the difference equation which does not have the form (1),(2) or (3) *i.e.* which is not linear is called a *non linear difference equation.* For example:

(i) The difference equation $(E^3 - 5E^2 + 6E + 3) y_k = 0$ is linear difference equation with constants coefficients.

(ii) The difference equation $[(2k+1)E^2 - 3kE + 4] y_k = 4k^3 - 3k$ is a linear difference equation with variable coefficients.

(iii) $y_k y_{k+1} = y_{k-1}^2$ is non-linear difference equation.

Solved Examples

Example 1: *Show that the difference eq.* $\frac{\Delta^2 y}{\Delta x^2} - 3\frac{\Delta y}{\Delta x} = 4x^{(2)}$ *can be written as* $f(x+2h) - (3h+2)$ $f(x+h) + (2h^2 + 3h + 1) f(x) = 4h^2 x^{(2)}$, *where* $y = f(x)$.

Solution: Putting $\Delta x = h$, $y = f(x)$ difference equation can be written as

$$\frac{\Delta^2 f(x)}{h^2} - 3\frac{\Delta f(x)}{h} + 2f(x) = 4x^{(2)} \qquad ...(1)$$

$$\Rightarrow \quad \frac{f(x+2h) - 2f(x+h) + f(x)}{h^2} - 3\left[\frac{f(x+h) - f(x)}{h}\right] + 2f(x) = 4x^{(2)}$$

$$\Rightarrow \quad f(x+2h) - (3h+2)f(x+h) + (2h^2 + 3h + 1)f(x) = 4h^2 x^{(2)}. \qquad ...(2)$$

Example 2: *Show that the general solution of the difference equation in Ex. 1 is given by*

$$y = c_1(x)(1+2h)^{x/h} + c_2(x)(1+h)^{x/h} + 2x^2 + (6-2h)x + 7 \qquad ...(1)$$

where $c_1(x)$ and $c_2(x)$ *have periods equal to h.*

Solution: $c_1(x+h) = c_1(x), c_2(x+h), = c_2(x)$

[$\because$ $c_1(x)$ and $c_2(x)$, both have periods equal to h.]

Also we have $y = c_1(x)(1+2h)^{x/h} + c_2(x)(1+h)^{x/h} + 2x^2 + (6-2h)x + 7$ ...(2)

$$\Rightarrow \quad \frac{\Delta y}{\Delta x} = \frac{c_1(x)}{h}[(1+2h)^{(x+h)/h} - (1+2h)^{x/h}] + \frac{c_2(x)}{h}[(1+h)^{(x+h)} - (1+h)^{x/h}]$$

$$+ \frac{2[(x+h)^2 - x^2] + (6-2h)[(x+h) - x]}{h}$$

$$= 2c_1(x)(1+2h)^{x/h} + c_2(x)(1+h)^{x/h} + 4x + 6$$

and $$\frac{\Delta^2 y}{\Delta x^2} = 4c_1(x)(1+2h)^{x/h} + c_2(x)(1+h)^{x/h} + 4$$

$$\Rightarrow \quad \frac{\Delta^2 y}{\Delta x^2} - 3\frac{\Delta y}{\Delta x} + 2y = [4c_1(x)(1+2h)^{x/h} + c_2(x)(1+h)^{x/h} + 4] - 3[2c_1(x)(1+2h)^{x/h}$$

$$+ c_2(x)(1+h)^{x/h} + 4x + 6] + 2[c_1(x)(1+2h)^{x/h} + c_2(x)(1+h)^{x/h} + 2x^2 + (6-2h)x + 7]$$

$$= 4x^2 - 4hx = 4x(x-h) = 4x^{(2)}$$

This shows that y given by (2) is the general solution of the difference equation of Ex. 1.

Again the difference equation (1) has the difference between the largest and smallest arguments divided by h equal to $\frac{(x+2h-x)}{h} = 2$; so it is of order 2.

Note: Solution (1) has two arbitrary independent periodic constants, so it is the general solution.

Differential Equations As Limits of Difference Equations

Example 3: *Show that limit of the difference equation*

$$\frac{\Delta^2 y}{\Delta x^2} - 3\frac{\Delta y}{\Delta x} + 2y = 4x^{(2)}$$

as Δx or h approaches to zero is $\dfrac{d^2 y}{dx^2} - 3\dfrac{dy}{dx} + 2y = 4x^{(2)}$.

Solution: We have

$$\lim_{\Delta x \to 0}\left[\frac{\Delta^2 y}{\Delta x^2} - 3\frac{\Delta y}{\Delta x} + 2y\right] = \frac{d^2 y}{dx^2} - 3\frac{dy}{dx} + 2y,$$

and $\lim_{h\to 0} 4x^{(2)} = \lim_{h\to 0} 4x(x-h) = 4x^2$. Hence the result follows at once.

Example 4: *Show that the limit, as Δx or h approaches zero, of the solution of the difference equation in Ex. 3 is the solution of the differential equation in that problem.*

Solution: By Ex. 2, the general solution of the difference equation in Ex. 3, is given by

$$y = c_1(x)(1+2h)^{x/h} + c_2(x)(1+h)^{x/h} + 2x^2 + (6-2h)x + 7 \qquad ...(1)$$

where $\Delta x = h$

But $$\lim_{n\to 0}\left(1+\frac{1}{n}\right)^n = e = 2.71828 \qquad ...(2)$$

$\Rightarrow$ $$\lim_{h\to 0}\left(1+\frac{h}{a}\right)^{a/h} = e = 2.71828\left[\text{Putting } n = \left(\frac{a}{h}\right) \text{ in (2)}\right] \qquad ...(3)$$

$\Rightarrow$ $$\lim_{h\to 0}\left(1+\frac{h}{a}\right)^{1/h} = e^{1/a} \qquad ...(4)$$

$\Rightarrow$ $$\lim_{h\to 0}\left(1+\frac{h}{a}\right)^{x/h} = e^{x/a} \qquad ...(5)$$

$\therefore$ $$\lim_{h\to 0}(1+2h)^{x/h} = e^{2x} \left[\text{Putting } a = \frac{1}{2} \text{ in (5)}\right] \qquad ...(6)$$

Also, we have $$\lim_{h\to 0}(1+h)^{x/h} = e^x \left[\text{Putting } a = 1 \text{ in (5)}\right] \qquad ...(7)$$

But $c_1(x+h) = c_1(x), c_2(x+h) = c_2(x)$; so we can say that

$$\lim_{h\to 0} c_1(x) = c_1, \lim_{h\to 0} c_2(x) = c_2,$$

where c_1 and c_2 are constants, provided these limits exist.

Hence the limit of the solution (1) as $h \to 0$ is given by

$$y = c_1 e^{2x} + c_2 e^x + 2x^2 = 6x + 7$$

This is the required general solution of the differential equation obtained in Ex. 3.

Difference Equations in Subscript Notation

Example 5: *Write the difference equation of Ex. 1 with subscript or k notation.*

Solution: By the definition of the subscript notation, we have

$$y_k = f(x), y_{k+1} = f(x+h), y_{k+2} = f(x+2h)$$

and $$x^{(2)} = x(x-h) = kh(kh-h) = h^2k(k-1) = h^2k^{(2)} \qquad [\text{using } x=kh]$$

$\therefore$ equation $f(x+2h)-(3h+2)f(x+h)+(2h^2+3h+1)f(x) = 4x^{(2)}$

$$\Rightarrow \quad y_{k+2}-(3h+2)y_{k+1}+(2h^2+3h+1)y_k = 4h^2k^{(2)}$$

Further in terms of the operator E, the above difference equation can be put as

$$E^2 y_k + (3h+2)Ey_k + (2h^2+3h+1)y_k = 4h^2k^{(2)}$$

$$\Rightarrow \quad [E^2-(3h+2)E+(2h^2+3h+1)]y_k = 4h^2k^{(2)}$$

Example 6: *Write the difference equation*

$$f(x+4h)+2f(x+3h)-4f(x+2h)+3f(x+h)-6f(x)=0$$

in the subscript or k notation.

Solution: $y_k = f(x), y_{k+1} = f(x+h), y_{k+2} = f(x+2h), y_{k+3} = f(x+3h), y_{k+4} = f(x+h).$

Hence the difference equation is given by $(E^4+2E^3-4E^2+3E-6)y_k = 0.$

Write each of the following difference equations in the subscript or k notation.

Example 7: $\Delta y_k = 0.$

Solution: $\Delta y_k = y_{k+1}-y_k, \Delta y_k = 0 \Rightarrow y_{k+1}-y_k = 0.$

Example 8: $\Delta y_k - 2y_k = 3.$

Solution: $\Delta y_k = y_{k+1}-y_k \Rightarrow y_{k+1}-y_k-2y_k = 3 \Rightarrow y_{k+1}-3y_k = 3.$

Example 9: $\Delta^3 y_k + \Delta^2 y_k + \Delta y_k + y_k = 0.$

Solution: We have $\Delta^3 y_k = \Delta(\Delta^2 y_k) = \Delta(y_{k+2}-2y_{k+1}+y_k) = \Delta y_{k+2}-2\Delta y_{k+1}+\Delta y_k$

$$= y_{k+3}-y_{k+2}-2(y_{k+2}-y_{k+1})+y_{k+1}-y_k = y_{k+3}-3y_{k+2}+3y_{k+1}-y_k$$

Now substituting these values in the left hand side of the given equation, we get

$$(y_{k+3}-3y_{k+2}+3y_{k+1}-y_k)+(y_{k+2}-2y_{k+1}+y_k)+(y_{k+1}-y_k)+y_k = 0$$

$$\Rightarrow \quad y_{k+3}-2y_{k+2}+2y_{k+1} = 0.$$

Example 10: *Show that* $y_k = \frac{1}{2}k(k-1)$ *is a solution of the difference equation* $y_{k+1}-y_k = k.$

Solution: Here $y_k = \frac{1}{2}k(k-1)$. $\therefore y_{k+1} = \frac{1}{2}(k+1).k$

Putting the values of y_k and y_{k+1} in the difference equation,

$$\text{L. H.S.} = \frac{1}{2}(k+1)k - \frac{1}{2}k(k-1) = \frac{1}{2}k\{(k+1)-(k-1)\} = k = \text{ the R. H. S.}$$

Therefore $y_k = \frac{1}{2}k(k-1)$ satisfies the given difference equation, hence it is solution the given difference equation.

Example 11: *Show that the function y given by* $y_k = 1 - \frac{2}{k}, k = 1, 2, 3, \ldots$ *is a solution of the first order diff. equation* $(k+1)y_{k+1} + ky_k = 2k-3$.

Solution: Given $y_k = 1 - \frac{2}{k}$ $\quad \therefore \; y_{k+1} = 1 - \frac{2}{k+1}$

Putting the value of y_k and y_{k+1} in the given difference equation, the L.H.S.

$$= (k+1)\left(1 - \frac{2}{k+1}\right) + k\left(1 - \frac{2}{k}\right) = k+1-2+k-2 = 2k-3 = \text{R.H.S.}$$

Therefore $y_k = 1 - \frac{2}{k}$ Satisfies the given difference equation, thus it is a solution of the given difference equation.

Linearly Independent Functions

Example 12: *Determine which of the following sets of functions are linearly dependent and which are linearly independent.*

(*a*) $2^k, 2^{k+3}$ (*b*) $2^k, 2^{k+3}, 4^k$

(*c*) $2^k, 4^k$ (*d*) $2^k, k.2^k, k^2.2^k$.

Solution: (a) $A_1 2^k + A_2 2^{k+3} = A_1 2^k + A_2 .2^3 2^k = (A_1 + 8A_2)2^k$ ...(1)

Hence we can find A_1 and A_2, not both zero, such that (1) is zero, *viz.* $A_2 = -1, A_1 = 8$, make (1) to be zero. Hence it follows that the functions $2^k, 2^{k+3}$, are linearly dependent.

(b) $A_1 2^k + A_2 2^{k+3} + A_3 4^k = (A_1 + 8A_2)2^k + A_3 4^k$. ...(2)

Hence we can find the three constants A_1, A_2, A_3 not all zero such that (2) is zero *viz.* $A_2 = -1, A_1 = 8$, make (1) to be zero. Hence it follows that the function $2^k, 2^{k+3}$ are linearly dependent.

(c) $A_1(2)^k + A_2 4^k = 2^k(A_1 + A_2 .2^k) = 0 \Rightarrow A_1 + A_2 2^k = 0$.

However this last equation cannot be true for all k unless $A_1 = A_2 = 0$. Hence it follows that 2^k and 4^k are linearly independent.

(d) $A_1 .2^k + A_2 k 2^k + A_3 k^2 .2^k = 2^k(A_1 + A_2 k + A_3 k^2) = 0 \Leftrightarrow A_1 + A_2 k + A_3 k^2 = 0$

However the last equation can not be true for all k unless $A_1 = A_2 = A_3 = 0$. Hence the functions are linearly independent.

***Remark* 1**: *Casorati (Analogous to the Wronskin differential equation).*

The set of functions $f_1(k), f_2(k), \ldots, f_n(k)$ is **L.I** *if and only if*

$$\begin{vmatrix} f_1(0) & f_2(0)\ldots & f_n(0) \\ f_1(1) & f_2(1)\ldots & f_n(1) \\ \ldots\ldots & \ldots\ldots & \ldots\ldots \\ \ldots\ldots & \ldots\ldots & \ldots\ldots \\ f_1(n-1) & f_2(n-1)\ldots & f_n(n-1) \end{vmatrix} \neq 0$$

Otherwise the functions are linearly dependent.

***Remark* 2**: *Superposition principle.*

If $f_1(k), f_2(k), \ldots, f_n(k)$ are n linearly independent solutions of the nth order difference equation, the general solution is given by

$$y_k = c_1 f_1(k) + c_2 f_2(k) + \ldots + c_n f_n(k).$$

Homogeneous Linear Difference Equations

A linear difference equation of order n is of the type

$$a_0(k)\, E^n y_k + a_1(k) E^{n-1} y_k + \ldots + a_n(k)\, y_k = R(k) \qquad \ldots(1)$$

$$i.e. \quad a_0(k)\, y_{k+n} + a_1(k) y_{k+n-1} + \ldots + a_n(k)\, y_k = R(k)$$

If $R(k) = 0$, then we obtain $\phi(E)\, y_k = 0$ ...(2)

where $$\phi(E) \equiv a_0(k) E^n + a_1(k) E^{n-1} + \ldots + a_n(k)\, I.$$

Equation (2) is known as *homogeneous linear difference equation.*

For Example: *Homogeneous linear difference equation with Constant coeffi-cients. If $a_0, \ldots, a_n$ are all constants, then the equation*

$$\phi(E)\; y_k = 0, \text{where } \phi(E) \cong a_0 E^n + a_1 E^{n-1} + \ldots + a_n I \qquad \ldots(1)$$

is known as *homogeneous linear difference equation with constant coefficient. Let $y_k = r^k$ be the solution of* (1); *then this implies*

$$a_0 r^{n+k} + a_1 r^{n+k-1} + a_2 r^{n+k-2} + \ldots + a_n r^k = 0$$

$$\Rightarrow \quad (a_0 r^n + a_1 r^{n-1} + a_2 r^{n-2} + \ldots + a_n)\, r^k = 0$$

which shows that r^k is a solution of (1) if r is a solution of

$$a_0 r^n + a_1 r^{n-1} + a_2 r^{n-2} + \ldots + a_n = 0 \qquad \ldots(2)$$

Equation (2) *is known as auxiliary equation or characteristic equation* and can be written as $\phi(r) = 0$. Let the roots of the auxiliary equation be given by $r_1, r_2, \ldots, r_n$ which may or not be different. In such case equation (1) can be written in *factor form* as $\{a_0(E - r_1)(E - r_2)\ldots(E - r_n)\}\, y_k = 0$ ...(3)

---

*A set of n functions $f_1(k), f_2(k), \ldots, f_n(k)$ is to said be linearly dependent if we can find a set of n constants $A_1, A_2, \ldots, A_n$ not all zero such that we have identically $A_1 f_1(k) + A_2 f_2(k) + \ldots + A_n f_n(k) = 0$.

Now, we shall discuss the following cases:

Case* 1: *Roots are all real and distinct.

In this case $r_1^k, r_2^k, \ldots, r_n^k$ are all solution of (1). Also it follows that $c_1 r_1^k, c_2 r_2^k, \ldots,$ are all solutions of (1). Again sums of solutions are also solutions; since $\phi(E)$ is a linear operator so we have

$$y_k = c_1 r_1^{\,k} + c_2 r_2^{\,k} + \ldots + c_n r_n^{\,k}.$$

Case* 2: *Auxiliary equation has repeated real roots.

Let two roots be equal, say $r_2 = r_1$; then $(c_1 + c_2 k) r_1^k$ is also a solution. Similarly if three roots are equal, say $r_1 = r_2 = r_3$, then the solution is given by $(c_1 + c_2 k + c_3 k^2) r_1^k$.

Case* 3: *Auxiliary equation has non-repeated complex roots.

If $\alpha + i\beta$ is a root, then so also is $\alpha - i\beta$ where α and β are real.

Thus in this case $(\alpha + i\beta)^k$ and $(\alpha - i\beta)^k$ are solutions implying $c_1(\alpha + i\beta)^k + c_2(\alpha - i\beta)^k$ is also a solution where $c_1$and c_2 are constants Putting. $\alpha + i\beta = \rho(\cos\theta + i\sin\theta)$ and $\alpha - i\beta = \rho(\cos\theta + i\sin\theta)$, the solution becomes $\rho^k[c_1\cos(k\theta) + c_2\sin(k\theta)]$ where $\rho = \sqrt{(\alpha^2 + \beta^2)}, \theta = \tan^{-1}[(\beta/\alpha)], c_1 = k_1 + k_2$ *and* $c_2 = i(k_1 + k_2)$.

Case* 4: *Auxiliary equation has repeated complex roots.

It can easily be proved that in such a case, the solution is

$$\rho^k\,[(k_1 + k_2 k)\cos(k\theta) + (k_3 + k_4 k)\sin(k\theta)] \qquad \text{where } \rho = (\alpha^2 + \beta^2)^{1/2}, \theta = \tan^{-1}(\beta/\alpha).$$

Theorem* 1: *If $y_k^{(1)}, y_k^{(2)}, \ldots, y_k^{(n)}$ *are any n solutions of the nth order homogeneous linear difference equation with constant coefficients*

$$(a_0 E^n + a_1 E^{n-1} + \ldots + a_n I)\, y_k = 0$$

i.e.
$$a_0\, y_{k+n} + a_1\, y_{k+n-1} + \ldots + a_n\, y_k = 0$$

then $\lambda_1 \lambda_k^{(1)} + \lambda_2 y_k^{(2)} + \ldots + \lambda_n y_k^{(n)}$ is also a solution, where $\lambda_1, \lambda_2, \ldots, \lambda_n$ are arbitrary constants.

***Proof*:** Since $y_k^{(1)}, y_k^{(2)}, \ldots, y_k^{(n)}$ are the n solutions of the difference equation $a_0 y_{k+n} + a_1 y_{k+n-1} + \ldots + a_n y_k = 0$; we must have

$$a_0\, y_{k+n}^{(1)} + a_1\, y_{k+n-1}^{(1)} + \ldots + a_n\, y_k^{(1)} = 0 \qquad \ldots(1)$$

$$a_0\, y_{k+n}^{(2)} + a_1\, y_{k+n-1}^{(2)} + \ldots + a_n\, y_k^{(2)} = 0 \qquad \ldots(2)$$

$$a_0\, y_{k+n}^{(3)} + a_1\, y_{k+n-1}^{(3)} + \ldots + a_n\, y_k^{(3)} = 0 \qquad \ldots(3)$$

$$\ldots \quad \ldots \quad \ldots \quad \ldots \quad \ldots$$

$$\ldots \quad \ldots \quad \ldots \quad \ldots \quad \ldots$$

$$a_0\, y_{k+n}^{(n)} + a_1\, y_{k+n-1}^{(n)} + \ldots + a_n\, y_k^{(n)} = 0 \qquad \ldots(4)$$

Multiplying (1) by λ_1;(2) by $\lambda_2,\ldots,(n)$ by λ_n and adding we get

$$a_0(\lambda_1 y_{k+n}^{(1)} + \lambda_2 y_{k+n}^{(2)} + \ldots + \lambda_n y_{k+n}^{(n)}) + a_1(\lambda_1 y_{k+n-1}^{(1)} + \lambda_2 y_{k+n-1}^{(2)}$$

$$+ \ldots \lambda_n y_{k+n-1}^{(n)}) + \ldots + a_n(\lambda_1 y_k^{(1)} + \lambda_2 y_k^{(2)} + \ldots + \lambda_n y_k^{(n)}) = 0$$

$\Rightarrow \lambda_1 y_k^{(1)} + \lambda_2 y_k^{(2)} + \ldots + \lambda_n y_k^{(n)}$ is also a solution of the given difference equation.

Theorem 2: *If Y is a solution of the nth order homogeneous equation with constant coefficients; viz*

$$a_0 y_{k+n} + a_1 y_{k+n-1} + \ldots + a_n\ y_k = 0,$$

and Y is the solution of the non-homogeneous equation*

$$a_0 y_{k+n} + a_1 y_{k+n-1} + \ldots + a_n\ y_k = R_k, \text{ then } Y + Y^* \text{ is a solution of}$$

$$a_0 y_{k+n} + a_1 y_{k+n} + \ldots a_n\ y_k = R_k.$$ **[Agra 2006]**

Proof: Y is a solution of $a_0 y_{k+n} + a_1 y_{k+n-1} + \ldots + a_n\ y_k = 0$

$\therefore \quad a_0 Y_{k+n} + a_1 Y_{k+n-1} + \ldots + a_n Y_k = 0$ ...(1)

Also Y^* is a solution of non-homogeneous equation $a_0 y_{k+n} + a_1 y_{k+n-1} + \ldots + a_n\ y_k = R_k$

$\therefore \quad a_0 Y^*_{k+n} + a_1 Y^*_{k+n-1} + \ldots + a_n Y^*_k = R_k$ ...(2)

Adding (1) and (2), we get

$$a_0(Y_{k+n} + Y^*_{k+n}) + a_1(Y_{k+n-1} + Y^*_{k+n-1}) + \ldots + a_n(Y_k + Y^*_k) = R_k$$

$\Rightarrow \quad Y + Y^*$ is solution of $a_0\ y_{k+n} + a_1\ y_{k+n-1} + \ldots + a_n\ y_k = R_k$.

Theorem 3: *If $y_k^{(1)}$ and $y_k^{(2)}$ are the two solutions of the second order linear diff. equation with constant coefficients; viz* $\quad a_0 y_{k+2} + a_1 y_{k+1} + a_2 = 0;$

$Y_k = c_1 y_k^{(1)} + c_2 y_k^{(2)}, c_1$ and c_2 *being arbitrary constants is the general solution of the some difference equation, provided*

$$\begin{vmatrix} y_0^{(1)} & y_0^{(2)} \\ y_1^{(1)} & y_1^{(2)} \end{vmatrix} \neq 0.$$

Proof: If $y_k^{(1)}$ and $y_k^{(2)}$ are two solution of $a_0 y_{k+2} + a_1 y_{k+1} + a_2\ y_k = 0$. Then by theorem 1, it follows that $Y_k = c_1 y_k^{(1)} + c_2 y_k^{(1)}$; c_1 and c_2 being arbitrary constants, is also a solution. Now we need only to prove that if y is any solution of the difference equation $a_0 y_{k+2} + a_1 y_{k+1} + a_2 y_k = 0$ then we can determine c_1 and c_2 such that Y_k and y_k are identical. By uniqueness theorem, we can also prove that the two solutions of the linear difference equation of order 2 are identical if they coincide in values at two consecutive values of k say $k = 0, k = 1$. Hence determine c_1 and c_2 so that for any choice of y_0 and $y_1, Y_0 = y_0$ and $Y_1 = y_1$;

implying $Y_0 = c_1 y_0^{(1)} + c_2 y_0^{(2)} = y_0$ and $Y_1 = c_1 y_1^{(1)} + c_2 y_1^{(2)} = y_1$

These equations have unique solutions only when

$$\begin{vmatrix} y_0^{(1)} & y_0^{(2)} \\ y_1^{(1)} & y_1^{(2)} \end{vmatrix} \neq 0.$$

Hence for each choice of y_0 and y_1, we can find unique pair of values of c_1 and c_2 implying there upon Y is a general solution.

Solution of simple Difference Equations

Many difference equations can be solved either by changing the form or on multiplication by some suitable function, being termed as *integrating factor* or by simply substitution. This procedure reduces the difference equation to an *integral form*.

Example 13: *Solve* $y_{k+1} - ay_k = 0, a \neq 1.$ **[Rohilkhand 2006; Agra 2003, 2006]**

Solution: Multiplying the given difference equation by a^{-k-1} we get

$$a^{-k-1}y_{k+1} - a^{-k}y_k = 0, \Rightarrow \Delta(a^{-k}y_k) = 0 \Rightarrow a^{-k}y_k = c$$

$\Rightarrow \quad y_k = ca^k$, where c is a periodic function of k of period 1.

Example 14: *Solve* $y_{k+1} - by_k = ca^k b$ *where c is a periodic function of period 1, when* **(a)** $b \neq a$, **(b)** $b = a$. **[Rohilkhand 2008, 2010; Agra 2005, 2008]**

Solution: ***Case a***: $b \neq a$.

Let $y_k = k' ca^k$ be the solution of the difference equation, then $k' ca^{k+1} - bk' ca^k = cab^k \Rightarrow k' = \{b/(a-b)\}, \Rightarrow y_k = \{b/(a-b)\} ca^k$ is a particular solution of the equation.

Aliter: we have $b^{-k-1} y_{k+1} - b^{-k} y_k = ca^k b^{-k}$

$$\Rightarrow \quad \Delta(b^{-k} y_k) = c(ab^{-1})^k, \Rightarrow b^{-k} y_k = c\Delta^{-1}(ab^{-1})^k \qquad ...(1)$$

Again $\Delta(a^k b^{-k}) = a^{k+1}b^{-k-1} - a^k b^{-k} = a^k b^{-k}(ab^{-1} - 1)$

i.e. $\quad a^k b^{-k} = \Delta^{-1}[a^k b^{-k}(ab^{-1} - 1)]$

$$\text{i.e.} \quad [a^k b^{-k}/(ab^{-1} - 1)] = \Delta^{-1}(a^k b^{-k}) \qquad ...(2)$$

Making use of (2) in (1), we get $b^{-k} y_k = ca^k b^{-k} a^k b^{-k}/(ab^{-1} - 1)$

$$\text{i.e.} \quad y_k = \frac{ca^k}{ab^{-1} - 1} = \frac{bca^k}{a-b}. \qquad ...(3)$$

Case b: $b = a$. The equation is $y_{k+1} - ay_k = ca^{k+1}$.

Let $y_k = k' kca^k$ be the solution of the above difference equation,then we obtain $k' ca^{k+1}(k+1) - ak' ca^k k = ca^{k+1} \Rightarrow k' = 1$.

$\therefore$ solution is $y_k = kca^k$.

Example 15: *Solve* $y_{k+1} - ay_k = bk$.

Solution: We know that $\Delta(a^{-k} y_k) = bka^{-k-1}$

$$\Rightarrow \quad a^{-k} y_k = b\Delta^{-1}[ka^{-k-1}] = ba^{-k}\Delta^{-1}(ka^{-k})$$

$$\Rightarrow \quad y_k = a^k C(k) - \frac{bk}{a-1} - \frac{b}{(a-1)^2}$$

Aliter: The given equation can be written as $a^{-(k+1)} \; y_{k+1} - a^{-k} y^k = bka^{-k-1}$

$$\Rightarrow \quad \Delta[a^{-k} y_k] = bka^{-k-1} (1) \qquad ...(1)$$

But the r.h.s of (1) can be made exact by indeterminate coefficients as follows

$$\Delta(a^{-k} y_k) = -b\left(\frac{k+1}{a-1} + \frac{1}{(a-1)^2}\right)a^{-k-1} + b\left(\frac{k}{a-1} + \frac{1}{(a-1)^2}\right)a^{-k}$$

$$= -\Delta\left(b\left\{\frac{k}{a-1} + \frac{1}{(a-1)^2}\right\}a^{-k}\right)$$

$$\Rightarrow \quad a^{-k} y_k = -b\left(\frac{k}{a-1} + \frac{1}{(a-1)^2}\right)a^k + C(k)$$

$$\Rightarrow \quad y_k = -b\left(\frac{k}{a-1} + \frac{1}{(a-1)^2}\right) + a^k C(k).$$

Example 16: *Solve* $y_{k+1} - y_k = (k^2 - 2k)\,2^k$.

Solution: We have $\Delta y_k = (k^2 - 2k)2^k \Rightarrow y_k = \Delta^{-1}[(k^2 - 2k)\,2^k]$

$$\Rightarrow \quad y_k = (k^2 - 6k + 10)\,2^k + C(k) \qquad ...(1)$$

Aliter: Let us assume $y_k = (Ak^2 + Bk + C)2^k$

$$\Rightarrow \quad y_{k+1} - y_k = [A(k+1)^2 + B(k+1) + C]\,2^{k+1} - [Ak^2 + Bk + C]\,2^k$$

$$= [2A(k+1)^2 + 2B(k+1) + 2\,C - Ak^2 - Bk - C]\,2^K$$

$$= [A(2k^2 + 4k + 2 - k^2) + B(2k + 2 - k) + C]\,2^k$$

$$= [A(k^2 + 4k + 2) + B(k+2) + C]\,2^k$$

$$\Rightarrow \quad (k^2 - 2k)\,2^k = [A(k^2 + 4k + 2) + B(k+2) + C]\,2^k$$

Comparing coefficients of like powers of k, we get

$$1 = A, -2 = 4A + B, 0 = 2A + 2B + C.$$

$$\Rightarrow \quad A = 1, B = -6 \text{ and } C = 10 \text{ implying } y_k = (k^2 - 6k + 10)\,2^k + C'(k).$$

Homogeneous Linear Difference Equations with Variable Coefficients

Example 17: *Solve* $y_{k+1} - A(k)\,y_k = 0$.

(homogeneous linear equation of order one)

Solution: We have, $y_1 = A(0)\,y_0 \qquad ...(1)$

$$y_2 = A(1)\,y_1 = A(1).A(0)\,y_0 \qquad ...(2)$$

$$y_3 = A(2)\,y_2 = A(2).A(1).A(0).\,y_0 \quad ...(3)$$

$$y_4 = A(3)\,y_3 = A(3)\,A(2)\,A(1)\,A(0)\,y_0 \quad ...(4)$$

... ...

$$y_k = A(k-1)\,y_{k-1} = [A(k-1)....A(3)\,A(2)\,A(1)\,A(0)]\,y_0 \quad ...(5)$$

Relation kth gives $y_k = C\prod_{k=0}^{k-1} A(k)$ where C is the arbitrary value assigned to y_0.

Aliter: $y_{k+1} = A(k)\,y_k \Rightarrow \log y_{k+1} = \log A(k) + \log y_k$

$$\Rightarrow \quad \log y_{k+1} - \log y_k = \log A(k), \Rightarrow \Delta \log y_k = \log A(k)$$

$$\Rightarrow \quad \log y_k = \Delta^{-1}[\log A(k)] \Rightarrow y_k = C\,\exp.[\Delta^{-1}\log A\,(k)]$$

$= C\prod_{k=0}^{k-1} A\,(k)$, where C is some arbitrary periodic function of k of period 1.

Example 18: *Solve* $y_{k+1} = 2^k\,y_k$.

Solution: Here $A\,(k) = 2^k$ [comparing with **Ex. 17.**]

Using Ex. 17., the required solution is given by

$$y_k = C\prod_{k=0}^{k-1} 2^k = C.2^0.2^1.2^2.2^{k-1} = C.2^{0+1+2...(k-1)} = C.2^{[k(k-1)/2]}$$

Example 19: *Solve* $y_{k+1} - (1/k)\,y_k = 0, k > 0.$

Solution: Here $A(k) = (1/k)$.

$$\therefore \quad y_k = c\prod_{k=1}^{k-1}(1/k) = C.\frac{1}{(k-1)!}$$

Aliter: We have $y_{k+1} = (1/k)\,y_k \Rightarrow \log y_{k+1} - \log y_k = -\log k$

$$\Rightarrow \quad \Delta \log y_k = -\log k \Rightarrow \log y_k = \Delta^{-1}\left[\log\left(\frac{1}{k}\right)\right]$$

$$\Rightarrow \quad y_k = C.\exp.[\Delta^{-1}\log(1/k)] = C\prod_{1}^{k-1}\left(\frac{1}{k}\right)$$

Example 20: *Show that* $y_{k+2} - 4\,y_{k+1} + 4\,y_k = 0...(i)(k = 0, 1...)$ *has the solution.*

[Agra 2005, 2007, 2010]

Solution: $y_k = 2^k(c_1 + kc_2), k = 0$ ...(1)

L.H.S. of the given difference equation gives

$$2^{k+2}\{c_1 + c_2(k+2)\} - 2^2.2^{k+1}\{c_1 + c_2(k+1)\} + 2^2.2^k(c_1 + kc_2)$$

$$= 2^{k+2}\{c_1 + c_2(k+2) - 2c_1 - 2c_2(k+1) + c_1 + c_2 k\} = 0.$$

i.e. we have found infinitely many solutions of the given equation.

Now suppose we want to find a solution of (1) for which

$y_0 = 1$ and $y_1 = 6$, **initial conditions** ...(2)

Putting $k = 0$ and $k = 1$ in (1), we obtain

$$y_0 = c \text{ and } y_1 = 2(c_1 + c_2) \text{ or } c_1 = 1 \text{ and } c_2 = 2$$

$$\Rightarrow \quad y_k = 2^k (1 + 2k) \quad ...(3)$$

This is a particular solution of (1) satisfying the prescribed intial conditions.

Now we shall show that this is the only solution.

9.4 Existence and Uniqueness Theorem

[Rohilkhand 2005, 2007, 2010; Agra 2004]

Some of the difference equations have infinitely many solutions where as others have no solution at all. In the case of linear difference equations, we can always find atleast one solution and, under certain conditions, only one solution and the theorems establishing such results are known as *existence and uniqueness theorems*.

First of all, we shall prove the theorem for the linear difference equation of order two simply to understand the general theorem.

Let the equation be

$$f_0(k)\, y_{k+2} + f_1(k)\, y_{k+1} + f_2(k)\, y_k = g(k), (k = 0, 1, 2, ...) \quad ...(1)$$

where $f_0(k) \neq 0, f_2(k) \neq 0$

Now let y_0 and y_1 be given, Putting $k = 0$ in (1),

$$f_0(0)\, y_2 + f_1(0)\, y_1 + f_2(0)\, y_0 = g(0)$$

$$\Rightarrow \quad f_0(0)\, y_2 = g(0) - f_1(0)\, y_1 - f_2(0)\, y_0$$

$$\Rightarrow \quad y_2 = \frac{g(0)}{f_0(0)} - \frac{f_1(0)}{f_0(0)} y_1 - \frac{f_2(0)}{f_0(0)} y_0, \text{ where } f_0(0) \neq 0 \quad ...(2)$$

Thus knowing y_0 and y_1, we have known y_2

Again to find y_3, we put $k=1$ in (1)

$$\Rightarrow \quad f_0(1)\, y_3 = g(1) - f_1(1)\, y_2 - f_2(1)\, y_1$$

$$\Rightarrow \quad y_3 = \frac{g(1)}{f_0(1)} - \frac{y_2 f_1(1)}{f_0(1)} - \frac{f_2(1)}{f_0(1)} y_1 \quad (\because f_0(1) \neq 0)$$

$\Rightarrow y_3$ is uniquely determined. We can continue this idea to get the unique solution of the second order equation (1) initiated by two values y_0 and y_1. By taking any other pair (say y_5 and y_0), we could have obtained a solution on the same lines.

General Theorem: *The linear difference equation of order n is given by*

$$f_0(k)\, y_{k+n} + f_1(k)\, y_{k+n-1} + ... + f_{n-1}(k)\, y_{k+1} + f_n(k)\, y_k = g(k) \quad ...(3)$$

over a set A of consecutive integral values of k has one and only one solution y for which values at n consecutives h-values are arbitrarily prescribed.

Proof: Here we shall establish that the above difference equation has a unique solution (over a set P of consecutive integrals values of y_k for which values at n consecutive k-values are arbitrarily fixed.

Let the theorem be true for jth order *i.e.* the difference equation,

$$f_0(k)\,y_{k+j}+f_1(k)\,y_{k+j-1}+\ldots+f_{j-1}(k)\,y_{k+1}+f_j(k)\,y_k=g(k)$$

of jth order has a unique solution y_{k+j} for the j prescribed values say $y_k, y_{k+1}, y_{k+2},\ldots, y_{k+j-1}$

Putting j for n in (3), we get

$$f_0(k)\,y_{k+j}+f_1(k)\,y_{k+j-1}+\ldots+f_{j-1}(k)\,y_{k+1}+f_j(k)\,y_k=g(k)$$

$$\Rightarrow\quad y_{k+j}=\frac{g(k)}{f_0(k)}-\frac{f_1(k)}{f_0(k)}\,y_{k+j-1}\ldots-\frac{f_{j-1}(k)}{f_0(k)}\,y_{k+1}-\frac{f_j(k)}{f_0(k)}\,y_k$$

$(\because\ f_0\ (k)\neq 0)$

i.e. y_{k+j} has a unique solution (**given**) ...(4)

Now we shall proceed to determine that the theorem is also true for $(j+1)^{th}$ *order.*

Putting $(j+1)$ for n in (3), we get

$$f_0(k)\,y_{k+(j+1)}+f_1(k)\,y_{k+j}+f_2(k)\,y_{k+(j-1)}+\ldots++f_{j+1}(k)\,y_k=g(k)$$

$$\Rightarrow\quad y_{k+(j+1)}=\frac{g(k)}{f_0(k)}-\frac{f_1(k)}{f_0(k)}\,y_{k+j}-\ldots-\frac{f_{j+1}(k)}{f_0(k)}\,y_k \qquad \ldots(5)$$

The values of y appearing on r.h.s. of this equation are known. Also $f_0(k)\neq 0$. Thus the division by $f_0(k)$ is permissible and therefore $y_{k+(j+1)}$ can be obtained easily. This further implies that $y_{k+(j+1)}$ is uniquely determined. But the theorem was true for second order, hence it must be true for third order and when it is true for third order, the theorem must be true for fourth order. Continuing in this way, we can say that it is universally true. In case the theorem is true for nth order,we must have

$$y_{k+n}=\frac{g(k)}{f_0(k)}-\frac{f_1(k)}{f_0(k)}\,y_{k+n-1}-\ldots-\frac{f_{n-1}(k)}{f_0(k)}\,y_{k+1}-\frac{f_n(k)}{f_0(k)}\,y_k$$

where $y_k, y_{k+1},\ldots, y_{k+n-1}$ are fixed.

If $y_k, y_{k+1},\ldots, y_{k+n-1}$ are not prescribed but instead. $y_m, y_{m+1},\ldots y_{m+n-1}$ $(m>k)$ are given then we may first successively determine unique values for y_{m-1} $y_{m-2},\ldots, y_{k+1}, y_k$ and then proceed as before to show that all other values uniquely determined. Putting $k=m-1$ in (3), We get

$$f_0(m-1)\,y_{m+n-1}+f_1(m-1)\,y_{m+n-2}+f_2(m-1)\,y_{m+n-3}+\ldots$$
$$+f_n(m-1)\,y_{m-1}=g(m-1)$$

$$\Rightarrow\ f_n(m-1)\,y_{m-1}=g(m-1)-f_0(m-1)\,y_{m-1+n}-f_1(m-1)\,y_{m-2+n}-f_{n-1}(m-1)\,y_m \qquad \ldots(6)$$

But $y_m, y_{m+1},\ldots, y_{m-1+n}, y_{m+1+n}$ are given, so y_{m-1} is known as $f_n(m-1)$ is never zero. Having determined y_{m-1}, we can obtain the values of $y_{m-2},\ldots, y_k$.

Homogeneous Linear Equations with Rational Coefficients

First consider the equation $y_{k+1} = ky_k$ ...(1)

gives $$y_k = (k-1)\,y_{k-1} = (k-1)(k-2)\,y_{k-2}$$

$$= (k-1)(k-2)(k-3)\ldots(k-\overline{k-2})\,y_2$$

$$= (k-1)!\,(1.\,y_1)$$

$$= \Gamma(k) \qquad (\because\ y_1 = 1) \qquad ...(2)$$

This shows that $y_k = \Gamma(k)$ is the particular solution of the equation

Now we proceed to determine the solution of $y_{k+1} = f_k y_k$ where f_k is a rational function

i.e. $$f_k = A\frac{(k-a_1)(k-a_2)\ldots(k-a_p)}{(k-b_1)(k-b_2)\ldots(k-b_l)} \qquad ...(3)$$

$$\therefore \quad y_{k+1} = A\frac{(k-a_1)(k-a_2)\ldots(k-a_p)}{(k-b_1)(k-b_2)\ldots(k-b_l)}\,y_k \qquad ...(4)$$

Now $y_{k+1} = f_k(f_{k-1}\,y_{k-1}) = (f_k\cdot f_{k-1}\,y_{k-2}) = f_k\cdot f_{k-1}\ldots f_1\,y_1 = f_k f_{k-1} f_{k-2}\ldots f_1$ as $y_1 = 1$

$$= \left\{A\frac{(k-a_1)(k-a_2)\ldots(k-a_p)}{(k-b_1)(k-b_2)\ldots(k-b_l)}\right\}\times\left\{A\frac{(k-1-a_1)(k-1-a_2)\ldots(k-1-a_p)}{(k-1-b_1)(k-1-b_2)\ldots(k-1-b_l)}\right\}\ldots$$

$$\ldots\left\{A\frac{(1-a_1)\ldots(1-a_p)}{(1-b_1)\ldots(1-b_l)}\right\}$$

← k factors ------------------------------->

$$= C_k A^k\frac{\Gamma(1+k-a_1)\,\Gamma(1+k-a_2)\ldots\Gamma(1+k-a_p)}{\Gamma(1+k-b_1)\,\Gamma(1+k-b_2)\ldots\Gamma(1+k-b_l)}$$

$$= A^k C_k\frac{\prod_{i=1}^{p}\Gamma(k+1-a_i)}{\prod_{i=1}^{l}\Gamma(k+1-b_i)} \qquad ...(5)$$

Hence the general solution of $y_{k+1} = f_k\cdot y_k$,

where $$f_k = A\frac{(k-a_1)(k-a_2)\ldots(k-a_p)}{(k-b_1)(k-b_2)\ldots(k-b_l)}$$ is given by

$$= y_{k+1} = C_k\frac{A^k\prod_{i=1}^{p}\Gamma(k+1-a_i)}{\prod_{i=1}^{l}\Gamma(k+1-b_i)} \qquad ...(6)$$

Example 21: *Solve* $(k^2-2k)\,y_{k+1}=(2k+1)\,y_k$.

Solution: The given equation may be written as $y_{k+1}=\dfrac{2k+1}{k^2-2k}\,y_k$

$$\therefore \qquad y_{k+1}=\frac{2k+1}{k(k-2)}=2\,.\frac{(k+\frac{1}{2})}{(k-0)(k-2)}.$$

Thus the general solution is $y_{k+1}=C_k 2^k \dfrac{\Gamma(k+\frac{3}{2})}{\Gamma(k+1)\,\Gamma(k-1)}$.

Homogeneous Linear Difference Equations with Constant Coefficients

Example 22: *Find linearly independent solution of the difference equation* $y_{k+2}-6\,y_{k+1}+8\,y_k=0$ *and thus write the general solution.* **[Agra 2006]**

Solution: Let $y_k=r^k$ be the solution of the given difference equation; then we have

$$r^{k+2}-6r^{k+1}+8r^k=0,\Rightarrow r^k(r^2-6r+8)=0 \qquad ...(1)$$

Dividing by r^k [assuming $r\neq 0$ which otherwise leads to the trivai solution $y_k=0$], we obtain the auxiliary equation as $r^2-6r+8=0\Rightarrow(r-2)(r-4)=0\Rightarrow r=2,4$.

Hence the two solution of (1) are 2^k and 4^k.

The set functions 2^k and 4^k is **L.I.** iff $\begin{vmatrix} 2^0 & 4^0 \\ 2^1 & 4^1 \end{vmatrix}\neq 0$

which is obvious and hence by ***Remark*** **1** we say that the solution 2^k and 4^k **L.I.** Now using ***Remark*** **2**, *viz,.* the superposition principle, the general solution is $y_k=c_1 2^k+c_2 4^k$.

> **Note:** The difference equation can be written as $(E^2-6E+8)y_k=0$.

$\therefore$ Auxiliary equation is $r^2-6r+8=0\Rightarrow r=2,4$.

Thus solutions are 2^k and 4^k.

Example 23: *Solve*

(a) $16\,y_{k+2}-8\,y_{k+1}+y_k=0$ ***(b)*** $y_{k+2}-4\,y_{k+1}+13\,y_k=0$. **[Agra 2008, 2009]**

Solution: (a) Auxiliary equation *viz.*, A.E. is given by

$$16r^2-8r+1=0\Rightarrow(4r-1)^2=0\Rightarrow r=(1/4),(1/4)$$

$\therefore$ Solution is $y_k=(c_1+c_2k)(1/4)^k$.

(b) A.E. is given by $r^2-4r+13=0,\Rightarrow r=2\pm 3\,i=\alpha\pm i\beta$ form.

Thus the solution is $y_k=(13)^{(k/2)}\,[c_1\cos(k\theta)+c_2\sin(k\theta)]$, where $\theta=\tan^{-1}(3/2)$.

Example 24: *Find the particular solution of* $y_{k+2} - 6y_{k+1} + 8y_k = 0$, *such that* $y_0 = 3$ $y_1 = 2$. *Also obtain* y_5. **[Agra 2007]**

Solution: We easily obtain $y_k = c_1 2^k + c_2 4^k$

Then from $y_0 = 3$, $y_1 = 2$, we have on putting $k = 0$ and $k = 1$ respectively,

$$3 = c_1 + c_2, 2 = 2c_1 + 4c_2 \Rightarrow c_1 = 5, c_2 = -2 \quad \therefore\ y_k = 5.2^k - 2.4^k.$$

Further, putting $k = 5$, we find $y_5 = 5.2^5 - 2.4^5 = 5\,(32) - 2\,(1024) = -1888$.

Example 25: *Solve the difference equation* $y_{k+2} - 2y_{k+1} + 5y_k = 0$.

Solution: The difference equation can be written as $(E^2 - 4E + 4)\,y_k = 0$,

and the auxiliary equation [*obtained by letting* $y_k = r^k$ in this equation] is given by

$$r^2 - 2r + 5 = 0$$

$$\Rightarrow \qquad r = \frac{2 \pm \sqrt{(4-20)}}{2} = \frac{2 \pm 4i}{2} = 1 \pm 2i = \alpha \pm i\beta$$

Hence the general solution can be written as

$$y_k = 5^{k/2}\,(c_1 \cos k\theta + c_2 \sin k\theta), \text{ where } \theta = \tan^{-1}(2).$$

Example 26: *Solve the difference equation* $y_{k+2} - 4y_{k+1} + 4y_k = 0$ *and find solution such that* $y_0 = 1$, $y_1 = 3$.

Solution: The difference equation can be written as $(E^2 - 4E + 4)\,y_k = 0$ ...(1)

Auxiliary equation is given by $r^2 - 4r + 4 = 0 \Rightarrow r = 2, 2$.

$\therefore$ $y_k = (c_1 + c_2 k)\,2^k$, which gives the required general solution.

Putting $k = 0$ and $k = 1$, we get $1 = c_1$ and $3 = 2(c_1 + c_2) \Rightarrow c_1 = 1, c_2 = \frac{1}{2}$

$$\Rightarrow \qquad y_k = 2^k\left(1 + \frac{k}{2}\right) = (k+2).2^{k-1}.$$

Example 27: *Solve* $2y_{k+2} - 5y_{k+1} + 2y_k = 0$

Also find the particular solution satisfying the initial conditions $y_0 = 0$ *and* $y_1 = 1$. **[Agra 2006]**

Solution: A.E. is given by $2r^2 - 5r + 2 = 0$ or $(2r-1)(r-2) = 0$ $\therefore$ $r = \frac{1}{2}, 2$

$\therefore$ General solution is $y_k = C_1 . \left(\frac{1}{2}\right)^k + C_2 . 2^k$

Putting $k = 0$ and $k = 1$ in the above solution we get

$$y_0 = C_1 + C_2 = 0 \quad \text{and} \quad y_1 = \frac{1}{2}C_1 + 2C_2 = 1$$

$$C_1 = -\frac{2}{3} \text{ and } C_2 = \frac{2}{3}$$

$$y_k = -\frac{2}{3}\left(\frac{1}{2}\right)^k + \frac{2}{3}2^k$$

Example 28: *Solve* $9y_{k+2} - 6y_{k+1} + y_k = 0$

Also find the particular solution satisfying the initial conditions $y_0 = 0$ *and* $y_1 = 1$.

Solution: A.E. is given by $9r^2 - 6r + 1 = 0$ or $(3r-1)^2 = 0$

$$\Rightarrow \qquad r = \frac{1}{3}, \frac{1}{3} \text{ (two roots repeated)}$$

∴ the general solution is given by

$$y_k = (C_1 + C_2 k).\left(\frac{1}{3}\right)^k$$

Putting $k = 0$ and $k = 1$ in the above solution, we get

$$y_0 = C_1 = 0 \text{ and } y_1 = (C_1 + C_2)\frac{1}{3} = 1$$

$$C_1 = 0 \text{ and } C_2 = 3.$$

∴ Particular solution satisfying the given initial conditions is equal to $y_k = 3k.\left(\frac{1}{3}\right)^k$.

Example 29: *Solve* $y_{k+4} - 4y_{k+3} + 6y_{k+2} - 4y_{k+1} + y_k = 0$.

Solution: A.E. is given by

$$r^4 - 4r^3 + 6r^2 - 4r + 1 = 0$$

or $\qquad (r-1)(r^3 - 3r^2 + 2r - 1) = 0$

or $\qquad (r-1)(r-1)(r^2 - 2r + 1) = 0$ or $(r-1)^4 = 0$

∴ $\qquad r = 1, 1, 1, 1.$

∴ General solution is

$$y_k = (C_1 + C_2 k + C_3 k^2 + C_4 k^3)(1^k)$$

$$= C_1 + C_2 k + C_3 k^2 + C_4 k^3.$$

Example 30: *Solve* $3y_{k+2} - 6y_{k+1} + 4y_k = 0$.

Solution: A.E. is given by $3r^2 - 6r + 4 = 0$

$$\Rightarrow \qquad r = \frac{6 \pm (36-48)^{1/2}}{6} = 1 \pm \frac{i}{\sqrt{3}} = \alpha \pm i\beta \text{ form}$$

∴ Solution is given by $y_k = A\left(\frac{2}{\sqrt{3}}\right)^k \cos\left(\frac{\pi k}{6} + B\right)$

Example 31: *Solve* $y_{k+2} - 2y_{k+1} + 2y_k = 0$.

Solution: Proceed as in Ex. 30.

Ans. $y_k = A(\sqrt{2})^k \cos\left(\frac{k\pi}{4} + B\right)$

Example 32: *Solve* $y_{k+2} + 6y_{k+1} + 25y_k = 0.$

Solution: A.E. is $r^2 + 6r + 25 = 0$

$$\Rightarrow \qquad r = \frac{-6 \pm \sqrt{(36-100)}}{2} = -3 \pm 4i = \alpha \pm i\beta \text{ form}$$

whence the solution is given by

$$y_k = C_1(5)^k \cos(k\theta + C_2), \text{ where } \theta = \tan^{-1}\left(-\frac{4}{3}\right)$$

Example 33: *Solve* $y_{k+3} + y_{k+2} - 8y_{k+1} - 12y_k = 0.$

Solution: A.E. is $r^3 + r^2 - 8r - 12 = 0 \Rightarrow r = 3, -2, -2$

$$\therefore \qquad y_k = C_1 3^k + (C_2 + C_3 k)(-2)^k.$$

Example 34: *Solve* $y_{k+2} - 3y_{k+1} + 2y_k = b^k$ ...(1)
where b is some constant.

Solution: A. E. is given by $r^2 - 3r + 2 = 0$

$$\Rightarrow \qquad (r-1)(r-2) = 0 \Rightarrow r = 1, 2.$$

$\therefore$ General solution of required homogeneous equation is $y_k = C_1 + C_2 . 2^k$

In order to find the particular solution of complete equation, let the trial function be

$$y_k^* = A . b^k \qquad \text{...(2)}$$

Substituting in the given equation, we get $A[b^{k+2} - 3b^{k+1} + 2b^k] = b^k$

$$\Rightarrow \qquad Ab^k(b^2 - 3b + 2) = b^k, \Rightarrow A(b-2)(b-1) = 1 \qquad \text{...(3)}$$

$$\therefore \qquad A = \frac{1}{(b-1)(b-2)}, \text{ provided } b \neq 1, b \neq 2$$

Thus the particular solution is $y_k^* = \frac{1}{(b-1)(b-2)} b^k$ ...(4)

Particular case $\qquad b = 2$ or $b = 1.$

In this case, we modify the trial solution by multiplying by k reducing it to

$$y_k^* = Ak2^k \qquad \text{...(5)}$$

Substituting in the given difference equation, we get

$$A.(k+2)2^{k+2} - 3.A.(k+1)2^{k+1} + 2.A.\,k.2^k = 2^k$$

$$\Rightarrow \qquad A(4k + 8 - 6k - 6 + 2k) = 1$$

$$\Rightarrow \qquad A = \left(\frac{1}{2}\right), \text{ whence from (5);}$$

$$y_k^* = \frac{1}{2} k . 2^k = 2^k = 2^{k-1} . k \text{ (Particular solution)}$$

$\therefore$ General solution is $y_k = C_1 + C_2 2^k + \frac{1}{(b-1)(b-2)} b^k \; (b \neq 1, b \neq 2)$

$$= C_1 + C_2 2^k + 2^{k-1}.k \qquad (b=2)$$

Similarly, the case can be discussed, when $b = 1$.

Example 35: *Solve* $y_{k+2} - 4y_{k+1} + 4y_k = 3k + 2^k$. **[Meerut 2005, 2007; Agra 2009]**

Solution: The corresponding homogeneous equation is given by

$$y_{k+2} - 4y_{k+1} + 4y_k = 0 \qquad ...(1)$$

Putting $y_k = r^k$ in (1), A.E. is given by

$$r^2 - 4r + 4 = 0 \quad \text{or } (r-2)^2 = 0 \quad \text{or } r = 2, 2$$

Hence the general solution of (1)is given by $y_k = (C_1 + C_2 k)2^k$

Now to find the particular solution of complete equation, let the trial solution be

$$y_k^* = A_0 + A_1 k + Bk^2 .2^k$$

Here $Bk^2 .2^k$ is taken corresponding to 2^k and not $B.2^k$, since 2^k is solution of (1), so we do not take $B.2^K$ as trial function, we multiply by k and try $Bk.2^k$ but since it is also a solution of (1), we again multiply by k and take the trial solution as $Bk^2 2^k$.

Putting the value of y_k in the given equation, we get

$$[A_0 + A_1(k+2) + B(k+2)^2 2^{k+2}] - 4[A_0 + A_1(k+1) + B(k+1)^2 2^{k+1}]$$
$$+ 4[A_0 + A_1 k + Bk^2 2^k] = 3k + 2^k$$

or $$(A_0 - 2A_1) + A_1 k + \{4B(k+2)^2 - 8B(k+1)^2 + 4Bk^2\}2^k = 3k + 2^k$$

or $$(A_0 - 2A_1) = A_1 k + 8B.2^k = 3k + 2^k \qquad ...(2)$$

On comparing the coefficients on both sides of (2), we get

$$A_0 - 2A_1 = 0, \; A_1 = 3, \; 8B = 1$$

or $$A_0 = 6, \; A_1 = 3, B = \frac{1}{8}$$

Thus the general solution of given equation is $y_k = (c_1 + c_2 k)2^k + 6 + 3k + \frac{1}{8}k^2 2^k$.

Example 36: *Solve* $y_{k+2} - 3y_{k+1} + 2y_k = 1$.

Solution: The corresponding homogeneous equation is given by

$$y_{k+2} - 3y_{k+1} + 2y_k = 0 \qquad ...(1)$$

Putting $y_k = r^k$ in (1), A.E. is given by

$$r^2 - 3r + 2 = 0 \quad \text{or } (r-2)(r-1) = 0 \quad \text{or } r = 2, 1$$

Hence the general solution of (1) is given by $y_k = C_1 + C_2 2^k$.

Now to find the particular solution of complete equation, let the trial function be $y_k^* = A$

Putting the value of y_k^* in the given equation, we have

$$A - 3A + 2A = 1 \quad \text{or } 0 = 1, \text{which is not true}$$

Now let the trial function be $y_k^* = Ak$

Putting the value of y_k^* in the given equation, we have

$$A(k+2) - 3A(k+1) + 2Ak = 1 \text{ or } A = -1$$

$$\therefore \quad y_k^* = -k$$

Thus the general solution of the given equation is $y_k = C_1 + C_2 2^k - k$.

Different Methods for finding Particular Solution in Case of Non-homogeneous Linear Equations

(1) Method of Undetermined Coefficients: This method is of great use in finding particular solution of the complete equation $\phi(E)\, y_k = R(k)$, when $R(k)$ consists of terms of special forms.

Corresponding to each such term, we consider a trial solution containing a number of unknown constant coefficients which have to be determined by substitution into the difference equation. The trial solutions to be used are depicted in the following table where A, B, A_0, A_1,... are the unknown constant coefficients to be determined.

Note. General solution = Complementary solution+Particular solution.

S.N.	Terms in $R(k)$	Trial solution
1.	β^k	$A\beta^k$
2.	$\sin(\alpha k)$ or $\cos(\alpha k)$	$A\cos(\alpha k) + B\sin(\alpha k)$
3.	$\beta^k P(k)$, where $P(k)$ is a poly. of mth degree in k.	$\beta^k[A_0 k^m + A_1 k^{m-1} + \ldots + \ldots A_m]$
4.	$\beta^k \sin(\alpha k)$ or $\beta^k \cos(\alpha k)$	$\beta^k[A\cos(\alpha k) + B\sin(\alpha k)]$
5.	$P(k)$, a polynomial of degree m	$A_0 k^m + A_1 k^{m-1} + \ldots + \ldots + A_m$

Example 37: *Solve* $y_{k+2} - 6y_{k+1} + 8y_k = 3k^2 + 2 - 5.3^k$.

Solution: The general solution of the *homogeneous equation* [also called as *complementary equation or reduced equation*] is given by $y_k = c_1 2^k + c_2 4^k$ ...(1)

Corresponding to the polynomial $3k^2 + 2$, we assume the trial solution as $A_1 k^2 + A_2 k + A_3$, since none of these terms occur in the complementary solution (1). But due to the presence of the term, -5.3^k, the trial solution can be written as $3^k.A_4$. Hence corresponding to the right hand side of the difference equation, the trial solution could be written as

$$y_k = A_1 k^2 + A_2 k + A_3 + A_4 3^k. \quad ...(2)$$

Substituting this in the difference equation, we obtain

$$y_{k+2} - 6y_{k+1} + 8y_k = A_1(k+2)^2 + A_2(k+2) + A_3 + A_4\,3^{k+2}$$
$$-6[A_1(k+1)^2 + A_2(k+1) + A_3 + A_4\,3^{k+1}] + 8[A_1k^2 + A_2k + A_3 + A_4 3^k]$$
$$= 3A_1k^2 + (3A_2 - 8A_1)k + 3A_3 - 4A_2 - 2A_1 - A_4 3^k$$

But this solution should be equal to the r.h.s of the given difference equation

$$\Rightarrow \quad 3A_1k^2 + (3A_2 - 8A_1)k + 3A_3 - 4A_2 - 2A_1 - A_4 3^k = 3k^2 + 2 - 5.3^k$$

Equation coefficients of like terms, we get

$$3A_1 = 3,\; 3A_2 - 8A_1 = 0,\; 3A_3 - 4A_2 - 2A_1 = 2,$$
$$A_4 = 5 \Rightarrow A_1 = 1,\; A_2 = (8/3),\; A_3 = (44/9) \text{ and } A_4 = 5$$

Hence, the particular solution is given by $k^2 + (8/3)k + (44/9) + 5.3^k$
Adding this to the complementary solution, we get the required solution as $y_k = c_1 2^k + c_2 4^k + k^2 + (8/3)k + (44/9) + 5.3^k$.

Example 38: *Solve* $y_{k+3} - 3y_{k+2} + 3y_{k+1} - y_k = 24(k+2)$.

Solution: Complementary equation is given by

$$(E^3 - 3E^2 + 3E - 1)\,y_k = 0 \Rightarrow (E-1)^3\,y_k = 0$$
$$\Rightarrow \quad y_k = (c_1 + c_2k + c_3k^2) = \text{ Complementary solution} \quad ...(1)$$

Now, we shall obtain particular solution. Corresponding to the term $24k + 48$, we assume the trial solution as $A_1k + A_2$. But these terms occur in (1); *so we multiply by a suitable power of k which is just sufficient to ensure that none of these terms will occur.* This is possibly k^3, so that trial solution becomes $y_k = A_1k^4 + A_2k^3$.

Now, substituting this in the difference equation, we obtain

$$A_1(k+3)^4 + A_2(k+3)^3 - 3\{A_1(k+2)^4 + A_2(k+2)^3\}$$
$$+ \{3A_1(k+1)^4 + A_2(k+1)^3\} - A_1k^4 - A_2k^3 = 24k + 48$$
$$\Rightarrow 24A_1k + 36A_1 + A_2 = 24k + 48 \Rightarrow A_1 = 1, A_2 = 12$$
$$\Rightarrow \text{Particular solution } = k^4 + 12k^3$$
$$\Rightarrow \text{Complete solution } = (c_1 + c_2k + c_3k^2) + k^4 + 12k^3 = y_k, \text{ say.}$$

Example 39: *Find the particular solution of the difference equation by the method of undetermined coefficients*

$$y_{k+2} - 2y_{k+1} + y_k = 2^k(k-1) + 5 + 3k + k^2 + \sin 2k\pi \qquad \textbf{[Agra 2006, 2008]}$$

Solution: Suppose the trial solution corresponding to the term $2^k(k-1)$ on the R.H.S. of the given difference equation be $y_k = 2^k(A_0 + A_1k)$.

Putting the values of y_k in the given equation, the L.H.S.

$$= y_{k+2} - 2y_{k+1} + y_k$$

$$= 2^{k+2}\{A_0 + A_1(k+2)\} - 2.2^{k+1}\{A_0 + A_1(k+1)\} + 2^k(A_0 + A_1 k)$$

$$= 2^k\{kA_1 + (4A_1 + A_0)\} \text{ Comparing it with } 2^k(k-1), \text{ we have}$$

$$A_1 = 1 \text{ and } 4A_1 + A_0 = -1 \Rightarrow A_1 = 1, A_0 = -5$$

Thus the particular solution corresponding to the term $2^k(k-1)$ on R.H.S. of (1) is $y_k = 2^k(-5+k)$.

Again let the trial solution corresponding to the term $5 + 3k + k^2$ on the R.H.S. of given equation be $y_k = k^2(A_2 + A_3 k + A_4 k^2)$.

The trial solution is not taken as $A_2 + A_3 k + A_4 k^2$ or $k(A_2 + A_3 k + A_4 k^2)$, since $c_1 + c_2 k$ is the solution of the reduced homogeneous equation. Putting this value of y_k in given equation, the

$$\text{L.H.S.} = y_{k+2} - 2y_{k+1} + y_k = (k+2)^2\{A_2 + A_3(k+2) + A_4(k+2)^2\}$$
$$-2(k+1)^2\{A_2 + A_3(k+1) + A_4(k+1)^2\} + k^2\{A_2 + A_3 k + A_4 k^2\}$$

$$= (2A_2 + 6A_3 + 14A_4) + (6A_3 + 24A_4)k + 12A_4 k^2$$

Comparing it with $5 + 3k + k^2$, we have

$$2A_2 + 6A_3 + 14A_4 = 5,\ 6A_3 + 24A_4 = 3,\ 12\ A_4 = 1$$

$$\Rightarrow \quad A_2 = 17/6,\ A_3 = 1/6, A_4 = 1/12.$$

Therefore the particular solution corresponding to the term $5 + 3k + k^2$ on R.H.S. of given equation is $y_k = k^2\left(\frac{17}{6} + \frac{k}{6} + \frac{k^2}{12}\right)$

Again let the trial solution corresponding to the term $\sin 2k\pi$ on the R.H.S. of given equation by $y_k = k^2(A_5 \sin 3k\pi + A_6 \cos 2k\pi)$.

Here we can verify that trial solutions

$$A_5 \sin 2k\pi + A_6 \cos 2k\pi \text{ and } kA_5 \sin 2k\pi + kA_6 \cos 2k\pi \text{ fail.}$$

Putting this trial solution in given equation the L.H.S. $= y_{k+2} - 2y_{k+1} + y_k$

$$= (k+2)^2[A_5 \sin 2(k+2)\pi + A_6 \cos 2(k+2)\pi]$$

$$-2(k+1)^2[A_5 \sin 2(k+1)\pi + A_6 \cos 2(k+1)\pi] + k^2[A_5 \sin 2k\pi + A_6 \cos 2k\pi]$$

$$= 2A_5 \sin 2k\pi + 3A_6 \cos 2k\pi.$$

On comparing it with $\sin 2k\pi$, we have $2A_5 = 1$ and $2A_6 = 0$ or $A_5 = 1/2$, $A_6 = 0$.

Therefore particular solution corresponding to the term $\sin 2k\pi$ on the R.H.S. of given equation is $y_k = \frac{k^2}{2}\sin 2k\pi$.

Hence the particular solution of the equation is given by

$$y_k = 2^k(-5+k) + \left(\frac{17}{6}k^2 + \frac{1}{6}k^3 + \frac{1}{12}k^4\right) + \frac{k^2}{2}\sin 2k\pi.$$

(2) Special Operator Methods: The non-homogeneous (general linear) difference equation with constant coefficients is of the form $\phi(E)\,y_k = R(k)$. **[Agra 2003]**

Let us define the operator $[1/\phi(E)]$, *called the inverse of* $\phi(E)$, by the relationship $\frac{1}{\phi(E)}R(k) = U$, where $\phi(E),\ U = R(k)$ ...(1)

Here we assume that U does not contain any arbitrary constants and so the particular solution of the equation (1) Such inverse operators lead to some special operator methods which are of great use and easy to apply in case $R(k)$ is of the form as indicated in the following table:

Method No. 1.	(i) $\frac{1}{\phi(E)}\beta^k = \beta^k\frac{1}{\phi(\beta)}$, provided $\phi(\beta) \neq 0$, (put $E=\beta$) (ii) $\frac{1}{E-\beta}\beta^k = k\beta^{k-1}$ (iii) $\frac{\beta^k}{(E-\beta)^2} = \frac{k(k-1)}{2!}\beta^{k-2}$ and so on.
Method No. 2	$\frac{1}{\phi(E)}\sin(\alpha k)$ or $\frac{1}{\phi(E)}\cos(\alpha k)$ Write $\sin\alpha k = \frac{e^{\alpha ki} - e^{-\alpha ki}}{2i}$ and $\cos\alpha k = \frac{e^{\alpha ki}+e^{-\alpha ki}}{2}$ and then apply method No. 1.
Method No. 3	$\frac{1}{\phi(E)}P(k) = \frac{1}{\phi(1+\Delta)}P(k)$ $= (b_0 + b_1\Delta + \ldots + b_m\Delta^m + \ldots +)P(k)$ where the expansion is to be carried out upto Δ^m since $\Delta^{m+1}P(k) = 0$.
Method No. 4.	$\frac{1}{\phi(E)}\beta^\kappa P(k) = \beta^\kappa\frac{1}{\phi(\beta E)}P(k)$ and then apply method No. 3. This result holds for any function $F(k)$ instead of $P(k)$.
Method No. 5	$\frac{1}{\phi(E)}T = \frac{T}{\phi(1)}$, where T is some constant and $\phi(1) \neq 0$.

Proof: (1) Let $R(k)$ = some constant, say T [Method No. 5]

we know that $ET = T$, implying $\phi(E)\,T = {}^*(a_0E^n + A_1E^{n-1} + \ldots + a_n)\,T$,

i.e. $\phi(E)\,T = a_0T + a_1T + \ldots + a_nT = \phi(1)\,T$

i.e. $\frac{1}{\phi(E)}.T = \frac{T}{\phi(1)}$ provided $\phi(1) \neq 0$,

---

$^*\phi(E) = a_0E^n + a_1E^{n-1} + \ldots + a_n$, where $a_0, a_1, a_2, \ldots, a_n$ are constants.

(2) Let $R(k) = T\beta^k$, where T and β are constant [Method No. 1]

we have $\phi(E)[T\beta^k] = \{a_0 E^n + \ldots + a_n\}(T\beta^k)$

$$= T[a_0\beta^{n+k} + a_1\beta^{n-1+k} + \ldots + a_n \beta^k]$$

$$\Rightarrow \quad \frac{1}{\phi(E)} T\beta^k = \frac{[T\beta^k]}{\phi(\beta)}, \quad \text{Provided } \phi(\beta) \neq 0$$

If $T = 1$, then $\dfrac{\beta^k}{\phi(E)} = \dfrac{\beta^k}{\phi(\beta)}$.

(3) Let $R(k) = P(k)$, a polynomial of degree m in k. [Method No. 3]

We can write $\phi(E) = \phi(1+\Delta)$ $(\because E \equiv 1+\Delta)$

$\Rightarrow \dfrac{1}{\phi(E)} = \dfrac{1}{\phi(1+\Delta)}$, which can be expanded ascending powers of Δ as far as upto Δ^m

$$\Rightarrow \quad \frac{1}{\phi(E)} = \frac{1}{\phi(1+\Delta)} = (b_0 + b_1\Delta + \ldots + b_m\Delta^m + \ldots)$$

$$\Rightarrow \quad \frac{1}{\phi(E)} P(k) = (b_0 + b_1\Delta + \ldots + b_m\Delta^m + \ldots) P(k)$$

$$= b_0 P(k) + b_1 \Delta P(k) + \ldots + b_m \Delta^m P(k) \text{ (since other terms will be zero).}$$

(4) Let $R(k) = \beta^k p(k)$, where $P(k)$ is a polynomial of degree m in k.

We have $E^r[\beta^k P(k)] = \beta^{k+r} p(k+r) = \beta^k \beta^r E^r p(k) = \beta^k (\beta E)^r p(k)$

and similarly $\dfrac{1}{\phi(E)} \beta^k p(k) = \beta^k \dfrac{1}{\phi(\beta E)} P[(k)] = \beta^k [\phi(\beta + \beta\Delta)]^{-1} P(k)$.

Example 40: *Solve* $y_{k+3} + y_{k+2} - 8y_{k+1} - 12y_k = 2k^2 + 5$. **[Bhopal 2002; Agra 2007]**

Solution: The given equation can be put as

$$E^3 y_k + E^2 y_k - 8Ey_k - 12 y_k = 2k^2 + 5$$

or as

$$(E^3 + E^2 - 8E - 12) y_k = 2k^2 + 5$$

or as

$$(E-3)(E+2)^2 y_k = 2k^2 + 5$$

Hence complementary solution is $c_1(3)^k + (c_2 + c_3 k)(-2)^k$.

The particular solution of this equation is

$$= [(E-3)(E+2)^2]^{-1}(2k^2+5)$$

$$= [(\Delta-2)(\Delta+3)^2]^{-1}(2k^2+5) \qquad [\because E \equiv 1+\Delta]$$

$$= [(\Delta^3 + 4\Delta^2 - 3\Delta - 18]^{-1}(2k^2+5)$$

$$= -\frac{1}{18}\left[1 + \frac{3\Delta - 4\Delta^2 - \Delta^3}{18}\right]^{-1}(2k^2+5)$$

$$= -\frac{1}{18}\left[1 - \frac{3\Delta - 4\Delta^2 - \Delta^3}{18} + \frac{(3\Delta - 4\Delta^2 - \Delta^3)^2}{(18)^2} + \ldots\right]^* (2k^2 + 5)$$

(expanding upto Δ^2 only)

$$= -\frac{1}{18}\left[1 - \frac{\Delta}{6} + \frac{\Delta^2}{4}\right](2k^{(2)} + 2k^{(1)} + 5)$$

$$= -\frac{1}{18}\left[2k^{(2)} + 2k^{(1)} + 5 - \frac{4k+2}{6} + \frac{4}{4}\right] = -\frac{k^2}{9} + \frac{k}{27} - \frac{17}{54}$$

Hence the general solution of the given difference equation is given by

$$y_k = [c_1 3^k + (c_2 + c_3 k)(-2)^k] - \frac{k^2}{9} + \frac{k}{27} - \frac{17}{54}.$$

Example 41: *Solve* $y_{k+1} - 2y_k = k + 1.$

Solution: The given equation can be put as $Ey_k - 2y_k = k + 1 \Rightarrow (E - 2)y_k = k + 1$

$\therefore$ complementary solution is $C_1(2)^k$

Now, particular solution is $\frac{1}{E-2}(k+1) = \frac{1}{1+\Delta-2}[k^{(2)} + k^{(0)}]$ $(\because\ k^{(1)} = k, k^{(0)} = 1)$

$$= -\frac{1}{1-\Delta}(k^{(1)} + k^{(0)}) = -(1-\Delta)^{-1}(k^{(1)} + k^{(0)})$$

$$= -(1 + \Delta + \Delta^2 + \ldots)[k^{(1)} + k^{(0)}] = -(k^{(1)} + k^{(0)} + 1)$$

$$= -(k + 1 + 1) = -(k + 2).$$

complete solution is $y_k = C_1 2^k - (k + 2).$

Example 42: *Solve the difference equation* $y_{k+2} - 2y_{k+1} + 5y_k = 2.3^k - 4.7^k.$

Solution: The given equation can be written as $(E^2 - 3E + 5)y_k = 2.3^k - 4.7^k.$

$\therefore$ Particular solution $= \frac{1}{E^2 - 2E + 5}(2.3^k - 4.7^k)$

$$= 2.\frac{1}{E^2 - 2E + 5}3^k - 4.\frac{1}{E^2 - 2E + 5}.7^k$$

$$= 2.\frac{3^k}{3^2 + 2(3) + 5} - 4.\frac{7^k}{7^2 - 2(7) + 6} = \frac{1}{4}.3^k - \frac{1}{10}7^k.$$

Also A.E. is $r^2 - 2r + 5 = 0 \Rightarrow r = 1 \pm 2i.$

Hence the complete solution is given by

$$y_k = 5^{k/2}(c_1 \cos k\theta + c_2 \sin k\theta) + \frac{1}{4}.3^k - \frac{1}{10}7^k, \text{where } \theta = \tan^{-1}2.$$

$^*2k^2 + 5 \equiv Ak^{(2)} + Bk^{(1)} + C = Ak(k-1) + Bk + c \Rightarrow C = 5, A = 2 = B \Rightarrow 2k^2 + 5 = 2k^{(2)} + 2k^{(1)} + 5.$

Example 43: *Find* $\frac{1}{E^2-4E+4}.2^k$.

Solution: The method no, 1 fails, since if $\phi(E)=E^2-4E+4$,

$\phi(2)=0$. So we apply method no. 4.

$$\frac{1}{\phi(E)}2^k=2^k.\frac{1}{\phi(2E)}(1)=2^k\frac{1}{(2E)^2-4(2E)+4}(1)=2^k\frac{1}{4E^2-8E+4}(1)$$

$$=2^k\frac{1}{4(1+\Delta)^2-8(1+\Delta)+4}(1)=2^k.\frac{1}{4\Delta^2}(1)$$

$$=\frac{2^k\Delta^{-1}}{4}[\Delta^{-1}(1)]=\frac{2^k}{4}\Delta^{-1}\{k^{(1)}\}=\frac{2^k}{4}\frac{k^{(2)}}{2}=\frac{k(k-1)2^k}{8}.$$

Example 44: *Solve the equation* $y_{k+2}+y_{k+1}+y_k=k.2^k$. **[Agra 2001, 2007]**

Solution: The equation can be put as

$$E^2y_k+Ey_k+y_k=k.2^k\Rightarrow(E^2+E+1)\,y_k=k.2^k$$

The particular solution of this equation is given by $2^k[(2E)^2+2E+1]^{-1}k$

$$=2^k[7+10\,\Delta+4\,\Delta^2]^{-1}k \qquad [\because\ E\equiv1+\Delta]$$

$$=\frac{2^k}{7}\left[1-\frac{10\Delta+4\Delta^2}{7}\right]k=\frac{2^k}{7}\left[k-\frac{10}{7}\right]=\text{ P.S}$$

The complementary solution of the equation is given by

C.S. $=c_1\cos k\theta+c_2\sin k\theta$, where $\theta=\tan^{-1}(-\sqrt{3})$.

Hence the general solution of the given difference equation is $y_k=$ C.S. + P.S

Example 45: *Find* $\frac{1}{E^2-6E+8}(3k^2+2)$.

Solution: We have

$$\frac{1}{E^2-6E+8}(3k^2+2)=\frac{1}{(1+\Delta)^2-6(1+\Delta)+8}(3k^2+2) \qquad [\because\ E\equiv1+\Delta]$$

$$=\frac{1}{3-4\Delta+\Delta^2}(3k^2+2)$$

$$=\frac{1}{3}[1+(\frac{4}{3}\Delta-\frac{1}{3}\Delta^2)+(\frac{4}{3}\Delta-\frac{1}{3}\Delta^2)^2+\ldots](3k^2+2)$$

$$=\frac{1}{3}[1+(\frac{4}{3}\Delta+\frac{13}{9}\Delta^2)+\ldots][3k^{(2)}+3k^{(1)}+\frac{13}{27}\Delta^2[3k^{(2)}+3k^{(1)}+$$

$$=\frac{1}{3}[3k^2+\frac{4}{3}[6k^{(1)}+3]+\frac{13}{27}[6]=k^2+\frac{8}{3}k+\frac{44}{9}.$$

Example 46: *Solve* $y_{k+2} - y_{k+1} - 2y_k = k^2$.

Solution: A.E. is given by

$$r^2 - r - 2 = 0 \Rightarrow r^2 - 2r + r - 2 = 0, \Rightarrow r(r-2) + 1(r-2) = 0$$

$$\Rightarrow \quad (r+1)(r-2) = 0, \Rightarrow r = -1, 2.$$

$\therefore$ Complementary solution is $C_1(-1)^k + C_2 2^k$

Also, particular solution $= \dfrac{1}{E^2 - E - 2} k^2 = \dfrac{1}{(I+\Delta)^2 - (I+\Delta) - 2I} k^2$

$$= \frac{1}{I + \Delta^2 + 2\Delta - I - \Delta - 2I} k^2 = \frac{1}{\Delta^2 + \Delta - 2I} k^2 = \frac{1}{-2\left\{I - \dfrac{\Delta^2 + \Delta}{2}\right\}} k^2$$

$$= -\frac{1}{2}\left\{I - \left(\frac{\Delta^2 + \Delta}{2}\right)\right\}^{-1} k^2$$

$$= -\frac{1}{2}\left[I + \left(\frac{\Delta^2 + \Delta}{2}\right) + \left(\frac{\Delta^2 + \Delta}{2}\right)^2 + \ldots\right] k^2$$

$$= -\frac{1}{2}\left[I + \frac{\Delta^2}{2} + \frac{\Delta}{2} + \left(\frac{\Delta^2}{4}\right) + \ldots\right] k^2 = -\frac{1}{2}\left[I + \frac{\Delta}{2} + \frac{3\Delta^2}{4} + \ldots\right] k^2$$

$$= -\frac{1}{2}\left[I + \frac{\Delta}{2} + \frac{3}{4}\Delta^2 + \ldots\right](k^{(2)} + k^{(1)})$$

$$= -\frac{1}{2}\left[\{k^{(2)} + k^{(1)}\} + \frac{1}{2}(2k^{(1)} + 1) + \frac{3}{4}(2.1k^{(0)})\right]$$

$$= -\frac{1}{2}(k^2 + k + 2)$$

$$\therefore \quad y_k = \text{C.S.} + \text{P.S.} = C_1(-1)^k + C_2 2^k - \frac{1}{2}(k^2 + k + 2).$$

Example 47: *Solve* $y_{k+2} - 5y_{k+1} + 6y_k = 5^k$.

Solution: Here we have $P(k) = 5^k$ and $\phi(E) = E^2 - 5E + 6$

$$\Rightarrow \quad \phi(5) = 25 - 25 + 6 = 6 \Rightarrow y_k = \frac{5^k}{\phi(5)} = \frac{5^k}{6}$$

Complementary solution of the equation is given by C.S. $= c_1 2^k + c_2 3^k$.

Hence, the general solution of the given difference equation is

$$y_k = c_1 2^k + c_2 .3^k + (5^k/6).$$

Example 48: *Solve* $y_{k+2} - 5y_{k+1} + 6y_k = 36$.

Solution: The equation can be put as $(E^2 - 5E + 6)y_k = 36 \Rightarrow \phi(E)y_k = 36$

Now, $\quad \phi(E) = (E-2)(E-3) \Rightarrow \phi(1) = (1-2)(1-3) = 2.$

$\therefore$ Particular solution of the equation is $y_k = \dfrac{36}{2} = 18$

Also complementary solution of this equation is $y_k = c_1 2^k + c_2 3^k$

Hence the general solution of the given equation is $y_k = c_1 2^k + c_2 3^k + 18$.

9.5 Method of Variation of Parameters

Example 49: *Solve* $y_{k+2} - 5\,y_{k+1} + 6\,y_k = k^2$, *by the method of variation of parameters.*

[Agra 2006]

Solution: The complementary solution *i.e.* the general solution of $y_{k+2} - 5\,y_{k+1} + 6\,y_k = 0$ is $c_1 2^k + c_2 3^k$. Now let the general solution of the complete difference equation be

$$y_k = K_1 2^k + K_2 3^k \qquad ...(1)$$

where K_1 and K_2 are function of k to be determined.

We have $$\Delta y_k = K_1 2^k + K_2 2.3^k + 2^{k+1}\Delta K_1 + 3^{k+1}\Delta K_2 \qquad ...(2)$$

$$= K_1 2^k + K_2\,.2.3^k \qquad ...(3)$$

provided $$2^{k+1}\Delta K_1 + 3^{k+1}\Delta K_2 = 0 \qquad ...(4)$$

Form (3), we have $$\Delta^2 y_k = K_1 2^k + K_2\,.4.3^k + 2^{k+1}\Delta K_1 + 2.3^{k+1}\Delta K_2 \qquad ...(5)$$

The given equation can be written as

$$(E^2 - 5E + 6)\,y_k = k^2 \Rightarrow (\Delta^2 - 3\Delta + 2)\,y_k = k^2 \qquad [\because \quad E \equiv 1 + \Delta] \qquad ...(6)$$

Using (1), (3) and (5) in (6), we obtain after simplifying,

$$2^{k+1}\Delta K_1 + 2.3^{k+1}\Delta K_2 = k^2 \qquad ...(7)$$

Solving (7) and $2^{k+1}\Delta K_1 + 3^{k+1}\Delta K_2 = 0$, we obtain $\Delta K_1 = \dfrac{-k^2}{2^{k+1}}$ and $\Delta\, K_2 = \dfrac{k^2}{3^{k+1}}$

$$\Rightarrow \qquad K_1 = -\Delta^{-1}\left(\frac{k^2}{2^{k+1}}\right), K_2 = \Delta^{-1}\left(\frac{k^2}{3^{k+1}}\right) \qquad ...(8)$$

Now we have $K_1 = -\dfrac{1}{\Delta}\left(\dfrac{k^2}{2^{k+1}}\right) = -\dfrac{1}{E-1}\left(\dfrac{1}{2}\right)^k\left(\dfrac{k^2}{2}\right) = -\left(\dfrac{1}{2}\right)^k \dfrac{1}{\frac{1}{2}E-1}\left(\dfrac{k^2}{2}\right)$

$$= -(1)^k \frac{1}{E-2}(k^2) = \frac{1}{1-\Delta}(k^2), \qquad \because \quad E \equiv 1 + \Delta$$

$$= \left(\frac{1}{2}\right)^k (1 + \Delta + \Delta^2 + \ldots)(k^{(2)} + k^{(1)})$$

$$= \left(\frac{1}{2}\right)^k [k^{(2)} + k^{(1)} + 2k^{(1)} + 1 + 2]$$

$$= \left(\frac{1}{2}\right)^k [k^2 + 2k + 3] + c_1 \qquad \text{(const., say } c_1.)$$

Similarly, we find $$K_2 = -\frac{1}{2.3^k}(k^2 + k + 1) + c_2$$

Hence the required solution is $y_k = \left[c_1 2^k + c_2 3^k + \dfrac{1}{2}k^2 + \dfrac{3}{2}k + \dfrac{3}{2}\right]$.

Example 50: $y_{k+1} - ry_k = R_k$, *where r is a constant.*

Solution: The complementary or homogeneous equation corresponding to the given equation is $y_{k+1} - ry_k = 0 \Rightarrow (E-r)\,y_k = 0$ ...(1)

$$\therefore \quad y_k = ry_{k-1},\, y_{k-1} = ry_{k-2}, \ldots, y_2 = ry_1,\, y_1 = ry_0$$

so that the solution of (1) is $y_k = r(ry_{k-2}) = r.r.ry_{k-3} = (r.r.r\ldots k \text{ times})\,y_0 = r^k y_0$

Thus $\quad y_k = r^k y_0$ or $y_k = c_0 r^k$,

where $c_0 = y_0$, as the arbitrary constant, gives the required solution of (1),

Now we shall apply the method of variation of parameters to solve the given equation.

Let $\quad y_k = K(k)\, r^k$ ...(2)

be the solution of given equation, $K(k)$ is a function of k.

Then proceeding as before, we obtain

$$K(k+1)r^{k+1} - K(k)r^{k+1} = R_k. \text{ i.e. } K(k+1) - K(k) = \Delta K = \frac{R_k}{r^{k+1}}$$

$$\therefore \quad K(k) = \Delta^{-1}\left(\frac{R^k}{r^{k+1}}\right) + c_1$$

$$\text{Thus,} \quad y_k = r^k \Delta^{-1}\left(\frac{R_k}{r^{k+1}}\right) + cr^k = r\sum_{p=1}^{k-1} \frac{R_p}{r^{p+10}} + cr^k.$$

Example 51: *Solve* $y_{k+2} - 5y_{k+1} + 6y_k = k^2$, *by the method of reduction of order.*

[Agra 2002]

Solution: The equation can be written as $(E-3)(E-2)\,y_k = k^2$ ...(1)

Putting $\quad z_k = (E-2)\,y_k$,

We have $(E-3)\,z_k = k^2$ ...(2)

Solving (2) as in Ex. 50, we have

$$z_k = 3^k \Delta^{-1}\left(\frac{k^2}{3^{k+1}}\right) + c_1 3^k = c_1 3^k - \frac{1}{2}(k^2 + k + 1) \quad \ldots(3)$$

$$\therefore \quad z_k = (E-2)\,y_k = c_1 3^k - \frac{1}{2}(k^2 + k + 1) \quad \ldots(4)$$

Again applying the method of Ex. 50. the solution is

$$y_k = 2^k \Delta^{-1}\left(\frac{c_1 3^k - \frac{1}{2}(k^2 + k + 1)}{3^{k+1}}\right) + c_2 2^k$$

$$= \frac{1}{2}k^2 + \frac{3}{2}k + \frac{5}{2} + c_2 2^k + c_3 3^k.$$

9.6 Methods of Generating Functions

The method of generating sequence is a powerful method to solve and study the solution of the difference equations. Let $y_0, y_1, y_2, \ldots$, be a sequence of real number, the function $G(t)$ defined for some interval of real numbers containing zero whose value at t is given by series $G(t) = y_0 + y_1 t + y_2 t^2 + \ldots + y_k t^k + \ldots$

is the generating function of the sequence $\{y_k\}$.

Example 52: *The function given by* $G(t) = [1/(1-t)]$.

is the generating function of the constant sequence 1, 1, 1, ..., **[Agra 2007]**

Solution: We have $G(t) = (1-t)^{-1} = 1 + t + t^2 + \ldots, \ldots \infty$ by Binomial Theorem.

$$y_0 = 1\ y_1 = 1, y_2 = 1; \text{etc.}$$

Then $\Rightarrow$ 1, 1, 1 ... be sequence

Example 53: *The function given by* $G(t) = (1-t)^{-2}$ *is the generating function of the sequence* 1, 2, 3, 4,.... .

Solution: We have $G(t) = \dfrac{1}{(1-t)^2} = (1-t)^{-2} = 1 + 2t + 3t^2 + \ldots \infty$

whence $y_0 = 1, y_1 = 2, y_3 = 3, \ldots$, *i.e.*, the sequence is 1, 2, 3, 4,.... .

Example 54: *Suppose* $B \neq 0$, *then find generating function of* $\{B^k\}$.

Solution: $y_0 = B^0 = 1, y_1 = B^1, y_2 = B^2$ etc. then we have

$G(t) = 1 + Bt + B^2t^2 + B^kt^k + \ldots = [1/(1-Bt)]$ which generates $\{B^k\}$ [we assumed here $|Bt| > 1$]

Now we express the above results in the following table:

S. N.	General term of $\{y_k\}$	Generating function $G(t)$
1	1	$1/(1-t)$
2	$(k+1)$	$1/(1-t)^2$
3	k	$t/(1-t)^2$
4	$k(k+1)$	$2t/(1-t)^3$
5	${}^nC_k B^{n-k}.C^k (k = 0, 1, 2, \ldots n) k > n$	$(B+Ct)^n$
6	B^k	$1/(1-Bt)$
7	y_k	$G(t)$
8	y_{k+1}	$[G(t) - y_0]/t$
9	y_{k+2}	$[G(t) - y_0 - y_1 t]/t^2$
10	y_{k+n}	$[G(t) - y_0 - y_1 t \ldots - y_{n-1} t^{n-1}]/t^n$
11	$\lambda_1 y_k^{(1)} + \lambda_2 y_k^{(2)}$	$\lambda_1 G_1(t) + \lambda_2 G_2(t)$

***Theorem* 4:** *If* $\{y_k^{(1)}\}$ has the generating function G_1 and $\{y_k^{(2)}\}$ has the generating function G_2, then $\{\lambda_1 y_k^{(1)} + \lambda_2 y_k^{(2)}\}$ has the generating function $\lambda_1 G_1 + \lambda_2 G_2$ for any constants λ_1 and λ_2.

***Proof*:** We have $\quad G_1(t) = y_0^{(1)} + y_1^{(1)} t + y_2^{(1)} t^2 + \ldots + y_k^{(1)} t^k + \ldots \qquad \ldots(1)$

and $\quad G_2(t) = y_0^{(2)} + y_1^{(2)} t + y_2^{(2)} t^2 + \ldots + y_k^{(2)} t^k + \ldots \qquad \ldots(2)$

$$\Rightarrow \quad \lambda_1 G_1 + \lambda_2 G_2 = \{\lambda_1 y_0^{(1)} + \lambda_2 y_0^{(2)}\} + \{\lambda_1 y_1^{(1)} + \lambda_2 y_1^{(2)}\}t + \{\lambda_1 y_2^{(1)} + \lambda_2 y_2^{(2)}\}t^2 + \ldots + \{\lambda_1 y_k^{(1)} + \lambda_2 y_k^{(2)}\}t^k + \ldots$$

$\Rightarrow$ that $\lambda_1 G_1 + \lambda_2 G_2$ is the generating function for the sequence with general term $\lambda_1 y_k^{(1)} + \lambda_2 y_k^{(2)}$.

***Theorem* 5:** *If we know the generating function for the sequence* $\{y_k\}$, *then we can easily find the generating function of the sequences* $\{y_{k+1}\}, \{y_{k+2}\}$.

***Proof*:** Let $G(t)$ be the generating function for the sequence whose general term is y_k, we have $G(t) = y_0 + y_1 t + y_2 t^2 + \ldots + y_k t^k + \ldots$

$$\Rightarrow \quad \frac{G(t) - y_0}{t} = y_1 + y_2 t + \ldots + y_k t^{k-1} + y_{k+1} t^k + \ldots$$

This shows that $\left\{\frac{G(t) - y_0}{t}\right\}$ is the generating for the sequence $\{y_{k+1}\}$

Similarly, $\frac{G(t) - y_0 - y_1 t}{t^2} = y_2 + y_3 t + y_4 t^2 + \ldots$ is the generating function for $\{y_{k+2}\}$.

Example 55: $y_{k+2} - 2y_{k+1} + y_k = 2^k$ *with* $y_0 = 2$ *and* $y_1 = 1$ *prescribed.*

Solution: From the results of the table on page 354, we get

$$\frac{G(t) - 2 - t}{t^2} - 2\frac{G(t) - 2}{t} + G(t) = \frac{1}{1 - 2t}$$

$$\Rightarrow \quad (1-t)^2 G(t) = 2 - 3t + \frac{t^2}{1-2t}$$

$$\Rightarrow \quad G(t) = \frac{2}{(1-t)^2} - \frac{3t}{(1-t)^2} + \frac{t^3}{(1-t)^2(1-2t)}$$

Let
$$\frac{t^2}{(1-t)^2(1-2t)} \equiv \frac{M}{1-t} + \frac{N}{(1-t)^2} + \frac{P}{(1-2t)}$$

$$= \frac{M(1-t)(1-2t) + N(1-2t) + P(1-t)^2}{(1-t)^2(1-2t)}$$

$$= \frac{(M+N+P) + (-3M-2N-2P)t + (2M+P)t^2}{(1-t)^2(1-2t)}$$

$$\therefore \quad M + N + P = 0, \; -3M - 2N - 2P = 0, \; 2M + P = 1$$

Solving, $M = 0, N = -1$ and $P = 1$

$$\Rightarrow \quad G(t) = \frac{1}{(1-t)^2} - \frac{3t}{(1-t)^2} + \frac{1}{(1-2t)}.$$

From the table of generating functions, we again obtain

$$y_k = (k+1) - 3k + 2^k = 1 - 2k + 2^k.$$

Example 56: *Find the generating functions of the sequence y_k, If $y_k = (k+1)(k+2)$.*

Solution: From the table, the generating function of $k(k+1)$ is $\frac{2t}{(1-t)^3}$

But $(k+1)(k+2) = k(k+1) + 2k + 2$

or generating function of $(k+1)(k+2)$ = generating function of a sequence of general term $= k(k+1) + 2k + 2$.

Hence form the table, the generating function is given by

$$G(t) = \frac{2t}{(1-t)^3} + \frac{2t}{(1-t)^2} + \frac{2}{(1-t)} = \frac{2}{(1-t)^3}.$$

Example 57: *Find the generating function of the sequence y_k if $y_k = k(k-1)/2$.*

[Agra 2007]

Solution: Now $\frac{k(k-1)}{2} = \frac{k}{2}[(k+1)-2] = \frac{k(k+1)}{2} - k$

$\Rightarrow$ the ***Required Generating Function*** is equal to the difference of the generating functions of two sequences whose general terms are $\frac{k(k+1)}{2}$ and k. The required generating function form the table is $G(t) = \frac{2t}{2(1-t)^3} - \frac{t}{(1-t)^2} = \frac{t^2}{(1-t)^3}$.

Example 58: **(a)** *Find the sequence $\{y_k\}$ having the generating function $G(t)$ given by*

$$G(t) = 3/(1-t) + 1/(1-2t).$$

(b) *Find the generating function of the sequence $\{y_k\}$ if*

$$y_0 = y_1 = 0, y_k = 1 \text{ if } k > 1.$$

Solution: (a) From the table, we have

Generating function	Sequence
$[1/(1-t)]$	$\{y_k\} = 1$
$[3/(1-t)]$	$\{y_k\} = 3$
$[1/(1-At)]$	$\{y_k\} = A^k$

Hence corresponding to the generating function $[3/(1-t)] + [1/(1-2t)]$; the sequence is $[3 + 2^k]$.

(b) Let the generating function be $G(t) = y_0 + y_1 t + y_2 t^2 + \ldots + y_k t^k + \ldots$

We have $\quad y_0 = y_1 = 0$ and $y_k = 1$, if $k > 1$

$$\therefore \quad G(t) = 0 + 0.t + 1.t^2 + 1.t^3 + \ldots + 1.t^k + \ldots$$
$$= t^2 + t^3 + t^4 + \ldots + t^k + \ldots = t^2\{1 + t + t^2 + \ldots\}$$
$$= t^2(1-t)^{-1} = t^2/(1-t).$$

Example 59: *If $\{y_k\}$ has a generating function $G(t)$, show that the generating function of $\{\Delta y_k\}$ where $\Delta y_k = y_{k+1} - y_k$ is given by $(1/t)[(1-t)\,G(t) - y_0]$.*

Solution: The generating function of the sequence whose general term is y_k is $G(t)$ and that of the sequence whose general term is y_{k+1} is $\{G(t) - y_0\}/t$.

Again $\Delta y_k = y_{k+1} - y_k$, therefore the required generating function is

$$= \frac{G(t) - y_0}{t} - G(t) = \frac{G(t) - y_0 - tG(t)}{t} = \frac{G(t)(1-t) - y_0}{t} = \frac{1}{t}[(1-t)\,G(t) - y_0].$$

Example 60: *Apply the generating function technique to find the solution of the difference equation $y_{k+2} - 5y_{k+1} + 6y_k = 2$ with initial conditions $y_0 = 1, y_1 = 2$.* **[Agra 2000, 2009]**

Solution: Taking generating function of both the sides, we get

$$\frac{G(t) - y_0 - y_1 t}{t^2} - \frac{5\{G(t) - y_0\}}{t} + 6\,G(t) = \frac{2}{1-t}$$

$$\frac{G(t) - 1 - 2t}{t^2} - 5\,\frac{G(t) - 1}{t} + 6\,G(t) = \frac{2}{1-t}$$

$$\Rightarrow \quad G(t) = \frac{5t^2 - 4t + 1}{(1-t)(1-2t)(1-3t)}$$

Again, let $\dfrac{5t^2 - 4t + 1}{(1-t)(1-2t)(1-3t)} \equiv \dfrac{A}{1-t} + \dfrac{B}{1-2t} + \dfrac{C}{1-3t}$

$$\Rightarrow \quad 5t^2 - 4t + 1 = A(1-2t)(1-3t) + B(1-t)(1-3t) + C(1-t)(1-2t) \qquad \ldots(1)$$

To find A put $t = 1$ both sides of (1), we have $2 = A(1-2)(1-3)$ or $1 = A$.

Similarly to find B put $t = \dfrac{1}{2}$ on both sides of (1), we have

$$\frac{5}{4} - \frac{4}{2} + 1 = B(1 - \frac{1}{2})(1 - \frac{2}{3}) \quad i.e.\, B = -1$$

To find C put $t = \dfrac{1}{3}$ on the both sides of (1), we have

$$\frac{5}{9} - \frac{4}{3} + 1 = C(1 - \frac{1}{3})(1 - \frac{2}{3}) \quad i.e. \quad C = 1$$

$$\Rightarrow \quad G(t) = \frac{1}{1-t} + \frac{-1}{1-2t} + \frac{1}{1-3t}$$

Applying inverse transformation $y_k = 1 - 2^k + 3^k$.

Example 61: *Solve the difference equation* $y_{k+2} - 3y_{k+1} + 2y_k = 0$; *if* $y_0 = 2$, $y_1 = 3$ *by the method of generating functions.* **[Agra 2007]**

Solution: Let $G(t) = \sum_0^{\infty} y_k t^k$

Now multiplying the given difference equation by t^k and summing from $k = 0$ to ∞, we have

$$\sum_0^{\infty} y_{k+2}\, t^k - 3\sum_0^{\infty} y_{k+1}\, t^k + 2\sum_0^{\infty} y_k\, t^k = 0$$

or $(y_2 + y_3 t + y_4 t^2 + \dots) - 3\,(y_1 + y_2 t + y_3 t^2 + \dots) + 2\,(y_0 + y_1 t + y_2 t^2 + \dots) = 0$

or $$\frac{G(t) - y_0 - y_1 t}{t^2} - 3\left(\frac{G(t) - y_0}{t}\right) + 2\,G(t) = 0 \qquad \dots(1)$$

$[\because \;\; G(t) = y_0 + y_1 t + y_2 t^2 + y_3 t^3 + \dots]$

Putting $y_0 = 2$ and $y_1 = 3$ in (1) and then solving for $G(t)$, we obtain

$$G(t) = \frac{2 - 3t}{1 - 3t + 2t^2} = \frac{2 - 3t}{(1-t)(1-2t)}$$

$$\Rightarrow \qquad G(t) = \frac{1}{1-t} + \frac{1}{1-2t} = \sum_{k=0}^{\infty} t^k + \sum_{k=0}^{\infty} (2t)^k = \sum_{k=0}^{\infty} (1 + 2^k)\, t^k = \sum_{k=0}^{\infty} y_k\, t^k$$

$$\Rightarrow \qquad y_k = 1 + 2^k \qquad \dots(2)$$

which is the required solution.

9.7 Non-homogeneous Linear Difference Equations with Variable Coefficients

Example 62: *Solve the first order linear difference equation with variable coefficients given by*

$$y_{k+1} - A_k y_k = R_k.$$

Solution: **Method (1),** Using variation of parameters.

The complementary equation corresponding to the given equation is given by

$$y_{k+1} - A_k y_k = 0 \qquad \dots(1)$$

$$\Rightarrow \qquad y_k = A_{k-1}\, y_{k-1},\; y_{k-1} = A_{k-2},\; y_{k-2}, \dots, y_2 = A_1\, y_1$$

$$\therefore \qquad y_k = A_{k-1}\, A_{k-2} \dots A_1 y_1 \Rightarrow y_k = c_1 A_1 A_2 \dots A_{k-1}, \qquad \dots(2)$$

where $c_1 = y_1$ is an arbitrary constant, (2) is a solution of (1)

Now replacing c_1 by $K(k)$, we have $y_k = K(k)\, A_1\, A_2\, A_3 \dots A_{k-1}$ ...(3)

Substitution of (3) in the given equation yields,

$$K(k+1)\, A_1\, A_2 \dots A_k - K(k)\, A_1\, A_2\, A_3 \dots A_{k-1}\, A_k = R_k$$

$$\Rightarrow \quad K(k+1) - K(k) = \Delta K(k) = \frac{R_k}{A_1 A_2 \dots A_k} \Rightarrow K(k) = \Delta^{-1}\left(\frac{R_k}{A_1 A_2 \dots A_k}\right) + C$$

$$\therefore \quad y_k = A_1 A_2 \ldots A_{k-1} \Delta^{-1} \left(\frac{R_k}{A_1 A_2 \ldots A_k} \right) + C A_1 A_2 \ldots A_{k-1}$$

$$= A_1 A_2 \ldots A_{k-1} \sum_{p=1}^{k-1} \frac{R_P}{A_1 A_2 \ldots A_p} + c A_1 A_2 \ldots A_{k-1} \quad \ldots(4)$$

where c is any arbitary constant.

Method (2), Multiplication by a suitable summation factor.

Multiplying the given equation by $[1/A_1 A_2 \ldots A_k]$, we have

$$\frac{y_{k+1}}{A_1 A_2 \ldots A_k} - \frac{y_k}{A_1 A_2 \ldots A_{k-1}} = \frac{R_k}{A_1 A_2 \ldots A_k}$$

$$\Rightarrow \quad \Delta \left(\frac{y_k}{A_1 A_2 \ldots A_{k-1}} \right) = \frac{R_k}{A_1 A_2 \ldots A_k}$$

$$\Rightarrow \quad y_k = A_1 A_2 \ldots A_{k-1} \left\{ \Delta^{-1} \left(\frac{R_k}{A_1 A_2 \ldots A_k} \right) + C \right\}$$

$$\Rightarrow \quad y_k = A_1 A_2 \ldots A_{k-1} \sum_{p=1}^{k-1} \frac{R_k}{A_1 A_2 \ldots A_P}$$

Note: The factor $[1/A_1 A_2 \ldots A_k]$, used to multiply the given equation is called the *Summation factor.*

Example 63: *Solve the equation* $y_{k+1} = Ay_k + C$.

Solution: We have $y_{k+1} = Ay_k + C; k = 0, 1, 2 \ldots$ ...(1)

where A and C are constant and $A \neq 0$.

Let us Now Find the Solution of (1) with y_0 Prescribed

$$k = 0 \Rightarrow y_1 = Ay_0 = C$$

$$k = 1 \Rightarrow y_2 = Ay_1 + C = A(Ay_0 + C) + C = A^2 y_0 + C(1 + A)$$

$$\therefore \quad y_3 = Ay_2 + C = A[A^2 y_0 + C(1 + A)] + C = A^3 y_0 + C(1 + A + A^2)$$

In general, we have, $y_k = A^k y_0 + C(1 + A + A^2 + \ldots + A^{k-1})$

This series on the right hand side is geometric series with first term 1 and common ratio A.

$$\therefore 1 + A + A^2 + \ldots + A^{k-1} = \frac{1 - A^k}{1 - A}, \text{if } A \neq 1$$

$$= k; \text{ if } A = 1$$

$$\therefore \quad y_k = \begin{cases} A^k y_0 + \dfrac{C(1 - A^k)}{1 - A}, & \text{if } A \neq 1 \\ y_0 + CK. & \text{if } A = 1 \end{cases} \quad \ldots(2)$$

***Theorem* 6**: *The function y given by* (2) *in Ex.* 63 *is a solution and the only solution of the difference equation* (1) *with* y_0 *prescribed.*

Proof: We have $y_{k+1} = A^{k+1} y_0 + C\dfrac{1-A^{k+1}}{1-A} (A \neq 1)$

Substituting in (1), we have $A^{k+1} + C\dfrac{1-A^{k+1}}{1-A} = A\left\{A^k y_0 + C\dfrac{1-A^k}{1-A} + C\right\}$

But R.H.S. is $= A^{k+1} y_0 + C\left\{1 + \dfrac{A - A^{k+1}}{1-A}\right\}$

$$= A^{k+1} y_0 + C\frac{1-A^{k+1}}{1-A},$$

which is equal to the left hand side expression.

When, $A = 1$ we have $y_k = y_0 + Ck$

$\therefore$ $y_{k+1} = y_0 + C(1+k)$

and R. H. S. $= Ay_k + C = A(y_0 + Ck) + C$

$$= y_0 + C(1+k) \qquad (\because \quad A = 1)$$

i.e. it reduces to an identity

Thus $y_0 + Ck, (A = 1)$ is also a unique solution

Example 64: *Find the solution of* $y_{k+1} = 2y_k - 1, k = 0,1,2,...$ *with initial condition* $y_0 = 5$.

Solution: Here $A = 2$ and $C = -1$. Therefore the solution is given by

$$y_k = A^k y_0 + C\frac{1-A^k}{1-A} = 2^k.5 - 1.\frac{1-2^k}{1-2}$$

$$= 5.2^k + 1 - 2^k = 4.2^k + 1, k = 0, 1, 2, ...$$

Starting with $y_0 = 5$, it gives the increasing sequence of the values [consecutive values of y from $y_0 = 5$] as 5,9,17, 33, 65, 129.

Example 65: *Solve* $y_{k+1} = -y_k + 2, k = 0,1,2,....$

Solution: Here $A = -1$ and $C = 2$, therefore the solution is given by

$$y_k = A^k y_0 + C\frac{1-A^k}{1-A} = -(-1)^k y_0 + 2.\frac{1-(-1)^k}{1+1}$$

$$= (-1)^k . y_0 + 1 - (-1)^k, k = 0, 1, 2, ...$$

Putting $k = 1, 2, ...;$ we have

$\therefore$ $y_1 = -y_0 + 1 + 1 = -y_0 + 2, \; y_2 = y_0 + 1 - 1 = y_0$

$$y_3 = -y_0 = 2, ...$$

This is the required sequence of values.

Example 66: *Solve* $2\,y_{k-1} - y_k = 4, k = 0, 1, 2, \ldots$ *with the initial condition* $y_0 = 3$.

Solution: Comparing the given equation with $y_{k+1} = Ay_k + C, A = \frac{1}{2}$, C = 2. Hence the solution is given by

$$y_k = A^k y_0 + C\,\frac{1-A^k}{1-A} = \left(\frac{1}{2}\right)^k .3 + 2 . \frac{1-\left(\frac{1}{2}\right)^k}{1-\frac{1}{2}}$$

$$= 3.\left(\frac{1}{2}\right)^k + 4\{1-\left(\frac{1}{2}\right)^k\} = 4 - \left(\frac{1}{2}\right)^k, k = 0, 1, 2, \ldots$$

We have the following sequence of values 3, 7/2, 15/4, 31/8,... .

Example 67: *Solve* $(E-a)\,y_k = 0,\ k = 0, 1, 2, \ldots$ *a is a constant.*

Solution: The given difference equation is $(E-a)\ y_k = 0$

or $\qquad y_{k+1} = ay_k$

Here $\qquad A = a,\ \ C = 0$

Hence solution of difference equation is given by $y_k = A^k y_0 + C\,\frac{1-A^k}{1-A} = a^k y_0$

we get following sequence of values $y_0, ay_0, a^2 y_0, \ldots$.

Example 68: *Solve* $y_{k+2} - (k+2)\,y_{k+1} + ky_k = k;\ y_1 = 0, y_2 = 1.$

Solution: First of all, we shall reduce the above equation in factored form.In operator, the given equation can be written as $[E^2 - (k+2)E + k]\,y_k = k$ ...(1)

Let us suppose $\{E^2 - (k+2)E + k\}\,y_k = \{(E-A_k)(E-B_k)\}\,y_k$ ...(2)

R.H.S. of (2) is $(E-A_k)(Ey_k - B_k y_k) = (E-A_k)(y_{k+1} - B_k y_k)$

$$= y_{k+2} - E(B_k y_k) - A_k y_{k+1} + A_k B_k y_k$$

$$= y_{k+2} - B_{k+1} y_{k+1} - A_k y_{k+1} + A_k B_k y_k$$

$$= y_{k+2} - (A_k + B_{k+1})\,y_{k+1} + A_k B_k y_k$$

$$= \{E^2 - (A_k + B_{k+1})E + A_k B_k\}\,y_k,$$

$$\therefore \quad \{E^2 - (k+2)E + k\}y_k = \{E^2 - (A_k + B_{k+1})E + A_k B_k\}y_k$$

$$\Rightarrow \quad A_k + B_{k+1} = k+2 \text{ and } A_k B_k = k \qquad ...(3)$$

Let us take $A_k = k, B_k = 1$ {or $A_k = 1, B_k = k$} (trial solutions)

Both the sets satisfy the second equation of (3). But the second set $A_k = 1$, $B_k = k$ satisfies the first equation of (3) also; this is the desired solution as other set deos not satisfy the first equation of (3).

Hence we are led to write $E^2 - (k+2)E + k \equiv (E-1)(E-k)$

$$\Rightarrow \quad (E-1)(E-k)y_k = k \qquad ...(4)$$

Let $\quad z_k = (E-k)y_k$ Then (4) becomes $(E-1)z_k = k$ or $\Delta z_k = k$

$$\Rightarrow \quad z_k = \Delta^{-1}k = \Delta^{-1}k^{(1)} = \frac{k^{(2)}}{2} + c_1 \qquad ...(5)$$

$$\Rightarrow \quad (E-k)y_k = \frac{k^{(2)}}{2} + c_1 = \frac{1}{2}k(k-1) + c_1 \qquad ...(6)$$

Now proceeding as in Ex. 62, we get

$$y_k = \{1,2,\ldots(k-1)\}\Delta^{-1}\left(\frac{\frac{1}{2}k(k-1)+c_1}{1.2\ldots k}\right) = (k-1)!\Delta^{-1}\left(\frac{\frac{1}{2}k(k-1)+c_1}{k!}\right)$$

or $$y_k = (k-1)\sum_{p=1}^{k-1}\left(\frac{\frac{1}{2}p(p-1)+c_1}{p!}\right) + c_2(k-1)!$$

$$= \frac{(k-1)!}{2}\sum_{p=1}^{k-1}\frac{p(p-1)}{p!} c_1(k-1)!\sum_{p=1}^{k-1}\frac{1}{p!} + c_2(k-1)! \qquad ...(7)$$

Substituting (1) in the given equation, we obtain

$$K(k+1)(k+1)! - (k+1)K(k)k! = 2^k(k-1)$$

$$\Rightarrow \quad \{K(k+1) - K(k)\}(k+1)! = 2^k(k-1)$$

$$\Delta\{K(k)\} = \frac{2^k(k-1)}{(k+1)!},\ K(k) = \Delta^{-1}\left[\frac{2^k(k+1)-2}{(k+1)!}\right]$$

$$\Rightarrow \quad K(k) = \Delta^{-1}\left[\frac{2^k}{k!} - \frac{2^{k+1}}{(k+1)!}\right] = -\Delta^{-1}\Delta\left\{\frac{2^k}{k!}\right\} = -\frac{2^k}{k!} + c(k)$$

Hence the complete solution is given by $y_k = k!\left\{\frac{-2^k}{k!} + c(k)\right\} = -2^k + c(k).k!$

Example 69: *Solve* $y_{k+1} - e^{2k-1} y_k = 5k e^{k^2}$.

Solution: The complementary equation corresponding to the given equation is given by

$y_{k+1} - e^{2k-1} y_k = 0, \Rightarrow \log y_{k+1} - \log y_k = (2k-1)$

$$\Rightarrow \quad \Delta \log y_k = (2k-1),$$

$$\Rightarrow \quad y_k = c_1 \exp.[\Delta^{-1}(2k-1)] = c_1 \exp.[(k-1)^2]$$

Now replacing c_1 by $K(k)$, we obtain the solution as $y_k = K(k).\exp.[(k-1)^2]$ ...(1)

Substituting (1) in the given equation, we obtain

$$e^{k^2} K(k+1) - e^{2k-1} K(k) e^{(k-1)^2} = 5k e^{k^2}$$

$$\Rightarrow \quad K(k+1) - e^{2k-1+1-2k} K(k) = 5(k), \Rightarrow \Delta K(k) = 5k$$

$$\Rightarrow \quad K(k) = 5\Delta^{-1}(k) = \frac{5}{2} k(k-1) + c_k \; [\because \; \Delta^{-1} K^{(r)} = \{k^{(r+1)}/(r+1)\}].$$

Thus the complete solution is given by $y_k = \left\{\frac{5}{2} k(k-1) + c_k\right\}. \exp.[(k-1)^2]$

Example 70: *Solve* $y_{k+1} - e^{2k} y_k = 3k^2 e^{k^2 + k + (1/6)}$. **[Agra 2002, 2007]**

Solution: The complementary equation is given by

$$y_{k+1} - e^{2k} y_k = 0, \Rightarrow \log y_{k+1} - \log y_k = 2k$$

$$\Rightarrow \quad \Delta \log y_k = 2k \Rightarrow \log y_k = \Delta^{-1}(2k)$$

$$\Rightarrow \quad \log y_k = 2\Delta^{-1}(k) = k^2 - k + c_1, \Rightarrow y_k = c_2 e^{k^2 - k}$$

Now, let the solution of the given equation be $y_k = K(k).\exp.[k^2 - k]$

Substituting this in the given equation, we obtain

$$K(k+1) - K(k) = e^{(1/6)}.3k^2 \Rightarrow \Delta\{K(k)\} = e^{(1/6)}.3k$$

$$\Rightarrow \quad K(k) = 3e^{(1/6)} \Delta^{-1}(k^2) = 3e^{(1/6)} \Delta^{-1}[k^{(2)} + k^{(1)}]$$

$$= 3e^{(1/6)}\left[c_3 + \frac{k^{(3)}}{3} + \frac{k(k-1)}{2}\right] \Rightarrow K(k) = 3e^{(1/6)}\left[c_3 + \frac{k^{(3)}}{3} + \frac{k^{(2)}}{2}\right]$$

Hence the solution of the given equation is given by

$$y_k = 3e^{(1/6)}\left\{c_3 + \frac{k^{(3)}}{3} + \frac{k^{(2)}}{2}\right\}.e^{k^2 - k}$$

$$= 3c_3 e^{(1/6)} e^{k^3 - k} + 3e^{(1/6)}.e^{k^2 - k}\left\{\frac{k^{(3)}}{3} + \frac{k^{(2)}}{2}\right\}$$

$$= ce^{k^2 - k + (1/6)} + e^{k^2 - k + (1/6)} + \{k^{(3)} + \frac{3}{2} k^{(2)}\}.$$

Example 71: *Solve* $(k+1)\, y_{k+2} - (3\,k+2)\, y_{k+1} + (2\,k-1)\, y_k = 0.$

Solution: We have $(k+1)\,\Delta^2\, y_k - k\,\Delta\, y_k - 2\, y_k = 0.$

Let us assume the solution as $y_k = \sum_{p=-\infty}^{\infty} c_p k^{(p)}$ where $c_p = 0$ for $p = -1, \; -2\,, \; -3\,, \ldots$ ...(1)

$$\therefore \qquad \Delta y_k = \sum_{P=-\infty}^{\infty} pc_p k^{(p-1)} \text{ and } \Delta^2\, y_k = \sum_{P=-\infty}^{\infty} p(p-1)\, c_p k^{(p-2)}$$

whence given equation gives

$$\Sigma\, p\,(p-1)\, c_p\, k^{(p-2)} + \Sigma\, p(p-1)\, c_p\, k^{\,(P-2)} - \Sigma\, pc_p\,.k.k^{(p-1)} - \Sigma\, 2c_p\, k^{(p)} = 0\,..$$

[using $k\,.\,k^{(m)} = k^{(m+1)} + mk^{(m)}$.]

Equation (1) can be written as

$$\Sigma\, p\,(p-1)\, c_p [k^{(p-1)} + (p-2)\, k^{(p-2)} + \Sigma\, p\,(p-1)\, c_p\, k^{(p-2)}]$$
$$- \Sigma\, pc_p\, [k^{(p)} + (p-1)k^{(p-1)}] - \Sigma\, 2\, c_p\, k^{(p)} = 0 \ldots \qquad ...(2)$$

Now collecting coefficients of $k^{(p)}$, we readily obtain

$$\Sigma\, \{(p+2)\,(p+1)^2 c_{p+2} - (p+2)c_p\}\, k^{(p)} = 0 \qquad ...(3)$$

But equation (3) is an identity, so each coefficient must be zero

i.e. $\qquad (p+2)(p+1)^2 c_{p+2} - (p+2)\, c_p = 0$ ...(4)

$\Rightarrow \qquad (p+1)^2 c_{p+2} - c_p = 0$ ...(5)

Putting $p = 0, 1, 2\,, \ldots$ in (5) , we find that

$$1^2 c_2 - c_0 = 0, 2^2 c_3 - c_1 = 0,\; 3^2 c_4 - c_2 = 0,\; 4^2 c_5 - c_3 = 0 \ldots$$

$$\Rightarrow \qquad c_2 = \frac{c_0}{1^2}, c_3 = \frac{c_1}{2^2}, c_4 = \frac{c_2}{3^2} = \frac{c_0}{1^2 .2^2}, c_5 = \frac{c_3}{4^2} = \frac{c_1}{2^2 .4^2}, \ldots$$

$\therefore$ Required solution becomes

$$y_k = c_0 \left[1 + \frac{k^{(2)}}{1^2} + \frac{k^{(4)}}{1^2\, 3^2} + \frac{k^{(6)}}{1^2\, 3^2\, 5^2} + \ldots\right] + c_1 \left[k^{(1)} + \frac{k^{(3)}}{2^2 .4^2} + \frac{k^{(5)}}{2^2 .4^2 .6^2} + \ldots\right].$$

9.8 Solution of Some Special Types of Difference Equations

(A) Form $p\,(k)\, u(k)\, u\,(k+1) + q\,(k)\, u\,(k+1) + r\,(k)\, u\,(k) = 0$ ...(1)

where $p\,(k), q\,(k), r\,(k)$ etc. are function of k.

In such equations, we divided by $u\,(k)\; u(k+1)$ so as to obtain

$$p\,(k) + \frac{q\,(k)}{u\,(k)} + r\,\frac{r\,(k)}{u\,(k+1)} = 0 \qquad ...(2)$$

Putting $V(k) = \dfrac{1}{u(k)}$, we get $p(k) + q(k).V(k) + r(k).V(k+1) = 0$,

which is linear and non-homogeneous, so it can be solved by any of the methods discussed earlier.

(B) Form $f(k+1)f(k) - B(k)\{f(k+1) - f(k)\} + 1 = 0$ ...(1)

This gives $$\frac{1}{B(k)} = \frac{f(k+1) - f(k)}{1 + f(k)\,f(k+1)}$$

Putting $f(k) = \tan[\phi(k)]$, we get

$$\frac{1}{B(k)} = \frac{\tan\phi(k+1) - \tan\phi(k)}{1 + \tan\phi(k)\tan\phi(k+1)} = \tan[\phi(k+1) - \phi(k)]$$

$$= \tan[\Delta\,\phi(k)]$$

$$\Rightarrow \quad \tan^{-1}\{B(k)\}^{-1} = \Delta\phi(k) \Rightarrow \phi(k) = \Delta^{-1}\left\{\tan^{-1}\frac{1}{B(k)}\right\} + A$$

$$\Rightarrow \quad f(k) = \tan\left[\Delta^{-1}\left\{\tan^{-1}\frac{1}{B(k)}\right\} + A\right] \qquad ...(2)$$

(C) *Any homogeneous equation of the form* $F\left\{\dfrac{f(k+1)}{f(k)}, k\right\} = 0$

can be converted into a linear equation by the substitution

$$\frac{f(k+1)}{f(k)} = V(k).$$

Example 72: *Solve* $y_{k+1} - y_k + k\,y_{k+1}\,y_k = 0, y_1 = 2$.

Solution: Dividing by $y_k\,y_{k+1}$, the equation can be written as $\dfrac{1}{y_{k+1}} - \dfrac{1}{y_k} = k$

Putting $1/y_k = V_k$, we get $V_{k+1} - V_k = k$, where $V_1 = \dfrac{1}{2}$ as $y_1 = 2$

$$\Rightarrow \quad V_k = \Delta^{-1} k^{(1)} = \frac{k^{(2)}}{2} + c_1 = \frac{k(k-1)}{2} + c_1$$

But $V_1 = \dfrac{1}{2} \Rightarrow c_1 = \dfrac{1}{2}$ Thus $V_k = \dfrac{k(k-1)}{2} + \dfrac{1}{2} = \dfrac{k^2 - k + 1}{2}$

$$\Rightarrow \quad y_k = (1/V_k) = (2/k^2 - k + 1)$$

Example 73: *Solve* $y_{k+1}\,y_k + 5\,y_{k+1} + y_k + 9 = 0$. **[Agra 2003]**

Solution: The given equation can be put as

$$y_{k+1}(y_k + 5) + y_k + 9 = 0 \qquad ...(1)$$

Putting $\qquad y_k + 5 = \dfrac{V_{k+1}}{V_k}$ in (1), we get

$$\left(\frac{V_{k+2}}{V_{k+1}} - 5\right)\frac{V_{k+1}}{V_k} + \left(\frac{V_{k+1}}{V_k} + 4\right) = 0 \Rightarrow V_{k+2} - 4V_{k+1} + 4V_k = 0 \qquad ...(2)$$

[Linear Homogeneous Equation]

Solving (2), we get $V_k = (c_1 + c_2 k) 2^k$,

$$\Rightarrow \qquad y_k = \frac{c_1 + c_2\,(k+1) 2^{k+1}}{c_1 + c_2 (k) 2^k} - 5. \qquad ...(3)$$

Example 74: *Solve* $y_{k+2} - 3y_{k+1} + 2y_k = 2^k$.

Solution: The complementary equation is given by

$$y_{k+2} - 3y_{k+1} + 2y_k = 0 \Rightarrow E^2 y_k - 3Ey_k + 2y_k = 0$$

$$\Rightarrow \quad (E^2 - 3E + 2) y_k = 0 \Rightarrow (E-2)(E-1) y_k = 0$$

$$\therefore \quad y_k = c_1 + c_2 . 2^k.$$

Now, Particular solution $= \dfrac{1}{E^2 - 3E + 2} 2^k = \dfrac{1}{\phi(E)} 2^k$,

where $\phi(E) = E^2 - 3E + 2$

$$= 2^k \frac{1}{\phi(2E)}.1 = 2^k \frac{1}{4E^2 - 6E - 2}.1$$

$$= 2^k \frac{1}{4(1+\Delta)^2 + 2 - 6(1+\Delta)}.1$$

$$= 2^k \frac{1}{2\Delta(1+2\Delta)}.1$$

$$= 2^k \left[\frac{1}{2\Delta}(1 - 2\Delta)\right] = 2^k \left[\frac{1}{2\Delta} - 1\right].1 = 2^k \left[\frac{k}{2} - 1\right]$$

Hence the complete solution is given by

$$y_k = c_1 + c_2 . 2^k + 2^k \left[\frac{k}{2} - 1\right] = c_1 + c_3 . 2^k + 2^{k-1} k, \text{ where } c_3 = c_2 - 1.$$

Example 75: *Solve* $y_{k+2}\, y_k^2 = y_{k+1}^3$, *if* $y_1 = 1, y_2 = 2$

Solution: Taking logarithms of the given difference equation, we get

$$\log y_{k+2} - 3 \log y_{k+1} + 2 \log y_k = 0 \qquad ...(1)$$

Putting $V_k = \log y_k$ in (1), we get

$$V_{k+2} - 3V_{k+1} + 2V_k = 0, \text{ where } V_1 = 0, V_2 = \log 2. \qquad ...(2)$$

Solving, we get $V_k = c_1 + c_2 . 2^k$

Using these conditions, we obtain $c_1 = -\log 2, c_2 = \frac{1}{2}\log 2$

$$V_k = (\log 2)(2^{k-1} - 1)$$

$$\log y_k = (\log 2)(2^{k-1} - 1)$$

$$y_k = \exp\{(\log 2)(2^{k-1} - 1)\}$$

$$y_k = 2^{[2^{k-1} - 1]}.$$

Example 76: *Solve* $y_{k+1}^2 - 3y_{k+1}y_k + 2y_k^2 = 0.$

Solution: Putting $\frac{y_{k+1}}{y_k} = z_k$ in the given difference equation, we get

$$z_k^2 - \frac{3y_{k+1}}{y_k} + 2 = 0 \Rightarrow z_k^2 - 3z_k + 2 = 0, \Rightarrow z_k = 2 \text{ or } 1.$$

$$y_{k+1} = 2y_k \text{ or } y_k,$$

***Case* 1:** $y_{k+1} - 2y_k = 0 \Rightarrow y_k = a.2^k$

***Case* 2:** $y_{k+1} - y_k = 0 \Rightarrow y_k = b.$

Example 77: *Solve the system* $y_{k+1} + z_k - 3y_k = k,$

$$3y_k + z_{k+1} - 5z_k = 4^k$$

Subject to the conditions $y_1 = 2, z_1 = 0.$

Solution: We have $\left\{\begin{matrix}(E-3)y_k + z_k = k \\ 3y_k + (E-5)z_k = 4^k\end{matrix}\right\}$ ...(1)

Operating (1) with $E-5$ and leaving the second equation as such, we obtain

$$\left\{\begin{matrix}(E-5)(E-3)y_k + (E-5)z_k = 1 - 4k \\ 3y_k + (E-5)z_k = 4^k\end{matrix}\right\} \quad ...(2)$$

Subtracting the second equation form the first equation in (2) yields

$$(E^2 - 8E + 12)y_k = 1 - 4k - 4^k$$

$$\therefore \quad y_k = c_1 2^k + c_2 6^k + \frac{4^k}{4} - \frac{4}{5}k - \frac{19}{25}$$

With this substitution in first equation (1), we get

$$z_k = c_1 2^k - 3c_2 6^k - \frac{1}{4}4^k - \frac{3}{5}k - \frac{34}{25}$$

Now $\quad y_1 = 2, z_1 = 0$

$$\Rightarrow \quad 2c_1 + 6c_2 = \frac{64}{25} \text{ and } 2c_1 - 18c_2 = \frac{74}{25}$$

$$\Rightarrow \quad c_1 = \left(\frac{133}{100}\right), c_2 = -\frac{1}{60}$$

$$\therefore \quad y_k = \frac{133}{100}.2^k - \frac{1}{66}.6^k + 4^{k-1} - \frac{4}{5}k - \frac{19}{25}$$

and
$$z_k = \frac{133}{100}.2^k + \frac{1}{20}.6^k - 4^{k-1} - \frac{3}{5}k - \frac{35}{25}.$$

Example 78: *Solve the system*

$$\begin{Bmatrix} y_{k+1} - y_k + 2z_{k+1} = 0 \\ z_{k+1} - z_k - 2y_k = 2^k \end{Bmatrix}.$$

Solution: The given system can be written as

$$(E-1)y_k + 2Ez_k = 0 \quad \text{...(1)}$$

$$-2y_k + (E-1)z_k = 2^k \quad \text{...(2)}$$

Operating (1) by $(E-1)$ and (3) by $2E$, we get

$$(E-1)^2 y_k + 2E(E-1)z_k = 0, \quad \text{...(3)}$$

$$-4Ey_k + 2E(E-1)z_k = -2E(2^k) \quad \text{...(4)}$$

Subtracting (4) from (3), we get

$$(E+1)^2 y_k = 2E(2^k) = -2^{k+2} \quad \text{...(5)}$$

Complementary solution of (5) is $\{c_1 + c_2(k)\}(-1)^k$

Also particular solution $= \dfrac{-1}{(E+1)^2} 2^{k+2} = \dfrac{2^{k+2}}{9}$

$$\Rightarrow \text{complete solution} = \{c_1 + c_2(k)\}(-1)^k - \frac{2^{k+2}}{9} = y_k \quad \text{...(6)}$$

Putting this value of y_k in (2), we get

$$-2\{c_1 + c_2(k)\}(-1)^k + \frac{2^{k+3}}{9} + (E-1)z_k = 2^k$$

$$\Rightarrow \quad (E-1)z_k = 2^k + 2\{c_1 + c_2(k)\}(-1)^k - \frac{2^{k+3}}{9} \quad \text{...(7)}$$

Solving (7), we get $z_k = \{c_1 + c_2(k - \frac{1}{2})\}(-1)^k + \dfrac{2^k}{9}$. ...(8)

Example 79: *Solve the differential-difference Equation*

$$y'_{k+1}(t) = y_k(t);\ y_0(t) = t,\ y_k(0) = k.$$

Solution: Putting $k = 0$, we obtain $y'_1(t) = y_0(t) = t \Rightarrow y_1(t) = \frac{t^2}{2} + c_1$

But $\quad y_1(0) = 1, \quad$ so have $c_1 = 1 \quad \Rightarrow \ y_1(t) = 1 + \frac{t^2}{2}$

Again putting $k = 1$, we find that $y'_2(t) = y_1(t) = 1 + \frac{t^2}{2}$ or $y_2(t) = t + \frac{t^3}{3!} + c_2$

But $\quad y_2(0) = 2 \ \Rightarrow c_2 = 2.$

$\therefore \quad y_2(t) = 2 + t + \frac{t^3}{3!}$

Continuing in this manner, we easily obtain

$$y_3(t) = 3 + 2t + \frac{t^2}{2!} + \frac{t^4}{4!},$$

$$y_4(t) = 4 + 3t + \frac{2t^2}{2!} + \frac{t^3}{3!} + \frac{t^5}{5!},$$

$$y_5(t) = 5 + 4t + \frac{3t^2}{2!} + \frac{2t^3}{3!} + \frac{t^4}{4!} + \frac{t^6}{6!},$$

and thus in general, we have

$$y_n(t) = \left[n + (n-1)t + \frac{(n-2)t^2}{2!} + \frac{(n-3)t^3}{3!} + \ldots + \frac{t^{n-1}}{(n-1)!} + \frac{t^{n+1}}{(n+1)}\right]$$

This is required solution.

Example 80: *Solve the difference equation.*

$$y'_{k+1}(t) = y_k(t),\ y_0(t) = t,\ y_k(0) = k$$

using the method of generating functions.

Solution: Let the generation function of $y_k(t)$ be given by $g(s,t) = \sum_{k=1}^{\infty} y_k(t)\, s^k.$

The given difference equation can be written as $y'_{k+1}(t) = y_k(t)$

$$\Rightarrow \quad \sum_{k=0}^{\infty} y'_{k+1}(t)\, s^k = \sum_{k=0}^{\infty} y_k(t)\, s^k \qquad \ldots(1)$$

$$\Rightarrow \quad \frac{1}{s}\sum_{k=0}^{\infty} y'_{k+1}(t)\, s^{k+1} = g(s,t)$$

$$\frac{1}{s}\frac{\partial}{\partial t}\left\{\sum_{k=0}^{\infty} y_{k+1}(t)\, s^{k+1}\right\} = g(s,t)$$

$$\Rightarrow \quad \frac{1}{s}\frac{\partial}{\partial t}\{g(s,t) - y_0(t)\} = g(s,t)$$

$$\Rightarrow \quad \frac{1}{s}\frac{\partial}{\partial t}\{g(s,t)-t\} = g(s,t)$$

$$\Rightarrow \quad \frac{1}{s}\frac{\partial}{\partial t}g(s,t,) - \frac{1}{s} - g(s,t) = 0$$

$$\Rightarrow \quad \frac{\partial g}{\partial t} - sg(s,t) = 1$$

$$\Rightarrow \quad ge^{-st} = \int e^{-st}\,dt + c = \frac{e^{-st}}{-s} + c \qquad (\because \text{ I.F. } = e^{-st}) \qquad \ldots(2)$$

Putting $t = 0$ in (2), we get $g(s,0) = -\frac{1}{s} + c$ ...(3)

But $$g(s,0) = \sum_{k=0}^{\infty} y_k(0)\, s^k = \sum_{k=0}^{\infty} k\, s^k \qquad \ldots(4)$$

Equation (3) and (4) $\Rightarrow$ $$c = \left[\sum_{k=0}^{\infty} k\, s^k + \frac{1}{s}\right]$$

Putting this value of c in (2), we get $ge^{-st} = -\frac{e^{-st}}{s} + \left\{\sum_{k=0}^{\infty} k\, s^k + \frac{1}{s}\right\}$,

$$\Rightarrow \quad g = \frac{1}{s}\left[(e^{st}-1) + e^{st}.\sum_{k=0}^{\infty} k\, s^{k+1}\right]$$

$$\Rightarrow \quad g(s,t) = \frac{1}{s}\left[e^{st}\left\{1 + \sum_{k=0}^{\infty} k\, s^{k+1}\right\} - 1\right]$$

$$= \frac{1}{s}\left[\left(\sum_{p=0}^{\infty}\frac{(st)^p}{p!}\right)\left\{1 + \sum_{p=0}^{\infty} k\, s^{k+1}\right\} - 1\right]$$

$$= \frac{1}{s}\left[\sum_{p=0}^{\infty}\frac{(st)^p}{p!} + \left(\sum_{p=0}^{\infty}\frac{(st)^p}{p!}\right)\left(\sum_{k=0}^{\infty} k\, s^{k+1}\right)\right]$$

$$= \frac{1}{s}\left[\sum_{p=1}^{\infty}\frac{(st)^p}{p!} + \sum_{p=0}^{\infty}\sum_{k=0}^{\infty}\left(\frac{s^{p+k+1}\, k\, t^p}{p!}\right)\right]$$

$$\leftarrow A_n - \rightarrow$$

Since the coefficient of s^n in the expansion is $y_n(t)$, so we have

$$y_n(t) = \frac{t^{n+1}}{(n+1)!} + \sum_{p=0}^{n}\frac{(n-p)\, t^p}{p!} \qquad \ldots(5)$$

Which is obtained by taking the term corresponding to $p = n+1$ in the first summation of A and $p+k+1 = n+1$ in the second summation of 5.

Example 81: *Solve the equation* $y_{k+2} - 4y_k = 9k^2$.

Solution: The complementary solution of the given equation is given by

$$y_k = c_1 2^k + c_2(-2)^k$$

Now for the particular solution of $9k^2$, we assume $y_k = Ak^2 + Bk + C$

$$\Rightarrow \quad [A(k+2)^2 + B(k+2) + C] - 4[Ak^2 + Bk + C] = 9k^2$$

$$\Rightarrow \quad (-3A-9)k^2 + k(4A - 3B) + (4A + 2B - 3C) = 0.$$

Equating coefficients of like powers of k, we obtain

$$-3A - 9 = 0,\ 4A - 3B = 0,\ 4A + 2B - 3C = 0$$

i.e. $$A = -3, B = -4,\ C = -\frac{20}{3}.$$

Hence the solution is given by $y_k = c_1 2^k + c_2(-2)^k - 3k^2 - 4k - \frac{20}{3}$.

Aliter: $$\text{P.I.} = \frac{1}{E^2 - 4} 9k^2 = \frac{1}{\Delta^2 + 2\Delta - 3} . 9k^2 \qquad (E \equiv 1 + \Delta)$$

$$= -3 . \frac{1}{1 + \left(\frac{2\Delta + \Delta^2}{3}\right)} k^2$$

$$= -3\left[k^{(2)} + \frac{2}{3} 2k^{(1)} + \frac{7}{9}.2 + k + \frac{2}{3}\right]$$

$$= -3\left[k^2 + \frac{4}{3}k + \frac{20}{9}\right] = -3k^2 - 4k - \frac{20}{3}$$

$\therefore$ General solution is given by $y_k = c_1 2^k + c_2(-2)^k - 3k^2 - 4k - \frac{20}{3}$.

Example 82: *Solve* $y(k+1) - ay(k) = \cos nk$. ...(1)

[Bhopal 2002]

Solution: Let $y_1(k)$ be the particular solution of (1), so that $y_1(k+1) - ay_1(k) = \cos nk$.

Now putting $y(k) = y_1(k) + V(k)$ in (1), we readily get

$$y(k+1) = y_1(k+1) + V(k+1) \Rightarrow V(k+1) = aV(k) \qquad ...(2)$$

Solving (2), we get $p(k) = ca^k$.

Further also equation (1) can be written as $Ey(k) - ay(k) = \cos nk$

$$\Rightarrow \quad y(k) = \frac{1}{E - a} \cos nk$$

$$= \text{R. P. of } \frac{1}{E-a} e^{ink}$$

$$= \text{R . P. of } e^{ink} \frac{1}{e^{in}-a} 1$$

$$\left[\because \frac{1}{f(E)} a^k = a^k . \frac{1}{f(a)} 1, f(a) \neq 0\right]$$

$$= R.P.of \ \frac{e^{ink}(e^{-in}-a)}{1-a(e^{in}+e^{-in})+a^2} = \frac{\cos(n-1)k - a\cos kn}{1-2\ a\ \cos\ n + a^2}$$

$\therefore$ Complete solution is given by $y_k = \dfrac{\cos(n-1)k - a\cos\ nk}{1-2a\cos n + a^2} + c(k)\, a^k.$

Example 83: *Solve the equation* $y_{k+4} - 5y_{k+3} + 9y_{k+2} + 7y_{k+1} + 2y_k = 0.$ **[Agra 2003]**

Solution: The given equation can be written as $(E^4 - 5E^3 + 9E^2 - 7E + 2)y_k = 0.$

Now, $$f(E) \equiv E^4 - 5E^3 - 9E^2 - 7E + 2$$
$$= (E-1)^3(E-2)$$

Auxiliary equation is given by $(m-1)^3(m-2) = 0,$

which gives $m = 1, 1, 1, 2.$

Hence the solution is given by $= c_1 + c_2 k + c_3 k^2 + c_4 (2)^k$

Example 84: *Solve* $\{y(k+1)\}^2 - ky(k+1)y(k) - 6k^2\{y(k)\}^2 = 0.$

Solution: Putting $\dfrac{y(k+1)}{y(k)} = V(k)$ we get

$$\{V(k)\}^2 - kV(k) - 6k^2 = 0, \Rightarrow V(k) = \frac{k \pm \sqrt{(25k^2)}}{2}$$

i.e. $$V(k) = 3k \quad \text{or } V(k) = -2k$$

i.e. $$y(k+1) = 3k\ y(k) \ \text{ or } \ y(k+1) = -2\ k\ y(k)$$

i.e. $$y(k) = C(k).3^k\Gamma(k) \quad \text{or } y(k) = C(k)(-2)^k\Gamma(k).$$

Example 85: *Solve* $2[u(k+1)^2] + u(k+1)u(k) - [u(k)]^2 = 0.$

Solution: Putting $\dfrac{u(k+1)}{u(k)} = V(k)$, we get

$$2[V(k)]^2 + V(k) - 1 = 0 \Rightarrow V(k) = \frac{-1 \pm \sqrt{(9)}}{4}$$

i.e. $$V(k) = -1 \text{ or } V(k) = \frac{1}{2}$$

i.e. $$u(k+1) = -u(k) \text{ or } u(k+1) = \frac{1}{2}u(k)$$

i.e. $$u(k) = C(k)(-1)^k \text{ or } u(k) = \left(\frac{1}{2}\right)^k C(k).$$

Example 86: *Find the solution of the difference equation* $u_{k+2} - 7u_{k+1} + 12\,u_k = \cos k$.

Solution: We have $u_{k+2} - 7u_{k+1} + 12\,u_k = E^2 u_k - 7E\,u_k + 12\,u_k = \{E^2 - 7E + 12)\,u_k$.

The auxiliary equation is $r^2 - 7r + 12 = 0 \Rightarrow r = 4$ or 3.

$\therefore$ General solution of the equation is given by $u_k = c_1 4^k + c_2 3^k$.

Now, particular solution $= \dfrac{1}{(E^2 - 7E + 12)} . \cos k = \dfrac{1}{(-1 - 7E + 12)} \cos k$

[Putting, $E^2 = -1$]

$$= \frac{1}{11 - 7E} \cos k = \frac{(11 + 7E)}{(11 - 7E)(11 + 7E)} \cos k$$

$$= \frac{11 + 7E}{(11^2 - 49E^2)} \cos k = \frac{11 + 7E}{121 + 49} \cos k \qquad (E^2 = -1)$$

$$= \frac{1}{170}(11 + 7E) \cos k = \frac{1}{170}[11 + 7(1 + \Delta)] \cos k$$

$$= \frac{1}{170}[18 \cos k + 7\Delta \cos k] = \frac{1}{170}[18 \cos k - 7 \sin k].$$

Hence the required solution is $u_k = c_1 4^k + c_2 3^k + \dfrac{1}{170}[18 \cos k - 7 \sin k]$.

Example 87: *Solve* $y_{n+1} - 3\,y_n = n,\ y_0 = 1$.

Solution: The equation can be put as $(E - 3)\,y_n = n$.

The auxiliary equation is $r - 3 = 0 \Rightarrow r = 3$. C. F. $\equiv c_1 3^n$.

Now P.S. $$= \frac{1}{E - 3} . n = -\frac{1}{1 + \Delta - 3} . n = \frac{1}{\Delta - 2} . n$$

$$= -\frac{1}{2}\left(1 - \frac{\Delta}{2}\right)^{-1} . n = -\frac{1}{2}\left(1 + \frac{\Delta}{2} + \ldots\right) n^{(1)}$$

$$= -\frac{1}{2}[n^{(1)} + \frac{1}{2}] = -\frac{1}{4}(2\,n + 1).$$

$\therefore$ Solution is $y_n = c_1 3^n - \dfrac{1}{4}(2\,n + 1)$.

Example 88: *Find the solution of* $u_{k+2} + a^2 u_k = \cos ak$. **[Bhopal 2002]**

Solution: The given equation can be put as $(E^2 + a^2)\,a_k = \cos ak$.

$\therefore$ The auxiliary equation is $r^2 + a^2 = 0 \Rightarrow r = 0 \pm ai$

$\therefore$ C.S. $= a^k[c_1 \cos(k\,\pi/2) + c_2 \sin(k\,\pi/2)]$.

Also P.S. $= \dfrac{1}{E^2 + a^2} \cos ak$

$$= \text{(Real part) of } \frac{1}{E^2 + a^2} e^{iak}$$

$$= \text{R.P. of } e^{iak} \frac{1}{(e^{ia})^2 + a^2}$$

$$= \text{R.P. of } e^{iak} \frac{1}{e^{2ia} + a^2}$$

$$= \text{R.P. of } e^{iak} \frac{(e^{-2ik} + a^2)}{(e^{2ia} + a^2)(e^{-2ai} + a^2)}$$

$$= \text{R.P. of } \frac{e^{iak}(e^{-2ia} + a^2)}{1 + a^2(e^{2ai} + e^{-2ia}) + a^4}$$

$$= \text{R.P. of } \frac{e^{iak}(e^{-2ia} + a^2)}{1 + 2a^2 \cos 2a + a^4} \quad \left(\because \quad \cos 2a = \frac{e^{2ai} + e^{-2ai}}{2}\right)$$

$$= \text{R.P. of } \frac{[\cos ak + i \sin ak][\cos 2a - i \sin 2a + a^2]}{[1 + 2a^2 \cos 2a + a^4]}$$

$$= [a^2 \cos ak + \cos a(k-2)]/[1 + 2a^2 \cos 2a + a^4]$$

Hence the required solution is

$$u_k = a^k \left[c_1 \cos\left(\frac{k\pi}{2}\right) + c_2 \sin k \frac{\pi}{2} \right] + \frac{a^2 \cos ak + \cos a(k-2)}{1 + 2a^2 \cos 2a + a^4}.$$

Example 89: *Solve* $u_k u_{k+1} - au_k + b = 0$.

Solution: Putting $u_k = \dfrac{V_{k+1}}{V_k}$, we get $\dfrac{V_{k+1}}{V_k} \cdot \dfrac{V_{k+2}}{V_{k+1}} - a\dfrac{V_{k+1}}{V_k} + b = 0$

$$\Rightarrow \quad V_{k+2} - aV_{k+1} + bV_k = 0 \quad \textit{i.e.} \quad \{E^2 - aE + b\} V_k = 0.$$

Auxiliary equation is given by $r^2 - ar + b = 0$

$$\Rightarrow \quad r = \frac{a \pm \sqrt{(a^2 - 4b)}}{2}$$

$$\therefore \quad V_k = c_1 \left(\frac{a + \sqrt{(a^2 - 4b)}}{2} \right)^k + c_2 \left(\frac{a - \sqrt{(a^2 - 4b)}}{2} \right)^k$$

$$\textit{i.e.} \quad u_k = \frac{c_1 \left(\frac{a + \sqrt{(a^2 - 4b)}}{2} \right)^{k+1} + c_2 \left(\frac{a - \sqrt{(a^2 - 4b)}}{2} \right)^{k+1}}{c_1 \left(\frac{a + \sqrt{(a^2 - 4b)}}{a} \right)^k + c_2 \left(\frac{a - \sqrt{(a^2 - 4b)}}{2} \right)^k}$$

Example 90: *Solve* $y_{k+2} + y_k = \sin \frac{k\pi}{2}$ ...(1)

Solution: The auxiliary equation is given by

$$m^2 + 1 = 0, \text{ i.e. } m = \pm i, \text{ i.e. } m = \cos \frac{\pi}{2} \pm i \sin \frac{\pi}{2} = \alpha \pm i\beta \text{ form}$$

∴ General solution of the reduced equation is given by

$$y_k = A \cos\left(\frac{k\pi}{2} + B\right)$$

From the table for the particular solution , we again have

$$y_k = A \sin\left(\frac{k\pi}{2}\right) + B \cos\left(\frac{k\pi}{2}\right) \quad ...(2)$$

Substituting this value of y_k in (1), we get

$$A \sin (k+2) \frac{\pi}{2} + B \cos (k+2) \frac{\pi}{2} + A \sin \frac{k\pi}{2} + B \cos \frac{k\pi}{2} = \sin\left(\frac{k\pi}{2}\right)$$

$$\Rightarrow \quad -A \sin\left(\frac{k\pi}{2}\right) - B \cos \frac{k\pi}{2} + A \sin \frac{k\pi}{2} + B \cos \frac{k\pi}{2} = \sin k \frac{\pi}{2}$$

$$\Rightarrow \quad 0 = \sin \frac{k\pi}{2} \Rightarrow y_k = A \sin \frac{k\pi}{2} + B \cos \frac{k\pi}{2} : \text{fails.}$$

Next, suppose the solution as $y_k = k A \sin \frac{k\pi}{2} + k B \cos(k\pi/2)$.

$$\therefore \quad A (k+2) \sin (k+2) \frac{\pi}{2} + B (k+2) \cos (k+2) \frac{\pi}{2} + k A \sin \frac{k\pi}{2} + B \cos \frac{k\pi}{2} = \sin \frac{k\pi}{2}$$

$$\Rightarrow \quad -A (k+2) \sin \frac{k\pi}{2} - B (k+2) \cos \frac{k\pi}{2} + A k \sin \frac{k\pi}{2} + k B \cos \frac{k\pi}{2} = \sin \frac{k\pi}{2}$$

$$\Rightarrow \quad \left(\sin \frac{k\pi}{2}\right)(-2A) + \left(\cos \frac{k\pi}{2}\right)(-2B) = \sin \frac{k\pi}{2}.$$

Comparing the coefficients of $\sin\left(\frac{k\pi}{2}\right)$ and $\cos\left(\frac{k\pi}{2}\right)$, we have

$$-2A = 1 \quad \text{or } A = -\frac{1}{2} \quad \text{and } -B = 0 \quad \text{or } B = 0.$$

∴ General solution of the complete equation is given by

$$y_k = A \cos\left(\frac{k\pi}{2} + B\right) - \frac{1}{2} k \sin \frac{k\pi}{2}.$$

Example 91: *Solve* $y_{k+2} - 2 y_{k+1} + y_k = 5 + 3k$.

Solution: The auxiliary equation is given by

$$m^2 - 2m + 1 = 0 \text{ i.e. } (m-1)^2 = 0 \Rightarrow m = 1, 1.$$

The general solution of the equation is given by $y_k = (C_1 + C_2 k)$.

Let us take the complete solution as $y_k = Ak^2 + Bk^3$. we have

$$A(k+2)^2 + B(k+2)^3 - 2A(k+1)^2 - 2B(k+1)^3 + Ak^3 + Bk^2 = 5 + 3k.$$

Comparing the coefficients of like powers on both sides, we have $A = 1$ and $B = \frac{1}{2}$,

∴ General solution of the complete equation is given by

$$y_k = (C_1 + C_2 k) + k^2 + \frac{1}{2}k^3.$$

Example 92: *Solve* $y_{k+2} - 4y_{k+1} + 3y_k = 5^k$.

Solution: Given equation in *symbolic form* is $(E^2 - 4E + 3)y_k = 5^k$

∴ The auxiliary equation is $r^2 - 4r + 3 = 0 \Rightarrow (r-1)(r-3) = 0$

$$\Rightarrow \quad r = 1, 3 \quad \therefore \text{C.F.} = c_1(1)^k + c_2(3)^k = c_1 + c_2 . 3^k$$

and
$$\text{P.I.} = \frac{1}{E^2 - 4E + 3} 5^k \qquad [\text{Put } E = 5]$$

$$= \frac{1}{25 - 4.5 + 3} 5^k = \frac{1}{8} . 5^k$$

Thus the complete solution is $y_n = c_1 + c_2 . 3^k + 5^k/8$.

Example 93: *Solve* $u_{k+2} - 4u_{k+1} + 4u_k = 2^k$.

Solution: Given equation in *symbolic form* is $(E^2 - 4E + 4)u_k = 2^k$.)

The auxiliary equation is $r^2 - 4r + 4 = 0 \ \therefore \ r = 2, 2$.

$$\therefore \quad \text{C.F.} = (c_1 + c_2 k) 2^k$$

$$\text{P.I.} = \frac{1}{(E-2)^2} . 2^k = \frac{k(k-1)}{2!} 2^{k-2} = k(k-1) 2^{k-3}$$

Then the complete solution is $u_k = (c_1 + c_2 k) 2^k + k(k-1) 2^{k-3}$.

Example 94: *Solve* $y_{k+2} - 2\cos\alpha \ y_{k+1} + y_k = \cos\alpha k$.

Solution: Given equation in *symbolic form* is $(E^2 - 2\cos\alpha . E + 1) y_k = \cos\alpha k$

The *auxiliary equation* is $r^2 - 2\cos\alpha . r + 1 = 0$.

$$\Rightarrow \quad r = \frac{2\cos\alpha \pm \sqrt{(4\cos^2\alpha - 4)}}{2} = \cos\alpha \pm i\sin\alpha$$

$$\Rightarrow \quad \text{C.F.} = (1)^k [c_1 \cos\alpha k + c_2 \sin\alpha k],$$

$$\text{P.I.} = \frac{1}{E^2 - 2E\cos\alpha + 1} \cos\alpha k$$

$$= \frac{1}{E^2 - E(e^{i\alpha} + e^{-i\alpha}) + 1} \left(\frac{e^{i\alpha k} + e^{-i\alpha k}}{2} \right)$$

$$= \frac{1}{2}\left[\frac{1}{(E-e^{i\alpha})(E-e^{-i\alpha})} e^{i\alpha k} + \frac{1}{(E-e^{i\alpha})(E-e^{i\alpha})} e^{-i\alpha k}\right]$$

$$= \frac{1}{2}\left[\frac{1}{(E-e^{i\alpha})}\left\{\frac{1}{e^{i\alpha}-e^{-i\alpha}} e^{i\alpha k}\right\} + \frac{1}{E-e^{-i\alpha}}\left\{\frac{1}{e^{-i\alpha}-e^{i\alpha}} e^{-i\alpha k}\right\}\right]$$

$$= \frac{1}{4\, i \sin\alpha}\left[\frac{1}{E-e^{i\alpha}} e^{i\alpha k} - \frac{1}{E-e^{-i\alpha}} e^{-i\alpha k}\right]$$

$$= \frac{1}{4\, i\sin\alpha}\left[k.e^{i\alpha(k-1)} - k.e^{-\alpha(k-1)}\right]$$

$$= \frac{k}{2\sin\alpha}\left[\frac{e^{i\alpha(k-1)} - e^{-i\alpha(k-1)}}{2i}\right] = \frac{k\sin(k-1)\alpha}{2\sin\alpha}$$

Hence the complete solution is $y_n = c_1 \cos \alpha k + c_2 \sin \alpha\, k + \dfrac{k \sin(k-1)\alpha}{2 \sin\alpha}$.

Example 95: *Solve* $y_{k+1} - y_k + k y_{k+1} y_k = 0$ *given* $y_1 = 2$.

Solution: Dividing throughout by $y_k\, y_{k+1}$, the given equation becomes $\dfrac{1}{y_{k+1}} - \dfrac{1}{y_k} = k$

Putting $1/y_k = u_k$, we get $u_{k+1} - u_k = k$ where $u_1 = \dfrac{1}{2}$ as $y_1 = 2$.

$\Rightarrow \quad \Delta u_k = k \Rightarrow u_k = \Delta^{-1}[k] = [k]^2/2 + c_1$

But $\quad u_1 = 1/2. \therefore \quad c_1 = 1/2$.

Thus $\quad u_k = \dfrac{1}{2} k(k-1) + \dfrac{1}{2} \Rightarrow y_k = \dfrac{1}{u_k} = \dfrac{2}{k^2 - k + 1}$.

Example 96: *Solve* $y_{k+1}\, y_k + (k+2)\, y_{k+1} + k y_k + k^2 + 2k + 2 = 0$.

Solution: We have $y_{k+1}[y_k + k + 2] + k y_k = -k^2 - 2k - 2$

Putting $\quad y_k = \dfrac{u_{k+1}}{u_k} - (k+2)$, it reduces to

$$\frac{u_{k+2}}{u_k} - 3\frac{u_{k+1}}{u_k} = -2 \Rightarrow u_{k+2} - 3u_{k+1} + 2u_k = 0.$$

Its A.E. is $\quad r^2 - 3r + 2 = 0, \Rightarrow r = 1, 2$

Thus the solution is $\quad u_k = c_1 = c_2 2^k$.

Hence the solution of the given equation is $y_k = \dfrac{c_1 + c_2 2^{k+1}}{c_1 + c_2 2^k} - k - 2$.

Example 97: *Solve the simultaneous difference equations*

$$u_{k+1} + v_k - 3u_k = k, 3u_k + v_{k+1} - 5v_k = 4^k$$

subject to the conditions $u_1 = 2,\ v_1 = 0.$

Solution: Given equation in symbolic form, are

$$(E-3)\,u_k + v_k = k \quad ...(1)$$

$$3\,u_k + (E-5)v_k = 4^k \quad ...(2)$$

Operating the first equation with $E-5$ and subtracting the second from it, we get

$$[E-5)(E-3)-3]\,u_k = (E-5)\,k - 4^k$$

or $$(E^2 - 8E + 12)\,u_k = 1 - 4k - 4^k$$

$$\Rightarrow \quad u_k = c_1 2^k + c_2 6^k - \frac{4}{5}k - \frac{19}{25} + \frac{4^k}{4} \quad ...(3)$$

Then substituting the value of u_k form (3) in (1), we get

$$u_x = c_1 2^k - 3c_2 6^k - \frac{3k}{5} - \frac{34}{25} + \frac{4^k}{4} \quad ...(4)$$

Taking $u_1 = 2, v_1 = 0$ in (3) and (4) we obtain

$$2c_1 + 6c_2 = \frac{64}{25}, 2c_1 - 18c_2 = \frac{74}{25}$$

whence $c_1 - 1.33, c_2 = -0.0167$

$$\therefore \quad u_k = 1.33\,2^k - 0.0167.6^k - 0.8k - 0.76 + 4^{k-1}$$

$$v_k = 1.33\,2^k - 0.05.6^k - 0.6^k - 1.36 - 4^{k-1}.$$

9.9 Application of Difference Equations to Social Sciences

[Meerut 2004, 2006, 2008, 2010; Rohilkhand 2006, 2008; M.D.U (Rohtak) 2008]

Here we shall study the national income of the country and then its variation with times

National income in any accounting period consists of the following three components:

(1) Consumer expenditure (for purchase of so called consumer goods).

(2) Induced private investment (for buying capital equipment *i.e.* machinery used to increase production.

(3) Government expenditure.

Let us denote above components by the following symbols.

I_t = national income, C_t = consumer expenditure,

P_t = induced private investment, G_t = Government expenditure,

where subscript t identifies the accounting period for which the variable is to be evaluated.

If we know the data yearly and t takes the integral values 1, 2,...; then we should have

$$I_t = C_t + P_t + G_t . \qquad ...(1)$$

In equation (1), we have four variables and one equation, therefore we require some more equations. These are obtained from the following postulates due to ***Sampson***:

(i) Consumption expenditure in any period is proportional to the national income of the preceding period, i.e. $C_t \propto I_{t-1}$ or $C_t = \alpha I_{t-1}$,

where α is constant and is termed as the ***Marginal Propensity*** to consume.

(ii) Induced private investment in any period is proportional to the increase in consumption of that period over the preceding period.

We usually call this as the ***Accelerating Principle***. From here we have

$$p_t \alpha (C_t - C_{t-1}), \ i.e. P_t = \beta (C_t - C_{t-1});$$

the constant of proportionality β is called the ***Relation***.

(iii) Government expenditure is the same in all periods.

Now we choose out unit so that Government expenditure is equal to 1; then we have

$$G_t = 1 \Rightarrow I_t = \alpha I_{t-1} + \beta (C_t - C_{t-1}) + 1 = \alpha I_{t-1} - \beta(\alpha I_{t-1} - \alpha I_{t-2}) + 1$$

$$= \alpha(1+\beta) I_{t-1} - \alpha\beta I_{t+2} + 1. \text{ Putting } t+2 \text{ for } t, \text{ we have}$$

$$I_{t+2} - \alpha(1+\beta) I_{t+1} + \alpha\beta I\, t = I. \qquad ...(2)$$

This is 2nd order non-homogeneous Difference equation for national income

As soon as two initial values I_0 and I_1 are specified, the income is determined for the later periods by (2).

To solve (2), we must known α and β also. Let them be as follows:

$$\alpha = 0.5 \text{ and } \beta = 1. \quad \therefore (2) \Rightarrow I_{t+2} - I_{t+1} + \frac{1}{2} I_t = 1 \qquad ...(3)$$

The auxiliary equation is given by $r^2 - r + \frac{1}{2} = 0$

$$\therefore \quad r_1 = \frac{1}{2}(1+i); r_2 = \frac{1}{2}(1-i).$$

In the polar form, the roots are $\frac{1}{\sqrt{2}}\left(\cos\frac{\pi}{4} \pm i\sin\frac{\pi}{4}\right)$

The solution of the corresponding homogeneous equations is given by

$$I_t = A\left(\frac{1}{\sqrt{2}}\right)^t \cos\left(\frac{t\pi}{4} + B\right) \qquad ...(3')$$

To find a particular solution of (3).

Choose the trial function $I_t = D$ where D is constant.

Then, $\quad D - D + \frac{1}{2} D = 1 \Rightarrow D = 2.$

The general solution of (3) is given by $I_t = A\left(\frac{1}{\sqrt{2}}\right)^t \cos\left(\frac{t\pi}{4} + B\right) + 2$. ...(4)

Let us choose the initial values as $I_0 = 2, I_1 = 3$.

These initial conditions enable us to determine A and B. On substituting $t = 0$ and $t = 1$ in (4), we get $A \cos B = 0$ ...(5)

and $$A.\frac{1}{\sqrt{2}} \cos\left(\frac{\pi}{4} + B\right) = 1 \quad ...(6)$$

Equation (5) $\Rightarrow \cos B = 0 = \cos\frac{\pi}{2} \Rightarrow B = \frac{\pi}{2}$

Hence the particular solution of (3) which satisfies the initial condition is given by

$$I_t = -2\left(\frac{1}{\sqrt{2}}\right)^t .\cos\left(\frac{t\pi}{4} + \frac{\pi}{2}\right) + 2.$$

or $$I_t = 2\left(\frac{1}{\sqrt{2}}\right)^t .\sin\left(\frac{t\pi}{4}\right) + 2. \quad ...(7)$$

The presence of sine term makes I as an oscillating function of time

Since $$r = \frac{1}{\sqrt{2}} < 1,$$

the oscillations are damped and the first term on the right in (7) approaches to zero as t increases. The constant term 2 remains, but the sequence $\{I_t\}$ converges to this limit.

Deduction: Samuelson's Conclusion

"*A constant continuing level of Government expenditure will result in damped oscillating movements of national income, gradually approaching the asymptote $[1/(1-\alpha)]$ times the constant level of the government expenditure*".

The constant level of Government expenditure was assumed in the beginning and we supposed that $G_t = 1$.

9.10 Matrix Method for Solving the System of two Simultaneous Linear Difference Equations

$$p_{t+1} = (1-\alpha)p_t + \beta q_t ; q_{t+1} = \alpha p_t + (1-\beta) q_t \ (t = 0, 1, 2, \ldots)$$

where α and β are constants p_0, q_0 being given such that $p_0 + q_0 = 1$.

The system of two simultaneous difference equation; *viz*

$$p_{t+1} = (1-\alpha)\, p_t + \beta q_t ; q_{t+1} = \alpha\, p_t + (1-\beta)\, q_t \ (t = 0, 1, 2, \ldots)$$

where α and β are constants can be written as

$$\begin{pmatrix} p_{t+1} \\ q_{t+1} \end{pmatrix} = \begin{pmatrix} 1-\alpha & \beta \\ \alpha & 1-\beta \end{pmatrix} \begin{pmatrix} p_t \\ q_t \end{pmatrix}, (t = 0, 1, 2, \ldots)$$

[in matrix notation]

i.e. $V_{t+1} = A\ V_t$

where $V_t = \begin{pmatrix} p_t \\ q_t \end{pmatrix}$ and $A = \begin{pmatrix} 1-\alpha & \beta \\ \alpha & 1-\beta \end{pmatrix}$, $V_0 = \begin{pmatrix} p_0 \\ q_0 \end{pmatrix}$ (given, as p_0 and q_0 are given)

Equation $V_{t+1} = AV_t \Rightarrow V_t = AV_{t-1} = A.AV_{t-2} = A^2V_{t-2} = \ldots$

$$= A^tV_{t-t} = A^tV_0 \ (t = 0, 1, 2, \ldots). \quad \text{.. (1)}$$

The problem of solving the system of difference equations

$$p_{t+1} = (1-\alpha)p_t + \beta q_t;\ q_{t+1} = \alpha\ p_t + (1-\beta)q_t \quad \text{...(2)}$$

has now been reduced to the problem of finding the tth power of the matrix A. For *with A^t known, we can perform the matrix multiplication* A^tV_0 and thus V_t(*i.e.* p_t *and* q_t) is obtained.

The tth Power of the matrix A is not easy to find directly, but the powers of a *diagonal* matrix are very easy to obtain

for if $D = \begin{pmatrix} \lambda_1 & 0 \\ 0 & \lambda_2 \end{pmatrix}$, then we have $D^2 = \begin{pmatrix} \lambda_1^2 & 0 \\ 0 & \lambda_2^2 \end{pmatrix}, \ldots, D^t = \begin{pmatrix} \lambda_1^t & 0 \\ 0 & \lambda_2^t \end{pmatrix}$ etc.

Hence now, our aim is to obtain a diagonal matrix similar to A_t.

We know that square matrix A is said to similar to another matrix B if there exists a non-singular matrix M such that $B = M^{-1}AM$ and this further suggests that A is similar to B.

To compute M, we proceed as follows

We have $D = M^{-1}AM$

Premultiplying by M we get

$$MD = MM^{-1}AM = IAM = AM \quad \text{...(3)}$$

respectively, then we get $M = (C_1, C_2)$. Putting of M and D in (3), we get

$$A(C_1C_2) = (C_1C_2)\begin{pmatrix} \lambda_1 & 0 \\ 0 & \lambda_2 \end{pmatrix} \Rightarrow (AC_1AC_2) = (\lambda_1C_1\lambda_2C_2)$$

$$\therefore \quad AC_1 = \lambda_1C_1 \text{ and } AC_2 = \lambda_2C_2 \quad \text{...(4)}$$

Both these equations satisfy a single equation $AX = \lambda X$ ...(5)

The non-zero column vector X is said to be a characteristic root of A corresponding to the characteristic vector X and vice versa. Characteristic vector are also called **eigen vectors** and **characteristic roots** are often called **latent roots** or **eigen values**.

Taking X to be $\begin{pmatrix} x_1 \\ x_2 \end{pmatrix}$, equation (5) givens $\begin{pmatrix} (1-\alpha) & \beta \\ \alpha & 1-\beta \end{pmatrix}\begin{pmatrix} x_1 \\ x_2 \end{pmatrix} = \lambda\begin{pmatrix} x_1 \\ x_2 \end{pmatrix}$

$$\Rightarrow \begin{pmatrix} (1-\alpha)x_1 + \beta x_2 \\ \alpha\ x_1 + (1-\beta)x_2 \end{pmatrix} = \begin{pmatrix} \lambda x_1 \\ \lambda x_2 \end{pmatrix} \quad \text{...(6)}$$

By the definition of equality of matrices, equation (6) gives

$$(1-\alpha)\,x_1 + \beta\,x_2 = \lambda\,x_1 \text{ and } \alpha\,x_1 + (1-\beta)\,x_2 = \lambda\,x_2 \quad \text{...(7)}$$

To obtain values, we put det $(A-\lambda I)=0$

i,e. $$\begin{vmatrix} 1-\alpha-\lambda & \beta \\ \beta & 1-\beta-\lambda \end{vmatrix}=0$$

$$\Rightarrow \quad \lambda^2-(2-\alpha-\beta)\lambda+(1-\alpha-\beta)=0$$

$$\Rightarrow \quad (\lambda-1)[\lambda-(1-\alpha-\beta)]=0 \qquad \text{...(8)}$$

$$\Rightarrow \quad \lambda_1=1, \lambda_2=1-\alpha-\beta.$$

Choosing $\lambda_1=1$

$$(7) \Rightarrow (1-\alpha)\,x_1+\beta\,x_2=x_1 \text{ and } \alpha\,x_1+(1-\beta)x_2=x_2$$

$$\Rightarrow -\alpha\,x_1+\beta\,x_2=0 \text{ and } \alpha\,x_1-\beta\,x_2=0 \;\; i.e.\; \alpha\,x_1-\beta\,x_2=0 \qquad \text{[only]}$$

From here x_1 and x_2 can be determined unlikely as there is only one equation for two unknows, but they are determined by choosing $x_1=\beta$ and $x_2=\alpha$.

Hence $$C_1=\begin{pmatrix} x_1 \\ x_2 \end{pmatrix}=\begin{pmatrix} \beta \\ \alpha \end{pmatrix} \qquad \text{...(9)}$$

Again choosing $\lambda_2=1-\alpha-\beta$, (7) implies

$$(1-\alpha)\,x_1+\beta\,x_2=(1-\alpha-\beta)\,x_1 \text{ and } \alpha\,x_1+(1-\beta)\,x_2=(1-\alpha-\beta)\,x_2$$

i.e. $$\beta x_2+\beta x_1=0 \text{ and } \alpha\,(x_1+x_2)=0,$$

which are satisfied by taking $x_1=1$ and $x_2=-1$.

$\therefore$ Characteristic vector corresponding to $\lambda=\lambda_2=1-\alpha-\beta$, is $C_2=\begin{pmatrix} x_1 \\ x_2 \end{pmatrix}=\begin{pmatrix} 1 \\ -1 \end{pmatrix}$

$$\therefore \quad M=(C_1,C_2)=\begin{pmatrix} \beta & 1 \\ \alpha & -1 \end{pmatrix} \qquad \text{...(10)}$$

Inverse of M (computing by usual methods) is given by $M^{-1}=\dfrac{1}{\alpha+\beta}\begin{pmatrix} 1 & 1 \\ \alpha & -\beta \end{pmatrix}$

$$\therefore \quad A^t=M\,D^t\,M^{-1}=\begin{pmatrix} \beta & 1 \\ \alpha & -1 \end{pmatrix}\times\begin{pmatrix} \lambda_1{}^t & 0 \\ 0 & \lambda_2{}^t \end{pmatrix}\frac{1}{\alpha+\beta}\begin{pmatrix} 1 & 1 \\ \alpha & -\beta \end{pmatrix}$$

$$=\begin{pmatrix} \beta & 1 \\ \alpha & -1 \end{pmatrix}_{2\times2}\times\begin{pmatrix} 1 & 0 \\ 0 & (1-\alpha-\beta)^t \end{pmatrix}_{2\times2}\frac{1}{\alpha+\beta}\begin{pmatrix} 1 & 1 \\ \alpha & -\beta \end{pmatrix}_{2\times2}$$

$$=\frac{1}{\alpha+\beta}\begin{pmatrix} \beta & (1-\alpha-\beta)^t \\ \alpha & -(1-\alpha-\beta)^t \end{pmatrix}_{2\times2}\begin{pmatrix} 1 & 1 \\ \alpha & -\beta \end{pmatrix}_{2\times2}$$

$$=\frac{1}{\alpha+\beta}\begin{pmatrix} \beta+\alpha\,(1-\alpha-\beta)^t & \beta-\beta(1-\alpha-\beta)^t \\ \alpha-\alpha\,(1-\alpha-\beta)^t & \alpha+\beta(1-\alpha-\beta)^t \end{pmatrix}_{2\times2}$$

$$\Rightarrow \quad V_t=A^tV_0=\frac{1}{\alpha+\beta}\begin{pmatrix} \beta+\alpha\,(1-\alpha-\beta)^t & \beta-\beta(1-\alpha-\beta)^t \\ \alpha-\alpha(1-\alpha-\beta)^t & \alpha+\beta(1-\alpha-\beta)^t \end{pmatrix}_{2\times2}\begin{pmatrix} p_0 \\ q_0 \end{pmatrix}_{2\times2}$$

$$\Rightarrow \quad \begin{pmatrix} p_t \\ q_t \end{pmatrix} = \frac{1}{\alpha+\beta}\begin{pmatrix} [\beta + \alpha(1-\alpha-\beta)^t]\, p_0 + q_0\, [\beta - \beta(1-\alpha-\beta)^t] \\ [\alpha - \alpha(1-\alpha-\beta)^t]\, p_0 + q_0\, [\alpha + \beta(1-\alpha-\beta)^t] \end{pmatrix}_{2\times 2}$$

$$\Rightarrow \quad p_t = \frac{p_0}{\alpha+\beta}[\beta + \alpha(1-\alpha-\beta)^t] + \frac{q_0}{(\alpha+\beta)}[\beta - \beta(1-\alpha-\beta)^t]$$

and
$$q_t = \frac{p_0}{\alpha+\beta}[\alpha - \alpha(1-\alpha-\beta)^t] + \frac{q_0}{(\alpha+\beta)}[\alpha + \beta(1-\alpha-\beta)^t]$$

$$\Rightarrow \quad p_t = \frac{\beta(p_0+q_0)}{\alpha+\beta} + (1-\alpha-\beta)^t\left\{\frac{\alpha p_0}{\alpha+\beta} - \frac{q_0\beta}{\alpha+\beta}\right\}$$

and
$$q_t = \frac{\alpha(p_0+q_0)}{\alpha+\beta} + (1-\alpha-\beta)^t\left\{\frac{-\alpha p_0}{\alpha+\beta} - \frac{\beta q_0}{\alpha+\beta}\right\}$$

Putting $p_0 + q_0 = 1$, we get

$$p_t = \frac{\beta}{\alpha+\beta} + (1-\alpha-\beta)^t\left\{p_0 - \frac{\beta}{\alpha+\beta}\right\};\ t = 0, 1, 2, \ldots$$

and
$$q_t = \frac{\alpha}{\alpha+\beta} + (1-\alpha-\beta)^t\left\{q_0 - \frac{\alpha}{\alpha+\beta}\right\}.$$

Short cut method to obtain A^t.

Let the distinct characteristic vector of a 2×2 matrix A be λ_1, λ_2.

These roots are obtained by solving the quadratic equation det $(A - \lambda I) = 0$. Having determined λ_1, λ_2; solve the following equations

$$a + b\lambda_1 = \lambda_1^t \quad \ldots(1)$$

$$a + b\lambda_2 = \lambda_2^t \quad \text{for } a \text{ and } b \quad \ldots(2)$$

Then, obtain $\quad A^t = aI + bA \quad \ldots(3)$

In this way, we can compute A^t and hence V_t *i.e.* (p_t and q_t) can be obtained as discused earlier.

To obtain A^t by the short cut method.

$$\det(A - \lambda I) = 0 \Rightarrow \begin{vmatrix} 1-\alpha-\lambda & \beta \\ \alpha & 1-\beta-\lambda \end{vmatrix} = 0$$

$$\Rightarrow \quad \lambda^2 - (2-\alpha-\beta)\lambda + (1-\alpha-\beta) = 0$$

$$\Rightarrow \quad (\lambda - 1)[\lambda - (1-\alpha-\beta)] = 0$$

$$\Rightarrow \quad \lambda_1 = 1, \lambda_2 = 1-\alpha-\beta.$$

$\therefore$ Equation (1) and (2), give

$$a + b = 1 \quad \ldots(4)$$

and
$$a + b(1-\alpha-\beta) = (1-\alpha-\beta)^t \quad \ldots(5)$$

Solving (4) and (5) we get

$$a = \frac{(1-\alpha-\beta)^t - (1-\alpha-\beta)}{\alpha+\beta} \quad \text{and} \quad b = \frac{1-(1-\alpha-\beta)^t}{\alpha+\beta}$$

$$\therefore \qquad A^t = aI + bA$$

$$= a\begin{pmatrix}1 & 0\\ 0 & 1\end{pmatrix} + b\begin{pmatrix}1-\alpha & \beta\\ \alpha & 1-\beta\end{pmatrix} = \begin{pmatrix}a+b-b\alpha & b\beta\\ b\alpha & a+b-b\alpha\end{pmatrix}$$

$$= \frac{1}{\alpha+\beta}\begin{pmatrix}\beta+\alpha\,[1-\alpha-\beta]^t & \beta-\beta[1-\alpha-\beta]^t\\ \alpha-\alpha\,[1-\alpha-\beta]^t & \alpha+\beta[1-\alpha-\beta]^t\end{pmatrix}$$

[As obtained earlier]

The example illustrates the advantage of using the rule than to calculate A^t. Once, the characteristic values are determined, the use of the rule eliminates the calculation of matrix M and its inverse.

Example 98: *Solve the second order difference equation*

$$x_{t+1} - 3x_t + 2x_{t-1} = 0, (t = 1, 2, 3, \ldots) \text{ given that } x_0 = 0, x_1 = 1.$$

[Meerut 2000, 2001, 2003, 2004, 2005]

Solution: We introduce a new function y (defined only for t value 1, 2, 3 ,...) in order to write the given difference equation as a system of two first order equation:

$$x_{t+1} = 3x_t - 2y_t,\ y_{t+1} = x_t \qquad (t=1, 2, 3,\ldots)$$

i.e.
$$\left.\begin{aligned}x_{t+1} &= 3x_t - 2y_t\\ y_{t+1} &= 1x_t + 0y_t\end{aligned}\right\} \Rightarrow \begin{pmatrix}x_{t+1}\\ y_{t+1}\end{pmatrix} = \begin{pmatrix}3 & -2\\ 1 & 0\end{pmatrix}\begin{pmatrix}x_t\\ y_t\end{pmatrix}$$

$$\Rightarrow \qquad V_{t+1} = AV_t \qquad \ldots(1)$$

Characteristic values are given by det $(A - \lambda I) = 0$

i.e. by
$$\begin{vmatrix}-3-\lambda & -2\\ 1 & -\lambda\end{vmatrix} = 0 \Rightarrow (\lambda-1)(\lambda-2) = 0 \Rightarrow \lambda_1 = 1, \lambda_2 = 2,$$

where a and b are given by $a + b = 1$ and $a + 2b = 2^t$,

Solving (2) for a,b ; we get $a = 2 - 2^t$ and $b = 2^t - 1$.

$$\therefore \qquad A^t = (2-2^t)\begin{pmatrix}1 & 0\\ 0 & 1\end{pmatrix} + (2^t-1)\begin{pmatrix}3 & -2\\ 1 & 0\end{pmatrix}$$

$$\Rightarrow \qquad V_{t+1} = A^t V_1 = A^t\begin{pmatrix}x_1\\ y_1\end{pmatrix} = A^t\begin{pmatrix}x_1\\ x_0\end{pmatrix} = A^t\begin{pmatrix}1\\ 0\end{pmatrix}$$

$$\Rightarrow \qquad \begin{pmatrix}x_{t+1}\\ y_{t+1}\end{pmatrix} = \begin{pmatrix}2^{t+1}-1\\ 2^t-1\end{pmatrix} (t = 0, 1, 2, \ldots)$$

$$\Rightarrow \qquad x_{t+1} = 2^{t+1} - 1 \text{ and } y_{t+1} = 2^t - 1 \Rightarrow x_t = 2^t - 1\ (t = 0, 1, 2, \ldots)$$

✦✦ Problem Set ✦✦

Solve the following difference equations by matrix method

1. $x_{t+1} - 4x_t + 3x_{t-1} = 0 (t = 1,\ 2,\ 3,...); x_0 = 0\ x_1 = 1$
2. $x_{t+1} - x_t - 2x_{t-1} = 0\ (t = 1, 2, 3, ...);\ x_0 = 1,\ x_1 = 0.$
3. $x_{t+1} - x_{t-1} = 0\ (t = 1,\ 2,\ 3, ...);\ x_0 = 1,\ x_1 = 3.$
4. $y_{k+2} - 5y_{k+1} + 6y_k = k^2;\ y_0 = 1,\ y_1 = 2.$
5. $y_{k+1} = 2y_k + z_k, z_{k+1} = y_k + 2z_k;\ y_1 = 1,\ z_1 = 0.$

✦✦ Answers ✦✦

1. $x_t = \frac{1}{3}(3^t - 1)$ 2. $x_t = \frac{1}{3}[2^t + 2(-1)^t]$ 3. $x_t = 2 - (-1)^t$

4. $y_k = [c_1 2^k + c_2 3^k + \frac{1}{2}k^2 + \frac{3}{2}k + \frac{3}{2}]$ 5. $z_h = -\frac{1}{2} + \frac{1}{6}h^6,\ y_h = \frac{1}{2} + \frac{1}{6}3^h$

9.11 Cobweb Phenomenon

Here we shall discuss a very important phenomenon known as ***Cobweb Phenomenon***. The so called Cobweb Phenomenon in economics efforts excellent examples in which first order difference equations may be used.

To be exact let us concentrate our ideas on the following situation.

Suppose that farmers decide on the basis of the years price for a certain commodity the acreage. They will plant with that crop. Anticipating that the price level will be maintained, if the price is high one year, farmers tend to plant heavily. The following year, when the crop is harvested and brought to the market, the supply exceeds the demand, prices fall, with the result the farmers cut acreage devoted to this particular commodity.

When the next crop is harvested, supply may be below the demand; price increase, demand prices fall and this cycle is repeated.

In this section, we wish to study this cycle on a mathematical basis.

We study three functions defined for $t = 0, 1, 2, 3,......$ as follows.

Let S_t done the number of units supplied in time t.

D_t stands for the units demanded in time t.

p_t=price per unit in period t.

We now make the following assumptions:

(i) A price demand relation is specified in which quantity demanded is determined by the price at the time of purchase or suppose a function g exists for which we have

$$D_t = g(p_t) \quad ...(1)$$

(ii) There exists a price supply curve that relates the supply in any period with the price one period before or in other words there exists a function h such that

$$S_{t+1} = h(p_t) \quad ...(2)$$

(iii) The market price is determined by the available supply, transactions occurring at the price at which that quantity demanded and the quantity supplied are equal,

$$S_t = D_t \quad ...(3)$$

Now suppose p_0 is prescribed if the function g and h are known, we may calculate S_1 from (2) and D_1 from (3) and so obtain p_1 from the price demand curve in (1). The process may be repeated. After obtaining p_1, we obtain p_2, and so on. Our main purpose is to study the sequence of prices $p_0, p_1, p_2, ..$

Here we are very particular to study the oscillatory behaviour.

If we wish to make a through study, we have to make certain hypothesis to study the functions g and h.

We suppose that g and h are linear functions or equivalently the price demand and price supply curve are straight lines. The equation in (1) and (2) are thereby simplified to

$$D_t = -n_d p_t + c_d \; ... \; x_d > 0, c_d > 0 \quad ...(4)$$

$$S_{t+1} = n_s p_t + c_s \quad n_s > 0, c_s > 0 \quad ...(5)$$

where $-n_d, c_d$ are the slope and intercept for the demand curve,

with n_s and c_s the corresponding constants for the supply curve.

Here the slope of the demand curve is taken to be negative and that of supply curve positive. The reason is evident that an increase of one unit in price produces a decrease in demand and increase in supply.

By hypothesis, (3) $\quad D_{t+1} = S_{t+1} \quad ...(6)$

and hence $\quad n_s y_t + c_s = -n_d p_{t+1} + c_d \quad ...(7)$

or $\quad p_{t+1} = Ap_t + B \quad ...(8)$

where $\quad A = \dfrac{-n_s}{n_d}$ and $B = \dfrac{c_d - c_s}{n_d} \quad ...(9)$

Remark: We have already studied the first order difference equation (8) and the following conclusions are worth-nothing.

Since A is negative, the solution sequence $\{p_t\}$ is always oscillatory.

(i) Being demped or convergent with limit $p^* = \dfrac{B}{1-A}$ if $-1 < A < 0$.

(ii) If $A = -1$, it undergoes finite oscillations.

(iii) If $A < -1$ it has infinite oscillations.

Thus the behaviour of price sequence is depending upon A which is the ratio of the supply and demand curves.

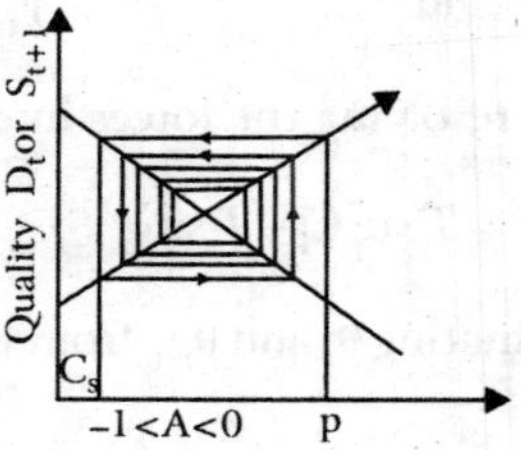

(a)

To have a more clear under-standing let us have a graphical analysis.

We start p_0 find S_1 by moving vertically to the supplier line, then move horizontally.

(Since $D_1 = \delta_1$) to find D_1, which determines the price p_1 on the price axis. The supply is δ is found on the supply line directly above p_1 and again $D_2 (= \delta)$ is found moving horizontally to the demand line etc.

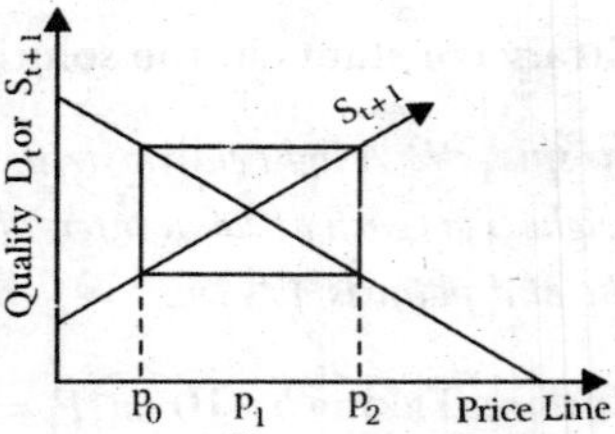

(b)

The intersection of the supply and demand line determines the equilibrium price p^* , in figure (a)

we find a Cobweb moving towards this equilibrium point prices alternating above and below but converging to p^*.

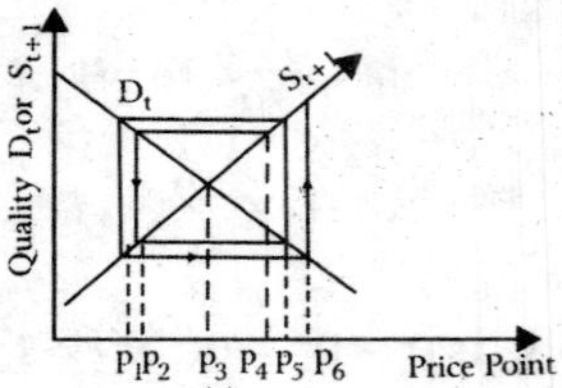

(c)

In fig. (b), the Cobweb consist of one square endlessly repeated prices oscillations finitely between just two values.

In the figure (c), the Cobweb moves from the intersection point, prices oscillating infinitely about the equilibrium value.

9.12 Application to Deflection of a Loaded String

Let us consider a light string of length l stretched tightly between A and B and let the forces p_i be acting perpendicular to AB at equispaced points $x_i (i = 1, 2, \ldots, n-1)$; giving small transverse displacements y_i at these points. Let the portion of the string in between x_i and x_{i+1} make a small angle θ_i with the horizontal, then we have

$$\sin\theta_i = \tan\theta_i = \theta_i \text{ and } \cos\theta_i = 1 \quad \ldots(1)$$

Let T be the tension of the string at x_i, then $T\cos\theta_i = T$

i.e. the tension may be taken as uniform.

Then taking $x_{i+1} - x_i = h$, we get $y_{i+1} \quad y_i = h\tan\theta_i = h\theta_i$

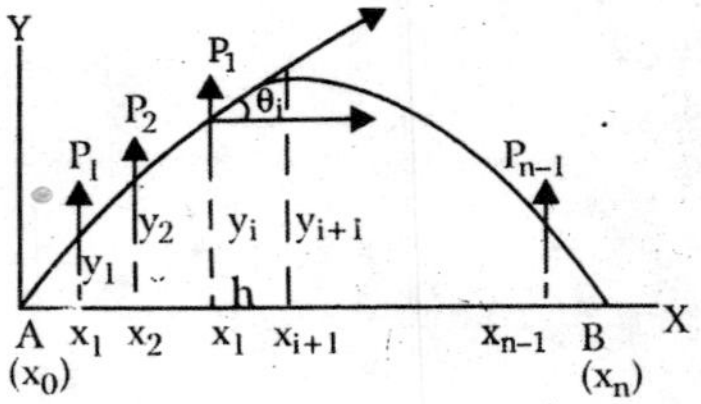

and $$y_i - y_{i-1} = h\tan\theta_{i-1} = h\theta_{i-1} \quad ...(2)$$

Now resolving the forces in equilibrium at (x_i, y_i) perpendicular to AB, we get

$$T\sin\theta_i - T\sin\theta_{i-1} + p_i = 0 \quad \Rightarrow T(\theta_i - \theta_{i-1}) + p_i = 0 \quad ...(3)$$

Eliminating θ_i and θ_{i-1} from (1), (2) and (3), we get

$$y_{i+1} - 2y_i + y_{i-1} = -(hp_i/T) \quad ...(4)$$

This is a difference equation and its solution gives y_i, the displacement. To obtain the arbitrary constants in the solution, we have $y_0 = y_n = 0$ as the ends A, B are fixed.

Example 99: *A light elastic string stretched between two fixed nails 120 cm apart, carries 11 loads of weight 5 gm each at equal intervals and the resulting tension in 500 gm weight.. Show that the sag at the mid-point is 1.8 cm.*

Solution: Taking $h = 10\,cm$, $P_i = 5$ gm and $T = 500$ gm wt. and using equation (4); we get

$$y_{i+1} - 2y_i + y_{i-1} = -(1/10)$$

$$\Rightarrow \quad y_{i+2} - 2y_{i+1} + y_i = -\frac{1}{10} \quad ...(1)$$

Its A.E. is $(r-1)^2 = 0$ *i.e.* $r = 1, 1.$ $\Rightarrow$ C.F. $= c_1 + c_2 i$

Now $$\text{P.I.} = \frac{1}{(E-1)^2}\left(-\frac{1}{10}\right) = -\frac{1}{10}\frac{1}{(E-1)^2}(1)$$

$$= -\frac{1}{10}\frac{i(i-1)}{2} = \frac{1}{20}(i - i^2)$$

$\Rightarrow$ The C.S. is $y_i = c_1 + c_2 i + \frac{1}{20}(i - i^2)$

But $y_0 = 0, \Rightarrow c_1 = 0$ and $y_2 = 0, \Rightarrow c_2 = \frac{11}{20}$

$\therefore$ $y_i = \frac{11}{20} i + \frac{1}{20}(i - i^2)$. Now at the mid-point $i = 6$, so that $y_6 = 1.8\,cm$.

✦✦ Problem Set ✦✦

1. Write down the order of

(i) $y_{k+4} - 5y_{k+2} + 6y_k = 0$, **[Agra 2009]**

(ii) $y_{k+2} + 3y_{k+1} + 2y_k = k^2$. **[Agra 2005]**

2. (i) Show that $y_k = c_1 3^k + c_2 4^k$ is a solution of $y_{k+2} - 7y_{k+1} + 12y_k = 0$,

(ii) $y_k = 2^k\left[c_1 \cos\dfrac{2\pi k}{3} + c_2 \sin\dfrac{2\pi k}{3}\right]$ is a solution of $y_{k+2} + 2y_{k+1} + y_k = 0$,

3. Solve the following equation

(i) $\Delta^2 y_k + \Delta y_k = k + \sin k$,

(ii) $y_{k+1} - 3y_k = 2^k$, **[Gwalior 2006]**

(iii) $y_{k+1} - ky_k = 0$,

(iv) $y_{k+2} - 3y_{k+1} - 4y_k = m^k$,

(v) $y_{k+2} - 2my_{k+1} + (m^2 + n^2)y_k = m^k$, **[Agra 2009]**

(vi) $y_{k+2} - 8y_k = 0$,

(vii) $y_{k+2} - 5y_{k+1} + 6y_k = 5^k$,

(viii) $y_{k+2} - 5y_{k+2} + 8y_{k+1} - 4y_k = k.2^k$, **[Gwalior 2008]**

(ix) $y_{k+1} - 9y_k = (2k+1)a^k$,

(x) $y_{k+2} + 2y_{k+1} + y_k = k(k-1)(k-2) + k(-1)^k$.

4. Determine which of the following sets of functions are linearly dependent and which are linearly independents

(i) $2k, k-3$,

(ii) $k+4, k-2, 2k+1$

(iii) $k^2 - 2k, 3k, 4$,

(iv) $2^k, 2^{2k}, 2^{3k}$,

(v) $1, k, k^2, k^3, k^4$,

(vi) $k^2 - 3k + 2,\ k^2 + 5k - 4, 2k^2, 3^k$,

(vii) $2^k \cos k\theta, 2^k \sin k\theta$,

(viii) $k^2, (k+1)^2, (k+2)^2, (k+3)^2$.

5. Solve $y_{k+3} - 6y_{k+2} + 11y_{k+1} - 6y_k = 0$ subject to the given conditions $y_0 = 0, y_1 = 1, y_2 = 1$. **[Gwalior 2001, 2005]**

6. Solve each of the following subject to the given conditions, if any

(i) $y_{k+2} - 3y_{k+1} + 2y_k = 4^k$,

(ii) $y_{k+1} = y_k + k, y_0 = 1$,

(iii) $y_{k+2} - y_k = \dfrac{1}{2}k$.

7. Solve the following difference equation by operator methods

(i) $y_{k+2} + 4y_{k+1} + 4y_k = k^2 - 3k + 5$, **[Agra 2008]**

(ii) $y_{k+2} - 4y_{k+1} + 4y_k = k^2\, 2^k$.

8. Solve each of the following difference equations by using the method of variation of parameters

(i) $y_{k+2} - 5y_{k+1} + 6y_k = k^2$, **[Agra 2004]**

(ii) $y_{k+2} + y_k = (1/k)$.

9. $ky_{k+1} + 2y_k = 2$.

10. Show $y_k + y_{k+1} = y_k\, y_{k+1}$.

[**Hint:** *Let* $1/y_k = V_k$]

11. Show that general solution of $y_{k+2} - 2(\cos\alpha)y_{k+1} + y_k = R_k$ is given by

$$y_k = c_1 \cos k\alpha + c_2 \sin k\alpha + \sum_{p=1}^{\infty} \frac{R_k \sin(k-p)\alpha}{\sin\alpha}$$ where it is assumed that

$\alpha \neq 0, \pm\pi, \pm 2\pi, \ldots\ldots$

12. Solve the difference equation $y_{k+1} = 2y_k + 3, k = 1, 2, 3, \ldots$ and $y_0 = 0$.

13. Solve the difference equation $y_{k+1} = 2y_k + 1, k = 0, 1, 2, \ldots$ and $y_0 = 5$.

14. Solve the difference equation $2y_{k+1} - 5y_k = 3k + 1$.

15. Solve the following difference equation $2y_{k+1} - y_k = 2$.

16. Apply the generating function technique to solve the initial value problem

$y_{k+2} - y_{k+1} + y_k = 0, \; y_0 = 0, y_1 = 1$. **[Agra 2004]**

17. Write down the order and degree of the difference equation $y_{k+2} - 2y_{k+1} + y_k = c$.

[Agra 2003, 2009]

✦✦ Objective Type Question ✦✦

❖ Multiple Choice Questions

1. If $y = f(x)$ is a given function and h is the interval of differentiating, the notation $\Delta^n y/\Delta^n x$ stands for: **[Agra 2004]**

(a) $f(x+h)/n.h$ (b) $f(x+nh)/n.h$

(c) $f(x+h^n)/h^n$ (d) $f(x+nh)/h^n$.

2. The order of the difference equation $\phi[x, f(x+2h), f(x+3h), \ldots f(x+ph)] = 0$ is: **[Agra 2004, 2005]**

(a) p (b) $p+2$

(c) $p-2$ (d) 2.

3. Which of the following is not a linear difference equation:

(a) $a_0(k)\, E^n y_k + a_1(k)\, E^{n-1} y_k + \ldots + a_n(k)\, y_k = R(k)$ where $a_0(k) \pm 0$

(b) $[E^3 - 5E^2 + 6E + 3]\, y_k = 0$

(c) $y_k y_{k+1} = y_{k-1}^2$

(d) $[(2k+1)\, E^2 - 3\, KE + 4]\, y_k = 4K^3 - 3K$.

4. The difference equation $\frac{\Delta^2 y}{\Delta x^2} - 3\frac{\Delta y}{\Delta x} + 2y = 4x^{(2)}$ can be written as:

(a) $3f(x+2h) - 2f(x+h) + f(x) = 4h\, x^{(2)}$

(b) $f(x+2h) - (3h+2)\, f(x+h) + (2h^2 + 3h + 1)\, f(x) = 4h^2 x^{(2)}$

(c) $f(x+2h) + (3h+2)\, f(x+h) - (2h^2 + 3h + 1)\, f(x) = 4h^2 x^{(2)}$

(d) None of these.

5. The difference equation $\Delta y_k - 2y_k = 3$ can be written in subscript notation as:

(a) $y_{k+2} - 2y_k = 0$ (b) $y_{k+1} + 2y_k = 3$

(c) $y_{k+1} - 3y_k = 0$ (d) $y_{k+1} - 3y_k = 3$.

6. The function y given by $y_k = 1 - \frac{2}{k}, k = 1, 2, 3, \ldots$ is a solution of the difference equation:

(a) $(k+2)\, y_{k+1} + ky_k = 2k - 3$ (b) $(k+1)\, y_{k+1} + ky_k = 2k - 3$

(c) $k\, y_{k+1} + (k+1)\, y_k = 2k - 3$ (d) None of these.

7. Which of the following sets of functions are linearly independent:

(a) $2^k, 2^{k+3}$ (b) $5^{k+5}, 5^k$

(c) $2^k, k, 2^k, k^2, 2^k$ (d) None of these.

8. The set of functions $f_1(k), f_2(k), \ldots, f_n(k)$ is linearly independent iff;

(a) $$\begin{vmatrix} f_1(0) & f_2(0) & \cdots\cdots & f_n(0) \\ f_1(1) & f_2(1) & \cdots\cdots & f_n(1) \\ \cdots & \cdots & & \cdots \\ \cdots & \cdots & & \cdots \\ f_1(n-1) & f_2(n-1) & \cdots\cdots & f_n(n-1) \end{vmatrix} = 0$$

(b) $$\begin{vmatrix} f_1(1) & f_2(1) & \cdots\cdots & f_n(1) \\ f_1(2) & f_2(2) & \cdots\cdots & f_n(2) \\ \cdots & \cdots & & \cdots \\ \cdots & \cdots & & \cdots \\ f_1(n) & f_2(n) & \cdots\cdots & f_n(n) \end{vmatrix} \neq 0$$

(c) $$\begin{vmatrix} f_1(0) & f_2(0) & \cdots\cdots & f_n(0) \\ f_1(1) & f_2(1) & \cdots\cdots & f_n(1) \\ \cdots & \cdots & & \cdots \\ \cdots & \cdots & & \cdots \\ f_1(n-1) & f_2(n-1) & \cdots\cdots & f_n(n-1) \end{vmatrix} \neq 0$$

(d) None of these.

9. Which of the following is homogeneous linear difference equation:

(a) $[a_0(k)E^n + a_1(k)E^{n-1} + \ldots + a_n(k)I]\, y_k = 0$

(b) $\phi(E)\, y_k = R(k)$

(c) Both

(d) None.

10. The solution of the difference equation $16\, y_{k+2} - 8 y_{k+1} + y_k = 0$ is:

[Agra 2008 , 2009]

(a) $y_k = C_1\left(\frac{1}{2}\right)^k + c_2\left(\frac{1}{4}\right)^k$ (b) $y_k = (c_1 + 2k\, c_2)\left(\frac{1}{2}\right)^k$

(c) $y_k = (c_1 + c_2)\left(\frac{1}{4}\right)^k$ (d) $y_k = (c_1 + kc_2)\left(\frac{1}{4}\right)^k$.

11. The solution of the linear difference equation $y_{k+1} - ay_k = 0,\ a \neq 1$ is:

(a) $y_k = ak$ (b) $y_k = ca^k$

(c) $y = ca^k$ (d) $y_{k+1} = c\, a^{k+1}$.

12. The solution of the linear difference equation $y_{k+2} - 4y_{k+1} + 13y_k = 0$ is:

(a) $y_k = (3)^{k/2}[c_1 \cos(k\theta) + c_2 \sin(k\theta)]$, where $\theta = \tan^{-1}\left(\frac{3}{2}\right)$

(b) $y_k = (13)^{k/2}[c_1 \cos\theta + c_2 \sin\theta]$, where $\theta = \tan^{-1}\left(\frac{3}{2}\right)$

(c) $y_k = (13)^{k/2}[c_1 \cos(k\theta) + c_2(\sin k\theta)]$, where $\theta = \tan^{-1}\left(\frac{3}{2}\right)$

(d) None of these.

13. The order of the equation $y_{k+2} - 6y_{k+1} + 8y_k = 0$ is:

(a) 1 (b) 0

(c) 3 (d) 2.

14. What is the degree of the difference equation $y_{k+1}^2 - 3y_{k+1}y_k + 2y_k^2 = 0$:

(a) 2 (b) 1

(c) 3 (d) 0.

15. The order and degree of the difference equation $y_{k+2} - 2y_{k+1} + y_k = c$ is: **[Agra 2003, 2009]**

(a) 2, 2 (b) 2, 1

(c) 1, 1 (d) 0, 2

16. Given $f(x) = 3^x + x\,3^{x-1}$, the corresponding difference equation is: **[Agra 2005]**

(a) $f(x+1) - f(x) = 3^x$ (b) $f(x+1) - 2f(x) = 3^x$

(c) $f(x+1) - 3f(x) = 3^x$ (d) $f(x+1) - x\,f(x) = 3^x$.

17. The order and degree of the difference equation

$f^3(x)\,f^4(x+1) - 2f(x)\,f(x+2) + 4f^2(x+3) = p(x)$ is: **[Agra 2006]**

(a) (3,4) (b) (1,2)

(c) (3,3) (d) (3,2)

18. Solution of the difference equation $y_{x+2} - 8y_{x+1} + 15y_x = 0$ is: **[Agra 2007]**

(a) $y_x(C_1 + C_2 x)5^x$ (b) $C_1 + 5^x C_2 3^x$

(c) $C_1 e^{5x} + C_2 e^{3x}$ (d) $(3c_1 + 5c_2 x)e^{3x} + 5x^2$

19. The function $G(t) = (1-t)^{-1}$ is the generating function of the sequence: **[Agra 2007]**

(a) 1, 1, 1, 1, ... (b) 1, 2, 3, 4, ...

(c) 1, −2, 3, −4 ... (d) $y_k = \frac{k(k-1)}{2}$.

20. The generating function for $k(k+1)$ is:

(a) $\frac{1}{(1-t)}$ (b) $2t(1-t)^{-3}$

(c) $t(1-t)^{-2}$ (d) $(1-Bt)^{-1}$.

21. The generating function of the sequence 0, 1, 2, 3, ...∞ is: **[Agra 2008]**

(a) $(1-t)^{-1}$ (b) $(1-t)^{-2}$

(c) $t(1-t)^{-3}$ (d) $t(1-t)^{-2}$.

22. The differential equation $\frac{dy}{dx} = \frac{xy + 2y^2}{x^2 + 3xy}$ is: **[Agra 2008]**

(a) Linear

(b) Homogeneous

(c) Of first order but not of first degree

(d) None of these.

✦✦ Examination Questions ✦✦

1. Derive the formula $y_0 = (y_{-2} - 8y_{-1} + 8y_1 - y_2)/12h$ for numerical differentiation at mid-point of a table. **[U.P.T.U. 2009]**

2. If $y = f(x)$ and y_n denotes $f(x_0 + nh)$ prove that, if powers of h above h^6 be neglected.

$$\left(\frac{dy}{dx}\right)_{x=x_0} = \frac{3}{4h}\left[y_1 - y_{-1} - \frac{1}{5}(y_2 - y_{-2}) + \frac{1}{45}(y_3 - y_{-3})\right]$$

[U.P.T.U. 2006]

3. When does the need of numerical differentiation arise? **[U.P .T.U. 2008]**

Answers

Problem Set

1. (i)	4	**(ii)**	2
3. (i)	$y_k = c_1 \cos(k\theta) + c_2 \sin(k\theta) + \frac{x^{(2)}}{2} - k + 1 + \sin(k+1)\theta,\ \theta = \tan h^{-}(\sqrt{3})$		
(ii)	$y_0 = (a.3^k - 2^k)$	**(iii)**	$[y_k = a(k-1)!]$
(iv)	$y_k = a_1(-1)^k + a_2 4^k + \frac{m^k}{(m \pm 1)(m-4)}$		
(v)	$y_k = a_1(-4)^k + [(5k-6)/25]$		
(iv)	$y_k = 2^k[c_1 + c_2 \cos(2\pi k/3) + c_3 \sin(2\pi k/3)]$		
(vii)	$y_k = c_1 2^k + c_2 .3^k + (5^k/6)$		
(viii)	$y_k = c_1(1)^k + (c_2 + c_3 k)2^k + [2^k k^{(3)}/24]$		
(ix)	$y_k = a^{k-1}(k^2 + b)$		
(x)	$y_k = (c_1 + c_2 k)(-1)^k + \frac{1}{4}[k^3 - 6k^2 + \frac{10}{2}k - 3] + \frac{(-1)^k}{6}(k)^{(3)}$		
4. (i)	(iii), (iv), (v), (vi), (vii) are linearly independent.		
(ii)	(viii) are linearly dependent.		
5.	$y_k = 5.2^k - 2.3^k - 3$.		
6. (i)	$y_k = c_1 + c_2 2^k + \frac{1}{2}4^k,$		
(ii)	$y_k = (k^2/2) - (k/2) + 1.$		
(iii)	$y_k = c_1 + c_2(-1)^k - \frac{9}{8}3^{-k}.$		
7. (i)	$y_k = (-2)^k(c_1 + c_2 k) + \frac{k^2}{7} - \frac{13k}{27} + \frac{7}{9}.$		
(ii)	$y_k = 2^k(c_1 + c_2 k) + \frac{2^k}{48}(k^4 - 4k^3 + 5k^2 - 2).$		
8. (i)	$y_k = c_1 .2^k + c_2 .3^k + \frac{1}{2}k^2 + \frac{3}{2}k - \frac{5}{2}.$		
(ii)	$y_k = c_1 \cos\frac{k\pi}{2} + c_2 \sin\frac{k\pi}{2} + \sum_{r=0}^{\infty}\frac{(-1)^r}{k+2^r}$		

9.	$y_k = \dfrac{c\,(-2)^k}{(k+1)} + \sum_{r=0}^{\infty} \dfrac{(-1)^k k^{(r)}}{2^{r+1}}$	**10.**	$y_k = 2/[2 - c\,(-1)^k]$
12.	$y_k = 3\,(2^k - 1).$	**13.**	$y_k = 6.2^k - 1.$
14.	$y_k = \lambda \left(\dfrac{5}{2}\right)^k - k - 1.$	**15.**	$y_k = \lambda \left(\dfrac{1}{2}\right)^k + 2.$
16.	$y_k = \dfrac{-\sqrt{5}}{5}\left(\dfrac{1-\sqrt{5}}{2}\right)^k + \dfrac{\sqrt{5}}{5}\left(\dfrac{1+\sqrt{5}}{2}\right)^k.$	**17.**	1, 2.

❖ Multiple Choice Questions

1.	(d)	**2.**	(c)	**3.**	(c)	**4.**	(b)	**5.**	(d)
6.	(b)	**7.**	(c)	**8.**	(c)	**9.**	(a)	**10.**	(d)
11.	(b)	**12.**	(c)	**13.**	(d)	**14.**	(a)	**15.**	(b)
16.	(c)	**17.**	(d)	**18.**	(c)	**19.**	(a)	**20.**	(b)
21.	(d)	**22.**	(b).						

◆◆◆

Theory | Solved Examples | Problem Set

Chapter

10

Approximations and Errors in Computation

Introduction, Accuracy of numbers, Errors, Errors in the approximation of a function, Error in a series approximation, Order of approximation, Progagation of error, Remainder terms in various formulae.

10.1 Numbers and their Accuracy

We often come across with two types of numbers, one exact and the other approximate. Exact numbers are 3, 5, 7, 9, 10, 12, $\frac{3}{5}, \frac{1}{2}, \ldots, \pi, e, \ldots$ etc., whereas approximate numbers are those which represent the numbers to a certain degree of accuracy. The approximate value of π is 3.1416 and to a better approximation it is 3.14159265 but not exact value. Further, the digits which are used to express any numbers are called ***significant digits*** (*figures*); *e.g.*, the 3.14167, 0.889876, 2.35698 and 6.06878 all contain six significant digits (*figures*) whereas the number 0.000034 has only two significant digits viz, 3 and 4 since the zeros serve only to fix the position of decimal point. Sometimes, we come across numbers with a large number of digits and in making calculations it might be necessary to cut them to a useable number of figures. This process is known *as rounding off and will be done by the following rule.*

To round off a number to a significant digit, we shall discard all digits right of the n-th digit. If discarded number is

(*i*) *greater than* $\frac{1}{2}$ *a unit in the nth place, the nth digit would be increased by unity;*

(*ii*) *less than* $\frac{2}{1}$ *a unit in the nth place, the nth digit would be left unaltered;*

(*iii*) *exactly half a unit in the nth place, the nth digit would be increased by unity, if odd otherwise left unchanged.*

Then we say that the number is rounded-off to *n* significant figures. The following numbers are rounded-off to five significant figures:

1.64789 to 1.6479; 32.0523 to 32.052

0.83791 to 0.8379; 2.13159 to 2.1316

10.2 Errors and their Analysis

In numerical analysis, the analysis of error is of great importance. So far we have used various data on the assumption that they are pure and the techniques of their computation are prefect, but this is not the case all the time, either the data can be impure or there can be error in computational procedure. In this chapter we shall discuss different types of errors that can occur and their determination in the case of various interpolation and quadrature formulae:

Different Types of Errors

We can classify errors in Numerical Analysis in two major categories called ***Inherent*** and ***Truncation Errors.***

(1) ***Inherent Errors***

Mostly, numerical computations are not exact because of the following reasons

(i) the given data is approximate,

(ii) limitations of computing aids, *viz.* mathematical tables, desk calculators and the digital computer.

With the above limitations, the numbers are rounded-off causing *rounding errors.* However, in computations such errors can be minimised by obtaining better data after correcting obvious errors in the data and using computing, aids of higher precision. While carrying hand computations, the rounding off errors can be reduced by making computations to mere significant figures at each step of calculation. Practically at each step of the calculation, retain at least one more significant figure than that given in the data. Finally, perform the last operation and round off.

(2) ***Truncation Errors***

In the evaluation of certain quantities, which involve infinite mathematical process, we simply work with finite terms only this leads to error in the final results and this error is called ***Truncation Error*** *e.g.* while representing any function by an infinite Taylor series, the remainder term gives us the measure of ***Truncation Error.***

In case of calculus of finite differences we always make polynomial approximation in a given interval; further only finite number of terms are used depending on the number of known observations. All this leads to error in the final result.

If $$e^x = 1 + x + \frac{x^2}{2!} + \frac{x^3}{3!} + \frac{x^4}{4!} + \ldots + \infty = X, \text{ say}$$

is approximated by $1 + x + \dfrac{x^2}{2!} + \dfrac{x^3}{3!} = X'$, say.

Then truncation error $= X - X'$ and this error is a type of *algorithm error.*

10.3 General Method of Finding Remainder Term

In case of finite differences formulae, the remainder term can be found in the same manner as in the case of well known series of differential calculus by employing ***Remainder Theorem***.

The Rolle's Theorem states that–

If $f(x)$ is any function of nth degree in the interval $[a,b]$, satisfying the properties:

(i) It is continuous in the closed interval $[a, b]$,

(ii) It is differentiable in the open interval $]a,b[$,

(iii) $f(a) = f(b)$.

Then $f'(x)$ vanishes at $(n-1)$ points in (a,b); $f''(x)$ vanishes at $(n-2)$ points in (a,b),....; $f^{n-1}(x)$ will vanish at least at one point in (a,b).

Now Rolle's Theorem will be applied to find the remainder term for any function $f(x)$ which is represented by means of a polynomial of nth degree say $p_n(x)$.

10.4 Absolute, Relative and Percentage Errors

Absolute error (*i.e.* E_A) is the numerical difference in the true value with the approximate value as obtained by the measurement calculation. Let X be the true value of the quantity and X_1 be its approximate value; then absolute error $= |X - X_1| = \delta X = E_A$ say.

Relative error *i.e.* E_R is defined as the absolute error divided by the true value of the quantity *i.e.* $\left|\frac{\delta X}{X}\right|$. Also the percentage error *i.e.*

E_P is 100 times the relative error *i.e.* $100 \times \left|\frac{\delta X}{X}\right|$.

It is to be noted that absolute error is expressed in terms of units used whereas the relative and percentage errors are independent of the units used. Let ΔX be a number such that $|X_1 - X| \le \Delta X$; then is ΔX is the upper limit for the magnitude of the absolute error and is said to measure *absolute accuracy.* On the same lines, the quantity $\frac{\Delta X}{|X|} \approx \frac{\Delta X}{|X_1|}$, is the measure for the relative accuracy.

Note 1: The relative and percentage errors are independent of the units while absolute error is expressed in terms of these units.

Note 2: If a number is correct to n decimal places then the error $= \frac{1}{2}10^{-n}$. *e.g.* if a number is 3.1416 correct to 4 decimal places, then the error $= \frac{1}{2}10^{-4} = 0.00005$.

Note 3: If the first significant of a number is k and the number is correct to n significant figures, then the relative error $< 1/(k \times 10^{n-1})$.

Let us find the relative error in the number 864.32 correct to five significant figures.

Here $k=8, n=5$ and absolute error $>0.01\times 1/2=0.005$.

$$\text{Hence the relative error} \le \frac{0.005}{864.32}=\frac{5}{864320}$$

$$=\frac{1}{2\times 86432}<\frac{1}{2\times 80000}=\frac{1}{2\times 8\times 10^4}$$

$$<\frac{1}{8\times 10^4} \quad i.e. \quad \frac{1}{k\times 10^{n-1}}.$$ Hence the result is verified.

Solved Examples

Example 1: *Round off the numbers 865250 and 37.46235 to four significant figures and compute E_A, E_R, E_P in each case.* **[Delhi (H) 2007]**

Solution: (a) Number rounded off to four significant figures = 865200. Then we have

$$E_A=|X-X_1|=|865250-865200|=50$$

$$E_R=\left|\frac{X-X_1}{X}\right|=\frac{50}{865250}=6.71\times 10^{-5},$$

$$E_R=\left|\frac{X-X_1}{X}\right|=\frac{50}{865250}=6.71\times 10^{-5},$$

and $E_P=E_R\times 100=6.71\times 10^{-3}$.

(b) Number rounded off to four significant figures = 37.46

Then we have

$$E_A=|X-X_1|=|37.46235-37.46000|=0.00235$$

$$E_R=\left|\frac{X-X_1}{X}\right|=\frac{0.00235}{37.46235}=6.27\times 10^{-5},$$

and $E_P=E_R\times 100=6.27\times 10^{-3}$.

✦✦ Problem Set ✦✦

1. $\sqrt{29}=5.385$ and $\sqrt{\pi}=3.317$ correct to 4 significant figures. Find the relative errors in their sum and difference.
2. Find the percentage error if 625.483 is approximated to three significant figures.
3. Find the relative error if 2/3 is approximated to 0.667.
4. The discharge Q over a notch for head H is calculated by the formula $Q=kH^{5/2}$ where k is a given constant. If the head is 75 cm and an error of 0.15 cm is possible in its measurement, estimate the percentage error in computing the discharge.
5. The height of an observation tower was estimated to be 47 m, whereas its actual height was 45 m. Calculate the percentage relative error in the measurement. **[Agra 2000]**

✦✦ Answers ✦✦

1.	1.149×10^{-4}	2.	0.077
3.	0.0005	4.	0.5
5.	4.44%		

10.5 Error in the Approximation of a Function

Let $y = f(x_1, x_2)$ be a function of two variables x_1, x_2. Further, let $\delta x_1, \delta x_2$ be errors in x_1, x_2, then the error δy in y is given by $y + \delta y = f(x_1 + \delta x_1, x_2 + \delta x_2)$

$$\Rightarrow \quad y + \delta y = f(x_1, x_2) + \left(\frac{\partial f}{\partial x_1} \delta x_1 + \frac{\partial f}{\partial x_2} \delta x_2 \right)$$

$$+ \text{ terms involving higher powers of } \delta x_1 \text{ and } \delta x_2 \qquad ...(1)$$

(by Taylor's series)

Now, if the errors $\delta x_1, \delta x_2$ are so small that their squares and higher powers can be neglected, then (i) gives

$$\delta y = \frac{\partial f}{\partial x_1} \delta x_1 + \frac{\partial f}{\partial x_2} \delta x_2 \text{ approximately.} \quad \Rightarrow \delta y = \frac{\partial y}{\partial x_1} \delta x_1 + \frac{\partial y}{\partial x_2} \delta x_2$$

Thus in general, the error δy for the function $y = f(x_1, x_2, \ldots\ldots x_n)$ corresponding to the errors δx_i in x_i $(i = 1, 2, \ldots\ldots n)$ is given by $\delta y = \frac{\partial y}{\partial x_1} \delta x_1 + \frac{\partial y}{\partial x_2} \delta x_2 + \ldots\ldots + \frac{\partial y}{\partial x_n} \delta x_n$.

the relative error in y is $E_R = \frac{\delta y}{y} = \frac{\partial y}{\partial x_1} \frac{\delta x_1}{y} + \frac{\partial y}{\partial x_2} \frac{\delta x_2}{y} + \ldots\ldots + \frac{\partial y}{\partial x_n} \frac{\delta x_n}{y}$.

Example 2: *If $u = 4x^2 y^3 / z^4$ and errors in x, y, z be 0.001, compute the relative maximum error in u when $x = y = z = 1$.* **[P.T.U. (Punjab) 2001, 2004, 2008]**

Solution: We have $\frac{\partial u}{\partial x} = \frac{8xy^3}{z^4}, \frac{\partial u}{\partial y} = \frac{12x^2 y^2}{z^4}, \frac{\partial u}{\partial z} = -4z^{-5} - \frac{16x^2 y^3}{z^5}$

$$\Rightarrow \quad \delta u = \frac{\partial u}{\partial x} \delta x + \frac{\partial u}{\partial y} \delta y + \frac{\partial u}{\partial z} \delta z = \frac{8xy^3}{z^4} \delta x + \frac{12x^2 y^2}{z^4} \delta y - \frac{16x^2 y^3}{z^5} \delta z$$

The errors $\delta x, \delta y, \delta z$ may be positive or negative, so we take the absolute values of the terms on the right side.

$$\Rightarrow \quad (\delta u)_{\max} = \left| \frac{8xy^3}{z^4} \delta x \right| + \left| \frac{12x^2 y^2}{z^4} \delta y \right| + \left| \frac{16x^2 y^2}{z^4} \delta z \right|$$

$$= 8\,(0.001) + 12\,(0.001) + 16\,(0\,001) = 0.036.$$

$$\therefore \text{ maximum relative error} = \left(\frac{\delta u}{u} \right)_{\max} = 0.036 / 4 = 0.009.$$

Example 3: *Find the relative error in the function* $y = ax_1^{m_1} x_2^{m_2} \ldots\ldots x_n^{m_n}$

[Coimbatore (B.E.) 2002, 2005]

Solution: $\log y = \log a + m_1 \log x_1 + m_2 \log x_2 + \ldots + m_2 \log x_n$

$$\Rightarrow \quad \frac{1}{y}\frac{\partial y}{\partial x_1} = \frac{m_1}{x_1}, \quad \frac{1}{y}\frac{\partial y}{\partial x_2} = \frac{m_2}{x_2} \text{ etc.}$$

$$\text{Hence } E_R = \frac{\partial y}{\partial x_1}\frac{\delta x_1}{y} + \frac{\partial y}{\partial x_2}\frac{\delta x_2}{y} + \ldots\ldots + \frac{\partial y}{\partial x_n}\frac{\delta x_n}{y} = m_1\frac{\delta x_1}{x_1} + m_2\frac{\delta x_2}{x_2} + \ldots + m_n\frac{\delta x_n}{x_n}$$

But the errors $\delta x_i, \delta x_2, \ldots, \delta x_n$ may be positive or negative so we take the absolute values of the terms on the right side.

$$\Rightarrow \quad (E_R)_{\max} \le m_1\left|\frac{\delta x_1}{x_1}\right| + m_2\left|\frac{\delta x_2}{x_2}\right| + \ldots\ldots + m_n + \left|\frac{\delta x_n}{x_n}\right|$$

> **Note:** Taking $a = 1, m_1 = m_2 = \ldots = m_n = 1$, we get
>
> $$y = x_1 x_2 \ldots\ldots x_n. \qquad \Rightarrow E_R = \frac{\delta x_1}{x_1} + \frac{\delta x_2}{x_2} + \ldots + \frac{\delta x_n}{x_n}$$
>
> $\Rightarrow$ The relative error of a product of n numbers is approximately equal to the algebraic sum of their relative errors.

Example 4: *Consider* $u = 3\frac{xy}{z^2} = f(x, y, z)$. *to find* $(E_R)_{\max}$.

[M.D.U. (Rohtak) 2008; Avadh 2004, 2008]

Solution: $\frac{\partial u}{\partial x} = \frac{3y}{z^2}, \quad \frac{\partial u}{\partial y} = \frac{3x}{z^2}, \quad \frac{\partial u}{\partial z} = \frac{-6xy}{z^3}$

$$\Rightarrow \quad \Delta u = \frac{\partial u}{\partial x}\Delta x + \frac{\partial u}{\partial y}\Delta y + \frac{\partial u}{\partial z}\Delta z$$

$$\Rightarrow \quad \Delta u = \frac{3y}{z^2}\Delta x + \frac{3x}{z^2}\Delta y - \frac{6xy}{z^3}\Delta z$$

$$\Rightarrow \quad |\Delta u| = \left|\frac{3y}{z^2}\Delta x + \frac{3x}{z^2}\Delta y - \frac{6xy}{z^3}\Delta z\right|$$

$$\le \left|\frac{3y}{z^2}\Delta x\right| + \left|\frac{3x}{z^2}\Delta y\right| + \left|\frac{6xy}{z^3}\Delta z\right|$$

$$\Rightarrow \quad (\Delta u)_{\max} = \left|\frac{3y}{z^2}\Delta x\right| + \left|\frac{3x}{z^2}\Delta y\right| + \left|\frac{6xy}{z^3}\Delta z\right|$$

In particular, if $\Delta x = \Delta y = \Delta z = 0.0001$ and $x = y = z = 1$,

Then we have $(\Delta u)_{\max} = 3 \times 0.0001 + 3 \times 0.0001 + 6 \times 0.0001$.

$$\Rightarrow \quad (E_R)_{\max} = \frac{(\Delta u)_{\max}}{Y} = \frac{12 \times 0.0001}{3} = 0.0004.$$

10.6 Error Committed in a Series Approximation

Taylor's expansion of $f(x)$ at $x = a$ gives

$$f(x) = f(a + \overline{x-a}) = f(a) + (x-a)f'(a) + \frac{(x-a)^2}{2!} f''(a) + \ldots + \frac{(x-a)^{n-1}}{(n-1)!} f^{n-1}(a) + R_n(x)$$

Where $\quad R_n(x) = \frac{(x-a)^n}{n!} f^n(\theta), a < \theta < x.$

For a convergent series, $R_n(x) \to 0$ as $n \to \infty$ and hence if we approximate $f(x)$ by the first n terms of a series, then the maximum error. *i.e.* $(E_n)_{\max}$ commited in this approximation is given by $R_n(x)$, the remainder term of $f(x)$. Conversely if the accuracy required is told in advance then it would be possible to find n such that the series up to finite numbers of terms (n) yields the required accuracy.

Convergent series, $R_n(x) \to 0$ as $n \to \infty$ and hence if we approximate $f(x)$ by the first n terms of a series, then the maximum error *i.e.* $(E_n)_{\max}$ committed in this approximation is given by $R_n(x)$, the remainder term of $f(x)$. Conversely if the accuracy required is told in advance then it would be possible to find n such that series up to finite numbers of terms (n) yields the required accuracy.

Illustration: *Consider the Expansion of e^x by Maclaurin's Theorem*

i.e. $$e^x = 1 + x + \frac{x^2}{2!} + \frac{x^3}{3!} + \ldots + \frac{x^{n-1}}{(n-1)} + \frac{x^n}{n!} e^{\theta}, \quad 0 < \theta < x.$$

Here we want to obtain the number of terms, say n such that their sum gives the value of e^x correct to 8 decimal places at $x = 1$.

Error term *i.e.* remainder term is $\frac{x^n}{n!} e^x$

$\Rightarrow$ Max. absolute error at $(\theta = x) = \frac{x^n}{n!} e^x$

$\Rightarrow$ Maximum, relative error $= \frac{\left(\frac{x^n}{n!} e^x\right)}{e^x} = \frac{x^n}{n!}$

$\Rightarrow$ $(E_R)_{\max}$ at $x = 1$ is $\frac{1}{n!}$

For an eight decimal accuracy at $x = 1$, *we have* $\frac{1}{n!} < \frac{1}{2} 10^{-8}$

$\Rightarrow n = 13$; *i.e.* we need 12 terms of the exponential series so that its sum is correct to 8 decimal places.

✦✦ Problem Set ✦✦

1. If $R = 4xy^2 / z^3$ and errors in x, y, z be 0.001, show that the maximum relative error at $x = y = z = 1$ is 0.006.

2. If $V = \frac{1}{2}\left(\frac{r^2}{h} + h\right)$ and the error in V is at the most 0.4%, find the percentage error allowable in r and h when $r = 5.1\ cm$ and $h = 5.8\ cm$.

3. Find the smaller root of the equation $x^2 - 400x + 1 = 0$, correct to 4 decimal places.

4. If $r = 3h(h^6 - 2)$, find the percentage error in r at $h = 1$, if the percentage error in h is 5.

5. Find the value of $I = \int_0^{0.8} \frac{\sin x}{x} dx$ correct to 4 decimal places.

6. If $R = 10x^3 y^2 z^2$ and errors in x, y, z are 0.03, 0.1., 0.02 respectively at $x = 3, y = 1, z = 2$. Calculate the absolute error and % relative error in evaluating R?

✦✦ Answers ✦✦

2.	0.23; 0.14	3.	0.0025
4.	0.75	5.	0.7721
6.	140.4; 13%		

10.7 Order of Approximation

We usually replace a function $f(h)$ with its approximation by $\phi(h)$ and the error bound is known to be $\mu(h^n)$, where n is a positive integer $\Rightarrow |f(h) - \phi(h)| \leq \mu |h^n|$,

for sufficiently small h. *We now say that $\phi(h)$ approximates $f(h)$ with order of approximation $o(h^n)$ and write $f(h) = \phi(h) + Of(h^n)$.*

e.g.
$$\frac{1}{1-h} = 1 + h + h^2 + h^3 + h^4 + h^5 + \ldots$$

is written as
$$\frac{1}{1-h} = 1 + h + h^2 + h^3 + O(h^4) \quad \ldots(1)$$

to the 4th order approximation.

Also
$$\cos(h) = 1 - \frac{h^2}{2!} + \frac{h^4}{4!} - \frac{h^6}{6!} + \frac{h^8}{8!} - \ldots$$

so, to the 6th order of approximation, we have

$$\cos(h) = 1 - \frac{h^2}{2!} + \frac{h^4}{4!} + o(h^6) \quad \ldots(2)$$

Adding (1) and (2), we get

$$(1-h)^{-1} + \cos(h) = 2 + h + h\frac{h^2}{2!} + h^3 + O(h^4) + \frac{h^4}{4!} + O(h^6) \quad \ldots(3)$$

Again $O(h^4) + \frac{h^4}{4!} = O(h^4)$ and $O(h^4) + O(h^6) = O(h^4)$. Hence (3) could be written as

$$(1-h)^{-1} + \cos(h) = 2 + h + \frac{h^2}{2} + h^3 + O(h^4)$$

which is of the 4th order of approximation.

and similarly

$$(1-h)^{-1}\cos(h)=(1+h+h^2+h^3)\left(1-\frac{h^2}{2!}+\frac{h^4}{4!}\right)+(1+h+h^2+h^3)\,O(h^6)$$

$$+\left(1-\frac{h^2}{2!}+\frac{h^4}{4!}\right)O(h^4)+O(h^4)\,O(h^6)$$

$$=1+h+\frac{h^2}{2}+\frac{h^3}{2}-11\frac{h^4}{24}+\frac{11}{24}h^5+\frac{h^6}{24}+\frac{h^7}{24}$$

$$+O(h^4)+O(h^6)+O(h^4)\,O(h^6) \qquad ...(4)$$

$$[\because O(h^4)\,O(h^6)=O(h^{10})$$

and $$-\frac{11h^4}{24}+\frac{11}{24}h^5+\frac{h^6}{24}+\frac{h^7}{24}+O(h^4)+O(h^6)+O(h^{10})$$

$$=1+h+\frac{h^2}{2}+\frac{h^3}{2}+O(h^4).$$

10.8 Remainder Term of Various Interpolation Formulae

[Agra 2003; Avadh 2003, 2004]

(1) Remainder Term in Lagrange's Interpolation Formulae

Let $f(x)$ be any function which is approximated by means of some polynomial $P_n(x)$ in x of n-th degree.

Now, Let the value of the function $f(x)$ be given at the points $x = x_0, x_1, x_2, \ldots, x_n$ and suppose the function $f(x)$ satisfies all the conditions of Rolle's theorem. But the function $f(x)$ is approximated by $P_n(x)$ so $P_n(x)$ has the same values as $f(x)$ at the points $x_0, x_1, \ldots, x_n$,

Further, let $$f(x) = P_n(x) + g(x) \qquad ...(1)$$

where $g(x)$, has the roots $x_0, x_1, \ldots, x_n$.

$$\Rightarrow \quad f(x) = P_n(x) + k(x)(x-x_0)(x-x_1)\ldots(x-x_n) \qquad ...(2)$$

Where $k(x)$ is to obtained.

To determine $k(x)$, we proceed as follows:

Let $$\phi(t) = f(t) - P_n(t) - k(x)(t-x_0)(t-x_1)\ldots\ldots(t-x_n) \qquad ...(3)$$

The function $\phi(t)$ vanishes for $(n+1)$ values of t *namely* $t = x_0, x_1, \ldots, x_n$; *also the function* $\phi(t)$ *varnishes for* $t = x$ by virtue of (2). Hence the function $\phi(t)$ vanishes for the $n+2$ real roots $x, x_0, x_1, \ldots, x_n$. It is also a continuous function of t possessing continuous derivatives of all orders within the interval $[x_0, x_n]$, so applying Rolle's theorem, $\varphi'(t)$ has at least $(n+1)$ roots lying between the smallest and greatest of the above roots. Similarly $\phi''(t)$ has at least n roots in the same interval and in the end $\phi^{n+1}(t)$ has at least on root, say $t = \xi$ in the interval $[x_0, x_n]$.

Using (3), $\phi^{n+1}(t) = f^{n+1}(t) - k(x).\{(n+1)!\}.$ $[\because P_n^{\ n+1}(t) = 0]$

$\Rightarrow$ $\phi^{n+1}(\xi) = f^{\,n+1}(\xi) - k(x).\{(n+1)!\}.$

But $\phi^{n+1}(t)$ vanishes at the points $t = \xi$ where $x_0 < \xi < x_n$ therefore, we have

$$f^{n+1}(\xi) - k(x)\{(n+1)!\} = 0; \qquad [x_0 < \xi < x_n]$$

$$\Rightarrow \quad k(x) = \frac{1}{(n+1)!} f^{n+1}(\xi). \qquad [x_0 < \xi < x_n] \qquad \text{...(4)}$$

Putting this values of $k(x)$ in (2), we get

$$f(x) = p_n(x) + f^{n+1}(\xi)\frac{(x-x_0)(x-x_1)\dots(x-x_n)}{(n+1)!}.$$

Thus, the required truncation error in approximating $f(x)$ by

$$P_n(x) = R_n = f(x) - p_n(x)$$

$$= \frac{(x-x_0)(x-x_1)\dots(x-x_n)}{(n+1)!} f^{n+1}(\xi) = \frac{f^{n+1}(\xi)}{(n+1)} \prod_{i=0}^{n}(x-x_i) \qquad \text{...(5)}$$

This is the remainder term in ***Lagrange's formula.***

(2) Remainder Term in Newton's Forward Interpolation Formula **[Avadh 2005]**

Let value $x_0, x_1, \dots. x_n$, be given at equal intervals, say, h

Then, we have $x - x_0 = hu, x - x_1 = x - (x_0 + h)$

$$= hu - h = h(u-1), \dots., x - x_n = h(u-n).$$

Now, putting the values of $x - x_0, x - x_1, x - x_n$, in (5)

we get $$R_n = \frac{u(u-1)\dots(u-n)}{(n+1)!} h^{n+1} f^{n+1}(\xi)$$

$$= \frac{u^{(n+1)}}{(n+1)!} h^{n+1} f^{n+1}(\xi) \; [x_0 < \xi < x_n] \qquad \text{...(6)}$$

This is the remainder term in Newton's formula to forward interpolation. Form (6) it is obvious R_n contains derivative of $(n+1)$ th order of the function $f(x)$ at $x = \xi$ and so we may not say anything about the error when the form of the function is not known to us. The only choice becomes that, if $f^{n+1}(\xi)$ can be expressed in terms of the differences of the function $f(x)$ then an approximate value of the error can be computed.

Again, From the relation between differences and deviates of a function $f(x)$, we have $\Delta^n f(x) = (\Delta x)^n f^n(x + \theta\, n\, \Delta x), 0 < \theta < 1.$ ...(7)

Whence putting $x = x_0$ and $\Delta x = h$ in (7) we readily obtain

$$f^n(x_0 + \theta\, n\, h) = \frac{\Delta^n f(x_0)}{h^n} \qquad \text{...(8)}$$

But $x_0 + \theta nh$ and ξ are the values of x at points with in the interval of interpolation *i.e.*, (x_0, x_n) so far practical purposes, we can put $\xi = x_0 0 + \theta nh$

Thus (8) $\Rightarrow \quad f^n(\xi) = \dfrac{\Delta^n f(x_n)}{h^n}$

$$\Rightarrow \quad f^{n+1}(\xi) = \frac{\Delta^{n+1} f(x_0)}{h^{n+1}} \qquad \text{...(9)}$$

Now, putting the values of $f^{n+1}(\xi)$ from (9) in (6), we obtain

$$R_n = \frac{u^{n+1}}{(n+1)!} \Delta^{n+1} f(x_0). \qquad \text{...(10)}$$

(3) Remainder Term in Newton's Formula for Backward Interpolation

[Agra 2002]

Let us write $f(x) = p_n(x) + k(x)(x - x_n)(x - x_{n-1})\ldots(x - x_0)$, ...(11)

where $k(x)$ is to be determined in terms of the function.

Now, consider the function

$$\phi(t) = f(t) - p_n(t) - k(x)(t - x_n)(t - x_{n-1})\ldots(t - x_0)$$

Proceeding in the same way as in (1) we readily get

$$k(x) = f^{n+1}(\xi) / \{(n+1)!\}, x_0 < \xi < x_n.$$

$$\therefore \quad \text{error } R_n = f(x) - P_n(x) = k(x)(x - x_n)(x - x_{n-1})\ldots(x - x_0)$$

$$= f^{n+1}(\xi) \frac{(x - x_n)(x - x_{n-1})\ldots(x - x_0)}{(n+1)!} \qquad \text{...(12)}$$

But, to obtain the value of R_n in terms of u we recall that

$$\frac{x - x_n}{h} = u, \quad \frac{x - x_{n-1}}{h} = u + 1, \ldots \frac{x - x_0}{h} = u + n$$

Substituting these values of $x - x_n, x - x_{n-1}, \ldots, x - x_0$ in (12)

we obtain $\quad R_n = u(u+1)\ldots(u+n) \dfrac{h^{n+1}}{(n+1)!} f^{n+1}(\xi).$ ...(13)

This is the required remainder term in Newton's Backward formula.

Note: If the analytical form of the given function is not known then to find a formula for R_n, we put $\nabla^{n+1} f(x_n) / h^{n+1}$ for $f^{n+1}(\xi)$ in (13)

and obtain $\quad R_n = \dfrac{\nabla^{n+1} f(x_n)}{(n+1)!} u(u+1)(u+2)\ldots(u+n)$ ...(14)

(4) Remainder Term in Stirling's Formula **[Agra 2000]**

Let the function $f(x)$ be approximated by a polyonomial $P_{2n}(x)$. In Stirling's formula there are $2n+1$ terms so, we say that $p_{2n}(x)$ coincides with function $f(x)$ at the $2n+1$ points given below:

$$u = -n, -(n-1), -(n-2), \ldots, -2, -1, 0, 1, 2, \ldots, n-2, n-1, n$$

i,e, at $\quad x = x_0 - nh, x_0 - (n-1)h, \ldots, x_0 - h, x_0, x_0 + h, \ldots, x_0 + (n-1)h, x_0 + nh$

Now, let us assume that

$$f(x) = p_{2n}(x) + k(x)(x-x_0)(x-x_1)(x-x_{-1})\ldots(x-x_n)(x-x_{-n}), \quad \ldots(15)$$

Where $k(x)$ is to be obtained in terms of $f(x)$.

Further, we consider the function

$$\phi(t) = f(t) - p_{2n}(t) - k(x)(t-x_0)(t-x_1)(t-x_{-1})\ldots(t-x_n)(t-x_{-n}). \quad \ldots(16)$$

It vanishes for the $2n+2$ values

$t = x, x_0, x_1, x_{-1}, \ldots, x_n, x_{-n}$ therefore by Rolle's theorem; we say that

$\phi^{2n+1}(t)$ has at least one root $t = \xi$ in the interval x_{-n} to x_n.

But $\phi^{2n+1}(t) = f^{2n+1}(t) - k(x)\{(2n+1)!\}$,

$$\Rightarrow \quad \phi^{2n+1}(\xi) = f^{2n+1}(\xi) - k(x)\{(2n+1)!\}$$

$$\Rightarrow \quad \phi^{2n+1}(\xi) = 0 \Rightarrow k(x) = f^{2n+1}(\xi)/\{(2n+1)!\}, (x_{-n} < \xi < x_n).$$

Now, putting the value of $k(x)$ in (15), we have

$$f(x)p_{2n}(x) + f^{2n+1}(\xi)\frac{(x-x_0)(x-x_1)(x-x_{-1})\ldots(x-x_n)(x-x_{-n})}{(2n+1)!}$$

Consequently, the error $R_n = f(x) - p_{2n}(x)$

$$= f^{2n+1}(\xi)\frac{(x-x_0)(x-x_1)(x-x_{-1})\ldots(x-x_n)(x-x_{-n})}{(2n+1)!}$$

To write this formula in terms of u we proceed as follows:

$$x - x_0 = hu, x - x_1 = h(u-1), \ldots, x - x_n = h(u-n),$$

and $\quad x - x_{-1} = x - (x_0 - h) = hu + h = h(u+1).$

$$x - x_{-2} = h(u+2), \ldots, x - x_{-n} = h(u+n),$$

$$\Rightarrow \quad R_n = \frac{h^{2n+1} f^{2n+1}(\xi)}{(2n+1)!} u(u^2-1^2)(u^2-2^2)\ldots(u^2-n^2) \quad \ldots(17)$$

[where $x_{-n} < \xi < x_n$].

To put the values of R_n in terms of difference, we replace

$f^{2n+1}(\xi)$ by $\dfrac{\Delta^{2n+1} f(x_{-n-1}) + \Delta^{2n+1} f(x_{-n})}{2}$ in (17) and putting $h = 1$, we immediately obtain

$$R_n = \frac{\Delta^{2n+1} f(x_{-n-1}) + \Delta^{2n+1} f(x_{-n})}{2.\{(2n+1)!\}} u(u^2-1^2)(u^2-2^2)\ldots(u^2-n^2)$$

(5) Remainder Term in Bessel's Formula

Consider $p_{2n+1}(x)$ as the polynomial of $(2n+1)$ th degree in x representing the given function $f(x)$. There are $2n+2$ terms Bessel's formula. The polynomial coincidies with the given function at the $2n+2$ points, given below:

$$u = -n, -(n-1), \ldots, -1, 0, 1, \ldots, n-1, n, n+1$$

i.e. at $\quad x = x_0 - nh, x_0 - (n-1)h, \ldots x_0 - h, x_0, x_0 + h, x_0 + nh, x_0 + (n+1)h.$

Let us now assume

$$f(x) = p_{2n+1}(x) + k(x)(x-x_0)(x-x_1)(x-x_{-1})\ldots(x-x_n)\ldots(x-x_{-n})(x-x_{n+1}), \quad \ldots(18)$$

Where $k(x)$ is to be obtained in terms of $f(x)$.

We now consider the function

$$\phi(t) = f(t) - p_{2n+1}(t) - k(x)(t-x_0)(t-x_1)(t-x_{-1})\ldots(t-x_n)(t-x_{-n})(t-x_{n+1}) \quad \ldots(19)$$

It obviously vanishes at the $2n+3$ points, *viz.* at

$$t = x, x_0, x_1, x_{-1}, \ldots, x_n, x_{-n}, x_{n+1}.$$

So by Rolle's theorem, $\phi^{2n+2}(\xi) = 0$ for some value $t = \xi$ in the interval (x_{-n}, x_{n+1}).

Now $\quad \phi^{2n+2}(t) = f^{2n+2}(t) - k(x)\{(2n+2)!\}$

[$\because$ $(2n+2)$ th derivative of $p_{2n+1}(t)$ is zero]

$$\Rightarrow \quad \phi^{2n+2}(\xi) = 0 \Rightarrow f^{2n+2}(\xi) - k(x)\{(2n+2)!\} = 0$$

$$\therefore \quad k(x) = f^{2n+2}(\xi)/(2n+2)!, x_{-n} < \xi < x_{n+1}$$

Now putting the value of $k(x)$ in (18), we obtain

$$f(x) = P_{2n+1}(x) + \frac{f^{2n+2}(\xi)}{(2n+2)}(x-x_0)(x-x_1)(x-x_{-1})\ldots(x-x_n)(x-x_{-n})(x-x_{n+1})$$

$\therefore$ error $R_n = f(x) - p_{2n+1}(x)$

$$= \frac{f^{2n+1}(\xi)}{(2n+2)!}(x-x_0)(x-x_1)(x-x_{-1})\ldots(x-x_n)(x-x_{-n})(x-x_{n+1}) \quad \ldots(20)$$

To find the value of R_n in terms of u, we put $x - x_0 = hu$

$$x - x_1 = h(u-1), x - x_{-1} = h(u+1), \text{etc.}$$

$$\Rightarrow \quad R_n = \frac{h^{2n+2}}{(2n+2)!} f^{2n+2}(\xi)\, u(u-1)(u+1)\ldots(u-n)(u+n)(u-n-1).$$

Again, putting $u = v + \frac{1}{2}$, we readily obtain

$$R_n = \frac{h^{2n+2}}{(2n+2)!} f^{2n+2}(\xi)\left(v^2 - \frac{1}{4}\right)\left(v^2 - \frac{9}{4}\right)\ldots\left(v^2 - \frac{(2n+1)^2}{4}\right) \quad \ldots(21)$$

which in terms of differences is reduced to

$$R_n = \frac{\Delta^{2n+2} y_{(-n-1)} + \Delta^{2n+2} y_{-n}}{2(2n+2)!}\left(v^2 - \frac{1}{4}\right)\left(v^2 - \frac{9}{4}\right)\ldots\left(v^2 - \frac{(2n+1)^2}{4}\right).$$

10.9 Errors in Different Quadrature Formulae

(1) Inherent Error in Simpson's one-third rule: Let $f(x)$ be a finite and continuous having continuous derivatives upto fourth order in the interval $x = x_0 - h$ to $x_0 + h$

Now, let $F(x)$ denote the integral of $f(x)$, then we have

$$F(x) = \int_a^x f(x)\,dx,\quad F'(x) = f(x),\quad F''(x) = f'(x), \text{etc.}$$

Also. $$I = \int_{x_0-h}^{x_0+h} f(x)\,dx = F(x_0+h) - F(x_0-h). \qquad ...(1)$$

But, by Simpson's '1/3' rule, the value of this integral comes out to be

$$I_s = (h/3)[f(x_0-h) + 4f(x_0) + f(x_0+h)]. \qquad ...(2)$$

The inherent error in Simpson's rule $= E_s$

$$= I - I_s = F(x_0+h) - F(x_0-h)$$

$$= (h/3)[f(x_0-h) + 4f(x_0) + f(x_0+h)] \qquad ...(3)$$

Now, by Taylor's theorem, we have

$$F(x_0+h) = F(x_0) + hF'(x_0) + \frac{h^2}{2}F''(x_0) + \frac{h^3}{3!}F'''(x_0) + \ldots$$

$$F(x_0-h) = F(x_0) - hF'(x_0) + \frac{h^2}{2}F''(x_0) - \frac{h^3}{3!}F'''(x_0) + \ldots$$

$$f(x_0+h) = f(x_0) + hf'(x_0) + \frac{h^2}{2}f''(x_0) + \frac{h^3}{3!}f'''(x_0) + \ldots$$

$$f(x_0-h) = f(x_0) - hf'(x_0) + \frac{h^2}{2}f''(x_0) - \frac{h^3}{3!}f'''(x_0) + \ldots$$

But $$F'(x) = f(x), = F''(x) = f'(x) \text{ etc.,}$$

$\therefore$ $$F(x_0+h) = F(x_0) + hf(x_0) + \frac{h^2}{2}f'(x_0) + \frac{h^3}{3!}f''(x_0) + \ldots$$

$$F(x_0-h) = F(x_0) - hf(x_0) + \frac{h^2}{2}f'(x_0) - \frac{h^3}{3!}f''(x_0) + \ldots$$

Now putting these values of $F(x_0+h), F(x_0-h), f(x_0+h)$ and $f(x_0-h)$ in (3), we obtain $E_s = -\frac{h^5}{90}[f^{iv}(x_0) + \ldots] = -\frac{h^5}{90}f^{iv}(x_0)$, where we have neglected derivates of order higher than four. This is the required error in the interval $x_0 - h$ to $x_0 + h$.

Hence the error over the interval $x_1 - h$ to $x_1 + h$ is given by $-\frac{h^5}{90}f^{iv}(x_1)$.

There fore the inherent error for the interval $b - a$ is

$$E_s = -\frac{h^5}{90}\left[f^{iv}(x_1) + f^{iv}(x_3) + \ldots + f^{iv}(x_{n-1})\right] \qquad ...(4)$$

Where $$x_0 = a, x_n = x_0 + nh = b, x_i = x_0 + ih$$

Let $f^{iv}(x_m)$ denote the greatest value of any of the $n/2$ terms within the bracket of (4); then putting $f^{iv}(x_m)$ for each $f^{iv}(x_i)$, we get

$$E_s \le -\frac{h^5}{90}\cdot\frac{n}{2} f^{iv}(x_m) = -\frac{b-a}{180} h^4 f^{iv}(x_m) \quad ...(5)$$

$[\because nh = b-a]$

Now the value of $E_s = 0$ when $f^{iv}(x) = 0$ *i.e.* when $f(x)$ is a polynomial of degree one, two or three. Then Simpson's rule gives the exact value of the integral

$$\int_a^b f(x)\,dx.$$

(2) Error in Trapezoidal Rule: Let the interval of integration be defined in the interval $(x_0, x_0 + h)$

Then we have $$I = \int_{x_0}^{x_0+h} f(x)\,dx = F(x_0 + h) - F(x_0) \quad ...(6)$$

But by trapezoidal rule, the value of this integral comes out to be

$$I_t = \frac{1}{2}\left[f(x_0) + f(x_0 + h)\right].$$

Thus the inherent error in the trapezoidal rule is gives by

$$E_t = I - I_t = \left[F(x_0 + h) - F(x_0)\right] - \frac{1}{2}\left[f(x_0) + f(x_0 + h)\right] \quad ...(7)$$

Now proceeding exactly as in case (1), we have

$$E_t = -\frac{h^3}{12} f''(x_0) + ... \quad ...(8)$$

$= -\frac{h^3}{12} f''(x_0)$, where derivatives of order higher than two have been neglected. Thus the error for the whole interval $x = a$ to $x = b$ is given by

$$E_t = -\frac{h^3}{12}\left[f''(x_0) + f''(x_1) + ... + f''(x_{n-1})\right].$$

Where $$x_0 = a, x_i = x_0 + ih, x_n = x_0 + nh = b.$$

If $f''(x_m)$ denotes the greatest value of any of the n quantities within the brackets; then putting $f''(x_m)$, for each $f''(x_i)$, we obtain

$$E_t \le -\frac{h^3}{12}.nf''(x_m) = -\frac{(b-a)}{12} h^2 f''(x_m) \quad ...(9)$$

Now, $E_t = 0$ when $f''(x) = 0$ *i.e.* if $f(x)$ is a polynomial of degree one.

Then trapezoidal rule gives of the exact value the integral $\int_a^b f(x)\,dx$.

(3) Error in Simpson's Three-Eighth Rule: Considering the interval of integration form $x = x_0$ to $x = x_0 + 3h$, we have

$$I = \int_{x_0}^{x_0+3h} f(x)\,dx = F(x_0 + 3h) - F(x_0). \qquad \text{...(10)}$$

The value of the integral by Simpson's '3/8' rule is

$$I_s = \frac{3h}{8}\left[f(x_0) + 3f(x_0 + h) + 3f(x_0 + 2h) + f(x_0 + 3h)\right] \qquad \text{...(11)}$$

$\therefore$ the inherent error $= I - I_s = \dfrac{-3}{80} h^3 f^{iv}(x_0)$

neglecting derivatives of order higher than four.

Hence the error for the whole interval $x = a$ to $x = b$ is given by

$$E_s = \frac{-3}{80} h^5 \left[f^{(iv)}(x_0) + f^{(iv)}(x_5) + \ldots + f^{(iv)}(x_{n-3})\right]$$

Where $\quad x_0 = a, \; x_i = x_0 + ih, \; x_n = x_0 + nh = b$

Let $f^{(iv)}(x_k)$ denote the greatest value of any of the $\left(\dfrac{n}{3}\right)$ quantities within the brackets.

Then

$$E_s \leq \frac{-3}{80} h^5 \cdot \frac{n}{3} f^{(iv)}(x_k) = -\frac{b-a}{80} h^4 f^{iv}(x_k)$$

when $f(x)$ is a polynomial of degree one, two or three.

Simpson's three-eight rule gives the exact value of the integral $\int_a^b f(x)\,dx$.

Example 5: *Find the maximum error the interpolation of* sin 52° *by Newton's Formula for forward interpolation, given*

sin 45° = 0.7071,	sin 50° = 0.7660
sin 55° = 0.8192,	sin 60° = 0.8660

Solution: Construct the following difference table:

x	$y = f(x)$	$\Delta f(x)$	$\Delta^2 f(x)$	$\Delta^3 f(x)$
45°	0.7071			
		0.0589		
50°	0.7660		– 0.0057	
		0.0532		– 0.0007
55°	0.8192		– 0.0064	
		0.0468		
60°	0.8660			

We have calculated sin 82° by Newton's interpolation formula earlier which comes out to be sin 52° = 0.78780032.

Now, we have $R_n = \dfrac{\Delta^{n+1}}{(n+1)!} u(u-1)(u-2)\ldots(u-n);$

Where $u = (x - x_0)/h$

Here, $u = \dfrac{52-45}{5} = 1.4$. Let us assume $n = 2$

$$\Rightarrow \quad R_n = \frac{\Delta^3 yo}{3!} u(u-1)(u-2)$$

$$= -(0.0007)\frac{(1.4)(.4)(-.6)}{3!} = .0000392.$$

✦✦ Problem Set ✦✦

1. Find the value of the integral $\int_{30^\circ}^{90^\circ} \log_{10} \sin x \, dx$ by Simpson's Rule taking ten sub-intervals and estimate the error in your answer.

2. Find the value of the integral $\int_{200}^{1000} \frac{dx}{\log_{10^x}}$. taking eight sub-intervals. Estimate the inherent error in your answer.

3. Find the expression for remainder term in Lagrange's formula.

4. Find an estimate of error in Gauss's interpolation formula. **[Patna 2002, 2007]**

5. Derive the expression for the remainder term in Newton's forward formula.

6. Find expression for the remainder term in Bassel's formula when terminated with a difference of even order. **[Patna 2009]**

◆◆◆

Theory | Solved Examples | Problem Set

Chapter 11 Numerical Solutions of Ordinary Differential Equations of First and Second Order

Introduction, Picard's Method, Tylor's Series Method, Euler's Method, Modified Euler's Method, Runge's Method, Runge-Kutta Method, Predictor-Corrector Method, Milne's Method, Adams-Bashforth Method, Simultaneous First Order Differential Equations, Second Order Differential Equations.

11.1 Introduction

Here we shall develop certain methods of obtaining the numerical solution of any desired degree of accuracy of first and second order differential equations, consisting of numerical coefficients under given conditions. The process consists of equal intervals, say h, in the independent variable, say x_r, and then the solution is evaluated step by step. Thus if the solution is carried to $x = x_r$ then the next step consists of evaluating the change in the solution in the interval h of x from x_r to x_{r+1}. In such methods, the nature of the equation is not so important as the nature of the boundary and other conditions to be satisfied by the solution; so it is very much essential to study the nature of the boundary conditions at one point of the range of integration, then they are termed as one point boundary conditions, but if the conditions are given at two points of the range of integration then they are termed as two points boundary conditions.

Further, we know that all differential equations cannot be integrated analytically. For example, consider the differential equation $\frac{dy}{dx} = x^2 + y^2 - a^2$. Of course, this is an ordinary differential equation of first order but it has not been possible up till now to find analytical solution of this differential equation. In equations of this type we try to find out their numerical solution. We will be considering here some methods of solving numerically ordinary differential equations of first order. There are method by which numerical coefficients and given initial condition can be found to any desired degree of accuracy.

The important methods of solving ordinary differential equations of first order, numerically, are as follows:

(i) Picard' method of successive approximations

(ii) Euler's method (iii) Modified Euler' method

(iv) Taylor's Series method (v) Milne's Series method

(vi) Runge's method (vii) Runge-Kutta method

(viii) Adams Bashforth method.

In case of ordinary differential equations of the first order, one arbitrary constant quantity comes in the solution and this will be determined by the condition given to us.

11.2 *Picard's Method of Successive Approximations

[Avadh 2004; Agra 2003, 2005; Bhopal 2000, 2001; Rohilkhand 2008]

Consider the following differential equation:

$$\frac{dy}{dx} = f(x, y); \text{ initial condition is that } y = y_0 \text{ at } x = x_0.$$

Integrating the above equation between the limits x_0 and x, we get

$$\int_{y_0}^{y} dy = \int_{x_0}^{x} f(x, y)\, dx \quad \text{or} \quad y - y_0 = \int_{x_0}^{x} f(x, y)\, dx,$$

$$y = y_0 + \int_{x_0}^{x} f(x, y)\, dx. \qquad \ldots(1)$$

For a first approximation, we replace y and y_0 in $f(x, y)$; for a second, we replace it by the first approximation, for a third by the second and so forth.

Now first approximation, $y^{(1)} = y_0 + \int_{x_0}^{x} f(x, y_0)\, dx,$ ...(2)

Second approximation, $y^{(2)} = y_0 + \int_{x_0}^{x} f(x, y^{(1)})\, dx;$ ...(3)

... ...

nth approximation $y^{(n)} = y_0 + \int_{x_0}^{x} f(x, y^{(n-1)})\, dx$, with $y^{(0)} = y_0$

As a matter of fact, the process is stopped when the two values of y *viz.* $y^{(n-1)}$ and $y^{(n)}$ are sensible the same *i.e.* they are same to the desired degree of accuracy.

Picard's method is of considerable theoretical value. In general, it is unsatisfactory as a practical means of approximation because of difficulties which arise in performing the necessary integrations.

> **Note:** Each approximation gives a better approximation of the required solution than the preceding one.

Solved Examples

Example 1: *Find the solution of* $\frac{dy}{dx} = 1 + xy$ *which passes through* $(0, 1)$ *in the interval* $(0, 0.5)$ *such that the value of* y *is correct to three decimcal places (use the whole interval as one interval only). Take* $h = 0.1$. **[Agra 2002, 2010]**

---

*Picard was a distinguished professor of Mathematics at the University of Paris famous for his researches on the theory of functions.

Solution: We have $\frac{dy}{dx} = 1 + xy$; giving $f(x, y) = 1 + xy$.

and $\quad y = 1$ at $x_0 = 0$; giving $y_0 = 1$ and $x_0 = 0$.

Now first approximation,

$$y^{(1)} = y_0 + \int_{x_0}^{x} f(x, y_0)\, dx = 1 + \int_0^x \{1 + (xy_0)\}\, dx$$

$$= 1 + \int_0^x (1 + x)\, dx = 1 + x + \frac{x^2}{2} \qquad \ldots(1)$$

Second approximation,

$$y^{(2)} = y_0 + \int_0^x f(x, y^{(1)})\, dx = y_0 + \int_0^x \{1 + xy^{(1)}\}\, dx$$

$$= 1 + \int_0^x \left(1 + x + x^2 + \frac{x^3}{2}\right) dx = 1 + x + \frac{x^2}{2} + \frac{x^3}{3} + \frac{x^4}{8} \qquad \ldots(2)$$

Third approximation,

$$y^{(3)} = 1 + \int_0^x \{1 + (xy^{(2)})\}\, dx$$

$$= 1 + \int_0^x \left\{1 + x\left(1 + x + \frac{x^2}{2} + \frac{x^3}{3} + \frac{x^4}{8}\right)\right\} dx$$

$$= 1 + x + \frac{x^2}{2} + \frac{x^3}{3} + \frac{x^4}{8} + \frac{x^5}{15} + \frac{x^6}{48} \qquad \ldots(3)$$

When $\quad x = 0, y = 1 \quad i.e. \quad y^{(0)} = 1$.

When $\quad x = 0.1, y^{(1)} = 1.105, y^{(2)} = 1.10533$.

But we want accuracy up to 3 decimal places.

Therefore when $x = 0.1,\ y = 1.105$.

When $\quad x = 0.2, y^{(1)} = 1.202, y^{(2)} = 1.2027$.

Therefore when $x = 0.2,\ y = 1.203$

When $\quad x = 0.3; y^{(1)} = 1.345, y^{(2)} = 1.35501, y^{(3)} = 1.3551$.

Therefore when $x = 0.3, y = 1.355$.

When $\quad x = 0.4; y^{(1)} = 1.48, y^{(2)} = 1.50453, y^{(3)} = 1.5052$.

Therefore when $x = 0.4, y = 1.505$.

When $\quad x = 0.5; y^{(1)} = 1.625, y^{(2)} = 1.6744725$ and $y^{(2)} = 1.6765$

Therefore, we have $y = 1.677$ when $x = 0.5$

Now we tabulate the results as obtained above.

x	0	0.1	0.2	0.3	0.4	0.5
y	1.000	1.105	1.203	1.355	1.505	1.677

Thus we have solved numerically the given differential equation for

$$x = 0, 0.1, 0.2, 0.3, 0.4, 0.5.$$

Example 2: *Use Picard's method to approximate* y *when* $x = 0.2$, *given that* $y = 1$ *when* $x = 0$ *and* $\dfrac{dy}{dx} = x - y$. **[Agra 2003; Avadh 2003]**

Solution: We have $f(x, y) = x - y$, $x_0 = 0$, $y_0 = 1$

Now first approximation,

$$y^{(1)} = y_0 + \int_{x_0}^{x} f(x, y_0)\, dx = 0 + \int_0^x (x-1)\, dx = \frac{x^2}{2} - x + 1.$$

Second approximation,

$$y^{(2)} = y_0 + \int_{x_0}^{x} f(x, y^{(1)})\, dx = 1 + \int_0^x \{x - (y)^{(1)}\}\, dx$$

$$= 1 + \int_0^x \left(x - \frac{x^2}{2} + x - 1\right) dx = -\frac{x^3}{6} + x^2 - x + 1.$$

Third approximation,

$$y^{(3)} = 1 + \int_0^x f(x, y^{(2)})\, dx = 1 + \int_0^x (x - y^{(2)})\, dx$$

$$= 1 + \int_0^x \left(x + \frac{x^3}{6} - x^2 + x - 1\right) dx = \frac{x^4}{24} - \frac{x^3}{3} + x^2 - x + 1$$

Fourth approximation,

$$y^{(4)} = 1 + \int_{x_0}^{x} f(x, y^{(3)})\, dx = 1 + \int_0^x (x - y^{(3)})\, dx$$

$$= 1 + \int_0^x \left(x - \frac{x^4}{24} + \frac{x^3}{3} - x^2 + x - 1\right) dx$$

$$= -\frac{x^5}{120} + \frac{x^4}{12} - \frac{x^3}{3} + x^2 - x + 1$$

Fifth approximation,

$$y^{(5)} = 1 + \int_{x_0}^{x} f(x, y^{(4)})\, dx = 1 + \int_0^x (x - y^{(4)})\, dx$$

$$= 1 + \int_0^x \left(\frac{x^5}{120} - \frac{x^4}{12} + \frac{x^3}{3} - x^2 + 2x - 1\right) dx$$

$$= \frac{x^6}{720} - \frac{x^5}{60} + \frac{x^4}{12} - \frac{x^3}{3} + x^2 - x + 1, \text{ etc. When } x = 0.2,$$

we have

$$y_0 = 1,\ y^{(1)} = 0.82,\ y^{(2)} = 0.83867,\ y^{(3)} = 0.83740.$$

$$y^{(4)} = 0.83746 \text{ and } y^{(5)} = 0.83746, \text{ i.e. } y = .837 \text{ at } x = 0.2.$$

Example 3: *Use Picard's method to approximate the value of y when $x = 0.1$, given that $y = 1$ when $x = 0$*

and $(dy/dx) = 3x + y^2$.

Solution: We have $f(x, y) = 3x + y^2$, $x_0 = 0$ and $y_0 = 1$.

Now first approximation,

$$y^{(1)} = y_0 + \int_{x_0}^{x} f(x, y_0)\,dx = 1 + \int_0^x (3x + y_0^2)\,dx$$

$$= 1 + \int_0^x (3x + 1)\,dx = \frac{3x^2}{2} + x + 1.$$

Second approximation, $y^{(2)} = y_0 + \int_0^x f(x, y^{(1)})\,dx$

$$= 1 + \int_0^x [3x + \{y^{(1)}\}^2]\,dx = 1 + \int_0^x \left(\frac{9}{4}x^4 + 3x^3 + 4x^2 + 5x + 1\right) dx$$

$$= \frac{9}{20}x^5 + \frac{3}{4}x^4 + \frac{4}{3}x^3 + \frac{5}{2}x^2 + x + 1.$$

Third approximation,

$$y^{(3)} = 1 + \int_0^x [3x + \{y^{(2)}\}^2]\,dx$$

$$= 1 + \int_0^x \left(\frac{81}{400}x^{10} + \frac{27}{40}x^9 + \frac{141}{80}x^8 + \frac{17}{4}x^7 + \frac{1157}{180}x^6 + \frac{136}{240}x^5 + \frac{125}{12}x^4 + \frac{23}{3}x^3 + 6x^2 + 5x + 1\right) dx$$

$$= \frac{81}{4400}x^{11} + \frac{27}{400}x^{10} + \frac{47}{240}x^9 + \frac{17}{32}x^8 + \frac{1157}{1260}x^7 + \frac{62}{45}x^6 + \frac{25}{12}x^5 + \frac{23}{12}x^4 + 2x^3 + \frac{5}{2}x^2 + x + 1$$

When $x = 0.1$, we get

$$y_0 = 1,\ y^{(1)} = 1.115,\ y^{(2)} = 1.1264,\ y^{(3)} = 1.12721;$$

$$\Rightarrow \quad y = 1.127 \text{ at } x = 0.1$$

Example 4: *Use Picard's method to approximate y when $x = 0.1$ given that $y = 1$ when $x = 0$ and* $\dfrac{dy}{dx} = \dfrac{y - x}{y + x}$,

[Bhopal 2002; Avadh 2005]

Solution: We have $f(x, y) = \dfrac{y - x}{y + x}$, $x_0 = 0$, $y_0 = 1$.

Now, first approximation,

$$y^{(1)} = y_0 + \int_0^x f(x, y_0)\,dx = 1 + \int_0^x \frac{1 - x}{1 + x}\,dx$$

$$y^{(1)} = 1 + \{2\log(1 + x) - x\}_0^x = 1 - x + 2\log(1 + x)$$

Second approximation,

$$y^{(2)} = x_0 + \int_{x_0}^{x} f(x, y^{(1)})\, dx = 1 + \int_0^x \frac{1-2x+2\log(1+x)}{1+2\log(1+x)}\, dx$$

$$= 1 + x - 2\int_0^x \frac{x}{1+2\log(1+x)}\, dx$$

$$= 1 + x - 2\int_0^x \frac{e^{2t}}{1+2t}\, dt + 2\int_0^t \frac{e^t}{1+2t}\, dt,$$

Where $t = \log(1 + x)$ which is difficult to integrate.

When $x = 0, y = 1.$

When $x = 0.1, y^{(1)} = 1 - 0.1 + 2\log(1.1) = 0.9828$

$y^{(2)}$ = can not be obtained.

Hence in this example, only first approximation, which is 0.9828, can be obtained.

Example 5: *Use Picard's method to approximate y when $x = 0.1, x = 0.2$ given that $y = 0$ when $x = 0, \frac{dy}{dx} = x + y$. Check the result with the exact value.*

Solution: We have $(dy/dx) = f(x, y) = x + y, x_0 = 0, y_0 = 1.$

Now first approximation,

$$y^{(1)} = y_0 + \int_{x_0}^{x} f(x, y_0)\, dx = 1 + \int_0^x (i + x)\, dx = 1 + x + \frac{x^2}{2}$$

Second approximation,

$$y^{(2)} = y_0 + \int_{x_0}^{x} f(x, y^{(1)})\, dx = 1 + \int_0^x \left\{x + \left(\frac{x^2}{2} + x + 1\right)\right\} dx$$

$$= (x^3/6) + x^2 + x + 1.$$

Third approximation,

$$y^{(3)} = y_0 + \int_0^x \left\{x + \left(\frac{x^3}{6} + x^2 + x + 1\right)\right\} dx = \frac{x^4}{24} + \frac{x^3}{3} + x^2 + x + 1.$$

When $x = 0.1$, we have

$$y^{(1)} = 1 + (0.1) + \frac{(0.1)^2}{2} = 1.105$$

$$y^{(2)} = 1 + (0.1) + (0.1)^2 + \frac{1}{6}(0.1)^3 = 1.11016$$

$$y^{(3)} = 1 + 0.1 + (0.1)^2 + \frac{1}{3}(0.i)^3 + \frac{1}{24}(0.1)^4 = 1.1103$$

Closer approximation.

When $x = 0.2$, we further have

$$y^{(3)} = \frac{1}{24}(0.2)^4 + \frac{1}{3}(0.2)^3 + (0.2)^2 + 0.2 + 1 = 1.2427$$

We can continue further to get the better approximations.

Now, we shall obtain the exact value

$$\frac{dy}{dx} = x + y, \qquad \Rightarrow \qquad \frac{dy}{dx} - y = x$$

$$\Rightarrow \qquad y e^{-x} = \int x e^{-x}\, dx + c = -e^{-x}(1 + x) + c$$

$$\Rightarrow \qquad y = -x - 1 + c e^{x}.$$

Putting $y = 1, x = 0$, we obtain

$$1 = -1 + c \Rightarrow c = 2, \qquad \therefore\ y = -x - 1 + 2e^{x}$$

When $x = 0.1,\ y = 2e^{0.1} - 0.1 - 1 = 1.11034.$

When $x = 0.2,\ y = 2e^{0.2} - 0.2 - 1 = 1.2428.$

These result reveal that the approximations obtained for $x = 0.1$ is correct to four decimal places while the approximation for $x = 0.2$ is correct to three decimal places.

Example 6: *Approximate y and z by using Picard's method for the particular solution of*

$$\frac{dy}{dx} = x + z,\ \frac{dz}{dx} = x - y^2,$$

[Avadh 2004]

Given that $y = 2,\ z = 1,$ *when* $x = 0.$

Solution: Let $f(x, y, z) = x + z$ and $\phi(x, y, z) = x - y^2$.

$$x_0 = 0,\ y_0 = 2,\ z_0 = 1.$$

$$\Rightarrow \qquad \frac{dy}{dx} = f(x, y, z) \quad \Rightarrow \quad y = y_0 + \int_{x_0}^{x} f(x, y, z)\, dx \qquad \text{...(1)}$$

Again, we have

$$\frac{dz}{dx} = \phi(x, y, z) \quad \Rightarrow \quad z = z_0 + \int_{x_0}^{x} \phi(x, y, z)\, dx \qquad \text{...(2)}$$

Now, first approximation of y is

$$y^{(1)} = y_0 + \int_0^x f(x, y_0, z_0)\, dx = 2 + \int_0^x f(x, y_0, z_0) \qquad \text{[using (1)]}$$

$$= 2 + \int_0^x (x + 1)\, dx = 2 + x + (x^2/2).$$

Also, first approximation of z is

$$z^{(1)} = z_0 + \int_0^x \phi(x, y_0, z_0)\, dx \quad \text{[using (2)]}$$

$$= 1 + \int_0^x (x - 4)\, dx = 1 - 4x + (x^2/2).$$

Hence the second approximation of $y^{(2)}$ and $z^{(2)}$ are

$$y^{(2)} = y_0 + \int_0^x f(x, y^{(1)}, z^{(1)})\, dx$$

$$= 2 + \int_0^x (x + z^{(1)})\, dx = 2 + \int_0^x \left(x + 1 - 4x + \frac{x^2}{2}\right) dx$$

$$= 2 + x - (3/2)\, x^2 + (1/6)\, x^3$$

and $$z^{(2)} = z_0 + \int_0^x \phi(x, y^{(1)}, z^{(1)})\, dx = 1 + \int_0^x [x - \{y^{(1)}\}^2]\, dx$$

$$= 1 + \int_0^x \left[x - \left(2 + x + \frac{x^2}{2}\right)^2\right] dx$$

$$= 1 - 4x - (3x^2/2 - x^3 - (x^4/4) - (x^5/20).$$

11.3 Euler's Method

[Agra 2003, 2006]

Euler's method, as such, is of very little practical importance, but illustrates in simple form, the basic idea of those numerical methods which seek to determine the change Δy in y corresponding to small increase in the argument x.

Let the differential equation be

$$\frac{dy}{dx} = f(x, y), \text{ where } y = y_0 \text{ at } x = x_0. \quad \ldots(1)$$

Again let $y = F(x)$ be the solution of (1) and let its graph be as shown in the adjoining diagram. We want to find out the value of y at $x = L$, say. For this divide the interval $l - x_0$ in 'n' equal parts. Let $x_1, x_2, \ldots\ldots, x_{n-1}$ be the intermediate points.

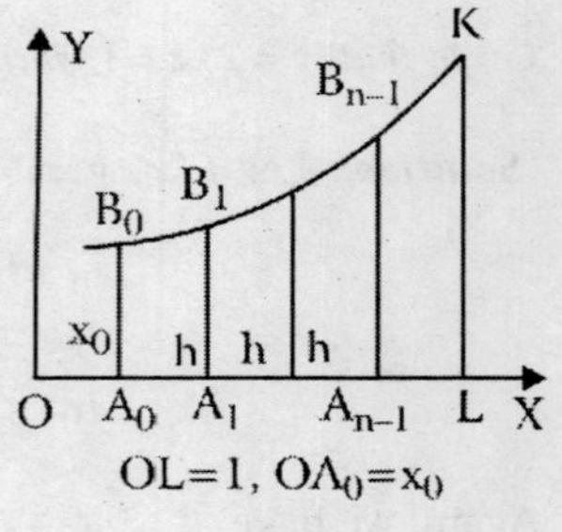

Now, in the interval (x_0, x_1) we have an approximate relation.

$$y_1 - y_0 \approx (x_1 - x_0)\left(\frac{dy}{dx}\right)_{x=x_0} = (x_1 - x_0) f(x_0, y_0) \quad \therefore\ y_1 \approx y_0 + hf(x_0, y_0)$$

$$\tan\theta = f(x_0, y_0) = \left(\frac{dy}{dx}\right)_{x=x_0} = \frac{MR}{B_0 R}$$

$$\approx \frac{B_1 R}{B_0 R} = \frac{y_1 - y_0}{x_1 - x_0} = \frac{\Delta y}{\Delta x}$$

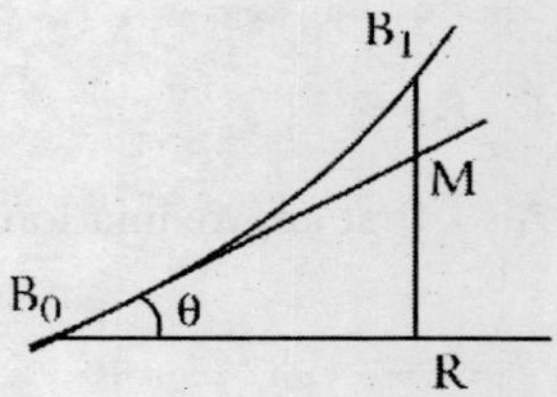

$$\Rightarrow \quad y_1 = y_0 + h(\Delta y / \Delta x)$$

$$\approx y_0 + hf(x_0, y_0)$$

This y_1 is approximate value of y for $x = x_1$.

On the same lines, the approximate value of y at $x = x_2$ is given by

$$y_2 \approx y_1 + hf(x_0 + h, y_1) = y_1 + hf(x_1, y_1) \quad \ldots(2)$$

Repeating this procedure n times, we get

$$y_n \text{ (i.e. } LK) \approx y_{n-1} + hf(x_0 + \overline{n-1}h, y_{n-1}) = y_{n-1} + hf(x_{n-1}, y_{n-1})$$

This is **Euler's Method**

Note 1: A great disadvantage of the above method lies in the fact that if $\frac{dy}{dx}$ changes rapidly over an interval then its value at the beginning of the interval may give a poor approximation as compared to its average value over the interval and thus the value of y calculated from this may be in much error from its true value. Errors of this type will be accumulated in the succeeding intervals. Finally value of y become so much in error thar it is completely useless.

Note 2: In Euler's method, the actual solution curve is approximated by the sequence of short straight lines, and some times the sequence of short lines diviates from the solution curve significantly. To avoid this difficulty. Euler's impoved method is preferred as there we consider the curvature of the actual curve instead of approximating the curve by the sequence of short lines.

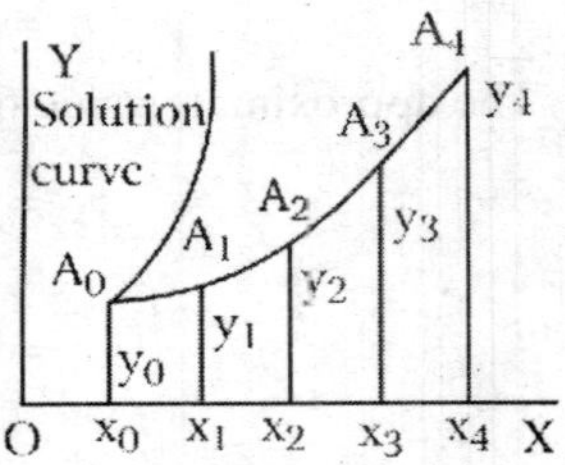

OL=I, OA0=x0

Example 7: **(a)** *Given* $\frac{dy}{dx} = \frac{y-x}{y+x}$ *with the initial condition* $y = 1$ *at* $x = 0$. *Find* y *for* $y = 0.1$. **[Agra 2003; Avadh 2003]**

(b) *Using Euler's method, find an approximate value of* y *corresponding to* $x = 1$, *given that* $(dy/dx) = x + y$ *and* $y = 1$ *where* $x = 0$.

Solution: (a) We have

$$\frac{dy}{dx} = \frac{y-x}{y+x} = f(x, y),\ x_0 = 0,\ y_0 = 1,\ h = 0.1.$$

Hence the approximate value of y at $x = 0.1$ is given by

$$y_1 = y_0 + hf(x_0, y_0) = 1 + .1\left\{\frac{1-0}{1+0}\right\} = 1.1.$$

Much better accuracy is obtained by breaking up the interval 0 to 0.1 into five steps.

The approximate value of y at $x_A = 0.02$ is given by

$$y_A = y_0 + hf(x_0, y_0)$$

$$= 1 + .02\,\frac{1-0}{1+0} = 1.0200,$$

$$\therefore \quad h = \frac{.1}{5} = 0.02$$

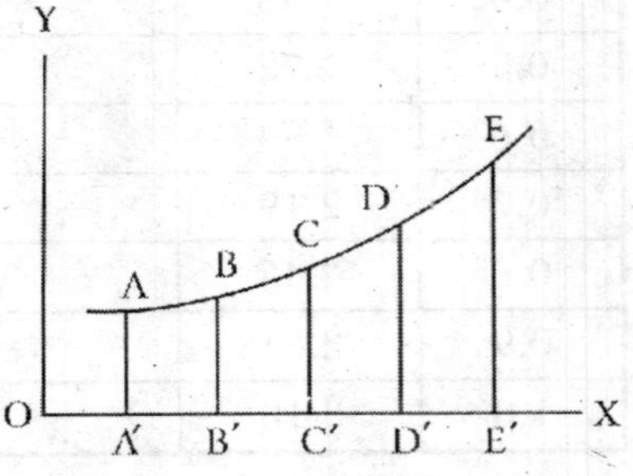

OE′ = 0.1

The approximate value of y at $x_B = 0.04$, is given by

$$y_B = y_A + h f(x_A, y_A)$$

$$= 1.0200 + .02\,\frac{1.02 - .02}{1.02 + .02} \qquad (\because\ x_A = .02,\ y_A = 1.02)$$

$$= 1.0200 + .02\,\frac{1}{1.04} = 1.02 + .0192 = 1.0392.$$

The approximate value of y at $x_C = 0.06$, is given by

$$y_C = y_B + h f(x_B, y_B) = 1.0392 + .02\,\frac{1.0392 - .04}{1.0392 + .04}$$

$$[\therefore\ x_B = .06,\ y_B = 1.0392]$$

$$= 1.0392 + .02\,\frac{.9992}{1.0792} - 1.0392 + .02\,(.926)$$

$$= 1.0392 + .0185 = 1.0577.$$

The approximate value of y at $x_D = .008$, is given by

$$y_D = y_C + h f(x_C, y_C) = 1.0571 + h\,\frac{h_C - x_C}{y_C + x_C}$$

$$= 1.0577 + 0.02\,\frac{(.9377)}{(1.1177)}$$

$$= 1.0577 + 0.02\,(.893) = 1.0577 + .0179 = 1.0756.$$

The approximate value of y at $x_E = .1$, is given by

$$y_E = y_D = h f(x_D, y_D) = y_D + h\,\frac{y_D - x_D}{y_D + x_D}$$

$$= 1.0756 + .02\,\frac{1.0756 - .08}{1.0756 + .08} = 1.0756 + 0.02\,\frac{0.9956}{1.1556}$$

$$= 1.0756 + .02\,(.862) = 1.0756 + 0.172 = 1.0928.$$

(b) Let us take $n=10$; $h=0.1$ (sufficiently small) Then various calculations are arranged as follows:

x	y	$x + y = (dy/dx)$	Old $y + 0.1\,(dy/dx) =$ new y
0.0	1.00	1.00	1.00 + .01 (1.00) = 1.10
0.1	1.10	1.20	1.10 + 0.1 (1.20) = 1.22
0.2	1.22	1.42	1.22 + 0.1 (1.42) = 1.36
0.3	1.36	1.66	1.36 + 0.1 (1.66) = 1.53
0.4	1.53	1.93	1.53 + 0.1 (1.93) = 1.72
0.5	1.72	2.22	1.72 + 0.1 (2.22) = 1.94
0.6	1.94	2.54	1.94 + 0.1 (2.54) = 2.19
0.7	2.19	2.89	2.19 + 0.1 (2.89) = 2.48
0.8	2.48	3.29	2.48 + 0.1 (3.29) = 2.81
0.9	2.81	3.71	2.81 + 0.1 (3.71) = 3.18
1.0	3.18		

Thus the required approximate value of $y = 3.18$.

11.4 Improved Euler's Method

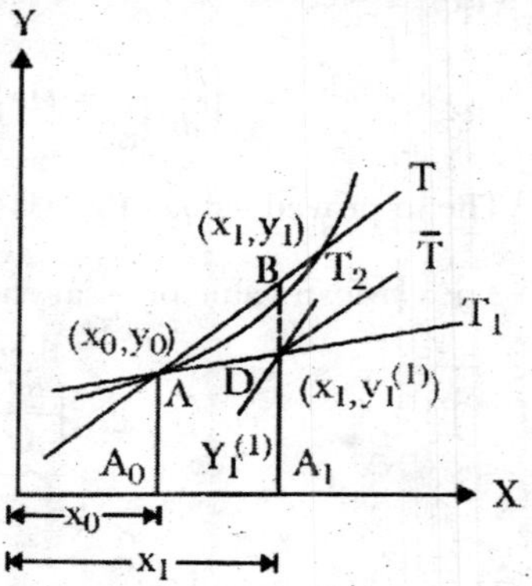

In this method, we consider a line passing through $(x_0\ y_0)$ whose slope is the average of the slopes at $(x_0\ y_0)$ and $(x_1\ y_1^{(1)})$ such that

$y_1^{(1)} = y_0 + hf(x_0, y_0)$ Geometrically, AT_1 is the tangent at $(x_0\ y_0)$. DT_2 is the line through $(x_1, y_1^{(1)})$ having slope $(x_1, y_1^{(1)})$ and DT is the line having slope

$$\frac{f(x_0\,, y_0) + f(x_1\ y_1^{(1)})}{2}$$

The line AT through $(x_0\ y_0)$ and parallel to DT is used to approximate the curve *i.e.* the ordinate of point B will give the value of y_1. Obviously the equation of the line ABT is given by

$$y - y_0 = (x - x_0)\left\{\frac{f(x_0, y_0) + f(x_1, y_1^{(1)})}{2}\right\} \qquad \ldots(1)$$

As we are assuming $A_1 B = y_1$, so co-ordinates of B will be (x_1, y_1). This point lies on the line AT, so we have

$$y - y_0 = (x_1 - x_0)\left\{\frac{f(x_0, y_0) + f(x_1, y_1^{(1)})}{2}\right\} \qquad \ldots(2)$$

Continuing further, we get

$$y_{m-1} - y_m = (x_{m+1} - x_m)\left\{\frac{f(x_m, y_m) + f(x_{m+1}, y_{m+1}^{(1)})}{2}\right\}$$

or $$y_{m-1} = y_m + \frac{h}{2}\{f(x_m, y_m) + f(x_{m+1}\,, y_{m+1}^{(1)})\}$$

where $$x_{m+1} - x_m = h \qquad \ldots(3)$$

Which agrees with the term obtained by the integration of $y' = f(x)$ using trapezoidal rule.

11.5 Modified Euler's Method

[Bangaluru 2004, 2007]

Starting with the initial value y_0 an approximate value for y_1 is computed from the relation

$$y_1^{(1)} \approx y_0 + h\left(\frac{dy}{dx}\right)_{x=x_0} = y_0 + f(x_0, y_0)\,h \qquad \ldots(1)$$

where $(dy/dx) = f(x, y)$

and $y_1^{(1)}$ is the first approximation of y at $x = x_1$

After obtaining the value of $y_1^{(1)}$, we substitute it in the differential equation

$\left(\frac{dy}{dx}\right) = f(x, y)$ so as to get the approximate value of $\left(\frac{dy}{dx}\right)$ at the end of first interval *viz.*,

$$\left(\frac{dy}{dx}\right)_1^{(1)} = f(x_1, y_1^{(1)}) \quad \ldots(2)$$

The improved value of Δy is then obtained as given below:

$\Delta y \approx$ [Mean value of $\frac{dy}{dx}$ at the end of the interval x_0 to x_1] h

$$= \frac{\left(\frac{dy}{dx}\right)_{x_0} + \left(\frac{dy}{dx}\right)_{x_1}^{(1)}}{2} h. \quad \ldots(3)$$

Hence, the second approximation for y is given by

$$y_1^{(2)} = y_0 + \frac{\left(\frac{dy}{dx}\right)_{x_0} + \left(\frac{dy}{dx}\right)_{x_1}^{(1)}}{2} h = y_0 + \frac{h}{2}[f(x_0, y_0) + f(x_0 + h, y_1^{(1)})] \quad \ldots(4)$$

The improved value $y_1^{(2)}$ is now substituted in the equation $\frac{dy}{dx} = f(x, y)$ so as to get second approximation for $\left(\frac{dy}{dx}\right)_1$ *viz*.

$$\left(\frac{dy}{dx}\right)_1^{(2)} = f(x_1, y_1^{(2)}) \quad \ldots(5)$$

The third approximation for y is therefore given by

$$y_1^{(3)} = y_0 + \frac{\left(\frac{dy}{dx}\right)_{x_0} + \left(\frac{dy}{dx}\right)_{x_1}^{(2)}}{2} h = y_0 + \frac{h}{2}[f(x_0, y_0) + f(x_0 + h, y_1^{(2)})] \quad \ldots(6)$$

The process is stopped, when the value of $y_1^{(n-1)}$ and $y_1^{(n)}$ are essentially the same

$$y_1^{(n)} = y_0 + \frac{\left(\frac{dy}{dx}\right)_{x_0} + \left(\frac{dy}{dx}\right)_{x_1}^{(n-1)}}{2} h = y_0 + \frac{h}{2}[f(x_0, y_0) + f(x_0 + h, y_1^{(n-1)})] \quad \ldots(7)$$

First approximation to $y_2, y_3, \ldots$ etc., could be found by means of formula.

$y_{n+1} \approx y_n + h\left(\frac{dy}{dx}\right)$, but as soon as two consecutive values of y are known, the first approximation to succeeding y's can be obtained more accurately by the formula

$$y_{n+1} = y_{n-1} + 2h\left(\frac{dy}{dx}\right) \quad \ldots(8)$$

Proof of (8) is not given here but is obtained by making use to Taylor's series in the neighbourhood of x_n.

By repeating this process, we can obtain the approximate value of y at $x = 1$

Geometrical Illustration: *For the improvement of this method over Euler's method.*

Δy by Euler's method as computed is represented by $R\ M$. If $B_0\ N$ is drawn parallel to the tangent at B_1, then $R\ N$ denotes the computed value of Δy by using the slope at B_1. But if we take the average value of the slopes, then the computed value of $(\Delta y / \Delta x)$ becomes

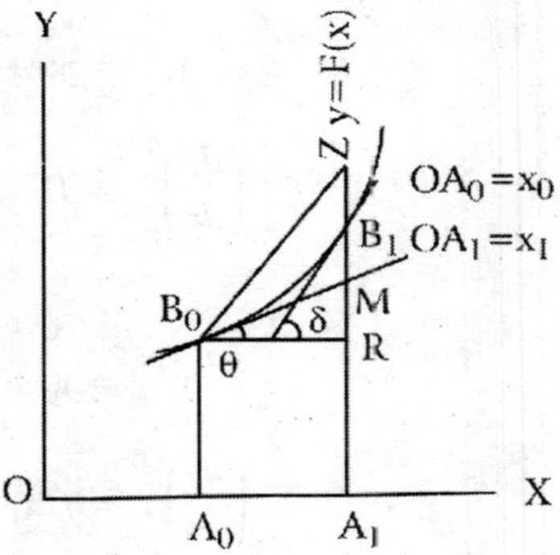

$$\frac{\Delta y}{\Delta x} = \frac{\left(\frac{dy}{dx}\right)_{x_0} + \left(\frac{dy}{dx}\right)_{x_1}}{2}$$

$$\Delta y = \frac{h}{2}\left\{\left(\frac{dy}{dx}\right)_{x_0} + \left(\frac{dy}{dx}\right)_{x_1}\right\}$$

Where $\quad h = x_1 - x_0$

$$= \frac{1}{2}\left\{h\left(\frac{dy}{dx}\right)_{x_0} + h\left(\frac{dy}{dx}\right)_{x_1}\right\}$$

$$= \frac{1}{2}[h \tan\theta + h \tan\delta]$$

$$= \frac{1}{2}[B_0\ R \tan\theta + B_0\ R \tan N\ B_0\ R]$$

$$= \frac{1}{2}[RM + RN]$$

Hence $\quad \Delta y = \frac{1}{2}[RM + RM + MN] = RM + \frac{MN}{2}$

which is in close approximation with its true value $R\ B_1$.

Example 8: *Given that $\frac{dy}{dx} = x + y$, with the initial condition that $y = 1$, When $x = 0$. Find y for $x = 0.05$, and $x = 0.1$. Give the correct result upto four decimal places.*

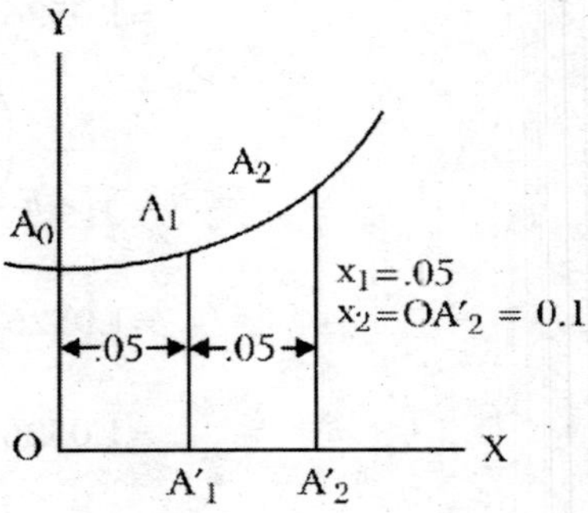

Solution: The given differential equation is

$$\frac{dy}{dx} = x + y = f(x, y), \text{ say.}$$

Initial condition is $x_0 = 0, y_0 = 1$.

This gives $\quad \left(\frac{dy}{dx}\right)_0 = x_0 + y_0 = 0 + 1 = 1.$

Now, $\quad y_1^{(0)} = y_0 + f(x_0, y_0) \times h = 1 + (0+1)(.05) = 1.05,$

$$\left(\frac{dy}{dx}\right)_0^{(1)} = f(x_1, y_1^{(1)}) = (x_1 + y_1^{(1)}) = .05 + 1.05 = 1.10$$

$$y_1^{(2)} = y_0 + \frac{\left(\frac{dy}{dx}\right)_0 + \left(\frac{dy}{dx}\right)_1^{(1)}}{2} h = 1 + \frac{1+1.10}{2}(0.05) = 1.0525,$$

$$\left(\frac{dy}{dx}\right)_1^{(2)} = f(x_1, y_1^{(2)}) = (x_1 + y_1^{(2)}) = .05 + 1.0525 = 1.1025,$$

$$y_1^{(3)} = y_0 + \frac{\left(\frac{dy}{dx}\right)_0 + \left(\frac{dy}{dx}\right)_1^{(2)}}{2} h = 1 + \frac{1+1.1025}{2}(0.05) = 1.05256,$$

$$\left(\frac{dy}{dx}\right)_1^{(3)} = f(x_1, y_1^{(3)}) = x_1 + y_1^{(3)} = .05 + 1.05256 = 1.10256,$$

$$y_1^{(4)} = y_0 + \frac{\left(\frac{dy}{dx}\right)_0 + \left(\frac{dy}{dx}\right)_1^{(3)}}{2} h = 1 + \frac{1+1.10256}{2}(0.05) = 1.05256.$$

It is obvious that $y_1^{(3)} = y_1^{(4)}$, so we stop here and say that

$$y = 1.05256, \left(\frac{dy}{dx}\right)_1 = 1.1026$$

As a first approximation to y_2, we have

$$y_2^{(1)} = y_0 + 2.h\left(\frac{dy}{dx}\right)_1 = 1 + 2(.05)(1.1026) = 1.1103$$

[Using equation (8) **11.5**]

Now $$y_2^{(2)} = y_1 + h\frac{\left(\frac{dy}{dx}\right)_1 + \left(\frac{dy}{dx}\right)_2^{(1)}}{2}$$

$$= 1.0526 + (0.05)\frac{1.1026 + (.1 + 1.1103)}{2} = 1.1104.$$

$$y_2^{(3)} = y_1 + h\frac{\left(\frac{dy}{dx}\right)_1 + \left(\frac{dy}{dx}\right)_2^{(2)}}{2}$$

$$= 1.0526 + (0.05)\frac{1.102 + (6.1 + y_2^{(2)})}{2}$$

$$= 1.0526 + (0.05)\frac{1.1026 + 1.1104)}{2} = 1.1104$$

Hence $$y_2^{(2)} = y_2^{(3)} = 1.1104.$$

This shows that the value of y at $x = 0.1$, is $y = 1.1104$

Also $$\left(\frac{dy}{dx}\right)_2 = .1 + 1.1104 = 1.2104$$

Collecting results in the tabulated form, we have the following table:

x	y	(dy / dx)
0.000	1.0000	1.0000
0.05	1.052	1.1026
0.10	1.1104	1.2104

Example 9: *Given that* $\frac{dy}{dx} = \log(x + y)$, *with the initial condition that* $y = 1$ *when* $x = 0$, *find* y *for* $x = 0.2$ *and* $x = 0.5$. **[Agra 2000]**

Solution: Let $x = 0, x_1 = 0.2,$ and $x_2 = 0.5$ then $y_0 = 1,$ while y_1 and y_2 are to be computed.

Here $\quad f(x, y) = \log(x + y), \quad \therefore \quad f(x_0, y_0) = \log(1) = 0$

Now, $\quad y_1^{(1)} = y_0 + hf(x_0, y_0) = 1 + (0.2)(0) = 1 \quad (\because \quad h = 0.2)$

$$\left(\frac{dy}{dx}\right)_1^{(1)} = f(x_1, y_1^{(1)}) = \log(x_1 + y_1^{(1)}) = \log(.2 + 1) = \log(1.2)$$

$$y_1^{(2)} = y_0 + h\frac{\left(\frac{dy}{dx}\right) + \left(\frac{dy}{dx}\right)_1^{(1)}}{2}h = 1 + \frac{f(x_0\ y_0) + \log(1.2)}{2} \times (0.2)$$

$$= 1 + \frac{0 + \log(1.2)}{2}(0.2) = 1 + .0079 = 1.0079,$$

$$\left(\frac{dy}{dx}\right)_1^{(2)} = f(x_1, y_1^{(2)}) = \log(x_1 + y_1^{(2)}) = \log[.2 + 1.0079],$$

$$y_1^{(3)} = y_0 + \frac{\left(\frac{dy}{dx}\right)_0 + \left(\frac{dy}{dx}\right)_1^{(2)}}{2}h = 1 + \frac{0 + \log(.2 + 1.0079)}{2} \times (0.2)$$

$$= 1 + .0082 = 1.0082,$$

$$\left(\frac{dy}{dx}\right)_1^{(3)} = f(x_1, y_1^{(3)}) = \log(x_1 + y_1^{(3)}) = \log(.2 + 1.0082)$$

$$y_1^{(4)} = y_0 + \frac{\left(\frac{dy}{dx}\right)_0 + \left(\frac{dy}{dx}\right)_1^{(3)}}{2}h = 1 + \frac{0 + \log(.2 + 1.0082)}{2} \times (0.2)$$

$$= 1 + .0082 = 1.0082.$$

It is obvious that $y_1^{(3)} = y_1^{(4)}$, so we stop here and say that $y_1 = 1.0082$.

To obtain y_2, the value of y at $x = 0.5$, we again make use of equation

$$y_2^{(1)} = y_1 + hf(x_1, y_1), \text{ giving that}$$

$$y_2^{(1)} = 1.0082 + .3 \log(.2 + 1.0082) = 1.0082 + .0246 = 1.0328.$$

$$(\because h = .5 - .2 = .3 \text{ here})$$

To improve this estimate of y_2, we have

$$y_2^{(2)} = y_1 + \frac{\left(\frac{dy}{dx}\right)_1 + \left(\frac{dy}{dx}\right)_2^{(1)}}{2} h$$

$$= y_1 + \frac{\{\log(x_1 + 1.0012) + \log(x_2 + y_2^{(1)}\}}{2}(.3)$$

$$= 1.0082 + \frac{\{\log(1.2 + 1.0082) + \log(0.5 + 1.0328\}}{2}(.3)$$

$$= 1.0082 + 0.0401 = 1.0483.$$

Now
$$y_2^{(3)} = y_1 + \frac{\left(\frac{dy}{dx}\right)_1 + \left(\frac{dy}{dx}\right)_2^{(2)}}{2} h$$

$$= 1.0082 + \frac{\{\log(.2 + 1.0082) + \log(.5 + 1.0483)\}}{2} \times (.3)$$

$$= 1.0082 + 0.0408 = 1.0490.$$

Another time, the value will not change and hence it is taken as the value of y at $x = 0.5$.

Example 10: *Using Euler's modified method, find a solution of the equation*

$$dy/dx = x + |\sqrt{y}| = f(x, y)$$

With initial condition $y = 1$ *at* $x = 0$ *for the range* $0 \le x \le 0.6$ *in steps of* 0.2

[Agra 2006, 2008; Bhopal 2002; M.N.U. Tamil Nadu 2004, 2006]

Solution: Here $f(x, y) = x + |\sqrt{y}|$, $x_0 = 0$, $y_0 = 1$, $h = 0.2$

$$f(x_0, y_0) = x_0 + |\sqrt{y_0}| = 1.$$

Now
$$y_1^{(1)} = y_0 + hf(x_0, y_0) = 1 + (0.2).1 = 1.2.$$

$$\therefore \quad \left(\frac{dy}{dx}\right)_1^{(1)} = f(x_1, y_1^{(1)}) = x_1 + |\sqrt{y_1^{(1)}}| = 0.2 + |\sqrt{(1.2)}|$$

$$= 1.2954$$

The second approximation to y_1 is given by

$$y_1^{(2)} = y_0 + \frac{f(x_0, y_0) + f(x_1, y_1^{(1)})}{2} h = 1 + \frac{1 + 1.2954}{2} \times 0.2 = 1.2295.$$

Again, $f(x_1, y_1^{(2)}) = x_1 + |\sqrt{y_1^{(2)}}| = 0.2 + \sqrt{(1.2295)} = 1.3018.$

$$\therefore \quad y_1^{(4)} = y_0 + \frac{f(x_0, y_0) + f(x_1, y_1^{(3)})}{2} h = 1.2309.$$

Since $y_1^{(4)} = y_1^{(3)}$, so we take $y_1 = 1.2309$.

Now $y_2^{(1)} = y_1 + hf(x_1, y_1) = 1.2309 + (0.2)[0.2 + \sqrt{(1.2309)}]$

$= 1.4927$

and $f(x_2, y_2^{(1)}) = 0.4 + \sqrt{(1.4927)} = 1.622.$

$$\therefore \quad y_2^{(2)} = y_1 + \frac{f(x_1, y_1) + f(x_2, y_2^{(1)})}{2} h$$

$$= 1.2309 + \frac{[0.2 + \sqrt{(1.2309)}] + 1.622}{2} \times 0.2$$

$= 1.5240$

Now
$$y_2^{(3)} = y_1 + \frac{f(x_1, y_1) + f(x_2, y_2^{(2)})}{2} h$$

$$= 1.2309 + \frac{[\{0.2 + \sqrt{(1.2309)}\} + \{0.4 + \sqrt{(1.5240)}\}]}{2} \times 0.2$$

$= 1.5253$

$$y_2^{(4)} = 1.2309 + \frac{[\{0.2 + \sqrt{(1.2309)}\} + \{0.4 + \sqrt{(1.5253)}\}]}{2} \times 0.2$$

$= 1.5253.$

Since $y_2^{(3)} = y_2^{(4)}$, therefore we take $y_2 = 1.5253$.

Again $y_3^{(1)} = y_2 + hf(x_2, y_2) = 1.5253 + (0.2)[0.4 + \sqrt{(1.5253)}]$

$= 1.8523$

$$y_3^{(2)} = y_2 + \frac{1}{2}\,[f(x_2, y_2) + f(x_3, y_3^{(1)})]\,h$$

$$= 1.5253 + \frac{1}{4} \times 0.2\ [\{0.4 + \sqrt{(1.5253)}\} + [0.6 + \sqrt{(1.8523)}\}]$$

$= 1.8849.$

Now
$$y_3^{(3)} = y_2 + \frac{1}{2} h[f(x_2, y_2) + f(x_3, y_3^{(2)})]$$

$$= 1.5253 + \frac{1}{2} \times 0.2\ [\{0.4 + \sqrt{(1.5253)}\} + [0.6 + \sqrt{(1.8849)}\}]$$

$= 1.8861.$

$$y_3^{(4)} = y_2 + \frac{1}{2} h[f(x_2, y_2) + f(x_3, y_3^{(3)})]$$

$$= 1.5253 + \frac{1}{2} \times 0.2\ [\{0.4 + \sqrt{(1.5253)}\} + [0.6 + \sqrt{(1.8861)}\}]$$

$= 1.8861$

Since $y_3^{(4)} = y_3^{(3)}$ therefore we take $y_3 = 1.8861$.

✦✦ Problem Set ✦✦

1. Using Euler's method, find approximate value of y when $x = 0.6$ of $(dy/dx) = 1 - 2xy$, given that $y = 0$ when $x = 0$ (take $h = 0.2$).

2. Using simple Euler's method solve for y at $x = 0.1$ from $(dy/dx) = x + y + xy$, $y(0) = 1$, taking step size $h = 0.025$.

3. Apply Euler's method to solve $y' = x + y$, $y(0) = 0$, choosing the step length $= 0.2$ (carry out 6 step).

4. Given $\dfrac{dy}{dx} = \dfrac{y - x}{y + x}$ with boundary conditions $y = 1$ when $x = 0$; find approximately y for $x = 0.1$, by Euler's modified method (5 steps). **[Agra 2004; Avadh 2005]**

✦✦ Answers ✦✦

1.	0.4748	2.	1.1448
3.	1.1831808	4.	1.0928

11.6 Taylor's Series Method

Let the first order differential equation be $\dfrac{dy}{dx} = f(x, y)$ ...(1)

where $y = y_0$ at $x = x_0$.

Let the solution of the above equation be $y = F(x)$ such that $F(x_0) \neq 0$, then expanding $F(x) = y$ *i.e.* in the neighborhood of x_0 by Taylor's expanding method, we obtain

$$y = y_0 + (x - x_0)\, y'_0 + \frac{(x - x_0)^2}{2!}\, y''_0 + \ldots$$

Putting $x = x_1 = x_0 + h$, we get

$$y = y_0 + h y'_0 + \frac{h^2}{2!} y''_0 + \ldots \qquad \ldots(2)$$

Which is a convergent series in the range $x_0 \leq x \leq x_n$.

The coefficient y'_0, y''_0, ... can be obtained in turn from (1) which can be re-written as $y' = f(x, y) = g_1(x, y)$, say ...(3)

Differentiating (3) successively, we get

$$y'' = \frac{\partial g_1}{\partial x} + \frac{\partial g_1}{\partial y} y' = g_2(x, y, y') \text{ say;}$$

$$y''' = \frac{\partial g_2}{\partial x} + \frac{\partial g_2}{\partial y} y' + \frac{\partial g_3}{\partial y'} y'' = g_3(x, y', y'')$$

$$y^{(iv)} = \frac{\partial g_3}{\partial x} + \frac{\partial g_3}{\partial y} y' + \frac{\partial g_3}{\partial y'} y'' + \frac{\delta g_3}{\delta y''} y''' = g_4(x, y, y', y'', y'''), \text{ say.}$$

Continuing in this way, we get

$$y^{(n)} = \frac{\partial g_{n-1}}{\partial x} + \frac{\partial g_{n-1}}{\partial y} y' + \frac{\partial g_{n-1}}{\partial y'} y'' + \ldots + \frac{\partial g_{n-1}}{\partial g^{n-2}} y^{(n-1)}$$

$$= g_n (x, y, y', \ldots y^{(n-1)}), \text{ say.}$$

Putting $x = x_0, y = y_0$ in the above result, we obtain

$$y_0', y_0'', y_0''', \ldots, y_0^{(n)}.$$

With these substitutions in (2), we obtain y *i.e.* the solution of the differential equation.

This method has not of much importance, since it involves partial derivatives, again h should be small enough so that the successive terms of series should diminish quite rapidly.

> **Note:** Putting $x - x_0 = m$ in (2), we obtain
>
> $$y = y_0 + m\, y_0' + \frac{r^2 h^2}{2!} y'' + \frac{r^3 h^3}{3!} y_0'' ,. + .. [r = \pm 1, \pm 2, \pm 3, \ldots]$$

Example 11: *Solve $(dy/dx) = x + y$ numerically. Start from $x = 1, y = 0$ and carry to $x = 1.2$ with $h = 0.1$. Compare the final result with the value of the explicit solution.* **[Agra 2004]**

Solution: Here, we have $x_0 = 1, y_0 = 0$

$\Rightarrow \quad y' = x + y \quad$ *i.e.* $\quad y_0' = x_0 + y_0 = 1$

$\Rightarrow \quad y'' = 1 + y' \quad$ *i.e.* $\quad y_0'' = 1 + y_0' = 2$

$\Rightarrow \quad y''' = y'' \quad$ *i.e.* $\quad y_0''' = y_0'' = 2$

$\Rightarrow \quad y^{(iv)} = y''' \quad$ *i.e.* $\quad y_0^{(iv)} = y_C''' = 2$

$\Rightarrow \quad y^{(v)} = y^{(iv)} \quad$ *i.e.* $\quad y_0^{(v)} = y_0^{(iv)} = 2$

By Taylor's series, we have

$$y_1 = y_0 + h\, y_0' + \frac{h^2}{2!} y_0'' + \frac{h^3}{3!} y_0''' + \frac{h^4}{4!} y_0^{(iv)} + \frac{h^5}{5!} y_0^{(v)} + \ldots$$

$$\Rightarrow \quad y_1 = 0 + (0.1)1 + \frac{(0.1)^2}{2!}(2) + \frac{(0.1)^3}{3!}(2) + \frac{(0.1)^4}{4!}(2) + \frac{(0.1)^5}{5!}(2)$$

$$y = 0.1103081 = .110 \text{ approx.}$$

Thus, we have $\quad x_1 = x_0 + h = 1.1$

Again $\quad y_1' = x_1 + y_1 = 1.1 + .11 = 2.21$

$$y_1'' = 1 + y_1' = 1 + 1.21 = 2.21$$

$$y_0''' = y_1'' = 2.21, y_1^{(iv)} = 2.21, y_1^{(v)} = 2.21$$

Substituting the values in

$$y_2 = y_1 + h\, y_1' + \frac{h^2}{2!} y_1'' + \frac{h^3}{3!} y_1''' + \frac{h^4}{4!} y_0^{(iv)} + \frac{h^5}{5!} y_0^{(v)} + \ldots$$

we get

$$y_2 = .11 + (.1)(1.21) + \frac{(.1)^2}{2!}(2.21) + \frac{(.1)^3}{3!}(2.21) + \frac{(.1)^4}{4!}(2.21) + \frac{(.1)^5}{5!}(2.21)$$

$$= 0.232 \text{ (Approx)}.$$

2nd Part: We have $y = -x - 1 + 2e^{x-1}$

Solving it as linear differential equation of first order we can get y. When $x = 1.2$, we get $y = -1.2 - 1 + 2e^2 = 0.242$.

Example 12: *Solve* $\frac{dy}{dx} = y^2 + 1$, *assuming* $y = 0$ *at* $x = 0$ *in the range* $0 \le x \le 1$. *Obtain* y *as series in power of x and check your result with the exact value.*

Solution: Initially $x_0 = 0,\ y_0 = 0$.

Also we have $\frac{dy}{dx} = y^2 + 1$

$\Rightarrow \quad y' = y^2 + 1 \qquad$ i.e. $\quad y_0' = 1$

$\Rightarrow \quad y'' = 2yy' \qquad$ i.e. $\quad y_0'' = 0$

$\Rightarrow \quad y''' = 2yy'' + 2y'^2 \qquad$ i.e. $\quad y_0''' = 2$

$\Rightarrow \quad y^{(iv)} = 2y'y'' + 2yy''' + 4y'y'', \qquad$ i.e. $\quad y_0^{(iv)} = 0$

$\Rightarrow \quad y^{(v)} = 2yy^{(iv)} + 6y''^2 + 2y'y'' + 6y'y''' \qquad$ i.e. $\quad y_0^{(v)} = 12$

Whence substituting these values in Taylor's series, we have

$$y = 0 + x.1 + \frac{x^2}{2!}0 + \frac{x^3}{3!}2 + \frac{x^4}{4!}0 + \ldots \quad \text{or} \quad y = x + \frac{x^3}{3!}2 + \ldots$$

Now choosing $h = 0.2$, we have

$$y_0 = y(0.2) = 0.2 + \frac{1}{3}(0.008) = 0.203$$

and $\quad y_1 = y'(0.2) = (0.008) = 0.0412.$

Solving the given equation, we get $y = \tan x$. Putting $x = 1$ we obtain $y = 0.422$, where $h = 0.2$, i.e. we have $y = 0.42$ at $x = 0.4$. Further choosing $x_0 = 0.4, h = 0.2, y = 0.422$, we obtain $y = 0.683$ at $x = 0.4 + 0.2 = 0.6$. Thus we prepare the following table:

x	0	0.2	0.4	0.6	0.8	1
y	0	0.203	0.422	0.683	1.027	1.546

Now correct value = 1.557, calculated value = 1.546.

$\therefore \quad$ Error = 0.011.

Example 13: *Using Taylor's series, find the solution of the differential equation $xy' = x - y$; $y(2) = 2$ at $x = 2.1$, correct to five places of decimal.*

Solution: We have $y' = \dfrac{x-y}{x} = 1 - (y/x) \Rightarrow y'_{(2)} = 0$, at $x = 2, y = 2$

$$\Rightarrow \quad y'' = -\frac{y'}{x} + \frac{y}{x^2} \qquad \Rightarrow \quad y''_{(2)} = \frac{1}{2}$$

$$\Rightarrow \quad y''' = -\frac{y''}{x} + \frac{2y'}{x^2} - \frac{2y}{x^3} \qquad \Rightarrow \quad y'''_{(2)} = -\frac{3}{4}$$

$$\Rightarrow \quad y^{(iv)} = -\frac{y'''}{x} + \frac{3y''}{x^2} - \frac{6y'}{x^3} + \frac{6y}{x^4} \qquad \Rightarrow \quad y^{iv}_{(2)} = \frac{3}{2}$$

Now Taylor's series expansion about $x = 2$ is $y(x) = y(2 + x - 2)$

$$= y(2) + (x-2)\, y'_{(2)} + \frac{(x-2)^2}{2!} y''_2 + \frac{(x-2)^3}{3!} y_2'''(2) + \frac{(x-2)^4}{4!} y_2^{iv}(2) +$$

$$= 2 + (x-2).0 + \frac{1}{4}(x-2)^2 - \frac{1}{3}(x-2)^3 + \frac{1}{16}(x-2)^4 + \ldots$$

$$\Rightarrow \quad y(2.1) = 2 + (2.1-2)\,0 + \frac{1}{4}(2.1-2)^2 - \frac{1}{8}(2.1-2)^3 + \frac{1}{16}(2.1-5)^4 + \ldots$$

$$= 2 + 0.0025 - 0.000125 + .0000062 \approx 2.00238.$$

If we now wish to obtain $y(2.2)$ to the same accuracy, we would have to carry the series through two additional terms. Alternatively, we could now make a new expansion about $x = 2.1$, re-evaluate the first four derivatives at $x = 2.1$ and then compute $y_{2.2}$.

✦✦ Problem Set ✦✦

1. Find an approximate value of y when $x = 0.1$, if $(dy/dx) = x - y^2$ and $y = 1$ at $x = 0$ using (i) Picard's method, (ii) Taylor's series.

2. Obtain Picard's second approximate solution of the initial value problem
$$y' = x^2/(y^2 + 1),\ y(0) = 0$$

3. Employ Picard's method to obtain, correct to four places of decimal, solution of the differential equation $(dy/dx) = x^2 + y^2$ for $x = 0.4$, given that $y = 0$ when $x = 0$.

4. Evaluate $y(0.1)$ correct to six places of decimals by Taylor's series method if $y(x)$ satisfies $y' = xy + 1, y(0) = 1$.

5. Using Taylor's series method, compute $y(0.2)$ to three places of decimal from $\dfrac{dy}{dx} = 1 - 2xy$ given that $y(0) = 0$.

✦✦ Answers ✦✦

1.	0.9138	2.	$y = \frac{x^3}{3} - \frac{x^9}{81} + \ldots$
3.	0.214	4.	1.1053425
5.	2.02061		

11.7 Runge's Method

This method is due to the German mathematical ***Carl Runge*** **(1856-1927)** and is as follows:

Let $\frac{dy}{dx} = f(x, y)$ be the given differential equation where $y = y_0$ at $x = x_0$

Now $\qquad dy = f(x, y)\, dx \qquad \ldots(1)$

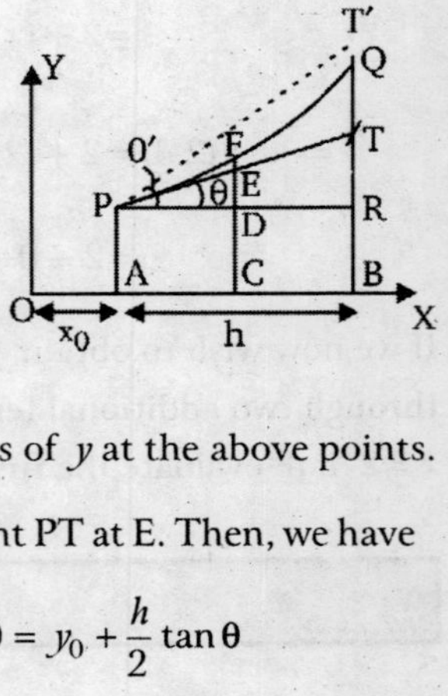

Integrating both sides of (1) from (x_0, y_0) to $(x_0 + h, y_0 + k)$

$$\int_{y_0}^{y_0+k} dy = \int_{x_0}^{x_0+h} f(x, y)\, dx \qquad \ldots(2)$$

To integrate the R.H.S., we consider C as the middle point of AB and obtain the values of (dy/dx) *i.e.* $f(x, y)$ at the points $x_0, x_0 + \frac{1}{2}h, x_0 + h$. For this, we first calculate the values of y at the above points.

Let the ordinate through C cut the curve PQ at F and the tangent PT at E. Then, we have

$$y_E = CE = CD + DE = AP + DE = y_0 + PD \tan\theta = y_0 + \frac{h}{2}\tan\theta$$

$$= y_0 + \frac{h}{2} f(x_0, y_0)$$

Also

$$y_T = BT = AP + RT = y_0 + h\tan\theta = y_C + h\,(dy/dx)_p = y_0 + hf(x_0, y_0)$$

Now the value of (dy/dx) is given by the point T' where the line drawn through P with slope at $T_E\ (x_0 + h, y_T)$ meets BQ.

$\therefore \qquad$ Slope at $T = \tan\theta' = f[(x_0 + h, y_T) = f[x_0 + h, y_0 + hf(x_0, y_0)]$

$\Rightarrow \qquad y_Q = BR + RT' = y_0 + PR\tan\theta'$

$\Rightarrow \qquad y_0 + hf[x_0 + h, y_C + hf(x_0, y_0)] \qquad \ldots(3)$

$\Rightarrow \qquad [f(x, y)]_p \quad i.e.\ [dy/dx]_p = f(x_0, y_0)$

$\qquad [f(x, y)]_F \quad i.e.\ [dy/dx]_F \quad f(x_0 + \frac{h}{2}, y_F)$

and $[f(x, y)]_Q$ i.e. $[dy/dx]_Q = f(x_0 + h, y_Q)$

$\therefore$ Relation (2)

$$\Rightarrow \quad k = \int_{x_0}^{x_0+h} f(x, y)\, dx = \frac{h}{6}\left[\{f(x, y)\} + 4\{f(x, y)\}_F + \{f(x, y)\}_Q\right]$$

by simpson's rule

$$= \frac{h}{6}[f(x_0, y_0) + 4f(x_0 + \frac{h}{2}, y_F) + f(x_0 + h, y_Q)]$$

This gives a sufficiently accurate value of k and then of $y = y_0 + k$. The repeated application of the result (4) gives the values of y for equispaced points.

Working Rule: To solve (1) by Runge's method:

Calculate successively $k_1 = hf(x_0, y_0)$,

$$k_2 = h f(x_0 + \frac{1}{2}h, y_0 + \frac{1}{2}k_1);\; k' = h f(x_0 + h, y_0 + k_1)$$

$$k_3 = h f(x_0 + h, y_0 + k') \text{ and then finally } k = \frac{1}{6}[k_1 + 4k_2 + k_3].$$

Example 14: *Use Runge's method to approximate y at $x = 1.6$, when $y = 0.4$ at $x = 1$ and $(dy/dx) = x - y$.* **[I.A.S. 2002]**

Solution: Here $x_0 = 1$, $y_0 = 0.4$; so that $f(x, y) = (dy/dx) = x - y$

and $$f(x_0, y_0) = x_0 - y_0 = 1 - 0.4 = 0.6.$$

Consequently $k_1 = h(x_0, y_0) = 0.6 \times h$ (consider $h = 0.6$)

and

$$f\left(x_0 + \frac{h}{2}, y_0 + \frac{k_1}{2}\right) = (x_0 - y_0) + \frac{1}{2}(h - k_1) = 0.6 + \frac{1}{2}(0.6 - 0.6h)$$

$$= 0.6 + \frac{1}{2}0.6(1 - h) = 0.6 + 0.3(1 - h)$$

$$\Rightarrow \quad k_2 = hf\left(x_0 + \frac{h}{2}, y_0 + \frac{k_1}{2}\right) = 0.6h + 0.3h(1 - h) = 0.6h + .12h = 0.72h,$$

$$f(x_0 + h, y_0 + k_1) = (x_0 - y_0) + h - k_1 = 0.6 + h - 0.6h$$

$$= 0.6 + h(.4)$$

$$\Rightarrow \quad k' = h f(x_0 + h, y_0 + k_1) = 0.6h + h(0.24) = 0.84h$$

and $$f(x_0 + h, y_0 + k') = x_0 - y_0 + h - k' = 0.6 + h - 0.84h$$

$$= 0.6 + h(1 - 0.84) = 0.6 + 0.16h$$

$$= 0.6 + 0.16 \times .6 = 0.6 + .096 = 0.696$$

$$\Rightarrow \quad k_3 = h f(x_0 + h, y_0 + k') = 0.696h$$

$\therefore \quad k = \frac{1}{6}(k_1 + 4k_2 + k_3) = \frac{1}{6}(.6h + 4 \times 0.72\,h + 0.696\,h)$

$= 0.1(.6 + 2.88 + 0.696) = .4176$

$\Rightarrow \quad [y]_{x=1.6} = 0.4 + 0.4176 = 0.8176.$

Example 15: *Use Runge's method to approximate y when $x = 0.1$, given that $y = 1$ at $x = 0$ and*

$$\frac{dy}{dx} = 3x + y^2.$$

Solution: Here $x_0 = 0,\ y_0 = 1;\ f(x, y) = 3x + y^2$, giving $f(x_0, y_0) = 1$.

Let $\quad h = 0.1.$

Then $\quad hf(x_0, y_0) = 0.1(1) = 0.1 = k_1$ say

$hf\{f(x_0 + h, y_0 + k_1)\} = 0.1\{3(x_0 + h) + (y_0 + k_1)^2\}$

$= 0.1\{3(0 + 0.1) + (1 + 0.1)^2\} = 0.151, = k'$, say

Now $\quad hf\{f(x_0 + h, y_0 + k')\} = h\{3(x_0 + h) + (y_0 + k')^2\}$

$= 0.1\{3(0 + 0.1) + (1 + 0.15)^2\} = 0.16225 = k_3.$

and $\quad k_2 = h\left\{f\left(x_0 + \frac{h}{2}, y_0 + \frac{k_1}{2}\right)\right\}$

$= h\left\{3\left(x_0 + \frac{h}{2}\right) + \left(y_0 + \frac{k_1}{2}\right)^2\right\}$

$= h\{3(0 + 0.05) + (1 + 0.05)^2\} = 0.1\{3(0.05) + (1.05)^2\} = \mathbf{0.12525.}$

Thus increment in the value of y in the range $(0, 0.1)$

$= \frac{1}{6}\{k_1 + 4k_2 + k_3\} = \frac{1}{6}\{0.1 + 4(0.12525) + 0.16225\} = \mathbf{0.12725}$

Hence the value of y at $x = 0.1$, is $y = 1 + 0.12725 = 1.12725$.

Example 16: *Use Runge's method to approximate y when $x = 0.8$ for the particular solution of $\frac{dy}{dx} = \sqrt{(x + y)}$ which satisfies the condition $y = 0.41$ at $x = 0.4$.*

Solution: Here $x_0 = 0.4,\ y_0 = 0.4;\ f(x, y) = \sqrt{(x + y)}$ giving

$f(x_0, y_0) = \sqrt{(x_0, y_0)} = \sqrt{(0.4 + 0.41)} = 0.9.$

Let $\quad h = 0.4 \qquad$ Then $\ k_1 = hf(x_0, y_0) = 0.4 \times 0.9) = 0.36.$

$k' = h\{f(x_0 + h, y_0 + k_1\} = 0.4\{\sqrt{(x_0 + h + y_0 + 0.36)}\}$

$= 0.4\{\sqrt{(0.4 + 0.41 + 0.36 + 0.4)}\} = 0.4\sqrt{(1.57)} = \mathbf{0.50120}$

and $\quad k_3 = h\{f(x_0 + h, y_0 + k')\} = \{\sqrt{(x_0 + h + y_0 + 0.50120)}\}$

$= 0.4\{\sqrt{(0.4 + 0.4 + 0.41 + 0.50120)}\} = \mathbf{0.4\sqrt{(1.7112)} = 0.52325,}$

$$\therefore \quad k_2 = h\left\{f\left(x_0 + \frac{h}{2}; y_0 + \frac{k_1}{2}\right)\right\} = h\left\{x_0 + y_0 + \frac{h}{2} + \frac{k_1}{2}\right\}^{1/2}$$

$$= 0.4\ \sqrt{\{0.4 + 0.41 + 0.2\,(1 + 0.9)\}} = 0.4\sqrt{(1.19)} = \mathbf{0.43635}$$

$\therefore$ Increment in the value of y in the range $(0.4, 0.8)$

$$= \frac{1}{6}(k_1 + 4k_2 + k_3) = \frac{1}{6}\{0.36 + 4\,(0.43635) + 0.52325\} = \mathbf{0.43811}$$

Hence the value of y at $x = 0.1$, is $y = 0.41 + 0.43811 = 0.84811$.

Example 17: *Use Runge's method to approximate y when $x = 1.1$, given that $y = 1.2$ at $x = 1$ and*

$$\frac{dy}{dx} = 3x + y^2.$$

Solution: Here $x_0 = 1, y_0 = 1.2; f(x, y) = 3x + y^2$, giving

$$f(x_0, y_0) = 3\,(1) + (1.2)^2 = 4.44.$$

Let $h = 0.1$ Then

$$k_1 = h\,f(x_0, y_0) = 0.1(3x_0 + y_0^2) = 0.1(3 \times 1 + 1.44) = 0.444,$$

$$k' = h\{f\,(x_0 + h, y_0 + k_1)\} = 0.1\{3\,(x_0 + h) + (y_0 + k_1)^2\}$$

$$= 0.1\{3\,(1 + 0.1) + (1.2 + 0.444)^2\} = 0.6002704,$$

$$k_3 = h\{f(x_0 + h, y_0 + k')\} = h\,\{3\,(x_0 + h) + (y_0 + k')^2\}$$

$$= 0.1\{3\,(1 + 0.1) + (1.2 + 0.600274)^2\} = 0.624097.$$

$$\Rightarrow \quad k_2 = h\left\{f\left(x_0 + \frac{h}{2}, y_0 + \frac{k_1}{2}\right)\right\} = h\left\{3\left(x_0 + \frac{h}{2}\right) + \left(y_0 + \frac{k_1}{2}\right)^2\right\}$$

$$= 0.1\{3\,(1 + .05) + (1.2 + 0.212)^2\} = 0.517208.$$

$\because$ Increment in the value of y in the range $(1, 1.1)$

$$= \frac{1}{6}(k_1 + 4k_2 + k_3) = \frac{1}{6}\{\mathbf{0.444 + 4 \times 0.517208 + 0.62409}\} = \mathbf{0.527822.}$$

Hence the value of y at $x = 1.1$, $y = 1.2 + 0.527822 = \mathbf{1.727822.}$

11.8 Runge Kutta Method

[Agra 2003, 2005]

Actually, Taylor's series method of solving differential equations numerically involves lot of labour in finding out the higher order derivatives. ***R-K method*** then was introduced and does not require the calculation of higher order derivatives and also gives greater accuracy. ***R-K method*** only requires the functional values at some selected points and agree with Taylor's series solution up to term in h^r where r differs from method to method and is known as the order of that method.

[A] R-K Method of First Order

[Agra 2007]

By Euler's method, we have $y_1^{(1)} = y_0 + h\,f(x_0, y_0) = y_0 + h\,y_0'$ where $(dy/dx) = f(x, y)$

Also expanding by Taylor's series method, we have

$$y_1^{(1)} = y_1 \text{ say} = y_0\,(x+h)$$
$$= y_0 + h\,y_0' + (h^2/2!)\,y_0'' + (h^2/3!)\,y_0''' + \ldots.$$

This means that Euler's method agrees with Taylor's series solution up to the term in h. *Hence Euler's method is nothing but R-K method of the first order.*

[B] R-K Method of Second Order

By modified Euler's method, we have

$$y_1 = y_0 + \frac{h}{2}\,[f(x_0, y) + f(x_0 + h, y_1)] \qquad \ldots(1)$$

Putting $y_1 = y_0 + h\,f(x_0, y_0)$ in the **r.h.s.**, we get

$$y_1 = y_0 + \frac{h}{2}\,[f_0 + f(x_0 + h, y_0 + h\,f_0)] \text{ where } f(x_0, y_0) = f_0 \qquad \ldots(2)$$

Again $\quad y_1 = y(x_0 + h)$

$$= y_0 + h\,y_0' + (h^2/2!)\,y_0'' + (h^3/3!)\,y_0''' + \ldots$$

by Taylor's series and

$$f(x_0 + h, y_0 + h\,f_0) = f(x_0, y_0) + h\left(\frac{\partial f}{\partial x}\right)_0 + h\,f_0\left(\frac{\partial f}{\partial y}\right)_0 + \text{terms having } h^2, h^3 \text{ etc.}$$

$\therefore$ Relation (2)

$$\Rightarrow \qquad y_1 = y_0 + \frac{h}{2}\left[f_0 + f_0 + h\left(\frac{\partial f}{\partial x}\right)_0 + h\,f_0\left(\frac{\partial f}{\partial y}\right)_0 + O(h)^3\right]$$

$$= y_0 + h\,f_0 + (h^2/2!)\left[\left(\frac{\partial f}{\partial x}\right)_0 + f_0\left(\frac{\partial f}{\partial y}\right)_0\right] + \ldots$$

$$\Rightarrow \qquad y_1 = y_0 + h\,f_0 + (h^2/2!)\left[\frac{d}{dx}f(x, y)\right]_0 + \ldots \qquad \left[\because \frac{\partial u}{\partial x} + \frac{\partial u}{\partial y}\frac{dy}{dx} = \frac{du}{dx}\right]$$

$$= y_0 + h\,y_0' + (h^2/2!)\left[\frac{d}{dx}\left(\frac{dy}{dx}\right)\right] + \ldots$$

$$= y_0 + hy_0' + (h^2/2!)\,y_0'' + O(h^3) \qquad \ldots(3)$$

Also $\quad y_1 = y_0\,(x+h)$

$$= y_0 + hy_0' + (h^2/2!)\,y_0'' + O(h^3) \qquad \ldots(4)$$

From (3) and (4), we see that the modified Euler's method is in agreement with Taylor's series solution up to the term in h^2. Thus, we can say that the modified Euler's method is nothing but ***R-K method*** of second order.

Working rule

R-K method of second order is $y_1 = y_0 + \frac{1}{2}(k_1 + k_2)$

where $\quad k_1 = hf(x_0, y_0), k_2 = hf(x_0 + h, y_0 + k_1)$

[C] R-K Method of Third Order

To find the increment k of y corresponding to an increment h of x by ***R-K method*** from $(dy/dx) = f(x, y)$ where $y(x_0) = y_0$, we proceed as follows:

Calculate $\quad k_1 = h\,f(x_0, y_0), k_2 = hf\left[x_0 + \frac{h}{2}, y_0 + \frac{k_1}{2}\right],$

$$k_3 = hf[x_0 + h, y_0 + k'];$$

where $\quad k' = hf\,[x_0 + h, y_0 + k_1]$ Finally compute

$$y_1 = y_0 + \frac{1}{6}(k_1 + 4k_2 + k_3)$$

[D] R-K Method of Fourth Order (or Simply Runge-Kutta Method)

To find the increment k of y corresponding to an increment h in x by ***R-K method*** from $(dy/dx) = f(x, y), y(x_0) = y_0$; we calculate:

$$k_1 = hf(x_0, y_0), k_2 = hf\left[x_0 + \frac{1}{2}h, y_0 + \frac{1}{2}k_1\right]$$

$$k_2 = hf\left(x_0 + \frac{h}{2}, y_0 + \frac{k_2}{2}\right), k_4 = hf\,[x_0 + h, y_0 + k_3]$$

and finally $\quad k = \frac{1}{6}[k_1 + 2\,k_2 + 2\,k_3 + k_4]$; so that $y_1 = y_0 + k$.

Example 18: *Apply Runge-Kutta fourth order method to find an approximate value of y when $x = 0.2$ given that $(dy/dx) = x + y$ and $y = 1$ when $x = 0$*

[Agra 2004; Meerut 2002]

Solution: $x_0 = 0, y_0 = 1, h = 0.2, f(x_0, y_0) = 1$

Hence, we get $k_1 = hf(x_0, y_0) = 0.2 \times 1 = 0.2000$

$$k_2 = hf(x_0 + \frac{1}{2}h, y_0 + \frac{1}{2}k_1) = 0.2 \times f(0.1, 1.1) = 0.2400$$

$$k_3 = hf\,(x_0 + \frac{1}{2}h, y_0 + \frac{1}{2}k_2) = 0.2 \times f(0.1, 1.12) = 0.2440$$

and $\quad k_4 = hf(x_0 + h, y_0 + k_3) = 0.2 \times f(0.2, 1.244) = 0.2888$

$$\Rightarrow \quad k = \frac{1}{6}(k_1 + 2k_2 + 2k_3 + k_4] = \frac{1}{6}(0.2000 + 0.4800 + 0.4880 + 0.2888)$$

$$= \frac{1}{6} \times 4.4568 = 0.2428$$

Hence the required approximate value of $y = y_0 + 0.2428 = 1.2428$

Example 19: *Apply Runge-Kutta method to find approximate value of y for $x = 0.2$, in steps of 0.1, if $(dy/dx) = x + y^2$, given that $y = 1$ where $x = 0$. Given $f(x, y) = x + y^2$.*

[Agra 2003]

Solution: Let us choose $h = 0.1$ and calculate various values as follows:

Step I: $x_0 = 0,\ y_0 = 1,\ h = 0.1$

$$\Rightarrow \quad k_1 = hf(x_0, y_0) = 0.1\, f(0,1) = 0.1000$$

$$k_2 = hf(x_0 + \frac{1}{2}h, y_0 + \frac{1}{2}k_1) = 0.1\, f(0.05, 1.1) = 0.1152$$

$$k_3 = hf(x_0 + \frac{1}{2}h, y_0 + \frac{1}{2}k_2) = 0.1 \times f(0.05, 1.1152) = 0.1168$$

$$k_4 = hf(x_0 + h, y_0 + k_3) = 0.1 f(0.1, 1.1168) = 0.1347$$

and $$k = \frac{1}{6}(k_1 + 2k_2 + 2k_3 + k_4)$$

$$= \frac{1}{6}(0.1000 + 0.2304 + 0.2336 + 0.1347) = \mathbf{0.1165}$$

So that $y(0.1) = y_0 + k = 1.1165$

Step II: $x_1 = x_0 + h = 0.1,\ y_1 = 1.1165,\ h = 0.1$

$$\Rightarrow \quad k_1 = hf(x_1, y_1) = 0.1\, f(0.1, 1.1165) = 0.1347$$

$$k_2 = hf(x_1 + \frac{1}{2}h, y_1 + \frac{1}{2}k_1) = 0.1\, f(0.15, 1.1838) = 0.1551$$

$$k_3 = hf(x_1 + \frac{1}{2}h, y_1 + \frac{1}{2}k_2) = 0.1 f(0.15, 1.194) = 0.1576$$

$$k_4 = hf(x_1 + h, y_2 + k_3) = 0.1 f(0.2, 1.1576) = 0.1823$$

and $$k = \frac{1}{6}(k_1 + 2k_2 + 2k_3 + k_4) = 0.1571$$

So that $y(0.2) = y_1 + k = 1.2736.$

Example 20: *Using Runge-Kutta method of fourth order, solve $\frac{dy}{dx} = \frac{y^2 - x^2}{y^2 + x^2}$ with $y(0) = 1$ at $x = 0.2, 0.4$.*

Solution: $f(x, y) = \frac{y^2 - x^2}{y^2 + x^2} = \frac{dy}{dx}$

To find $y(0.2)$:

we have $x_0 = 0,\ y_0 = 1,\ h = 0.2$

$$\Rightarrow \quad k_1 = hf(x_0, y_0) = 0.2\ f(0.1) \qquad = 0.2000$$

$$k_2 = hf\left(x_0 + \frac{1}{2}h, y_0 + \frac{1}{2}k_1\right) = 0.2\ f(0.1, 1.1) \qquad = 0.19672$$

$$k_3 = hf\left(x_0 + \frac{1}{2}h, y_0 + \frac{1}{2}k_2\right) = 0.2\ f(0.1, 1.09836) \quad = 0.1967$$

$$k_4 = hf(x_0 + h, y_0 + k_3) = 0.2\ f(0.2, 1.1967) \qquad = 0.1891$$

and $$k = \frac{1}{6}(k_1 + 2k_2 + 2k_3 + k_4)$$

$$= \frac{1}{6}[0.2 + 2(0.19672) + 2(0.1967) + 0.1891] \quad = 0.19599$$

so that $y(0.2 = y_0 + k = 1.196)$.

To find $y(0.4)$:

we have $x_1 = 0.2,\ y_1 = 1.196,\ h = 0.2.$

$$\Rightarrow \quad k_1 = hf(x_1, y_1) \qquad = 0.1891$$

$$k_2 = hf\left(x_1 + \frac{1}{2}h, y_1 + \frac{1}{2}k_1\right) = 0.2\ f(0.3, 1.2906) \quad = 0.1795$$

$$k_3 = hf\left(x_1 + \frac{1}{2}h, y_1 + \frac{1}{2}k_2\right) = 0.2\ f(0.3, 1.2858) \quad = 0.1793$$

$$k_4 = hf(x_1 + h, y_1 + k_3) = 0.2\ f(0.4, 1.3753) \qquad = 0.1688$$

and $$k = \frac{1}{6}(k_1 + 2k_2 + 2k_3 + k_4)$$

$$= \frac{1}{6}[0.1891 + 2(0.1795) + 2(0.1793) + 0.1688] = 0.1792$$

so that $y(0.4) = y_1 + k = 1.196 + 0.1792 = 1.3752.$

✦✦ Problem Set ✦✦

1. Using Runge-Kutta method of order 4, find $y(0.2)$ given that

$$(dy/dx) = 3x + \frac{1}{2}y,\ y(0) = 1, \text{ taking } h = 0.1$$

2. Use Runge's method to approximate y when $x = 1.1$, given that $y = 1.2$ when $x = 1$ and $(dy/dx) = 3x + y^2$. **[Agra 2003; Avadh 2003]**

3. Find by Runge-Kutta method an approximate value of y for $x = 0.8$, given that $y = 0.41$ when $x = 0.4$ and $(dy/dx) = \sqrt{(x + y)}$.

4. Given that $(dy/dx) = (y^2 - 2x)/(y^2 + x)$ and $y = 1$ as $x = 0$; find y for $x = 0.1, 0.2, 0.3, 0.4$ and 0.5.

5. Using Runge-Kutta method of order 4, find $y(0.2)$ for the equation

$$\frac{dy}{dx} = \frac{y-x}{y+x},\ y(0) = 1.\ \text{Take } h = 0.2$$

6. Using Runge-Kutta method of order 4, compute $y(.2)$ and $y(.4)$ from

$$10\frac{dy}{dx} = x^2 + y^2,\ y(0) = 1, \text{taking } h = 0.1$$

[Agra 2006; Meerut 2003]

✦✦ Answers ✦✦

1.	2.5005	**2.**	1.7278
3.	1.1678	**4.**	1.0911, 1.1677, 1.2352, 1.2902, 1.338.
5.	1.1749	**6.**	1.0207, 1.038

11.9 Predictor and Corrector Method

[Agra 2005]

Let x_{n-1} and x_n be the two consecutive mesh points, then we can write $x_n = x_{n-1} + h$. Also by Euler's method, we have $y_n = y_{n-1} + hf[x_0 + \overline{n-1}h, y_{n-1}]$

$$(n = 1, 2, 3, \ldots) \qquad \ldots(1)$$

Also modified Euler's method gives

$$y_n = y_{n-1} + \frac{h}{2}[f(x_{n-1}, y_{n-1}) + f(x_n, y_n)] \qquad \ldots(2)$$

From relation (1), we just estimate y_n and then insert this value in the **r.h.s.** of (2). This gives a better approximation of y_n. Again substituting this value in (2), we again get the new value.

This step is repeated till two consecutive values of y_n are in close agreement. This technique of refining the crude estimate of y_n by means of a more accurate formula is known as ***Predictor-Corrector*** method.

Hence equation (1) is therefore called the ***Predictor*** and (2) as a ***Corrector*** of y_n. In the above methods, we solved a **d.e** over an interval knowing the value of y at the beginning of the interval. In predictor corrector methods, four prior values are needed to find y at x_n. As a matter of fact, these method are complex but yield the estimate of error from successive approximations to y_n. We now describe two such methods.

11.10 Milne's Method

[Agra 2007]

In order to solve the differential equation $y' = f(x, y)$ by this method, we first obtain the approximate value of y_{n+1} by predictor formula and then improve this value by means of a corrector formula. Newton's interpolation formula in terms of y' and u is given by

$$y' = y'_0 + u\Delta y'_0 + \frac{u(u-1)}{2}\Delta^2 y'_0 + \frac{u(u-1)(u-2)}{6}\Delta^3 y'_0 + \ldots$$

$$+ \frac{u(u-1)(u-2)(u-3)}{24}\Delta^4 y'_0 + \ldots \quad \ldots(1)$$

Where $\qquad u = \dfrac{x - x_0}{h} \Rightarrow x = x_0 + uh.$

Now, integrating (1) over the interval x_0 to $(x_0 + 4h)$ (*i.e.* $u = 0$ *to* 4), we obtain

$$\int_{x_0}^{x_0+4h} y'\,dx = h\int_0^4 \left[y'_0 + u\Delta y'_0 + \frac{u(u-1)}{2}\Delta^2 y'_0 \right.$$

$$\left. + \frac{u(u-1)(u-2)}{6}\Delta^3 y'_0 + \frac{u(u-1)(u-2)(u-3)}{24}\Delta^4 y'_0 + \ldots \right] du$$

$[\because dx = h\,du]$

$$\Rightarrow \qquad y_4 - y_0 = h\left[4y'_0 + 8\Delta y'_0 + \frac{20}{3}\Delta^2 y'_0 + \frac{8}{3}\Delta^3 y'_0 + \frac{28}{90}\Delta^4 y'_0 \right]$$

up to fourth difference only.

Where y_0 and y_4 stand for the value of y at $x = x_0$ and $x = x_0 + 4h$ respectively.

Now, substituting the values of first, second and third differences, in the above relation, we get

$$y_4 - y_0 = h\left[4y'_0 + 8(E-1)y'_0 + \frac{20}{3}(E-1)^2 y'_0 + \frac{8}{3}(E-1)^3 y'_0 + \frac{28}{90}\Delta^4 y'_0 \right] \quad \ldots(2)$$

$$\Rightarrow \qquad y_4 - y_0 = \frac{4h}{3}(2y'_1 - y'_2 + 2y'_3) + \frac{28}{90}h\Delta^4 y'_0$$

$$\Rightarrow \qquad y_4 = y_0 + \frac{4h}{3}(2y'_1 - y'_2 + 2y'_3) + \frac{28}{90}h\Delta^4 y'_0 \quad \ldots(3)$$

This is ***Milne's Extrapolation (Predictor) Formula***

It is used to predict the value of y_4 when the value of y_0, y_1, y_2 and y_3 are known.

To obtain the corrector formula we integrate (1) over the interval x_0 to $x_0 + 2h$ or $u = 0$ to 2 and consequently

$$y_2 - y_0 = h\left[2y'_0 + 2\Delta y'_0 + \frac{1}{3}\Delta^2 y'_0 - \frac{1}{90}\Delta^4 y'_0 \right]$$

Now expressing the first, second and third differences in terms of the function value by using $\Delta \equiv E - 1$, we at once obtain

$$y_2 - y_0 = \frac{h}{3}(y'_0 + 4y'_1 + y'_2) - \frac{h}{90}\Delta^4 y'_0$$

$$\Rightarrow \quad y_2 = y_0 + \frac{h}{3}(y'_0 + 4y'_1 + y'_2) - \frac{h}{90}\Delta^4 y'_0 \qquad \ldots(4)$$

This is Milne's corrector formula: The value of y_4 obtained from the formula (3) and (4) can be put as

$$y_{n+1} = y_{n-3} + \frac{4h}{3}(2y'_{n-2} - y'_{n-1} + 2y'_n) \qquad \ldots(5)$$

$$y_{n+1}^{(1)} = y_{n-1} + \frac{h}{3}(y'_{n-1} + 4y'_n + y'_{n+1}) \qquad \ldots(6)$$

It is to be noted that we have considered the differences upto the third order, because we fit up a polynomial of degree four. The terms containing $\Delta^4 y'_0$ are not used explicitly in the formulae, but they give the principal parts of the errors in the two values of y_{n+1} as computed from (5)and (6). It is worth mentioning that error in (6) is of opposite sign to that in (5) but it is very small in magnitude.

Again, we have taken $+\frac{28}{90}h\Delta^4 y'$ and $-\frac{h}{90}\Delta^4 y'$ as the principal parts of the errors, so we may take

$$(y_{n+1})_{exact} = y_{n+1} + \frac{28}{90}h\Delta^4 y'$$

and $$(y_{n+1})_{exact} = y_{n+1}^{(1)} - \frac{h}{90}\Delta^4 y'$$

where y_{n+1} and $y_{n+1}^{(1)}$ denote the predicted and first corrected value of y at $x = x_{n+1}$.

Equating these two values, we obtain

$$y_{n+1} + \frac{28}{90}h\Delta^4 y' = y_{n+1}^{(1)} - \frac{h}{90}h\Delta^4 y'$$

$$\Rightarrow \quad y_{n+1} - y_{n+1}^{(1)} = -\frac{29}{90}h\Delta^4 y' = 29\left(-\frac{h}{90}h\Delta^4 y'\right) = 29\delta,$$

where δ denotes the principle part of the error in (6). Thus it gives

$$\delta = \frac{1}{29}(y_{n+1} - y_{n+1}^{(1)}) \qquad \ldots(7)$$

Hence the error in (6) is (1/29)th of the difference between the predicted and corrected values. From the above discussion we can say that to solve first order differential equation, we first find three consecutive values of y and y' in addition to the initial value and then we obtain the next value of y by using (5). Putting this value in $y' = f(x, y)$, we get new y', *i.e.*, the value of y' at the value of y.

Then Putting the new y' in (6) we get the corrected value of the new y. If the corrected value agrees closely with the predicted value then we proceed to the next interval, whereas, on the other hand if the corrected value differs significantly from the predicted value then we compute δ by (7). If δ is too small then we proceed to the next interval. But if δ is large enough, the value of h is large and must be reduced by taking its half value etc.

Example 21: *Tabulate by Milne's method the numerical solution of* $\frac{dy}{dx} = x - y$ *with initial conditions* $x_0 = 0$, $y_0 = 1$ *from* $x = .20$ *to* $x = .30$. **[Agra 2004, 2008, 2009]**

Solution: To obtain the solution $\frac{dy}{dx} = x + y$, with $x_0 = 0$, $y_0 = 1$ ...(1)

by Milne's Method, we shall obtain three consecutive values of y and y' corresponding to $x = 0.05$, 0.10 and 0.15 *i.e.* $h = 0.05$.

x	y	$\frac{dy}{dx} = y'$
0.00	1.0000	1.0000
0.05	1.0525	1.1025
0.10	1.1103	1.2103
0.15	1.1736	1.3236

We also get

$$y_{n+1} - y_{n-3} = -\frac{4h}{3}[2y'_{n-2} - y'_{n-1} + 2y'_n]. \quad \text{...(2)}$$

which is corrected by

$$y^{(1)}{}_{n+1} = y_{n-1} + \frac{h}{3}[y'_{n-1} + 4y'_n + y'_{n+1}]. \quad \text{...(3)}$$

Putting $n = 3$, $h = 0.05$ in (2), we get

$$y_4 = y_0 + \frac{4h}{3}[2y'_1 - y'_2 + 2y'_3]$$

$$= 1 + \frac{4(0.05)}{3}[2.205 - 1.2103 + 2.6472] = 1.2428 = \text{predicted value which is corrected by}$$

$$y_4^{(1)} = y_2 + \frac{h}{3}[y'_2 - 4y_3 + y'_4]$$

$$= 1.1103 + \frac{0.05}{3}[1.2103 + 5.2944 + 1.4428] = 1.2428,$$

Which is the same as the predicted value.

$\because$ $y_4 = y_{.20} = 1.2428$, and $y_4 = 1.4428$ $\left[\text{From } \frac{dy}{dx} = x + y\right]$

Again Putting $n=4, h=.05$, we get

$$y_5 = y_1 + \frac{4h}{3}[2y_2' - y_3' + 2y_4']$$

$$=1.0525 + \frac{4(.05)}{4}[2.4206 - 1.3236 + 2.8856] = 1.3180,$$

which is corrected by

$$y_5^{(1)} = y_3 + \frac{h}{3}[y_3' - 4y_4' + y_5']$$

$$=1.1736 + \frac{.05}{3}[1.3236 + 5.7712 + 1.568] = 1.3180,$$

same as the predicted value.

Thus $\quad y_5 = y_{.25} = 1.3180$ and $y_5' = 1.5680$.

Again putting $n=5, h=.05$, we get

$$y_6 = y_2 + \frac{4h}{3}[2y_3' - y_4' + 2y_5']$$

$$=1.1103 + \frac{4\times.05}{3}[2.6472 - 1.4428 + 3.1360] = 1.3997,$$

which is corrected by $y_6^{(1)} = y_4 + \frac{h}{3}[y_4' - 4y_5' + y_6']$

$$=1.2428 + \frac{.05}{3}\times[1.4428 + 6.2720 + 1.6997]$$

$$=1.2428 + \frac{.05}{3}\times 9.41459 = 1.3997 = y_{.30}$$

The same as the predicted value,

$\therefore \quad y^6 = 1.3997,\ y_6' = 1.6997 \quad (\because\ y' = x + y)$

x	y	$dy/dx = y'$
$.20 = x_4$	$1.2428 = y_4$	$1.4428 = y_4'$
$.25 = x_5$	$1.3180 = y_5$	$1.5680 = y_5'$
$.30 = x_6$	$1.3997 = y_6$	$1.6997 = y_6'$

Example 22: *Tabulate by Predictor-corrector formula the numerical solution of*

$$\frac{dy}{dx} = x + y = f(x, y) \text{ with initial conditions}$$

$$x_0 = 0, y_0 = 1 \text{ from } x = .10 \ to\ x = .30.$$

Solution: Let $h = .10$. To solve $\frac{dy}{dx} = x + y$, with $x_0 = 0, y_0 = 1$ by Predictor-correct pair

$$\left[\overline{y_1} = y_0 + \frac{h}{2}(3f_0 - f_{-1}), y_1 = y_0 + \frac{h}{2}(f_0 + f_1)\right]$$

We require the value of y and y' corresponding in $x = -.10$. This can be taken from the table since the exact solution of the above equation is $y = 2e^x - x - 1$.

Putting $\qquad x = -.10$, we get

$$y = 2\,e^{-.10} + 10 - 1 = .90968$$

Also we have $\qquad y'_{-.10} = x + y = -\ .10 + .90968 = .80968$

In order to obtain the next value of y and y', we proceed as follows:

$$\overline{y_1} = y_0 + \frac{h}{2}(3\,f_0 - f_{-1}),$$

i.e. $$\overline{y_{.10}} = 1 + \frac{.1}{2}[3 - .80968] = 1.1095,$$

which is corrected by

$$y_1 = y_0 + \frac{h}{2}[f_0 + f_1] = 1 + \frac{.1}{2}[1 + 1.2095] = 1.21047$$

$$\Rightarrow \qquad (y_1)_{exact} \approx y_1 - \frac{1}{6}(y_1 - \overline{y_1})$$

$$= 1.110475 - \frac{1}{6}[1.110475 - 1.1095] = 1.1103, \text{ upto four decimal places.}$$

Hence $y_1 = 1.113$, $y_1' = f_1 = 1.2103$

Again, we have

$$\overline{y_2} = y_1 + \frac{h}{2}(3\,f_1 - f_0),\ = 1.1103 + \frac{.1}{2}[3\,(.10 + 1.1106) - 1] = 1.2418,$$

which is corrected by

$$y_2 = y_1 + \frac{h}{2}[f_2 + \overline{f_2}],\ = 1.1103 + \frac{.1}{2}[1.2103 + 1.4418] = 1.2429$$

Thus $$(y_2)_{exact} \approx y_2 - \frac{1}{6}(y_2 - \overline{y_2}) \approx 1.2429 - \frac{1}{6}[1.2429 - 1.2418]$$

$$= 1.2429 - \frac{1}{6}[.0011] = 1.2428.$$

To sum up, $\qquad y_2 = 1.2428. \qquad$ Also $\ y_2' = f_2 = 1.4428.$

Further $$\overline{y_2} = y_2 + \frac{h}{2}[3\,f_2 - f_1] = 1.2428 + \frac{.1}{2}[3\,(1.4428) - 1.2103] = 1.3987$$

And is corrected by $y_3 = y_2 + \frac{h}{2}[f_0 + \overline{f_3}] = 1.2428 + \frac{.1}{2}[1.4428 + 1.6987] = 1.3999$

Thus $$(y_3)_{exact} \approx y_3 - \frac{1}{6}(y_3 - \overline{y_3}) = 1.3999 - \frac{1}{6}[1.3999 - 1.3987]$$

$$= 1.399 - \frac{1}{6}[.0012] = 1.3997.$$

Also $y_3' = 1.6997$. Hence the result in tabular from is a follows:

x	y	y'
$x_1 = .10$	$y_{1(ex)} = 1.1103$	1.2103
$x_2 = .20$	$y_{2(ex)} = 1.2428$	1.4428
$x_3 = .30$	$y_{3(ex)} = 1.3997$	1.6697

Example 23: *Find* $y(2)$, *if* $y(x)$ *is the solution of* $\frac{dy}{dx} = \frac{1}{2}(x+y)$ *assuming* $y(0) = 2$, $y(0.5) = 2.636$, $y(1.0) = 3.595$ *and* $y(1.5) = 4.968$.

Solution: Let $x_0 = 0, x_1 = 5, x_2 = 1.00, x_3 = 1.5$; then we have given: $y_0 = 2$, $y_{0.5} = 2.636 = y_1$, say, $y_2 = y_{1.00} = 3.595$, $y_3 = 4.968$ and we want to find $y_4 = y_{2.00}$.

By the Predictor formula, we have

$$y_4 = y_0 + \frac{4h}{3}\{2y_1' - y_2' + 2y_3'\} \qquad \text{...(1)}$$

Also, we have

$$y' = \frac{1}{2}(x+y), y_1' = \frac{1}{2}(x_1 + y_1) = \frac{1}{2}(.5 + 2.636) = 1.568$$

$$y_2' = \frac{1}{2}(x_2 + y_2) = \frac{1}{2}(1 + 3.595) = 2.2975,$$

$$y_3' = \frac{1}{2}(x_3 + y_3) = \frac{1}{2}(1.5 + 4.968) = 3.234.$$

$$\therefore \quad \overline{y_4} = 2 + \frac{4 \times .5}{3}[2 \times 1.568 - 2.2975 + 2 \times 3.234] = 6.8710.$$

This is corrected by $y_4^{(1)} = y_2 + \frac{h}{3}\{y_2' + 4y_3' + y_4'\}$

$$= 3.595 + \frac{.5}{3}\{2.2975 + 4 \times (3.234) + 4.4355\} = 6.87317.$$

$$\left[\because \quad \overline{y_4'} = \frac{1}{2}(x_4 + y_4)\right]$$

Above gives the first corrected value of y_4 *i.e.* $y_{2.00}$. Again applying the Corrector formula, we get

$$y_4^{new} = y_2 + \frac{h}{3}\{y_2' + 4y_3' + y_4'\}$$

$$= 3.595 + \frac{.5}{3}\{1.2975 + 4 \times (3.234) + 4.43659\} = 6.87335.$$

$$\left[\because \quad y_4' = \frac{1}{2}\{x_4 + y_4\} = \frac{1}{2}(2 + 6.87316) = 4.43659\right]$$

11.11 Adams-Bash Forth Method

We have $\dfrac{dy}{dx} = f(x, y)$ where $y_0 = y(x_0)$.

Then $y_{-1} = y(x_0 - h)$, $y_{-2} = y(x_0 - 2h)$, $y_{-3} = y(x_0 - 3h)$ are calculated by ***Taylor's series*** or ***Euler's method*** or ***Runge-Kutta method***.

Next calculate
$$y'_{-1} = [f(x, y)]_{-1} = f(x_0 - h, y_{-1})$$
$$y'_{-2} = [f(x, y)]_{-2} = f(x_0 - 2h, y_{-2})$$
$$y'_{-3} = [f(x, y)]_{-3} = f(x_0 - 3h, y_{-3})$$

To obtain y_1, we now take Newton's Backward Interpolation formula *i.e.*
$$f(x, y) = f_0 + n\nabla f_0 + \frac{n(n+1)}{2!}\nabla^2 f_0 + \frac{n(n+1)(n+2)}{3!}\nabla^3 f_0 + \ldots$$

in
$$y_1 = y_0 + \int_{x_0}^{x_0+h} f[x, y]\, dx \qquad \ldots(1)$$
$$= y_0 + \int_{x_0}^{x_1} \left\{f_0 + n\nabla f_0 + \frac{n(n+1)}{2!}\nabla^2 f_0 + \frac{n(n+1)(n+2)}{3!}\nabla^3 f_0 + \ldots\right\} dx$$

Putting $x = x_0 + nh$ *i.e.* $dx = h\,dn$, we get
$$y_1 = y_0 + h\int_0^1 \left[f_0 + n\nabla f_0 + \frac{n(n+1)}{2!}\nabla^2 f_0 + \frac{n(n+1)(n+2)}{3!}\nabla^3 f_0 + \ldots\right] dn$$
$$= y_0 + h\left[f_0 + \nabla f_0 + \nabla f_0\left(\frac{1}{2}\right) + \frac{\nabla^2 f_0}{2!}\left(\frac{1}{3} + \frac{1}{2}\right) + \frac{\nabla^3 f_0}{3!}\left(\frac{9}{4}\right) + \ldots\right]$$
$$= y_0 + h\left[f_0 + \frac{\nabla f_0}{2} + \frac{5}{12} + \nabla^2 f_0 + \frac{3}{8}\nabla^3 f_0 + \ldots\right]$$

But, we know that $\nabla f_0 = f_0 - f_{-1}$, $\nabla^2 f_0 = \nabla f_0 - \nabla f_{-1}$
$$= (f_0 - f_{-1}) - (f_{-1} - f_{-2}) = f_0 - 2f_{-1} + f_{-2}$$

and
$$\nabla^3 f_0 = \nabla f_0 - 2\nabla f_{-1} + \nabla f_{-2} = (f_0 - f_{-1}) - 2(f_{-1} - f_{-2}) + (f_{-2} - f_{-3}) = f_0 - 3f_{-1} + 3f_{-2} - f_{-3}$$

$$\Rightarrow \quad y_1 = y_0 + \left[f_0 + \frac{1}{2}(f_0 - f_{-1}) + \frac{5}{12}(f_0 - 2f_{-1} + f_{-2}) + \frac{3}{8}(f_0 - 3f_{-1} + 3f_{-2} - f_{-3})\right] h$$

$$\Rightarrow \quad y_1 = y_0 + \frac{h}{24}[55 f_0 - 59 f_{-1} + 37 f_{-2} - 9 f_{-3}] \qquad \ldots(2)$$

This is called ***Adams-Bash forth Predictor formula***

After computing y_1, we will obtain $f_1 = f(x_0 + h, y_1)$.

In order to obtain a better approximation for y_1, we shall derive a Corrector formula by putting Newton's Backward formula at f_1 *i.e.*

$$f(x, y) = f_1 + n\nabla f_1 + \frac{n(n+1)}{2!}\nabla^2 f_1 + \frac{n(n+1)(n+2)}{3!}\nabla^3 f_1 + \ldots \text{ in}$$

$$y_1 = y_0 + \int_{x_0}^{x_0+h} f(x, y)\, dx, \text{ we obtain}$$

$$y_1 = y_0 + \int_{x_0}^{x_0+h}\left[f_1 + n\nabla f_1 + \frac{n(n+1)}{2!}\nabla^2 f_1 + \frac{n(n+1)(n+2)}{3!}\nabla^3 f_1 + \ldots\right] dx$$

putting $x = x_1 + nh$ *i.e.* $dx = h\, dn$

$$= y_0 + h\int_{-1}^{0}\left[f_1 + n\nabla f_1 + \frac{n(n+1)}{2!}\nabla^2 f_1 + \frac{n(n+1)(n+2)}{2!}\nabla^3 f_1\right] dn$$

$$= y_0 + h\left[f_1 - \frac{1}{2}\nabla f_1 - \frac{1}{12}\nabla^2 f_1 - \frac{1}{24}\nabla^3 f_1 \ldots\right] \quad \ldots(3)$$

Now $\quad \nabla f_1 = f_1 - f_0,\ \nabla^2 f_1 = \nabla f_1 - \nabla f_0 = (f_1 - f_0) - (f_0 - f_{-1}) = f_1 - 2f_0 + f_{-1}$

$$\nabla^3 f_1 = \nabla f_1 - 2\nabla f_0 + \nabla f_{-1} = (f_1 - f_0) - 2(f_0 - f_{-1}) + (f_{-1} - f_{-2})$$

$$= -3f_0 + f_1 + 3f_{-1} - f_{-2}$$

Feeding these values in (3), we obtain

$$y_1 = y_0 + h\left[f_1 - \frac{1}{2}(f_1 - f_0) - \frac{1}{12}(f_1 - 2f_0 + f_{-1}) - \frac{1}{24}(-3f_0 + f_1 + 3f_{-1} - f_{-2} + \ldots\right]$$

$$\Rightarrow \quad y_1 = y_0 + \frac{h}{24}[9f_1 + 19f_0 - 5f_{-1} + f_{-2}] \quad \ldots(4)$$

This is called ***Adams-Moulton Corrector Formula***

> **Note:** While applying **Milne and Adams-Bash forth methods,**
> we need four starting values of y calculated by **Picard's Method / Taylor's Series method/Euler's Method / R-K method** and in practice the formula (2) and (4) given above with **R-K method** of **order 4** have been found most useful.

11.12 General Approach to Predictors and Correctors

Here we are going to develop a formula which uses the information of the function $y(x)$ and its first derivatives $y'(x)$ at the past three points together with one more old value of the derivative. The most general formula can be written as

$$y_{n+1} = A_0 y_n + A_1 y_{n-1} + A_2 y_{n-2} + h[C_0 y'_n + C_1 y'_{n-1} + C_2 y'_{n-2} + C_3 y'_{n-3}] \quad \ldots(1)$$

Formula (1) consists of seven constants. Let it be exact for polynomial upto degree four *i.e.* we can assume $y(x)$ as $1,\ x,\ x^2, x^3, x^4$. Putting $h = 1$, *i.e.* unit spacing between consecutive values of x and $y(x) = 1, x, x^2, x^3, x^4$, respectively, in (1) we get

$$1 = A_0 + A_1 + A_2\,,\ 1 = -\,A_1 - 2\,A_2 + C_0 + C_1 + C_2 + C_3$$

$$1 = A_1 + 4\,A_2 - 2\,C_1 - 4\,C_2 - 6\,C_3\,,$$

$$1 = -\,A_1 - 8\,A_2 + 3\,C_1 + 12\,C_2 + 27\,C_3\,,$$

$$1 = A_1 + 16\,A_2 - 4\,C_1 - 32\,C_2 - 108\,C_3\,,$$

But equations are five and constants are seven so taking A_1 and A_2 as parameters and solving the above set of equations, we obtain

$$A_0 = 1 - A_1 - A_2\,, C_0 = \frac{1}{24}(55 + 9A_1 + 8A_2),$$

$$C_1 = \frac{1}{24}(19A_1 + 32A_2 - 59)\,, C_2 = \frac{1}{24}(8A_2 - 5A_1 + 37).$$

$$C_3 = \frac{1}{24}(A_1 - 9)$$

Choosing $A_1 = A_2 = 0$ (as they are arbitrary), we further obtain

$$A_0 = 1,\ C_0 = \frac{55}{24},\ C_1 = -\frac{59}{34},\ C_2 = \frac{37}{24},\ C_3 = -\frac{9}{24} \qquad \text{...(2)}$$

Substituting these values in (1), we get

$$y_{n+1} = y_n + \frac{h}{24}[55\,y'_n - 59\,y'_{n-1} + 37\,y'_{n-2} - 9\,y'_{n-3}] \qquad \text{...(3)}$$

This is known as **Adam's Predictor formula.**

Taking other value of A_1 and A_2, we can find other Predictor formulae. The formulae obtained from equation (1) are known Adam's Bashford type predictors.

Now We Shall Find the Local Turncation Error of Adam's Predictor

We have $$y_k = y_0 + (k\,h)\ y'_0 + \frac{1}{2}(k\,h)^2\ y_0^{(2)} + \frac{(k\,h)^3}{6}\,y_0^{(3)} + \frac{(k\,h)^4}{24}\,y_0^{(4)} + \frac{(k\,h)^5}{120}\,y_0^{(5)}$$

$$\therefore \quad y_{n+1} = y_0 + (n+1)\,h\,y'_0 - \frac{(n+1)^2\,h^2}{2}\,y_0^{(2)} + \frac{(n+1)^3\,h^3}{6}\,y_0^{(3)} + \frac{(n+1)^4\,h^4}{24}\,y_0^{(4)} + \frac{(n+1)^5\,h^5}{120}\,y_0^{(5)} + \ldots \qquad \text{...(4)}$$

Putting $n - 1$ for n in (4), we get

$$y_n = y_0 + n\,h\,y'_0 + \frac{n^2\,h^2}{2}\,y_0^{(2)} + \frac{n^3\,h^3}{6}\,y_0^{(3)} + \frac{n^4\,h^4}{24}\,y_0^{(4)} + \frac{n^5\,h^5}{120}\,y_0^{(5)} + \ldots \qquad \text{...(5)}$$

Further, we have

$$y'_k = y'_0 + (kh)\, y_0^{(2)} + \frac{(kh)^2}{2} y_0^{(3)} + \frac{(kh)^3}{6} y_0^{(4)} + \frac{(kh)^4}{24} y_0^{(5)} + \ldots \quad \ldots(6)$$

Putting n for k, we get

$$y'_n = y_0 + nh\, y_0^{(2)} + \frac{n^2 h^2}{2} y_0^{(3)} + \frac{n^3 h^3}{6} y_0^{(4)} + \frac{n^4 h^4}{24} y_0^{(5)} + \ldots \quad \ldots(7)$$

Again putting $n-1, n-2, n-3$ etc. for n in (7), we get

$$y'_{n-1} = y'_0 + (n-1)\, h\, y_0^{(2)} + \frac{(n-1)^2 h^2}{2} y_0^{(3)} + \frac{(n-1)^3 h^3}{6} y_0^{(4)} + \frac{(n-1)^4 h^4}{24} y_0^{(5)} + \ldots \quad \ldots(8)$$

$$y'_{n-2} = y'_0 + (n-2)\, h\, y_0^{(2)} + \frac{(n-2)^2}{2} h^2 y_0^{(3)} + \frac{(n-2)^3}{6} h^3 y_0^{(4)} + \frac{(n-2)^4}{24} h^4 y_0^{(5)} + \ldots \quad \ldots(9)$$

$$y'_{n-3} = y'_0 + (n-3)\, h\, y_0^{(2)} + \frac{(n-3)^2}{2} h^2 y_0^{(3)} + \frac{(n-3)^2}{6} h^3 y_0^{(4)} + \frac{(n-3)^3}{24} h^4 y_0^{(5)} + \ldots \quad \ldots(10)$$

$$\Rightarrow \quad (y_{n+1} - y_n) - \frac{h}{24}[55\, y'_n - 59\, y'_{n-1} + 37\, y'_{n-2} - 9\, y'_{n-3}] = \frac{251}{720} h^5 y_0^{(5)} + \ldots \quad \ldots(11)$$

$$\Rightarrow \quad \text{The local truncation error is} = \frac{251}{720} h^5 y_0^{(5)} + \ldots$$

Using the first term of this error as an estimate, the local turncation error is

$$(251/720)\, h^5\, y_0^{(5)}.$$

Proceeding in this manner, we can obtain the local turncation error of the other predictor also.

To Find Correctors. Most general corrector formula which uses the function and its first derivative at the past three points together with the value of the derivative at the point being computed is given by

$$y_{n+1} = a_0\, y_n + a_1\, y_{n-1} + a_2\, y_{n-2} + h(b_{-1}\, y'_{n+1} + b_0\, y'_n + b_1\, y'_{n-1} + b_2\, y'_{n-2}) \quad \ldots(12)$$

Again making (12) exact successively for $y(x) = 1, x, x^2, x^3, x^4$ and choosing $h = 1$; we get

$$a_0 + a_1 + a_2 = 1, a_1 + 24\, b_{-1} = 9$$

$$13\, a_1 + 8\, a_2 - 24\, b_0 = -19, 13\, a_1 + 32\, a_2 - 24\, b_1 = 5.$$

$$a_1 - 8\, a_2 + 24\, b_2 = 0.$$

Thus there exist five equations in seven unknowns.

Hence taking a_1 and a_2 as parameters, we get

$$a_0 = 1 - a_1 - a_2, b_{-1} = \frac{1}{24}(9 - a_1), b_0 = \frac{1}{24}(19 + 13\, a_1 + 8\, a_2).$$

$$b_1 = \frac{1}{24}(-5 + 13\, a_1 + 32\, a_2), b_2 = \frac{1}{24}(1 - a_1 + 8\, a_2).$$

Choosing $a_1 = 0 = a_2$, we get

$$a_0 = 1, b_{-1} = \frac{9}{24}, b_0 = \frac{9}{24}, b_1 = -\frac{5}{24} \text{ and } b_2 = \frac{1}{24}.$$

Substituting these values in (12), we get

$$y_{n+1} = y_n + \frac{h}{24}[9\, y'_{n+1} + 19\, y'_n - 5\, y'_{n-1} + y'_{n-2}). \quad ...(13)$$

By taking other suitable values of a_1 and a_2 various correctors can be found.

Proceeding as earlier, we can show that corrector (13) has local turncation error

$$\left[-\frac{19}{720} h^5\, y_0^{(5)}\right].$$

$\therefore$ The error in (13) is less enough than that of its predictor (2).

Example 24: *For the solution of first order differential equation $y' = f(x, y)$, obtain the 'Predictor' formula of the form*

$$y_{n+1} = a_1\, y_n + h(a_2\, y'_n + a_3\, y'_{n-1} + a_4\, y'_{n-2})$$

and its corresponding corrector formula. Also find their local tumcation error.

Solution: It is Adam's type Predictor. Making it exact for $y = 1, x, x^2, x^3$, respectively, we get

$1 = a_1$ when $y = 1$

$1 = a_2 + a_3 + a_4$ when $y = x$, $y' = 1$

$1 = -2\, a_3 - 4\, a_4$ when $y = x^2$, $y' = 2x$

and $1 = 3\, a_3 + 12\, a_4$ when $y = x^3$, $y' = 3x^2$

$$\Rightarrow \quad a_1 = 1,\ a_2 = \frac{1}{6},\ a_3 = \frac{13}{6},\ a_4 = -\frac{4}{3},$$

$$\Rightarrow \quad y_{n+1} = y_n + h\left(\frac{1}{6} y'_n - \frac{13}{6} y'_{n-1} - \frac{4}{3} y'_{n-2}\right)$$

$$\Rightarrow \quad y_{n+1} = y_n + \frac{h}{6}(y'_n - 13\, y'_{n-1} - 8\, y'_{n-2}) \quad ...(1)$$

(Predictor Formula)

Turncation error can be computed by using 11.11.

The corresponding corrector formula is given by

$$y_{n+1} = a_0\, y_n + h(b_{-1}\, y'_{n+1} + b_0\, y'_n + b_1\, y'_{n-1})$$

Making it exact for $y = 1, x, x^2, x^3$, we get

$$a_0 = 1, \quad 2\, b_{-1} - 2\, b_1 = 1, \quad b_{-1} + b_0 + b_1 = 1, \quad 3\, b_{-1} + 3\, b_1 = 1.$$

Solving $a_0 = 1,\ b_{-1} = \frac{5}{12},\ b_0 = \frac{8}{12},\ b_1 = -\frac{1}{12}.$

$\Rightarrow$ Corresponding corrector is

$$y_{n+1} = y_n + \frac{h}{12}(5\,y'_{n+1} + 8\,y'_n - y'_{n-1}) \qquad \ldots(2)$$

Turncation error can be computed by using **11.11**

Example 25: *For the solution of the first order differential equation, $y' = f(x, y)$ obtain the 'Predictor' formula of the form*

$$y_{n+1} = a_1\,y_n + \frac{h}{12}(a_2\,f_n + a_3\,f_{n-1} + a_4\,f_{n-2}),$$

and its corresponding "Corrector" formula. Also find their local turncation error.

Solution: Exactly example 24.

Example 26: *Apply Milne's method, to find a solution of the differential equation $y' = x - y^2$ in the range $0 \le x \le 1$ for the boundary condition $y = 0$ at $x = 0$*

Solution: Using Picard's method, we have

$$y = y(0) + \int_0^x f(x, y)\,dx, \quad \text{where } f(x, y) = x - y^2$$

To obtain the first approximation, we put $y = 0$ in $f(x, y)$,

$$\Rightarrow \qquad y_1 = 0 + \int_0^x x\,dx = (x^2/2)$$

To find the second approximation, we put $y = (x^2/2)$ in $f(x, y)$,

$$\Rightarrow \qquad y_2 = \int_0^x \left(x - \frac{x^4}{4}\right)dx = \frac{x^2}{2} - \frac{x^5}{20}$$

Similarly, the third approximation is given by

$$y_3 = \int_0^x \left[x - \left(\frac{x^2}{2} - \frac{x^5}{20}\right)^2\right]dx = \frac{x^2}{2} - \frac{x^5}{20} + \frac{x^8}{160} - \frac{x^{11}}{4400} \qquad \ldots(1)$$

We now determine the starting values of the Milne's method from (1), by choosing $h = 0.2$.

x	y	$(dy/dx) = y'$
$x_0 = 0.0,$	$y_0 = 0.0000,$	$y'_0 = 0.0000$
$x_1 = 0.2,$	$y_1 = 0.020,$	$y'_1 = 0.1996$
$x_2 = 0.4,$	$y_2 = 0.0795,$	$y'_2 = 0.3937$
$x_3 = 0.6,$	$y_3 = 0.1762,$	$y'_3 = 0.5689$

Using Predictor, we have $y_4 = y_0 + \frac{4h}{3}(2y_1' - y_2' + 2y_3')$

$$\Rightarrow \qquad y_{0.8} = y_4 = 0.3049, \quad \text{and } y_4' = 0.7070$$

And the *corrector* is given by $y_4^{(1)} = y_2 + \frac{h}{3}(y_2' + 4y_3' + y_4')$

$$= 0.3046, \text{ Also } y_4' = 0.7072 \qquad \ldots(2)$$

Further using the Corrector, we again in obtain $y_4 = 0.3046$, which is same as obtained in (2).

Now using the Predictor, we get

$$y_5 = y_1 + \frac{4h}{3}(2y_2' - y_3' + 2y_4'),$$

$$\Rightarrow \qquad y_5 = y_{1.0} = 0.4554, \text{ and } y_5' = 0.7926$$

Also the *corrector* gives $y_5 = y_3 + \frac{h}{3}(y_3' + 4y_4' + y_5')$, gives.

$$\Rightarrow \qquad y_5 = 0.4555, \text{ and } y_5' = 0.7925$$

Again using the corrector, we get $y_5 = 0.4555$, a value which is the same as before,

Hence $\qquad y(1) = 0.4555.$

Example 27: *Using Runga-Kutta method of order 4, find y for $x = 0.1, 0.2, 0.3$ given that $(dy/dx) = xy + y^2$, $y(0) = 1$. Continue the solution to $x = 0.4$ using Milne's method.*

Solution: We have $f(x, y) = xy + y^2 = (dy/dx)$.

Step 1: To find $y(0.1)$:

we have $x_0 = 0$, $y_0 = 1$, $h = 0.1$.

$$\Rightarrow \qquad k_1 = hf(x_0, y_0) = (0.1)\, f(0, 1) = 0.1000$$

$$k_2 = hf\left(x_0 + \frac{1}{2}h, y_0 + \frac{1}{2}k_1\right) = (0.1)\, f(0.05, 1.05) = 0.1155$$

$$k_3 = hf\left(x_0 + \frac{1}{2}h, y_0 + \frac{1}{2}k_2\right) = (0.1)\, f(0.05, 1.0577) = 0.1172$$

$$k_4 = hf(x_0 + h, y_0 + k_3) = (0.1)\, f(0.1, 1.1172) = 0.13598$$

and $\qquad k = \frac{1}{6}(k_1 + 2k_2 + 2k_3 + k_4) = \frac{1}{6}(0.1 + 0.231 + 0.2343 + 0.13598) = 0.11087$

$$\Rightarrow y(0.1) = y_1 = y_0 + k = 1.1169.$$

Step 2: To find $y(0.2)$:

we have $\quad x_1 = 0.1,\ y_1 = 1.1169,\ h = 0.1,$

$\Rightarrow \quad k_1 = hf(x_1, y_1) = (0.1)\, f(.1, 1.1169) = 0.1359$

$$k_2 = hf\left(x_1 + \frac{1}{2}h, y_1 + \frac{1}{2}k_1\right) = (0.1)\, f(0.15, 1.1848) = 0.1581$$

$$k_3 = hf\left(x_1 + \frac{1}{2}h, y_1 + \frac{1}{2}k_2\right) = (0.1)\, f(0.15, 1.1959) = 0.1609$$

$$k_4 = hf(x_1 + h, y_1 + k_3) = (0.1)\, f(0.2, 1.2778) = 0.1888$$

and $\quad k = \frac{1}{6}(k_1 + 2k_2 + 2k_3 + k_4) = 0.1605$

$\Rightarrow \quad y(0.2) = y_2 = y_1 + k = 1.2773.$

Step 3: To find $y(0.3)$:

$$x_2 = 0.2,\ y_2 = 1.2773,\ h = 0.1.$$

$\Rightarrow \quad k_1 = hf(x_2, y_2) = (0.1)\, f(0.2, 1.2773) = 0.1887$

$$k_2 = hf\left(x_2 + \frac{1}{h}, y_2 + \frac{1}{2}k_1\right) = (0.1)\, f(0.25, 1.3716) = 0.2224$$

$$k_3 = hf\left(x_2 + \frac{1}{2}h, y_2 + \frac{1}{2}k_2\right) = (0.1)\, f(0.25, 1.3885) = 0.2275$$

$$k_4 = hf(x_2 + h, y_2 + k_3) = (0.1)\, f(0.3, 1.5048) = 0.2716$$

and $\quad k = \frac{1}{6}(k_1 + 2k_2 + 2k_3 + k_4) = 0.2267$

$\Rightarrow \quad y(0.3) = y_3 = y_2 + k = 1.504$

Thus the starting values for the Milne's method are as follows:

$x_0 = 0.0$	$y_0 = 1.0000$	$y_0' = 1.0000$
$x_1 = 0.1$	$y_1 = 1.1169$	$y_1' = 1.3591$
$x_2 = 0.2$	$y_2 = 1.2773$	$y_2' = 1.8869$
$x_3 = 0.4$	$y_3 = 1.5049$	$y_3' = 2.7132$

Then, using the Predictor, we easily obtain

$$y_4 = y_0 + \frac{4h}{3}(2y_1' - y_2' + 2y_3') = 1.8344$$

$\Rightarrow \quad x_4 = 0.4,\ y_4 = 1.8344$ and $y_4' = 4.0988$

Also, the Corrector, then gives

$$y_4 = y_2 + \frac{h}{3}(y_2' + 4y_3' + y_4')$$

$\Rightarrow y_4 = 1.2773 + \frac{0.1}{3}[1.8869 + 4(2.7123) + 4.098] = 1.8386$ and also $y_4' = 4.1159.$

Again using the *Corrector* formula, we obtain

$$y_4 = 1.2773 + \frac{0.1}{3}[1.8869 + 4(2.7132) + 4.1159]$$

$$= 1.8392. \qquad y_4' = 4.1182. \qquad ...(1)$$

And then using the Corrector we readily obtain

$$y_4 = 1.2773 + \frac{0.1}{3}[1.8869 + 4(2.7132) + 4.1182]$$

$= 1.8392$. This is the same as (1). $\quad \therefore \quad y(0.4) = 1.8392.$

Example 28: *Given* $\frac{dy}{dx} = x^2(1+y)$ *and* $y(1) = 1, y(1.1) = 1.233, \ y(1.2) = 1.548,$

$y(1.3) = 1.979$, *evaluate* $y(1.4)$ *by Adams-Bashforth method.*

Solution: $f(x, y) = x^2(1 + y)$. Choose $h = 0.1$

Starting values of the Adams-Bashforth method are

$$x = 1.0, \quad y_{-3} = 1.000, \quad f_{-3} = (1.0)^2(1 + 1.000) = 2.000$$

$$x = 1.1, \quad y_{-2} = 1.233, \quad f_{-2} = 2.702$$

$$x = 1.2, \quad y_{-1} = 1.548, \quad f_{-1} = 3.669$$

$$x = 1.3, \quad y_0 = 1.979, \quad f_0 = 5.035$$

Then using the Predictor, we have

$$y_1 = y_0 + \frac{h}{24}(55 f_0 - 59 f_{-1} + 37 f_{-2} - 9 f_{-3})$$

$$x = 1.4, \ y_1 = 2.753, \ f_1 = 7.004$$

Using the Corrector, we then obtain

$$y_1 = y_0 + \frac{h}{24}(9 f_1 + 19 f_0 - 5 f_{-1} + f_{-2})$$

$$= 1.979 + \frac{0.1}{24}(9 \times 7.004 + 19 \times 5.035 - 5 \times 3.669 + 2.702)$$

$$= 2.575 \qquad \therefore \quad y(1.4) = 2.575.$$

Example 29: *Solve the Initial values problem* $(dy/dx) = x - y^2, y(0) = 1$ *to find* $y(0.4)$ *by Adam's method. Starting solutions required are to be obtained using Runge-Kutta method of order 4 using step value* $h = 0.1$.

Solution: $f(x, y) = x - y^2$

Step I: To find $y(0.1)$:

$x_0 = 0, \ y_0 = 1, \ h = 0.1$. Let us now compute

$$k_1 = hf(x_0, y_0) = (0.1) f(0, 1) = -0.1000$$

$$k_2 = hf\left(x_0 + \frac{1}{2}h, y_0 + \frac{1}{2}k_1\right) = (0.1)\, f(0.05, 0.95) = -0.08525$$

$$k_3 = hf\left(x_0 + \frac{1}{2}h, y_0 + \frac{1}{2}k_2\right) = (0.1)\, f(0.05, 0.9574) = -0.0867$$

$$k_4 = hf\,(x_0 + h, y_0 + k_3) = (0.1)\, f(0.1, 0.9137) = -0.07341$$

and $$k = \frac{1}{6}(k_1 + 2k_2 + 2k_3 + k_4) = -0.0833$$

$$\therefore \quad y(0.1) = y_1 = y_0 + k = 1 - 0.0833 \quad = 0.9117$$

Step II: To find $y(0.2)$:

$$x_1 = 0.1,\ y_1 = 0.9117,\ h = 0.1$$

$$\Rightarrow \quad k_1 = h\,f\,(x_1, y_1) = (0.1)\, f\,(0.1)\, f\,(0.1, 0.9117) = -0.0731$$

$$k_2 = hf\left(x_1 + \frac{1}{2}h, y_1 + \frac{1}{2}k_1\right) = (0.1)\, f\,(0.15, 0.8751) = -0.0616$$

$$k_3 = hf\left(x_1 + \frac{1}{2}h, y_1 + \frac{1}{2}k_2\right) = (0.1)\, f\,(0.15, 0.8809) = -0.0626$$

$$k_4 = hf\,(x_1 + h, y_1 + k_3) = (0.1)\, f(0.2, 0.8491) = -0.0521$$

and $$k = \frac{1}{6}(k_1 + 2\,k_2 + 2\,k_3 + k_4) = -0.0623$$

$$\Rightarrow \quad y(0.2) = y_2 = y_1 + k \quad = 0.8494.$$

Step III: To find $y(0.3)$:

$$x_2 = 0.2,\ y_2 = 0.8494,\ h = 0.1.$$

$$\Rightarrow \quad k_1 = hf\,(x_2, y_2) = (0.1)\, f(0.2, 0.8494) = -0.0521$$

$$k_2 = hf\left(x_2 + \frac{1}{2}h, y_2 + \frac{1}{2}k_1\right) = (0.1)\, f(0.25, 0.8233) = -0.0428$$

$$k_3 = hf\left(x_2 + \frac{1}{2}h, y_2 + \frac{1}{2}k_2\right) = (0.1)\, f(0.25, 0.828) = -0.0436$$

$$k_4 = h\,f\,(x_2 + h, y_2 + k_3) = (0.1)\, f(0.3, 0.8058) = -0.0349$$

and $$k = \frac{1}{6}(k_1 + 2k_2 + 2k_3 + k_4) = -0.0438$$

$$\therefore \quad y(0.3) = y_3 = y_2 + k \quad = 0.8061$$

Thus the starting values of Adam's method with $h = 0.1$ are given as

$x = 0.0$	$y_{-3} = 1.0000$	$f_{-3} = 0.0 - (1.0)^2$	$= -1.0000$
$x = 0.1$	$y_{-2} = 0.9117$	$f_{-2} = 0.1 - (0.9117)^2$	$= -0.7312$
$x = 0.2$	$y_{-1} = 0.8494$	$f_{-1} = 0.2 - (0.8494)^2$	$= -0.5215$
$x = 0.3$	$y_0 = 0.8061$	$f_0 = 0.3 - (0.8061)^2$	$= -0.3498$

Now, using the *Predictor*, we get

$$y_1 = y_0 + \frac{h}{24}(55 f_0 - 59 f_{-1} + 37 f_{-2} - 9 f_{-3})$$

at $\quad x = 0.4 \quad y_1 = 0.8061 + \frac{0.1}{24}[55(-0.3498) - 59(-0.5215)$

$$+ 37(-0.7312) - 9(-1)] = .77789; \quad f_1 = -0.2067$$

Then using the *Corrector*, we obtain

$$y_1 = y_0 + \frac{h}{24}(9 f_1 - 19 f_0 - 5 f_{-1} + f_{-2})$$

$$= 0.8061 + \frac{0.1}{24}[9(-0.2067) + 19(-0.3498) - 5(-0.5215) - 0.7312] = 0.7785$$

$\Rightarrow \quad y(0.4) = 0.7785.$

11.13 Simultaneous Differential Equation (first order)

Simultaneous differential equation of the type

$$\frac{dy}{dx} = f(x, y, z) \qquad \ldots(1)$$

and

$$\frac{dz}{dx} = \phi(x, y, z) \qquad \ldots(2)$$

With initial conditions $y(x_0) = y_0$ *and* $z(x_0) = z_0$ *can be solved by the methods discussed in the preceding sections, especially Picard's or Runge-Kutta method.*

(i) Picard's Method

we have $\quad y_1 = y_0 + \int f(x, y_0, z_0)\, dx, \quad z_1 = z_0 + \int \phi(x, y_0, z_0)\, dx$

$$y_2 = y_0 + \int f(x, y_1, z_1)\, dx, \quad z_2 = z_0 + \int \phi(x, y_1, z_1)\, dx$$

$$y_3 = y_0 + \int f(x, y_2, z_2)\, dx, \quad z_3 = z_0 + \int \phi(x, y_2, z_2)\, dx \text{ etc.}$$

(ii) Taylor's Series Method

Let h be the step-size then $y_1 = y(x_0 + h)$ and $z_1 = z(x_0 + h)$.

Taylor's Algorithm for (1) and (2)

$$\Rightarrow \quad y_1 = y_0 + h y_0' + \frac{h^2}{2!} y_0'' + \frac{h^3}{3!} y_0''' + \ldots \qquad \ldots(3)$$

and

$$z_1 = z_0 + h z_0' + \frac{h^2}{2!} z_0'' + \frac{h^3}{3!} z_0''' + \ldots \qquad \ldots(4)$$

Now differentiating (1) and (2) successively, we get y'', z'', etc. So the value $y'_0, y''_0, y'''_0 \ldots$ and $z'_0, z''_0, z'''_0 \ldots$ are known. Putting these in (3) and (4), we obtain y_1, z_1 for the next calculation.

And similarly $y_2 = y_1 + h\,y'_1 + \dfrac{h^2}{2!} y''_1 + \dfrac{h^3}{3!} y'''_1 + \ldots$ ...(5)

$$z_2 = z_1 + h\,z'_1 + \frac{h^2}{2!} z''_1 + \frac{h^3}{3!} z'''_1 + \ldots \qquad \ldots(6)$$

As y_1 and z_1 are known, we can calculate $y'_1, y''_1, \ldots$ and $z'_1, z''_1, \ldots$. Substituting these in (5) and (6), we get y_2 and z_2.

Thus proceeding further, we can calculate other values of y and z.

(iii) Runge-Kutta Method

Starting initially (x_0, y_0, z_0) and taking the step-sizes for x, y, z to be h, k, l respectively, the Runge-Kutta method

$$\Rightarrow \quad k_1 = hf(x_0, y_0, z_0)$$

$$l_1 = h\,\phi(x_0, y_0, z_0)$$

$$k_2 = hf\left(x_0 + \frac{1}{2}h,\ y_0 + \frac{1}{2}k_1,\ z_0 + \frac{1}{2}l_1\right)$$

$$l_2 = h\,\phi\left(x_0 + \frac{1}{2}h,\ y_0 + \frac{1}{2}k_1,\ z_0 + \frac{1}{2}l_1\right)$$

$$k_3 = hf\left(x_0 + \frac{1}{2}h,\ y_0 + \frac{1}{2}k_2,\ z_0 + \frac{1}{2}l_2\right)$$

$$l_3 = h\,\phi\left(x_0 + \frac{1}{2}h,\ y_0 + \frac{1}{2}k_2,\ z_0 + \frac{1}{2}l_2\right)$$

$$k_4 = h\,f(x_0 + h,\ y_0 + k_3,\ z_0 + l_3)$$

$$l_4 = h\,\phi(x_0 + h,\ y_0 + k_3,\ z_0 + l_3)$$

$$\therefore \quad y_1 = y_0 + \frac{1}{6}(k_1 + 2k_2 + 2k_3 + k_4)$$

and
$$z_1 = z_0 + \frac{1}{6}(l_1 + 2l_2 + 2l_3 + l_4)$$

To calculate y_2 and z_2 we simply replace x_0, y_0, z_0, by x_1, y_1, z_1 in the above formulae and proceed.

Example 30: *Using Picard's method, find approximate values of y and z corresponding to* $x = 0.1$, *given that* $y(0) = 2$, $z(0) = 1$ *and* $(dy/dx) = x + z$, $(dz/dx) = x - y^2$.

Solution: $x_0 = 0,\ y_0 = 2,\ z_0 = 1$, Now $\dfrac{dy}{dx} = f(x, y, z) = x + z$

$$\frac{dz}{dx} = \phi(x, y, z) = x - y^2 \qquad \Rightarrow \qquad y = y_0 + \int_{x_0}^{x} f(x, y, z)\,dx$$

and
$$z = z_0 + \int_{x_0}^{x} \phi(x, y, z)\,dx.$$

First Approximations $y_1 = y_0 + \int_{x_0}^{x} f(x, y_0, z_0)\, dx = 2 + \int_0^x (x+1)\, dx = 2 + x + \frac{1}{2}x^2$

and $$z_1 = z_0 + \int_{x_0}^{x} \phi(x, y, z_0)\, dx = 1 + \int_0^x (x-4)\, dx = 1 - 4x + \frac{1}{2}x^2.$$

Second Approximations $y_2 = y_0 + \int_{x_0}^{x} f(x, y_1, z_1)\, dx$

$$= 2 + \int_0^x (x + 1 - 4x + \frac{1}{2}x^2)\, dx = 2 + x - \frac{3}{2}x^2 + \frac{x^3}{6}$$

and $z_2 = z_0 + \int_{x_0}^{x} \phi(x, y_1, z_1)\, dx = 1 + \int_0^x [x - (2 + x + \frac{1}{2}x^2)^2]\, dx = 1 - 4x + \frac{3}{2}x^2 - x^3 - \frac{x^4}{4} - \frac{x^5}{20}.$

Third Approximations $y_3 = y_0 + \int_{x_0}^{x} f(x, y_2, z_2)\, dx$

$$= 2 + x - \frac{3}{2}x^2 - \frac{1}{2}x^3 - \frac{1}{4}x^4 - \frac{1}{20}x^5 - \frac{1}{120}x^6$$

and $z_3 = z_0 + \int_{x_0}^{x} \phi(x, y_2, z_2)\, dx = 1 - 4x - \frac{3}{2}x^2 + \frac{5}{3}x^3 + \frac{7}{12}x^4 - \frac{31}{60}x^5 + \frac{1}{12}x^6 - \frac{1}{252}x^7$; etc.

Thus at $x = 0.1$, we have $y_1 = 2.105$, $y_2 = 2.08517$, $y_3 = 2.08447$

$$z_1 = 0.605, z_2 = 0.58397, z_3 = 0.58672$$

Thus the correct to 4 decimal places, we have $y(0.1) = 2.0845$, $z(0.1) = 0.5867$.

Example 31: *Find solution of the simultaneous equations*

$$\frac{dy}{dx} = xy + 2t \quad \text{...(1)}$$

$$\frac{dy}{dt} = 2ty + x \quad \text{...(2)}$$

Subject to the Initial conditions $x = 1, y = -1, t = 0$.

Solution: Taylor's Series method

It is evident that x and y are dependent variables whereas t is an independent variable and x, y (both) functions of t therefore by Taylor's series, we have

$$x(t) = x_0 + t\, x'_0 + \frac{t^2}{2!} x''_0 + \frac{t^3}{3!} x'''_0 + \ldots + \frac{t^r}{r!} x^r_0 + \ldots$$

and

$$y(t) = y_0 + t\, y'_0 + \frac{t^2}{2!} y''_0 + \frac{t^3}{3!} y'''_0 + \ldots + \frac{t^r}{r!} y^r_0 + \ldots \quad \text{...(A)}$$

Where dashes denote the differentials w.r.t. 't'.

Differentiating the given equations successively w.r.t. 't' we get

$$x'' = xy' + x'y + 2, \qquad y'' = 2ty' + 2y + x'$$

$$x''' = (xy'' + x'y') + x''y + x'y', \qquad y''' = 2ty'' + 2y' + 2y'' + x'' \text{ etc.} \quad \text{...(B)}$$

Putting $x = 1, y = -1, t = 0$ in (i), (ii) and (B), we get

$$x_0' = (-1) + 2.0 = -1 \qquad y_0' = 1$$

$$x_0'' = x_0 y_0' + x_0' y_0 + 2, \qquad y_0'' = 0 + 2 y_0 + x_0'$$

$$= 1.1 + 1.1 + 2 = 4 \qquad = 2(-1) - 1 = -3$$

$$x_0''' = x_0 y'' + x_0' y_0' + x_0'' y_0 + x_0' y_0' ; \; y_0''' = 2 y_0' + 2 y_0' + x_0''$$

$$= 1(-3) + (-1)(1) + 4.(-1) + (-1).1; \; y_0''' = 4 + 4 = 8 \text{ etc.}$$

$$= -3 - 1 - 4 - 1 = -9.$$

Putting these values in (A), we get

$$x(t) = 1 - t + t^2 .2 + \frac{t^3}{6}(-9) + \ldots = 1 - t + 2t^2 - \frac{3}{2}t^3 + \ldots$$

and $$y(t) = -1 + t + \frac{t^2}{2}(-3) + \frac{t^3}{6}.8 + \ldots = -1 + t - \frac{3}{2}t^2 + \frac{4}{3}t^3 + \ldots$$

11.14 Differential Equation of Second Order

Consider a second order differential equation as

$$\frac{d^2 x}{dt^2} = \phi[x, (dx/dt), t), t]$$

Under the initial conditions $(x)\,t_0 = x_0$ and $(x')\,t_0 = x_0'$. This second order equation can be reduced to a system of simultaneous differential equations of first order as follows:

Take $\frac{dx}{dt}$ to be y i.e. $\frac{dx}{dt} = y$ or $x' = y$ ...(1)

and $\frac{dx}{dt} = \phi[x, y, t]$ ...(2)

Initial conditions being $(x)_{t_0} = x_0$ and $(y)_{t_0} = x_0'$.

It is worth noticing that an nth order differential equation yields n simultaneous differential equations of first order.

Example 32: *Use Taylor's series method to obtain the power series in t for x and y satisfying the differential equations*

$$(dx/dt) = x + y + t, (d^2 y/dt^2) = x - t$$

Under the Initial conditions

$$x_{t=0} = 0, \; y_{t=0} = 1, \; (dy/dt)_{t=0} = -1.$$

Solution: Consider $dy/dt = z$, so that the given equations are

$$dx/dt = x + y + t, \; dz/dt = x - t \text{ and } dy/dt = z.$$

The Initial conditions become $x_{t=0} = 0, \; y_{t=0} = 1,$ and $(z)_{t=0} = -1.$

Expanding $x, y, z,$ in power series of t, we get

$$\left.\begin{aligned} x &= x_0 + x_0' t + (t^2/2!)\, x_0'' + (t^3/3!)\, x_0''' + \ldots \\ y &= y_0 + y_0' t + (t^2/2!)\, y_0'' + (t^3/3!)\, y_0''' + \ldots \\ \text{and} \quad z &= z_0 + z_0' t + (t^2/2!)\, z_0'' + (t^3/3!)\, z_0''' + \ldots \end{aligned}\right\} \quad \ldots(A)$$

Now, we have $x' = x + y + t,\ y' = z,\ z' = x - t$

$$\begin{aligned} x'' &= x' + y' + 1 = x + y + z + t + 1 \\ y'' &= z' = x - t \\ z'' &= x' - 1 = x + y + t - 1 \\ x''' &= x'' + y'' \quad = 2x + y + z + 1 \\ y''' &= z'' \quad = x + y + t - 1 \\ z''' &= x''' \quad x + y + z + t + 1 \text{ etc.} \end{aligned}$$

Whence substituting $x_0 = 0,\ y_0 = 1,\ z_o = -1$, we get

$$\begin{aligned} x_0' &= 1,\ y_0' = -1,\ z_0' = 0 \\ x_0'' &= 1,\ y_0'' = 0,\ z_0'' = 0 \\ x_0''' &= 1,\ y_0''' = 0,\ z_0''' = 1 \text{ etc.} \end{aligned}$$

Making these substitutions in (A), we get

$$\begin{aligned} x &= x_0 + x_0' t + x''(t^2/2!) + x_0'''(t^3/3!) + \ldots \\ &= t + (t^2/2!) + (t^3/3!) + (t^4/4!) + (2t^5/5!) + \ldots \\ y &= 1 - t + (t^4/4!) + (t^5/5!) + \ldots \\ z &= -1 + (t^3/3!) + (t^4/4!) + (t^5/5!) + \ldots \end{aligned}$$

Example 33: *Using Runge-Kutta method, solve $y'' = xy'^2 - y^2$ for $x = 0.2$ correct to 4 decimal places. Initial conditions are $x = 0, y = 1, y' = 0$.*

Solution: Let $(dy/dx) = z = f(x, y, z)$ Then $\dfrac{dz}{dx} = xz^2 - y^2 = \phi(x, y, z)$

But $\quad x_0 = 0, y_0 = 1, z_0 = 0, h = 0.2.$

Then Runge-Kutta formulae become:

$k_1 = hf(x_0, y_0, z_0) = 0.2\,(0) = 0$

$l_1 = h\phi(x_0, y_0, z_0) = 0.2\,(-1) = -0.2$

$k_2 = hf\left(x_0 + \frac{1}{2}h, y_0 + \frac{1}{2}k_1, z_0 + \frac{1}{2}l_1\right)$
$= 0.2\,(-0.1) = -0.02$

$l_2 = h\phi\left(x_0 + \frac{1}{2}h, y_0 + \frac{1}{2}k_1, z_0 + \frac{1}{2}l_1\right)$
$= 0.2\,(-0.999) = -0.1998$

$k_3 = hf\left(x_0 + \frac{1}{2}h, y_0 + \frac{1}{2}k_2, z_0 + \frac{1}{2}l_2\right)$
$= 0.2\,(-0.0999) = -0.02$

$l_3 = h\phi\left(x_0 + \frac{1}{2}h, y_0 + \frac{1}{2}k_2, z_0 + \frac{1}{2}l_2\right)$
$= 0.2\,(-0.9791) = -0.1958$

$k_4 = hf(x_0 + h, y_0 + k_3, z_0 + l_3)$
$= 0.2\,(-0.1958) = -0.0392$

$l_4 = h\phi(x_0 + h, y_0 + k_3, z_0 + l_3)$
$= 0.2\,(0.9527) = -0.1905$

$$\therefore \quad k = \frac{1}{6}(k_1 + 2k_2 + 2k_3 + k_4) \qquad l = \frac{1}{6}(l_1 + 2l_2 + 2l_3 + l_4)$$

$$= -0.0199 \qquad\qquad = -0.1970$$

Thus at $x = 0.2$, we have

$$y = y_0 + k = 1 - 0.0199 = 0.9801$$

and $$y' = z = z_0 + l = 0 - 0.1970 = -0.1970.$$

11.15 Numerov's Method

This method is used only when there is a second order equation without * $y^{(1)}$ *i.e.* the differential equation is of the type * $y^{(2)} = \phi(x, y)$. We shall develop the formula by using the method of undertermined coefficients. Let $x_1, x_2, x_3 \ldots, x_k$, be the equidistant values of x at the equispaced points 1, 2, 3 ..., k, ... Let y_{k-1} and y_k be known, so that $\phi_{k-1} = \phi(x_{k-1}, y_{k-1})$ and $\phi_k = \phi(x_k, y_k)$ also become known.

To integrate the differential equation, we assume a corrector type formula of the form

$$y_{k+1} = A\, y_k + B\, y_{k-1} + h^2\, [C\, \phi_{k+1} + D\, \phi_k + E\, \phi_{k-1}] + R \qquad \ldots (1)$$

Where R denotes the error term and A, B, C, D, E, are unknown coefficients to be determined.

Let $y_k^{(p)}$ denote the pth derivative of y at $x = x_k$ then by Taylor's series expansion, we get

$$y_{k+1} = y_k + h y_k^{(1)} + \frac{h^2}{2!} y_k^{(2)} + \frac{h^3}{3!} y_k^{(3)} + \frac{h^4}{4!} y_k^{(4)} + \frac{h^5}{5!} y_k^{(5)} + \frac{h^6}{6!} y_k^{(6)}$$

$$y_{k-1} = y_k - h y_k^{(1)} + \frac{h^2}{2!} y_k^{(2)} - \frac{h^3}{3!} y_k^{(3)} + \frac{h^4}{4!} y_k^{(4)} - \frac{h^5}{5!} y_k^{(5)} + \frac{h^6}{6!} y_k^{(6)}$$

$$\text{and } \phi_{k+1} = \phi_k + h\phi_k^{(1)} + \frac{h^2}{2!}\phi_k^{(2)} + \frac{h^3}{3!}\phi_k^{(3)} + \frac{h^4}{4!}\phi_k^{(4)} + \ldots$$

Again, we have $\phi = y^{(2)}$

$$\therefore \quad \phi^{(1)} = y^{(3)}, \phi^{(2)} = y^{(4)}, \phi^{(3)} = y^{(5)}, \phi^{(4)} = y^{(6)}, \text{ etc.}$$

$$h^2\, \phi_{k-1} = h^2\, y_k^{(2)} + h^3\, y_k^{(3)} + \frac{h^4}{2!} y_k^{(4)} + \frac{h^5}{3!} y_k^{(5)} + \frac{h^6}{4!} y_k^{(6)}$$

and $$h^2\phi_{k-1} = h^2\, y_k^{(2)} - h^3\, y_k^{(3)} + \frac{h^4}{2!} y_k^{(4)} - \frac{h^5}{3!} y_k^{(5)} + \frac{h^6}{4!} y_k^{(6)}$$

The unknown coefficients are so determined that the corrector type formula agrees with the Taylor's expansion of y_{k+1} up to fourth order. Now substituting the values of $y_{k+1}, y_k, y_{k-1}, \phi_{k+1}, \phi_k, \phi_{k-1}$ in (1) and then comparing the coefficients of various powers of h (up to fourth power of h) on both sides, we get

$$A + B = 1, B = -1, (B/2) + C + D + E = (1/2)$$

$$-(B/6) + C - E = (1/6), (B/24) + (E/2) + (C/2) = (1/24)$$

These give $A = 2, B = -1, C = (1/12), D = (5/6), E = (1/12).$

It is worth noticing that the coefficient of fifth powers of h are also equal; of course we matched the terms only up to fourth power.

Making these sustitutions in the corrector type formula, we at once obtain

$$y_{k+1} = 2\, y_k - y_{k-1} + (h^2/12)\,[\phi_{k+1} + 10\,\phi_k + \phi_{k-1}] + R \qquad \text{...(B)}$$

It is known as ***Numerov's formula***.

This formula involves an error of order six and if we assume all the terms of $y^{(6)}$ to be equal, then the estimate of the error is $-[h^6\ y k^{(6)}/240]$.

Again in (B), y_{k+1} appears on both sides hence this formula becomes a corrector formula. Thus to obtain y_{k+1}, some previous approximation for y is necessary.

For this reason, ignoring the term ϕ_{k+1}, in (B), we readily obtain

$$y_{k+1} = 2\, y_k - y_{k-1} + (h^2/12)\,[10\,\phi_k + \phi_{k-1}] \qquad \text{...(C)}$$

The formula (C) can now be used as Predictor formula.

Example 34: *Using Numerov's formula, solve $y'' = y$ given that*

$$y_0 = 1,\ y'(0) = -1.$$

Solution: Taking the interval of differencing to be 0.5 and equal throughout, we may take $x_0 = 0$, $x_1 = 0.5$, $x_2 = 1$. The corresponding values of y shall be denoted by y_0, y_1 and y_2 respectively. We are interested in finding out the value of y_2. By putting $k = 1$ in (C), we get

$$y_2 = 2\, y_1 - y_0 + (h^2/12)\,[10\,\phi_1 + \phi_0]. \qquad \text{...(1)}$$

Now $\quad y_0 = 1,\ y_0' = -1,\ y_0'' = 1,\ y_0''' = -1,\ y_0^{iv} = 1$ etc.

$$\therefore \quad y_1 = y_0 + h\, y_0' + \frac{h^2}{2!} y_0'' + \frac{h^3}{3!} y_0''' + \ldots$$

$$= 1 - 0.5 + 0.125 - 0.0208 + 0.0026 - 0.0003 = .6065$$

And from (1)

$$y_2 = 2(.6065) - 1 + \{(0.5)^2/12\}\,[10 \times .6065 + 1] = 0.3602$$

$$\Rightarrow \quad \phi_2 = \phi(x_2, y_2) = y_2 = 0.3602.$$

Hence using (B), the first corrected value of y_2 is given by

$$y_2 = 2\, y_1 - y_0 + (h^2/12)\,[\phi_2 + 10\,\phi_1 + \phi_0]$$

$$= 2 \times (.6065) - 1 + \{(0.5)^2/12\}\,[.3602 + 6.065 + 1] = 0.3677.$$

Again using Corrector formula, we get

$$y_2 = .2130 + \{(0.5)^2/12\}\,[.3677 + 6.065 + 1] = 0.3678.$$

$$\Rightarrow \quad (y)_{x=1} = 0.3678.$$

Example 35: *Given $y'' + xy' + y = 0, y(0) = 1, y'(0) = 0$, obtain y for $x = 0, (0.1), (0.3)$, by any method. Further, continue the solution by Milne's method to calculate $y(0.4)$.*

Solution: Putting $y' = z$, the given equation reduces to:

$$z' + xz + y = 0, y' = z \quad \dots(1)$$

Now, we use Taylor's series method to find y.

Differentiating the given equation n times, we have

$$y_{n+2} + x\, y_{n+1} + n\, y_n + y_n = 0 \;\Rightarrow\; (y_{n+2})_0 = -(n+1)\,(y_n)_0$$

$\therefore$ $y(0) = 1$, gives. $y_2(0) = -1, y_4(0) = 3, y_6(0) = -5 \times 3, \dots$

and $y_1(0) = 0$ yields $y_3(0) = y_5(0) = \dots = 0$.

Then expanding $y(x)$ by Taylor's series, we get

$$y(x) = y(0) + x\, y_1(0) + \frac{x^2}{2!} y_2(0) + \frac{x^3}{3!} y_3(0) + \dots$$

$$\Rightarrow \quad y(x) = 1 - \frac{x^2}{2!} + \frac{3}{4!} x^4 - \frac{5 \times 3}{6!} x^6 + \dots \quad \dots(2)$$

and $$z(x) = y'(x) = -x + \frac{1}{2} x^3 - \frac{1}{8} x^5 + \dots = -xy \quad \dots(3)$$

Then from (2), we have

$$y(0.1) = 1 - \frac{(0.1)^2}{2} + \frac{1}{8}(0.1)^4 - \dots = 0.995$$

$$y(0.2) = 1 - \frac{(0.2)^2}{2} + \frac{(0.2)^4}{8} - \dots = 0.9802$$

$$y(0.3) = 1 - \frac{(0.3)^2}{2} + \frac{(0.3)^4}{8} - \frac{(0.3)^6}{48} + \dots = 0.956$$

From (3), we also have

$$z(0.1) = -0.0995, z(0.2) = -0.196, z(0.3) = -0.2863.$$

Further from (1), $z'(x) = -(xz + y)$

$$z'(0.1) = 0.985, z'(0.2) = -0.941, z'(0.3) = -0.87$$

Now applying Milne's Predictor formula, first to z and then to y, we readily obtain

$$z(0.4) = z(0) + \frac{4}{3}(0.1)\{2z'(0.1) - z'(0.2) + 2z'(0.3)\}$$

$$= 0 + \left(\frac{0.4}{3}\right)\{-1.79 + 0.941 - 1.74\} = -0.3692$$

and $$y(0.4) = y(0) + \frac{4}{3}(0.1)\{2y'(0.1) - y'(0.2) + 2y'(0.3)\}$$

$$0 + \left(\frac{0.4}{3}\right)\{-0.199 + 0.196 - 0.5736\} \qquad [\because y' = z]$$

$$= 0.9231. \text{ Also } z'(0.4) = -\{x(0.4)\, z(0.4) + y(0.4)\}$$

$$= -\{0.4(-0.3692) + 0.9231\} = -0.7754.$$

Further applying Milne's Corrector formula, we readily get

$$z(0.4) = z(0.2) + \frac{h}{3}\{z'(0.2) + 4z'(0.3) + z'(0.4)\}$$

$$= -0.196 + \left(\frac{0.1}{3}\right)\{-0.941 - 3.48 - 0.7754\} = -0.3692$$

and $$y(0.4) = y(0.2) + \frac{h}{3}\{y'(0.2) + 4y'(0.3) + y'(0.4)\}$$

$$= 0.9802 + \left(\frac{0.1}{3}\right)\{-0.196 - 1.1452 - 0.3692\} = 0.9232$$

$$\therefore \quad y(0.4) = 0.9232 \text{ and } z(0.4) = -0.3692.$$

11.16 Boundary Value Problems

Such type of problems require the solution of a differential equation in a region. R subject to various conditions on the boundary of R. We shall discuss two-points linear boundary value problems as given below:

(i) $$\frac{d^2y}{dx^2} + \lambda(x)\frac{dy}{dx} + \mu(x)\, y = y(x);\ y(x_0) = a,\ y(x_n) = b$$

(ii) $$\frac{d^4y}{dx^4} + \lambda(x)\, y = \mu(x);\ y(x_0) = y'(x_0) = a;\quad y(x_n) = y'(x_n) = b.$$

As a matter of fact, there exist many numerical methods for solving such Boundary Value problems but the method of finite-differences is most common.

Finite-Difference method: The finite-difference approximations to the various derivatives are derived below:

Let $y(x)$ and its derivatives be single-valued continuous functions of x then by Taylor's expansion, we get

$$y(x+h) = y(x) + hy'(x) + \frac{h^2}{2!}y''(x) + \frac{h^3}{3!}y'''(x) + \ldots \qquad \ldots(1)$$

$$y(x-h) = y(x) - hy'(x) + \frac{h^2}{2!}y''(x) - \frac{h^3}{3!}y'''(x) + \ldots \qquad \ldots(2)$$

$$\Rightarrow \quad y'(x) = \frac{1}{h}[y(x+h) - y(x)] - \frac{h}{2}y''(x) - \ldots$$

$$= \frac{1}{h}[y(x+h) - y(x)] + O(h)$$

This is the forward difference approximation of $y'(x)$ with an error of order h.

Similarly (2) gives $y'(x) = \frac{1}{h}[y(x) - y(x-h)] + O(h)$

This is the backward difference approximation of $y'(x)$ with an error of order h.

Now subtracting (2) from (1), we get

$$y'(x) = \frac{1}{2h}[y(x+h) - y(x-h)] + O(h^2)$$

This is the central-difference approximation of $y'(x)$ with an error of order h^2. Clearly central difference approximation to $y'(x)$ is better than the forward or backward difference approximations and hence it should be preferred.

Then adding (1) and (2), we obtain

$$y''(x) = \frac{1}{h^2}[y(x+h) - 2y(x) + y(x+h)] + O(h^2)$$

This is the central difference approximation of $y''(x)$. Similarly, we can obtain central difference approximations of higher derivatives.

Now the working expressions for the central difference approximations of the first four derivatives of y_i are as given below:

$$y_i' = \frac{1}{2h}(y_{i+1} - y_{i-1}), \qquad \ldots(3)$$

$$y_i'' = \frac{1}{h^2}(y_{i+1} - 2y_i + y_{i-1}) \qquad \ldots(4)$$

$$y_i''' = \frac{1}{2h^3}(y_{i+2} - 2y_{i+1} + 2y_{i-1} - y_{i-2}) \qquad \ldots(5)$$

$$y_i^{iv} = \frac{1}{h^4}(y_{i+2} - 4y_{i+1} + 6y_i - 4y_{i-1} + y_{i-2}) \qquad \ldots(6)$$

As a matter of fact, the accuracy of the method depends of the sub-interval h and also on the order of approximation. As we reduce h, though the accuracy improves but the number of equations to be solved also increases.

Example 36: *Solve the equation $y'' = x + y$ with the Boundary conditions $y(0) = y(1) = 0$.*

Solution: Let us divide the interval (0, 1) into four sub-intervals, so that $h = 1/4$. The pivot points are $x_0 = 0$, $x_1 = 1/4$, $x_2 = 1/2$, $x_3 = 3/4$ and $x_4 = 1$.

Now the differential equation is approximated as

$$\frac{1}{h^2}[y_{i+1} - 2y_i + y_{i-1}] = x_i + y_i$$

$$\Rightarrow \qquad 16y_{i+1} - 33y_i + 16y_{i-1} = x_i, \quad i = 1, 2, 3. \quad (\because h = \frac{1}{4})$$

Then using $y_0 = y_4 = 0$, we get the system of equations

$$16y_2 - 33y_1 = \frac{1}{4}, 16y_3 - 33y_2 + 16y_1 = \frac{1}{2}, \quad \text{and } -33y_3 + 16y_2 = \frac{3}{4}.$$

Solving: $\quad y_1 = -0.03488, \; y_2 = -0.05632, \; y_3 = -0.05003.$

Note: The exact solution is $y(x) = \dfrac{\sin h\,x}{\sin h\,1} - x$. Now, we frame the following table:

x	Computed value $y(x)$	Exact value $y(x)$	Error
0.25	−0.03488	−0.03505	0.00017
0.5	−0.05632	−0.05659	0.00027
0.75	−0.05003	−0.05028	0.00025

Example 37: *The deflection of a beam is governed by the equation* $\dfrac{d^4 y}{d x^4} + 81\, y = \phi(x)$ *where* $\phi(x)$ *is given by the table*

x :	1/3	2/3	1
$\phi(x)$:	81	162	243

and Boundary condition $y(0) = y'(0) = y''(1) = 0$.

Evaluate the deflection at the pivotal points of the beam using three sub-intervals.

Solution: Here $h = (1/3)$ and the pivotal points are $x_0 = 0, x_1 = 1/3, x_2 = 2/3, x_3 = 1$. The corresponding y-values are $y_0\,(=0), y_1, y_2, y_3$.

Now, the given differential equation is approximated as

$$\frac{1}{h^4}(y_{i+2} - 4\,y_{i+1} + 6\,y_i - 4\,y_{i-1} + y_{i-2}) + 81\,y_i = \phi(x_i)$$

Putting $i = 1$, $$y_3 - 4\,y_2 + 7\,y_1 - 4\,y_0 + y_{-1} = 1 \quad \ldots(1)$$

Putting $i = 2$, $$y_4 - 4\,y_3 + 7\,y_2 - 4\,y_1 + y_0 = 2 \quad \ldots(2)$$

Putting $i = 3$, $$y_5 - 4\,y_4 + 7\,y_3 - 4\,y_2 + y_1 = 3 \quad \ldots(3)$$

We have $$y_0 = 0 \quad \ldots(4)$$

and $y'_i = \dfrac{1}{2h}(y_{i+1} - y_{i-1})$ so for $i = 0$, $0 = y'_0 = \dfrac{1}{2h}(y_1 - y_{-1}) \Rightarrow y_{-1} = y_1$ ...(5)

Also $y'' = \dfrac{1}{h^2}(y_{i+1} - 2\,y_i + y_{i-1})$

Putting $i = 3$, we get $0 = y''_3 = \dfrac{1}{h^2}(y_4 - 2\,y_3 + y_2)$, $\Rightarrow y_4 = 2\,y_3 - y_2$ ...(6)

Also, we have $y'''_i = \dfrac{1}{2h^3}(y_{i+2} - 2\,y_{i+1} + 2\,y_{i-1} - y_{i-2})$

$\Rightarrow$ $0 = y'''_3 = \dfrac{1}{2h^3}(y_5 - 2\,y_4 + 2\,y_2 - y_1)$ (for $i = 3$)

$\Rightarrow$ $y_5 = 2\,y_4 - 2\,y_2 + y_1$ ...(7)

Using (4), and (5); (1) $\Rightarrow$ $y_3 - 4\,y_2 + 8\,y_1 = 1$ ...(8)

Again Using (4) and (6), the equation (2) yields:

$$-y_3 + 3y_2 - 2y_1 = 1 \qquad \ldots(9)$$

Then using (6) and (7), the equation (3) implies

$$3y_3 - 4y_2 + 2y_1 = 3 \qquad \ldots(10)$$

Now solving (8), (9) and (10) we obtain

$$y_1 = 8/13,\ y_2 = 22/13,\ y_3 = 37/13.$$

$$\Rightarrow \quad y(1/3) = 0.6154,\ y(2/3) = 1.6923,\ y(1) = 2.8462.$$

Example 38: *Determine values of y at the pivotal points of the interval* $(0, 1)$ *if y satisfies the Boundary value problem* $y^{iv} + 81y = 81x^2$,

$$y(0) = y(1) = y''(1) = 0. \text{ (Take } n = 3\text{)}.$$

Solution: Note $h = 1/3$ and the pivotal points are $x_0 = 0$, $x_1 = 1/3$, $x_2 = 2/3$, $x_3 = 1$. The corresponding y-values are $y_0 (= 0)$, y_1, y_2, $y_3 (= 0)$.

Then replacing y^{iv} by its central difference approximation, the differential equation yields:

$$\frac{1}{h^4}(y_{i+2} - 4y_{i+1} + 6y_i - 4y_{i-1} + y_{i-2}) + 81y_i = 81x_i^2$$

$$\Rightarrow \quad y_{i+2} - 4y_{i+1} + 7y_i - 4y_{i-1} + y_{i-2} = x_i^2,\ i = 1, 2$$

Putting $i = 1$, $\quad y_3 - 4y_2 + 7y_1 - 4y_0 + y_{-1} = 1/9$

Putting $i = 2$, $\quad y_4 - 4y_3 + 7y_2 - 4y_1 + y_0 = 4/9$

Now, using $y_0 = y_3 = 0$, we obtain

$$-4y_2 + 7y_1 + y_{-1} = 1/9 \qquad \ldots(1)$$

$$y_4 + 7y_2 - 4y_1 = 4/9 \qquad \ldots(2)$$

Further, regarding the conditions $y_0'' = y_3'' = 0$, we have

$$y_i'' = \frac{1}{h^2}(y_{i+1} - 2y_i + y_{i-1})$$

Putting $\quad i = 0,\ y_0'' = 9(y_1 - 2y_0 + y_{-1})$

$$\Rightarrow \quad y_{-1} = -y_1 \qquad [\because y_0 = y_0'' = 0] \qquad \ldots(3)$$

Putting $\quad i = 3,\ y_3'' = 9(y_4 - 2y_3 + y_2)$

$$\Rightarrow \quad y_4 = -y_2 \qquad [\because y_3 = y_3'' = 0] \qquad \ldots(4)$$

Using (3), the equation (1) $\Rightarrow -4y_2 + 6y_1 = 1/9 \qquad \ldots(5)$

Using (4), equation (2) $\Rightarrow 6y_2 - 4y_1 = 4/9 \qquad \ldots(6)$

Solving (5) and (6), we get $y_1 = 11/90$ and $y_2 = 7/45$.

$$\therefore \quad y(1/3) = 0.1222 \text{ and } y(2/3) = 0.1556.$$

Problem Set

1. Solve the equation $y'' - 4y' + 4y = e^{3x}$, with the conditions $y(0) = 0$, $y(1) = -2$, taking $n = 4$.
2. Solve the equation $y'' + y = 0$, with the conditions $y(0) = 1$, $y'(0) = 0$. Compute the value $y(0.2)$ and $y(0.4)$.
3. The Boundary value problem governing the deflection of a beam of length 3 meters is given by $\frac{d^4y}{dx^4} + 2y = \frac{1}{9}x^2 + \frac{2}{3}x + 4$, $y(0) = y'(0) = y(3) = y'(3) = 0$.
   The beam is built-in at the left end ($x = 0$) and simply supported at the right end ($x = 3$). Determine y at the pivotal points $x = 1$ and $x = 2$.
4. Solve the equation $y^{iv} - y''' + y = x^2$, subject to the Boundary conditions $y(0), = y'0 = 0$ and $y(1) = 2, y'(1) = 0$. (Take $n = 5$).

Answers

1.	$y(.25) = -0.3473, y(.5) = -0.9508$ and $y(.75) = -1.7257$		
2.	1.204, 1.0	3.	$y(1) = 1.0171, y(2) = 1.094$
4.	0.189, 0.642, 1.217, 1.740		

11.17 Error Analysis

The numerical solution of a differential equation certainly differs from its exact solution. The difference between the computed value y_i and its true value $y(x_i)$ at any stage is defined as the **total error.** The total error comprises of **truncation error** and **round-off error.** As a matter of fact, the application of numerical methods is to minimize the error and obtain the solutions with least errors.

In any method, the truncation-error can be minimised by making smaller sub-intervals and the round-off error cannot be controlled easily until-unless the computer has the double precision arithmetic-facility.

This error is more elusive than the truncation error.

The truncation error in Euler's method is $\frac{1}{2}h^2\ y_n''$ *i.e.* of $O(h^2)$ and that of modified Euler's method is $\frac{1}{2}h^3\ y_n'''$ *i.e.* or $O(h^3)$. Also in Runge-Kutta 4th order method, the truncation error comes out to be of $O(h^5)$; whereas in Milne's method, the truncation error due to Predictor formula is $\frac{14}{45}\ y_n^v\ h^5$ *i.e.* of $O(h^5)$ and due to Corrector formula $-\frac{1}{90}\ y_n^v\ h^5$ *i.e.* of $O(h^5)$. Also the error in Adams-Bashforth method is of $O(h^5)$. The predictor error T_p and the corrector error T_C are connected by $19\,T_P \approx -251\,T_C$. Further, the relative error of an approximate solution is defined by the ratio of the total error to the exact value.

Example 39: *Applying Euler's method to the differential equation*

$$(dy/dx) = f(x, y),\ y(x_0) = y_0;\ \textit{estimate the total error?}$$

When $f(x, y) = -y$, $y(0) = 1$, *compute this error neglecting the round-off error.*

Solution: **I Part:** The Euler's solution of the given differential equation is given by

$$y_{n+1} = y_n + h f(x_n, y_n) \text{ where } x_n = x_0 + nh.$$

$$\Rightarrow \quad y_{n+1} = y_n + h y'_n \quad \ldots(1)$$

Now, denoting the exact solution of the given equation at $x = x_n$ by $y(x_n)$ and expanding $y(x_{n+1})$ by Taylor's series, we readily obtain

$$y(x_{n+1}) = y(x_n) + h y'(x_n) + \frac{h^2}{2!} y''(\xi_n),\ x_n \le \xi_n \le x_{n+1} \quad \ldots(2)$$

Hence the truncation error

$$T_{n+1} = y(x_{n+1}) - y(x_n) = \frac{1}{2} h^2\ y''(\xi_n) = O(h^2) \quad \ldots(3)$$

In order to introduce the effect of round-off error, R_n, we now introduce a new approximation $\bar{y}_n$ as defined below:

$$\bar{y}_{n+1} = \bar{y}_n + hf(x_n, \bar{y}_n) - R_{n+1} \quad \ldots(4)$$

Whence the total error is defined by $E_{n+1} = y(x_{n+1}) - \bar{y}_{n+1}$

$$= y(x_n) + hy'(x_n) + \frac{h^2}{2!} y''(\xi_n) - \{\bar{y}_n + hf(x_n, y_n) - R_{n+1}\}$$

$$= [y(x_n) - \bar{y}_n] + h[y'(x_n) - f(x_n, y_n)] + T_{n+1} + R_{n+1} \quad \ldots(5)$$

Further allowing the continuity of $(\partial f / \partial y)$ and using Mean-Value theorem, we readily obtain

$$= f[x_n - y(x_n)] - f(x_n, y_n)] = [y(x_n) - y_n]\ f_y(x_n, \xi_n)$$

where $\quad y(x_n) < \xi_n < y_n \quad \ldots(6)$

Then $\quad E_{n+1} = [y(x_n) - \bar{y}_n][1 + h f_y(x_n, \xi_n)] + T_{n+1} + R_{n+1}$

$$= E_n [1 + h f_y(x_n, \xi_n)] + T_{n+1} + R_{n+1} \quad \ldots(7)$$

This is the recurrence formula for finding the total error and the first terms on the right hand side is the inherited error.

II Part: $(dy/dx) = -y,\ y(0) = 1$.

Then taking $h = 0.01$ and applying the relation (1), successively; we obtain

$$y(0.01) = 1 + 0.01(-1) = 0.99$$

$$y(0.02) = 0.99 + 0.01(-0.99) = 0.9801$$

$$y(0.03) = 0.9703,\ y(0.04) = 0.9606$$

Whence, we get the truncation error

$$T_{n+1} = \frac{1}{2} h^2 y'(\xi) = 0.00005\, y(\xi) \quad \le 5 \times 10^{-5}\, y(x_n)$$

[**Note:** (dy/dx) is $-$ve]

$$\Rightarrow \qquad T_1 \le 5 \times 10^{-5}\; y(0) = 5 \times 10^{-5}$$

$$T_2 \le 5 \times 10^{-5}\, y(0.01) = 5 \times 10^{-5}\,(0.99) < 5 \times 10^{-5}$$

$$T_3 \le 5 \times 10^{-5}\, y(0.02) = 5 \times 10^{-5}\,(0.9801) < 5 \times 10^{-5}$$

$$T_4 \le 5 \times 10^{-5}\, y(0.03) = 5 \times 10^{-5}\,(0.9703) < 5 \times 10^{-5} \text{ etc.}$$

Further also $\quad 1 + h\, f_0\,(x_n, y_n) = 1 + 0.01(-1) = 0.99$

Then reglecting round-off error and using the above result, (7) we readily obtain

$$E_0 = 0,\ E_1 = E_0\,(0.99) + T_1 = 5 \times 10^{-1} - 0.00005$$

$$E_2 = E_1\,(0.99) + T_2 < 5 \times 10^{-5} + 5 \times 10^{-5} = 0.0001$$

$$E_3 = E_2\,(0.99) + nT_3 < 10^{-4} + 5 \times 10^{-5} = 0.00015$$

$$E_4 = E_3\,(0.99) + T_4 < 1.5 \times 10^{-4} + 5 \times 10^{-5} = 0.0002 \text{ etc.}$$

Note: The exact solution of $y' = -y,\ y(0) = 1$ is $y = e^{-x}$.

Then the actual error in $y\,(0.03) = e^{-0.03} - 0.9703 = 0.00014$

and actual error in $y\,(0.04) = e^{-0.04} - 0.9606 = 0.00019$

Obviously the total error E_4 agrees with the actual error in $y\,(0.04)$.

11.18 Convergence of a Method

Any numerical method applied to solve a differential equation is said to be convergent, if the approximate solution y_n approaches to the exact solution $y\,(x_n)$ as h tends to zero provided the rounding-off errors arising from the initial conditions also tend to zero; which implies that as the method is continually refined by taking smaller and smaller step-sizes, the sequence of approximate solutions must converge to the exact solution.

Now, Taylor's series method is convergent, provided $f(x, y)$ has sufficient continuous derivatives. The Runge-Kutta methods are also convergent under similar conditions and Predictor-corrector methods are convergent if $f(x, y)$ satisfies the Lipschitz condition *i.e.*

$$|\, f\,(x, y) - f\,(x, \overline{y})\,| \le k\,|\, y - \overline{y}\,|,$$

Where k is a constant. The sequence of approximations to the numerical solution converges to the exact solution.

11.19 Stability Analysis

The reduction of step size h gives rise to control the ***Truncation Error*** but there exists a limit of reduction beyond which a further reduction in h gives rise to increase the ***Round-Off*** error causing a increase in the total error. In such cases, we make use of stable methods which do not allow the magnification of error introduced at any stage. If any method produces a bounded solution which imitates the exact solution is said to be a ***Stable Method*** otherwise the method is said to unstable. Further, the method is said to be ***Obsolutely*** or ***Unconditionally Stable*** if it is stable for all parametric values and in case the method is stable for some values of the parameter, it is said to be ***Conditionally Stable***. ***Euler's*** and ***Runge-Kutta*** method are conditionally stable whereas ***Taylor's*** and ***Adams-Bashforth*** method are relatively stable. On the other hand ***Milne's Method*** is purely unstable.

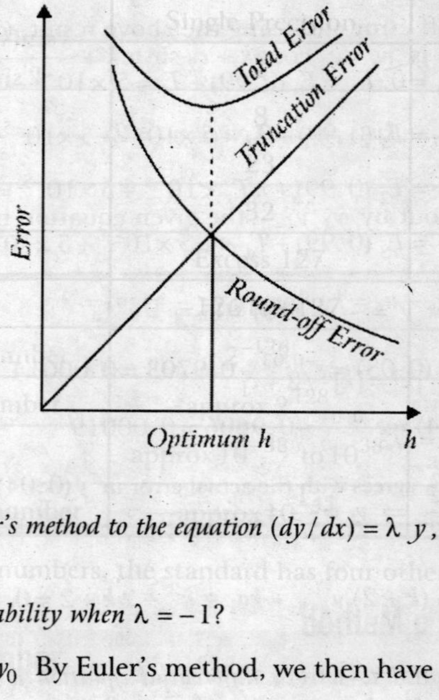

Example 40: *Applying Euler's method to the equation* $(dy/dx) = \lambda\, y$, *given* $y(x_0) = y_0$, *test its stability zone?*

What would be the range of stability when $\lambda = -1$?

Solution: $y' = \lambda y,\ y(x_0) = y_0$ By Euler's method, we then have

$$y_n = y_{n-1} + h\, y'_{n-1} = y_{n-1} + \lambda\, h\, y_{n-1} \qquad (\because\ y' = \lambda y)$$

$$= (1 + \lambda\, h)\, y_{n-1} \qquad \ldots[A]$$

$$\Rightarrow \quad y_{n-1} = (1 + \lambda\, h)\, y_{n-2} \qquad \ldots(1)$$

$$\ldots\ldots\ldots\ldots\ldots\ldots\ldots\ldots$$

$$y_2 = (1 + \lambda h)\, y_1 \quad \ldots\ldots\ldots \quad (n-2)$$

and $$y_1 = (1 + \lambda h)\, y_0 \quad \ldots\ldots\ldots \quad (n-1)$$

Then multiplying all these equations, we get

$$y_n = (1 + \lambda\, h)^n\, y_0 \qquad \ldots[B]$$

Again $$y' = \lambda\, y \Rightarrow y = c\, e^{\lambda x}$$

But $$y(x_0) = y_0 \Rightarrow y_0 = c\, e^{\lambda x_0} \qquad \therefore \quad y = y_0\, e^{\lambda (x - x_0)}$$

Then, the exact solution through (x_n, y_n) is given by

$$y_n = y_0\, e^{\lambda(x_n - x_0)} = y_0\, e^{\lambda nh} \qquad [\because x_n = x_0 + nh]$$

$$\Rightarrow \qquad y_n = y_0\,(e^{\lambda h})^n = y_0 \left[1 + \lambda h + \frac{(\lambda h)^2}{2} + \ldots\right]^n \qquad \ldots [C]$$

The numerical solution (B) agrees with exact solution (C) for small values of h. The solution (B) increases if $|1 + \lambda h| > 1$.

$\Rightarrow \qquad |1 + \lambda h| < 1$ defines a stable zone.

In case λ is real; the method is stable if $|1 + \lambda h| < 1 \Rightarrow -2 < \lambda h < 0$. Further, when λ is complex $(= a + ib)$, then it is stable if $|1 + (a + ib)\,h| < 1$

$\Rightarrow \qquad |(1 + ah) + i\,b\,h| < 1$

$\Rightarrow \qquad (1 + ah)^2 + (bh)^2 < 1$

$\Rightarrow \qquad (x + 1)^2 + y^2 < 1,$

$\Rightarrow \lambda h$ lies within the unit circle as shown in Fig.

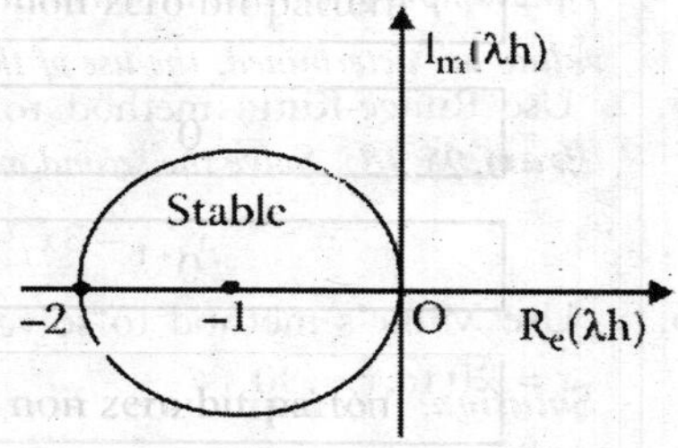

where $x = ah$, $y = bh$.

When λ is purely imaginary $(= ib)$ then $|1 + \lambda h| = 1$, i.e. we have a periodicstability. This implies that Euler's method is absolutely stable if and only if (i) $\exists$ real $\lambda : -2 < \lambda h < 0$.

(ii) $\exists$ complex $\lambda : \lambda h$ lies within the unit circle *i.e.* Eyler's method is conditionally convergent.

And case $\lambda = -1$, the solution is stable in the range $-2 < -h < 0$ *i.e.* $0 < h < 2$.

✦✦ Problem Set ✦✦

1. Using Runge-Kutta method of order 4, solve $y'' = y + xy'$, $y(0) = 1$, $y'(0) = 0$ to find $y(0.2)$ and $y'(0.2)$.

2. Use Euler's method to find $y(1)$ from the differential equation $\frac{dy}{dx} = \frac{-y}{1+x}$, $y(3) = 2$. Take for each step $h = 0.1$.

3. Use Picard's method to solve $\frac{dy}{dx} = 1 + xy$, with $x_0 = 2$, $y_0 = 0$.

4. Solve $y' = x - y^2$ by series expansion for $x = 0.2$ to 0.6 with $h = 0.2$. Initially $x = 0$, $y = 1$.

5. Use Runge-Kutta method to solve $y' = xy$ for $x = 1.4$. Initially $x = 1, y = 2$ (take $h = 0.2$)

[Bhopal 2002; Agra 2006]

6. Use Milne's method to solve $dy/dx = x + y$ with initial condition $y(0) = 1$ from $x = .20$ to $x = .30$. **[Agra 2009]**

7. Use Taylor's-series method to start the numerical solution of

   (i) $dy/dx = x^2 + y^2$ with $x_0 = 1$, $y_0 = 0$,

   (ii) $xy'' + y' + xy = 0$ where $y(0) = 1$, $y(0) = 0$ for $x = 0.$ to $x = 1.5$

8. Obtain by Taylor's series five consecutive starting values for the numerical solution of $dy/dx = 2y + 3e^x$ where $x_0 = 0$, $y_0 = 0$.

   Check the values.

9. Solve numerically at $x = 0.4, 0.5$ by Milne's Predictor-corrector method given their values at four points.

$$x = 0, 0.1, 0.2, 0.3. \quad dy/dx = 2e^x - y,$$

$$y_0 = 2, \; y_1 = 2.010, \; y_2 = 2.040, \; y_2 = 2.090.$$

10. Solve the differential equation (i) $y' = 1/(x + y)$ for $x = 0.5$ to 2 by using Runge-Kutta's method. Initial value; $x = 0$, $y = 1$. $[h = .5]$.

    (ii) $y'' = (x^2 - y^2)(1 + x y^2)$ for $x = 0.5, 1.00, 1.5$ using Runge-Kutta's method, initial value $x = 0$, $y = 1$ $y' = 0$.

11. Evaluate to three significant figures the integral of

$$dy/dx = 3e^x + 2y$$

with $x_0 = 0$ at $y_0 = 0$ at $x = 0.4, 0.5, 0.6$, using Adam Bashforth's formula with difference upto the third order.

12. Solve $\frac{dy}{dx} = \frac{1}{x+y}$ for $x = 0.5$ to $x = 2$ $[h = .5]$ by using Runge-Kutta's method, with $x_0 = 0, y_0 = 1$.

13. (i) Integrate for $x = 0.1, 0.2$ the following initial value problem by Runge-Kutta's fourth order method.

$$y' = x - y^2, \quad y(0) = 1$$

(ii) Use Runga-Kutta method to calculate the value of y at $x = 0.1$, to five places of decimal, after a single step of 0.1 if

$$y' = 0.31 + 0.25\,y + 0.3\,x^2$$

and $\quad y = 0.72$ when $x = 0$.

14. Determine Predictor and Corrector formulae, as given below, which are known as Milne's fourth order in case of Initial Value problem

$$dy/dx = f(x, y), \; y(x_0) = y_0$$

$$y_{i+1} = y_{i-3} + (4h/3)(2f_i - 2f_{i-1} + 2f_{i-2}) \text{ Predictor}$$

$$y_{i+1} = y_{i-1} - (h/3)(f_{i+1} - 4f_i + f_{i-1}) \text{ Corrector.}$$

15. Solve Initial Value problem

$$dy/dx = 1 + xy^2, \; y(0) = 1$$

for $x = 0.4, 0.5$ by using Milne's method when it is given

$x =$	.1	.2	.3
$y =$	1.105	1.223	1.355

16. Solve $x\,y'' + y' + x\,y = 0$, where

$$y(0) = 1, \; y'(0) = 1, \text{ for } x = 0 \text{ to } x = 1.5.$$

17. Solve the equation $\frac{dy}{dx} = x + y$ with initial condition $y^{(0)} = 1$ by Runge-Kutta's rule from $x = 0$ to $x = .4$ with $h = .1$

18. Use Runge-Kutta's quadratic method calculate these additional point on the solution curve of the problem

$$\frac{dy}{dx} = 1 - 2xy, \; y^{(0)} = 0, \; h = .1$$

19. Solve Initial Value problem.

$$dy/dx = 1 + x\,y^2, \; y^{(0)} = 0, \; h = .1$$

for $x = 0.4, 0.5$ by using Milne's method when it is given

$x =$	.1	.2	.3
$y =$	1.105	1.223	1.355

20. Solve $xy'' + y' + xy = 0$, where $y(0) = 1, y'(0) = 1, x = 0$ to $x = 1.5$.

21. Solve $dy/dx = [1/(x+y)]$ for $x = .5$ to $x = 2$ $(h = .5)$ by using Runge-Kutta's method, with $x_0 = 0$, $y_0 = 1$.

22. Show that the modified Euler's method is convergent.

23. Apply fourth order Runge-Kutta method to the equation $(dy/dx) = \mu\, y,\ y(x_0) = y_0$ and show that the range of absolute stability is $-2.78 < \mu h < 0$.

24. Find the range of absolute stability of the equation

$$y' + 10\, y = 0,\ y(0) = 1, \text{ using}$$

(i) Euler's method (ii) Runge-Kutta method.

25. Show that the local truncation error in the Milne's Predictior and Corrector formulae are $\frac{14}{45} h^5 y^v$ and $-\frac{1}{90} h^5 y^v$ respectively.

✦✦ Objective Type Question ✦✦

❖ Multiple Choice Questions

1. In Runge-Kutta method, value of k_2 is:

(a) $hf(x_0, y_0)$ (b) $hf\left(x_0 + \frac{h}{2}, y_0 + \frac{k_1}{2}\right)$

(c) $hf\left(x_0 + \frac{h}{2}, y_0 + \frac{k_3}{2}\right)$ (d) $hf\left(x_0 - \frac{h}{2}, y_0 - \frac{k_3}{2}\right)$

[Rohilkhand 2010]

2. Which of the following formulae is used in Euler's method to solve the differential equation of the form $\frac{dy}{dx} = f(x, y)$?

(a) $y_{n+1} = x_n + hf(x_n, y_n)$ (b) $y_{n+1} = y_n + hf(x_n, y_n)$

(c) $y_{n+1} = y_n + \frac{1}{2} hf(x_n, y_n)$ (d) $y_{n+1} = y_n + 2h\, f(x_n, y_n)$

3. Which of the following formulae is used in Picard's method to solve the differential equation $\frac{dy}{dx} = f(x, y)$?

(a) $y^{(n)} = y_0 + \int_{x_0}^{x} f(x, y^{(n-1)})\, dx$ (b) $y^{(n)} = y_0 - \int_{x_0}^{x} f(x, y^{(n-1)})\, dx$

(c) $y^{(n)} = y_0 - \frac{1}{2}\int_{x_0}^{x} f(x, y^{(n-1)})\, dx$ (d) $y^{n} = y_0 + \frac{1}{2}\int_{x_0}^{x} f(x, y^{(n-1)})\, dx$

[I.A.S. 2005]

4. Principal part of the error in Milne's formula of solving differential equation is

(a) $y_{n+1} - y_{n+1}^{(1)}$ (b) $\frac{1}{29}(y_{n+1} - y_{n+1}^{(1)})$

(c) $\frac{1}{29}[y_{n+1} - y_{n+1}^{(1)}]$ (d) $y_{n+1}^{(1)} - \frac{h}{90}\Delta^4 y^1$ **[P.C.S. (M.P.) 2009]**

5. Which of the following formulae is used in modified Euler's method to solve the differential equations $\frac{dy}{dx} = f(x, y)$?

(a) $y^{(n+1)} = y_0 + h[f(x_0, y_0) + f(x_1, y_1^{(n)})]$ (b) $y^{(n+1)} = y_0 + h[f(x_0, y_0) - f(x_1, y_1^{(n)})]$

(c) $y^{(n+1)} = y_0 + \frac{h}{2}[f(x_0, y_0) - f(x_1, y_1^{(n)})]$ (d) $y^{(n+1)} = y_0 + \frac{h}{2}[f(x_0, y_0) + f(x_1, y_1^{(n)})]$

[Rohilkhand 2009]

6. Milne's predictor formula is

(a) $y_4 = y_0 + \frac{4}{3}h(2y_1' - y_2' + 2y_3') + \frac{28}{90}h\Delta^4 y_0'$

(b) $y_4 = y_0 + \frac{4}{3}h(2y_1' + y_2' + 2y_3') + \frac{28}{90}h\Delta^4 y_0'$

(c) $y_4 = y_0 + \frac{h}{3}(2y_1 + 4y_2' + 2y_3') - \frac{8}{90}h\Delta^4 y_0'$

(d) None of these.

✦✦ Examination Questions ✦✦

1. Using Runge-Kutta's method with third order accuracy, solve $\frac{dy}{dx} = y - x$ with Initial condition $y = 2, x = 0$.

2. Given that $\frac{dy}{dx} = y - \frac{2x}{y}$, $y(0) = 1$, $y(0.1) = 1.0954$, $y(0.2) = 1.1832$ and $y(0.3) = 1.2649$, find $f(0.5)$ by Adam's Predictor-corrector method.

3. Solve by Runge-Kutta's method $\frac{dy}{dx} = x + y$ with initial conditions $x_0 = 0, y_0 = 1$ correct upto four decimal places, by evaluating upto second increment of y. (Take $h = 0.1$).

4. For the differential equation

$$\frac{dy}{dx} = y - x^2, \ y(0) = 1$$

starting values are given as

$$y(0.2) = 1.2186, \ y(0.4) = 1.4682 \text{ and } y(0.6) = 1.7379.$$

Using Milne's Predicutor corrector method advance the solution to $x = 0.8$ and compare it with the analytical solution. (carry four decimals).

5. Solve the system of differential equations $\frac{dy}{dx} = xz + 1,\ \frac{dz}{dx} = -xy$ for $x = 0.3$ given that $y = 0$ and $z = 1$ when $x = 0$, using Runge-Kutta's method of order four.

6. By the Fourth-order Runge-Kutta's method, tabulate the solution of the differential equation

$$\frac{dy}{dx} = \frac{xy+1}{10y^2+4},\ y(0) = 0$$

in $[0; .4]$ with step length 0.1 correct to five decimal places.

7. Using Fourth order Classical Runge-Kutta's method for the Initial value problem $\frac{du}{dt} = -2tu^2, u(0) = 1,$

with $h = 0.2$ on the interval $[0, 1]$, calculate $u(0.4)$ correct to six places of decimal.

8. Given: $\frac{dy}{dx} = y - x$ where $y(0) = 2$, using the Runge-Kutta's Fourth order method, find $y(0.1)$ and $y(0.2)$. Compare the appeoximate solution with its exact solution.

$(e^{0.1} = 1.10517,\ e^{0.2} = 1.2214)$ **[I.A.S. 2002]**

9. Apply the Second order Runge-Kutta's method, to find an approximate value of y at $x = 0.2$ taking $h = 0.1$, given that y satisfies the differential equation and the initial condition

$$y' = x + y$$
$$y(0) = 1$$

[I.A.S. 2007]

10. Using Runge-Kutta's method, solve $y'' = xy'^2 - y^2$ for $x = 0.2$. Initial conditions are at $x = 0$, $y = 1$ and $y' = 0$ use four decimal places for computations. **[I.F.S. 2008]**

11. $\frac{dy}{dx} = xy; y = 2$, when $x = 1$, use Runge-Kutta fourth order rule to find y at $x = 1.4$ taking the step length $h = 0.2$ **[I.F.S. 2002]**

12. Apply modified Euler's method to determine $y(0.1)$, given that $\frac{dy}{dx} = x^2 + y$ when $y(0) = -1$ **[I.F.S. 2003]**

13. Solve the Initial Value problem $\frac{dy}{dx} = \frac{1}{x+y},\ y(0) = 1$

using Range-Kutta method of fourth order to evaluate $y(0.5)$ in a single step.

[I.F.S. 2004]

14. For the solution of the differential equation $\frac{dy}{dx} = f(x, y)$, obtain the Predictor formula of the form

$$y_{n+1} = y_n + \frac{h}{6}(y'_n + 13\, y'_{n-1} - 8\, y'_{n-2})$$

and also obtain the corresponding corrector formula.

15. Obtain Runge-Kutta's type formulae of fourth order, also discuss its advantages and disadvantags.

16. Using Runga-Kutta method, find $y(0.2)$ given that

$$\frac{dy}{dx} = 1 + y^2, \; y(0) = 0$$

17. Use Euler's method and an interval of $h = 0.1$ to find a solution of the differential equation $\frac{dy}{dx} = x^2 + y^2$ with Boundary conditions $y = 1$ for $x = 0$ in $0 \le x \le 1$.

18. Using Runge-Kutta method, find $y(2)$, given that $\frac{dy}{dx} = y - \frac{2x}{y}$, $y(0) = 1$.

19. Drive Euler's method to solve an Initial value problem of first order. How can this method be improved to obtain Runge-Kutta's explicit method of fourth order for the same problem? Explain.

20. When the Initial value problem is $y' = 1 + y^2$, $y(0) = 0$. Find $y(0.6)$ by Runge-Kutta fourth order method Taking $h = 0.2$.

[U.P.T.U. 2006, 2008]

21. Find the value of $y(1.1)$ using Runge-Kutta method of Fourth order, given that

$$\frac{dy}{dx} = y^2 + 3x, \; y(1) = 1.2. \qquad [\text{take } h = 0.1]$$

[U.P.T.U. 2007; I.A.S. 2009]

Answers

Problem Set

1. $y(0.2) = 0.9802,\ y'(0.2) = 0.196$

2. 0.9477

3. $y^{(3)} = \dfrac{x^5}{15} - \dfrac{x^4}{4} + \dfrac{x^3}{3} - \dfrac{x^2}{2} + x - \dfrac{22}{15}$

4.

x	0.2	0.4	0.6
y	0.8512	0.8798	0.7620

5. $y_{1.4} = 2.99485866$

6. $y_{.2} = 1.2428,\ y_{.3} = 1.3997.$

8. $y(1) = 13.91,\ y(1.1) = 17.87$

9. $y_4 = 2.162,\quad y_5 = 2.256$

10. (i)

x	0.5	1.0	1.5	2.00
y	1.3571	1.5837	1.7565	1.8950

(ii)

x	0.5	1.0	1.5
y	0.8891	.6674	.5794

11. $y(0.4) = 2.20,\ y(0.5) = 3.20,\ y(0.6) = 4.49.$

12. $y_{.5} = 1.3571,\ y_1 = 1.5837,\ y_{1.5} = 1.7565,\ y_2 = 1.8950.$

13. 0.76972.

17. $y_1 = 1.1103,\ y_2 = 1.2428,\ y_3 = 1.5836$

21. $y_{.5} = 1.3571,\ y_1 = 1.5837,\ y_{1.5} = 1.7565;\ y_2 = 1.8950.$

24. (i) $0 < h < 0.2$; (ii) $0 < h < 0.278$.

Multiple Choice Questions

1. (b) 2. (b) 3. (a) 4. (b) 5. (d)
6. (a)

Examination Questions

1. $y = 4.2214$

2. 1.4572

3. $y = 1.2104$

4. $y = 0.3046$

7. $u(0.4) = 0.8602978$

9. $x_2 = 0.2,\ y_2 = 1.2428$

10. $\begin{cases} z(0.2) = 0.20133347 \\ y(0.2) = 0.9799326 \end{cases}$

11. $y = 2.99486$

12. $y = -1.105$

13. $y = 1.357$

16. $y = 0.20271$

17. $y = 1, 1.1, 1.222, 1.375, 1.573$

20. $y = 0.6828$

21. $y = 1.727$

Theory | Solved Examples | Problem Set

Chapter 12

Solution of Algebraic and Transcendental Equations

Introduction, Properties of Equations, Descarte's rule of signs, Transformations of Equations, Synthetic Division, Diminishing of Roots, Sturm's Theorem, Computation of Roots of an Equation, Convergence of Bisection method, Approximate value of the Roots, Regula Falsi Method, Secant method, Iteration method, Aitken's Δ^2 method, Newton Raphson method, Muller's method, Lin–Bairstow's method, Convergence of Newton's method, Horner's method, Comparison of Iterative method.

12.1 Introduction

An expression of the form $f_n(x) = a_0 x^n + a_1 x^{n-1} + \ldots + a_{n-1}x + a_n$

where a's are constants, and n is a positive integer, is said to be a *polynomial* in x of degree n provided $a_0 \neq 0$. The values of x which make $f_n(x)$ to zero are called as *zeroes or the roots* of the polynomial $f_n(x)$ and every polynomial of nth degree has *n zeroes*.

The equations of the form $f_n(x) = 0$ are called *Algebraic or Transcendental* according as $f_n(x)$ is purely a polynomial in x or contains some other functions such as logarithmic, exponential and trigonometric functions etc. *e.g.*, the equations $x^7 + 7x^6 + 5x^3 - 10 = 9$ and $8x^2 + \log(x+2) + e^{-x}\cos x = 0$ are called *algebraic and transcendental* respectively. By obtaining the solution of an equation $f_n(x) = 0$, we mean to find *roots or zeroes* of $f_n(x)$. Geometrically, a root of equation is that value of x where the graph of $y = f(x)$ crosses the x-axis and the process of finding the roots of an equation is known as the solution of the equation. If $f_n(x)$ is a quadratic, cubic or a biquadratic expression, algebraic solutions of equations are available. But the need arises to solve higher degree or transcendental equations for which no direct methods are available. Such equations can best be solved by approximate methods.

Some Properties of Equations

(a) *If $f(x)$ is exactly divisible by $x - \alpha$, then α is a root of $f(x) = 0$.*

(b) *Every equation of the nth degree has only n roots (real or complex)* and conversely if α_1, α_2 ...., α_n are the roots of the nth degree equation $f_n(x) = 0$, then

$$f_n(x) = A(x - \alpha_1)(x - \alpha_2)\ldots(x - \alpha_n)$$

where A is a constant.

Further, if a polynomial of degree n vanishes for more than n values of x, it must be identically zero.

(c) ***Intermediate Value Property***: *If $f(x)$ is continuous in the interval $[a, b]$ and $f(a)$, $f(b)$ have different signs, then the equation $f(x) = 0$ has at least one root between $x = a$ and $x = b$.*

(d) *In an equation with real coefficients, imaginary roots occur in conjugate pairs, i.e.* if $\alpha + i\beta$ is a root of the equation $f(x) = 0$, then $\alpha - i\beta$ must also be its second root.

Similarly if $\alpha + \sqrt{b}$ is an irrational root of an equation, then $\alpha - \sqrt{b}$ must also be its second root.

> **Note:** *Every equation of the odd degree has at least one real root...*

(e) ***Descarte's Rule of Signs***: *The equation $f(x) = 0$ cannot have more positive roots than the changes of signs in $f(x)$; and more negative roots than the changes of signs in $f(-x)$. For example, let us consider the equation $f(x) = 12x^7 - x^5 + 4x^3 - 15 = 0$.* ...(1)

Signs of $f(x)$ are $+ \quad - \quad + \quad -$

Hence $f(x)$ has three changes of signs. Thus (1) cannot have more than three positive roots,

Hence (1) cannot have more than 3 positive roots. Also, we have

$$f(-x) = 12(-x)^7 - (-x)^5 + 4(-x)^3 - 15$$
$$= -12x^7 + x^5 - 4x^3 - 15 \quad \textit{i.e. } \exists \text{ two changes of signs.}$$

Hence (1) cannot have more than 2 negative roots.

(f) ***Existence of Imaginary Roots***: *If an equation of nth degree has at the most p positive roots and at the most q negative roots, then the equation has at least $n - (p + q)$ imaginary roots.*

(g) ***Relations between Roots and Coefficients***: *If $\alpha_1, \alpha_2, \alpha_3, \ldots, \alpha_n$ be the roots of the equation*

$$a_0 x^n + a_1 x^{n-1} + a_2 x^{n-2} + \ldots + a_{n-1} x + a_n = 0 \qquad \ldots(1)$$

then $$\sum \alpha_1 = -\frac{a_1}{a_0}, \quad \sum \alpha_1 \alpha_2 = \frac{a_2}{a_0}, \quad \sum \alpha_1 \alpha_2 \alpha_3 = -\frac{a_3}{a_0}, \ldots$$

$$\alpha_1 \alpha_2 \alpha_3 \ldots \alpha_n = (-1)^n \frac{a_n}{a_0}$$

(h) ***Transformation of the Equations***

(i) ***To Find an Equation whose Roots are m Times the Roots of the Given Equation***: Multiply the second term by m, third term by m^2 and so on (all missing terms supplied with zero coefficients).

Let the given equation be $13x^4 + 16x^3 + 4x^2 - 8x + 11 = 0$ ...(1)

To multiply its roots by m, let us put $y = mx$ (or $x = y/m$) in (1).

Then $13\,(y/m)^4 + 16\,(y/m)^3 + 4\,(y/m)^2 - 8\,(y/m) + 11 = 0$

$$\Rightarrow \quad 13\,y^4 + m\,(16\,y^3) + m^2\,(4\,y^2) - m^3\,(8\,y) + m^4\,(11) = 0$$

which is same as multiplying the second term by m, third term by m^2 and so on in (1).

(i) ***To Find an Equation whose Roots are with Opposite Signs to those of the Given Equation***: Change the signs of every alternative term of the given equation beginning with the second.

(j) ***To Find an Equation whose Roots are Reciprocal of the Roots of the Given Equation***: Change x to $(1/x)$.

(k) ***Reciprocal Equations***: If an equation remains unaltered on changing x to $(1/x)$. It is called **reciprocal equation.**

(i) A reciprocal equation of an odd degree having coefficients of terms equidistant from the beginning and end equal and has root = – 1.

(ii) A reciprocal equation of an odd degree having coefficients of terms equidistant from the beginning and equal but opposite in sign and has a root = 1.

(iii) A reciprocal of an even degree having coefficients of terms equidistant from the beginning and end equal but opposite in sign and has two roots = 1 and – 1.

The substitution $x + (1/x) = y$ reduces the degree of the equation to half its former degree.

(l) ***Synthetic Division of a Polynomial by Linear Expression***: The division of the polynomial

$$f(x) = a_0\,x^n + a_1\,x^{n-1} + a_2\,x^{n-2} + \ldots + a_{n-1}\,x + a_n$$

by a binomial $x - \alpha$ is done by synthetic division as follows:

α	a_0	a_1	a_2	a_{n-1}	a_n
		$\alpha\,b_0$	$\alpha\,b_1$	$\alpha\,b_{n-2}$	$\alpha\,b_{n-1}$
	a_0	$a_1 + \alpha b_0$	$a_2 + \alpha\,b_1$	$a_{n-1} + \alpha\,b_{n-1}$	$a_n + \alpha\,b_{n-1}$
	$(= b_0)$	$(= b_1)$	$(= b_2)$	$(= b_{n-1})$	$(= R)$

Hence quotient $= b_0\,x^{n-1} + b_1\,x^{n-2} + \ldots. + b_{n-1}$; while remainder $= R$

Rule (i) Write the coefficients of the power of x (supplying missing powers of x by zero and write α on extreme left.

(ii) Put $a_0\,(= b_0)$ as the first term of 3rd row and multiply it by α and write the product under a_1 and add, giving $a_1 + \alpha\,b_0\;(= b_1)$.

(iii) Multiply b_1 by α and write the product under a_2 and add, giving $a_2 + \alpha\,b_1\;(= b_2)$; etc. and continue this process, till we get R.

(m) ***To Diminish the Roots of an Equation*** $f(x) = 0$ ***by*** h: Let us divide $f(x)$ by $x - h$ successively; the successive remainders, then determine the coefficients of the required equation.

Let the given equation be

$$a_0 x^n + a_1 x^{n-1} + ... + a_{n-1} x + a_n = 0 \quad ...(1)$$

We want to diminish its roots h ; $y = x - h$ (or $x = y + h$) in (1)

$$\Rightarrow \quad a_0 (y + h)^n + a_1 (y + h)^{n-1} + ... + a_n = 0 \quad ...(2)$$

$$\Rightarrow \quad A_o y^n + A_1 y^{n-1} + ... + A_n = 0 \quad ...(3)$$

where the coefficients $A_0, A_1, ..., A_n$ can easily be found with help of *synthetic division*. For this, we put $y = x - h$ in (3), so that

$$A_0 (x - h)^n + A_1 (x - h)^{n-1} + ... + A_n = 0 \quad ...(4)$$

Clearly (1) and (4) are identical. If we divide L.H.S. of (4) by $x - h$, the remainder is A_n and the quotient $Q = A_0 (x - h)^{n-1} + A_1 (x - h)^{n-2} + ... A_{n-1}$.

Similarly, if we divide Q by $x - h$, the remainder is A_{n-1} while the quotient is Q_1 (say). Further divide Q_1 by $x - h$, A_{n-2} will be obtained and so on.

12.2 Quotient & Remainder by Synthetic Division (Problem)

Solved Examples

Example 1: *Find the quotient and remainder when* $x^4 + 6x^2 - 4x + 1$ *is divided by* $2x + 3$, *using the process of synthetic division.* **[Chennai (B.E.) 2004]**

Solution: The synthetic division in the tabular form by $2(x + 3/2)$ is given below

	1	0	6	– 4	1
– 3/2		– 3/2	9/4	– 99/8	393/16
	1	– 3/2	33/4	– 131/8	| 409/16 |

Therefore, Quotient $= \dfrac{1}{2}\left[x^3 - \dfrac{3}{2}x^2 + \dfrac{33}{4}x - \dfrac{131}{8}\right]$

$= \dfrac{x^3}{2} - \dfrac{3}{4}x^2 + \dfrac{33}{8}x - \dfrac{131}{16}$;

and remainder $R = (409/16)$.

Derivatives of a Polynomial by Synthetic Division

Consider the polynomial

$$f_n(x) = a_0 x^n + a_1 x^{n-1} + ... + a_{n-1} x + a_n \quad ...(1)$$

where $a_0, a_1, \ldots, a_n$ are defined by the polynomials

$$f_0(x) = a_0$$
$$f_1(x) = x\, f_0(x) + a_1$$
$$f_2(x) = x\, f_1(x) + a_2$$
$$\ldots \quad \ldots \quad \ldots \quad \ldots \quad \ldots$$
$$\ldots \quad \ldots \quad \ldots \quad \ldots \quad \ldots$$
$$f_{n-1}(x) = x\, f_{n-2}(x) + a_{n-1}$$
$$f_n(x) = x\, f_{n-1}(x) + a_n \qquad \ldots(2)$$

The value of $f_n(x)$ at $x = \alpha$ may not be known by first calculating $f_0(\alpha)$, then $f_1(\alpha)$, $f_2(\alpha)$, and so on from (2). The process of equation is best done by the synthetic division as follows:

	a_0	a_1	a_2	$\ldots,$	a_{n-1}	a_n
		αf_0	αf_1	$\ldots,$	αf_{n-2}	αf_{n-1}
α	$f_0 = a_0$	f_1	f_2	$\ldots,$	f_{n-1}	$f_n(\alpha)$

Differentiating equations (2) once, we get

$$f_0'(x) = 0$$
$$f_1'(x) = x\, f_0'(x) + f_0(x) = f_0(x)$$
$$f_2'(x) = x\, f_1'(x) + f_1(x)$$
$$\ldots \quad \ldots \quad \ldots \quad \ldots \quad \ldots \quad \ldots$$
$$f_n'(x) = x\, f_{n-1}'(x) + f_{n-1}(x) \qquad \ldots(3)$$

Putting $x = \alpha$ in equation (3) and then comparing with equation (2) for $x = \alpha$, we find $f_1'(\alpha), f_2'(\alpha), \ldots, f_n'(\alpha)$, are obtained from $f_0(\alpha), f_1(\alpha), \ldots, f_{n-1}(\alpha)$ in the same manner as $f_0(\alpha), f_1(\alpha), \ldots, f_{n-1}(\alpha)$ were obtained from $a_0, a_1, \ldots, a_{n-1}$.

Further, differentiating (3), we find that

$$f_0''(x) = 0,\ f_1''(x) = x\, f_0''(x) + 2\, f_0' = 0$$
$$f_2'' = x\, f_1'' + 2\, f_1' = 2\, f_1' \quad \text{or} \quad \frac{1}{2!} f_2'' = f_1'$$
$$\ldots \quad \ldots \quad \ldots \quad \ldots \quad \ldots \quad \ldots \quad \ldots \quad \ldots$$
$$f_n'' = x\, f_{n-1}'' + 2\, f_{n-1}' \quad \text{or} \quad \frac{1}{2!} f_n'' = x\left[\frac{1}{2!} f_{n-1}''\right] + f_{n-1} \qquad \ldots(4)$$

Similarly, by differentiating (2) n times we get

$$f_0^{(n)}(x) = 0,\ f_1^{(n)}(x) = 0, \ldots\ldots, f_{n-1}^{(n)}(x) = 0$$
$$f_n^{(n)}(x) = n\, f_{n-1}^{(n-1)}, \quad \text{or} \quad \frac{1}{n!} f_n^{(n)} = \frac{1}{(n-1)!} f_{n-1}^{(n-1)} \qquad \ldots(5)$$

The results (2), (3), (4), (5) for $x = \alpha$ in the form of synthetic division may be written as under:

α	a_0	a_1	a_2	a_{n-2}	a_{n-1}	a_n
		αf_0	αf_1	αf_n	αf_{n-2}	αf_{n-1}
α	$f_0 = \alpha_0$	f_1	f_2	f_{n-2}	f_{n-1}	$f_n(\alpha)$
		$\alpha f_1'$	αf_2	αf_{n-2}	$\alpha f_{n-1}'$	
α	$f_1' = f_0$	f_2'	f_3	f_{n-1}	$f_n'(\alpha)$	1
		$\frac{\alpha}{2!} f_2'$	....	$\frac{\alpha}{2} f_{n-1}''$		
	$\frac{1}{2!} f_2' = f_1'$	$\frac{1}{2!} f_3''$	$\frac{1}{2!} f_n''$			
	... ...	... ...	... ...	... ...		
	... ...	... ...	... ...	... ...		
α						
	$\frac{1}{n!} f_n^{(n)} = \frac{1}{(n-1)!} f_{n-1}^{(n-1)}$					

Corollary:

$$f_n(x) = a_0 x^n + a_1 x^{n-1} + \ldots.. + a_{n-2} x^2 + a_{n-1} x + a_n.$$

$$f_n'(x) = n a_0 x^{n-1} + \ldots\ldots + 2a_{n-2} x + a_{n-1}$$

$$f_n''(x) = n(n-1) a_0 x^{n-2} + \ldots\ldots + 2 a_{n-2}$$

$$\ldots \quad \ldots \quad \ldots \quad \ldots \quad \ldots \quad \ldots \quad \ldots \quad \ldots \quad \ldots \quad \ldots.$$

$$f_n^{(n)}(x) = n!\, a_0$$

$$\Rightarrow \quad a_n = f_n(0),\ a_{n-1} = f_n'(0),\ a_{n-2} = \frac{1}{2!} f_n''(0), \ldots\ldots, a_0 = \frac{1}{n!} f_n^{(n)}(0).$$

Example 2: *For the polynomial* $f(x) = 2x^3 - 6x + 13$, *find* $f(2)$, $f'(2)$, $f''(2)$ *and* $f'''(2)$.

Solution: Using the method of synthetic division, we have

2	2	0	–6	13
		4	8	4
2	2	4	2	$17 = f(2)$
		4	16	
2	2	8	$18 = f'(2)$	
		4		
	2	$12 = \frac{1}{2!} f''(2)$		

$$2 = \frac{1}{3!} f'''(2)$$

Hence $f(2) = 17,\ f'(2) = 18,\ f''(2) = 24$ and $f'''(2) = 12$.

Example 3: *Apply Descarte's rule of signs to discuss the nature of the roots of the equation*

(a) $x^{2n} - 1 = 0,$

(b) $x^4 - 3x^3 + 4x^2 + 3x - 2 = 0$

Solution: (a) Let $f_{2n}(x) = x^{2n} - 1$, then $f_{2n}(-x) = (-x)^{2n} - 1 = x^{2n} - 1$. Obviously there is one variation sign each in $f_{2n}(x)$ and $f_{2n}(-x)$. Therefore the equation has almost two real roots one opposite and the other negative. Clearly, roots are $x = \pm 1$.

(b) Let $f_4(x) = x^4 - 3x^3 + 4x^2 + 3x - 2$

$\therefore$ $f_4(-x) = x^4 + 3x^3 + 4x^2 - 3x - 2$

Obviously $f_4(x)$ has three variations of sign and $f_4(-x)$ only one variation of sign. Hence the equation may have all the four real roots and none imaginary roots.

Example 4: *Show that one of the roots of the equation* $e^x \log_e x = 1$ *lies in the interval* $[1, 2]$.

Solution: Let $f(x) = e^x \log_e x - 1$. Clearly, $f(1) = -\,ve$ and $f(2) = +\,ve$.

Hence $\exists$ at least one root (odd number) lies in the interval [1, 2].

Example 5: *Show that the equation* $x^5 - 5x + 2 = 0$ *has three real roots. Also find the interval in which they lie.*

Solution: Let $f_n(x) = x^5 - 5x + 2$

$\Rightarrow$ $f_n(-x) = -x^5 + 5x + 2$

Hence there are two variations of signs in $f_n(x)$ and one in $f_n(-x)$.

Hence there are atmost three real roots. Further, the equation is odd degree and its last term is positive.

Therefore, it possesses at least one negative root.

Positive or negative signs of $f_n(x)$ for some of the values of x are as follows:

x:	-2	-1	0	1	2
$f_n(x)$:	$-$	$+$	$+$	$-$	$+$

This shows that there are exactly three real roots and the intervals are $(-2,-1)$; $(0, 1)$; and $(1, 2)$.

Theorem 1: Position of Real Roots

If $f_n(x)=0$ be the given polynomial equation and $x_1, x_2, \ldots, x_k$ (say) are the successive real roots of $f'_n(x)=0$, then positive or negative sign of the values of the expressions $f_n(-\infty)$, $f_n(x_1), \ldots, f_n(x_k)$, $f_n(\infty)$ will determine the intervals in which the roots of $f_n(x)=0$ will lie. Whenever, there is a change of sign from $f_n(x_r)$ to $f_n(x_{r+1})$, the root lies in the interval $[x_r, x_{r+1}]$.

Example 6: *Separate the real roots of the equation $x^5-80x+6=0$*

Solution: Let $f_n(x)=x^5-80x+6$

$$\Rightarrow \quad f'_n(x)=5x^4-80=5(x-2)(x+2)(x^2+4)$$

Now $\quad f'_n(x)=0$ for $x=2,-2$.

$\because$ Signs of $f_n(x)$ at $x=-\infty, -2, 2, \infty$ are

x	$-\infty$	-2	2	∞
$f_n(x)$	$-$	$+$	$-$	$+$

This shows that there are three real roots of $f_n(x)=0$ which lie in the intervals $(-\infty,-2)$; $(-2,2)$ and $(2,\infty)$.

Example 7: *Find the range of values of k which all the roots of the following equation are real*

$$x^3-3x+k=0.$$

Solution: Let $f_n(x)=x^3-3x+k \Rightarrow f'_n(x)=3x^2-3$.

Now, $\quad f'_n(x)=0$ for $x=-1,1$

The values of $f_n(x)=0$ at $\quad x=-\infty,-1,1$, and ∞, are:

x:	$-\infty$	-1	1	∞
$f_n(x)$:	$-\infty$	$k+2$	$k-2$	$+\infty$

Now, all the roots of $f_n(x)=0$ are real if

$$k+2>0 \text{ and } k-2<0 \text{ i.e. if } -2<k<2$$

$\therefore$ Range of k is $-2<k<2$.

Theorem 2: Limits of The Roots of an Equation

Let $\qquad f_n(x)=0 \qquad \ldots(1)$

be a polynomial equation of degree n and let $a_1, a_2, \ldots, a_k$; $(k \le n)$ be the real roots of (1), then we define upper and lower limits of the roots as below:

Upper limit of Root: A number M is said to be upper limit (*or superior limit*) of the roots of the equation $f_n(x) = 0$, if

$$a_i \le M, \forall\, i = 1, 2, \ldots, k.$$

Lower limit of the Root: A number m is said to be lower limit (*or inferior limit*) of the roots of the equation $f_n(x) = 0$, if

$$a_i \ge m, \forall\, i = 1, 2, \ldots, k$$

Determination of Upper Limit of Positive Roots

(i) Method of grouping: If $f_n(x)$ is positive for all values of $x \ge M$, then M is the upper limit of positive roots.

Procedure: (i) The terms of $f_n(x) = 0$ are grouped in such a manner that there is always a positive sign between two groups.

(ii) Find a number M such that each group is positive $\forall\, x \ge M$.

(iii) The number M, so determined, is the upper limit of the positive roots of $f_n(x) = 0$.

Example 8: *Find the upper limit of positive roots of the following equation*

$$x^6 - 13x^5 - 14x^4 + x^2 - 6x - 20 = 0.$$

Solution: Let $f_n(x) = x^6 - 13x^5 - 14x^4 + x^2 - 6x - 20 = 0$

Arranging the terms of $f_n(x)$, we have

$$f_n(x) = x^4(x - 14)(x + 1)[(x - 3)^2 - 29]$$

Here both the groups are positive for $x \ge 14$.

Hence $\quad f_n(x) > 0$ for $x \ge 14$.

Therefore, 14 is the upper limit of roots.

(ii) Newton's Method: If $f_n(x)$ and all its derivative are positive for $x \ge \alpha$. Then α is the upper limit of positive roots of $f_n(x) = 0$.

Example 9: *Find the upper limit of the positive roots of the following equation*

$$x^3 - 3x^2 - 2x + 7 = 0$$

Solution: Let $f_n(x) = x^3 - 3x^2 - 2x + 7 \Rightarrow f_n'(x) = 3x^2 - 6x - 2$

$$\Rightarrow \quad f_n''(x) = 6x - 6 \quad \Rightarrow f_n'''(x) = 6$$

Obviously, $f_n(x)$, $f_n'(x)$, $f_n''(x)$, and $f_n'''(x)$ are all positive $x \ge 3$.

Therefore, upper limit of positive roots of is 3.

Determination of Lower Limit of Positive Roots:

If α is the upper limit of positive roots of $f_n(1/x) = 0$, then $(1/\alpha)$ is the lower limit of positive root of $f_n(x) = 0$.

Example 10: *Find the lower limit of the positive roots of following equation*

$$x^5 - 4x - 2 = 0$$

Solution: Let $f_n(x) = x^5 - 4x - 2$

$$\Rightarrow \quad f_n(1/x) = (1/x^5) - (4/x) - 2 = -(1/x^5)[2x^5 + 4x^4 - 1] = -(1/x^5)\, Q_n(x)$$

where
$$Q_n(x) = 2x^5 + 4x^4 - 1$$
$$Q_n'(x) = 10x^4 + 16x^3$$
$$Q_n''(x) = 40x^3 + 48x^2$$
$$Q_n'''(x) = 120x^2 + 96x$$
$$Q_n^{iv}(x) = 240x + 96$$

Obviously $Q_n(x)$ and its various derivatives are positive for $x > 1$.

Therefore, 1 is the upper limit of the roots of $f_n(1/x) = 0$. Hence the lower limit of the roots of $f_n(x) = 0$ is also 1.

Determination of Limits of Negative Roots

Let $f_n(x) = 0$.........(1) be a polynomial equation of degree n and let the negative roots of (1) lie in the interval $(-\alpha, -\beta)$; $\alpha > 0, \beta > 0$ where $\alpha > \beta$. Therefore, the positive roots of $f_n(-x) = 0$ would lie in the interval (β, α).

Thus α is the upper limit of the roots of $f_n(-x) = 0$.

Therefore, $(-\alpha)$ is the lower limit of the roots $f_n(x) = 0$.

Similarly, if β is the lower limit of the roots $f_n(-x) = 0$.

then $(-\beta)$ is the upper limit of the roots of $f_n(x) = 0$.

Example 11: *Find the range in which the roots of equation* $3x^5 - 15x^3 + 4x - 4 = 0$, *lie.*

Solution: Let $f_n(x) = 3x^5 - 15x^3 + 4x - 4$

$$= 3x^3(x^2 - 5) + 4(x - 1)$$

Here $\quad f_n(x) = 0$ for $x \geq 3$

$\therefore$ 3 is the upper limit of the roots $f_n(x) = 0$.

Further $f_n(-x) = 3(-x)^5 - 15(-x)^3 + 4(-x) - 4$

$$= -3x^5 + 15x^3 - 4x - 4$$
$$= -(3x^5 - 15x^3 + 4x + 4)$$
$$= -Q_n(x)$$

where $\quad Q_n(x) = 3x^5 - 15x^3 + 4x + 4 = 3x^3(x^2 - 5) + 4(x + 1)$

Here $\quad Q_n(x) > 0$, for $x \geq 3$.

Therefore, (-3) is the lower limit of $f_n(x) = 0$.

Hence the range of the roots of $f_n(x) = 0$ is $[-3, 3]$

Theorem 3: Sturm's Theorem

Sturm's Function: Let $f(x)$ be a given polynomial of degree n and let $f_1(x)$ denote its first order derivative. Divide $f(x)$ by $f_1(x)$ and let the remainder *with its sign changed* be denoted by $f_2(x)$. Similarly $f_3(x)$ is obtained as the remainder with its sign changed when $f_1(x)$ is divided by $f_2(x)$ and so on. The sign of the last remainder is also to be changed.

We thus obtain a sequence of functions

$$f(x), f_1(x), f_2(x), \ldots\ldots\ldots, f_n(x).$$

These functions are called *Sturm's Functions of Sturm's sequence.*

If $q_1, q_2, \ldots q_{n-1}$, are the successive quotients in the process of the obtaining Sturm's functions, we have the following relations.

$$f = q_1 f_1 - f_2$$

$$f_1 = q_2 f_2 - f_3$$

$$\ldots\ldots\ldots\ldots\ldots\ldots$$

$$\ldots\ldots\ldots\ldots\ldots\ldots$$

$$f_{n-2} = q_{n-1} f_{n-1} - f_n$$

Sturm's Theorem: *The number of real roots of the equation $f(x) = 0$ in an interval $[a, b]$ equals to the difference between the number of changes of the sign in the Sturm's sequence at $x = a$ and $x = b$, provided that $f(a) \neq 0, f(b) \neq 0$.*

Example 12: **(a)** *Find the number and position of the real roots of the equation*

$$f(x) = x^3 - 3x^2 - 4x + 13 = 0.$$

Solution: The Sturm's function are as given below:

$$f = x^3 - 3x^2 - 4x + 13$$

$$f_1 = 3x^2 - 6x - 4$$

$$f_2 = 14x - 35$$

$$f_3 = (7/2)$$

$[f(x)]$ is multiplied by 3 before division and f_1 is multiplied by 14 before dividing it by f_2].

Now the following table gives us the signs of Sturm's functions for different values of x:

x	$-\infty$	0	∞	1	2	3	1	-2	-3
f	$-$	+	+	+	+	+	+	+	$-$
f_1	+	$-$	+	$-$	$-$	+	+	+	+
f_2	$-$	$-$	+	$-$	$-$	+	$-$	$-$	$-$
f_3	+	+	+	+	+	+	+	+	+
No. of changes of sign	3	2	0	2	2	0	2	2	3

From the columns obtained by giving the value $-\infty, 0, \infty$ to x we see that difference between the number of changes of signs of signs between the value $Q-\infty$ and 0 is one while between the values 0 and ∞ is two. Hence the equation has one negative root and two positive roots. Further giving the values $\pm 1, \pm 2, \pm 3$ to x and applying the same principal we notice that the negative roots lies in $[-2,-3]$ and two positive roots lie in $[2, 3]$.

12.2.1 Method for the Finding the Roots (Zeros) of an Equation

We shall now discuss few methods which are applicable to both algebraic (with numerical coefficients) and transcendental equations. In finding the real roots of an equation, we first find an approximate value of the root of the given equation and then successively improve it to some desired degree of accuracy. The general technique is that we start with an initial approximate value, say x_0, and then find the better approximations successively $x_1, x_2, \ldots, x_n$ by repeating the same method. If the successive approximations at each step of a method approach the root more and more closely, we say that the method *converges*. **[U.P.T.U. 2007, 2008]**

12.2.2 Convergence

Let $x_0, x_1, x_2 \ldots$ be the value of a root ($\alpha = 2.5567$) of an equation at the zeroeth, first, second ... iterations. The actual value of the root being 2.5567. We calculated the value of this root by three different methods and the results were tabulated as given below.

Inspection of the above table reveals that the roots computed by Ist method do not converge to the root 2.5567. In method No. 2, the roots converge after sixth iteration while in method No. 3, the roots converge after fourth iteration. Obviously in method No. 3 the roots converge faster than second method. The fastness of Convergence of any method is represented by its **rate of convergence**. Let e be the error, then $e_i = \alpha - x_i = x_{i+1} - x_i$. When (e_{i+1} / e_i) is nearly constant, then the convergence is said to be linear while if (e_{i+1} / e_1^2) is nearly constant then the convergence is said to be quadratic *i.e.*, faster.

S.No. of Iteration	Root value	1st method	2nd method	3rd method
0	x_0	4	4	4
1	x_1	4.6	2.8527	2.8327
2	x_2	5.4	2.5693	2.56834
3	x_3	7.3	2.55798	2.55743
4	x_4	8.7	2.55687	2.55672
5	x_5	9.6	2.55676	
6	x_6	10.9	2.55671	

(A) Bisection Method (Bolzano Method) **[U.P.T.U. 2009]**

If a function $f(x)$ is continuous between a and b and $f(a)$ and $f(b)$ are the opposite signs then there exists at least one root between a and b. Let $f(x_0)$ be negative and $f(b)$ be positive so that the approximate value of the root between them is $x_0 = (a+b)/2$. If $f(x_0) = 0$, then it asserts that x_0 is the correct root of $f(x) = 0$. On the other hand, if $f(x_0) \neq 0$, then the root

a– – – • – – –b

either lies in between $\left(a, \frac{a+b}{2}\right)$ or $\left(\frac{a+b}{2}, b\right)$

depending on wether $f(x_0)$ is negative or positive. We again bisect the interval and repeat the process until the root is obtained to desired accuracy.

Example 12: **(b)** *To find a real root of the equation.*

$$f(x) = x^3 - x - 1 = 0$$

Solution: Here $f(1) = 1-1-1 = -1$, $f(2) = 8-2-1 = 5$; hence the root lies in between (1, 2) *i.e.,* the first approximation is $x_0 = (3/2)$, again $f(3/2) = (7/8)$ *i.e.,* positive hence the root is in between (1, 3/2); the second approximation being $x_1 = \frac{1+1.5}{2} = 1.25$.

Repeating this process, we get the successive approximations as

$$x_2 = \frac{1.25+1.5}{2} = 1.375,\; x_3 = 1.3125$$

$$x_4 = 1.34375 \text{ etc.}$$

12.2.3 Convergence of Bisection Method Convergence of Sequence

The sequence $\langle x_n \rangle$ of successive approximations of a root $x = \alpha$ of the equation $f(x) = 0$, is said to *converge to $x = \alpha$ with order $q \geq 1$*, if $|x_{n+1} - \alpha| \leq c\,|x_n - \alpha|\; q, n \geq 0$, where c is some constant greater than zero.

When $q = 1$ and $0 < c < 1$, then the convergence is said to be of *first order or linear* and constant c is called the *rate of linear convergence; convergence is rapid or slow according as 'c' is near* 0 *or* 1.

Further, if $|x_{n+1} - \alpha| = c.|x_n - \alpha|$, $n \geq 0, 0 < c < 1$, then the convergence is said to be **geometric**. Proceeding in this way and using principal of induction, *the condition for linear convergence can be simplified to the form*

$$|x_n - \alpha| \leq c^n |x_0 - \alpha|, n \geq 0, 0 < c < 1.$$

12.2.4 To Show that Bisection Method Always Converges

Let $[p_n, q_n]$ be the interval at the nth step of bisection, having a root of the equation $f(x) = 0$. Let x_n be the nth approximation of the root, then initially $p_1 = a$ and $q_1 = b \Rightarrow x_1$ = first approximation $= (p_1 + q_1)/2$. *i.e.,* $p_1 < x_1 < q_1$.

Now, either the root lies in $[a, x_1]$ or in $[x_1, b]$. Therefore either $[p_2, q_2] = [p_1, x_1]$ or $[p_2, q_2] = [x_1, q_1]$.

$\Rightarrow$ either $p_2 = p_1, q_2 = x_1$ or $p_2 = x_1, q_2 = q_1$

$\Rightarrow$ $p_1 \le p_2, q_2 \le q_1$

Further, we have $x_2 = (p_2 + q_2)/2$ so that $p_2 < x_2 < q_2$. Continuing in this way, we see that at the *n*th step $x_n = (p_n + q_n)/2$, $p_n < x_n < q_n$ and $p_1 \le p_2 \le ...... \le p_n$ and $q_1 \ge q_2 \ge ..... \ge q_n$.

Thus $\langle p_1, p_2, ..., p_n .... \rangle$ is a bounded non-decreasing sequence (bounded by b) and $\langle q_1, q_2, ..., q_n ...... \rangle$ is a bounded non-increasing sequence of number (bounded by a).

Hence both these sequences converge. Let $\lim_{n \to \infty} p_n = p$ and $\lim_{n \to \infty} q_n = q$. But the length of the interval is decreasing at every step, we see that

$$\lim_{n \to \infty} (q_n - p_n) = 0 \Rightarrow q = p$$

Also $\quad p_n < x_n < q_n \Rightarrow \lim p_n < \lim x_n < \lim q_n$

$$\Rightarrow \quad p \le \lim x_n \le q \Rightarrow \lim x_n = p = q \qquad ...(1)$$

Again as the root lies in the interval $[p_n, q_n]$, we have

$$f(p_n).f(q_n) < 0 \Rightarrow 0 \ge \lim_{n \to \infty} [f(p_n).f(q_n)]$$

$$\Rightarrow \quad 0 \ge f(p).f(q) \Rightarrow 0 \ge [f(p)]^2 \qquad ...(2)$$

But $[f(p)^2] \ge 0$, being square. So we get $f(p) = 0$

$\Rightarrow$ p is a root of the sequence $f(x) = 0$ ...(3)

Thus (1) and (2) imply that the sequence $\langle x_n \rangle$ converges necessarily to a root of the equation $f(x) = 0$.

But $|x_n - \alpha| \le (1/2)^n (b - a)$, hence the method shows a linear convergence with a rate $(1/2)$. So the method is not rapidly converging. But it is useful the sense that is converges surely.

Now we shall discuss few methods which are applicable to both algebraic (*constant coefficient*) and transcendental equations.

(B) Method for Finding the Initial Approximate Value of the Root

(i) Graphical Method: To solve the equation $f(x) = 0$, we draw the graph of the function $y = f(x)$ *w.r.t.* x and y-axis and then obtain x-co-ordinates of those points for which y-co-ordinations are zero. These x-co-ordinations will then determine the real roots of the equation $f(x) = 0$. In other words, the real roots may be interpreted as the x-co-ordinates of the points of intersection of the curve $y = f(x)$ with x-axis. In case, $f(x)$ involves difference of two functions etc, then we usually write $f(x) = 0$ as $f_1(x) = f_2(x)$ where $f_1(x)$ and $f_2(x)$ are both functions of x. To solve the above equation we draw the graphs of the two functions $y = f_1(x)$ and $y = f_2(x)$ on the same axes. The real roots of the given equation are the abscissae of these two curves, at these points $y_1 = y_2$ and so $f_1(x) = f_2(x)$.

(ii) Analytical Method: (*Solved via examples in the following pages*).

(iii) Regula Falsi Method: (*Method of false position*).

[Agra 2003, 2004, 2007; U.P.T.U. 2004]

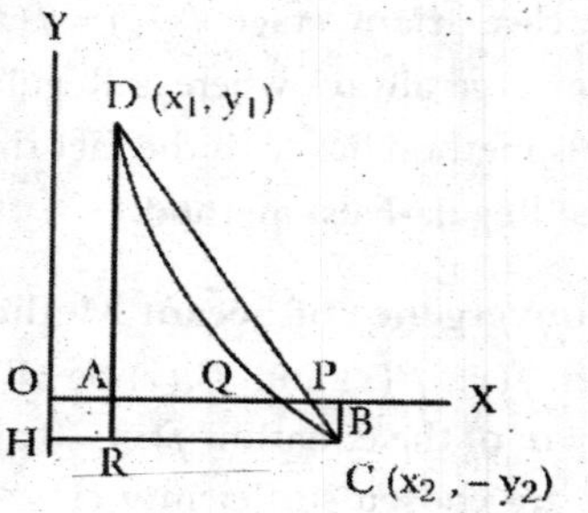

This is the most oldest method for finding the real root of a numerical equation $f(x) = 0$. To find the real root of the equation $f(x) = 0$, we consider a sufficiently small interval (x_1, x_2) in which the root lies. Since the root lies in the interval (x_1, x_2), the curve must cross the axis of x in between (x_1, x_2) and hence $y_1 = f(x_1)$, $y_2 = f(x_2)$ have opposite signs.

This method is based on the principal that any portion of a smooth curve is practically straight for a short distance and hence we may say that the x-co-ordinate of the point of intersection of the straight line joining (x_1, y_1), (x_2, y_2) and the axis of x gives an approximate value of the desired root. By the figure it is obvious that $x = OP$ is the approximate value of the desired root whereas $x = OQ$ is the actual value of the root. Now we shall derive a formula to compute the root.

We have $\quad OP = OA + AP = x_1 + AP$ ...(1)

The triangles DPA and DRC are similar, so we have

$$\frac{DA}{AP} = \frac{DR}{CR} \Rightarrow AP = \frac{CR}{DR} DA = \frac{(x - x_1)\, DA}{DA + AR} = \frac{(x_2 - x_1)|y_1|}{|y_1| + |y_2|}$$

$$\therefore \quad OP - OA = \frac{|x_2 - x_1|\,|y_1|}{|y_1| + |y_2|} \Rightarrow OP = x_1 + \frac{|x_2 - x_1|\,|y_1|}{|y_1| + |y_2|}$$

= Desired value of the root.

Let the desired value (which is approximate) be represented by $x^{(1)}$; then to find the better approximation, we evaluate $y^{(1)}$ by $y^{(1)} = f(x)^{(1)}$. Now either $y^{(1)}$ and y_1 or y_2 will be of opposite signs. In case $y^{(1)}$ and y_1 are of opposite signs then one root will lie the interval $(x_1, x^{(1)})$. Now again apply the method of false position to this interval to get second approximation. In case $y^{(1)}$ and y_2 are of opposite signs then second approximation is obtained by using the method of false position to the interval $(x^{(1)}, x_2)$.

Continuing this process we can obtain the root to the desired degree of accuracy.

(iv) The Secant Method: This method is quite similar to that of Regula-falsi method except for the condition $f(x_1) \cdot f(x_2) < 0$. Here the graph of the function $y = f(x)$ in the neighborhood of the root is approximated by a secant line (chords), further the interval at each iteration may not contain the root. Let initially the limits of interval be x_1 and x_2, then the first approximation is given by

$$x_3 = x_2 + \frac{(x_2 - x_1)\, f(x_2)}{f(x_1) - f(x_2)},$$

Again the formula for successive approximation in general from is

$$x_{n+1} = x_n + \frac{(x_n - x_{n-1}) \cdot f(x_n)}{f(x_{n-1}) - f(x_n)}, n \geq 1.$$

In case at any stage $f(x_n) = f(x_{n-1})$, this method will fail. Thus this method does not converge always whereas Regula-falsi method will always converge. Only advantage in this method lies with the fact that if it converges then it will converge more rapidly than the Regula-Falsi method.

Convergence of Secant Method

Let $f(x)$, $f'(x)$ and $f''(x)$ be all continuous functions in the neighborhood of the root $x = \alpha$ of the equation $f(x) = 0$ and let $f'(\alpha) \neq 0$. We will now show that if initially x_1 and x_2 are chosen sufficiently close to the root $x = \alpha$, then the sequence $\langle x_n \rangle$ converges to $x = \alpha$ and the order of convergence is 1.62 approximately.

Let $\quad x_n - \alpha = \varepsilon_n$, then ...(I')

$$x_{n+1} = \frac{x_n f(x_{n-1}) - x_{n-1} f(x_n)}{f(x_{n-1}) - f(x_n)}$$

$$\Rightarrow \quad \alpha + \varepsilon_{n+1} = \frac{(\alpha + \varepsilon_n) f(\alpha + \varepsilon_{n-1}) - (\alpha + \varepsilon_{n-1}) f(\alpha + \varepsilon_n)}{f(\alpha + \varepsilon_{n-1}) - f(\alpha + \varepsilon_n)}$$

$$= \alpha + \frac{\varepsilon_n (\alpha + \varepsilon_{n-1}) - \varepsilon_{n-1} f(\alpha + \varepsilon_n)}{f(\alpha + \varepsilon_{n-1}) - f(\alpha + \varepsilon_n)}$$

$$\left\{\varepsilon_n \left[f(\alpha) + \varepsilon_{n-1} f'(\alpha) + \frac{1}{2} \varepsilon^2_{n-1} f''(\alpha) \ldots \right] - \varepsilon_{n-1} \left[f'(\alpha) + \frac{1}{2} \varepsilon_n^2 f''(\alpha) + \ldots \right]\right\}$$

$$\Rightarrow \quad \varepsilon_{n+1} = [f(\alpha) + \varepsilon_{n-1} f'(\alpha) + \ldots] - [f(\alpha) + \varepsilon_n f'(\alpha) + \ldots]$$

$$= \frac{1}{2} \varepsilon_n \varepsilon_{n-1} \frac{f''(\alpha)}{f'(\alpha)} + 0(\varepsilon_n^2), \text{ as } f(\alpha) = 0, f'(\alpha) \neq 0$$

$M\varepsilon_n \cdot \varepsilon_{n-1}$, where $M = [f''(\alpha) / 2 f'(\alpha)]$. ...(I'')

Now we want to determine a number p.s.t. $\varepsilon_{n+1} = c\, \varepsilon_n^p$ satisfying (I'')

Again $\quad \varepsilon_{n+1} = c\, \varepsilon_n^p, \Rightarrow \varepsilon_n = c\, \varepsilon_{n-1}^p$ and hence $\varepsilon_{n-1} = c^{-1/p} \varepsilon_n^{(1/p)}$

whence (I'')

$$\Rightarrow \quad c\, \varepsilon_n^p = M \varepsilon_n c^{-1/p} \varepsilon^{p-1} \Rightarrow p = 1 + p^{-1} \Rightarrow p^2 - p - 1 = 0.$$

$$\therefore \quad p = (1 \pm \sqrt{5})/2 \quad \Rightarrow p = (1 + \sqrt{5})/2 = 1.62$$

(neglecting the negative value)

$\Rightarrow \quad \varepsilon_{n+1} \approx c\, \varepsilon_n^{1.62}$ *i.e.* $\langle x_n \rangle$ converges with order 1.62 app.

Example 13: *Find the root of the equation $xe^x = \cos x$ using the secant method correct to four decimal places.*

Solution: Let $f(x) = \cos x - xe^x = 0$ and let us consider the initial approximations as $x_0 = 0, x_1 = 1$. Then we have

$$f(x_0) = 1, f(x_1) = \cos 1 - e = -2.17798.$$

Now by Secant method, we have

$$x_2 = x_1 + \frac{x_1 - x_0}{f(x_0) - f(x_1)} f(x_1)$$

$$= 1 + \frac{1}{3.17798}(-2.7798) = 0.31467 \qquad \text{Now } f(x_2) = 0.51987$$

$$\Rightarrow \qquad x_3 = x_2 + \frac{x_2 - x_1}{f(x_1) - f(x_2)} f(x_2) = 0.44673, f(x_3) = 0.20354$$

$$\Rightarrow \qquad x_4 = x_3 + \frac{x_3 - x_2}{f(x_2) - f(x_3)} f(x_3) = 0.53171.$$

Then repeating this process, the successive approximations are given as $x_5 = 0.51690$, $x_6 = 0.51775$, $x_7 = 0.51776$ etc. This implies that the root is 0.5177 correct to 4 decimal places.

(v) Iteration Method: This method is used when we can find the value of α in terms of a function of x, *i.e.*, $x = f(x)$, from

$$F(x) = 0 \qquad \text{...(1)}$$

In this method, we first obtain the approximate value of the root, say x_0 of the given equation and then substitute it in $f(x)$ giving the second approximation as

$$x_1 = f(x_0) \qquad \text{...(2)}$$

Again putting $x = x_1$ in $f(x)$, we obtain the third approximation as $x_2 = f(x_1)$ ...(3)

Continuing in this manner, we can get

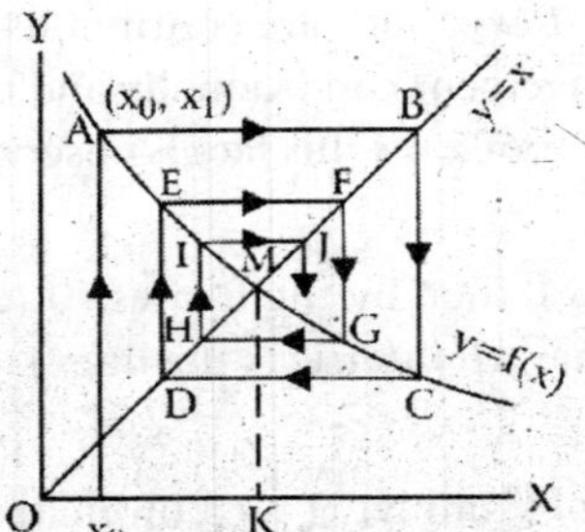

−1 < f′(x) < 0

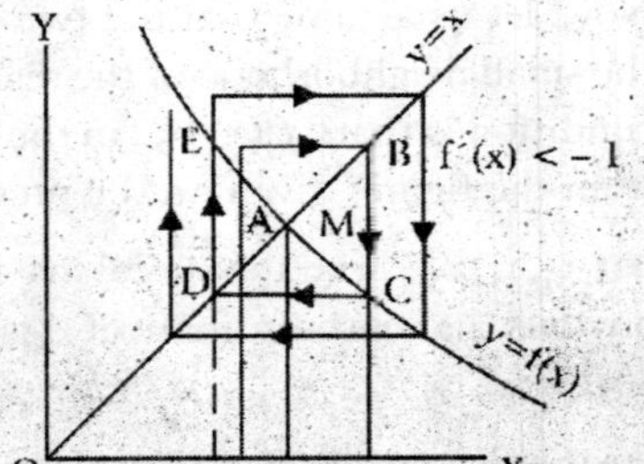

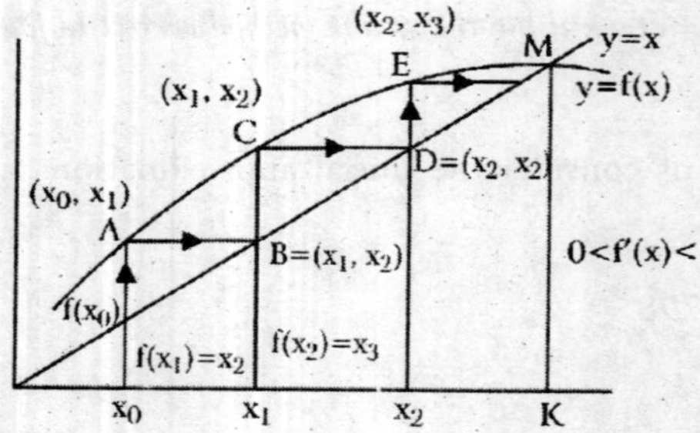

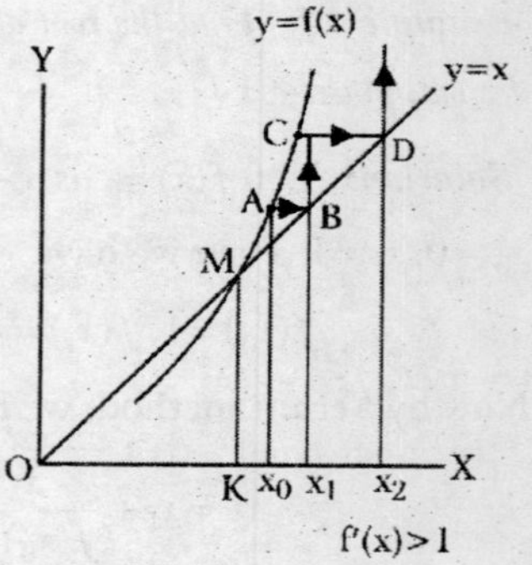

$$x_n = f(x_{n-1}) \quad \text{or} \quad x_{n+1} = f(x_n) \qquad \text{...(4)}$$

In this way, we obtain a sequence of successive approximation $x_2, x_3, \ldots,$ which may converge to the desired root.

Let us consider $F(x) = 0$, viz., $x^2 - x - 1 = 0$,

where $F(x) \equiv x^2 - x - 1$

This can be written in different forms as follows:

(i) $x = x - (x^2 - x - 1) = 2x - x^2 + 1.$ (ii) $x^2 = x + 1$ or $x = 1 + \frac{1}{x}$

(iii) $x^2 = x + 1$ or $x = \sqrt{(x+1)}$ (iv) $x = x^2 - 1$, etc.

***Theorem* 4**: *Let $x = a$ be a root of $f(x) = 0$ and let I be an interval containing the point $x = a$. Let $f(x)$ and $f'(x)$ be continuous in I where $f(x)$ is defined by the equation $x = f(x)$ which is equivalent to $F(x) = 0$.*

Then if $|f'(x)| < 1$ for all x in I, the sequence of approximations $x_0, x_1, x_2, \ldots, x_n$ defined by $x_{n+1} = f(x_n)$ converges to the root a, provided that the initial approximation x_0 is chosen in I.

Proof: In order to obtain the root of $F(x) = 0$, *i.e.*, $x = f(x)$ we are to find the abscissa of the point of intersection of the line $y = x$ with the curve $y = f(x)$ which may or may not intersect. In case the two curves do not intersect, then no real exists to the equation $F(x) = 0$.

Now, let us assume that the two curve intersect and $f(x), f'(x)$, both are continuous in the small neighborhood of the real root. This method is convergent conditionally and the condition is that $|f'(x)| < 1$ in the neighborhood of the real root $x = a$ this fact is observed from the figures given on the previous page.

Let $x_0, x_1, x_2, \ldots,$ be the successive iterations and $0 < f'(x) < 1$, then by the figures (*i*) it is obvious that y-co-ordinate of A is $f(x_0)$. The horizontal line AB intersects the line $y = x$ at $B \equiv (x_1, x_2)$.

Further x-co-ordinate of B is the same as the x-co-ordinate of C implying y-co-ordinate of $C = f(x_1) = x_2$, *i.e.*, co-ordinates of C are (x_1, x_2). Continuing in this manner, we can say that the sequence $x_1, x_2, \ldots, x_n,$ converges to $x = a$.

Further also as obvious by the figures on page 505 given above, sequence $x_1, x_2, \ldots, x_n$ converges to $x = a$ in figure (*ii*) whereas the sequence $x_1, x_2, \ldots, x_n$ diverges in figure (*iii*) and (*iv*) respectively.

Let $x = a$ be a root of the equation $x = f(x)$.

$$\therefore \quad a = f(a) \quad \ldots(1)$$

The first approximation satisfies

$$x_1 = f(x_0) \quad \ldots(2)$$

Subtracting (2) from (1), we have

$$a - x_1 = f(a) - f(x_0) \quad \ldots(3)$$

Again from the mean value theorem of differential calculus, the right hand side of (3)

$$f(a) - f(x_0) = (a - x_0)\, f'(a_0),\ x_0 < a_0 < a$$

Therefore from (3), we have

$$a - x_1 = (a - x_0)\, f'(a_0),\ x_0 < a_0 < a \quad \ldots(4)$$

Similarly, we have

$$(a - x_2) = (a - x_1)\, f'(a_1),\ x_1 < a_1 < a \quad \ldots(5)$$

$$(a - x_3) = (a - x_2)\, f'(a_2),\ x_2 < a_2 < a \quad \ldots(6)$$

$$\ldots \quad \ldots \quad \ldots \quad \ldots \quad \ldots \quad \ldots \quad \ldots \quad \ldots$$

and $$(a - x_{n+1}) = (a - x_n)\, f'(a_n),\ x_n < a_n < a \quad \ldots(7)$$

Multiplying together all these equations, member-wise and dividing the resulting equation throughout by the common factor

$$(a - x_1)(a - x_2) \ldots (a - x_n), \text{ we get}$$

$$(a - x_{n+1}) = (a - x_0)\, f'(a_0)\, f'(a_1) \ldots f'(a_n) \quad \ldots(8)$$

Let $|f'(a_i)| \le K < 1$, for all *i*. Then from (8), we have

$$|a - x_{n+1}| \le |a - x_0|\, K^{n+1} \quad \ldots(9)$$

Now when $n \to \infty$, the R.H.S. of (9) tends to zero and it implies that the sequence of approximations $x_0, x_1, \ldots$ converges to the root *a if* $K < 1$.

Acceleration of Convergence: Aitken's Δ^2- Method:

We have the relation

$$|a - x_{n+1}| = |f(a) - f(x_n)| \le K\,|a - x_n|,\ K < 1.$$

We observe from this relation the iteration method is linearly convergent.

This slow rate of convergence can be accelerated as given below.

Suppose the three successive approximations of the desired root $x = a$ the equation $x = f(x)$ are x_{i-1}, x_i, x_{i+1}. Then we know that

$$a - x_i \simeq K(a - x_{i-1}) \text{ and } a - x_{i+1} \simeq K(a - x_i).$$

Dividing, we get $\dfrac{a-x_i}{a-x_{i+1}} \simeq \dfrac{a-x_{i-1}}{a-x_i}$

or $$a \simeq x_{i+1} - \frac{(x_{i+1}-x_i)^2}{x_{i+1}-2x_i+x_{i-1}} \qquad ...(1)$$

Again in the sequence of successive approximations, we have

$$\Delta x_i = x_{i-1} - x_i \quad \text{and} \quad \Delta^2 x_i = \Delta(\Delta x_i).$$

Now $\Delta^2 x_{i-1} = \Delta(\Delta x_{i-1}) = \Delta(x_i - x_{i-1}) = \Delta x_i - \Delta x_{i-1}$

$$= (x_{i+1}-x_i) - (x_i - x_{i-1}) = x_{i+1} - 2x_i + x_{i-1}$$

Therefore (1) can be written as

$$a \simeq x_{i+1} - \frac{(\Delta x_i)^2}{\Delta^2 x_{i-1}}, \qquad ...(2)$$

which gives the new approximate value of the root in terms of three previously known successive approximations. Now we can be obtain the next approximation by putting the value of x_{i-1}, x_i, x_{i+1} in the formula

$$x_{i+2} = x_{i+1} - \frac{(\Delta x_i)^2}{\Delta^2 x_{i-1}},$$

This modified iterative scheme is known as **Aitken's Δ^2-method or Aitken's extrapolation method.**

(vi) Newton-Raphson Method: **[Agra 2003, 2004, 2008, 2009; U.P.T.U. 2004]**

Let x_0 be an approximate value of a root of the equation $f(x)=0$, and let x_0+h be the exact value of the corresponding root, where h is very small quantity.

Then $$f(x_0+h)=0 \qquad ...(1)$$

Since x_0+h is the root of the equation $f(x)=0$.

Expanding (1) by Taylor's theorem, we get

$$f(x_0+h) = f'(x_0) + hf'(x_0) + \frac{h^2}{2!}f''(x_0) + \ldots = 0$$

Since h is very small, neglecting second and higher order terms and taking the first approximation, we have

$$f(x_0) + hf'(x_0) = 0 \;\Rightarrow\; h = -\frac{f(x_0)}{f'(x_0)}, \text{ provided } f'(x_0) \neq 0.$$

$$\therefore \quad x_1 = x_0 + h = x_0 - \frac{f(x_0)}{f'(x_0)}. \qquad ...(2)$$

Relation (2) gives the improved value of the root over the previous one. Now substituting x_1 for x_0 and x_2 for x_1 in (2), we get

$$x_2 = x_1 - \frac{f(x_1)}{f'(x_1)} \qquad ...(3)$$

In general, we can get an approximation or the iteration formula

$$x_{n+1} = x_n - \frac{f(x_n)}{f'(x_n)} \qquad \ldots(4)$$

From this formula, we can calculate successive better values of the root. Formula (4) is known as ***Newton-Raphson Method.***

From above it is obvious that this method is applicable only when h is very small *i.e.*, when $f'(x)$ is large, in other words when the graph of the function near the root is nearly vertical.

If $f(x)$ is small in the neighbourhood of the root then the value of h is large and so by this method the computation of the root will be slow process or may fail altogether. Therefore, this method is not suitable in those cases where graph of $f(x)$ is nearly horizontal where it crosses the x-axis. This method can be used for both the algebraic and transcendental equations and also works for complex coefficients of an equation.

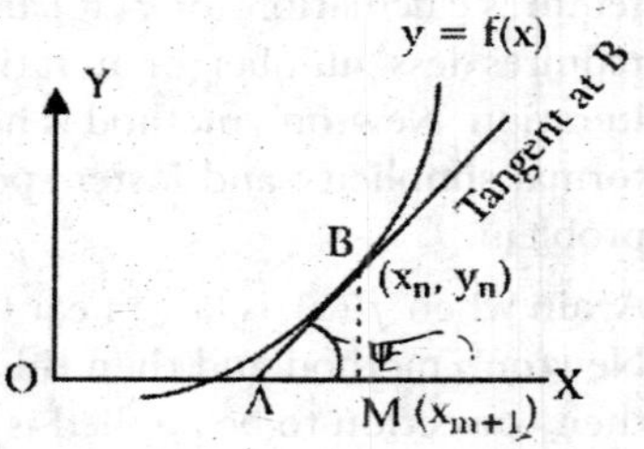

Geometrical interpretation of Newton-Raphson's Method.

Equation of the curve is $y = f(x)$

$\Rightarrow \qquad (dy/dx) = f'(x),$

$\Rightarrow$ Slope of the tangent at B $= f'(x_n)$. $\qquad \ldots(5)$

At the point A, $y = 0$ *i.e.* $f(x) = 0$ or in other words, the point A is closer to the desired root than B. Let the co-ordinates of the point be $(x_{n+1}, 0)$. Then we have

$$f'(x_n) = \frac{BM}{AM} = \frac{f(x_n)}{OM - OA} = \frac{f(x_n)}{x_n - x_{n+1}} \text{ implying } x_{n+1} - x_n = \frac{-f(x_n)}{f'(x_n)} \qquad \ldots(6)$$

Cases of Failure of Newton's Method **[U.P.T.U. 2009]**

As discuss earlier, Newton's method fails if $f(x_0)/f'(x_0)$ is not small enough. This happens, when the graph of the function $y = f(x)$ near the root is flat. Sometimes, the curve is not rather flat but a wrong choice of initial approximation leads to the failure of Newton's method.

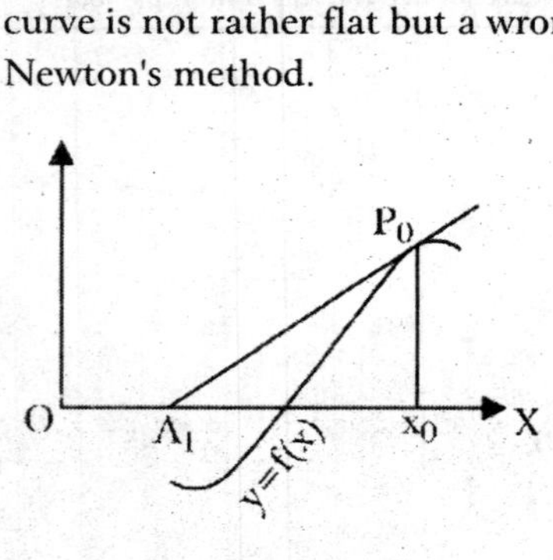

(i)

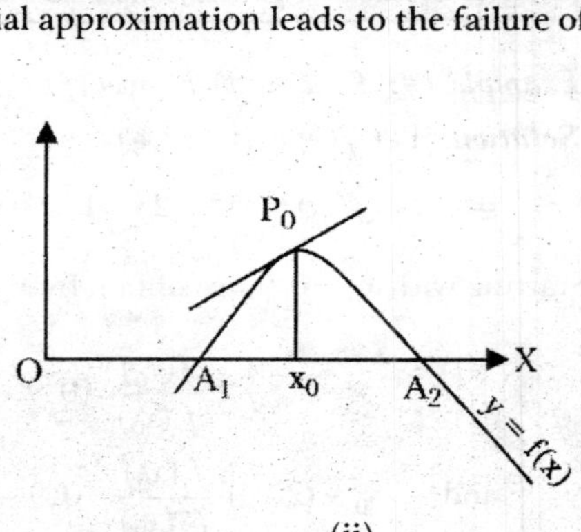

(ii)

The tangent at P_0 $(x = x_0)$ meets the x-axis at A_1 thus giving more worse approximation of the root. This situation can be avoided by choosing initial approximation more close to P_0.

Another case of failure is the situation where two roots of the equation are close together. In this case, the simplest initial approximation x_0 is also nearly parallel to x-axis.

Comparison of Newton's Method with the Regul-Falsi Method. **[Agra 2005]**

Newton's method is conditionally convergent while Regula-Falsi is surely convergent. Once Newton's method converges, it converges faster. In Regula-Falsi method we calculate only one more value of function at each step *i.e.* $f(x)^{(n)}$, while Newton's method requires calculations of $f(x_n)$ and $f'(x_n)$ at each step. Hence Newton's method generally requires less number of iterations but requires more time for computations at each iteration. Newton's method is not always the best method a given problem, but due to its formal simplicity and faster speed, people often use it as the first method to solve the problem.

Again when $f'(x)$ is large near the root, the correction to be applied is smaller in case of Newton's method and then this method is preferred while if $f'(x)$ is small near the root then correction to be applied is large and the curve becomes parallel to x-axis, so in this case Regula-falsi method must be applied.

Generalised Newton's Method for Multiple Roots: If α is a root of $f(x) = 0$ which is repeated m times, then we have

$$x_{n+1} = x_n - m\frac{f(x_n)}{f'(x_n)}$$

This is called *generalised Newton's formula.* It reduces to Newton-Rephson formula at $m = 1$.

Note 1: If α is a root of $f(x) = 0$ with multiplicity m, then it is also a root of $f'(x) = 0$ with multiplicity $m - 1$, or $f''(x) = 0$ with multiplicity $m - 2$ and so on. Hence, if initial approximation x_0 is sufficiently close to the root, then the expressions.

$$x_0 - m\frac{f(x_0)}{f'(x_0)},\ x_0 - (m-1)\frac{f'(x_0)}{f''(x_0)},\ x_0 - (m-2)\frac{f''(x_0)}{f'''(x_0)},\ldots$$

will have the same value.

Note 2: *Generalised Newton's formula has a second order of convergence for determining a multiple root.*

Example 14: *Find the double root of the equation* $x^3 - x^2 - x + 1 = 0$

Solution: Let $f(x) = x^3 - x^2 + 1 - x$

$$\Rightarrow \qquad f'(x) = 3x^2 - 2x - 1,\ f''(x) = 6x - 2$$

Starting with $x_0 = 0.9$, we obtain by $x_0 - m\dfrac{f(x_0)}{f'(x_0)}, m = 2$

$$x_0 - 2\frac{f(x_0)}{f'(x_0)} = 0.9 - \frac{2 \times 0.019}{-0.37} = 1.003$$

$$\text{and} \qquad x_0 - (2-1)\frac{f'(x_0)}{f''(x_0)} = 0.9 - \frac{(-0.37)}{3.4} = 1.009$$

Then the closeness of these values simply indicates that there is a double root at $x = 1$. Further taking $x_1 = 1.01$ for the next approximation

we have $x_1 - 2\dfrac{f(x_1)}{f'(x_1)} = 1.01 - \dfrac{2 \times .0002}{.0403} = 1.0001$

$x_1 - (2-1)\dfrac{f'(x_1)}{f''(x_1)} = 1.01 - \dfrac{0.0403}{4.06} = 1.0001$ which means that $\exists$ a double root at $x = 1.0001$ close to $x = 1$.

(C) Newton's Iterative Formula for Obtaining Square Root, Inverse Square Root etc.

(a) **Square Root:** The square root b is nothing but the root of the equation $x^2 - b = 0$, solvable by Newton's method. Here $f(x) = x^2 - b \Rightarrow f'(x) = 2x$.

Hence $x_{n+1} = x_n - \dfrac{f(x_n)}{f'(x_n)} \Rightarrow x_{n+1} = x_n - \dfrac{x_n^2 - b}{2x_n} \Rightarrow x_{n+1} = \dfrac{1}{2}\left(x_n + \dfrac{b}{x_n}\right)$ ...(7)

(b) **Inverse:**

The inverse of b is nothing but the root of the equation $\dfrac{1}{x} - b = 0$. Here

$$f(x) = x^{-1} - b \Rightarrow f'(x) = -x^{-2}$$

$\therefore$ $x_{n+1} = x_n - \dfrac{x_n^{-1} - b}{-x_n^{-2}} = x_n(2 - bx_n)$ ...(8)

(c) **Inverse Square Root:** The inverse square root of b is the root of the equation $\dfrac{1}{x^2} - b = 0$. Here $f(x) = x^{-2} - b,\ f'(x) = -2x^{-3}$.

$\Rightarrow$ $x_{n+1} = x_n - \dfrac{f(x_n)}{f'(x_n)} = x_n - \dfrac{x_n^{-2} - b}{-2x_n^{-3}} = \dfrac{1}{2}x_n(3 - bx_n^2)$ ...(9)

(d) **pth Root and Reciprocal pth Roots of a Given Number:** **[I.F.S. 2008]**

Let $f(x) = x^p - N$, where N is a given number.

Now $x_{n+1} = x_n - \dfrac{f(x_n)}{f'(x_n)} = x_n - \dfrac{(x_n^p - N)}{p\,x_n^{p-1}} = \dfrac{(p-1)x_n^p + N}{p\,x_n^{p-1}}$

(required iteration formula)

Again in order to obtain the reciprocal pth root of N, we assume

$$f(x) = N - x^{-p} \Rightarrow f'(x) = px^{-p-1}$$

so that $x_{i+1} = x_i - \dfrac{f(x_i)}{f'(x_i)} = x_i\dfrac{(p + 1 - N\,x_i^p)}{p}$

(required iteration formula)

Example 15: *Obtain the cube root of* 12. **[Manipal (B.E.) 2005, 2008]**

Solution: Let $f(x) = N - x^3, \Rightarrow f'(x) = -3x^2$.

$$\Rightarrow \qquad x_{n+1} = x_n - \frac{f(x_n)}{f'(x_n)} - = x_n - \frac{N - x_n^3}{-3x_n^2} = \frac{1}{3}\left[2x_n + \frac{N}{x_n^2}\right]$$

(General formula of cube root of N)

Now we shall obtain cube root of 12.

We have $(8)^{1/3} = 2$ and $(27)^{1/3} = 3$; talking $x_0 = 2.5$, we obtain

$$x_1 = \frac{1}{3}\left[2 \times 2.5 + \frac{12}{(2.5)^2}\right] = \frac{1}{3}\left[5 + \frac{48}{25}\right] = 2.3066$$

$$x_2 = \frac{1}{3}\left[2 \times 2.306 + \frac{12}{(2.3006)^2}\right] = 2.2901$$

Similarly, higher approximations can be obtained.

(D) Rate of Convergence of Newton's Method. **[I.A.S. (Agra) 2004; U.P.T.U. 2007]**

Let p be the exact value of the root and let ε_n be the small quantity by which x_n differs from b *i.e.* $x_n = b + \varepsilon_n$, implying $x_{n+1} = b + \varepsilon_{n+1}$, whence Newton-Rephson's method gives

$$x_{n+1} = x_n - \frac{f(x_n)}{f'(x_n)} \quad i.e.\ b + \varepsilon_{n+1} = b + \varepsilon_n - \frac{f(b+\varepsilon_n)}{f'(b+\varepsilon_n)}$$

$$\varepsilon_{n+1} = \varepsilon_n - \frac{f(b+\varepsilon_n)}{f'(b+\varepsilon_n)}\, b \qquad \text{...(10)}$$

By Taylor's theorem, we have

$$f(b+\varepsilon_n) = f(b) + \varepsilon_n f'(b) + \frac{\varepsilon_n^2}{2!} f''(b)$$

$$= \varepsilon_n f'(b) + \frac{\varepsilon_n^2}{2!} f''(b) + \ldots \qquad (\because\ f(b) = 0)$$

and $f'(b+\varepsilon_n) = f'(b) + \varepsilon_n f''(b) + \ldots$ Putting these values in (10), we obtain

$$\varepsilon_{n+1} = \varepsilon_n - \varepsilon_n \frac{f'(b) + \frac{\varepsilon_n}{2!} f''(b) + \ldots}{f'(b) + \varepsilon_n f''(b) + \ldots}$$

$$= \frac{\varepsilon_n^2 f''(b)}{2\,[f'(b) + \varepsilon_n f''(b)]} = \varepsilon_n^2 \frac{f''(b)}{2f'(b)} \frac{1}{\left[1 + \varepsilon_n \frac{f''(b)}{2f'(b)}\right]}$$

$$= \frac{\varepsilon_n^2}{2f'(b)} f''(b) \left\{1 + \varepsilon_n \frac{f''(b)}{f'(b)}\right\}^{-1} \approx \varepsilon_n^2 \frac{f''(b)}{2f'(b)} \qquad \text{...(11)}$$

From (11) it is obvious that the subsequent error is proportional to the square of the previous error and hence we may say that the convergence is quadratic.

(E) Muller's Method: Let x_{i-2}, x_{i-1}, x_i be three approximations of the root α of the equation $f(x) = 0$ and let y_{i-2}, y_{i-1}, y_i be the corresponding values of $f(x)$.

Now let us consider $\quad y = ax^2 + bx + c \quad$ ...(1)

The parabola, through the points (x_{i-2}, y_{i-2}), (x_{i-1}, y_{i-1}) and (x_i, y_i); so that we obtain

$$\left.\begin{aligned} y_{i-2} &= a x_{i-2}^2 + bx_{i-2} + c \\ y_{i-1} &= z x_{i-1}^2 + b x_{i-1} + c \\ \text{and } y_1 &= a x_i^2 + b x_i + c \end{aligned}\right\} \quad \text{...(2)}$$

Then eliminating *a, b, c* from (1) and (2) we readily obtain

$$\begin{vmatrix} y & x^2 & x & 1 \\ y_{i-2} & x_{i-2}^2 & x_{i-2} & 1 \\ y_{i-1} & x_{i-1}^2 & x_{i-1} & 1 \\ y_i & x_i^2 & x_i & 1 \end{vmatrix} = 0$$

$$\Rightarrow \quad y = \frac{(x - x_{i-1})(x - x_i)}{(x_{i-2} - x_{i-1})(x_{i-2} - x_i)} y_{i-2} + \frac{(x - x_{i-2})(x - x_i)}{(x_{i-1} - x_{i-2})(x_{i-1} - x_i)} y_{i-1}$$

$$+ \frac{(x - x_{i-2})(x - x_{i-1})}{(x_i - x_{i-2})(x_i - x_{i-1})} y_i \quad \text{...(3)}$$

Putting $\quad \lambda = \dfrac{x - x_i}{x_i - x_{i-1}}, \ \lambda_i = \dfrac{x_i - x_{i-1}}{x_{i-1} - x_{i-2}}$ and $\delta_i = \dfrac{x_i - x_{i-2}}{x_{i-1} - x_{i-2}}$

in (3), we get

$$y = \frac{(y_{i-2}\lambda_i + y_{i-1}\delta_i + y_i)\lambda_i \lambda^2}{\delta_i} + \frac{y_{i-2}\lambda_i^2 - y_{i-1}\delta_i^2 + y_i(\lambda_i + \delta_i)}{\delta_i}\lambda + y_i \quad \text{...(4)}$$

Also, we have $x = x_i + \lambda (x_i - x_{i-1})$ ...(5)

To obtain λ, we put $y = 0$ in (4)

$$\Rightarrow \quad (y_{i-2}\lambda_i - y_{i-1}\delta_i + y_i)\lambda_i \lambda^2 + \mu_i \lambda + \delta_i y_i = 0 \quad \text{...(6)}$$

where $\quad \mu_i = y_{i-2}\lambda_i^2 - y_{i-1}\delta_i^2 + y_i(\lambda_i + \delta_i)$

$$\Rightarrow \quad \frac{1}{\lambda} = \frac{-\mu_i \pm \sqrt{[\mu_i^2 - 4 y_i \delta_i \lambda_i (y_{i-2}\lambda_i - y_{i-1}\delta_i + y_i)]}}{2 y_i \delta_i} \quad \text{...(7)}$$

As x is close to x_i, λ must be small in magnitude and hence the sign should be chosen so as to make the numerator largest in magnitude. Then (5) gives a better approximation of the root.

The root of this quadratic is taken as the next approximation x_{i+1} to the root $f(x) = 0$. This method is iterative and converges for almost all initial approximations quadratically. When no better approximations are known, we usually take $x_{i-2} = -1$, $x_{i-1} = 0$ and $x_i = 1$.

Note: In this method, $y = f(x)$ is the approximated by a second degree curve passing through the points (x_{i-2}, y_{i-2}), (x_{i-1}, y_{i-1}) and (x_i, y_i) in the vicinity of the root.

Example 16: *Apply Muller's method to find the root of the equation* $\cos x = x e^x$, *which lies between* 0 *and* 1.

Solution: Let $y = \cos x - x e^x$

Now taking initial approximations as

$$x_{i-2} = -1,\ x_{i-1} = 0,\ x_i = 1;$$

we get $$y_{i-2} = \cos 1 + e^{-1},\ y_{i-1} = 1,\ y_i = \cos 1 - e$$

$$\lambda = x - 1,\ \lambda_i = 1,\ \delta_i = 2$$

and $$\mu_i = (\cos 1 + e^{-1}) - 4 + 3\,(\cos 1 - e)$$

Then (7) implies two values of $(1/\lambda)$ ...(1)

Choosing – ve sign as the numerator in (1) is largest in magnitude and obtain $\lambda = -0.5585$.

Further, the next approximation to the root is given by (5) as

$$x_{i+1} = x_i + \lambda\,(x_i - x_{i-1}) = 1 - 0.5585 = 0.4415.$$

Then, repeating the above process. we get

$$x_{i+2} = 0.5125,\ x_{i+3} = 0.5177,\ x_{i+4} = 0.5177$$

Thus the root is 0.518, correct to 3 places of decimal.

(vii) Lin-Bairstow's Method **[Agra 2002; M.K.U. (Tamilnadu) 2005, 2009]**

This method is widely used for determining the complex roots of the polynomial equation

$$f_n(x) = x^n + a_1 x^{n-1} + \ldots + a_{n-1} x + a_n = 0 \qquad \text{...(1)}$$

which is an algebraic equation with real coefficients.

All complex root appear in pairs $a \pm i\,b$. Each such pair corresponds to a quadratic factor.

$$\{x - (a + ib)\}\,\{x - (a - ib)\} = x^2 - 2\,a\,x + (a^2 + b^2)$$

i.e. of the form $x^2 + px + q$ with the real coefficients. If we divide $f_n(x)$ by $x^2 + px + q$. then we get

$$\frac{f_n(x)}{x^2 + xp + q} = f_{n-2}(x) + \frac{(R\,x + S)}{x^2 + xp + q}$$

where $f_{n-2}(x)$ is a polynomial of degree $n - 2$ and can be expressed in the form

$f_{n-2}(x) = x^{n-2} + b_1 x^{n-3} + \ldots + b_{n-2}$ and $R\,x + S$ is the remainder.

Thus we have $x^n + a_1 x^{n-1} + a_2 x^{n-2} + \ldots + a_{n-1} x + a_n$

$$\equiv (x^2 + x\,p + q)(x^{n-2} + b_1 x^{n-3} + \ldots + b_{n-2}) + R\,x + S \qquad \ldots(2)$$

When $x^2 + x\,p + q$ divides $f_n(x)$ completely, the remainder $R x + S = 0$ i.e. $R = 0 = S$. Obviously R and S both are functions of p, q. So our problem is to find $R(p, q) = 0$; $S(p, q) = 0$. ...(3)

These relation are not satisfied in general for arbitrary values of p and q.

Let $p + \Delta P$, $q + \Delta q$ be the actual values of the p and q which satisfy (3); then we have

$$R(p + \Delta p, q + \Delta q) = 0; S(p + \Delta p, q + \Delta q) = 0 \qquad \ldots(4)$$

Expanding (4) by Taylor's theorem and neglecting the second and higher order term of Δp and Δq, we get

$$\left.\begin{aligned} R(p, q) + \frac{\partial R}{\partial p}\Delta p + \frac{\Delta R}{\Delta q}\Delta q = 0 \\ S(p, q) + \frac{\partial S}{\partial p}\Delta p + \frac{\Delta S}{\Delta q}\Delta q = 0 \end{aligned}\right\} \qquad \ldots(5)$$

We regard this as a linear system of equations for Δp and Δq, and when the system has been solved, the procedure is repeated with the corrected values for p and q. In order to compute the coefficients $b_1, \ldots, b_{n-2}$, R and S, we use the following identity:

$$(x^n + a_1 x^{n-1} + a_2 x^{n-2} + \ldots + a_{n-1} x + a_n)$$

$$\equiv (x^2 + x\,p + q)(x^{n-2} + b_1 x^{n-3} + \ldots + b_{n-2}) + R\,x + S \qquad \ldots(6)$$

Comparing the coefficients of like powers of x in (6) we obtain

$$\left.\begin{aligned} b_1 + p = a_1 \\ b_2 + p\,b_1 + q = a_2 \\ \ldots \quad \ldots \quad \ldots \\ b_k + p\,b_{k-2} + q\,b_{k-2} = a_k \\ \ldots \quad \ldots \quad \ldots \quad \ldots \\ p\,b_{n-3} + q\,b_{n-4} + b_{n-2} = a_{n-2} \\ p\,b_{n-2} + q\,b_{n-3} + R = a_{n-1} \\ q\,b_{n-2} + S = a_n \end{aligned}\right\} \qquad \ldots(7)$$

The quantities $b_1, b_2, \ldots b_{n-2}$, R and S can be found recursively. Conveniently, we introduce two other quantities b_{n-1} and b_n and define;

$$b_k = a_k - p\,b_{k-1} - q\,b_{k-2} \qquad (k = 1, 2, \ldots, n) \qquad \ldots(8)$$

where $\quad b_{-1} = 0 = b_{-2}$

$\therefore \quad b_{n-1} = a_{n-1} - p\,b_{n-2} - q\,b_{n-3} = R$ [Using (7)]

and $\quad b_n = a_n - p\,b_{n-1} - q\,b_{n-2} = S - p\,b_{n-1}$ [Using (7)]

These give $R = b_{n-1}$ and $S = b_n + p\,b_{n-1}$ ...(9)

Putting the values in (5), we get

$$\left.\begin{aligned} & b_{n-1} + \frac{\partial b_{n-1}}{\partial p}\Delta p + \frac{\partial b_{n-1}}{\partial q}\Delta q = 0 \\ & \left(\frac{\partial b_n}{\partial p} + p\frac{\partial b_{n-1}}{\partial p} + b_{n-1}\right)\Delta p + \left(\frac{\partial b_n}{\partial q} + p\frac{\partial b_{n-1}}{\partial q}\right)\Delta q + b_n + pb_{n-1} = 0 \end{aligned}\right\} \quad ...(10)$$

Multiplying the first of equation (10) by p and subtracting it from second, we obtain

$$\left.\begin{aligned} & \frac{\partial b_{n-1}}{\partial p}\Delta p + \frac{\partial b_{n-1}}{\partial q}\Delta q + b_{n-1} = 0 \\ & \left(\frac{\partial b_n}{\partial p} + b_{n-1}\right)\Delta p + \frac{\partial b_n}{\partial q}\Delta q + b_n = 0 \end{aligned}\right\} \quad ...(10')$$

Differentiating (8) w.r.t. p and q, keeping in view that all a_k's are constants and all b_k's are functions of p and q, we get

$$\left.\begin{aligned} & \frac{\partial b_k}{\partial p} = -b_{k-1} - p\frac{\partial p_{k-1}}{\partial p} - q\frac{\partial b_{k-2}}{\partial p};\ \frac{\partial b_{-1}}{\partial p} = \frac{\partial b_{-2}}{\partial p} = 0 \\ & \leftarrow - - - - - - A - - - - - \rightarrow \quad \leftarrow - - - - B - - - \rightarrow \\ & \frac{\partial b_k}{\partial q} = -b_{k-2} - p\frac{\partial b_{k-1}}{\partial q} - q\frac{\partial b_{k-2}}{\partial q};0 = \frac{\partial b_{-1}}{\partial q} = \frac{\partial b_{-2}}{\partial q} \\ & \leftarrow - - - - - - C - - - - - \rightarrow \quad \leftarrow - - - - D - - - \rightarrow \end{aligned}\right\} \quad ...(11)$$

Equating (11) imply

$$\left.\begin{aligned} & 0 = \frac{\partial b_1}{\partial q} \\ & \frac{\partial b_1}{\partial p} = -1;\ \frac{\partial b_2}{\partial q} = -b_0 - p\frac{\partial b_1}{\partial q} = -1 \\ & \frac{\partial b_2}{\partial p} = -b_1 - p\frac{\partial b_1}{\partial p} = -b_1 + p.1 \\ \text{and}\quad & \frac{\partial b_3}{\partial q} = -b_1 - p\frac{\partial b_2}{\partial q} - q\frac{\partial b_1}{\partial q} = -b_1 + 1.p \end{aligned}\right\} \text{[Using (7)]} \quad ...(12)$$

From (12), it is obviously $\frac{\partial b_3}{\partial q} = \frac{\partial b_2}{\partial p}, \frac{\partial b_1}{\partial q} = 0, \frac{\partial b_2}{\partial q} = \frac{\partial b_1}{\partial p}$ ...(13)

Now, we shall prove $\frac{\partial}{\partial q}(b_{k+1}) = \frac{\partial}{\partial p}(b_k)$ [for all k]

by mathematical induction ...(14)

Let the result be true for $k = r$; then we have

$$\frac{\partial}{\partial q}(b_{r+1}) = \frac{\partial}{\partial p}(b_r) \quad ...(15)$$

$$\left.\begin{aligned} &\text{Now} \quad \frac{\partial}{\partial q} b_{r+2} = -b_r - p\frac{\partial}{\partial q} b_{r+1} - q\frac{\partial}{\partial p} b_r \\ &\text{and} \quad \frac{\partial}{\partial p} b_{r+1} = -b_r - p\frac{\partial b_r}{\partial p} - q\frac{\partial}{\partial p} b_{r-1} \end{aligned}\right\} \qquad \text{[Using (11)]}$$

which shows that

$$\frac{\partial}{\partial q} b_{r+2} = \frac{\partial}{\partial p} b_{r+1} \quad \left[\because \frac{\partial}{\partial q} b_{r+1} = \frac{\partial}{\partial p} b_r, \frac{\partial}{\partial q} b_r = \frac{\partial}{\partial p} b_{r-1}\right]$$

i.e. the result is true for $k = r + 1$. But the result was true for $r = 1, 2$ and hence it is true for $r = 2+1, 3+1, 4+1, \ldots$, *i.e.* the result holds for all values of r.

Now setting $\frac{\partial}{\partial q} b_{k+1} = \frac{\partial}{\partial p} b_k = -c_{k-1} \quad (k = 0, 1, 2, \ldots, n-1)$ ...(16)

in the two equations (*A*) and (*C*) of (11), we have

$$\left.\begin{aligned} c_{k-1} &= b_{k-1} - pc_{k-2} - qc_{k-3} \\ \text{and} \quad c_{k-2} &= b_{k-2} - pc_{k-3} - qc_{k-4} \end{aligned}\right\} \qquad \text{...(17)}$$

The two equations of (17) can be written as

$$c_k = b_k - pc_{k-1} - qc_{k-2} \qquad [k = 1, 2, \ldots, n-1] \qquad \text{...(18)}$$

where $c_{-1} = 0$, and $c_0 = \frac{\partial b_1}{\partial p} = 1$

Relation (18) is of the form (8) with the exception that (18) does not contain the term c_{-2} while equation (8) has the term of the type b_{-2}.

From equation (18), we can obtain c_k's from b_k's just as b_k's were obtained from a_k's.

To find the derivatives in terms of c_k's

From above, we have $R = b_{n-1}$ and $S = b_n + pb_{n-1}$

$$\therefore \quad \frac{\partial R}{\partial p} = \frac{\partial b_{n-1}}{\partial p} = -c_{n-2}, \frac{\partial R}{\partial q} = \frac{\partial b_{n-1}}{\partial q} = -c_{n-3}$$

$$\text{and} \quad \frac{\partial S}{\partial p} = \frac{\partial b_n}{\partial q} + b_{n-1} + p\frac{\partial b_{n-1}}{\partial p} = -c_{n-1} - pc_{n-2} + b_{n-1}$$

$$\frac{\partial S}{\partial q} = \frac{\partial b_n}{\partial q} + p\frac{\partial b_{n-1}}{\partial q} = -c_{n-2} - pc_{n-3}.$$

Substituting the above values in (5), we get $b_{n-1} - c_{n-2}\,\Delta p - c_{n-3}\,\Delta q = 0$

and $\quad b_n + pb_{n-1} + (-c_{n-1} + b_{n-1} - pc_{n-2})\,\Delta p + (-c_{n-2} - pc_{n-3})\,\Delta q = 0$

which can be written as

$$\left.\begin{aligned} c_{n-2}\,\Delta p + c_{n-3}\,\Delta q &= b_{n-1} \\ \text{and} \quad ^{*}(c_{n-1} - b_{n-1})\,\Delta p + c_{n-2}\,\Delta q &= b_n \end{aligned}\right\} \quad \ldots(19)$$

After finding c_k's and b_k's [from (8) and (18)], and then inserting these values in (19), we can obtain the approximate values of Δp and Δq. Let the approximate values of Δp and Δq be denoted by $\Delta\bar{p}$ and $\Delta\bar{q}$. Now talking the new values of $p+\Delta\bar{p}$ and $q+\Delta\bar{q}$, as the initial values and then repeating the process again, we can obtain better values of p and q.

The values of b's and c's are determined with the help of synthetic division as shown in the following table:

$1\ p\ q$	1	a_1	a_2	a_3	...	a_{n-2}	a_{n-1}	a_n
	–	$-p$	$-pb_1$	$-pb_2$	...	$-pb_{n-3}$	$-pb_{n-2}$	$-pb_{n-1}$
	–	–	$-q$	$-qb_1$	...	$-qb_{n-4}$	$-qb_{n-3}$	$-qb_{n-2}$
$1\ p\ q$	1	b_1	b_2	b_3	...	b_{n-2}	b_{n-1}	b_n
							$=R$	
	–	$-pc_0$	$-pc_1$	$-pc_2$	...	$-pc_{n-3}$		
	–	–	$-qc_0$	$-qc_1$	...	$-qc_{n-4}$		
	c_0	c_1	c_2	c_3	...	c_{n-2}		

Example 17: *Solve $x^4 - 5x^3 + 20x^2 - 40x + 60 = 0$, given that all the roots of $f(x) = 0$ are complex, by using Lin-Bairstow Method.* **[Agra 2003, 2004, 2008, 2009]**

Solution: Let us start with the values $p_0 = -4, q_0 = 8$, implying

1	−5	20	−40	60	
—	4	−4	32	0	4
—	—	−8	8	−64	−8
1	−1	8	$0\ (=b_{n-1})$	$-4\ (=b_n)$	
	4	12	48		4
		−8	−24		−8
1	$3\ (=c_{n-3})$	$12\ (=c_{n-2})$	$24\ (=c_{n-1})$		

Hence $c_{n-1} - b_{n-1} = 24 - 0 = 24$

Then, Corrections Δp_0 and Δq_0 are given by

$$\left.\begin{aligned} c_{n-2}\,\Delta p_0 + c_{n-3}\,\Delta q_0 = b_{n-1} &\quad i.e.\ 12\,\Delta p_0 + 3\,\Delta q_0 = 0 \\ (c_{n-1} - b_{n-1})\,\Delta p_0 + c_{n-2}\,\Delta q_0 = b_n &\quad i.e.\ 24\,\Delta p_0 + 12\,\Delta q_0 = -4 \end{aligned}\right\}$$

$^{*}b_n + pb_{n-1} + (-c_{n-1} + b_{n-1} - pc_{n-2})\,\Delta p + (-c_{n-2} - pc_{n-3})\,\Delta p = 0$

$\Rightarrow \quad b_n - (c_{n-1} - b_{n-1})\,p - c_{n-2}\,\Delta q + p\,(b_{n-1} - c_{n-2}\,\Delta p - c_{n-3})\,\Delta q = 0$

$\Rightarrow \quad b_n - (c_{n-1} - b_{n-1})\,\Delta p - c_{n-2}\,\Delta q = 0 \quad [\because\ b_{n-1} - c_{n-2}\,\Delta p - c_{n-3}\,\Delta q = 0]$

Δp and Δq are the approximate values. Since we have neglected higher powers of Δp and Δq in (5).

Solving these, we get $\Delta p_0 = 0.1667, \Delta q_0 = -0.6667$

Now, we have $p_1 = p_0 + \Delta p_0 = -3.8333$ and $q_1 = q_0 + \Delta q_0 = 7.3333$

Then repeating the same process *i.e.* dividing $f(x)$ by

$x^2 - 3.8333\,x + 7.3333$, we readily get

1	– 5	20	– 40	60	
	3.8333	– 4.4723	31.4116	– .125	3.8333
		– 7.3333	– 8.5558	– 60.092	–7.3333
1	– 1.1667	8.1944	– .0326 $(= b_{n-1})$	– .217 $(= b_n)$	
	3.8333	10.2219	42.4845		3.8333
		– 7.3333	– 19.555		– 7.3333

$1 \quad 2.6666\,(= c_{n-3})\; 11.083\,(= c_{n-2})\; 22.8969\,(= c_{n-1})$

$\Rightarrow \quad c_{n-1} - b_{n-1} = 22.8969 + .0326 = 22.9295$

Then corrections Δp_1 and Δq_1 are given by

$$11.083\,\Delta p_1 + 2.6666\,\Delta q_1 = -0.0326$$

$$22.9295\,\Delta p_1 + 11.083\,\Delta q_1 = -0.217$$

Solving these we get $\Delta p_1 = 0.0033$ and $\Delta q_1 = -0.0269$

$\Rightarrow \quad p_2 = p_1 + \Delta p_1 = -3.83,\; q_2 + \Delta q_1 = 7.3064$

Hence one of the quadratic factor of $f(x)$ is

$$x^2 - 3.83\,x + 7.3064 \qquad \text{...(1)}$$

Let $a \pm i\,b$ be its roots, then $2\,a = 3.83,\; a^2 + b^2 = 7.3064$

$\Rightarrow \quad a = 1.9149$ and $b = 1.9077$

Hence a pair of roots is $1.9149 \pm 1.9077\,i$.

To obtain the remaining two roots of $f(x) = 0$, let us divide $f(x)$ by (1) implying:

1	– 5	20	– 40	60	
	3.83	– 4.4811	31.4539		3.83
		– 7.3064	8.5485	– 60.0038	– 7.3064
1	– 1.17	8.2125	0.0024	– 0.0038	
			≈ 0	≈ 0	

* The sign ≥ indicates "much greater than".

Hence the other quadratic factor is $x^2 - 1.17x + 8.2125$

Let $c \pm i\,d$ be its roots, then $2d = 1.17, c^2 + d^2 = 8.2125$.

$\Rightarrow \quad c = 0.585$ and $d = 2.8054$.

Then the pair of the roots is $0.585 \pm 2.8054\,i$.

(viii) Graeffe's root squaring Method: The method is applicable to polynomial equations only and sometimes it gives all the roots of the polynomial equation. The advantage of this method is that it does not require any prior information of the roots such as approximation value of the roots etc., as in the case of *Newton's Raphson Method*. For the sake of simplicity, we shall discuss this method when all the roots of the polynomial equation are real and distinct.

$$a_0 x^n + a_1 x^{n-1} + a_2 x^{n-2} + \ldots + a_{n-1} x + a_n = 0.$$

This can be rewritten as

$$x^n + (a_1/a_0)\, x^{n-1} + (a_2/a_0)\, x^{n-2} + \ldots + (a_{n-1}/a_0)\, x + (a_n/a_0) = 0$$

or as $\quad x^n + b_1 x^{n-1} + b_2 x^{n-2} + \ldots + b_{n-1} x + b_n = 0$

where $\quad b_i = (a_i/a_0) \ [i = 1, 2, \ldots, n]$ ...(1)

Now collecting all even terms on one side and all odd terms on the other side, than square we get

$$(x^n + b_2 x^{n-2} + \ldots + \ldots)^2 = (b_1 x^{n-1} + b_3 x^{n-3} + \ldots)^2$$

Putting $x^2 = y$, we get

$$y^n + c_1 y^{n-1} + c_2 y^{n-2} \ldots + c_n = 0 \qquad \ldots(2)$$

where
$$\left.\begin{aligned} c_1 &= -b_1^2 + 2b_2 \\ c_2 &= b_2^2 - 2b_1 b_3 + 2b_4 \\ c_3 &= -b_3^2 + 2b_2 b_4 - 2b_1 b_5 + 2b_6 \\ &\cdots\cdots\cdots\cdots \\ c_n &= (-1)^n b_n^2 \end{aligned}\right\} \qquad \ldots(3)$$

or in other words, $(-1)^r c_r = b_r^2 - 2b_{r-1} b_{r+1} + 2b_{r-2} b_{r+2} - \ldots$ ...(4)

$[r = 1, 2, \ldots, n]$

Roots of the equation (2) are the squares of the roots of the equation (1).

Let us now assume that after m squaring, the new transformed equation is

$$z^n + \lambda_1 z^{n-1} + \ldots + \lambda_n = 0$$

with the roots $q_1, q_2, \ldots, q_n$ while the original equation has roots $p_1, p_2, \ldots, p_n$. Then $q_i = p_i^{2m}$ $(i = 1, 2, 3, \ldots n)$. Also if the magnitude to the roots

$$|p_1| > |p_2| > \ldots > |p_n|, \text{ then}$$

$$|q_1|^* \geq |q_2| \geq |q_3| \ldots \geq |q_n|.$$

---

* If there does not exist a solution like $x = d$ and $f(x)$ is small in a small neighbourhood of the point $x = d$ then further modification is needed

Hence $\quad \dfrac{|q_2|}{|q_1|} = \dfrac{q_2}{q_1}$ etc. can be neglected in comparison with unity.

Further also q_i is an even power of p_i so q_i is always positive.

Again we know that, if the roots of the equation

$x^n + a_1 x^{n-1} + a_2 x^{n-2} + \ldots + a_{n-1} x + a_n = 0$ are $\alpha_1, \alpha_2, \ldots, \alpha_n$, then from theory of equations we know that

$$\sum \alpha_1 = -a_1 = (-1)\, a_1$$
$$\sum \alpha_1 \alpha_2 = (-1)^2\, a_2$$
$$\sum \alpha_1 \alpha_2 \alpha_3 = (-1)^3\, a_3$$
$$\ldots\ldots\ldots\ldots\ldots\ldots$$
$$\alpha_1 \alpha_2 \alpha_3 \ldots \alpha_n = (-1)^n\, a_n$$

So from (5), we have

$$\left.\begin{aligned} &\sum q_1 = q_1 + q_2 \ldots + q_n = (-1)^1 \lambda_1 \\ &\sum q_1 q_2 = q_1 q_2 + q_2 q_3 + \ldots = (-1)^2 \lambda_2 \\ &\sum q_1 q_2 q_3 = q_1 q_2 q_3 + q_1 q_2 q_4 + \ldots = (-1)^3 \lambda_3 \\ &\ldots\ldots\ldots\ldots\ldots\ldots\ldots\ldots\ldots\ldots \\ &q_1 q_2 q_3 \ldots q_n = (-1)^n \lambda_n \end{aligned}\right\}$$

or $\quad \lambda_1 = -(q_1 + q_2 + \ldots + q_n) = (-1)^1 q_1 \left(1 + \dfrac{q_2}{q_1} + \ldots + \dfrac{q_n}{q_1}\right)$

$$\lambda_2 = (-1)^2\, (q_1 q_2 + q_1 q_3 + q_3 q_4 + \ldots) = (-1)^2\, q_1 q_2 \left(1 + \frac{q_3}{q_1} + \ldots\right)$$

$$\lambda_3 = (-1)^3\, (q_1 q_2 q_3 + q_1 q_2 q_4 + \ldots) = (-1)^3\, q_1 q_2 q_3 \left(1 + \frac{q_4}{q_3} + \ldots\right)$$

$$\ldots \quad \ldots \quad \ldots \quad \ldots \quad \ldots \quad \ldots \quad \ldots \quad \ldots \quad \ldots \quad \ldots$$

$$\lambda_n = (-1)^n\, q_1 q_2 \ldots q_n.$$

But the quantities (q_2 / q_1) etc, are negligible as compared to unity, so we get

$$\left.\begin{aligned} &\lambda_1 \approx -q_1 \\ &\lambda_2 \approx q_1 q_2 \\ &\lambda_3 \approx -q_1 q_2 q_3 \\ &\ldots \quad \ldots \quad \ldots \quad \ldots \quad \ldots \\ &\lambda_n = (-1)^n\, q_1 q_2 \ldots q_n \\ \text{But} \quad &q_i = p_i^{2m} \Rightarrow p_i = (\sqrt{q_i})^m \end{aligned}\right\} \text{using (6)}$$

Dividing each equation by its proceeding equation, we get

$$\left.\begin{aligned} q_1 &= -\lambda_1 \\ q_2 &= -\lambda_2/\lambda_1 \\ q_3 &= -\lambda_3/\lambda_2 \\ \ldots & \;\ldots\;\ldots\;\ldots \\ q_n &= -\lambda_n/\lambda_{n-1} \end{aligned}\right\}$$

i.e., p_i is obtained by m successive square-root extractions of q_i, the sign of p_i is to determined by substituting p_i into the equation.

> **Note:** *Double root.* If the magnitude of λ_i is half the square of the magnitude of the corresponding coefficient in the previous equation after a few squarings, then it shows that q_i is a double root and could be calculated as follows:

$$p_k = \frac{\lambda_k}{\lambda_{k-1}} \quad \text{and} \quad p_{k+1} = -\frac{\lambda_{k+1}}{\lambda_k}$$

$$\Rightarrow \quad p_k\, p_{k+1} \approx p_k^2 \approx \left|\frac{\lambda_{k+1}}{\lambda_{k-1}}\right| \Rightarrow q_k^{2m} = p_k^2 = \left|\frac{\lambda_{k+1}}{\lambda_{k-1}}\right|$$

This gives the magnitude of the double root and then we can get its sign easily.

Complex Roots: If p_k, p_{k+1} from a complex pair $\rho_\kappa e^{\pm i\phi_k}$ then the coeff. of x^{n-k} in successive squarings would fluctuate both in magnitude and sign by the amount $2\rho_k^m \cos m\phi_k$. For sufficiently large value of m; c_k and ϕ_k can be obtained by

$$\rho_k^{2(2^m)} = \left|\frac{\lambda_{k+1}}{\lambda_{k-1}}\right|, 2\,p_k^m \cos m\,\phi_k = \frac{\lambda_{k+1}}{\lambda_{k-1}}.$$

If equation (1) has only one complex root, say $e_k\, e^{\pm i\phi_k} = \xi + i\eta$. This determines complex root.

Example 18: *Find all roots of the equation $x^3 - 2x^2 - 5x + 6 = 0$ by Graeffe's Method, squaring thrice.*

Solution: Let $f(x) = x^3 - 2x^2 - 5x + 6 = 0$ ...(1)

$$+ \quad - \quad - \quad +$$

By Descartes rule of signs, there are two changes of two sign. Hence (1) has two positive roots. Also $f(-x) = -x^3 - 2x^2 + 5x + 6$.

$$- \quad - \quad + \quad +$$

i.e., change in sign *i.e.* there is only one negative root.

Further, rewriting (1) as $x^3 - 5x = 2x^2 - 6$

and squaring, $y(y-5)^2 = (2y-6)^2$ where $y = x^2$

$$\Rightarrow \quad y(y^2 + 49) = 14y^2 + 36 \qquad \text{...(2)}$$

Squaring again and putting $y^2 = z$, we obtain

$$z(z+49)^2 = (14z+36)^2 \text{ or } z(z^2 + 1393) = 98z^2 + 1296 \qquad \text{...(3)}$$

Squaring once again and putting $z^2 = u$, we get

$$u(u+1393)^2 = (98u+1296)^2$$

or $$u^3 - 6818u^2 + 1686433u - 1679616 = 0 \quad ...(4)$$

Let the roots of (4) be u_1, u_2, u_3, then $u_1 = 6818$,

$$u_1 u_2 = 1686433 \Rightarrow u_2 = 247.3501.$$

and $$u_1 u_2 u_3 = 1679616 \Rightarrow u_3 = \frac{1679616}{1686433}$$

If p_1, p_2, p_3 be the roots of (1) then we have

$$|p_1| = (u_1)^{1/8} = 3.014443 \approx 3, \; |p_2| = (u_2)^{1/8} = 1.991425 \approx 2$$

$$|p_3| = (u_3)^{1/8} = 0.999499 \approx 1$$

The sign of a root is found by substituting the root in $f(x) = 0$. We find $f(3) = 0$, $f(-2) = 0$, $f(1) = 0$. Hence the roots are $3, -2, 1$.

Example 19: *Apply Graeffe's Method to find al the roots of the equation* $x^4 - 3x + 1 = 0$.

Solution: We have $f(x) = x^4 - 3x + 1 = 0 \quad ...(1)$

$\Rightarrow$ there exist two changes in sign so (1) has two positive real roots and no negative real root. The remaining two roots are complex.

Now rewriting (1) as $x^4 + 1 = 3x$,

and squaring, we get $(y^2+1)^2 = 9y$ where $y = x^2$.

Again squaring and putting $y^2 = z$, we obtain

$$(z+1)^4 = 81z \text{ or, } z^4 + 4z^3 + 6z^2 - 77z + 1 = 0 \quad ...(2)$$

$$z^4 + 6z^2 + 1 = -z(4z^2 - 77)$$

Squaring once again and putting $z^2 = u$, we get

$$(u^2 + 6u + 1)^2 = u(4u - 77)^2$$

$$\Rightarrow \quad u^4 - 4u^3 + 654u^2 - 5917u + 1 = 0 \quad ...(3)$$

If p_1, p_2, p_3, p_4 be the roots of (1), then the roots of (3) are $p_1^8, p_2^8, p_3^8, p_4^8$.

Thus (3)

$$\Rightarrow \left.\begin{aligned} p_1^8 &= 4 \\ p_2^8 &= \frac{654}{4} = 163.5 \\ p_3^8 &= \frac{5917}{654} = 9.0474 \\ p_4^8 &= \frac{1}{5917} = 0.00017 \end{aligned}\right\} \Rightarrow \left.\begin{aligned} p_1 &= 1.1892 \\ p_2 &= 1.891 \\ p_3 &= 1.3169 \\ p_4 &= 0.3379 \end{aligned}\right]$$

From (2) and (3), we see that the magnitudes of the coefficients c_1 and c_4 have become constant, so p_1 and p_4 are the real roots whereas p_2 and p_3 are a pair of complex roots.

Thus real roots $p_1 = 1.1892$ and $p_4 = 0.3379$

Now let us find the complex roots $\rho_2 \, e^{\pm i\phi_2} = \xi + i\eta$.

From (3), its magnitude is given by

$$\rho_2^{2\,(2^3)} \approx \frac{\lambda_{2+1}}{\lambda_{2-1}} \quad \text{or} \quad \rho_2^{16} \approx \frac{5917}{4} \approx 1479.25 \quad \Rightarrow \rho_2 = 1.5781.$$

Also, $\quad p_1 + 2\,\xi + p_4 = 0 \Rightarrow \xi = -\frac{1}{2}(p_1 + p_4) = -0.7636$

and $\quad \eta = \sqrt{(\rho_2^2 - \xi^2)} = 1.381$

Thus the complex roots are $-0.7636 \pm 1.381\,i$.

12.3 Nearly Equal Roots

We know that Newton's Method is applicable only when $f(x) \neq 0$ in the neighbourhood of the actual root $x = b$ *i.e.* in the interval $(b - h, b + h)$. But in practice the above restriction may not be satisfied and further, the quantity h which satisfies this may be very small. This situation arises when the roots are very close to each other. To avoid this difficulty, we proceed as follows:

By Rolle's Theorem, we know that $f'(x) = 0$ vanishes at least one time between two roots of $f(x) = 0$ and hence we can choose h sufficiently small to satisfy the interval $(b - h, b + h)$ in case of nearly equal roots. When two roots are equal, say $x = b$, then $f(x)$ and $f'(x)$ both vanish at $x = b$. Hence while carrying Newton's method if x_i is very nearly the roots of $f(x)$ and $f'(x)$ *i.e.* $f(x_j)$ and $f'(x_j)$ both are very small, then we shall proceed to obtain two new starting values for the two nearly equal roots. In order to obtain these two values for the two nearly equal roots. In order to obtain these two values we shall first apply Newton's method to the equation $f'(x) = 0$ *i.e.*, we use iteration formula

$$x_{j+1} = x_j - \frac{f'(x_j)}{f''(x_j)} \qquad \text{...(1)}$$

*Let $x = d$ be the solution obtained by (1), then applying Taylor's Theorem, we get

$$f(x) = (d + \overline{x - d})$$

$$= f(d) + (x - d)\, f'(d) + \frac{(x-d)^2}{2\,!} f''(d) + \ldots$$

$$\Rightarrow \qquad f(x) = f(d) + \frac{1}{2\,!}(x - d)^2 f''(d) + \ldots \qquad [\because\ f'(d) = 0]$$

Leaving cube and higher powers of $(x - d)$, we get

$$f(x) = f(d) + \frac{(x-d)^2}{2\,!} f''(d) \qquad \text{...(2)}$$

Hence the zeroes of $f(x)$ near $x = d$ are approximately given by

$$f(x) = 0 \Rightarrow f(d) + \frac{1}{2!}(x-d)^2 f''(d) = 0$$

$$\Rightarrow \quad x = d \pm \sqrt{\{-2 f(d) / f''(d)\}}. \quad ...(3)$$

Now assuming these values as the starting values, we can find the two close roots by Newton's method. [See example 19]

12.4 Rate of Convergence of Newton's Method When there Exist Double Roots

Let b be the exact value of the root and x_n differs from b by the small quantity ε_n. Then

$x_n = b + \varepsilon_n \Rightarrow x_{n+1} = b + \varepsilon_{n+1}$ By Newton-Raphson Method we have $x_{n+1} - x_n - \dfrac{f(x_n)}{f'(x_n)}$

$$\text{or} \quad b + \varepsilon_{n+1} = b + \varepsilon_n - \frac{f(b+\varepsilon_n)}{f'(b+\varepsilon_n)}$$

$$\text{or} \quad \varepsilon_{n+1} = \varepsilon_n - \frac{f(b+\varepsilon_n)}{f'(b+\varepsilon_n)}$$

$$= \varepsilon_n - \frac{f(b) + \varepsilon_n f'(b) + \frac{\varepsilon_n^2}{2!} f''(b) + \frac{\varepsilon_n^3}{3!} f'''(b) + \dots}{f'(b) + \varepsilon_n f''(b) + \frac{\varepsilon_n^2}{2!} f'''(b) + \frac{\varepsilon_n^3}{3!} f^{(iv)}(b) + \dots}$$

(By Tailor's Theorem)

$$= \varepsilon_n - \frac{\frac{\varepsilon_n^2}{2!} f''(b) + \frac{\varepsilon_n^3}{3!} f'''(b) + \dots}{\varepsilon_n f''(b) + \frac{\varepsilon_n^2}{2!} f'''(b) + \dots}$$

[$\because$ $f(b) = 0 = f'(b)$ as there exist double roots]

$$= \varepsilon_n - \varepsilon_n \frac{\frac{1}{2} f''(b) + \frac{\varepsilon_n}{6} f'''(b)}{f''(b) + \frac{\varepsilon_n}{2} f'''(b)} \quad \text{[leaving higher powers]}$$

$$= \varepsilon_n \frac{\frac{1}{2} f''(b) + \frac{\varepsilon_n}{3} f'''(b)}{f''(b) + \frac{\varepsilon_n}{2} f'''(b)}$$

$$= \varepsilon_n \cdot \frac{1}{2} \frac{f''(b)}{f''(b)} = \frac{1}{2} \varepsilon_n = \frac{2-1}{2} \varepsilon_n,$$

which shows that the convergence is linear. Proceeding in the same manner we can prove that if $x = b$ is root of multiplicity $m > 1$, then the speed of convergence is given by $\varepsilon_{n+1} \approx \dfrac{m-1}{m} \varepsilon_n$, which is also linear.

Example 20: *Find the approximation value of the smallest real of* $e^{-x} - \sin x = 0$.

[Agra 2005; P.C.S. (UP) 2004, 2007; I.A.S. 2004]

Solution: Using graphical method, we draw the graphs of $y = e^{-x}$ and $y = \sin x$ on the same set of axes as shown in the figure. The intersection of the two curves is in the neighbourhood of $x = 0.6$. This gives the approximate value of the smallest real root of the equation $e^{-x} = \sin x$.

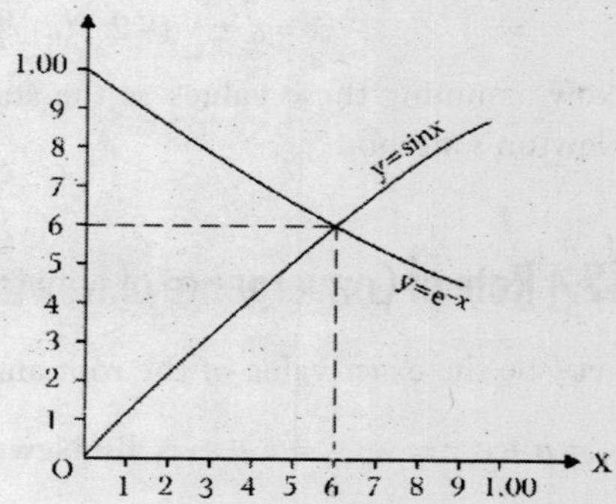

Example 21: *Find approximate value of the root of the equation* $3x - \sqrt{(1 + \sin x)} = 0$.

Solution: Let $f(x) = 3x - (1 + \sin x)^{(1/2)}$

Then $f(0) = 3 \times 0 - \sqrt{(1 + \sin 0)} = -1$,

$f(1) = 3 - (1 + \sin 1)^{(1/2)} = 3 - (1 + .8147)^{(1/2)} = 3 - 1.3570 = 1.6430$.

So we can say that at least one root lies in the interval $(0, 1)$ as $f(0)$ and $f(1)$ are of opposite signs.

Further also $f(.3) = 3 \times 9.3 - \sqrt{[1 + \sin (.3)]}$

$= .9 - \sqrt{[1 + 1.29552]} = .9 - 1.1381 = -0.2381$.

$f(.4) = 3 \times .4 - \sqrt{[1 + \sin (.4)]}$

$= 1.2 - \sqrt{[1.38912]} = 1.2 - 1.1787 = 0.0213$.

This suggest that at least one real root lies between $x = .3$ and $x = .4$

Again $f(.38) = 3 \times .38 - \sqrt{[1 + \sin (.38)]}$

$= 1.14 - \sqrt{[1 + 37092]}$

$= 1.14 - 1.1708 = -0.0808$, and $f(40) = 0.0213$.

$\therefore$ There exists at least one real root between $x = .38$ and $x = .40$. From the discussion, we conclude that $x = .38$ is an approximate value of the root in the range $(.38, .40)$.

Example 22: *Find the approximate value of the root of the equation* $x - 1 = \sin x$.

Solution: Using graphical method we draw the graphs of $y = x - 1$ and $y = \sin x$ on the same set of axes as shown in the diagram; and then find that the abscissa of the points of intersection of the two curves in the neighbourhood of the point $x = 1.9$. This gives the approximate value of the root as $x = 1.9$.

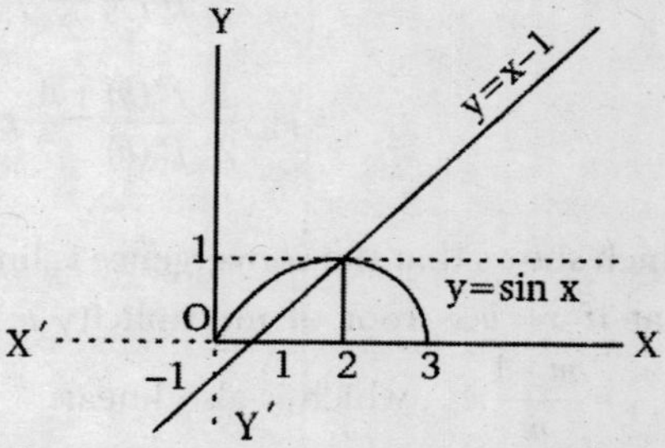

Example 23: *Find graphically an approximate value of the root of the equation* $3 - x = e^{x-1}$.

Solution: Let $f(x) = e^{x-1} + x - 3 = 0$ ...(1)

Then, we have $f(1) = 1 + 1 - 3 = -ve$;

$f(2) = e + 2 - 3 = 2.718 - 1 = +ve$

$\therefore$ A root of (1) lies between 1 and 2. We now write (1) as $e^{x-1} = 3 - x$ and draw the graphs of $y = e^{x-1}$ and $y = 3 - x$.

The abscissa of the point of intersection of the curves $y = e^{x-1}$ ...(2)

and $y = 3 - x$ ...(3)

will give the required root.

Let us frame the following table to plot the graph of $y = e^{x-1}$.

$x =$	1.1	1.2	1.3	1.4	1.5	1.6	1.7	1.8	1.9	2.0
$y = e^{x-1}$	1.11	1.22	1.35	1.49	1.65	1.82	2.01	2.23	2.46	2.72

The graph of $y = 3 - x$ is obviously a st. line $(x/3) + (y/3) = 1$.

Considering the origin at (1.1) and 1 small unit along either axis = 0.02, we plot these points.

From the figure, we get the required root as $x = 1.44$ nearly.

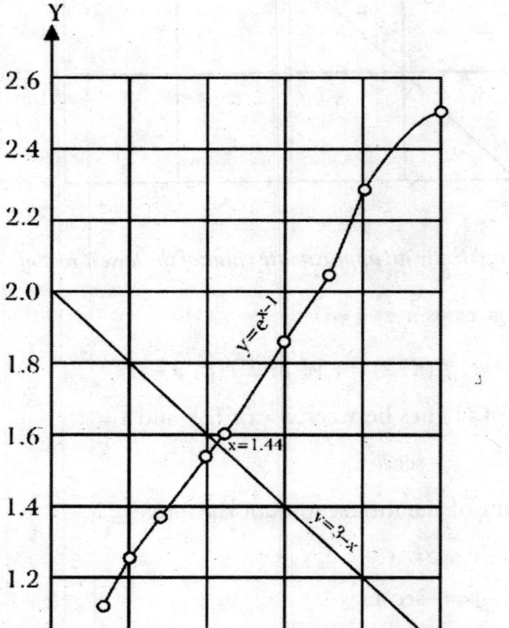

Example 24: *Obtain graphically an approximate value of the root* $x = \sin x + (\pi/2)$.

Solution: Let us write the given equation as $\sin x = x - (\pi/2)$, we now draw the graphs of $y = \sin x$ and $y = x - (\pi/2)$.

The abscissas of the point of intersection of curve $y = \sin x$ and the line $y = x - (\pi/2)$ gives a rough estimate of the root.

x	0	$\pi/4$	$\pi/2$	$3\pi/4$	π
y	0	0.71	1	0.71	0

The curve $y = x - (\pi/2)$ is purely a straight line.

From the graph, we get $x = 2.3$ radians approximately.

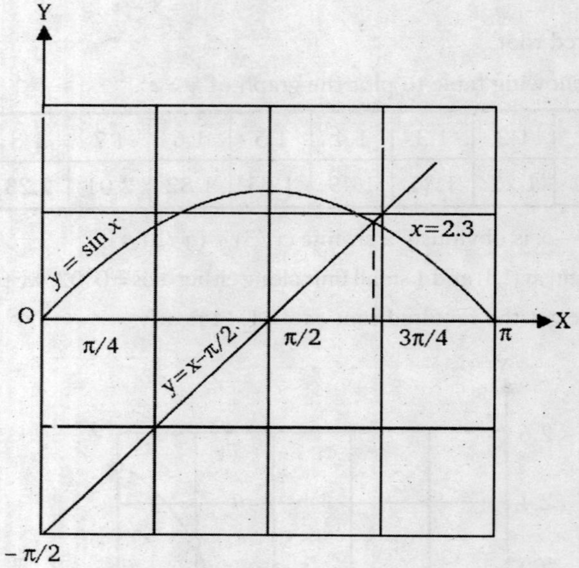

Example 25: *Obtain graphically an approximate value of the lowest root of* $\cos x \cos hx = -1$.

Solution: Let $f(x) = \cos x \cos h\,x + 1 = 0$ ...(1)

Then, we have $f(0) = +ve$, $f(\pi/2) = +ve$ and $f(\pi) = -ve$.

Hence the lowest root of (1) lies between $x = (\pi/2)$ and $x = \pi$.

We now write (1) as $\cos x = -\operatorname{sec} h\,x$.

The abscissa of the point of the intersection of the curves

$$y = \cos x \quad ...(2)$$

and

$$y = -\operatorname{sec} h\,x \quad ...(3)$$

Then gives the required root.

$y = \cos x$ (Table)

x	$\pi/2 = 1.57$	$3\pi/4 = 2.36$	$\pi = 3.14$
y	0	-0.71	-1

Further, taking the origin at (1.57, 0) and 1 unit along either axis = $\pi/8, = 0.4$ nearly, we plot the cosine curve as shown in the figure.

$y = -\text{sec}\,h\,x$ (Table)

x	1.57	2.36	3.14
$\cos h\,x$	2.51	5.34	11.57
$y = -\sec h\,x$	− 0.4	−0.19	−0.09

We plot the curve (3) to the same scale with the same axis and see from the figure, that the lowest root is approximately

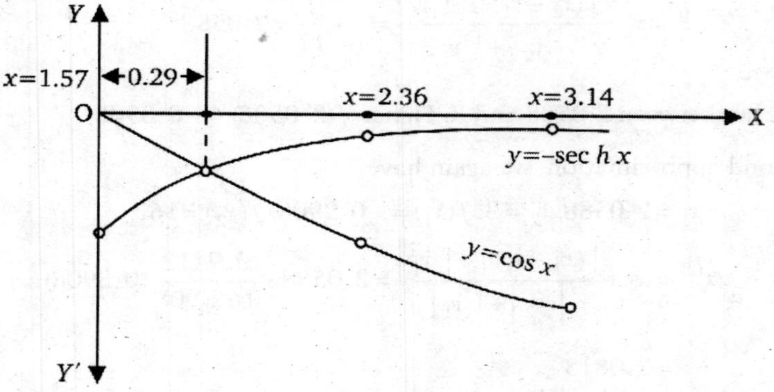

$$x = 1.57 + 0.29 = 1.86$$

Example 26: *The equation $x^6 - x^4 - x^3 - 1 = 0$ hcs one real root between 1.4 and 1.5. Find the root to four places of decimal by false position method.*

Solution: For the first approximation, we take

$$\left.\begin{aligned} x_1 &= 1.4, y_1 = -.056061 \\ x_2 &= 1.5, y_2 = 1.953125 \end{aligned}\right\}$$

$$\therefore \quad x^{(1)} = x_1 + \frac{|(x_2 - x_1)|.|y_1|}{|y_2| + |y_1|} = 1.4 + \frac{(.1)(.056061)}{1.953125 + 0.056061}$$

$$= 1.4 + .003 = 1.403.$$

For the second approximation, we have

$$\left.\begin{aligned} x_1 &= 1.403, y_1 = -.0167 \\ x_2 &= 1.402, y_2 = 1.0056 \end{aligned}\right\} \Rightarrow x^{(2)} = 1.403 + \frac{(.001)(.0167)}{(.0056) + (.0167)}$$

$$= 1.4037.$$

Again, for the third approximation, we have

$$\left.\begin{aligned} x_1 &= 1.4036, y_1 = -.0001 \\ x_2 &= 1.4037, y_2 = 1.0004 \end{aligned}\right\} \Rightarrow x^{(3)} = 1.4036 + \frac{(.0001)(.0001)}{(.0004) + (.0001)}$$

$$= 1.4036$$

$\Rightarrow$ that the root is 1.4036.

Example 27: *Find a real root of the equation $x^3 - 2x - 5 = 0$ by the method of false position correct to three decimal places.*

[S. Patel B.E. 2009; Bhopal 2002; M.K.U. (Tamilnadu 2005, 2008); Agra 2009; I.A.S. 2002]

Solution: Let $f(x) = x^3 - 2x - 5$. Then, we have

$$f(2) = -1 \text{ and } f(3) = 16.$$

$\Rightarrow$ a root lies between 2 and 3. For the first approximation, we have

$$x_1 = 2, x_2 = 3, y_1 = f(x_1) = -1, f(x_2) = 16 = y_2.$$

Then, we have

$$x^{(1)} = x_1 + \frac{|(x_2 - x_1)| \cdot |y_1|}{|y_2| + |y_1|} = 2 + \frac{1}{17} = 2.0588.$$

Hence root lies between 2.0588 and 3. Hence $f(2.0588) = -0.3908$

For the second approximation, we again have

$$x_1 = 2.0588, x_2 = 3, f(x_1) = -0.3908, f(x_2) = 16.$$

$$\Rightarrow \quad x^{(2)} = x_1 + \frac{|(x_2 - x_1)| \cdot |y_1|}{|y_2| + |y_1|} = 2.0588 + \frac{0.9412}{16.3908}(0.3908)$$

$$= 2.0813$$

$\Rightarrow$ The root lies between 2.0813 and 3.

Repeating this process, the successive approximations are given as

$$x^{(3)} = 2.0862, x^{(4)} = 2.0915, x^{(5)} = 2.0934,$$

$$x^{(6)} = 2.0941, x^{(7)} = 2.0943 \text{ etc.}$$

Hence the root is 2.094 correct to 3 decimal places.

Example 28: *Find the root of the equation $x e^x = \cos x$ using the Regula-Falsi Method correct to four decimal places.* **[Chennai B.E. 2007; I.A.S. 2008; U.P.T.U. 2004]**

Solution: Let $f(x) = \cos x - x e^x = 0$

$$\Rightarrow \quad f(0) = 1, f(1) = \cos 1 - e = -2.17798$$

$\Rightarrow$ the root lies between 0 and 1. Let us take

$$x_1 = 0, x_2 = 1, f(x_1) = y_1 = 1$$

$$\therefore \quad f(x_2) = -2.17798 = y_2.$$

By Regula-Falsi Method, we then obtain

$$x = x_1 + \frac{|(x_2 - x_1)| \cdot |y_1|}{|y_2| + |y_1|} = 0 + \frac{1}{3.17798} \times 1 = 0.31467 \quad \text{...(1)}$$

Hence the root lies in between $(0.31467, 1)$.

Now $\quad f(0.31467) = 0.51987$

Then taking $x_1 = 0.31467, x_2 = 1, f(x_1) = 0.51987$,

$f(x_2) = -2.17798$ in (1), we get

$$x^{(2)} = 0.31467 + \frac{0.68533}{2.69785} \times 0.51987 = 0.44673$$

i.e., the root lie between 0.44673 and 1.

Then $f(0.4673) = 0.20356$. Then taking $x_1 = 0.44673, x_2 = 1$

$f(x_1) = 0.20356$, and $f(x_2) = -2.17798$ in (1), we obtain

$$x^{(3)} = 0.44673 + \frac{0.55327}{2.38154} \times 0.20356 = 0.49402$$

Repeating this process, the successive approximations are given as

$$x^{(4)} = 0.50995, x^{(5)} = 0.51520, x^{(6)} = 0.51692$$

$$x^{(7)} = 0.51748, x^{(8)} = 0.51767, x^{(9)} = 0.51775 \text{ etc.}$$

Thus the root is 0.5177 correct to 4 decimal places.

Example 29: *Find the real root of the equation* $x \log_{10} x - 1.2 = 0$, *correct to five places of decimal.*

[Agra 2006]

Solution: Let $y = f(x) = x \log_{10} x - 1.2$, when we have

$$f(2) = 2 \log_{10} 2 - 1.2 = 2 \times (.30103) - 1.2 = -.59794$$

$$f(3) = 3 \log_{10} 3 - 1.2 = 3 \times (.44712) - 1.2 = -.23138$$

Hence there exists at least one real root of the equation $f(x) = 0$ in the interval $(2, 3)$ and it is closer to 3.

For the first approximation, we get

$$\begin{cases} x_1 = 2, y_1 = -.59794 \\ x_2 = 3, y_2 = .23136 \end{cases} \Rightarrow x^{(1)} = x_1 + \frac{|(x_2 - x_1)|\,|y_1|}{|y_1| + |y_2|} = 2 + \frac{.59704}{.82990} = 2.719$$

Also, we have

$$f(2.721) = 2.719 \times \log_{10}(2.719) - (1.2)$$

$$= 2.719 \times (.43473) - 1.2$$

$$= 1.1829 - 1.2 = -.0188$$

Further $f(2.721)$ and $f(3)$ are the opposite signs; so the root lies in between $x = 2.721$ and $x = 3.00$. For the second approximation, we take

$$\begin{cases} x_1 = 2.719, y_1 = -.3171 \\ x_2 = 3, y_2 = .23136 \end{cases}$$

$$\Rightarrow \quad x^{(2)} = 2.719 + \frac{(3 - 2.719)(.3171)}{(.3171) + (.23136)} = 2.88$$

Also, we have $f(2.702) = 2.7402 \times \log_{10}(2.7402) - 1.2$

$$= 2.740 + (0.43778) - 1.2$$

$$= 1.1996 - 1.2 = -.0004$$

Again as $f(2.740200)$ and $f(3)$ are of opposite sign, so that root lies in the interval $(2.7402, 3)$ and it is closer to $x = 2.7402$.

For the third approximation, we have

$$\begin{cases} x_1 = 2.7402, \; y_1 = .0004 \\ x_2 = 3, \; y_2 = .23136 \end{cases} \Rightarrow x^{(3)} = 2.7402 + \frac{(3 - 2.7402)(.0004)}{.0004 + .23136}$$

$$= 2.7385 + .00044844 = 2.7405967$$

$\Rightarrow$ The root is 2.7406.

Example 30: *Find a real root of the equation* $f(x) = x^3 - x - 1 = 0$.

[Purvanchal 2007; M.K.U. (Tamilnadu) 2005, 2007]

Solution: $f(1) = 1 - 1 - 1 = -1$; $f(2) = 2^3 - 2 - 1 = 5$. Now $f(1)$ is negative and $f(2)$ is positive so at least one root lies between 1 and 2.

So we take $x_0 = \frac{1}{2}(1 + 2) = (3/2)$.

Again $f(x_0) = (27/8) - (3/2) - 1 = (7/8)$, which is positive. But $f(1)$ and $f(1.5)$ are of opposite signs so the root lies between 1 and 1.5 and therefore, we obtain

$$x_1 = \frac{1 + 1.5}{2} = 1.25$$

Further, $f(x_1) = -19/64$, which is negative. Hence we conclude that the root lies between 1.25 and 1.5 implying

$$x_2 = \frac{1.25 + 1.5}{2} = 1.375.$$

Whence repeating the procedure, we obtain the successive approximations as

$$x_3 = 1.3125, \; x_4 = 1.34375, \; x_5 = 1.328125 \text{ etc.}$$

Example 31: *Find the real root of the equation* $x^2 + 4 \sin x = 0$ *correct to four places of decimal by using Newton's-Raphson Method.* **[Rajasthan 2001]**

Solution: We have $x_{n+1} = x_n - \dfrac{f(x_n)}{f'(x_n)}, n = 0, 1, 2, \ldots$

Let us take $f(x) = x^2 + 4 \sin x$,

$$\Rightarrow \quad f'(x) = 2x + 4 \cos x.$$

$$\Rightarrow \quad x_{n+1} = x_n - \frac{x_n^2 + 4 \sin x_n}{2 x_n + 4 \cos x_n}$$

By the equation it is obvious that it is satisfied only by a negative value of x as x^2 is to be positive always for all real values of x. By the graphical method, approximate value of the root is given by $x_2 = -1.9$.

Again starting from $x_0 = -1.9$, relation (1)gives

$$x_1 = x_0 - \frac{x_0^2 + 4 \sin x_0}{2 x_0 + 4 \cos x_0}$$

$$= -1.9 - \frac{(-1.9)^2 + 4\sin(-1.9)}{2(-1.9) + 4\cos(-1.9)} = 1.9 - \frac{3.61 - 4(0.945)}{-3.8 + (0.323)}$$

$$= -1.93$$

The second approximation,

$$= x_1 - \frac{x_1^2 + 4\sin x_1}{2x_1 + 4\cos x_1}$$

$$= -1.93 - \frac{(-1.93)^2 + 4\sin(-1.93)}{2(-1.93 + 4\cos(-1.93)} = -1.93 - 0.0038$$

$$= 1.9338$$

Example 32: *Obtain* $\sqrt{(12)}$, *to five places of decimals by Newton's Raphson Method.*

[Agra 2004, 2007, 2009]

Solution: Let us take $x = \sqrt{(12)}$, so that $x^2 - 12 = 0$. From this it is obvious that $x^2 - 12$ becomes negative for $x = 3$, whereas it is positive for $x = 3.5$. Hence the root of $x^2 - 12 = 0$ lies in the interval $(3, 3.5)$. Further $f(x) = x^2 - 12$, so that the given equation is $f(x) = 0$. Again $f'(x) = 2x$.

Now by Newton's-Raphson Method, we have

$$x_{n+1} = x_n - \frac{f(x_n)}{f'(x_n)}$$

$$\Rightarrow \quad x_1 = x_2 - \frac{f(x_0)}{f'(x_0)} = 3.5 - \frac{f(3.5)}{f'(3.5)} \qquad \text{[Taking } x_0 = 3.5\text{]}$$

$$= 3.5 - \frac{(3.5)^2 - 12}{2(3.5)} = 3.464.$$

Again, we have

$$x_2 = x_1 - \frac{x_1^2 - 12}{2x_1} = 3.464 - \frac{(3.464)^2 - 12}{2(3.464)} = 3.4641$$

$$x_3 = x_2 - \frac{x_2^2 - 12}{2x_2} = 3.4641 - \frac{(3.4641)^2 - 12}{2(3.4641)} = 3.4641$$

Hence up to four places of decimals, we get

$$\sqrt{(12)} = 3.4641.$$

Example 33: *The equation* $x^6 - x^4 - x^3 - 1 = 0$ *has one real root between* $(1.4, 1.5)$. *Find this root to four decimal places by False Position Method.*

[Agra 2007]

Solution: For the first approximation, we take

$$\begin{cases} x_1 = 1.4, \ y_1 = -0.56064 \\ x_2 = 1.5, \ y_2 = 1.953125 \end{cases} \Rightarrow x^{(1)} = x_1 + \frac{|x_2 - x_1||y_1|}{|y_1| + |y_2|}$$

$$= 1.4 + \frac{.0056064}{2.009189} = 1.403.$$

For the second approximation, we have

$$\begin{cases} x_1 = 1.403, \; y_1 = -.0167 \\ x_2 = 1.404, \; y_2 = .0056 \end{cases} \Rightarrow \quad x^{(2)} = 1.403 + \frac{(.001)\,(.0167)}{(.0056)+(.0167)}$$

$$= 1.403 + .0007 = 1.4037$$

For third approximation, we have

$$\begin{cases} x_1 = 1.4036, \; y_1 = -.0001 \\ x_2 = 1.4037, \; y_2 = .0004 \end{cases} \Rightarrow \quad x^{(2)} = 1.4036 + \frac{(.0001)\,(.0001)}{(.0001)+(.0004)}$$

$$= 1.4036 + 0.00002 = 1.4036$$

Hence the root is 1.4036

Example 34: *Find the approximate value for the real root of* $x \log_{10} x - 1.2 = 0$ *correct to five decimal places by Newton-Raphson Method.* **[Manglore (B.E.) 2008; U.P.T.U. 2004]**

Solution: We have $x_{n+1} = x_n - \dfrac{f(x_n)}{f'(x_n)}$; $n = 0, 1, 2 \ldots$

Here, $\quad f(x) = x \log_{10} x - 1.2$

$$\Rightarrow \quad f'(x) = \log_{10} x + x \cdot \frac{1}{x} \cdot \log_{10} e = \log_{10} x + .43429$$

$$\therefore \quad x_{n+1} = x_n - \frac{x_n \log_{10}(x_n) - 1.2}{\log_{10} x_n + .43429} = \frac{.43429\, x_n + 1.2}{\log_{10} x_n + .43429}.$$

Now, putting $n = 0$, we get

$$x_1 = \frac{.43429\,(2) + 1.2}{\log_{10} 2 + .43429} = 2.81 \qquad [\text{starting with } x_0 = 2]$$

Similarly, $\quad x_2 = \dfrac{.13429\,(2.81 + 1.2)}{\log_{10} 2.81 + .43429} = 2.741$

$$x_3 = \frac{.43429\,(2.741) + 1.2}{\log_{10} 2.741 + .43429} = 2.74064$$

$$x_4 = \frac{.43429\,(2.74064) + 1.2}{\log_{10} 2.74064 + .43429} = 2.74065$$

$$x_5 = \frac{.43429\,(2.74065) + 1.2}{\log_{10} 2.74065 + .43429} = 2.74065$$

Hence the required root is 2.74065.

Example 35: *Apply Newton's method to obtain the root of the equation* $x \log_{10} x = 4.7772393$, *correct to six decimal places.* **[Bulbarga 2002, 2007]**

Solution: By the logarithmic table, we have $6 \log_{10} 6 = 4.64$ and $7 \log_{10} 7 = 5.92$; so we take the first approximation as $x_0 = 6$. Now applying Newton's method, we have

$$x_1 = x_0 - \frac{f(x_0)}{f'(x_0)} \quad \Rightarrow \quad x_1 = 6 - \frac{5 \times 0.77815 - 4.7772393}{\log_{10} 6 + \log_{10} e}$$

$$\Rightarrow \quad x_1 = 6 + \frac{0.1083}{0.778 + 0.434} = 6 + \frac{0.1083}{1.212} = 6.089.$$

The second approximation is given by

$$x_2 = x_1 - \frac{f(x)}{f'(x_1)} \Rightarrow x_2 = 6.89 - \frac{(6.089)\log_{10}(6.089) - 0.47772393}{\log_{10}(6.089) + \log_{10} e}$$

$$\Rightarrow \quad x_2 = 6.089 - \frac{6.089 + 0.784460 - .47772303}{\log_{10} 6.089 + 0.434}$$

$$= 6.089 + \frac{1.0001387}{\log_{10} 6.089 + 0.434}$$

$$= 6.089 + (.0001387)(0.825) = 6.089114.$$

Example 36: *Find the root of $x^2 - 5x + 2 = 0$ correct to the five decimal places by Newton-Raphson Method.* **[Agra 2007]**

Solution: The given equation has two real roots, and from the graph it can be verified that the approximate value of the roots are 0, 4.

Let $f(x) = x^2 - 5x + 2 \quad \Rightarrow f'(x) = 2x - 5$.

By Newton's Raphson formula, we have

$$x_{n+1} = x_n - \frac{f(x_n)}{f'(x_n)} = x_n - \frac{x_n^2 - 5x_n + 2}{2x_n - 5} = \frac{x_n^2 - 2}{2x_n - 5}$$

Putting $n = 0$, we get, $x_1 = \frac{-2}{-5} = .4$ [starting with $x_0 = 0$]

Again, we have $x_2 = \frac{(.4^2 - 2)}{2(.4) - 5} = \frac{-1.84}{-4.20} = .438095$,

$$x_3 = \frac{(.438095)^2 - 2}{2(.438095) - 5} = .438447, \quad \text{and } x_4 = \frac{(.438447)^2 - 2}{2(.438447) - 5} = .438447$$

From here it is clear that $x_3 = x_4$; that real root is .438447.

For the second real root, we start with $x_0 = 4.0$ and thus we have obtain

$$x_2 = \frac{(4)^2 - 2}{2(4) - 5} = \frac{14}{3}.$$

Further also,

$$x_2 = \frac{\left(\frac{14}{3}\right)^2 - 2}{2\left(\frac{14}{3}\right) - 5} = 4.564104; \qquad x_3 = \frac{(4.564104)^2 - 2}{2(4.564104) - 5} = 4.561554,$$

$$x_4 = \frac{(4.561554)^2 - 2}{2(4.561554) - 5} = 4.561553; \text{ and } x_5 = \frac{(4.561553)^2 - 2}{2(4.561553) - 5} = 4.561553,$$

Obviously $x_5 = x_4$ so the real of $f(x) = 0$ is 4.561553.

Example 37: *Find to four places of decimal the smaller root of the equation* $e^{-x} - \sin x = 0$.

[Manipal 2007; Baroda 2007]

Solution: We have $f(x) = e^{-x} - \sin x = 0$

$$\text{Now } x_{n+1} = x_n + \frac{e^{-x_n} - \sin x_n}{e^{-x_n} + \cos x_n} \qquad ...(1)$$

$$\Rightarrow \quad x_1 = .6 + \frac{e^{.6} - \sin(.6)}{e^{.6} + \cos(.6)} = .6 \frac{.54881 - .56464}{.54881 + .82524}$$

$$= .6 - \frac{.01583}{1.37415} = .6 - .01151 = .58848$$

Aiso $$x_2 = .58848 + \frac{e^{-.58848} - \sin(.58848)}{e^{-.58848} - \cos(.58848)}$$

$$= .58848 + \frac{.55519 - .55508}{.55519 + .8311} = .58848 + .000079287 = .588559287$$

Thus the desired root is $.5885$.

Example 38: *By using Newton-Raphson Method find the root of* $x^4 - x - 10 = 0$, *which is nearer to* $x = 2$, *correct to three places of decimal.* **[Agra 2006; M.K.U. (Tamilnadu) 2008]**

Solution: The approximate value of the root is given to be 2.

Now $f(x) = x^4 - x - 10, \Rightarrow f'(x) = 4x^3 - 1$

$$\therefore \quad x_{n+1} = x_n - \frac{f(x_n)}{f'(x_n)} = x_n - \frac{x_n^4 - x_n - 10}{4x_n^3 - 1} = \frac{3x_n^4 + 10}{4x_n^3 - 1}$$

$\Rightarrow \quad x_1 =$ first approximation

$$= \frac{3x_0^4 + 10}{4x_0^3 - 1} = \frac{3\,2^4 + 10}{4\,2^3 - 1} = 1.871,$$

$$x_2 = \text{second approximation} = \frac{3x_1^4 + 10}{4x_1^3 - 1} = 1.85578 = 1.856.$$

$x_3 =$ third approximation,

$$= \frac{3x_2^4 + 10}{4x_2^3 - 1} = \frac{3\,(1.856)^4 + 10}{4\,(1.856)^3 - 1} = 1.856$$

Obviously $x_2 = x_3$ and hence the required root $= 1.856$.

Example 39: *Using the staring value* $x_0 = i$, *find a zero of* $x^4 + x^3 + 5x^2 + 4x + 4 = 0$.

[Agra 2005]

Solution: By Newton's Method, we have

$$\text{First approx,} \quad x_1 = x_0 - \frac{f(x_0)}{f'(x_0)} = i - \frac{3i}{1 + 6i} = .486 + 0.919\,i$$

Second approx, $x_2 = 0.486 + 0.919\,i - \dfrac{f(0.486 + 0.919\,i)}{f'(0.486 + 0.919\,i)}$

$$= 0.486 + 0.919\,i - \frac{-0.292 + 0.174\,i}{1.780 + 6.005\,i} = -0.499 + 0.866\,i$$

The actual root is $x = \dfrac{-1 + i\sqrt{3}}{2}$

Example 40: *Find the cube root of* 10. **[I.F.S. 2003; Ranchi (B.E.) 2005]**

Solution: The Iterative formula for finding successive approximation of cube roots is given by

$$x_{n+1} = \frac{2x_n^3 + N}{3\,x_n^2} = \frac{1}{3}\left(2x_n + \frac{N}{x_n^2}\right) \qquad \text{...(1)}$$

$\because \quad (8)^{1/3} = 2, (27)^{1/3} = 3$, we may take initially $x_0 = 2.5$.

$$\Rightarrow \quad x_1 = \frac{1}{3}\left[2 \times 2.5 + \frac{10}{(2.5)^2}\right] = 2.2\,;\; x_2 = \frac{1}{3}\left[2 \times 2.2 - \frac{10}{(2.2)^2}\right] = 2.155,$$

and $$x_3 = \frac{1}{3}\left[2 \times 2.155 + \frac{10}{(2.155)^2}\right] = 2.15466.$$

Hence $\sqrt[3]{(10)} \approx 2.15466$.

Example 41: *Apply* **(a)** *False Position Method* **(b)** *Newton-Raphson Method to solve the equation*

$$3x - \cos x - 1 = 0.$$

Solution: Let $f(x) = 3x - \cos x - 1 = 0$.

$f(.60) = -.025$ = negative quantity, $f(.61) = .010$ = positive quantity.

$\therefore$ Real root lies in the interval $(.60, .61)$.

(a) False Position Method

$$\begin{cases} x_1 = .60, \; y_1 = -.025 \\ x_2 = .61, \; y_2 = .010 \end{cases} \Rightarrow x^{(1)} = x_1 + \frac{(x_2 - x_1)\,|\,y_1\,|}{|\,y_2\,| + |\,y_1\,|} = .60 + \frac{(.01)\,(.025)}{.025 + .010}$$

$$= .60 + \frac{(.01)\,(.025)}{.01 + .025} = .607$$

For the second approximation, we take

$$\begin{cases} x_1 = .607, \; y_1 = -.00036 \\ x_2 = .608, \; y_2 = .00321 \end{cases} \Rightarrow x^{(2)} = .607 + \frac{(.00321)\,(.00036)}{.00321 + .00036} = .6071$$

For the third approximation, we have

$$\begin{cases} x_1 = .6071, \; y_1 = -.00000 \\ x_2 = .6072, \; y_2 = .00035 \end{cases} \Rightarrow x^{(3)} = .6071 + \frac{(.0001)\,(.00000)}{.00000 + .00035} = .60710.$$

(b) Newton's Raphson Method

For the first approximation, we take

$$f(x) = 3x - \cos x - 1 \quad \Rightarrow \quad f'(x) = 3 + \sin x$$

Now $$x_{n+1} = x_n - \frac{3x_n - \cos x_n - 1}{3 + \sin x_n}$$

$$\Rightarrow \quad x_1 = .60 - \frac{3\,(.60) - \cos .60 - 1}{3 + \sin .60} \quad \text{[starting from } x_0 = .60]$$

$$= .60 - \frac{1.8 - .82534 - 1}{3 + .56464} = .60710$$

Further, we have $$x_2 = .60710 - \frac{3\,(.60710) - \cos\,(.60710) - 1}{3 + \sin\,(.60710)}$$

$$= .60710 - \frac{1.82130 - 821321 - 1}{3 + .57070} = .60710$$

Obviously $x_1 = x_2$ so the real root of $f(x) = 0$ is $.60710$.

Example 42: *Find a real root of the equation* $f(x) = x^3 + x^2 - 1 = 0$. *by using Iteration Method.*

[M.K.U. (Tamilnadu) 2004, 2006]

Solution: Here $F(0) = -1$ and $F(1) = 1 + 1 - 1 = 1$, so that the root lies in between 0 and 1.

We have $x^2 (x + 1) = 1$

$$\Rightarrow \quad x^2 = \frac{1}{x+1}, \quad \Rightarrow x = \frac{1}{\sqrt{(x+1)}} \quad \Rightarrow x = f(x).$$

where $$f(x) = \frac{1}{\sqrt{(x+1)}}$$

Now $$f'(x) = -\frac{1}{2\,(x+1)^{3/2}}$$

Again $$|f'(x)| = \left| \frac{1}{2\,(x+1)^{3/2}} \right| < 1, \text{ for } x < 1.$$

Hence Iterative Method is applicable.

Starting with $x_0 = .5$, we get

$$x_1 = f(x_0) = \frac{1}{\sqrt{(1.5)}} = .81649; \quad x_2 = f(x_1) = \frac{1}{\sqrt{(1.81649)}} = .74196$$

$$x_3 = f(x_2) = \frac{1}{\sqrt{(1.74196)}} = .75767; \quad x_4 = f(x_3) = \frac{1}{\sqrt{(1.75767)}} = .75427$$

$$x_5 = f(x_4) = \frac{1}{\sqrt{(1.75427)}} = .75500; \quad x_6 = f(x_5) = \frac{1}{\sqrt{(1.75500)}} = .75485$$

$$x_7 = f(x_6) = \frac{1}{\sqrt{(1.75485)}} = .75488; \quad x_8 = f(x_7) = \frac{1}{\sqrt{(1.75488)}} = .75487, \text{ etc.}$$

Example 43: *Starting with* $x = .12$, *solve* $x = .21 \sin(.5 + x)$ *by using Iteration Method.*

[M.K.U. (Tamilnadu) 2003]

Solution: $x = .21\sin(.5 + x) \Rightarrow f(x) = .21\sin(.5 + x)$ so that $|f(x)| < 1$. Thus Iterative Method can be applied.

Hence, first approximation of x is given by

$$x^{(1)} = .21\sin(.5 + .12) = .21\sin(.62)$$
$$= .21(.58104) = .1220$$

Also, the second approximation is given by

$$x^{(2)} = .21\sin(.5 + .122) = .21\sin(.622)$$
$$= .21(.58267) = .1224$$

Further, $x^{(3)} = .21\sin(.5 + .1224) = .21\sin(.6224)$

$$= .21(.58299) = .12243$$

and $x^{(4)} = .21\sin(.5 + .12243) = .21\sin(.62243)$

$$= .21(0.58301) = .12243$$

Obviously $x^{(3)} = x^{(4)}$

So the required root is .12243.

Example 44: *Find a real root of the equation* $\cos x = 3x - 1$ *correct three decimal places using*

[Nagarjuna 2003, 2007]

***(a)** Iteration method* ***(b)** Aitken's* Δ^2 *method*

Solution: (a) We have $f(x) = \cos x - 3x + 1 = 0$

$\Rightarrow$ $f(0) = 2 = +ve$ and $f(\pi/2) = -3(\pi/2) + 1 = -ve$

Hence a root lies between 0 and $(\pi/2)$.

Rewriting the given equation as given below:

$$x = \frac{1}{3}(\cos x + 1) = \phi(x), \text{ say}$$

Then we have $\phi'(x) = -\dfrac{\sin x}{3}$

So that $|\phi'(x)| = \dfrac{1}{3}|\sin x| < 1$ in $(0, \pi/2)$.

Thus the Iteration method can be applied and we start with $x_0 = 0$. The successive approximations are as follows:

$$x_1 = \phi(x_0) = \frac{1}{3}(\cos 0 + 1) = 0.6667$$

$$x_2 = \phi(x_1) = \frac{1}{3}(\cos .6667 + 1) = 0.5953$$

$$x_3 = \phi(x_2) = \frac{1}{3}(\cos .5953 + 1) = 0.6093$$

$$x_4 = \phi(x_3) = \frac{1}{3}(\cos .6093 + 1) = 0.6067$$

$$x_5 = \phi(x_4) = \frac{1}{3}(\cos .6067 + 1) = 0.6072$$

$$x_6 = \phi(x_5) = \frac{1}{3}(\cos .6072 + 1) = 0.6071$$

Now x_5 and x_6 being almost the same, the root is surely 0.607 correct to 3 decimal places.

(b) Calculate x_1, x_2, x_3 as computed above. to use Aitken's method, we proceed as;

x	Δx	$\Delta^2 x$
$x_1 = 0.6667$		
	-0.0714	
$x_2 = 0.5953$		0.0854
	0.014	
$x_3 = 0.6093$		

Then we have $x_4 = x_3 - \dfrac{(\Delta x_2)^2}{\Delta^2 x_1} = 0.6093 - \dfrac{(0.014)^2}{0.0854} = 0.607.$

This corresponds to six iterations in normal form. Hence the required root is 0.607.

Example 45: *Find a real root of $2x - \log_{10} x = 7$ correct to four decimal places using Iteration Method.*

Solution: Let $f(x) \equiv 2x - \log_{10} - 7 = 0$

Then $\quad f(3) = 6 - \log_{10} 3 - 7 = 6 - 0.04771 - 7 = -1.4471$

and $\quad f(4) = 8 - \log_{10} 4 - 7 = 8 - 0.602 - 7 = 0.398$

Thus a root lies between 3 and 4.

Rewriting the given equation as given below:

$$x = \frac{1}{2}(\log_{10} x + 7) = \phi(x), \text{ say}$$

Then $\quad \phi'(x) = \dfrac{1}{2}\left(\dfrac{1}{x}\log_{10} e\right).$

Evidently $|\phi'(x)| < 1$ when $3 < x < 4$ $\qquad [\because \log_{10} e = 0.4343]$

Now $|f(4)| < |f(3)|$, hence the root is near to 4.

We can apply Iteration method now. Taking $x_0 = 3.6$, the successive approximations are computed as follows:

$$x_1 = \phi(x_0) = \frac{1}{2}(\log_{10} 3.6 + 7) = 3.77815,$$

$$x_2 = \phi(x_1) = \frac{1}{2}(\log_{10} 3.77815 + 7) = 3.7886,$$

$$x_3 = \phi(x_2) = \frac{1}{2}(\log_{10} 3.78863 + 7) = 3.78924,$$

$$x_4 = \phi(x_3) = \frac{1}{2}(\log_{10} 3.78924 + 7) = 3.78927,$$

Now x_3 and x_4 being almost equal, it implies that the root is 3.7892 correct to four decimal points.

Example 46: *Find the smallest root of the equation*

$$1 - x + \frac{x^2}{(2\,!)^2} - \frac{x^3}{(3\,!)^2} + \frac{x^4}{(4\,!)^2} - \frac{x^5}{(5\,!)^2} + \ldots = 0$$

[UP (P.C.S.) 2003]

Solution: The given equation can be written as

$$x = 1 + \frac{x^2}{(2\,!)^2} - \frac{x^3}{(3\,!)^2} + \frac{x^4}{(4\,!)^2} - \frac{x^5}{(5\,!)^2} + \ldots = \phi(x), \text{ say}$$

Omitting x^2 and higher powers of x, we readily get $x = 1$ approximately.

So taking $x_0 = 1$ we successively obtain

$$x_1 = \phi(x_0) = 1 + \frac{1}{(2\,!)^2} - \frac{1}{(3\,!)^2} + \frac{1}{(4\,!)^2} - \frac{1}{(5\,!)^2} + \ldots = 1.2239$$

$$x_2 = \phi(x_1) = 1 + \frac{(1.2239)^2}{(2\,!)^2} - \frac{(1.2239)^3}{(3\,!)^2} + \frac{(1.2239)^4}{(4\,!)^2} - \frac{(1.2239)^5}{(5\,!)^2} + \ldots = 1.3263$$

$$x_3 = 1.38,\ x_4 = 1.409,\ x_5 = 1.425$$

and $x_6 = 1.434,\ x_7 = 1.439,\ x_8 = 1.442$.

Thus the values x_7 and x_8 indicate that the root is 1.44 correct to 2 decimal places.

Example 47: *Solve* $x^4 - 5x^3 + 20x^2 - 40x + 60 = 0$, *by Newton-Raphson method given all the roots of the given equation are complex.*

Solution: Let $f(x) = x^4 - 5x^3 + 20x^2 - 40x + 60$, then

$$f'(x) = 4x^3 - 15x^2 + 40x - 40.$$

Now $$x_{n+1} = x_n - \frac{f(x_n)}{f'(x_n)}$$

$$= x_n - \frac{x_n^4 - 5x_n^3 + 20x_n^2 - 40x_n + 60}{4x_n^3 - 15x_n^2 + 40x_n - 40} = \frac{3x_n^4 - 10x_n^3 + 20x_n^2 - 60}{4x_n^3 - 15x_n^2 + 40x_n - 40}$$

Starting with $x_0 = 2(1 + i)$, we get

$$x_1 = \frac{3(2+2i)^4 - 10(2+2i)^3 + 20(2+2i)^2 - 60}{4(2+2i)^3 - 15(2+2i)^2 + 40(2+2i) - 40} = \frac{-92i}{24i - 24}$$

$$= \frac{23}{12}(1 + i) = 1.92 + 1.92\,i, \qquad \ldots(1)$$

$$x_2 = \frac{3\,(1.92+1.92\,i)^4 - 10\,(1.92+1.92\,i)^3 + 20\,(1.92+1.92\,i) - 60}{4\,(1.92+1.92\,i)^3 - 15\,(1.92+1.92)^2 + 40\,(1.92+1.92) - 40}$$

$$= 1.915 + 1.908\,i \qquad \text{...(2)}$$

Imaginary roots occur in pairs, so the roots of $f(x)=0$ are $1.915 \pm 1.908\,i$ up to three places of decimal. Let the other roots of the given equation be $\alpha \pm i\beta$.

Then the sum of the roots is given by

$$(\alpha + i\beta) + (\alpha - i\beta) = (1.915 + 1.908\,i) + (1.915 - 1.908\,i) = -(-5) = 5 \qquad \text{...(3)}$$

Also the product of roots is given by

$$(\alpha^2 + \beta^2) = \{(1.95)^2 + (1.908)^2\} = 60 \qquad \text{...(4)}$$

Solving (3) and (4), we get $\alpha = .585,\ \beta = 2.805$.

Hence the other two roots are $(.585 \pm 2.805\,i)$.

Example 48: *Obtain* e^{-1}, *where* $e = 2.71$, *starting with* $x_0 = 0.3$

Solution: We have $x_{n+1} = x_n\,(2 - b\,x_n)$ **[formula for inverse of b]**

Here, we have $b = 2.71$ and $x_0 = 0.3$

$$\therefore \quad x_1 = x_0\,\{2 - b\,x_0\} = 0.3\,\{2 - 2.71 \times 0.3\} = .3561$$

$$x_2 = x_1\,\{2 - b\,x_1\} = .3561\,\{2 - 2.71 \times .3561\} = .36854$$

$$x_3 = x_2\,\{2 - b\,x_2\} = .36854\,\{2 - 2.71 \times .36854\} = .3686$$

$$x_4 = x_3\,\{2 - b\,x_3\} = .36860\,\{2 - 2.71 \times .36860\} = .369007671600$$

This gives the inverse of e.

Example 49: *Solve the equation* $\log x = \cos x$ *to five decimal places by Newton-Raphson Method.*

[R.A.S. 2004, 2007]

Solution: Let $f(x) = \log_e x - \cos x = 0$.

Then it is clear that $f(x)$ is negative for $x = 1.3$ and is positive for $x = 1.4$, so the root lies between 1.3 and 1.4.

$$\text{Now,} \quad x_{n+1} = x_n - \frac{f(x_n)}{f'(x_n)};\ n = 0, 1, 2, \ldots$$

$$\Rightarrow \quad x_{n+1} = x_n - \frac{\log_e x_n - \cos x_n}{\frac{1}{x_n} + \sin x_n} \qquad \left[\because\ f'(x) = \frac{1}{x} + \sin x\right]$$

$$\Rightarrow \quad x_1 = 1.3 - \frac{\log_e 1.3 - \cos(1.3)}{\frac{1}{1.3} + \sin(1.3)} \qquad [\text{starting from } x_0 = 1.3]$$

$$= 1.3 - \frac{(2.3026)\,(.11394) - .26750}{.76923 + .96356} = 1.3029.$$

Again putting $n = 2$, we get

$$x_2 = 1.3029 - \frac{\log_e 1.3029 - \cos(1.3029)}{\frac{1}{1.3029} + \sin(1.3029)} = 1.30295.$$

Finally, $$x_3 = 1.30295 - \frac{\log_e 1.30295 - \cos(1.30295)}{\frac{1}{1.30295} + \sin(1.30295)} = 1.30295$$

Obviously $x_2 = x_3$, Hence the root is 1.30295.

Example 50: *Using synthetic division with $x = 1$, solve the equation*

$$f(x) \equiv x^3 - x^2 - 1.0001\,x + 0.9999 = 0.$$

Solution: By synthetic division with $x = 1$, we get

	1	−1	−1.0001	0.9999
1		1	0	−1.0001
	1	0	−1.0001	−0.0002 = f(1)
1		1	1.0000	
	1	1	−0.0001 = f′(1)	

Now $\quad f(1) = 0.0002.\ f'(1) = -0.0001$ ...(1)

Thus $f'(1)$ and $f(1)$ very small *i.e.* two nearly equal roots exist, and hence we shall first solve that equation

$$f'(x) \equiv 3x^2 - 2x - 1.0001 = 0.$$

Now $\quad x_{j+1} = x_j - \frac{f'(x_j)}{f''(x_j)} \Rightarrow x_1 = 1 - \frac{f'(1)}{f''(1)}$, putting $j = 0$ $\quad [\because \quad x_0 = 1]$ ...(2)

To obtain $f''(1)$, we apply synthetic division method

	3	−2	−1.0001
1		3	1.0000
	3	1	−.0001 = f(1)
1		3	
	3	4 = f″(1)	

$$\Rightarrow \quad x_1 = 1 + \frac{.0001}{4} = 1.000025 = d \text{ say.} \quad ...(3)$$

Further, we also have

$$x = d \pm \left\{\frac{-2f(d)}{f''(d)}\right\}^{1/2} = 1.000025 \pm \left\{\frac{-2f(1.000025)}{f(1.000025)}\right\}^{1/2} \quad ...(4)$$

In order to obtain $f(1.000025)$ and $f''(1.000025)$, we again use the method of synthetic division.

1.000025	1	−1.000000	−1.0001000	0.999900
		1.000025	0.000025	−1.000100
1.000025	1	0.000025	−1.000075	−0.000200 = $f(1.000025)$
		1.000025	1.000075	
1.000025	1	1.000050	0 = $f'(1.000025)$	
		1.000025		
		2.000075 = $\frac{1}{2}f''(1.000025)$		

Thus, we have

$$f(1.000025) = -0.000200,\ f''(1.000025) = \frac{(2.000075)\times 2}{1}$$

$$\Rightarrow \quad x = 1.000025 \pm \left(\frac{0.000200}{2.000075}\right)^{1/2} = 1.000025 \pm .009$$

$$= 1.009025, 0.991025.$$

Example 51: *Find a real root of the polynomial equation*

$$P(x) \equiv x^5 - 0.346284\, x^4 + x^3 + 3.768\, x + 10 = 0$$

correct to six decimal places by using Newton-Raphson's formula and the method of synthetic division.

Solution: First of all, we shall obtain the value of $f(-1)$, $f(-2)$ by the method of synthetic division.

−1	1	−0.346284	1	0	3.768	10
		−1.000000	1.346284	−2.346284	−2.346284	−6.114284
	1	−1.346284	2.346284	−2.346284	6.114284	3.885716 = $f(-1)$
	1	−0.346284	1	0	3.768	10
		−2.000000	4.692568	−11.385136	22.770272	−60.612544
	1	−2.346284	5.692568	−11.385136	26.530372	−50.612544 = $f(-2)$

Obviously $f(-1)$ and $f(-2)$ are opposite sign, so the root lies in the interval $(-1, -2)$. Starting from $x_0 = -1$, we have

$$x_1 = -1 - \frac{f(-1)}{f'(-1)}, \quad \textit{i.e.}, \text{ we have}$$

$$x_1 = -1 - \frac{3.885716}{13.153136} = -1 - .295 = -1.295,$$

where $f'(-1) = 13.153136$ and $f'(x) = 5x^4 - 1.385136\, x^3 + 3x^2 + 3.768$

Again by synthetic division, we obtain

	1	−0.346284	1	0	3.768	10
−1.295						
		−1.295	2.12546	−4.0447	5.24147	−11.66726
	1	−1.641284	3.12546	−4.04747	9.00947	−1.66726 = f(−1.295)

To obtain $f'(-1.295)$ by synthetic division, we proceed as follows:

	5	−1.385136	3	0	3.768
−1.295					
		−6.475	10.17888	−17.06665	22.10131
	5	−7.86014	13.17888	−17.06665	25.86391 = f′(−1.295)

Further, we have $x_3 = -1.295 - \dfrac{f(-1.295)}{f'(-1.295)}$

$$= -1.295 - \frac{(-1.66726)}{25.86931} = -1.295 + 1.064 = -1.231$$

Also, $x_3 = -1.231 - \dfrac{f(-1.231)}{f'(-1.231)}$, *(next improved value)*

Now, we shall compute $f(-1.231)$, $f'(-1.231)$,

	1	0.34628	1	0	3.768	10
−1.231		−1.231				
			1.94163	−2.62114	4.45762	−10.12573
	1	−1 577284	2.94163	−2.62114	8.25562	−0.12573 = f′(−1.231)

To find $f'(-1.231)$, by synthetic division, we have

	5	1.385136	3	3	3.768
−1.231					
		−6.155	9.28190	−15.11901	11.61150
	5	−7.540136	12.28190	−15.11901	22.37950 = f′(−1.231)

$$\Rightarrow \qquad x_3 = -1.231 + \frac{0.12573}{22.37950} = -1.22539.$$

Further $x_4 = -1.22539 - \dfrac{f(-1.22539)}{f'(-1.22539)}$ (improved the value over x_3)

Now we shall compute $f(-1.22539)$ and $f'(-1.22539)$ by synthetic division.

	1	−0.346284	1	0	3.768	10
−1.22539						
		−1.22539	1.92590	−3.58536	4.39346	−10.00097
	1	−1.371674	2.91590	−3.58536	8.16146	−.00097 = $f(-1.22539)$

$$\therefore \qquad f(-1.22539) = -.00097$$

To find $f'(-1.22539)$ by synthetic division, we have

	5	−1.384136	3	0	3.76
−1.22539					
		−26.12695	9.20523	−14.95616	18.32712
	5	−7.512036	12.20523	−14.95616	22.09512 = $f'(-1.22539)$

$$\therefore \qquad f'(-.22539) = 25.09512$$

For better approximation, we should have by Newton-Raphson's Method.

$$x_4 = -1.22539 + \frac{.00097}{22.09512} = -1.22539 + .000004$$

$$= -1.225386 \qquad \text{(correct to six places of decimal).}$$

Example 52: *Obtain the more general formula for the root of*

$$f(x) = 0, \, x_1 = x_0 - \frac{f(x_0)}{f'(x_0)} - \frac{1}{2}\frac{\{f(x_0)\}^2 \, f''(x_0)}{\{f'(x_0)\}^3}$$

Solution: Expanding $f(x)$ *in the neighbourhood of* $^*x_0$ *and using Taylor's series, we readily obtain,* $-f(x) = f(x_0) + (x - x_0)\, f'(x_0) \qquad (\because \, f(x) = 0)$

$$\Rightarrow \qquad x_1 - x_0 = -\frac{f(x_0)}{f'(x_0)} \qquad \Rightarrow \qquad x_1 = x_0 - \frac{f(x_0)}{f'(x_0)}$$

(for the first approximation)

Again, we have, $f(x_1) = f(x_0) + (x_1 - x_0)\, f'(x_0) + \frac{1}{2}(x_1 - x_0)^2 \, f''(x_0)$

$$\Rightarrow \qquad 0 = f(x_0) + (x_1 - x_0)\, f'(x_0) + \frac{1}{2}\frac{\{f(x_0)\}^2}{\{f'(x_0)\}^2} f''(x_0) \qquad (\because \, f(x) = 0)$$

$$\Rightarrow \qquad x_1 = x_0 - \frac{f(x_0)}{f'(x_0)} - \frac{1}{2}\frac{\{f(x_0)\}^2 \, f''(x_0)}{\{f'(x_0)\}^3}$$

Example 53: *Show that the modified Newton-Raphson's Method.*

$$x_{n+1} = x_n - \frac{2f(x_n)}{f'(x_n)}$$

Gives a quadratic convergence when the equation $f(x) = 0$ has a pair of double root in the neighbourhood of $x = x_n$. **[Purvanchal 2005]**

Solution: $\varepsilon_{n+1} = \varepsilon_n - \dfrac{2f(a+\varepsilon_n)}{f'(a+\varepsilon_n)}$, where a, ε_n, ε_{n+1} have their usual meanings. Further expanding $f(a+\varepsilon_n)$ and $f'(a+\varepsilon_n)$ in powers of ε_n and using $f(a) = 0$, $f'(a) = 0$, since $x = a$ is a double root near $x = x_n$ we readily obtain

$$\varepsilon_{n+1} = \varepsilon_n - \frac{2\varepsilon_n^2\left[\frac{1}{2!}f''(a) + \frac{1}{3!}\varepsilon_n f'''(a) + \ldots\right]}{\varepsilon_n\left[f''(a) + \frac{\varepsilon_n}{2!}f'''(a) + \ldots\right]}$$

$$\simeq \varepsilon_n - \frac{2\varepsilon_n\left[\frac{1}{2!}f''(a) + \frac{1}{3!}\varepsilon_n f'''(a)\right]}{\varepsilon_n\left[f''(a) + \frac{\varepsilon_n}{2!}f'''(a)\right]}$$

$$\simeq \varepsilon_n^2 \frac{f'''(a)}{\left[f''(a) + \frac{\varepsilon_n f'''(a)}{2!}\right]} \simeq \frac{\varepsilon_n^2}{6}\frac{f'''(a)}{\left\{f''(a) + \frac{\varepsilon_n f'''(a)}{2}\right\}}$$

Thus $\varepsilon_{n+1} \simeq \frac{1}{6}\varepsilon_n^2 \frac{f'''(a)}{f''(a)}$ implying that $\varepsilon_{n+1} \propto \varepsilon_n^2$ and hence the convergence is quadratic.

Example 54: *Show that the following two sequences, both have convergence of the second order with the limit $\sqrt{a}$.*

$$x_{n+1} = \frac{1}{2}x_n\left(1 + \frac{a}{x_n^2}\right) \text{ and } x_{n+1} = \frac{1}{3}x_n\left(3 - \frac{x_n^2}{a}\right)$$

Solution: $x_{n+1} = \frac{1}{2}x_n\left(1 + \frac{a}{x_n^2}\right) \Rightarrow (x_{n+1} - \sqrt{a}) = \frac{1}{2}x_n\left(1 + \frac{a}{x_n^2}\right) - \sqrt{a}$

$$= \frac{1}{2}\left(x_n + \frac{a}{x_n} - 2\sqrt{a}\right) = \frac{1}{2}\left(\sqrt{x_n} - \frac{\sqrt{a}}{\sqrt{x_n}}\right)^2$$

$$= \frac{1}{2x_n}(x_n - \sqrt{a})^2 \quad \ldots(A)$$

or $\quad \varepsilon_{n+1} = (1/2x_n) \cdot \varepsilon_n^2$

And hence the convergence is quadratic.

Similarly for the second; we have

$$x_{n+1} - \sqrt{a} = \frac{1}{2} x_n \left(3 - \frac{x_n^{\,2}}{a}\right) - \sqrt{a}$$

$$= \frac{1}{2} x_n \left(1 + \frac{x_n^2}{a}\right) + (x_n - \sqrt{a})$$

$$= (x_n - \sqrt{a}) \left[1 - \frac{x_n}{2a}(x_n + \sqrt{a})\right]$$

$$= -\frac{(x_n - \sqrt{a})^2}{2}(x_n + 2\sqrt{a})$$

$$\Rightarrow \quad \varepsilon_{n+1} = -\frac{(x_n + 2\sqrt{a})}{2a}\varepsilon_n^2,$$

$\Rightarrow$ The convergence is quadratic.

Example 55: *If x_n is suitable close approximation to $\sqrt{a}$, show that the error in the first formula for x_{n+1} is about one-third in the second formula and deduce that* $x_{n+1} = (x_n/8)\ [6 + (3a/x_n^2) - (x_n^2/a)]$, *gives a sequence with third order convergence.*

Solution: Proceeding as in Ex. 40 we get

$$\varepsilon_{n+1} = -\frac{(x_n + \sqrt{a})}{2a}\varepsilon_n^2 \qquad \text{...(1)}$$

Further, since x_n is very close to $\sqrt{a}$, we must have

$$\varepsilon_{n+1} \simeq -\frac{(x_n + 2x_n)}{2x_n^2}\varepsilon_n^2 = -\frac{3}{2x_n}\varepsilon_n^2. \qquad \text{...(2)}$$

Inspection of equs. [A. ex. 40] and (2) reveals that the error in the first formula for x_{n+1} is about one-third of that in the second formula. In order to obtain the rate of 3rd order, we have

$$x_{n+1} - \sqrt{a} = \frac{1}{8} x_n \left(6 + \frac{3a}{x_n^2} - \frac{x_n^2}{a}\right) - \sqrt{a}$$

$$= \frac{x_n (6x_n^{\,2} a + 3a^2 - x_n^{\,4})}{8x_n^{\,2} a} - \sqrt{a}$$

$$= \frac{6x_n^{\,2} a + 3a^2 - x_n^4 - 8x_n a\sqrt{a}}{8x_n a}$$

$$= -\frac{(x_n + 3\sqrt{a})(x_n^{\,3} - 3x_n^{\,2}\sqrt{a} + 3x_n a - a\sqrt{a})}{8x_n a}$$

$$= -\frac{-(x_n + 3\sqrt{a})(x_n - \sqrt{a})^3}{8x_n a} = -\frac{(x_n + 3\sqrt{a})}{8x_n a}.\epsilon_n^{\,3}$$

$$\Rightarrow \quad \varepsilon_{n+1} = -[(x_n + 3\sqrt{a})/8a\,x_n]\,\varepsilon_n^3$$

$\Rightarrow$ That the above formula has a convergence of third order.

Example 56: *Solve* $x^4 - 5x^3 + 20x^2 - 40x + 60 = 0$, *given that all the roots of* $f(x) = 0$ *are complex, by using Bairstow's Method.* **[I.A.S. 2004]**

Solution: Starting with the value $p_0 = -4$, $q_0 = -8$, we proceed as follows:

	p	q	a_k	$1\ (a_0)$	$-5\ (a_1)$	$20\ (a_2)$	$-40\ (a_3)$	$60\ (a_4)$
1	−4	8	$-p\,b_{k+1}$	–	4	−4	32	0
			$-q\,b_{k+2}$	–	–	−8	8	−64
			b_k	$1\ (b_0)$	$-1\ (b_1)$	$8\ (b_2)$	$0\ (b_3)$	$-4\ (b_4)$
1	−4	8	$-p\,c_{k-1}$	–	4	12	48	
			$-q\,c_{k-2}$	–	–	−8	−24	
			c_k	1	3	12	24	
				(c_0)	(c_1)	(c_2)	(c_3)	

Using the value of the above table, the corrections Δp and Δq are given by

$$\begin{cases} c_2\,\Delta p + c_1\,\Delta q = -b_3 \\ (c_3 - b_3)\,\Delta p + c_2\,\Delta q = b_4 \end{cases}$$

or by

$$\begin{cases} 12\,\Delta p + 3\,\Delta q = 0 \\ 24\,\Delta p + 12\,\Delta q = -4 \end{cases}$$

Solving, we get $\Delta p = 1/6$, $\Delta q = -2/3$

i.e., $\Delta p = .16667$ and $\Delta q = -.66667$

Hence the new values of p and q are given by

$$p_1 = p_0 + \Delta p, \qquad q_1 = q_0 + \Delta q$$

$$= -4 + .16667 \qquad = 8 - .66667$$

$$= -3.83333, \qquad = 7.33333.$$

Now repeating the same computation with the new value of p and q *i.e.*, we divide the original equation by

$$x^2 - 3.83333\,x + 7.33333$$

1	−3.83333	−7.33333	a_k	1	−5	20	−40	60
			–		3.83333	−4.47223	+31.41199	−.12431
			–	–	–	−7.33333	+8.55558	−6.09253
1	−3.83333	−7.33333	a_k	1	−1.16667	8.19444	−.03243	−.21684
			–		+3.83333	+10.22219	+42.48595	
			–	–		−7.33333	−19.55550	
			c_k	1	2.66666	11.08330	22.89802	
				c_0	c_1	c_2	c_3	

The corrections Δp and Δq are given by

$$\begin{cases} 11.08330\,\Delta p + 2.66666\,\Delta q = -.03243. \\ 22.93045\,\Delta p + 11.08330\,\Delta q = -.21684. \end{cases}$$

Solving, we get $\Delta p = .00354$ and $\Delta q = -.02690$

$$\Rightarrow \quad p_2 = p_1 + \Delta p = -3.83333 + .00354 = -3.82979.$$

$$q_2 = q_1 + \Delta q = 7.33333 + .02690 = 7.306442.$$

The above results can be improved by further repeating the above procedure.

Hence one of the quadratic factors of $f(x)$ is

$$x^2 - 3.82979\,x + 7.30643.$$

Other quadratic factors can be obtained by dividing $f(x)$ by this factor.

Let the roots of the factor (1) be $\alpha \pm i\beta$, then we have

$$-2\alpha = -3.82979 \quad \text{and} \quad \alpha^2 + \beta^2 = 7.30643.$$

$$\Rightarrow \quad \alpha = 1.914895 \pm 1.907776\,i$$

i.e., roots are $1.914895 \pm 1.907776\,i$.

On the same lines, the roots of the other quadratic factor can be obtained.

Illustration: *Solve the equation $x^3 - 5x^2 - 17x + 20 = 0$ by Graeffe's Method (squaring three times).*

Example 57: *Find a quadratic factor of the polynomial*

$$P_4(x) \equiv x^4 + 5x^3 + 3x^2 - 5x - 9 = 0$$

starting with $p_0 = 3$, $q_0 = -5$, by using Bairstaw's Method. **[Agra 2004]**

Solution:

1, 3, −5	a_k	$1\,(a_0)$	$5\,(a_0)$	$3\,(a_2)$	$-5\,(a_3)$	$-9\,(a_4)$
	$(-p\,b_k)$		$-3\,(-p\,b_0)$	$-6\,(-p\,b_1)$	$-6\,(p\,b_2)$	$3\,(-p\,b_3)$
	$(-q\,b_k)$			$5\,(-q\,b_0)$	$10\,(-q\,b_1)$	$10\,(-p\,b_3)$
1, 3, −5	b_k	$1\,(b_0)$	$2\,(b_1)$	$2\,(b_2)$	$-1\,(b_3)$	$4\,(b_4)$
	$-p\,c_{k-1}$		$-3\,(-p\,c_0)$	$3\,(-p\,c_1)$	$-30\,(-p\,c_2)$	
	$-q\,c_{k-2}$			$5\,(-p\,c_0)$	$-5\,(-q\,c_1)$	
	(c_k)	$1\,(c_0)$	$-1\,(c_1)$	$10\,(c_2)$	$-36\,(c_3)$	

Using the values of the above table, the correction Δp_0 and Δq_0 are given by

$$\left.\begin{aligned} c_{n-2}\,\Delta p_0 + c_{n-3}\,\Delta q_0 &= b_{n-1} \\ (c_{n-1} - b_{n-1})\,\Delta p_0 + c_{n-2}\,\Delta q_0 &= b_n \end{aligned}\right\} \quad i.e. \quad \begin{aligned} \text{by } 10\,\Delta p_0 - \Delta q_0 &= -1 \\ -35\,\Delta p_0 + 10\,\Delta q_0 &= 4 \end{aligned}$$

Solving, we get $\Delta p_0 = -0.09$, $\Delta q_0 = 0.08$.

Thus p_1, q_1 the first approximation of p and q are given by

$$p_1 = p_0 + \Delta p_0 = -3 - 0.09 = 2.91$$

and $$q_1 = q_0 + \Delta q_0 = -5 + .8 = -4.92$$

Now, repeating the same computation with the new values of p and q *i.e.* we divide the original equation by $x^3 + 2.91x - 4.92$.

1, 2.91, −4.92	(a_k)	1	5	3	−5	−9
			−2.91	−6.08	−5.35	0.20
				4.92	10.28	9.05
	(b_k)	1	2.09	1.84	−0.07	0.25
			−2.91	2.37	−26.57	
				4.92	−4.03	
	(c_k)	1	−0.82	9.13	−30.67	
		c_0	c_1	c_2	c_3	

Hence the corrections Δp_1 and Δq_1 are given by

$$\left.\begin{aligned} 9.13\,\Delta p_1 - 0.82\,\Delta q_1 &= -0.07 \\ -30.60\,\Delta p_1 + 9.13\,\Delta q_1 &= 0.25 \end{aligned}\right\}$$

Now solving the above equations; we get

$$\Delta p_1 = -.00745,\ \Delta q_1 = 0.00241.$$

$$\Rightarrow \left.\begin{aligned} p_2 &= p_1 + \Delta p_1 = 2.91 - .00745 = 2.90255 \\ q_2 &= q_1 + \Delta q_1 = -4.92 + .00241 = -4.91756 \end{aligned}\right\}$$

$$\Rightarrow \quad (x^2 + p_2 x + q_2) - x^2 + 2.90255\,x - 4.91759 \text{ is factor of } P_4(x).$$

Dividing the given equation by this factor, we obtain another quadratic factor.

Example 58: *Solve* $x^3 - 8x^2 + 17x - 10 = 0$, *by Graeffe's Method. (squaring three times).*

[Agra 2008]

Solution: Let $f(x) \equiv x^3 - 8x^2 + 17x - 10 = 0$, then collecting all even terms on one side and all odd terms on the other side, we get

$$x^3 + 17x = 8x^2 + 10$$

Squaring both sides, $(x^3 + 17x)^2 = (8x^2 + 10)^2$

Putting $x^2 = y$, we obtain $y(y + 17)^2 = (8y + 10)^2$ ...(1)

$$\Rightarrow \quad y^3 - 30y^2 + 129y - 100 = 0.$$

$$y^3 + 129y = 30y^2 + 100 \quad \Rightarrow y^2(y^2 + 129)^2 = (30y^2 + 100)^2.$$

Putting $y^2 = z$,

we get $\quad z(z + 129)^2 = (30z + 100)^2$

$$\Rightarrow \quad z^3 - 642z^2 + 10641z + 10^4 = 0 \qquad \text{...(2)}$$

This gives $\quad z(z^2 + 10641) = 642z^2 + 10^4.$ ...(3)

Squaring both sides of (3) and then putting $z^2 = u$, we get

$$u^3 - 390882u^2 + 10039081u - 10^3 = 0$$

Let the roots of (4) be u_1, u_2, u_3, then we have

$$\left.\begin{aligned} u_1 &\approx 39882 \\ u_1 u_2 &\approx 100390881 \\ u_1 u_2 u_3 &\approx 10^8 \end{aligned}\right\} \Rightarrow \left\{\begin{aligned} u_1 &\approx 390882 \\ u_2 &\approx (100390881/390882) \\ u_3 &\approx (10^8/100390881) \end{aligned}\right.$$

Hence the roots of the original equation are

$$\left.\begin{array}{l|l} p_1 & \approx (u_1)^{1/8} \\ p_2 & \approx (100390881/390882)^{1/8} \\ p_3 & \approx (10)^8/(100390881)^{1/8} \end{array}\right) \Rightarrow \left|\begin{array}{l|l} p_1 & \approx 5.00041 \\ p_2 & \approx 2.00081 \\ p_3 & \approx 0.999512 \end{array}\right)$$

Thus the exact roots of the given equation are 5, 2, 1.

Example 59: *Find the roots of the equation* $2x = \cos x + 3$ *correct to three decimal places.*

Solution: We have $x = \frac{1}{2}(\cos x + 3)$

Let $f(x) = \frac{1}{2}(\cos x + 3)$, $\Rightarrow f'(x) = \frac{1}{2}(-\sin x)$

$$\Rightarrow |f'(x)| = \left|\frac{\sin x}{2}\right| < 1.$$

Thus the Iterative method is applicable and starting with $x_0 = \frac{\pi}{2}$,

we obtain successive approximations as follows:

$$x_1 = 1.5, x_2 = 1.535, x_3 = 1.518, x_4 = 1.526,$$

$$x_5 = 1.522, x_6 = 1.524, x_7 = 1.523, x_8 = 1.524.$$

So we can take the value of the root as 1.524 correct to three decimal places.

Aliter: *Solution by Aitken's Δ^2-Method.*

We get 3 approximation x_1, x_2, x_3 as above:

x_i	Δx_i	$\Delta^2 x_i$
$x_1 = 1.5$		
	0.035	
$x_2 = 1.535$		−0.052
	−0.017	
$x_3 = 1.518$		

Thus we get $x_4 = 1.518 - \frac{(0.017)^2}{-0.052} = 1.524$,

This value is corresponding to six normal iterations.

12.5 Solution of Numerical Equations (Contd)

(i) Algebraic Equations: The equations whose coefficients are merely algebraic symbols like *a, b, c* etc, and not numerical numbers are called algebraical equations e.g. $ax^2 + bx + c = 0$.

(ii) Numerical Equations: The equation whose coefficients are given numbers (numericals) is called a numerical equation e.g.

$$3x^2 + 4x + 1 = 0.$$

(iii) Commensurable Roots: A real root of an equation is called commensurable root, if it is either an integral or a rational number.

(iv) Incommensurable Roots: A real root of a given equation is said to be incommensurable if it is an rational number as $\sqrt{2}$, π etc.

By Horner's Method, we can find both commensurable and incommensurable roots of a given equation.

Horner's Method: First, we find integral pat of the root and then proceed to find its decimal parts as follows:

This method consists of in diminishing the roots of the given equation by suitable numbers. For example if the required root is 25.672, then the roots of the given equation shall be successively diminished by 20, 5, 0.6, .07, .002 respectively. Each new figure of the root is found by Newton's Method. By this method, we find positive roots only. To find the negative roots of $f(x) = 0$, we shall obtain the positive roots of $f(-x) = 0$.

Explanation: Let

$$f(x) \equiv a_0 x^n + a_1 x^{n-1} + a_2 x^{n-2} + \ldots + a_n \equiv 0 \qquad \ldots(1)$$

have its roots α (between p and $p+1$) as $p.\,qrs\ldots$ where $q, r, s\ldots$ are the decimal parts of the root.

Step 1: Let us diminish the roots of (1) by p getting the transformed equation as

$$b_0 x^n + b_1 x^{n-1} + \ldots + b_{n-1} x + b_n = 0 \qquad \ldots(2)$$

Step 2: The above equation has a root between 0 and 1 *i.e.* $0.\,qrs$.

To find out the value of q we multiply the roots of (2) by 10, getting the transformed equation as

$$b_0 x^n + 10\, b_1 x^{n-1} + 10^2 b_2 x^{n-2} + \ldots + 10^{n-1} b_{n-1} x + 10^n b_n = 0 \qquad \ldots(3)$$

The root of this equation $q.rs$

Step 3: Diminish the root of (3) by q, obtaining the transformed equation as

$$c_0 x^n + c_1 x^{n-1} + c_2 x^{n-2} + \ldots + c_{n-1} x + c_n = 0 \qquad \ldots(4)$$

It is to be noted that the sign of the last term of (4) is the same as that of the term of (3) and so on.

Example 60: *Find by Horner's Method the positive root of the equation* $x^3 + x^2 + x - 100 = 0$, *correct to four places of decimal.*

Solution: **Step 1**: Let $f_1(x) = x^3 + x^2 + x - 100 = 0$ ...(1)

Then we have $f_1(0) = -100$, $f_1(1) = -97$, $f_1(2) = -86$,

$$f_1(3) = -61,\ f_1(4) = -16,\ f_1(5) = +55$$

Here $f_1(4)$ and $f_1(5)$ are opposite in sign, so the root lies between 4 and 5.

Step 2: *The integral part of the root is* 4, *so we diminish the roots by* 4 *implying;*

4	1	1	1	− 100
	0	4	20	84
	1	5	21	− 16
	0	4	36	
	1	9	57	
	0	4		
	1	13		

Whence the transformed equation is

$$\phi_1(x) \equiv x^3 + 13x^2 + 57x - 16 \qquad ...(2)$$

Step 3: *By Newton's Method, the approximate root of* (2) *is given*

by $$x_1 = 0 - \frac{\phi_1(0)}{\phi_1'(0)} = 0 - \frac{-16}{57} = 0.28$$

$$\phi_1(.2) = -4.072 \quad \phi_1(.3) = +2.297$$

∴ Root of (2) lies between .2 and .3

then multiplying the roots of the equation (2) by 10, we have

$$x^3 + 130x^2 + 5700x - 16000 = 0 \qquad ...(3)$$

Now the root of (3) lies between 2 and 3.

Step 4: *Let us diminish the root of* (3) *by* 2, *implying*

2	1	130	5700	− 16000
	0	2	264	11928
	1	132	5964	− 4072
	0	2	268	
	1	134	6232	
	0	2		
	1	136		

The transformed equation is then given by

$$\phi_2(x) = x^3 + 136x^2 + 6232x - 4072 = 0 \qquad ...(4)$$

Step 5: *By Newton's Method, approximate root of* (4) *is given by*

$$x_1 = 0 - \frac{\phi_2(0)}{\phi_2'(0)} = -\frac{-4072}{6232} = 0.65$$

Also, $\phi_2(.6) = -283.624$ and $\phi(.7) = +357.383$.

i.e. the root of (4) lies between 0.6 and 0.7.

Step 6: *Multiply the root of* (4) *by* 10, *so that we obtain*

$$x^3 + 1360x^2 + 623200x - 4072000 = 0 \qquad ...(5)$$

Hence the root of (5) lies between 6 and 7.

Step 7: *Diminishing the roots of* (5) *by* 6, *we again obtain*

6	1	1360	623200	– 4072000
	0	6	8196	3788376
	1	1366	631396	– 283624
	0	6	8232	
	1	1372	639628	
	0	6		
	1	1378		

The transformed equation is therefore given by

$$\phi_3(x) = x^3 + 1378x^2 + 639628x - 283624 = 0 \qquad ...(6)$$

Step 8: *Applying Newton's Method we get*

$$x_1 = 0 - \frac{\phi_3(0)}{\phi_3'(0)} = -\frac{-283624}{639628} = 0.44$$

$\Rightarrow \quad \phi_3(.4) = -27552.256$ and $\phi_3(.5) = +36534.625$

$\Rightarrow$ The root of (6) lies between 0.4 and 0.5

Then multiplying the roots of (6) by 10, so that the new equation is

$$x^3 + 13780x^2 + 63962800x - 283624000 = 0 \qquad ...(7)$$

Evidently the root of (7) lies between 4 and 5.

Step 9: *Diminishing the roots of* (7) *by* 4, *we readily get*

4	1	13780	63962800	– 283624000
	0	4	55136	26071744
	1	13784	64017936	– 27552256
	0	4	55152	
	1	13788	64073088	
	0	4		
	1	13792		

The transformed equation is then given by

$$\phi_4(x) = x^3 + 13792x^2 + 64073088x - 27552256 = 0$$

Step 10: *By Newton's Method, we have*

$$x_1 = 0 - \frac{\phi_4(0)}{\psi_4'(0)} = 0 - \frac{-27552256}{64073088} = .4$$

The next digit is 4, so that the root of the given equation is 4.2644

Aliter: In short we can proceed as follows: $x^3 + x^2 + x - 100 = 0$

4	1	1	1	– 100
		4	20	84
		5	21	– 16000
		4	36	11928
		9	5700	– 4072000
		4	264	3788376
2		130	5964	– 283624000
		2	268	256071744
		132	623200	– 27552256000
		2	8196	
		134	631396	
		2	8232	
6		1360	63962800	
		6	55136	
		1366	64017936	
		6	55152	
		1372	6407308800	
		6		
4		13780		
		4		
		13784		
		4		
		13788		
		4		
		137920		

Root = 4.2644

Example 61: *Find the real root of the equation* $x^3 + 3x - 7 = 0$; *correct to two places of decimals.*

[Bhopal 2002]

Solution: Let $f(x) \equiv x^3 + 3x - 7 = 0$ ...(1)

then we have $f(0) = -7,\ f(1) = -3,\ f(2) = +7.$

Here $f(1)$ and $f(2)$ are of opposite sign. so the root of (1) lies between 1 and 2, *i.e.*

The integral part of the root is 1.

Then diminishing the root of (1) by 1, we obtain

1	1	0	3	−7
	0	1	1	4
	1	1	4	−3
	0	1	2	
	1	2	6	
	0	1		
	1	3		

Whence the transformed equation is given by

$$\phi_1(x) \equiv x^3 + 3x^2 + 6x - 3 = 0 \qquad \text{...(2)}$$

Now by Newton's Method; we get

$$x_1 = 0 - \frac{\phi_1(0)}{\phi_1'(0)} = 0 - \frac{-3}{6} = 5$$

and $\phi_1(.4) = -0.056$ and $\phi_1(.5) = +0.875$

Hence the root of (2) lies between 0.4 and 0.5

Now multiplying the roots of (2) by 10, we get

$$\phi(x) \equiv x^3 + 30x^2 + 600x - 3000 = 0 \qquad \text{...(3)}$$

The root of (3) then lies between 4 and 5.

Now diminishing the root of (3), by 4. we have

4	1	30	600	−3000
	0	4	136	2944
	1	34	736	−56
	0	4	152	
	1	38	888	
	0	4		
	1	42		

Whence the transformed equation is given by

$$\phi_3(x) \equiv x^3 + 42x^2 + 888x - 56 = 0 \qquad \text{...(4)}$$

Now by Newton's Method; we obtain

$$x_1 = 0 - \frac{\phi_3(0)}{\phi_3'(0)} = 0 - \frac{-56}{888} = 0.06$$

Then multiplying the root of (4) by 10, we get

$$\phi_4(x) \equiv x^3 + 420x^2 + 88800x - 56000 = 0 \qquad \text{...(5)}$$

Now, we have $\phi_4(0) = -56000$ and $\phi_4(1) = +33221$

The second decimal place of the root is 0. Further multiplying roots of (5) by 10, we again obtain

$$\phi_5(x) \equiv x^3 + 4200x^2 + 8880000x - 56000000 = 0 \qquad ...(6)$$

$$\therefore \quad \phi_5(6) = -2568584 \text{ and } \phi_5(7) = +6366143$$

Thus the thirds decimal place of the root is 6

Thus the root is 1.406

Whence the required root upto two decimal places is 1.41

Example 62: *Find the Horner's Method, the positive root of the equation is:*

$$x^3 + 2x^2 - 7x - 9 = 0$$

Solution: Let $f(x) = x^3 + 2x^2 - 7x - 9 = 0 \qquad ...(1)$

Then, we have $f(1) = -13$, $f(2) = -7$, $f(3) = +15$.

Hence the root lies between 2 and 3.

The integral part of the root is obviously 2.

Now diminishing the root by 2, we get

2	1	2	−7	−9
	0	2	8	2
	1	4	1	−7
	0	2	12	
	1	6	13	
	0	2		
	1	8		

Whence the transformed equation is given by

$$f_1(x) \equiv x^3 + 8x^2 + 13x - 7 = 0 \qquad ...(2)$$

Applying Newton's Method, the approximate root of equation (2) is given by

$$x_1 = 0 - \frac{f_1(0)}{f_1'(0)} = 0 - \frac{-7}{13} = 0.5385$$

Also, we have $f_1(.4) = -0.456$, $f_1(.5) = 1.625$.

Now the approximately root may be 0.4 or 0.5.

i.e. the root of the equation (2) lies between 0.4 and 0.5; then multiplying the roots of (2) by 10, we readily obtain

$$x^3 + 80x^2 + 1300x - 7000 = 0 \qquad ...(3)$$

Then root of (3) lies between 4 and 5 whence diminishing the root of (3) by 4, we obtain

4	1	80	1300	– 7000
	0	4	336	6544
	1	84	1636	– 456
	0	4	352	
	1	88	1988	
	0	4		
	1	92		

Thus the transformed equation is given by

$$f_2(x) \equiv x^3 + 92\,x^2 + 1988\,x - 456 = 0 \qquad \text{...(4)}$$

The root of this equation lies between 0 and 1.

Now we have $x_2 = -\dfrac{f_2(0)}{f_2'(0)} = -\dfrac{-456}{1988} = 0.2294$

Also $f_2(.2) = -54.712$ and $f_2(.3) = +148.707$

whence the root (4) lies between 0.2 and 0.3. Multiplying the root of (4) by 10, we readily obtain

$$x^3 + 920\,x^2 + 198800\,x - 456000 = 0 \qquad \text{...(5)}$$

The root of this equation lies between 2 and 3.

Then diminishing the root of (5) by 2; we get

2	1	920	198800	– 456000
	0	2	1844	401288
	1	922	200644	– 54712
	0	2	1848	
	1	924	202492	
	0	2		
	1	926		

Whence the transformed equation is given by

$$f_3(x) \equiv x^3 + 926\,x^2 + 202492\,x - 54712 = 0 \qquad \text{...(6)}$$

Now by Newton's Method; we have

$$x_1 = 0 - \frac{f_3(0)}{f_3'(0)} = 0 - \frac{-54712}{202492} = 0.2702$$

Again we have $f_3(.2) = -14176.552$ and $f_3(.3) = +6118.967$

Thus the root of (6) lies between 0.2 and 0.3

Hence the root of (1) is 2.422

✦✦ Problem Set ✦✦

*Find the positive root of the following equations by **Horner's Method**.*

1. The root of the equation $x^3 - 3x + 1 = 0$ lies between 1 and 2, find it correct to third decimal places.
2. Find the root of the equation $x^3 - 2x - 7 = 0$ between 2 and 3 correct to three places of decimals.
3. Find the real root of the equation $x^3 + 2x - 10 = 0$ up to three decimal places.

✦✦ Answers ✦✦

1.	1.532	2.	2.258	3.	1.847

12.6 Contracton of Horner's Method

When we want to find out the root of an equation up to 10 places of decimals, the process of multiplying the roots by 10 at every stage too lengthy. We illustrate this process by taking the last example. After evaluating the root up to second decimal place, the transformed equation is

$$x^3 + 9260\,x^2 + 20249200\,x - 54712000 = 0 \qquad ...(1)$$

Then dividing the equation by 1000, we obtain

$$0.001\,x^3 + 9.26\,x^2 + 20249.2x - 54712 = 0 \qquad ...(2)$$

Making approximations of the fractional coefficients of (2), we say that the roots will not change very much; 0.001 may be taken as zero, 9.26 equal to 9 and 20249.2 equal to 20249.

Whence the equation (2) changes to

$$0.x^3 + 9x^2 + 20249x - 54712 = 0 \qquad ...(3)$$

or $\quad f(x) = 0$, where $f(x) \equiv 9\,x^2 + 20249\,x - 54712$

$\therefore \quad f(2) = -14178,\ f(3) = +6116$ *i.e.* the root lies between 2 and 3. The next digit is therefore 2.

Rather annexing zero to the right of the coefficients of the transformed equation, we now cut off one figure from the right of the coefficient of x, two from the right of coefficient of x^2 and so on. Also retain the figures of the constant term and neglect the leading taken as 1 and the fractions less than 0.5 to be neglected. By this repeated method all the figures of the last but two coefficients are exhausted and the process reduces to the ordinary process of division. This can be continued until all the figures of the trial divisor are exhausted. For example, in example the equation was

$$x^3 + 926\,x^2 + 202492\,x - 54712 = 0$$

Rather annexing zero's we cut off one figure from the right of last but one coefficient and cut off two figures *i.e.* 26 from the last but two coefficients and neglect the leading coefficient,

$$\Rightarrow \qquad 9x^2 + 20249x - 54712 = 0 \qquad ...(4)$$

Then by Newton's method, we have

$$x_1 = 0 - \frac{f(0)}{f'(0)} = -\frac{-54712}{20249} = 2.7$$

Whence diminishing the roots of (3) by 2, we get

2	9	20249	– 54712	2
	0	18	40534	
	9	20267	– 14178	6
	0	18	12171	
	9	20285	– 2007	9
		2028	1825	
		202	– 182	9
		20	182	
		2	0	
			0	
			0	

Hence the required root is 2.4226990.

> **Note:** After obtaining 2.422 as a root of the given equation, we apply contraction. There are 5 digits (20285) in the last but one coefficient and hence we can find (5 – 1) *i.e.* 4 additional places of decimal. Let us now cut off 5 from 20285 and 9 from 9. 2028. $5 \times 6 = 12171$.

Then cut off 8 from 202.8 then $202.8 \times 9 = 1825.2 = 1825$ (rounding off) cut off 2 from 202, then $202 \times 9 = 1818 = 182$ (round off) and cut off 0 from $20, 2 \times 0 = 0$.

Where Horner's Contraction Process Begins:

Let the last but one coefficient contain *n* integers, then we can obtain (*n* – 1) figures of the root in addition to those already obtained. We must be sure that the number of integers in the last one coefficient should be one more than the number of figures of the root excluding the figures already found. Let after calculating three places of decimal, we apply contraction process to find seven additional figures; then last but one coefficient should contain (7 + 1) *i.e.* 8 digits. But when the last but one coefficient consists of only 7 figures then we should obtain four places of decimal by usual Horner's method and then apply its contraction process.

Example 63: *Find the positive root of the equation* $x^3 - x^2 - x - 2000 = 0$ *up to 7 places of decimal.*

Solution: Let $f(x) \equiv x^3 - x^2 - x - 2000 = 0$ ...(1)

Then we have $f(12) = -ve$, $f(13) = +ve$

and hence the root of the equation lies between 12 and 13. Now let us diminishing the root by 10 and then by 2. Then completing the method we get the required root $= 12.9686724$

1	−1	−1	−2000	
0	10	90	890	10
1	9	89	−1110	
0	10	190	682	+2
1	19	279	−428000	
0	10	62	395379	9
1	29	341	−32621000	
0	2	66	28481736	6
1	31	40700	−4139264	
0	2	3231	3818144	8
1	33	43931	−321120	6
0	2	3312	286543	
1	350	4724300	−34577	
0	9	22656	33430	7
1	359	4746956	−1147	
0	9	22692	955	2
1	368	4769648	−192	4
0	9	303	191	
1	3770	477268	−1	0
0	6	303	0	
1	3776	477571	−1	
0	6	47757	−1	
1	3782	4775		
0	6	477		
1	3788	47		
	37	4		

Example 64: *Solve the equation $x^3 - 2x - 5 = 0$ correct to nine places of decimal.*

Solution: Let $f(x) \equiv x^3 - 2x - 5 = 0$ ...(1)

Then $f(2) = 8 - 4 - 5 = -1,\ f(3) = 27 - 6 - 5 = +16$

Hence the root lies between 2 and 3. The root is 2.094551483

1	0	−2	−5	2
0	2	+4	4	
1	2	2	−1000	0
0	2	8	−1000000	9
1	4	1000	949329	
0	2	100000	−50671000	4
1	60	5481	44517584	
0	600	105481	−6153416	5
1	9	5562	5578825	
0	609	11104300	−574591	5
1	9	25096	558040	
0	618	11129396	−16551	1
1	9	25112	11160	
0	6270	11154508	−5391	4
1	4	314	4464	
0	6274	1115765	−926	8
1	4	314	893	
0	6278	111607~~9~~	−33	3
1	4	11160~~7~~	33	
0	6282	1116~~0~~	0	
1	6~~2~~	111~~6~~		
0		11~~1~~		
1				
0				
~~1~~				

Illustration: *Find the root of the equation* $x^3 - 7x + 7 = 0$ *up to four places of decimals. The root lies between* 1.5 *and* 2. *(Multiplying the root of the equation by* 2*).*

✦✦ Problem Set ✦✦

1. Find the real root of (i) $x = \frac{1}{2} + \sin x$, (ii) $e^x - 3x = 0$.

2. Find the real root to four decimal of the equation.
$x^6 - x^4 - x^3 - 1 = 0$ [lying between (1, 2)].

3. The equation $x^4 - 5x^3 - 12x^2 + 76x - 79 = 0$ has two roots close to $x = 2$. Find the roots up to four places of decimal.

4. Evaluate (i) $\sqrt{(29)}$, (ii) $\left(\frac{1}{3}\right)^{1/4}$

5. Find the root of $\log x = \cos x$, by Newton's Method to five places of decimal.

6. Find $\sqrt{(30)}$ by using Iterative process.

7. Find the roots of $x^3 - 2x^2 - 5x + 6 = 0$, squaring three times.

8. Determine the real root of $2x - 3\sin x - 5 = 0$, up to six decimal places, by Newton's Method.

9. Find a root $x = \frac{1}{2} + \sin x$ near $x = 1.5$.

10. Solve the equation $x^4 - 8x^3 + 39x^2 - 62x + 50 = 0$, starting with $p = q = 0$.

11. Find the quadratic factor of $x^3 - 3.7x^2 + 6.25x - 4.069$, after two iteration. Use $p_0 = -2.5$, $q_0 = 0$.

12. Use Newton's Method for nearly equal roots to solve
$x^3 - x^2 - 16.0001x - 19.9985 = 0$

13. Determine the real root of $\tan x = x$ the Iteration Method.

14. Solve $x^3 + 1.2x^2 - 4x - 4.8 = 0$ by False Position Method.

15. Find the root of $x^3 - 5x^2 - 7x + 20 = 0$, squaring three times.

16. Find a double root of $x^3 - 15.87x + 24.34 = 0$, correct to three significant figures.

17. Show that the square root of $N = AB$ is given by
$\sqrt{N} = (S/4) + (N/S)$, where $S = A + B$

18. Describe Graeffes squaring Method for obtaining the root of a polynomial equation.

19. Find the pth and reciprocal p^{th} root of a given number N by Newton-Raphson's Method. Hence obtain the cube root of 12.

20. Solve $x^3 - 8x^2 + 7x - 10 = 0$ by Graeffe's Method (Squaring two times).

[Bhopal 2002]

21. (i) Find the root of the equation $2x = \cos x + 3$ correct to three decimal places.

(ii) Solve the above equation by Aitken's Δ^2 – Method.

22. Using Newton's formula with $x_0 = 1$, obtain a zero of

$$x^4 + x^3 + 5x^2 + 4x + 4 = 0.$$

23. Find the root of $x^2 - 5x + 2 = 0$ correct to five decimal places by Newton-Raphson Method.

[Agra 2003]

24. Find a root of the equation $x^4 + x^3 - x^2 - 10x + 1 = 0$, which lies 0 and 1, correct to four places of decimal.

25. Find a root of a equation $x^3 + 29x - 97 = 0$, which lies between 2 and 3, correct to five places of decimal.

✦✦ Objective Type Question ✦✦

❖ Multiple Choice Questions

1. a is the root of the equation $f(x) = 0$ iff

(a) $f(a) = 0$ (b) $f(a) \neq 0$

(c) $f'(a) = 0$ (d) $f'(a) \neq 0$ **[Rohilkhand 2008]**

2. The real roots of the equation $f(x) = 0$ are the abscissae of the points where the graph crosses the

(a) y-axis (b) x-axis

(c) Line $y = x$ (d) Line $y = -x$ **[Rohilkhand 2010]**

3. Let x_0 be an approximate value of the disired root of the equation $f(x) = 0$. Then by Newton-Raphson method the improved value of the root is $x_0 + h$ where h is

(a) $\dfrac{f(x_0)}{f'(x_0)}$ (b) $-\dfrac{f(x_0)}{f'(x_0)}$

(c) $\dfrac{f'(x_0)}{f(x_0)}$ (d) $-\dfrac{f'(x_0)}{f(x_0)}$ **[Kanpur 2005, 2009]**

4. Newton's iterative formula for obtaining a^{-1} is

(a) $x_{n+1} = x_n(2 + ax_n)$ (b) $x_{n+1} = x_n(2 - ax_n)$

(c) $x_{n+1} = x_n(1 + ax_n)$ (d) $x_{n+1} = x_n(1 - ax_n)$ **[Bhopal 2006, 2009]**

5. The exact roots of the equation $x^3 - 8x^2 + 17x - 10 = 0$ are

(a) 1, 2, 3 (b) 1, 2, 5

(c) 2, 3, 5 (d) 1, 3, 5 **[Indore 2010]**

6. One root of the equation $x^3 - x - 1 = 0$ lies between

(a) 1 and 2 (b) 0 and 1

(c) 2 and 3 (d) None of these **[Kanpur 2007]**

7. An algebraic equation of degree n, where n is a positive integer, has

(a) n roots (b) n^2 roots

(c) n^3 roots (d) None of these

8. In Regula-Falsi method if a root of $f(x) = 0$ lies between x_1 and x_2 then the approximate value of the desired root is $x_1 + h$ where h is

(a) $\dfrac{(x_1 - x_2)|y_1|}{|y_1| + |y_2|}$ (b) $\dfrac{(x_2 - x_1)|y_1|}{|y_1| + |y_2|}$

(c) $\dfrac{(x_1 - x_2)|y_2|}{|y_1| + |y_2|}$ (d) $\dfrac{(x_2 - x_1)|y_2|}{|y_1| + |y_2|}$ **[I.A.S. 2009]**

✦✦ Answers ✦✦

❖ Problem Set

1.	(i) 1.4471, (ii) 0.6190	**2.**	1.4036 [lying between (1, 2)]
3.	1.7684, .2410	**4.**	(i) 5.385165, (ii) 0.75
5.	1.3029	**6.**	5.47722
7.	Exact roots are $3, -2, 1$.	**8.**	2.883238
9.	1.4973	**10.**	$1 \pm i,\ 3 \pm 4i$
11.	$x^2 - 2.40246\,x + 3.13232$		
12.	$-2.990007,\ -2.310007$. Actual roots are $-1.99,\ -2.31, 5$		
13.	4.43464	**21.**	1.524
23.	4.561553	**24.**	0.3131
25.	2.68061		

❖ Multiple Choice Questions

1.	(a)	**2.**	(b)	**3.**	(b)	**4.**	(b)
5.	(b)	**6.**	(a)	**7.**	(a)	**8.**	(b)

◆◆◆

Theory | Solved Examples | Problem Set

Chapter 13

Solution of Simultaneous Linear Algebraic Equations

Cramer's Rule, Gauss Elimination Method, Gauss Jaurdan Method, Crout's Method, Factorisation Method, Iterative Method (Jacobi's Gauss Seidel, Relaxation) Well Conditioned and Ill Conditioned Equations, Comparison of Different Methods, Newton Raphson Method to Solve Non Linear Simultaneous Equations.

13.1 Introduction

Consider the following "m" first degree equations consisting of n unknowns $x_1, x_2, x_3, \ldots x_n$:

$$\left.\begin{array}{l} a_{11}x_1 + a_{12}x_2 + \ldots + a_{1j}x_j + \ldots + a_{1n}x_n = b_1 \\ a_{21}x_1 + a_{22}x_2 + \ldots + a_{2j}x_j + \ldots + a_{2n}x_n = b_2 \\ \ldots \quad \ldots \quad \ldots \quad \ldots \quad \ldots \quad \ldots \\ a_{i1}x_1 + a_{i2}x_2 + \ldots + a_{ij}x_j + \ldots + a_{in}x_n = b_i \\ \ldots \quad \ldots \quad \ldots \quad \ldots \quad \ldots \quad \ldots \\ a_{m1}x_1 + a_{m2}x_2 + \ldots + a_{mj}x_j + \ldots + a_{mn}x_n = b_m \end{array}\right\}$$

or in matrix notation, we have

$$\underbrace{\begin{bmatrix} a_{11} & a_{12} & \ldots & a_{1j} & \ldots & a_{1n} \\ a_{21} & a_{22} & \ldots & a_{2j} & \ldots & a_{2n} \\ \ldots & \ldots & & \ldots & & \ldots \\ a_{i1} & a_{i2} & \ldots & a_{ij} & \ldots & a_{in} \\ \ldots & \ldots & & \ldots & & \ldots \\ a_{m1} & a_{m2} & \ldots & a_{mj} & \ldots & a_{mn} \end{bmatrix}_{m\times n}}_{A} , \underbrace{\begin{bmatrix} x_1 \\ x_2 \\ \ldots \\ x_i \\ \ldots \\ x_n \end{bmatrix}_{m\times n}}_{X} = \underbrace{\begin{bmatrix} b_1 \\ b_2 \\ \\ b_i \\ \\ b_m \end{bmatrix}_{m\times n}}_{B}$$

$\Rightarrow$ $$AX = B$$

Where $A = (a_{ij})_{m\times n}$, $X = \begin{bmatrix} x_1 \\ x_2 \\ \cdot \\ \vdots \\ x_n \end{bmatrix}$, $B = \begin{bmatrix} b_1 \\ b_2 \\ \vdots \\ \cdot \\ b_m \end{bmatrix}$

By finding a solution of a system of equation we mean to obtain the value of $x_1, x_2, \ldots, x_n$ (the n unknowns) such that they satisfy the given equations. The system of equations, given above, is said to be *homogeneous* if all the b_i $(i = 1, \ldots. m)$ vanish otherwise it is called as *Non-Homogeneous System.* A number of methods have been discussed by the authors in their books on matrices for finding the solution of such equations. Some of the methods we shall discuss in brief as they are not of much practical importance in comparison to the methods of successive elimination, Crout and Gauss-Siedel etc, while using desk calculating machines.

Hence we shall restrict ourselves to the case where number of rows is equal to the number of columns *i.e.* $m = n$.

13.2 Different Methods of Obtaining the Solutions

We have $\qquad AX = B$ * $\qquad$ ...(1)

Where $\qquad A = (a_{ij})_{m \times n}, \quad X = \begin{bmatrix} x_1 \\ x_2 \\ \cdot \\ \cdot \\ x_n \end{bmatrix}_{n \times 1}, \quad B = \begin{bmatrix} b_1 \\ b_2 \\ \cdot \\ \cdot \\ b_m \end{bmatrix}_{m \times 1}$

Where A is the coefficient matrix, X the solution vector and B is known as right-hand-side vector.

The necessary and sufficient condition for the existence of a solution of the system $AX = B$ is that $r(A) = r(AB)$ *i.e.* in other words: rank of the coefficient matrix is the same as the rank of the augmented matrix.

We now give some rules to give the information about the existence of a solution of the system $AX = B$.

(i) If $B = 0$, det $A = 0$, then there exist infinite number of non-trivial solutions besides trivial solution $X = 0$.

(ii) If $B = 0$ and det $A \neq 0$; then the system has the only unique trivial solution $X = 0$. In this case $r(A) = m$.

(iii) If $B \neq 0$ and det $A \neq 0$; then system has only unique solution and in this case we have $r(A) = m$.

(iv) If $B \neq 0$, det $A = 0$; then there exist infinite number of solutions provided the equations are consistent. In this case we have $r(A) < m$.

13.2.1 Method of Solution using Inverse of the Matrix: We know, if A is invertible, then det $A \neq 0$.

Now $\qquad AX = B \Rightarrow A^{-1} AX = A^{-1} B \Rightarrow X = A^{-1} B,$

---

* A is called the coefficient matrix of the system and X and B are called column vectors with components $x_1, x_2, \ldots, x_n$ and $b_1, b_2, \ldots, b_n$ respectively.

Where $A^{-1} = \dfrac{1}{\det(A)} \text{Adj}(A)$.

Thus $X = \dfrac{\text{adj}(A)}{\det(A)} B$ and hence the solution is determined.

13.2.2 Cramer's Rule: We have

$$AX = B, \qquad \ldots(1)$$

Where, $A = \begin{bmatrix} a_{11} & a_{12} \cdots & a_{1n} \\ a_{21} & a_{22} \cdots & a_{2n} \\ \cdots & \cdots & \cdots \\ a_{n1} & a_{n2} \cdots & a_{nn} \end{bmatrix}$, $X = \begin{bmatrix} x_1 \\ x_2 \\ \vdots \\ \cdot \\ x_n \end{bmatrix}$, $B = \begin{bmatrix} b_1 \\ b_2 \\ \vdots \\ b_n \end{bmatrix}$

$$x_j \; (\det A) = x_j \begin{vmatrix} a_{11} & a_{12} & a_{1j} & a_{1n} \\ a_{21} & a_{22} & a_{2j} & a_{2n} \\ \cdots & \cdots & \cdots & \cdots \\ a_{i1} & a_{i2} & a_{ij} & a_{in} \\ \cdots & \cdots & \cdots & \cdots \\ a_{n1} & a_{n2} & a_{nj} & a_{nn} \end{vmatrix} = \begin{vmatrix} a_{11} & a_{12} \cdots & a_{1j}\, x_j \cdots & a_{1n} \\ a_{21} & a_{22} \cdots & a_{2j}\, x_j \cdots & a_{2n} \\ \cdots & \cdots & \cdots & \cdots \\ a_{i1} & a_{i2} \cdots & a_{ij}\, x_j \cdots & a_{in} \\ \cdots & \cdots & \cdots & \cdots \\ a_{n1} & a_{n2} & a_{nj}\, x_j & a_{nn} \end{vmatrix}$$

Oprating $[C_j - C_1 x_1 - C_2 x_2 \ldots - C_{j-1} x_{j-1} - C_{j+1} x_{j+1} - \ldots - C_n x_n]$

$$= \begin{vmatrix} a_{11} & a_{12} \cdots & b_1 \cdots & a_{1n} \\ a_{21} & a_{22} \cdots & b_2 \cdots & a_{2n} \\ \cdots & \cdots & \cdots & \cdots \\ a_{i1} & a_{i2} \cdots & b \ldots & a_{in} \\ \cdots & \cdots & \cdots & \cdots \\ a_{n1} & b_{n2} & b_n \cdots & a_{nn} \end{vmatrix}$$ *and using the equations* given $AX = B$.

$= \det(A_j)$, where $\det A_j$ is the determinant obtained form

det (A) by replacing its jth column by the column $\begin{bmatrix} b_1 \\ b_2 \\ \cdot \\ \vdots \\ b_n \end{bmatrix}$

$\Rightarrow x_j = \dfrac{\det(A_j)}{\det(A)}$; where $\det A_j$ is the determinant obtained by replacing jth column of det A by B.

Giving different values to j, we can obtain $x_1, x_2, \ldots, x_n$ and hence the solution is determined. This method is feasible when $m = 3$ or 4.

13.2.3 The Elimination Method by Gauss: We have seen that any system of linear algebraic equations can be solved by the use of determinants. If the order of the determinant is large, then the evaluations becomes tedious. To avoid these unnecessary computations, from the practical computation point of view, various mathematicians have tried to develop simpler and less time consuming procedures, and various methods for solving system of linear equations have been suggested.

$$\left.\begin{array}{l} a_{11}x_1 + a_{12}x_2 + \ldots + a_{1n}x_n = b_1 \\ a_{21}x_1 + a_{22}x_2 + \ldots + a_{2n}x_n = b_2 \\ \ldots \quad \ldots \quad \ldots \quad \ldots \\ \ldots \quad \ldots \quad \ldots \quad \ldots \\ a_{n1}x_1 + a_{n2}x_2 + \ldots + a_{nn}x_n = b_n \end{array}\right] \quad \ldots(1)$$

One of the most important methods is the so called **Gauss-Algorithm**, which is a systematic elimination method. In this method for solving (1) we proceed step wise as follows:

First Step: *Elimination of x_1 form the second, third ,...., nth equation.* We assume here that the order of the equation and the order of the unknowns in each equations are such that $a_{11} \neq 0$. The variable x_1 can then be eliminated form the second equation by subtracting (a_{21}/a_{11}) times the first equation from the second equation, (a_{31}/a_{11}) times the first equation from the third equation, etc. This gives new system as follows:

$$\left.\begin{array}{l} a_{11}x_1 + a_{12}x_2 + \ldots + a_{1n}x_n = b_1 \\ \ldots \quad a'_{22}x_2 + \ldots + a'_{2n}x_n = b'_2 \\ \ldots \quad \ldots \quad \ldots \quad \ldots \\ \ldots \quad \ldots \quad \ldots \quad \ldots \\ \quad a'_{n2}x_2 + \ldots + a'_{nn}x_n = b'_n \end{array}\right] \quad \ldots(2)$$

Second Step: Elimination of x_2 form the third ,....., nth equation (2).

If the coefficient $a'_{22}, \ldots, a'_{nn}$ in (2) are not all zero, we may assume that the order of equation and the unknowns is such that $a'_{22} \neq 0$. Then we may eliminate x_2 from the third, fourth,...., n th equations of (2) by subtracting.

(a'_{33}/a'_{22}) times the second equation from the third equation, (a'_{42}/a'_{22}) times the second equation from the fourth equation, etc. The fourth steps are now obvious. In the third step, we eliminate x_3 and in the fourth step, we eliminate x_4 etc.

By successive elimination, we arrive at a single equation in the unknown x_n which can be solved and substituting this in the preceding equation we obtain the value of $x_{(n-1)}$. In this manner, we find x_1 when the elimination is completed. Also when the elimination is complete, the system takes the form

$$\left.\begin{array}{l} c_{11}x_1 + c_{12}x_2 + \ldots + c_{1n}x_n = d_1 \\ \quad c_{22}x_2 + \ldots + c_{2n}x_n = d_2 \\ \ldots \quad \ldots \quad \ldots \quad \ldots \\ \ldots \quad \ldots \quad \ldots \quad c_{nn}x_n = d_n \end{array}\right] \quad \textit{Triangular form.}$$

In this case there exists a unique solution. The new coefficient matrix is an upper triangular matrix, the diagonal element c_{ii} are usually equal to 1.

13.2.4 Gauss-Jordan Method: It is a modification of the method due to Gauss. In this method, the elimination is performed not only in the equations below but also in the equations above. In this way,we finally obtain a diagonal (even unit) coefficient, matrix, and we have the solution without further computation.

13.2.5 Crout's Method: This method is advantageous over Gauss method in the sense that it requires less computation. We shall explain this method by taking a set of three equations.

Consider the system

$$AX = B \quad \text{...(1)}$$

i.e.

$$\begin{bmatrix} a_{11} & a_{12} & a_{13} \\ a_{21} & a_{22} & a_{23} \\ a_{31} & a_{32} & a_{33} \end{bmatrix} \begin{bmatrix} x_1 \\ x_2 \\ x_3 \end{bmatrix} = \begin{bmatrix} b_1 \\ b_2 \\ b_3 \end{bmatrix} \Rightarrow \left. \begin{aligned} a_{11} x_1 + a_{12} x_2 + a_{13} x_3 &= b_1 \\ a_{21} x_1 + a_{22} x_2 + a_{23} x_3 &= b_2 \\ a_{31} x_1 + a_{32} x_2 + a_{33} x_3 &= b_3 \end{aligned} \right\}$$

The augmented matrix of (1) is $\begin{bmatrix} a_{11} & a_{12} & a_{13} & b_1 \\ a_{21} & a_{22} & a_{23} & b_2 \\ a_{31} & a_{32} & a_{33} & b_3 \end{bmatrix}$ ...(2)

Then we consider derived matrix $\begin{bmatrix} a'_{11} & a'_{12} & a'_{13} & b'_1 \\ a'_{21} & a'_{22} & a'_{23} & b'_2 \\ a'_{31} & a'_{32} & a'_{33} & b'_3 \end{bmatrix}$ ...(3)

which is obtained in order as given below:

(i) *To determine the first column,* $a'_{i1} = a_{i1}$ for i, *i.e.* the first column of the augmented matrix is same as the first column of the coefficient matrix A.

(ii) *To determine the first row to the right of the first column*

$$a'_{1j} = \frac{a_{1j}}{a_{11}} : j = 2, 3, b'_1 = \frac{b_1}{a_{11}};$$

i.e. the first row except the first element is obtained by dividing the corresponding elements of the first row of the matrix (2) *by the first element of that row.*

(iii) *To determine the elements of second column except* a'_{12},

$$a'_{i2} = a_{i2} - a'_{12} a'_{i1} : i = 2, 3$$

(iv) *To determine the elements of second row except* a'_{21}, a'_{22},

$$a'_{2j} = \frac{a_{2j} - a'_{1j} a'_{21}}{a'_{22}}, j = 3 \text{ and } b'_2 = \frac{b_2 - b'_1 a'_{21}}{a'_{22}}$$

(v) *To determine the elements of third column except* a'_{13}, a'_{33}

$$a'_{33} = a_{33} - a'_{23} a'_{32} - a'_{13} a'_{31}.$$

(vi) *To determine the remaining elements of third row*

$$b'_3 = \frac{b_3 - b'_2 a'_{32} - b'_1 a'_{31}}{a'_{33}}$$

The solution is given by

$$x_3 = b'_3, x_2 = b'_2 - a'_{23} x_3, x_1 = b'_1 - a'_{13} x_3 - a'_{12} x_2.$$

Hence the elements of the derived matrix are obtained as follows; first obtain first column, then elements of the first row to the right of the first column. After this compute elements of second column below the first row and then elements of the second row to the right of second column etc.

13.2.6 Method of Factorization: (Triangularisation Method).

This method is based on the fact that a square matrix A can be factorized into the form LU where L is unit lower triangular matrix and U is upper triangular, if all the principal minors of A are nonsingular,

i.e. if $$a_{11} \neq 0, \begin{vmatrix} a_{11} & a_{12} \\ a_{21} & a_{22} \end{vmatrix} \neq 0, \begin{vmatrix} a_{11} & a_{12} & a_{13} \\ a_{21} & a_{22} & a_{23} \\ a_{31} & a_{32} & a_{33} \end{vmatrix} \neq 0, \text{ etc.}$$

We shall explain this method by taking a set of three equations.

$$\left.\begin{aligned} a_{11} x_1 + a_{12} x_2 + a_{13} x_3 &= b_1 \\ a_{21} x_1 + a_{22} x_2 + a_{23} x_3 &= b_2 \\ a_{31} x_1 + a_{32} x_2 + a_{33} x_3 &= b_3 \end{aligned}\right] \qquad \ldots(1)$$

Put (1) in the form

$$\mathbf{AX = B}. \qquad \ldots(2)$$

Let $A = LU$

Where $L = \begin{bmatrix} 1 & 0 & 0 \\ l_{21} & 1 & 0 \\ l_{31} & l_{32} & 1 \end{bmatrix}$ and $U = \begin{bmatrix} u_{11} & u_{12} & u_{13} \\ 0 & u_{22} & u_{23} \\ 0 & 0 & u_{33} \end{bmatrix}$

Writing $A = LU$ in (2), we have

$$LUX = B. \qquad \ldots(3)$$

Putting $UX = Y$, the equation (3)

$$\Rightarrow \qquad LY = B. \qquad \ldots(4)$$

Equation (4) is equivalent to the system

$$\left.\begin{aligned} y_1 &= b_1 \\ l_{21} y_1 + y_2 &= b_2 \\ l_{31} y_1 + l_{32} y_2 + y_3 &= b_3 \end{aligned}\right\} \qquad \ldots(5)$$

The values of y_1, y_2, y_3 are obtained by the forward substitution.

When we know Y, the system $UX = Y$ gives:

$$\left.\begin{aligned} u_{11} x_1 + u_{12} x_2 + u_{13} x_3 &= y_1 \\ u_{22} x_2 + u_{23} x_3 &= y_2 \\ u_{33} x_3 &= y_3 \end{aligned}\right\} \qquad \ldots(6)$$

By the backward substitution, we get the values of x_1, x_2 and x_3.

The procedure of computing the matrices L and U is discussed below. From the relation $A = LU$, we have

$$\begin{bmatrix} 1 & 0 & 0 \\ l_{21} & 1 & 0 \\ l_{31} & l_{32} & 1 \end{bmatrix} \begin{bmatrix} u_{11} & u_{12} & u_{13} \\ 0 & u_{22} & u_{23} \\ 0 & 0 & u_{33} \end{bmatrix} = \begin{bmatrix} a_{11} & a_{12} & a_{13} \\ a_{21} & a_{22} & a_{23} \\ a_{31} & a_{32} & a_{33} \end{bmatrix}.$$

On multiplying the matrices on the left hand side and then equating the corresponding elements on both sides, we get

$$u_{11} = a_{11}; u_{12} = a_{12}; u_{13} = a_{13},$$

$$l_{21} u_{11} = a_{21} \Rightarrow l_{21} = a_{21}/a_{11},$$

$$l_{21} u_{12} + u_{22} = a_{22} \Rightarrow u_{22} = a_{22} - (a_{21}/a_{11}) a_{12},$$

$$l_{21} u_{13} + u_{23} = a_{23} \Rightarrow u_{23} = a_{23} - (a_{21}/a_{11}) a_{13},$$

$$l_{31} u_{11} = a_{31} \Rightarrow l_{31} = a_{31}/a_{11},$$

$$l_{31} u_{12} + l_{32} u_{22} = a_{32} \Rightarrow l_{32} = \frac{a_{31} - (a_{31}/a_{11}) a_{12}}{u_{22}},$$

and $\quad l_{31} u_{13} + l_{32} u_{23} + u_{33} = a_{33}$ which gives u_{33}.

Thus in a systematic way the elements of L and U can be obtained.

Let the lower and upper triangular matrices be denoted by L and U respectively, then we have

$$LA = U \Rightarrow L^{-1} LA = L^{-1}U \Rightarrow A = L^{-1}U \qquad ...(1)$$

But L^{-1} is also a lower triangular matrix, we can find a factorization of A as the product of one L-matrix and one R-matrix. Replacing L^{-1} by L, we get $LU = A$. Conveniently, we choose diagonal elements of one as 1. Thus the system $Ax = y$ is resolved into two Simpler systems:

$$Lz = y; \; Ux = z;$$

13.2.7 Iterative Method: So far, we have discussed some methods related with the solution of Simultaneous Linear Equation. Now we are going to discuss various indirect or Iterative Methods. Here we start with an approximate solution and if convergent, derive a sequence of closer approximations. This cycle of computation is repeated so as to obtain the required accuracy. Hence we conclude that in Direct Methods, the amount of computation is fixed whereas in any iterative method, the amount of computation depends on the accuracy required.

13.2.8 Jacobi Iterative Method: Consider the equations

$$\left.\begin{aligned} a_1 x + b_1 y + c_1 z = d_1 \\ a_2 x + b_2 y + c_2 z = d_2 \\ a_3 x + b_3 y + c_3 z = d_3 \end{aligned}\right\} \qquad ...(1)$$

Let a_1, b_1, c_3 be large as compared to other coefficients, then the system can written as

$$x = \frac{1}{a_1}(d_1 - b_1\, y - c_1\, z),$$

$$y = \frac{1}{b_2}(d_2 - a_2 x - c_2 z), \quad \text{...(2)}$$

and $$z = \frac{1}{c_3}(d_3 - a_3 x - b_3\, y)$$

If we start with the Initial approximations x_0, y_0, z_0 for the values of x, y, z respectively then substituting these on the right sides of (2), the first approximations are given by

$$x_1^{(1)} = \frac{1}{a_1}(d_1 - b_1\, y_0 - c_1\, z_0)$$

$$y_1^{(1)} = \frac{1}{b_2}(d_2 - a_2\, x_0 - c_2\, z_0)$$

$$z_1^{(1)} = \frac{1}{c_3}(d_3 - a_3\, x_0 - b_3\, y_0)$$

Again substituting the values $x_1^{(1)}, y_1^{(1)}, z_1^{(1)}$ on the right sides of (2), the second approximations are given by

$$x_2^{(2)} = \frac{1}{a_1}(d_1 - b_1\, y_1^{(1)} - c_1\, z_1^{(1)})$$

$$y_2^{(2)} = \frac{1}{b_2}(d_2 - a_2\, x_1^{(1)} - c_2\, z_1^{(1)})$$

$$z_2^{(2)} = \frac{1}{c_3}(d_3 - a_3\, x_1^{(1)} - b_3\, y_1^{(1)})$$

Continue this process till the difference between two consecutive approximations is as small as we please.

Solved Examples

Example 1: *Solve, by Jacobi's Iteration method, the equations*

$$20x + y - 2z = 17; 3x + 20\,y - z = -18; 2x - 3\,y + 20z = 25.$$

Solution: The given equations can be put in the form

$$\left.\begin{aligned} x &= \frac{1}{20}\,(17 - y + 2\,z) \\ y &= \frac{1}{20}\,(-18 - 3\,x + z) \\ z &= \frac{1}{20}\,(25 - 2\,x + 3\,y) \end{aligned}\right\} \quad \text{...(1)}$$

Let us start by an approximation $x_0 = y_0 = z_0 = 0$.

Substituting these on the right sides of the equations (1), we get

$$\left.\begin{aligned} x_1^{(1)} &= \frac{17}{20} = 0.85, \\ y_1^{(1)} &= -\frac{18}{20} = -0.9, \\ z_1^{(1)} &= \frac{25}{20} = 1.25 \end{aligned}\right\} \qquad ...(2)$$

Again putting these values on the right sides of the equations (1),

we obtain
$$\left.\begin{aligned} x_2^{(2)} &= \frac{1}{20}(17 - y_1^{(1)} + 2z_1^{(1)}) = 1.02 \\ y_2^{(2)} &= \frac{1}{20}(-18 - 3x_1^{(1)} + z_1^{(1)}) = -0.965 \\ z_2^{(2)} &= \frac{1}{20}(25 - 2x_1^{(1)} + 3y_1^{(1)}) = 1.515 \end{aligned}\right\} \qquad ...(3)$$

Further substituting these values on the right sides of the equations (1), we have

$$\left.\begin{aligned} x_3^{(3)} &= \frac{1}{20}(17 - y_2^{(2)} + 2z_2^{(2)}) = 1.0134 \\ y_3^{(3)} &= \frac{1}{20}(-18 - 3x_2^{(2)} + z_2^{(2)}) = -0.9954 \\ z_3^{(3)} &= \frac{1}{20}(25 - 2x_2^{(2)} + 3y_2^{(2)}) = 1.0032 \end{aligned}\right\} \qquad ...(4)$$

Also

$$\left.\begin{aligned} x_4^{(4)} &= \frac{1}{20}(17 - y_3^{(3)} + 2z_3^{(3)}) = 1.0009 \\ y_4^{(4)} &= \frac{1}{20}(-18 - 3x_3^{(3)} + z_3^{(3)}) = -1.0018 \\ z_4^{(4)} &= \frac{1}{20}(25 - 2x_3^{(3)} + 3y_3^{(3)}) = 0.9993 \end{aligned}\right\} \qquad ...(5)$$

Putting these values, we have

$$\left.\begin{aligned} x_5^{(5)} &= \frac{1}{20}(-17 - y_4^{(4)} + 2z_4^{(4)}) = 1.0000 \\ y_5^{(5)} &= \frac{1}{20}(-18 - 3x_4^{(4)} + z_4^{(3)}) = -1.0002 \\ z_5^{(5)} &= \frac{1}{20}(25 - 2x_4^{(4)} + 3y_4^{(4)}) = 0.9996 \end{aligned}\right\} \qquad ...(6)$$

and
$$\left.\begin{aligned} x_6^{(6)} &= \frac{1}{20}(-17 - y_5^{(5)} + 2z_5^{(5)}) = 1.0000 \\ y_6^{(6)} &= \frac{1}{20}(-18 - 3x_5^{(5)} + z_5^{(5)}) = -1.0000 \\ z_6^{(6)} &= \frac{1}{20}(25 - 2x_5^{(5)} + 3y_5^{(5)}) = 1.0000 \end{aligned}\right\} \qquad ...(7)$$

So the values in the 5th and 6th Iterations are practically the same, hence we stop here. Thus the solution is $x = 1, y = -1, z = 1$.

13.2.9 Gauss-Seidal Iteration Method: This is the modification of Jacobi's method. As before the system of equations:

$$\left.\begin{aligned} a_1 x + b_1 y + c_1 z = d_1 \\ a_2 x + b_2 y + c_2 z = d_2 \\ a_3 x + b_3 y + c_3 z = d_3 \end{aligned}\right\} \qquad ...(1)$$

Can be written as

$$\left.\begin{aligned} x &= \frac{1}{a_1}(d_1 - b_1 y - c_1 z), \\ y &= \frac{1}{b_2}(d_2 - a_2 x - c_2 z), \\ z &= \frac{1}{c_3}(d_3 - a_3 x - b_3 y) \end{aligned}\right\} \qquad ...(2)$$

Let us start with initial approximations x_0, y_0, z_0 for x, y, z respectively. Then substituting $y = y_0, z = z_0$ in the first of the equations (2), we get

$$x_1^{(1)} = \frac{1}{a_1}(d_1 - b_1 y_0 - c_1 z_0)$$

Then putting $x = x_1, z = z_0$ in the second of the equations (2) we have

$$y_1 = \frac{1}{b_2}(d_2 - a_2 x_1^{(0)} - c_2 z_0)$$

Next substituting $x = x_1^{(1)}, y = y_1^{(1)}$ in the third of the equations (2), we get

$$z_1 = \frac{1}{c_3}(d_3 - a_3 x_1^{(1)} - b_3 y_1^{(1)}) \text{ etc.}$$

Note: Jacobi and Gauss-Seidal methods converge for any choice of the initial approximations if in each equation of the system, the absolute value of the largest co-efficient is greater than the sum of the absolute values of all the remaining coefficients.

Example 2: *Apply Gauss-Seidal iteration method to solve the equations*

$$20x + y - 2z = 17, 3x + 20y - z = -18, 2x - 3y + 20z = 25$$

[M.K.U. (Tamil Nadu) 2005, 2006; I.A.S. 2001; I.A.S. 2004]

Solution: We have

$$x = \frac{1}{20}(17 - y + 2z) \qquad ...(1)$$

$$y = \frac{1}{20}(-18 - 3x + z) \qquad ...(2)$$

$$z = \frac{1}{20}(25 - 2x + 3y) \qquad ...(3)$$

First Iteration: Putting $y = y_0, z = z_0$ is (1), we get

$$x_1^{(1)} = \frac{1}{20}(17 - y_0 + 2z_0) = 0.8500$$

Putting $x = x_1^{(1)}, z = z_0$ in (2), we have $y_1^{(1)} = \frac{1}{20}(-18 - 3x_1^{(1)} + z_0) = -1.0275$

Putting $x = x_1^{(1)},\ y = y_1^{(1)}$ in (3), we obtain $z_1^{(1)} = \frac{1}{20}(25 - 2\,x_1^{(1)} + 3\,y_1^{(1)}) = 1.0109$

Second Iteration: Putting $y = y_1^{(1)}, z = z_1^{(1)}$ in (1), we get

$$x_2^{(2)} = \frac{1}{20}(17 - y_1^{(1)} + 2z_1^{(1)}) = 1.0025$$

Putting $x = x_2^{(2)}, z = z_1^{(1)}$ in (2), we get $y_2^{(2)} = \frac{1}{20}(-18 - 3x_2^{(2)} + z_1^{(1)}) = -0.9998$

Again putting $x = x_2^{(2)},\ y = y_2^{(2)}$ in (3), we have

$$z_2^{(2)} = \frac{1}{20}(25 - 2x_2^{(2)} + 3\,y_2^{(2)}) = 0.9998$$

Third Iteration:

$$x_3^{(3)} = \frac{1}{20}(17 - y_2^{(2)} + 2\,z_2^{(2)}) = 1.0000$$

$$y_3^{(3)} = \frac{1}{20}(-18 - 3x_3^{(3)} + z_2^{(2)}) = -1.0000$$

$$z_3^{(3)} = \frac{1}{20}(25 - 2x_3^{(3)} + 3\,y_3^{(3)}) = 1.0000$$

Now the values in the 2nd and 3rd iterations are nearly the same,so we stop here. Hence the solution is $x = 1,\ y = -1, z = 1$.

Example 3: *Solve the equations:*

$$10x_1 - 2x_2 - x_3 - x_4 = 3$$
$$-2x_1 + 10x_2 - x_3 - x_4 = 15$$
$$-x_1 - x_2 + 10x_3 - 2x_4 = 27$$
$$-x_1 - x_2 - 2x_3 + 10x_4 = -9$$

By Guass- Seidal Iteration Method.

Solution: Rewriting the given equations as given below:

$$x_1 = 0.3 + 0.2x_2 + 0.1x_3 + 0.1x_4 \quad ...(1)$$
$$x_2 = 1.5 + 0.2\,x_1 + 0.1\,x_3 + 0.1\,x_4 \quad ...(2)$$
$$x_3 = 2.7 + 0.1x_1 + 0.1x_2 + 0.2x_4 \quad ...(3)$$
$$x_4 = -0.9 + 0.1x_1 + 0.1x_2 + 0.2x_3 \quad ...(4)$$

First Iteration

Putting $x_2 = 0, x_3 = 0, x_4 = 0$ in (1) we get $x_1^{(1)} = 0.3$

Putting $x_1^{(1)} = 0.3$, $x_3 = 0$, $x_4 = 0$ in (2), we obtain $x_2^{(1)} = 1.56$

Putting $x_1^{(1)} = 0.3$, $x_2^{(1)} = 1.56$, $x_4 = 0$ in (3) we obtain $x_3^{(1)} = 2.886$

Putting $x_1^{(1)} = 0.3$, $x_2^{(1)} = 1.56$, $x_3^{(1)} = 2.886$ in (4) we get $x_4^{(1)} = -0.1366$

Second Iteration

Putting $x_2^{(1)} = 1.56, x_3^{(1)} = 2.886, x_4^{(1)} = -0.1368$ in (1) we obtain $x_1^{(2)} = 0.8869$

Putting $x_1^{(2)} = 0.8869, x_3^{(1)} = 2.886, x_4^{(1)} = -0.1368$ in (2), we obtain $x_2^{(2)} = 1.9523$

Putting $x_1^{(2)} = 0.8869, x_2^{(2)} = 1.9523, x_4^{(1)} = -0.1368$ in(3) we have $x_3^{(2)} = 2.9566$

Putting $x_1^{(2)} = 0.8896, x_2^{(2)} = 1.9523, x_3^{(2)} = 2.9566$ in (4), we get $x_4^{(2)} = -0.0248.$

Third Iteration

Putting $x_2^{(2)} = 1.9523, x_3^{(2)} = 2.9566, x_4^{(2)} = -0.0248$ in (1), we have $x_1^{(3)} = 0.9836$

Putting $x_1^{(3)} = 0.9836, x_3^{(2)} = 2.9566, x_4^{(2)} = -0.0248$ in (2) we get $x_2^{(3)} = 1.9899$

Putting $x_1^{(3)} = 0.9836, x_2^{(3)} = 1.9899, x_4^{(2)} = -0.0248$ in (3), we get $x_3^{(3)} = 2.9924$

Then putting $x_1^{(3)} = 0.9836, x_2^{(3)} = 1.9800, x_3^{(3)} = 2.9924$ in (4), we get

$$x_4^{(3)} = -0.0042.$$

Fourth Iteration: Proceeding as above, we readily obtain

$$x_1^{(4)} = 0.9968, x_2^{(4)} = 1.9928, x_3^{(4)} = 2.9987, x_4^{(4)} = -0.0008.$$

Fifth Iteration

$$x_1^{(5)} = 0.9994, x_2^{(5)} = 1.9997, x_3^{(5)} = 2.9997, x_4^{(5)} = -0.0001.$$

Sixth Iteration

$$x_1^{(6)} = 0.9999, x_2^{(6)} = 1.9999, x_3^{(6)} = 2.9999, x_4^{(6)} = -0.0001$$

Hence the solution is $x_1 = 1, x_2 = 2, x_3 = 3, x_4 = 0.$

13.2.10 Relaxation Method: This method was originally developed by R.V South Well in 1935, for Application to Structural Engineering Problems.

Let us now consider the equations:

$$\left.\begin{aligned} a_1 x + b_1 y + c_1 z &= d_1 \\ a_2 x + b_2 y + c_2 z &= d_2 \\ a_3 x + b_3 y + c_3 z &= d_3 \end{aligned}\right\}$$

Let us now define residuals R_x, R_y, R_z by the following relations

$$\left.\begin{aligned} R_x &= d_1 - a_{1x} - b_1 y - c_1 z \\ R_y &= d_2 - a_2 x - b_2 y - c_2 z \\ R_z &= d_3 - a_3 x - b_3 y - c_3 z \end{aligned}\right\} \quad \ldots(1)$$

To start with we assume $x = y = z = 0$ and calculate the initial residuals. Then the residuals are reduced step by step, by giving some increments to the variables. We now construct the following *table*:

	δR_x	δR_y	δR_z
$\delta x = 1$	$-a_1$	$-a_2$	$-a_3$
$\delta y = 1$	$-b_1$	$-b_2$	$-b_3$
$\delta z = 1$	$-c_1$	$-c_2$	$-c_3$

From the above equations we see that if x is increased by 1 (keeping y and z constant); R_x, R_y and R_z decrease by a_1, a_2, a_3 respectively.

Similarly effects on the residuals when y and z are given unit increments are exhibited in the above table.

At each step. the numerically largest residual is reduced almost to zero. To reduce a particular residual, the value of the corresponding variable is changed. For example to reduce R_x by p, x must be increased by (p/a_1) etc.

In case all the residuals have been reduced to almost zero, the increments in x, y, z are added separately to obtain the desired solution.

Note 1: *In case the computed values of x, y, z are substituted in* (1) *and the residuals are calculated and if these residuals are not all negligible, then it means that there is some mistake and the entire process is to be rechecked.*

Note 2: *Relaxation method can be applied successfully only when the diagonal elements of* coefficient matrix dominate the other coefficients in the corresponding row *i.e. if in the equations* (1), *we have*

$$|a_1| \geq |b_1| + |c_1|$$
$$|b_2| \geq |a_2| + |c_2|$$
$$|c_3| \geq |a_3| + |b_3|$$

where > sign should be valid for at least one row.

Example 4: *Solve by Relaxation method, the equations*:

$$9x - 2y + z = 50; x + 5y - 3z = 18; -2x + 2y + 7z = 19.$$

Solution: The residuals are evidently given by

$$R_x = 50 - 9x + 2y - z;$$
$$R_y = 18 - x - 5y + 3z;$$
$$R_z = 19 + 2x - 2y - 7z$$

We Now Compute the Following Tables:

Residuals / Increments	δR_x	δR_y	δR_z
$\delta x = 1$	-9	1	2
$\delta y = 1$	2	-5	-2
$\delta z = 1$	-1	3	-7

Relaxation Table:

S.No.	Variables	R_x	R_y	R_z
1	$x = y = z = 0$	50	18	19
2	$\delta x = 5$	5	13	29
3	$\delta z = 4$	1	25	1
4	$\delta y = 5$	11	0	-9
5	$\delta x = 1$	2	-1	-7
6	$\delta z = -1$	3	-4	0
7	$\delta y = -0.8$	1.4	0	1.6
8	$\delta z = 0.23$	1.17	0.69	$-.09$
9	$\delta x = 0.13$	0	0.56	0.17
10	$\delta y = 0.112$	0.224	0	-0.054

$$\Sigma\delta x = 6.13, \Sigma\delta y = 4.312, \Sigma\delta z = 3.23.$$

$$\therefore \quad x = 6.13, y = 4.312, z = 3.23 \Rightarrow x = 6.13, y = 4.31, z = 3.23.$$

From above it is obvious that in (1), the largest residual is 50 so to reduce it, we give an increment $\delta x = 5$ and the residuals are given in (2) Here $R_z = 29$ is the largest residual and we give an increment $\delta z = 4$ to get the results in (3) In (6) $R_y = -4$ is numerically largest and we have an increment $\delta z = 4$ to get the result in (3). In (6) $R_y = -4$ is numerically largest and we have an increment $\delta y = -(4/5) = -0.8$ so as to get the results in (7). Similarly other steps could be carried out as explained in the above table.

Example 5: *Solve the equations:*

$$10x - 2y - 3z = 205; -2x + 10y - 2z = 154; -2x - y + 10z = 120$$

By Relaxation method.

Solution: The residuals are given by

$$R_x = 205 - 10x + 2y + 3z;$$

$$R_y = 154 + 2x - 10y - 2z$$

$$R_z = 120 + 2x + y - 10z.$$

Now the operations table is given by:

Variables / Increments	δR_x	δR_y	δR_z
$\delta x = 1$	-10	2	2
$\delta y = 1$	2	-10	1
$\delta z = 1$	3	2	-10

Also the Relaxation tables is as follows;

S. No.	Variables and increments	R_x	R_y	R_z
1	$x = y = z = 0$	205	154	120
2	$\delta x = 20$	5	194	160
3	$\delta y = 19$	43	4	179
4	$\delta z = 18$	97	40	−1
5	$\delta x = 10$	−3	60	19
6	$\delta y = 6$	9	0	25
7	$\delta z = 2$	15	4	5
8	$\delta x = 2$	−5	8	9
9	$\delta z = 1$	−2	10	−1
10	$\delta y = 1$	0	0	0

It is obvious that $\Sigma\delta x = 32, \Sigma\delta y = 26, \Sigma\delta z = 21.$

$$\Rightarrow \qquad x = 32,\ y = 26,\ z = 21.$$

Example 6: *Solve the system* $2x_1 + 3x_2 + x_3 = 9;$

$$x_1 + 2x_2 + 3x_3 = 6,$$

$$3x_1 + x_2 + + x_3 = 8.$$

Solution: Coefficient matrix $= A = \begin{bmatrix} 2 & 3 & 1 \\ 1 & 2 & 3 \\ 3 & 1 & 2 \end{bmatrix}$

$$\det(A) = \begin{vmatrix} 2 & 3 & 1 \\ 1 & 2 & 3 \\ 3 & 1 & 2 \end{vmatrix} = 18.$$

Further, we also have adj. $(A) = \begin{bmatrix} 1 & -5 & 7 \\ 7 & 1 & -5 \\ -5 & 7 & 1 \end{bmatrix}$

$$\Rightarrow \qquad A^{-1} = \frac{1}{18}\begin{bmatrix} 1 & -5 & 7 \\ 7 & 1 & -5 \\ -5 & 7 & 1 \end{bmatrix}. \text{ Also } B = \begin{bmatrix} 9 \\ 6 \\ 8 \end{bmatrix}$$

Now inverse of A has been obtained.

So $$X = A^{-1}B = \frac{1}{18}\begin{bmatrix} 1 & -5 & 7 \\ 7 & 1 & -5 \\ -5 & 7 & 1 \end{bmatrix}\begin{bmatrix} 9 \\ 6 \\ 8 \end{bmatrix} = \frac{1}{18}\begin{bmatrix} 35 \\ 29 \\ 5 \end{bmatrix}_{3\times 1} = \begin{bmatrix} x_1 \\ x_2 \\ x_3 \end{bmatrix}$$

$\therefore$ Solution is $x_1 = \frac{35}{18}, x_2 = \frac{29}{18}, x_3 = \frac{5}{18}$,

Aliter: By Cramer's rule, we have $D_1 = \begin{vmatrix} 9 & 3 & 1 \\ 6 & 2 & 3 \\ 8 & 1 & 2 \end{vmatrix} = 35$,

and similarly we obtain $D_2 = 29$ and $D_3 = 5$.

$$\therefore \quad x_1 = \frac{D_1}{D} = \frac{35}{18}, x_2 = \frac{D_2}{D} = \frac{29}{18}\ x_3 = \frac{D_3}{D} = \frac{5}{18}.$$

Example 7: *Solve the equations* $3x + y + 2z = 3$

$$2x - 3y - z = -3$$
$$x + 2y + z = 4.$$

Solution: $A = \begin{bmatrix} 3 & 1 & 2 \\ 2 & -3 & -1 \\ 1 & 2 & 1 \end{bmatrix}$, $\det(A) = |A| = \begin{vmatrix} 3 & 1 & 2 \\ 2 & -3 & -1 \\ 1 & 2 & 1 \end{vmatrix} = 8$

$\Rightarrow$ Transpose of $A = A' = \begin{bmatrix} 3 & 1 & 2 \\ 1 & -3 & 2 \\ 2 & -1 & 1 \end{bmatrix}$, adj $A = \begin{bmatrix} -1 & 3 & 5 \\ -3 & 1 & 7 \\ 7 & -5 & -11 \end{bmatrix}$.

$$\Rightarrow \quad A^{-1} = \frac{Adj(A)}{|A|} = \frac{1}{8}\begin{bmatrix} -1 & 3 & 5 \\ -3 & 1 & 7 \\ 7 & -5 & -11 \end{bmatrix}.$$

$$\therefore \quad X = A^{-1}B \Rightarrow \begin{bmatrix} x \\ y \\ z \end{bmatrix} = \frac{1}{8}\begin{bmatrix} -1 & 3 & 5 \\ -3 & 1 & 7 \\ 7 & -5 & -11 \end{bmatrix}\begin{bmatrix} 3 \\ -3 \\ 4 \end{bmatrix} = \frac{1}{8}\begin{bmatrix} 8 \\ 16 \\ -8 \end{bmatrix} = \begin{bmatrix} 1 \\ 2 \\ -1 \end{bmatrix}$$

$$\Rightarrow \quad x = 1,\ y = 2,\ z = -1.$$

Example 8: *Solve the Given system by Cramer's rule:*

$$\left.\begin{array}{r} 3x + 2y - z + t = 1 \\ x - y - 2z + 4t = 3 \\ 2x - 3y + z - 2t = -2 \\ 5x - 2y + 3z + 2t = 0 \end{array}\right\} \quad \ldots(1)$$

Solution: We have $D = \begin{vmatrix} 3 & 2 & -1 & 1 \\ 1 & -1 & -2 & 4 \\ 2 & -3 & 1 & -2 \\ 5 & -2 & 3 & 2 \end{vmatrix} = 50$, while

$$D_1=\begin{vmatrix}1&2&-1&1\\3&-1&-2&4\\-2&-3&1&-2\\0&-2&3&2\end{vmatrix}=19,\quad D_2=\begin{vmatrix}3&1&-1&1\\1&3&-2&4\\2&-2&1&-2\\5&0&3&2\end{vmatrix}=-29,$$

$$D_3=\begin{vmatrix}3&2&1&1\\1&-1&3&4\\2&-3&-2&-2\\5&-2&0&2\end{vmatrix}=-51,\quad D_4=\begin{vmatrix}3&2&-1&1\\1&-1&-2&3\\2&-3&1&-2\\5&-2&3&0\end{vmatrix}=0.$$

$$\Rightarrow\quad x=\frac{D_1}{D}=\frac{19}{50},\ y=\frac{D_2}{D}=-\frac{29}{50},\ z=\frac{D_3}{D}=-\frac{51}{50},\ t=\frac{D_4}{D}=0.$$

Example 9: *Solve the following equations in x, y, z and w, with the help of matrices:*

$$\left.\begin{aligned}x-3y+z&=a,\\2x+y-w&=b,\\3x-2y-z-2w&=c,\\4x-y+3w&=d.\end{aligned}\right\}$$

Solution: The Given system is $AX=B$, where

$$A=\begin{bmatrix}1&-3&1&0\\2&1&0&-1\\3&-2&-1&-2\\4&-1&0&3\end{bmatrix},\ X=\begin{bmatrix}x\\y\\z\\w\end{bmatrix},\ B=\begin{bmatrix}a\\b\\c\\d\end{bmatrix}$$

$$\text{adj. }(A)=\begin{bmatrix}1&2&3&3\\-3&1&-2&-1\\1&0&-1&0\\0&-1&-2&8\end{bmatrix},\ \text{Now det }(A)=\begin{vmatrix}1&-3&1&0\\2&1&0&-1\\3&-2&-1&-2\\4&-1&0&3\end{vmatrix}=-70;$$

$$\begin{vmatrix}1&0&-1\\-2&-1&-2\\-1&0&3\end{vmatrix}=-2;\ \begin{vmatrix}-3&-2&-1\\1&-1&0\\2&-2&3\end{vmatrix}=17.$$

$$\Rightarrow\quad A^{-1}=\frac{1}{70}\begin{bmatrix}2&17&2&7\\-10&20&-10&0\\38&43&-32&-7\\-6&-16&-6&14\end{bmatrix}$$

$$\Rightarrow\quad \begin{bmatrix}x\\y\\z\\w\end{bmatrix}=\frac{1}{70}\begin{bmatrix}2&17&2&7\\-10&20&-10&0\\38&43&-32&-7\\-6&-16&-6&14\end{bmatrix}\begin{bmatrix}a\\b\\c\\d\end{bmatrix}\quad [\because X=A^{-1}B]$$

$$\Rightarrow\quad x=\frac{1}{70}(2a+17b+2c+7d),\ y=-\frac{1}{35}(5a-10b+5c),$$

$$z=\frac{1}{70}(38a+43b-32c-7d),\ w=-\frac{1}{35}(3a+8b+3c-7d).$$

Example 10: *Solve* $10x - 7y + 3z + 5u = 6$,

$$-6x + 8y - z - 4u = 5,$$
$$3x + y + 4z + 11u = 2,$$
$$5x - 9y - 2z + 4u = 7.$$

By Gauss,s Elimination method.

Solution: The Given system can be written as

$$\left.\begin{aligned} x - 0.7y + 0.3z + 0.5u &= 0.6 \\ -6x + 8y - z - 4u &= 5 \\ 3x + y + 4z + 11u &= 2 \\ 5x - 9y - 2z + 4u &= 7 \end{aligned}\right] \quad ...(1)$$

The variable x can be eliminated from the second, third and forth equations by subtracting (– 9) times the first equation from the second equation, 3 times the first equation from the third equation and 5 times the first equation from the forth equation and thus new system becomes

$$\left.\begin{aligned} x - 0.7y + 0.3z + 0.5u &= 0.6 \\ 3.8y + 0.8z - u &= 8.6 \\ 3.1y + 3.1z + 9.5u &= 0.2 \\ -5.5y - 3.5z + 1.5u &= 4 \end{aligned}\right\} \quad ...(2)$$

In this system, coeff. of y is maximum (numerically) in fourth equation, so now, we shall permutate the second and fourth equation.

After that y is eliminated:

$$\left.\begin{aligned} x - 0.7y + 0.3z + 0.5u &= 0.6 \\ y + 0.6363z - 0.27275u &= -0.72727 \\ -1.61818z + 0.03636u &= 11.36364 \\ 1.12727z + 10.34545u &= 2.45455 \end{aligned}\right\} \quad ...(3)$$

Further elimination of z gives

$$\left.\begin{aligned} x - 0.7y + 0.3z + 0.5u &= 0.6 \\ y + 0.63636z - 0.27273u &= -0.72727 \\ z - 0.02247u &= -7.02247 \\ 10.3607947u &= 10.37079 \end{aligned}\right\} \quad ...(4)$$

These give $u = 1, z = -7, y = 4$ and $x = 5$.

Example 11: *Solve* $x + \frac{1}{2}y + \frac{1}{3}z = 1$,

$$\frac{1}{2}x + \frac{1}{3}y + \frac{1}{4}z = 0,$$

$\frac{1}{3}x + \frac{1}{4}y + \frac{1}{5}z = 0$, *by Gauss' s Elimination method*

Solution: Elimination of x gives

$$\left.\begin{aligned} x+\frac{1}{2}y+\frac{1}{3}z &= 1 \\ \frac{1}{12}y+\frac{1}{12}z &= -\frac{1}{2} \\ \frac{1}{12}y+\frac{4}{45}z &= -\frac{1}{3} \end{aligned}\right\} \quad \text{...(1)}$$

Now, we shall eliminate y from the third and fourth equations.

Subtracting second equation from third equation, we immediately get

$$\left.\begin{aligned} x+\frac{1}{2}y+\frac{1}{3}z &= 1 \\ \frac{1}{12}y+\frac{1}{12}z &= -\frac{1}{2} \\ -\frac{1}{180}z &= -\frac{1}{6} \end{aligned}\right\} \quad \text{...(2)}$$

This gives $z=30,\ y=-36,\ x=9.$

Example 12: (*a*) *By Gauss's Elimination method, solve*

$$5x-y-2z=142,$$
$$x-3y-z=-30 \qquad \textbf{[Bhopal 2002]}$$
$$2x-y-3z=-5.$$

(*b*) *Applying Gauss's Elimination method, solve*

$$x+4y-z=-5,\ x+y-6z=-12;\ 3x-y-z=4.$$

Solution: (a) Elimination of x from IInd and third equations we get

$$\left.\begin{aligned} 5x-y-2z &= 142 \\ -\frac{14}{5}y-\frac{3}{5}z &= -\frac{292}{5} \\ -\frac{5}{6}y-\frac{11}{5}z &= -\frac{250}{5} \end{aligned}\right\} \quad \text{...(1)}$$

Further eliminating y from the third and fourth equations, we get

$$\left.\begin{aligned} 5x-y-2z &= 142 \\ -\frac{14}{5}y-\frac{3}{5}z &= -\frac{292}{5} \\ -\frac{29}{14}z &= -\frac{275}{7} \end{aligned}\right\} \quad \text{...(2)}$$

This gives $x=39.2$ approx, and $y=16.7$ approx.

(b) We have check sum

$$x+4y-z=-5 \qquad \text{...(1)} \quad -1$$
$$x+y-6z=-12 \qquad \text{...(2)} \quad -16$$
$$3x-y-z=4 \qquad \text{...(3)} \quad +5$$

Eliminating x from (2) and (3) with the help of (1)

[(2) – (1) and (3) – 3 (1)]; we get **_Check Sum_**

$$-3y-5z=-17 \qquad ...(4) \quad -15$$

$$-13y+2z=19 \qquad ...(5) \quad 8$$

To eliminate y let us operate $(5)-\frac{13}{4}[4]$ **_Check Sum_**

$$\Rightarrow \quad \frac{71z}{3}=\frac{148}{3} \qquad ...(6) \quad 73$$

Then substituting backwards, we get $z=(148/71)$ (from 6),

$$y=\frac{7}{3}-\frac{5}{3}\left(\frac{148}{71}\right)=-\frac{81}{71} \qquad \text{(from 4)},$$

and

$$x=-5-4\left(\frac{-81}{71}\right)+\frac{148}{71}=\frac{117}{71}.$$

Example 13: *Apply Jordan's methods to solve*

$$10x-7y+3z+5u=6,$$
$$-6x+8y-z-4u=5,$$
$$3x+y+4z+11u=2,$$
$$5x-9y-2z+4u=7.$$

Solution: Elimination of x (as usual) gives

$$\left.\begin{aligned} x-0.7y+0.3z+0.5&=0.6\\ 3.8y+0.8z-u&=8.6\\ 3.1y+3.1z+9.5u&=0.2\\ 5.5y-3.5z+1.5u&=4 \end{aligned}\right\} \qquad ...(1)$$

Now appalling Jordan's method, we get

$$\left.\begin{aligned} x+0.74545z+0.30909u&=0.09091\\ y+0.63636z-0.27273u&=-0.72727\\ -1.61818z+0.03636u&=11.36364\\ 1.12727z+10.34545u&=2.45455 \end{aligned}\right\} \qquad ...(2)$$

and

$$\left.\begin{aligned} x+0.32584u&=5.32582\\ y-0.25843u&=3.74156\\ z-0.02447u&=7.02248\\ 10.37078u&=10.37078 \end{aligned}\right\} \qquad ...(3)$$

The last step in the elimination is trivial and gives the same result as before *i.e.* we have

$$x=5, y=4, z=-7, u=1.$$

Example 14: *Apply Jordan's method to solve*

$$x+2y+z=8,$$
$$2x+3y+4z=20,$$
$$4x+3y+2z=16.$$

Solution: Elimination of x, from the last two equations gives

$$\left.\begin{aligned} x+2y+z&=8 \\ -y+2z&=4 \\ -5y-2z&=-16 \end{aligned}\right\} \quad ...(1)$$

Elimination of y from the first and third equation gives

$$\left.\begin{aligned} x+0+5z&=16 \\ -y+2z&=-36 \\ -12z&=-36 \end{aligned}\right\} \quad ...(2)$$

Further eliminating z from the first two equations with the help of Third equation,

we get
$$\left.\begin{aligned} x&=1 \\ -y&=-2 \\ 12z&=36 \end{aligned}\right\}$$

This gives $x=1, y=2, z=3.$

Example 15: (*a*) *Solve the system* $\begin{cases} x_1+x_2+x_3=1, \\ 3x_1+x_2-3x_3=5, \\ x_1-2x_2-5x_3=10, \end{cases}$

(*b*) *Solve the system:*

$$3x_1+2x_2+7x_3=4, 2x_1+3x_2+x_3=5, 3x_1+4x_2+x_3=7;$$

by Crout's Method.

Solution: (a) Coefficient matrix is given by $\begin{pmatrix} a_{11} & a_{12} & a_{13} \\ a_{21} & a_{22} & a_{23} \\ a_{31} & a_{32} & a_{33} \end{pmatrix} = \begin{pmatrix} 1 & 1 & 1 \\ 3 & 1 & -3 \\ 1 & -2 & -5 \end{pmatrix}$

The augmented matrix of the coefficient matrix is given by $\begin{pmatrix} a_{11} & a_{12} & a_{13} & b_1 \\ a_{21} & a_{22} & a_{23} & b_2 \\ a_{31} & a_{32} & a_{33} & b_3 \end{pmatrix}$

and the derived matrix is $\begin{pmatrix} a'_{11} & a'_{12} & a'_{13} & 1 & b'_1 \\ a'_{21} & a'_{22} & a'_{23} & 5 & b'_2 \\ a'_{31} & a'_{32} & a'_{33} & 10 & b'_3 \end{pmatrix}$

Where $a'_{i1}=a_{i1}, (i=1,2,3)$ *i.e.* $a'_{11}=1, a'_{21}=3, a'_{31}=1.$ ...(1)

$$a'_{12}=\frac{a_{12}}{a_{11}}, =\frac{1}{1}=1, a'_{13}=\frac{a_{13}}{a_{11}}=\frac{1}{1}=1, b'_1=\frac{b_1}{a_{11}}=\frac{1}{1}=1. \quad ...(2)$$

$$a'_{22}=a_{22}-a'_{12}.a'_{21}=1-1\times3=-2,$$
$$a'_{32}=a_{32}-a'_{12}.a'_{31}=-2-1\times1=-3. \quad ...(3)$$

$$a'_{23} = \frac{a_{23} - a'_{13}\,a_{21}}{a'_{22}} = \frac{-3-1\times 3}{-2} = 3, b'_2 = \frac{5-1\times 3}{-2} = -1 \qquad \text{...(4)}$$

$$a'_{32} = a_{33} - a'_{22}\,.\,a'_{32} - a'_{13}\,a'_{31} = -5-3(-3)-(1)\times(1) = 3 \qquad \text{...(5)}$$

$$b'_3 = \frac{b_3 - b'_2\,a'_{32} - b'_1\,a'_{31}}{a'_{33}} = \frac{10-(-1)(-3)-1(1)}{3} = 2. \qquad \text{...(6)}$$

$$\therefore \qquad \text{Derived matrix} = \begin{pmatrix} 1 & 1 & 1 & 1 \\ 3 & -2 & 3 & -1 \\ 1 & -3 & 3 & 2 \end{pmatrix}.$$

Thus $\qquad x_3 = b'_3 = 2, x_2 = b'_2 - a'_{23}, x_3 = -1-3\times 2 = -7$

and $\qquad x_1 = b'_1 - a'_{13}\,x_3 - a'_{12}\,x_2 = 1 - x_3 - x_2 = 1-2+7 = 6.$

(b) The coefficient matrix is given by

$$A = \begin{pmatrix} a_{11} & a_{12} & a_{13} \\ a_{21} & a_{22} & a_{23} \\ a_{31} & a_{32} & a_{33} \end{pmatrix} = \begin{pmatrix} 3 & 2 & 7 \\ 2 & 3 & 1 \\ 3 & 4 & 1 \end{pmatrix}$$

is $\begin{pmatrix} a_{11} & a_{12} & a_{13} & b_1 \\ a_{21} & a_{22} & a_{23} & b_2 \\ a_{31} & a_{32} & a_{33} & b_3 \end{pmatrix} = \begin{pmatrix} 3 & 2 & 7 & 4 \\ 2 & 3 & 1 & 5 \\ 3 & 4 & 1 & 7 \end{pmatrix}$

Also the derived matrix is $\begin{pmatrix} a_{11}' & a_{12}' & a_{13}' & b_1' \\ a_{21}' & a_{22}' & a_{23}' & b_2' \\ a_{31}' & a_{32}' & a_{33}' & b_3' \end{pmatrix}$ where $a_{i1}' = a_{i1}\ (i=1,2,3)$

$$\Rightarrow \qquad a_{11}' = a_{11} = 3, a_{21}' = a_{21} = 2, a_{31}' = a_{31} = 3; b_1' = \frac{b_1}{a_{11}} = \frac{4}{3},$$

$$a_{12}' = \frac{a_{12}}{a_{11}} = \frac{2}{3}, a_{13}' = \frac{a_{13}}{a_{11}} = \frac{7}{3}, \ a_{i2}' = a_{i2} - a_{12}'\,a_{i1}'\ (i=2,3)$$

$$\Rightarrow \qquad a_{22}' = a_{22} - a_{12}'\,a_{21}' = 3 - \frac{2}{3}.2 = \frac{5}{3}$$

$$a_{32}' = a_{32} - a_{12}'\,a_{31}' = 4 - \frac{2}{3}.3 = 2$$

$$a_{2j}' = \frac{a_{2j} - a_{1j}'\,a_{21}'}{a_{22}'}\ (j=3)$$

$$\Rightarrow \qquad a_{23}' = \frac{a_{23} - a_{13}'\,a_{21}'}{a_{22}'} = 1 - \frac{(14/3)}{(5/3)} = -\frac{11}{5} \quad b_2' = \frac{b_2 - b_1'\,.\,a_{21}'}{a_{22}'} = \frac{5-(8/3)}{(5/3)} = \frac{7}{5}.$$

$$a_{33}' = a_{33} - a_{23}'\,.\,a_{32}' - a_{13}'\,a_{31}' = 1 + \frac{11}{5}(2) - \frac{7}{3}.3 = -\frac{8}{5}$$

and $\qquad b_3' = (b_3 - b_2'\,a_{32}' - b_1'\,a_{31}')\,/\,a_{33}' = -\frac{1}{8}.$

$$\Rightarrow \qquad x_3 = b_3' = -\frac{1}{8}, x_2 = b_2' - a_{23}' x_3 = \frac{7}{5} + \frac{11}{5} \times \left(-\frac{1}{8}\right) = \frac{56}{40} - \frac{11}{40} = \frac{45}{40} = \frac{9}{8}$$

and
$$x_1 = b_1' - a_{13}' x_3 - a_{12}' x_2 = \frac{4}{3} - \frac{7}{3} \cdot \left(-\frac{1}{8}\right) - \frac{2}{3}(9/8) = \frac{4}{3} + \frac{7}{24} - \frac{18}{24} = \frac{7}{8}.$$

Example 16: *Solve the following system of equations by* **(a)** *Gauss Seidel Iteration Method,* **(b)** *Jacobi Iterative Method.* **[Agra 2006, 2008, 2009]**

$$27x + 6y - z = 85,$$
$$6x + 15y + 2z = 72,$$
$$x + y + 54z = 110.$$

Solution: (a) We solve each equation of the system of the unknown with the largest coefficient in terms of the remaining unknowns, *viz.*

$$x = \frac{1}{27}(85 - 6y + z)$$

$$y = \frac{1}{15}(72 - 6x - 2z). \text{ and } z = \frac{1}{54}(110 - x - y).$$

Starting with $y = 0, z = 0$ we obtain

$$x = x^{(1)} = \frac{85}{27} = 3.15 = \text{first approximation.}$$

Now putting $x = 3.15, z = 0$ in the second equation, we get

$$y = (1/15)(72 - 18.90) = 3.54 = y^{(1)} = \text{first approx.}$$

Again putting $x = 3.15, y = 3.54$ in third equation, we get

$$z = z^{(1)} = (1/54)(110 - 3.15 - 3.54) = 1.91 = \text{first approx.}$$

Now, we proceed to obtain the second approximations.

$$x^{(2)} = (1/27)[85 - 6y^{(1)} + z^{(1)}] = (1/27)[85 - 21.24 + 1.91] = 2.43,$$

$$y^{(2)} = (1/15)[72 - 6x^{(2)} - 2z^{(1)}] = (1/15)[72 - 14.58 - 3.82] = 3.57,$$

$$z^{(2)} = (1/54)[110 - x^{(2)} - y^{(2)}] = (1/54)[110 - 2.43 - 3.57] = 1.926,$$

Similarly,

$$x^{(3)} = (1/27)[85 - 6y^{(2)} + z^{(2)}] = 2.426,$$

$$y^{(3)} = (1/15)[72 - 6x^{(3)} - 2z^{(2)}] = 3.572$$

$$z^{(3)} = (1/54)[110 - x^{(3)} - y^{(3)}] = 1.926$$

These values are sufficiently close to $x^{(2)}, y^{(2)}, z^{(2)}$ receptively.

Hence the values 2.426, 3.572, 1.926 can be considered as the solution of the Given System.

(b) Jacobi-Iterative Method: Starting with $x=0, y=0, z=0$, we obtain

$$x^{(1)}=\frac{85}{27}=3.15,\ y^{(2)}=\frac{72}{15}=4.8,\ z^{(1)}=\frac{110}{54}=2.04;$$

which are the first approximations. We now proceed to obtain the second approximations as follows:

$$x^{(2)}=\frac{1}{27}(85-6y^{(1)}+z^{(1)})=\frac{1}{27}(85-28.8+2.04)=2.16,$$

$$y^{(2)}=\frac{1}{15}(72-6x^{(1)}-2z^{(1)})=\frac{1}{15}(72-18.9-4.08)=3.27,$$

$$z^{(2)}=\frac{1}{54}(110-x^{(1)}-y^{(1)})=\frac{1}{54}(110-3.15-4.8)=1.89.$$

Similarly, next approximations can be obtained as

$$x^{(3)}=\frac{1}{27}(85-6y^{(2)}+z^{(2)}),\ y^{(3)}=\frac{1}{15}(72-6x^{(2)}-2z^{(2)}),$$

$$z^{(3)}=\frac{1}{54}(110-x^{(2)}-y^{(2)}).$$

Proceeding in this way further Iterations can be calculated.

Example 17: ***(a)*** *Solve the equations*

$$2x+3y+z=9$$
$$x+2y+3z=6$$
$$3x+y+2z=8$$

by the Factorization method,

(b) *Applying Factorization method to solve the equations:*

$$3x+2y+7z=4;\ 2x+3y+z=5;\ 3x+4y+z=7.$$

Solution: (a) We have $A=\begin{bmatrix}2&3&1\\1&2&3\\3&1&2\end{bmatrix}$.

Now, let $A=LU$, where $L=\begin{bmatrix}1&0&0\\l_{21}&1&0\\l_{31}&l_{32}&1\end{bmatrix}$ and $U\begin{bmatrix}u_{11}&u_{12}&u_{13}\\0&u_{22}&u_{23}\\0&0&u_{33}\end{bmatrix}$.

Thus, we have $u_{11}=2,\ u_{12}=3,\ u_{13}=1,$

$$l_{21}u_{11}=1\Rightarrow l_{21}=1/2,\ l_{31}u_{11}=3\Rightarrow l_{31}=3/2,$$

$$l_{21}u_{12}+u_{22}=2\Rightarrow u_{22}=1/2,\ l_{21}u_{13}+u_{23}=3\Rightarrow u_{23}=5/2,$$

$$l_{31}u_{12}+l_{32}u_{22}=1\Rightarrow l_{32}=-7,$$

$$l_{31}u_{13}+l_{32}u_{23}+u_{33}=2\Rightarrow u_{33}=18.$$

Hence we can now write $A=LU=\begin{bmatrix}1&0&0\\1/2&1&0\\3/2&-7&1\end{bmatrix}\begin{bmatrix}2&3&1\\0&1/2&5/2\\0&0&18\end{bmatrix}$.

Further, the Given system can be written as

$$\begin{bmatrix} 1 & 0 & 0 \\ \frac{1}{2} & 1 & 0 \\ \frac{3}{2} & -7 & 1 \end{bmatrix} \begin{bmatrix} 2 & 3 & 1 \\ 0 & \frac{1}{2} & \frac{5}{2} \\ 0 & 0 & 18 \end{bmatrix} \begin{bmatrix} x \\ y \\ z \end{bmatrix} = \begin{bmatrix} 9 \\ 6 \\ 8 \end{bmatrix}$$

$$\Rightarrow \quad \begin{bmatrix} 1 & 0 & 0 \\ \frac{1}{2} & 1 & 0 \\ \frac{3}{2} & -7 & 1 \end{bmatrix} \begin{bmatrix} y_1 \\ y_2 \\ y_3 \end{bmatrix} = \begin{bmatrix} 9 \\ 6 \\ 8 \end{bmatrix} \qquad \ldots(1)$$

where
$$\begin{bmatrix} y_1 \\ y_2 \\ y_3 \end{bmatrix} = \begin{bmatrix} 2 & 3 & 1 \\ 0 & 1/2 & 5/2 \\ 0 & 0 & 18 \end{bmatrix} \begin{bmatrix} x \\ y \\ z \end{bmatrix} \qquad \ldots(2)$$

Now Relation (1) gives $y_1 = 9, (y_1/2) + y_2 = 6$ *i.e.* $y_2 = (3/2)$ and $(3/2)\, y_1 - 7\, y_2 + y_3 = 8 \Rightarrow y_3 = 5.$

Now, using (2), solution of the original system is given by

$$\begin{bmatrix} 2 & 3 & 1 \\ 0 & \frac{1}{2} & \frac{5}{2} \\ 0 & 0 & 18 \end{bmatrix} \begin{bmatrix} x \\ y \\ z \end{bmatrix} = \begin{bmatrix} 9 \\ \frac{3}{2} \\ 5 \end{bmatrix}$$

$$\Rightarrow \quad 2x + 3y + z = 9. \frac{y}{2} + \frac{5z}{2} = \frac{3}{2} \text{ and } 18z = 5$$

i.e. $$x = \frac{35}{18}, y = \frac{29}{18} \text{ and } z = 5/18$$

(b) Let $\begin{bmatrix} 1 & 0 & 0 \\ l_{21} & 1 & 0 \\ l_{31} & l_{32} & 1 \end{bmatrix} \begin{bmatrix} u_{11} & u_{12} & u_{13} \\ 0 & u_{22} & u_{23} \\ 0 & 0 & u_{33} \end{bmatrix} = \begin{bmatrix} 3 & 2 & 7 \\ 2 & 3 & 1 \\ 3 & 4 & 1 \end{bmatrix}$ (*i.e.* A),

$\leftarrow L \text{-------} \rightarrow \quad \longleftrightarrow U$

$\Rightarrow$ (i) R_1 of U: $u_{11} = 3$ $u_{12} = 2,$ $u_{13} = 7.$

(ii) C_1 of L: $l_{21}\, u_{11} = 2,$ $\therefore$ $l_{21} = 2/3,$

$l_{31}\, u_{11} = 3,$ $\therefore$ $l_{31} = 1.$

(iii) R_2 of U: $l_{21}\, u_{12} + u_{22} = 3,$ $\therefore$ $u_{22} = 5/3,$

$l_{21}\, u_{13} + u_{23} = 1,$ $\therefore$ $u_{23} = -11/3.$

(iv) C_2 of L: $l_{31}\, u_{12} + l_{32}\, u_{22} = 4,$ $\therefore$ $l_{32} = 6/5.$

(v) R_3 of U: $l_{31}\, u_{13} + l_{32}\, u_{23} + u_{33} = 1 \qquad \therefore\ u_{33} = -8/5.$

$$\therefore \qquad A = \begin{bmatrix} 1 & 0 & 0 \\ 2/3 & 1 & 0 \\ 1 & 6/5 & 1 \end{bmatrix} \begin{bmatrix} 3 & 2 & 7 \\ 0 & 5/3 & -11/3 \\ 0 & 0 & -8/5 \end{bmatrix}$$

Then writing $UX = V$, the Given System is reduced to

$$A = \begin{bmatrix} 1 & 0 & 0 \\ 2/3 & 1 & 0 \\ 1 & 6/5 & 1 \end{bmatrix} \begin{bmatrix} v_1 \\ v_2 \\ v_3 \end{bmatrix} = \begin{bmatrix} 4 \\ 5 \\ 7 \end{bmatrix}$$

$$\Rightarrow \quad \begin{cases} v_1 = 4, \\ \frac{2}{3} v_1 + v_2 = 5 \quad \text{or} \quad v_2 = \frac{7}{3} \\ v_1 + \frac{6}{5} v_2 + v_3 = 7 \quad \text{or} \quad v_3 = \frac{1}{5} \end{cases}$$

Thus the original system becomes

$$\begin{bmatrix} 3 & 2 & 7 \\ 0 & 5/3 & -11/3 \\ 0 & 0 & -8/5 \end{bmatrix} \begin{bmatrix} x \\ y \\ z \end{bmatrix} = \begin{bmatrix} 4 \\ 7/3 \\ 1/5 \end{bmatrix}$$

$$\Rightarrow \quad 3x + 2y + 7z = 4, 5\,(y/3) - (11/3)\,z = (7/3)$$

and $\quad -(8z/5) = (1/5);$ so that $x = (7/8), y = (9/8), z = -\frac{1}{8}$

Example 18: *Solve the equations*

(a) $x_1 + 2x_2 + 3x_3 = 14, 2x_1 + 5x_2 + 2x_3 = 18, 3x_1 + x_2 + 5x_3 = 20.$ **[Bhopal 2002]**

(b) $10x - 7y + 3z + 5u = 6, -6x + 8y - z - 4u = 5,$

$3x + y + 4z + 11u = 2, 5x - 9y - 2z + 4u = 7.$

by Factorization method.

Solution: (a) We have $A = \begin{pmatrix} 1 & 2 & 3 \\ 2 & 5 & 2 \\ 3 & 1 & 5 \end{pmatrix}$

Now, let $\qquad A = LU$, where $L = \begin{pmatrix} 1 & 0 & 0 \\ l_{21} & 1 & 0 \\ l_{31} & l_{32} & 1 \end{pmatrix}$ and $U = \begin{pmatrix} u_{11} & u_{12} & u_{13} \\ 0 & u_{22} & u_{23} \\ 0 & 0 & u_{33} \end{pmatrix}$

$$\Rightarrow \quad \begin{pmatrix} 1 & 2 & 3 \\ 2 & 5 & 2 \\ 3 & 1 & 5 \end{pmatrix} = \begin{pmatrix} u_{11} & u_{12} & u_{13} \\ l_{21} u_{11} & l_{21} u_{12} + u_{22} & l_{21} u_{13} + u_{23} \\ l_{31} u_{11} & l_{31} u_{12} + l_{32} u_{22} & l_{31} u_{13} + l_{32} u_{23} + u_{33} \end{pmatrix}$$

$$\Rightarrow \left.\begin{matrix} u_{11}=1, & u_{12}=2, & u_{13}=3 \\ l_{21}u_{11}=2, & l_{21}u_{12}+u_{22}=5, & l_{21}u_{13}+u_{23}=2, \\ l_{31}u_{11}=3, & l_{31}u_{12}+l_{32}u_{22}=1 & l_{31}u_{13}+l_{32}u_{23}+u_{33}=5 \end{matrix}\right\}$$

$$\Rightarrow \begin{matrix} u_{11}=1, & u_{12}=2, & u_{13}=3 \\ l_{21}=2, & u_{22}=1, & u_{23}=-4 \\ l_{31}=3, & l_{32}=-5 & u_{33}=-24. \end{matrix}$$

$$\Rightarrow \begin{pmatrix} 1 & 2 & 3 \\ 2 & 5 & 2 \\ 3 & 1 & 5 \end{pmatrix} = \begin{pmatrix} 1 & 0 & 0 \\ 2 & 1 & 0 \\ 3 & -5 & 1 \end{pmatrix} \begin{pmatrix} 1 & 2 & 3 \\ 0 & 1 & -4 \\ 0 & 0 & -24 \end{pmatrix}$$

Further, the Given system can be written as $\begin{pmatrix} 1 & 2 & 3 \\ 2 & 5 & 2 \\ 3 & 1 & 5 \end{pmatrix} \begin{pmatrix} x_1 \\ x_2 \\ x_3 \end{pmatrix} = \begin{pmatrix} 14 \\ 18 \\ 20 \end{pmatrix}$

$$\Rightarrow \begin{pmatrix} 1 & 0 & 0 \\ 2 & 1 & 0 \\ 3 & -5 & 1 \end{pmatrix} \begin{pmatrix} 1 & 2 & 3 \\ 0 & 1 & -4 \\ 0 & 0 & -24 \end{pmatrix} \begin{pmatrix} x_1 \\ x_2 \\ x_3 \end{pmatrix} = \begin{pmatrix} 14 \\ 18 \\ 20 \end{pmatrix}$$

$$\Rightarrow \begin{pmatrix} 1 & 0 & 0 \\ 2 & 1 & 0 \\ 3 & -5 & 1 \end{pmatrix} \begin{pmatrix} z_1 \\ z_2 \\ z_3 \end{pmatrix} = \begin{pmatrix} 14 \\ 18 \\ 20 \end{pmatrix} \text{ where } \begin{pmatrix} z_1 \\ z_2 \\ z_3 \end{pmatrix} = \begin{pmatrix} 1 & 2 & 3 \\ 0 & 1 & -4 \\ 0 & 0 & -24 \end{pmatrix} \begin{pmatrix} x_1 \\ x_2 \\ x_3 \end{pmatrix}$$

$$\Rightarrow \quad LZ = \begin{pmatrix} 14 \\ 18 \\ 20 \end{pmatrix} \quad \Rightarrow Z = L^{-1} \begin{pmatrix} 14 \\ 18 \\ 20 \end{pmatrix} = \left\{ \begin{pmatrix} 1 & 0 & 0 \\ 2 & 1 & 0 \\ 3 & -5 & 1 \end{pmatrix} \right\}^{-1} \begin{pmatrix} 14 \\ 18 \\ 20 \end{pmatrix}$$

$$\Rightarrow \begin{pmatrix} z_1 \\ z_2 \\ z_3 \end{pmatrix} = \begin{pmatrix} 1 & 0 & 0 \\ -2 & 1 & 0 \\ -13 & 5 & 1 \end{pmatrix} \begin{pmatrix} 14 \\ 18 \\ 20 \end{pmatrix} = \begin{pmatrix} 14 \\ -10 \\ -12 \end{pmatrix}$$

$$\Rightarrow \begin{pmatrix} 1 & 2 & 2 \\ 0 & 1 & -4 \\ 0 & 0 & -24 \end{pmatrix} \begin{pmatrix} x_1 \\ x_2 \\ x_3 \end{pmatrix} = \begin{pmatrix} 14 \\ -10 \\ -12 \end{pmatrix} \Rightarrow \begin{pmatrix} x_1 \\ x_2 \\ x_3 \end{pmatrix} = \begin{pmatrix} 1 & 2 & 3 \\ 0 & 1 & -4 \\ 0 & 0 & -24 \end{pmatrix}^{-1} \begin{pmatrix} 14 \\ -10 \\ -12 \end{pmatrix}$$

$$= \begin{pmatrix} 1 & -2 & 11/24 \\ 0 & 1 & -1/6 \\ 0 & 0 & -1/24 \end{pmatrix} \begin{pmatrix} 14 \\ -10 \\ -12 \end{pmatrix} = \begin{pmatrix} 14+20-33 \\ -10+12 \\ 3 \end{pmatrix} = \begin{pmatrix} 1 \\ 2 \\ 3 \end{pmatrix}$$

$$\Rightarrow \quad x_1 = 1, x_2 = 2, x_3 = 3.$$

(b) Let $\begin{bmatrix} 1 & 0 & 0 & 0 \\ l_{21} & 1 & 0 & 0 \\ l_{31} & l_{32} & 1 & 0 \\ l_{41} & l_{42} & l_{43} & 1 \end{bmatrix} \begin{bmatrix} u_{11} & u_{12} & u_{13} & u_{14} \\ 0 & u_{22} & u_{23} & u_{24} \\ 0 & 0 & u_{33} & u_{34} \\ 0 & 0 & 0 & u_{44} \end{bmatrix} = \underbrace{\begin{bmatrix} 10 & -7 & 3 & 5 \\ -6 & 8 & -1 & -4 \\ 3 & 1 & 4 & 11 \\ 5 & -9 & -2 & 4 \end{bmatrix}}_{\longleftarrow A \longrightarrow}$

(i) R_1 of U: $u_{11} = 10,\ u_{12} = -7,\ u_{13} = 3,\ u_{14} = 5$

(ii) C_1 of L: $l_{21} = -.6, l_{31} = 0.3, l_{41} = 0.5$

(iii) R_2 of U: $u_{22} = 3.8, u_{23} = 0.8, u_{24} = -1$

(iv) C_2 of L: $l_{32} = 0.81579, l_{42} = -1.44737$

(v) R_3 of U: $u_{33} = 2.44737, u_{34} = 10.31579$

(vi) C_3 of L: $l_{43} = -0.95699$

(vii) R_4 of U: $u_{44} = 9.92474$

$$\Rightarrow \quad A = \begin{bmatrix} 1 & 0 & 0 & 0 \\ -0.6 & 1 & 0 & 0 \\ 0.3 & 0.81579 & 1 & 0 \\ 0.5 & -1.44737 & -.95699 & 1 \end{bmatrix} \times \begin{bmatrix} 10 & -7 & 3 & 5 \\ 0 & 3.8 & 0.8 & -1 \\ 0 & 0 & 2.44737 & 10.31579 \\ 0 & 0 & 0 & 9.92474 \end{bmatrix}$$

Then writing $UX = V$,

$$\begin{bmatrix} 1 & 0 & 0 & 0 \\ -0.6 & 1 & 0 & 0 \\ 0.3 & 0.81577 & 1 & 0 \\ 0.5 & -1.44737 & -.95699 & 1 \end{bmatrix} \begin{bmatrix} v_1 \\ v_2 \\ v_3 \\ v_4 \end{bmatrix} = \begin{bmatrix} 6 \\ 5 \\ 2 \\ 7 \end{bmatrix}$$

where $v_1 = 6. v_2 = 8.6, v_3 = -6.81579, v_4 = 9.92474.$

Thus original system becomes

$$\begin{bmatrix} 10 & -7 & 3 & 5 \\ 0 & 3.8 & 0.8 & -1 \\ 0 & 0 & 2.44737 & 10.31579 \\ 0 & 0 & 0 & 9.92474 \end{bmatrix} \begin{bmatrix} x \\ y \\ z \\ u \end{bmatrix} = \begin{bmatrix} 6 \\ 8.6 \\ -6.81579 \\ 9.92474 \end{bmatrix}$$

$$\Rightarrow \quad 10x - 7y + 3z + 5u = 6, 3.8y + 0.8z - u = 8.6$$

$$2.44737z + 10.31579u = -6.81579, u = 1$$

$$\Rightarrow \quad u = 1, z = -7, y = 4, x = 5.$$

✦✦ Problem Set ✦✦

Solve the following equations by Cramer's Rule:

1. $x + 3y + 6z = 2;\ 3x - y + 4z = 9;\ x - 4y + 2z = 7.$

2. $x + y + z = 6.6;\ x - y + z = 2.2;\ x + 2y + 3z = 15.2.$

3. Solve by matrix Inversion method;

$$x + y + 2z = 4;\ 2x - y + 3z = 9; 3x - y - z = 2.$$

4. In a given electrical network, the equations for the currents i_1, i_2, i_3 are

$$3i_1 + i_2 + i_3 = 8;\ 2i_1 - 3i_2 - 2i_3 = -5;\ 7i_i + 2i_2 - 5i_3 = 0.$$

Calculate i_1 and i_3 by (*i*) *Cramer's Rule,* (*ii*) *Matrix Inversion*

5. $2x + y + z = 10; 3x + 2y + 3z = 18; x + 4y + 9z = 16.$

✦✦ Answers ✦✦

1.	(2, – 1, 1/2)	2.	(1.2, 2.2, 3.2)
3.	(1, – 1, 2)	4.	$i_1 = 1.5,\ i_3 = 2.5$
5.	(7, –9, 5)		

13.2.11 Well Conditioned and Ill Conditioned Equations: A linear system is said to be well-conditioned, if small changes in the coefficients of the system produce small changes in the values of the unknowns whereas the system is said to be Ill -Conditioned if small changes in the coefficients of the equations produce large changes in the values of unknowns. We generally face Ill Conditioned Systems in practical life situation. When the determinant of the coefficient matrix is small, there exist a hope for an Ill-Conditioned system. For an Ill-Conditioned system, its coefficient matrix is called as an *Ill-Conditional Matrix.* In case, we are Solving Simultaneous equations, we usually have two types of instabilities: Induced and inherent. Induced instability occurs due to in correct choice of the method while the inherent instability is a property and occurs due to the problem being ill conditioned and further it can be avoided by the reformulation of the problem in a proper manner.

To improve accuracy of an Ill Conditioned system by the Iterative method.

***Consider the System*:**

$$a_1 x + b_1 y + c_1 z = b_1,\ a_2 x + b_2 y + c_2 z = d_2,\ a_3 x + b_3 y + c_3 z = d_3$$

Let x^1, y^1, z^1 be the approximate solution of the above system, then substituting these values on the L.H.S., we get

$$a_1 x^1 + b_1 y^1 + c_1 z^1 = d_1^1,\ a_2 x^1 + b_2 y^1 + c_2 z^1 = d_2^1,\ a_3 x^1 + b_3 y^1 + c_3 z^1 = d_3^1,,$$

Where d_1^1, d_2^1, d_3^1 are the new values of d_1, d_2, d_3. Then we have

$$\left.\begin{aligned} a_1(x - x^1) + b_1(y - y^1) + c_1(z - z^1) &= d_1 - d_1^1 \\ a_2(x - x^1) + b_2(y - y') + c_2(z - z^1) &= d_2 - d_2^1 \\ a_3(x - x^1) + b_3(y - y^1) + c_3(z - z^1) &= d_3 - d_3' \end{aligned}\right\}$$

$$\Rightarrow \left.\begin{aligned} a_1x_e + b_1\, y_e + c_1\, z_e &= k_1 \\ a_2x_e + b_2\, y_e + c_2\, z_e &= k_2 \\ a_3x_e + b_3\, y_e + c_3\, z_e &= k_3 \end{aligned}\right\}$$

where $x - x^1 = x_e,\ y - y^1 = y_e,\ z - z^1 = z_e$ and $k_i = d_i - d_i^1\ (i = 1, 2, 3)$

Solving this system, we can obtain the values of x_e, y_e, z_e and hence $x = x^1 + x_e$, $y = y^1 + y_e, z = z^1 + z_e$. This would be a better approximation for x, y, z.

Then repeating this procedure again and again we can obtain results to the desired accuracy.

Example 19: *An approximate solution of the system* $2x + 2y - z = 6; x + y + 2z = 8;$ $-x + 3y + 2z = 4$ *is given by* $x = 2.8,\ y = 1,\ z = 1.8.$ *Using the above Iterative method, improve this solution.*

Solution: Putting the approximate values $x^1 = 2.8,\ y^1 = 1, z^1 = 1.8$ in the given equations,

we obtain
$$\left.\begin{aligned} 2(2.8) + 2(1) - 1.8 &= 5.8 \\ 2.8 + 1 + 2(1.8) &= 7.4 \\ -2.8 + 3(1) + 2(1.8) &= 3.8 \end{aligned}\right\} \quad \text{...(1)}$$

Then subtracting each equation in (1) from the corresponding given equations, we get

$$\left.\begin{aligned} 2x_e + 2y_e - z_e &= 0.2 \\ x_e + y_e + 2z_e &= 0.6 \\ -x_e + 3y_e + 2z_e &= 0.2 \end{aligned}\right\} \quad \text{...(2)}$$

Where $x_e = x - 2.8,\ y_e = y - 1, z_e = z - 1.8.$

Again solving equations (2) we get $x_e = 0.2,\ y_e = 0, z_e = 0.2.$

Hence the better solution is $x = 3,\ y = 1, z = 2$. This evidently is the exact solution.

Example 20: *Extablish whether the system* $1.01x + 2y = 2.01;\ x + 2y = 2$ *is Well-conditioned or not?*

Solution: The solution is $x = 1$ and $y = 0.5$. ...(1)

Let us now consider the system

$$\left.\begin{aligned} x + 2.01y &= 2.04 \\ x + 2y &= 2 \end{aligned}\right\}$$

This has the solution $x = -6$ and $y = 4$.

Thus the system is Ill-Conditioned.

Example 21: *Establish whether the system of equation*

$$\begin{aligned} 10x + 8y + 9z + 6w &= 33, \\ 6x + 7y + 5z + 5w &= 23, \\ 8x + 10y + 7z + 7w &= 32, \\ 9x + 7y + 10z + +5w &= 31 \end{aligned}$$

Is well-conditioned or not?

Solution: Proceed as above example. **Ans:** *Ill*-conditioned.

13.2.12 Comparison of Different Methods

Direct methods and Methods of Iteration have their advantages and disadvantages over each other on a particular system of equations. As a matter of fact, the Direct methods yield a solution for any Non-Singular Set of equations in a finite number of steps whereas in the application of Iterative Methods, the desired accuracy depends on the amount of computation. In usual practice, we use a Direct Method for the solution of the Linear System. On the other hand for large systems, the application of an Iterative Method makes the solution faster and hence must be preferred.

Gauss Elimination Method is more expensive more of recording and is time consuming for operations. Crout's Method (Triangularistion Method) is one of the Direct methods which is best suited for the solution of a Linear system and is also a software for the computer. In the Elimination Method, the rounding off errors are also generally generated where the rounding off erros come in final iteration while applying Iteration methods. As a mater of fact, in general the Iteration method have smaller round-off errors as the iteration Process is the self correcting technique. The Iterative method does not converge necessarily and incase it converges then the Iterative method is decidedly a better method as compared to other Direct methods.

When, we are solving a Linear System of equations then generally we come across with two types of instabilities as induced in stability and inherent instability. The induced instability occurs due to an incorrect choice of the technique of solution whereas inherent instability arrises due to the set of equations being Ill-Conditioned *i.e.* it is the property of the problem itself and can be avoided by re-formulating the problem.

13.3 Newton-Raphson Method for Solving Non-Linear Simultaneous Equations

Let us consider the equations as $f(x, y) = 0, g(x, y) = 0$ ...(1)

Further by Graphical or another methods, let (x_0, y_0) be the initial approximation then we proceed to obtain a better approximation (x_1, y_1) as follows.

$$\text{Let } x_1 = x_0 + h, y_1 = y_0 + k \Rightarrow f(x_0 + h, y_0 + k) = 0, g(x_0 + h, y_0 + k) - 0 \quad ...(2)$$

$$\Rightarrow \left.\begin{aligned} f(x_0, y_0) + h\left(\frac{\partial f}{\partial x}\right)_{x_0, y_0} + k\left(\frac{\partial f}{\partial y}\right)_{x_0, y_0} &= 0 \\ g(x_0, y_0) + h\left(\frac{\partial g}{\partial x}\right)_{x_0, y_0} + k\left(\frac{\partial f}{\partial y}\right)_{x_0, y_0} &= 0 \end{aligned}\right\} \quad ...(3)$$

By Taylor's expansion to first degree terms.

Solving these equations, we can get h, k and hence x_1 and y_1 are determined. The process can be repeated till, we get the values to the desired accuracy. This method does not converge unless the starting values of the roots are chosen close to the actual roots. This method can also be extended to three equations involving three unknowns. To obtain the meaningful solution, the method becomes very cumbersome unless the complete information about the equation and their physical significance is available.

Note: In case one of the variables is eliminated from the given equations so as yield a polynomial equation in another variable, then this variable could be easily obtained by Newton-Raphson method to the desired degree of accuracy. As a matter of fact, sometimes the root of the polynomial equation could be easily obtained by trial. In this case the degree of the polynomial equation could be depressed easily by one. Again obtain the root, by Newton Raphson method. After Obtaining this variable to the desired degree of accuracy, the other variable can be readily obtained from one of the given equations.

Example 22: *Solve the system of Non-Linear equations:*

$$x^2 + y = 11,\ y^2 + x = 7. \qquad ...(1)$$

Solution: By Graphical method, the initial approximation is $x_0 = 3.5$, $y_0 = -1.8$. now

$$f = x^2 + y - 11 \text{ and } g = y^2 + x - 7 \Rightarrow \frac{\partial f}{\partial x} = 2x,\ \frac{\partial f}{\partial y} = 1 \text{ and } \frac{\partial g}{\partial x} = 1,\ \frac{\partial g}{\partial y} = 2y.$$

Applying then Newton-Raphson's equations (3) above

$\Rightarrow 7h + k = 0.55,\ h - 3.6k = 0.26.$

Solving these $h = 0.0855$ and $k = -0.0485$

Hence the better approximation to the root is $x_1 = x_0 + h = 3.5855$ and $y_1 = y_0 + k = -1.8485$

Repeating the procedure *i.e.* replacing (x_0, y_0) by (x_1, y_1); we obtain $x_2 = 3.5844$, $y_2 = -1.8482$.

✦✦ Problem Set ✦✦

1. Use Matrix Method to solve the system

$$\left.\begin{aligned} 5x_1 + 3x_2 + 7x_3 &= 4, \\ x_1 + 5x_2 + 3x_3 &= 2, \\ 2x_1 + 2x_2 + 10x_3 &= 5 \end{aligned}\right]$$

2. Solve the system $\left.\begin{aligned} 10x_1 + 2x_2 + x_3 &= 59. \\ x_1 + 8x_2 + 2x_3 &= -4. \\ 7x_1 - x_2 + 20x_3 &= 5. \end{aligned}\right]$ by Cramer's Rule

3. Apply Gauss's Elimination Method to solve the following system:

(i) $16x_1 - 19x_2 + 40x_3 - 17x_4 = 89,$

$82x_1 + 42x_2 + 32x_3 - 8x_4 = 73,$

$55x_1 - 35x_2 + 45x_3 - 25x_4 = 67,$

$7x_1 + 19x_2 + 33x_3 + 85x_4 = 111.$

(ii) $5x_1 - x_2 - 2x_3 = 142,$

$x_1 - 3x_2 - x_3 = -31,$

$2x_1 - x_2 - 3x_3 = 5.$

(iii) $2x_1 + 4x_2 + x_3 = 3,$

$$3x_1 + 2x_2 - 2x_3 = -2,$$

$$x_1 - x_2 + x_3 = 6.$$

4. Apply Crout's Method to solve

$$2x - 6y + 8z = 24;$$

$$5x + 4y - 3z = 2,$$

5. Solve the following system of equations by Relaxation method, giving the results correct to three places of decimal:

(i)
$$\left.\begin{aligned} 3x_1 + 9x_2 - 2x_3 &= 11, \\ 4x_1 + 2x_2 + 13x_3 &= 24, \\ 4x_1 - 4x_2 + 3x_3 &= -8. \end{aligned}\right]$$

(ii)
$$\left.\begin{aligned} -10x_1 + 6x_2 + 3x_3 + 100 &= 0, \\ 6x_1 - 5x_2 + 5x_3 + 100 &= 0, \\ 3x_1 + 6x_2 - 10x_3 + 100 &= 0 \end{aligned}\right]$$

(iii)
$$\left.\begin{aligned} 15x_1 + 3x_2 - 4x_3 + 2x_4 &= 49.207, \\ 3x_1 + 27x_2 - 5x_3 - x_4 &= 18.024, \\ -4x_1 - 5x_2 + 16x_3 + 5x_4 &= -23.871, \\ 2x_1 - x_2 + 5x_3 + 19x_4 &= 54.907 \end{aligned}\right]$$

6. Solve the system

$$\begin{aligned} 2x_1 - x_2 &= 1, \\ -x_1 + 2x_2 - x_3 &= 1, \\ -x_2 + 2x_3 - x_4 &= 1, \\ -x_3 + 2x_4 - x_5 &= 1, \\ -x_4 + 2x_5 - x_6 &= 1, \\ -x_5 + 2x_6 &= 1, \end{aligned}$$

7. Apply Gauss-Siedal Iteration Method to solve

$$10x + y + z = 12,$$

$$2x + 10y + z = 13,$$

$$2x + 2y + 10z = 14.$$

Unknown	1	2	3	4
x	1.20	90	1.00	1.00
y	1.06	1.00	1.00	
z	0.95	1.00	1.00	

8. Solve the following system by the Iteration method, continuing the iterating the Iteration Process until the maximum difference between successive value of x, y and z is less than 0.02

$$20x+2y+6z=28,$$
$$x+20y+9z=-23,$$
$$2x-7y+2z=-57.$$

9. Solve by Gauss-Elimination Method

$$2x+y+4z=12,$$
$$8x-3y+2z=23,$$
$$4x+11y-z=33,$$

10. Factorize the matrix

$$A=\begin{bmatrix}5 & -2 & 1\\ 7 & 1 & -5\\ 3 & 7 & 4\end{bmatrix}$$

Into the from LU, where L is unit lower triangular matrix and U is upper triangular and triangular hence solve the system of equations

$$5x-2y+z=4,$$
$$7x+y-5z=8,$$
$$3x+7y+4z=10.$$

11. Solve the system of equations

$$2x-3y+10z=3,\ -x+4y+2z=20,\ 5x+2y+z=-12$$

By Factorization Method.

✦✦ Objective Type Question ✦✦

❖ Multiple Choice Questions

1. If $AX = B$ is the matrix form of a system of algebraic equations, which of the following is not correct:

   (a) If $B = 0$, and $\det A = 0$; then there exist infinite number of non-trivial solutions besides trivial solution $X = 0$.

   (b) If $B = 0$ and $\det A \neq 0$; then the system has the only unique trivial solution $X = 0$.

   (c) If $B \neq 0$ and $\det A \neq 0$; then the system has only unique solution.

   (d) If $B \neq 0$ and $\det A = 0$; then there exist infinite number of solutions provided the equations are inconsistent.

2. Due to Gauss-Elimination Method, when the elimination is complete, then the system takes the form:

   (a) Upper triangular Form (b) Lower triangular Form

   (c) Rectangular Form (d) None of these.

3. Which of the following are Iterative Methods:

   (a) Jacobi's Method (b) Gauss-Seidel Method

   (c) Relaxation Method (d) All of the above.

4. The concept of dividing the matrix into upper and Lower Triangular Form is used by

   (a) Crout's Triangular Method (b) Jacobi's Method

   (c) Gauss-Elimination Method (d) Cramer's Rule.

5. The solution of Simultaneous Linear Algebraic Equation can not be found by

   (a) Gauss Jardon Method (b) Gauss-Elimination Method

   (c) Gauss-Seidel Method (d) None of these.

6. Which of the following is not correct:

   (a) By Newton-Raphson Method the Non Linear Simultaneous Equations can be solved

   (b) The Newton-Raphson Method is not applicable to Non-Linear Simultaneous Equation

   (c) Jacobi's Method is an Iterative Method

   (d) None of these.

7. The Relaxation Method can be applied successfully only when:
   (a) The diagonal elements of coefficient matrix are non-dominant to the other coefficients in the corresponding row.
   (b) The sum of elements in each row must be greater than the diagonal element in the corresponding row.
   (c) The diagonal elements of coefficient matrix dominate the other coefficient and diagonal element must be greater than the sum of the corresponding row for at least one row.
   (d) None of these.
8. Which of the following is a Direct Method:
   (a) Relaxation Method (b) Crout's Method
   (c) Gauss-Seidel Method (d) None of these
9. Which of the following is not a Direct Method:
   (a) Gauss-Elimination Method (b) Cramer's Rule
   (c) Gauss-Jordon Method (d) Jacobi's Method.
10. Which of the following the best method for finding the solution of Linear Algebraic equation:
    (a) Crout's Triangularisation Method
    (b) Gauss Elimination Method
    (c) Jacobi's Iterative Method
    (d) Gauss-Jordon Method.
11. The fact which is not correct is
    (a) The Iterative Method converges necessarily
    (b) The Iterative Method does not converge necessarity.
    (c) Rounding of errors exist in Iteration Methods
    (d) None of these.
12. Jordan's Method is a modification of the method due to:
    (a) Gauss Method (b) Relaxation Method
    (c) Triangularisation Method (d) Jacobi's Method.
13. Relaxation method converges .... in comparison to Gauss-Seidel Iterative method:
    (a) Less rapidly (b) More rapidly
    (c) Remains constant (d) None of these.
14. The Gauss-Seidel Method is called the method of .... displacements and Jacobi Method is called the method ....displacements.
    (a) Simultaneous, successive (b) Successive, continuous
    (c) Successive, simultaneous (d) None of these.

✦✦ Examination Questions ✦✦

1. Solve the following system of Linear equations, using Gauss-Elimination Method:

$$x_1 + 6x_2 + 3x_3 = 6$$
$$2x_1 + 3x_2 + 3x_3 = 117$$
$$4x_1 + x_2 + 2x_3 = 283.$$

[I.A.S. 2000]

2. Using Gauss-Seidel Iterative Method and the starting solution $x_1 = x_2 = x_3 = 0$, determine the solution of the following system of equations in two iterations.

$$10x_1 - x_2 - x_3 = 8$$
$$x_1 + 10x_2 + x_3 = 12$$
$$x_1 - x_2 + 10x_3 = 10$$

Compare the approximate solution with the exact solution. **[I.A.S. 2001]**

3. Using Gauss-Seidel Iterative Method, find the solution of the following system:

$$4x_1 - x_2 + 8x_3 = 26$$
$$5x_1 + 2x_2 - x_3 = 6$$
$$x_1 - 10x_2 + 2x_3 = -13.$$

Upto three iterations. **[I.A.S. 2004]**

$$-x_1 - x_2 + 6x_3 = 42$$
$$6x_1 - x_2 - x_3 = 11.33$$
$$-x_1 + 6x_2 - x_3 = 32$$

With initial values (4.67, 7.62, 9.05). upto two iterations. **[I.A.S. 2008]**

4. Solve the following system of equations by Gauss's Elimination Method:

$$10x_1 - 7x_2 + 3x_3 + 5x_4 = 6$$
$$-6x_1 + 8x_2 - x_3 - 4x_4 = 5$$
$$3x_1 + x_2 + 4x_3 + 11x_4 = 2$$
$$5x_1 - 9x_2 - 2x_3 + 4x_4 = 7$$

[I.F.S. 2002]

5. Using Gauss-Seidel Iteration Method find the solution, correct to three decimal places, of the Linear system

$$7x_1 + 52x_2 + 13x_3 = 104$$
$$3x_1 + 8x_2 + 29x_3 = 71$$
$$83x_1 + 11x_2 - 4x_3 = 95$$

with $(x_1^0, x_2^0, x_3^0) = (1.145, 1.846, 1.821)$. upto two iterations. **[I.F.S. 2004]**

6. Solve the Given System of equations using Gauss Elimination Method with partial pivoting:

$$x - y + 3z = 13; \quad 4x - 2y + z = 15; \quad -3x - y + 4z = 8.$$

[U.P.T.U. 2009]

Answers

Problem Set

1.	$x_1 = \frac{7}{11}, x_2 = \frac{3}{11}, x_3 = 0$
2.	$x_4 = 6.36, x_2 = -0.2996, x_3 = -3.33$
3. (i)	$x_1 = -1.339, x_2 = 2.5, x_3 = 0.288, x_4 = -8.61$
(ii)	$x_1 = 39.378, x_2 = 17.17, x_3 = 18.86$ approx.
(iii)	$x_1 = 2, x_2 = -1, x_3 = 3$
4.	$x = 1, y = 3, z = 5$
5. (i)	$x_1 = 1.94, x_2 = 2.11, x_3 = 6.9$
(ii)	$x_1 = 175, x_2 = 195, x_3 = 160$
(iii)	$x_1 = 195, x_2 = 2.683, x_3 = -1.118, x_4 = 3.111$
6.	$x_1 = 3, x_2 = 5, x_3 = 6, x_4 = 6, x_5 = 5, x_6 = 3$
7.	$x = 1.163, y = 1.14, z = -.77$
9.	3.36, 1.8, 0.8
10.	$L = \begin{bmatrix} 1 & 0 & 0 \\ 7/5 & 1 & 0 \\ 3/5 & 41/19 & 1 \end{bmatrix}, U = \begin{bmatrix} 5 & -2 & 1 \\ 0 & 19/5 & -32/5 \\ 0 & 0 & 327/19 \end{bmatrix}, x = \frac{122}{109}, y = \frac{284}{327}, z = \frac{46}{327}$
11.	$x = -4, y = 3, z = 2$

Multiple Choice Questions

1.	(d)	2.	(a)	3.	(d)	4.	(a)	5.	(d)
6.	(b)	7.	(c)	8.	(b)	9.	(d)	10.	(a)
11.	(a)	12.	(a)	13.	(b)	14.	(c)		

Examination Questions

1.	$x_1 = 72, x_2 = -13, x_3 = 4$	2.	$x_1 = 1, x_2 = 1, x_3 = 1$
3.	$x_1 = 1, x_2 = 2, x_3 = 3$	4.	$x_1 = 5, x_2 = 4, x_3 = -7, x_4 = 1$
5.	$x = 1.06, y = 1.37, z = 1.96$	6.	$x = 2, y = -2, z = 3$

Theory | Solved Examples | Problem Set

Chapter 14

Matrix Inversion

Gauss Elimination Method, Gauss-Jordan Method, Crout's Method, Doolitte Method, Choleskies Method, Iterative Method.

14.1 Introduction

A square matrix A (order m say) is said to be the inverse of the square matrix B, if $AB = BA = I_m$, where I_m is an $m \times m$ order identity matrix. As studied earlier, the inverse of a matrix is always unique. It is to be noted that a matrix "A" can be inverted if it is non-singular *i.e.* det $A \neq 0$. This implies further that a singular matrix (for which det $A = 0$) has no inverse. There are several methods to obtain the inverse of a matrix. One method of finding out the inverse of a matrix is based on computing the adjoint of this matrix, but it requires a lot of calculation work. So we try to discuss those methods which requires less computational work to find the inverse of matrix. Few methods are given below:

(i) Gauss Elimination Method
(ii) Gauss Jordan Method
(iii) Triangularisation Method
(iv) Crout's Method
(v) Doolittle Method
(vi) Choleski's Method
(vii) Iterative Method
(viii) Escalator Method
(ix) Complex Matrices and Inversion

14.2 Gauss Elimination Method

Here we consider an identity matrix of the same order as A has got and keep it with A and then try to convert A into an upper triangular matrix by the usual method. Again making row transformations, this upper triangular matrix is also transformed into an identity matrix. In the end when the matrix A is transformed into an identity matrix, the adjacent matrix gives inverse of A. In order to increase the accuracy, the largest element is fixed as the pivot element by making row transformations only.

Solved Examples

Example 1: *Find the inverse of* $A = \begin{bmatrix} 0 & 2 & 4 \\ 2 & 4 & 6 \\ 6 & 2 & 2 \end{bmatrix}$ *by Gauss Elimination method.*

Solution: We have $A = AI$

$$\Rightarrow \quad A = \underset{\leftarrow A \rightarrow}{\begin{bmatrix} 0 & 2 & 4 \\ 2 & 4 & 6 \\ 6 & 2 & 2 \end{bmatrix}} \underset{\leftarrow I \rightarrow}{\begin{bmatrix} 1 & 0 & 0 \\ 0 & 1 & 0 \\ 0 & 0 & 1 \end{bmatrix}} \underset{\sim}{R_{13}} \begin{bmatrix} 6 & 2 & 2 \\ 2 & 4 & 6 \\ 0 & 2 & 4 \end{bmatrix} \begin{bmatrix} 0 & 0 & 1 \\ 0 & 1 & 0 \\ 1 & 0 & 0 \end{bmatrix}$$

[To bring the maximum element 6 at the place a_{11}, we interchange to first and third rows.]

$$\underset{\sim}{R_1(1/3)} \begin{bmatrix} 2 & 2/3 & 2/3 \\ 2 & 4 & 6 \\ 0 & 0 & 4 \end{bmatrix} \begin{bmatrix} 0 & 0 & \frac{1}{3} \\ 0 & 1 & 0 \\ 1 & 0 & 0 \end{bmatrix} \text{(multiplying 1st row by } \frac{1}{3}\text{)}$$

$$\underset{\sim}{R_{21}(-1)} \begin{bmatrix} 2 & 2/3 & 2/3 \\ 0 & 10/3 & 16/3 \\ 0 & 2 & 4 \end{bmatrix} \begin{bmatrix} 0 & 0 & 1/3 \\ 0 & 1 & -1/3 \\ 1 & 0 & 0 \end{bmatrix} \text{(operation is } R_2 - R_1\text{)}$$

$$\underset{\sim}{R_2(3/5)} \begin{bmatrix} 2 & 2/3 & 2/3 \\ 0 & 2 & 16/5 \\ 0 & 2 & 4 \end{bmatrix} \begin{bmatrix} 0 & 0 & 1/3 \\ 0 & 3/5 & -1/5 \\ 1 & 0 & 0 \end{bmatrix} \text{(operation is } 3/5\, R_2\text{)}$$

$$\underset{\sim}{R_{32}(-1)} \begin{bmatrix} 2 & 2/3 & 2/3 \\ 0 & 2 & 16/5 \\ 0 & 0 & 4/5 \end{bmatrix} \begin{bmatrix} 1 & 0 & 1/3 \\ 0 & 3/5 & -1/5 \\ 1 & -3/5 & 1/5 \end{bmatrix} \text{(operation is } R_3 - R_2\text{)}$$

$$\underset{\sim}{R_3(5/2)} \begin{bmatrix} 2 & 2/3 & 2/3 \\ 0 & 2 & 16/5 \\ 0 & 0 & 2 \end{bmatrix} \begin{bmatrix} 1 & 0 & 1/3 \\ 0 & 3/5 & -1/5 \\ 5/2 & -3/2 & 1/2 \end{bmatrix}$$

Evidently A has been converted into an upper triangular matrix. Now by making row transformations, A will be converted into an identity matrix.

$$\begin{matrix} R_{13}(-1/3) \\ \sim \\ R_{32}(-8/5) \end{matrix} \begin{bmatrix} 2 & 2/3 & 0 \\ 0 & 2 & 0 \\ 0 & 0 & 2 \end{bmatrix} \begin{bmatrix} -5/6 & 1/2 & 1/6 \\ -4 & 3 & -1 \\ 5/2 & -3/2 & 1/2 \end{bmatrix}$$

$$\underset{\sim}{R_{12}(-1/3)} \begin{bmatrix} 2 & 0 & 0 \\ 0 & 2 & 0 \\ 0 & 0 & 2 \end{bmatrix} \begin{bmatrix} 1/2 & -1/2 & 1/2 \\ -4 & 3 & -1 \\ 5/2 & -3/2 & 1/2 \end{bmatrix} \text{[operation is } R_1 - R_2/3\text{]}$$

$$\begin{bmatrix} 1 & 0 & 0 \\ 0 & 1 & 0 \\ 0 & 0 & 1 \end{bmatrix} \quad \begin{bmatrix} 1 & -1 & 1 \\ -8 & 6 & -2 \\ 5 & -3 & 1 \end{bmatrix}$$

$\leftarrow$Identity matrix$\rightarrow \leftarrow A^{-1} \rightarrow$

The adjacent matrix of $I_{3\times 3}$ gives $A^{-1} = \begin{bmatrix} 1 & -1 & 1 \\ -8 & 6 & -2 \\ 5 & -3 & 1 \end{bmatrix}$.

14.3 Gauss-Jordan Method

[Agra 2004]

In this method A is written for the given matrix and I the unit matrix side by side. Then on every step, we get column in the unit matrix to the left and at the end, we have I to the left and A^{-1} to the right. As a matter of fact, the following formula for the p-th reduction of the

p-th row: $a_{pk}^{p} = (a_{pk}^{p-1} / a_{pp}^{p-1})$. For rest of the rows, we have

$a_{jk}^{p} = a_{jk}^{p-1} - a_{jp}^{p-1}.[a_{pk}^{p-1} / a_{pp}^{p-1}]$. Now, for example consider the matrix

$A = \begin{pmatrix} a_{11} & a_{12} & a_{13} \\ a_{21} & a_{22} & a_{23} \\ a_{31} & a_{32} & a_{33} \end{pmatrix}$. Then we write the whole procedure as follows:

$$(\text{Pivot element} = \boldsymbol{a}_{11}) \begin{pmatrix} \boldsymbol{a}_{11} & a_{12} & a_{13} \\ a_{21} & a_{22} & a_{23} \\ a_{31} & a_{32} & a_{33} \end{pmatrix} \begin{pmatrix} 1 & 0 & 0 \\ 0 & 1 & 0 \\ 0 & 0 & 1 \end{pmatrix}$$

We consider the pivot element as $\boldsymbol{a}_{11}$. Then the first row of the new matrix becomes

$\frac{a_{12}}{a_{11}}, \frac{a_{13}}{a_{11}}, \frac{1}{a_{11}}$ i.e. $a'_{11} = \frac{a_{12}}{a_{11}}, a'_{12} = \frac{a_{13}}{a_{11}}, a'_{13} = \frac{1}{a_{11}}$.

The elements of the second row are $a'_{21} = a_{22} - a_{21}.(a_{12} / a_{11}), a'_{22} = a_{23} - a_{21}\,(a_{13} / a_{11})$, $a'_{23} = 0 - a_{21}(1/a_{12})$. Also, the elements of third row are:

$a_{32} - a_{31}(a_{12} / a_{11}) = a'_{31};\ a'_{32} = a_{33} - a_{31}.(a_{13} / a_{11});\ a'_{33} = 0 - a_{31}.(1/a_{12})$,

$$\text{Then we write: } \begin{matrix} 1 \\ 0 \\ 0 \end{matrix} \quad \begin{pmatrix} a_{11}' & a_{12}' & a_{13}' \\ \boldsymbol{a}_{21}' & a_{22}' & a_{23}' \\ a_{31}' & a_{32}' & a_{33}' \end{pmatrix} \quad \begin{matrix} 0\ 0 \\ 1\ 0 \\ 0\ 1 \end{matrix}$$

Further, the pivot element becomes $\boldsymbol{a}_{21}'$ and procedure is repeated starting from second row. To make the procedure clear, we consider the matrix.

Example 2: $A = \begin{pmatrix} 50 & 107 & 36 \\ 25 & 54 & 20 \\ 31 & 66 & 21 \end{pmatrix}$ *to find its inverse.*

Solution: For this we write:

Pivot element is **50** $\begin{pmatrix} \mathbf{50} & 107 & 36 \\ 25 & 54 & 20 \\ 31 & 66 & 21 \end{pmatrix} \begin{pmatrix} 1 & 0 & 0 \\ 0 & 1 & 0 \\ 0 & 0 & 1 \end{pmatrix}$

The elements $a_{11}', a_{12}', a_{13}', a_{21}', a_{22}', a_{23}', a_{31}', a_{32}', a_{33}'$ are obtained and the matrix A after first operation becomes

$$\begin{matrix} 1 \\ 0 \\ 0 \end{matrix} \begin{bmatrix} \frac{107}{50} = 2.14 = a_{11}', & \frac{36}{50} = 0.72 = a_{12}', & \frac{1}{50} = .02 = a_{13}' \\ 54 - 25 \times 2.14 & 20 - 25 \times .72 & 0 - 25 \times .02 \\ = 0.5 = a_{21}' & = 2 = a_{22}' & = -0.5 = a_{23}' \\ 66 - 31 \times 2.14 & 21 - 31 \times 0.72 & 0 - 31 \times .02 \\ = -0.34 = a_{31}' & = -1.32 = a_{32}' & = -0.62 = a_{33}' \end{bmatrix} \begin{matrix} 0 & 0 \\ 1 & 0 \\ 0 & 1 \end{matrix}$$

$$\Rightarrow \begin{matrix} 1 \\ 0 \\ 0 \end{matrix} \begin{pmatrix} 2.14 & 0.72 & .02 \\ \mathbf{0.5} & 2.00 & -0.5 \\ -0.34 & -1.32 & -0.62 \end{pmatrix} \begin{matrix} 0 & 0 \\ 1 & 0 \\ 0 & 1 \end{matrix}$$

For further calculations, we consider the pivot element **0.5** and proceed as follows:

$$\begin{matrix} 1 & 0 \\ 0 & 1 \\ 0 & 0 \end{matrix} \begin{bmatrix} 0.72 - 2.14 \times 4 & .02 - 2.14(-1) & 0 - 2.14 \times 2 \\ = -7.84 & = 2.16 & = -4.28 \\ 2/.5 = 4 & -.5/.5 = -1 & 1/.5 = 2 \\ -1.32 - (-.34) \times 4 & -0.62 - (.34)(-1) & 0 - (-.34)2 \\ = .04 & = -.96 & = 0.68 \end{bmatrix} \begin{matrix} 0 \\ 0 \\ 1 \end{matrix}$$

$$\Rightarrow \begin{matrix} 1 & 0 \\ 0 & 1 \\ 0 & 0 \end{matrix} \begin{pmatrix} -7.84 & 2.16 & -4.28 \\ 4 & -1 & 2 \\ .04 & -0.96 & 0.68 \end{pmatrix} \begin{matrix} 0 \\ 0 \\ 1 \end{matrix}$$

Finally taking the pivot element as **.04**, we get the next operation as

$$\begin{matrix} 1 & 0 & 0 \\ 0 & 1 & 0 \\ 0 & 0 & 1 \end{matrix} \begin{pmatrix} 2.16 - (-7.84)(-24) & -4.28 - (-7.84)17 & 0 - (-1.84)25 \\ = -186 & = 129 & = 196 \\ -1 - 4(-24) = 95 & 2 - 4(17) = -66 & 0 - 4(25) = -100 \\ -0.96/.04 = -24 & .68/.04 = 17 & 1/.04 = 25 \end{pmatrix}$$

$$\Rightarrow \begin{matrix} 1 & 0 & 0 \\ 0 & 1 & 0 \\ 0 & 0 & 1 \end{matrix} \begin{pmatrix} -186 & 129 & 196 \\ 95 & -66 & -100 \\ -24 & 17 & 25 \end{pmatrix}$$

$$\Rightarrow IA^{-1} \text{ i.e. } A^{-1} = \begin{pmatrix} -186 & 129 & 196 \\ 95 & -66 & -100 \\ -24 & 17 & 25 \end{pmatrix}$$

Example 3: *To find the inverse of matrix.*

$$A=\begin{pmatrix}1 & 1/3 & 1/5\\ 1/3 & 1/5 & 1/7\\ 1/5 & 1/7 & 1/9\end{pmatrix}, \textit{using Jordan's method.}$$

[Agra 2004]

Solution: For this, we write Pivot element = **1**

$$\begin{pmatrix}\mathbf{1} & 1/3 & 1/5\\ 1/3 & 1/5 & 1/7\\ 1/5 & 1/7 & 1/9\end{pmatrix}\begin{pmatrix}1 & 0 & 0\\ 0 & 1 & 0\\ 0 & 0 & 1\end{pmatrix}$$

$$\Rightarrow \begin{matrix}1\\0\\0\end{matrix}\begin{pmatrix}\frac{1}{3}\div 1=\frac{1}{3} & \frac{1}{5}\div 1=\frac{1}{5} & 1\div 1=1\\ \frac{1}{5}-\frac{1}{3}.\frac{1}{3}=\frac{4}{45} & \frac{1}{7}-\frac{1}{3}.\frac{1}{5}=\frac{8}{105} & 0-\frac{1}{3}=-\frac{1}{3}\\ \frac{1}{7}-\frac{1}{5}.\frac{1}{3}=\frac{8}{105} & \frac{1}{9}-\frac{1}{5}.\frac{1}{5}=\frac{16}{225} & 0-\frac{1}{5}=-\frac{1}{5}\end{pmatrix}\begin{matrix}0 & 0\\ 1 & 0\\ 0 & 1\end{matrix}$$

$$\Rightarrow \begin{matrix}1\\0\\0\end{matrix}\begin{pmatrix}1/3 & 1/5 & 1\\ \mathbf{4/45} & 8/105 & -1/3\\ 8/105 & 16/225 & -1/5\end{pmatrix}\begin{matrix}0 & 0\\ 1 & 0\\ 0 & 1\end{matrix} \text{ where pivot element is } \mathbf{4/45}.$$

$$\Rightarrow \begin{matrix}1 & 0\\ 0 & 1\\ 0 & 0\end{matrix}\begin{bmatrix}\frac{1}{5}-\frac{6}{5}\times\frac{1}{3}=-\frac{3}{35} & 1-\left(-\frac{15}{4}\right)\frac{1}{3}=\frac{9}{4} & 0-\frac{45}{4}\times\frac{1}{3}=-\frac{15}{4}\\ \frac{8}{105}\times\frac{45}{4}=\frac{6}{7} & -\frac{1}{3}\times\frac{45}{4}=-\frac{15}{4} & 1\times\frac{45}{4}=\frac{45}{4}\\ \frac{16}{225}-\frac{8}{105}\times\frac{6}{7} & -\frac{1}{5}-\frac{8}{105}=\left(-\frac{15}{4}\right) & 0-\frac{8}{105}\times\frac{45}{4}\\ =\frac{64}{225\times 49} & =\frac{3}{35} & =-\frac{6}{7}\end{bmatrix}\begin{matrix}0\\0\\1\end{matrix}$$

$$\Rightarrow \begin{matrix}1 & 0\\ 0 & 1\\ 0 & 0\end{matrix}\begin{pmatrix}-3/35 & 9/4 & -15/4\\ 6/7 & -15/4 & 45/4\\ 64/(225\times 49)=.058 & 3/35 & -9/7\end{pmatrix}\begin{matrix}0\\0\\1\end{matrix}$$

Now the pivot element is taken as $\frac{64}{225\times 49}=.058$

$$\Rightarrow \begin{matrix}1 & 0 & 0\\ 0 & 1 & 0\\ 0 & 0 & 1\end{matrix}\begin{bmatrix}\frac{9}{4}-\left(-\frac{3}{35}\right)\frac{945}{64} & -\frac{15}{4}\left(-\frac{3}{35}\right)\times\left(\frac{-9450}{64}\right) & 0-\left(-\frac{3}{35}\right)\frac{11025}{64}\\ -\frac{15}{4}-\frac{6}{7}\times\frac{945}{64} & \frac{45}{4}-\frac{6}{7}\left(-\frac{9450}{64}\right) & 0-\left(\frac{6}{7}\right)\frac{11025}{64}\\ \frac{3}{35}\times\frac{225\times 49}{64} & -\frac{6}{7}\times\frac{225\times 49}{64} & 225\times\frac{49}{64}\end{bmatrix}$$

$$\Rightarrow \begin{matrix}1 & 0 & 0\\ 0 & 1 & 0\\ 0 & 0 & 1\end{matrix}\begin{pmatrix}(15/64)\times 15 & (15/64)(-70) & (15/64)(63)\\ (15/64)\times(-70) & (15/64)(588) & (15/64)(-630)\\ (15/64)\times 63 & (15/64)(-630) & (15/64)(735)\end{pmatrix}$$

$$\Rightarrow IA^{-1}, \text{where } A^{-1}=\frac{15}{64}\begin{pmatrix}15 & -70 & 63\\ -70 & 588 & -630\\ 63 & -630 & 735\end{pmatrix}$$

Example 4: *(a) Apply Gauss-Jordan method to find the inverse of* $\begin{bmatrix} 2 & 6 & 6 \\ 2 & 8 & 6 \\ 2 & 6 & 8 \end{bmatrix}$.

(b) Apply G-J method to find A^{-1}, *where* $A = \begin{bmatrix} 1 & 1 & 3 \\ 1 & 3 & -3 \\ -2 & -4 & -4 \end{bmatrix}$

Solution: (a) Let $AI = \begin{bmatrix} 2 & 6 & 6 \\ 2 & 8 & 6 \\ 2 & 6 & 8 \end{bmatrix} \begin{bmatrix} 1 & 0 & 0 \\ 0 & 1 & 0 \\ 0 & 0 & 1 \end{bmatrix} \underset{R_{31}(-1)}{\overset{R_{21}(-1)}{\sim}} \begin{bmatrix} 2 & 6 & 6 \\ 0 & 2 & 2 \\ 0 & 0 & 2 \end{bmatrix} \begin{bmatrix} 1 & 0 & 0 \\ -1 & 1 & 0 \\ -1 & 0 & 1 \end{bmatrix}$

$$\overset{R_{12}(-3)}{\sim} \begin{bmatrix} 2 & 0 & 6 \\ 0 & 2 & 0 \\ 0 & 0 & 2 \end{bmatrix} \begin{bmatrix} 4 & -3 & 0 \\ -1 & 1 & 0 \\ -1 & 0 & 1 \end{bmatrix}$$

$$\overset{R_{13}(-3)}{\sim} \begin{bmatrix} 2 & 0 & 0 \\ 0 & 2 & 0 \\ 0 & 0 & 2 \end{bmatrix} \begin{bmatrix} 7 & -3 & -3 \\ -1 & 1 & 0 \\ -1 & 0 & 1 \end{bmatrix} \approx \underset{\leftarrow I_{3\times 3} \rightarrow}{\begin{bmatrix} 1 & 0 & 0 \\ 0 & 1 & 0 \\ 0 & 0 & 1 \end{bmatrix}} \underset{\leftarrow A^{-1} \rightarrow}{\begin{bmatrix} 14 & -6 & -6 \\ -2 & 2 & 0 \\ -2 & 0 & 2 \end{bmatrix}}$$

$$\therefore \quad A^{-1} = \begin{bmatrix} 14 & -6 & -6 \\ -2 & 2 & 0 \\ -2 & 0 & 2 \end{bmatrix}$$

(b) Proceed as above example. **Ans:** $\begin{pmatrix} 3 & 1 & 3/2 \\ -5/4 & -1/4 & -3/4 \\ -1/4 & -1/4 & -1/4 \end{pmatrix}$

14.4 Triangularization Method

Let $A = LU$ where

$$L = \begin{pmatrix} 1 & 0 & 0 \\ l_{21} & 1 & 0 \\ l_{31} & l_{32} & 1 \end{pmatrix} \quad \text{and} \quad U = \begin{pmatrix} u_{11} & u_{12} & u_{13} \\ 0 & u_{22} & u_{23} \\ 0 & 0 & u_{33} \end{pmatrix}$$

be two triangular matrices; one lower and the other upper.

Then we have $A^{-1} = (LU)^{-1} = U^{-1}L^{-1}$ ...(1)

The method is clear by the example given below:

Example 5: *Find the inverse of* $A = \begin{pmatrix} 50 & 107 & 36 \\ 25 & 54 & 20 \\ 31 & 66 & 21 \end{pmatrix}$

Solution: Let $A = LU$

$$\Rightarrow \quad \begin{pmatrix} 50 & 107 & 36 \\ 25 & 54 & 20 \\ 31 & 66 & 21 \end{pmatrix} = \begin{pmatrix} 1 & 0 & 0 \\ l_{21} & 1 & 0 \\ l_{31} & l_{32} & 1 \end{pmatrix} \cdot \begin{pmatrix} u_{11} & u_{12} & u_{13} \\ 0 & u_{22} & u_{23} \\ 0 & 0 & u_{33} \end{pmatrix}$$

$$\begin{bmatrix} 50 & 107 & 36 \\ 25 & 54 & 20 \\ 31 & 66 & 21 \end{bmatrix} = \begin{pmatrix} u_{11} & u_{12} & u_{13} \\ l_{21}u_{11} & l_{21}u_{12} + u_{22} & l_{21}u_{13} + u_{23} \\ l_{31}u_{11} & l_{31}u_{12} + l_{32}u_{22} & l_{31}u_{13} + l_{32}u_{23} + u_{33} \end{pmatrix}$$

$\Rightarrow \quad u_{11} = 50, u_{12} = 107, u_{13} = 36,\ 25 = l_{21}u_{11} = 50l_{21}$ *i.e.* $l_{21} = \left(\frac{1}{2}\right)$,

$54 = l_{21}u_{12} + u_{22} = 107/2 + u_{22} \Rightarrow u_{22} = \left(\frac{1}{2}\right)$,

$20 = l_{21}u_{13} + u_{23} = \frac{1}{2}.36 + u_{23} \Rightarrow u_{23} = 2$,

$31 = u_{11}l_{31} = 50l_{31} \Rightarrow l_{31} = (31/50)$,

$66 = l_{31}u_{12} + l_{32}u_{22} = (31/50).107 + l_{32} \Rightarrow l_{32} = 2\,[66 - (3317/50)] = -17/25$,

and $\quad 21 = l_{31}\, u_{33} + l_{32}\, u_{23} + u_{33} \Rightarrow u_{33} = 1/25$.

Thus $\quad L = \begin{bmatrix} 1 & 0 & 0 \\ 1/2 & 1 & 0 \\ 31/50 & -17/25 & 1 \end{bmatrix}$ and $U = \begin{bmatrix} 50 & 107 & 36 \\ 0 & \frac{1}{2} & 2 \\ 0 & 0 & 1/25 \end{bmatrix}$

$$L^{-1} = \begin{bmatrix} 1 & 0 & 0 \\ -\frac{1}{2} & 1 & 0 \\ -\frac{24}{25} & \frac{17}{25} & 1 \end{bmatrix} \text{ and } U^{-1} = \begin{bmatrix} \frac{1}{50} & -\frac{107}{25} & 196 \\ 0 & 2 & -100 \\ 0 & 0 & 25 \end{bmatrix}$$

$\Rightarrow \quad A^{-1} = U^{-1}L^{-1}$

$$= \begin{bmatrix} \frac{1}{50} & -\frac{107}{25} & 196 \\ 0 & 2 & -100 \\ 0 & 0 & 25 \end{bmatrix}_{3\times 3} \begin{bmatrix} 1 & 0 & 0 \\ -\frac{1}{2} & 1 & 0 \\ -\frac{24}{25} & \frac{17}{25} & 1 \end{bmatrix}_{3\times 3}$$

$$= \begin{bmatrix} -186 & 129 & 196 \\ 95 & -66 & -100 \\ -24 & 17 & 25 \end{bmatrix}$$

Aliter: We have

$$\Rightarrow \quad U = \begin{pmatrix} 50 & 107 & 36 \\ 0 & \frac{1}{2} & 2 \\ 0 & 0 & \frac{1}{25} \end{pmatrix} \text{ and } L = \begin{bmatrix} 1 & 0 & 0 \\ \frac{1}{2} & 1 & 0 \\ \frac{31}{50} & -\frac{17}{25} & 1 \end{bmatrix} \quad \text{where } A = LU$$

Now let U be further decomposed as $U = D\overline{U}$ where D is a diagonal matrix and $\overline{U}$, the upper triangular matrix, *i.e.* we can write

$$\begin{bmatrix} 50 & 107 & 36 \\ 0 & \frac{1}{2} & 2 \\ 0 & 0 & \frac{1}{25} \end{bmatrix} = \begin{bmatrix} 50 & 0 & 0 \\ 0 & \frac{1}{2} & 0 \\ 0 & 0 & \frac{1}{25} \end{bmatrix} \begin{bmatrix} 1 & \bar{u}_{12} & \bar{u}_{13} \\ 0 & 1 & \bar{u}_{23} \\ 0 & 0 & 1 \end{bmatrix}$$

$$\Rightarrow \quad 107 = \bar{u}_{12}.50 \Rightarrow \bar{u}_{12} = (107/50), 36 = 50.\bar{u}_{13} \Rightarrow \bar{u}_{13} = (36/50)$$

$$2 = \bar{u}_{23}\cdot\frac{1}{2} \Rightarrow \bar{u}_{23} = 4.$$

Now $$A = LU = LD\overline{U} \Rightarrow A^{-1} = (LD\overline{U})^{-1} = (\overline{U})^{-1}D^{-1}L^{-1} \quad \ldots(1)$$

Now $$(\overline{U})^{-1} = \begin{pmatrix} 1 & 107/50 & 36/50 \\ 0 & 1 & 4 \\ 0 & 0 & 1 \end{pmatrix}^{-1} = \begin{pmatrix} 1 & 107/50 & -7.84 \\ 0 & 1 & -4 \\ 0 & 0 & 1 \end{pmatrix}$$

$$D^{-1} = \begin{bmatrix} 50 & 0 & 0 \\ 0 & \frac{1}{2} & 2 \\ 0 & 0 & \frac{1}{25} \end{bmatrix}^{-1} = \begin{bmatrix} \frac{1}{50} & 0 & 0 \\ 0 & 2 & 0 \\ 0 & 0 & 25 \end{bmatrix}, L^{-1} = \text{given above}$$

$$\therefore \quad A^{-1} = (\overline{U})\, D^{-1}\, L^{-1}$$

$$= \begin{pmatrix} 1 & 107/50 & -7.84 \\ 0 & 1 & -4 \\ 0 & 0 & 1 \end{pmatrix} \times \begin{pmatrix} \frac{1}{50} & 0 & 0 \\ 0 & 2 & 0 \\ 0 & 0 & 25 \end{pmatrix} \begin{pmatrix} 1 & 0 & 0 \\ -\frac{1}{2} & 1 & 0 \\ -24/25 & 17/25 & 1 \end{pmatrix}$$

$$= \begin{bmatrix} -186 & 129 & 196 \\ 95 & -66 & -100 \\ -24 & 17 & 25 \end{bmatrix}$$

Example 6: *Factorize the matrix* $A = \begin{bmatrix} -2 & 4 & 8 \\ -4 & 18 & -16 \\ -6 & 2 & -20 \end{bmatrix}$ *in the form* $LD\overline{U}$ *and use the result* $A^{-1} = (\overline{U})^{-1}D^{-1}L^{-1}$ *to obtain* A^{-1}.

Solution: Let $$A = LU$$

$$\Rightarrow \begin{bmatrix} -2 & 4 & 8 \\ -4 & 18 & -16 \\ -6 & 2 & -20 \end{bmatrix} = \begin{bmatrix} 1 & 0 & 0 \\ l_{21} & 1 & 0 \\ l_{31} & l_{32} & 1 \end{bmatrix} \begin{bmatrix} u_{11} & u_{12} & u_{13} \\ 0 & u_{22} & u_{23} \\ 0 & 0 & u_{33} \end{bmatrix}$$

$$\begin{bmatrix} -2 & 4 & 8 \\ -4 & 18 & -16 \\ -6 & 2 & -20 \end{bmatrix} = \begin{pmatrix} u_{11} & u_{12} & u_{13} \\ l_{21}u_{11} & l_{21}u_{12}+u_{22} & l_{21}u_{13}+u_{23} \\ l_{31}u_{11} & l_{31}u_{12}+l_{32}u_{22} & l_{31}u_{13}+l_{32}u_{23}+u_{33} \end{pmatrix}$$

$\Rightarrow \quad u_{11}=-2, u_{12}=4, u_{13}=8,\ l_{21}\,u_{11}=-4$

$l_{21}\,u_{12}+u_{22}=18, l_{21}\,u_{13}+u_{23}=-16$

$l_{31}\,u_{11}=-6,\ l_{31}\,u_{12}+l_{32}\,u_{22}=2$ and $l_{31}\,u_{13}+l_{32}\,u_{23}+u_{33}=-20$

$\Rightarrow \quad l_{21}=2, l_{31}=3, l_{32}=-1, u_{11}=-2, u_{12}=4, u_{13}=8, u_{22}=10,$

$u_{23}=-32$ and $u_{33}=-76$

Thus $$\underset{\leftarrow A \rightarrow}{\begin{bmatrix} -2 & 4 & 8 \\ -4 & 18 & -16 \\ -6 & 2 & -20 \end{bmatrix}} = \underset{\leftarrow L \rightarrow}{\begin{bmatrix} 1 & 0 & 0 \\ 2 & 1 & 0 \\ 3 & -1 & 1 \end{bmatrix}} \underset{\leftarrow U \rightarrow}{\begin{bmatrix} -2 & 4 & 8 \\ 0 & 10 & -32 \\ 0 & 0 & -76 \end{bmatrix}} \quad \ldots(1)$$

Again let, $$\underset{\leftarrow U \rightarrow}{\begin{bmatrix} -2 & 4 & 8 \\ 0 & 10 & -32 \\ 0 & 0 & -76 \end{bmatrix}} = \underset{\leftarrow D \rightarrow}{\begin{bmatrix} -2 & 0 & 0 \\ 0 & 10 & 0 \\ 0 & 0 & -76 \end{bmatrix}} \underset{\leftarrow \bar{U} \rightarrow}{\begin{bmatrix} 1 & \bar{u}_{12} & \bar{u}_{13} \\ 0 & 1 & \bar{u}_{23} \\ 0 & 0 & 1 \end{bmatrix}} \quad \ldots(2)$$

$\Rightarrow \quad \bar{u}_{12}=-2, \bar{u}_{13}=-4, \bar{u}_{23}=-3.2$

$$\begin{bmatrix} -2 & 4 & 8 \\ 0 & 10 & -32 \\ 0 & 0 & -76 \end{bmatrix} = \begin{bmatrix} -2 & 0 & 0 \\ 0 & 10 & 0 \\ 0 & 0 & -76 \end{bmatrix} \begin{bmatrix} 1 & -2 & -4 \\ 0 & 1 & -3.2 \\ 0 & 0 & 1 \end{bmatrix}$$

Hence $\quad A = LU = LD\bar{U} \Rightarrow A^{-1} = (LD\bar{U})^{-1} = (\bar{U})^{-1}D^{-1}L^{-1} \quad \ldots(3)$

Now $$(\bar{U})^{-1} = \begin{pmatrix} 1 & -2 & -4 \\ 0 & 1 & -3.2 \\ 0 & 0 & 1 \end{pmatrix}^{-1} = \begin{pmatrix} 1 & 2 & 10.4 \\ 0 & 1 & 3.2 \\ 0 & 1 & 1 \end{pmatrix},\ D^{-1} = \begin{pmatrix} 1 & 0 & 0 \\ -2 & 1 & 0 \\ -5 & 1 & 1 \end{pmatrix}$$

and $$L^{-1} = \begin{pmatrix} 1 & 0 & 0 \\ -2 & 1 & 0 \\ -5 & 1 & 1 \end{pmatrix}$$

$$\Rightarrow \quad A^{-1} = (\bar{U})^{-1}D^{-1}L^{-1} = \begin{pmatrix} 1 & 2 & 10.4 \\ 0 & 1 & 3.2 \\ 0 & 1 & 1 \end{pmatrix} \begin{pmatrix} 1 & 0 & 0 \\ -2 & 1 & 0 \\ -5 & 1 & 1 \end{pmatrix} \begin{pmatrix} 1 & 0 & 0 \\ -2 & 1 & 0 \\ -5 & 1 & 1 \end{pmatrix}$$

$$= \begin{pmatrix} -\frac{41}{90} & \frac{6}{95} & -\frac{13}{95} \\ \frac{1}{95} & \frac{11}{190} & -\frac{4}{95} \\ \frac{5}{76} & -\frac{1}{76} & -\frac{1}{76} \end{pmatrix}.$$

Example 7: *Let* $A = \begin{pmatrix} 3 & 12 & 9 \\ 2 & 10 & 12 \\ 1 & 12 & 2 \end{pmatrix}$, *then find two triangular matrices; L (lower triangular) and U (upper triangular) such that* $A = LU$, *using the diagonal elements of L as* 3, 1, 5. *Hence obtain* A^{-1}.

[Lucknow 2007, 2009; Allahabad 2008; M.D.U. (Rohtak) 2010; Agra 2004, 2009]

Solution: Let $A = LU = \begin{bmatrix} 3 & 0 & 0 \\ l_{21} & 1 & 0 \\ l_{31} & l_{32} & 5 \end{bmatrix} \begin{bmatrix} u_{11} & u_{12} & u_{13} \\ 0 & u_{22} & u_{23} \\ 0 & 0 & u_{33} \end{bmatrix}$

$$= \begin{pmatrix} 3u_{11} & 3u_{12} & 3u_{13} \\ l_{21}u_{11} & l_{21}u_{12} + u_{22} & l_{21}u_{13} + u_{23} \\ l_{31}u_{11} & l_{31}u_{12} + l_{32}u_{22} & l_{31}u_{13} + l_{32}u_{23} + 5u_{33} \end{pmatrix} = \begin{pmatrix} 3 & 12 & 9 \\ 2 & 10 & 12 \\ 1 & 12 & 2 \end{pmatrix} \quad \ldots(1)$$

$3u_{11} = 3, 3u_{12} = 12, 3u_{13} = 9$, [*i.e.* $u_{11} = 1, u_{12} = 4, u_{13} = 3$]

$l_{21}u_{11} = 2$, $l_{21}u_{12} + u_{22} = 10$ $l_{21}u_{13} + u_{23} = 12$ [*i.e.* $l_{21} = 2, u_{22} = 2, u_{23} = 0$]

$l_{31}u_{11} = 1$, $l_{31}u_{12} + l_{32}u_{22} = 12$, $l_{31}u_{13} + l_{32}u_{23} + 5u_{33} = 2$

[*i.e.* $l_{31} = 1, l_{32} = 4, u_{33} = -5$]

$$\rightarrow \underset{\leftarrow A \rightarrow}{\begin{pmatrix} 3 & 12 & 9 \\ 2 & 10 & 12 \\ 1 & 12 & 2 \end{pmatrix}} = \underset{\leftarrow L \rightarrow}{\begin{pmatrix} 3 & 0 & 0 \\ 2 & 1 & 0 \\ 1 & 4 & 5 \end{pmatrix}} \underset{\leftarrow U \rightarrow}{\begin{pmatrix} 1 & 4 & 3 \\ 0 & 2 & 6 \\ 0 & 0 & -5 \end{pmatrix}} \quad \ldots(2)$$

$$\Rightarrow \quad A^{-1} = (LU)^{-1} = U^{-1}L^{-1}$$

$$= \begin{pmatrix} 1 & -2 & -\frac{9}{5} \\ 0 & \frac{1}{2} & \frac{3}{5} \\ 0 & 0 & -\frac{1}{5} \end{pmatrix} \begin{pmatrix} \frac{1}{3} & 0 & 0 \\ -\frac{2}{3} & 1 & 0 \\ \frac{7}{15} & -\frac{4}{5} & \frac{1}{5} \end{pmatrix}$$

$$= \begin{pmatrix} \frac{1}{3} + \frac{4}{3} - \frac{21}{25} & -2 + \frac{36}{25} & -\frac{9}{25} \\ -\frac{1}{3} + \frac{21}{25} & \frac{1}{2} - \frac{12}{25} & \frac{3}{25} \\ -\frac{7}{75} & \frac{4}{25} & -\frac{1}{25} \end{pmatrix} = \begin{pmatrix} \frac{62}{75} & -\frac{14}{25} & -\frac{9}{25} \\ -\frac{4}{15} & \frac{1}{50} & \frac{3}{25} \\ -\frac{7}{75} & \frac{4}{25} & -\frac{1}{25} \end{pmatrix}$$

$$= \frac{1}{25} \begin{pmatrix} \frac{62}{3} & -14 & -9 \\ -\frac{4}{3} & \frac{1}{2} & 3 \\ -\frac{7}{3} & 4 & -1 \end{pmatrix}.$$

14.5 Crout's Triangularisation Method

[Kumaon 2003, 2005, 2008]

In this method, we write the given matrix

$$A = LU \quad \ldots(1)$$

Where L is a lower triangular matrix and U is an upper triangular matrix with diagonal elements unity.

Evidently, $$A^{-1} = U^{-1}L^{-1} \quad \ldots(2)$$

$(\because \; A^{-1}A = I)$.

Let A be a matrix of 3rd order, then let

$$L = \begin{bmatrix} l_{11} & 0 & 0 \\ l_{21} & l_{22} & 0 \\ l_{31} & l_{32} & l_{33} \end{bmatrix} \quad \text{and} \quad U = \begin{bmatrix} 1 & u_{12} & u_{13} \\ 0 & 1 & u_{23} \\ 0 & 0 & 1 \end{bmatrix}$$

$\therefore$ $A = LU$, implies

$$\begin{bmatrix} a_{11} & a_{12} & a_{13} \\ a_{21} & a_{22} & a_{23} \\ a_{31} & a_{32} & a_{33} \end{bmatrix} = \begin{bmatrix} l_{11} & 0 & 0 \\ l_{21} & l_{22} & 0 \\ l_{31} & l_{32} & l_{33} \end{bmatrix} \begin{bmatrix} 1 & u_{12} & u_{13} \\ 0 & 1 & u_{23} \\ 0 & 0 & 1 \end{bmatrix}$$

$$\Rightarrow \begin{bmatrix} a_{11} & a_{12} & a_{13} \\ a_{21} & a_{22} & a_{23} \\ a_{31} & a_{32} & a_{33} \end{bmatrix} = \begin{bmatrix} l_{11} & l_{11}u_{12} & l_{11}u_{13} \\ l_{21} & l_{21}u_{12} + l_{22} & l_{21}u_{13} + l_{22}u_{23} \\ l_{31} & l_{31}u_{12} + l_{32} & l_{31}u_{13} + l_{32}u_{23} + l_{33} \end{bmatrix} \quad \ldots(3)$$

Equating the corresponding elements, we get

$$\left.\begin{array}{lll} l_{11} = a_{11}, & l_{21} = a_{21}, & l_{31} = a_{31} \ldots (a) \\ l_{11}u_{12} = a_{12}, & l_{11}u_{13} = a_{13}, & \ldots\ldots \quad \ldots (b) \\ l_{21}u_{12} + l_{22} = a_{22}, & l_{31}u_{12} + l_{32} = a_{32}, & \ldots\ldots \quad \ldots (c) \\ & l_{21}u_{13} + l_{22}u_{23} = a_{23}, & \ldots\ldots \quad \ldots (d) \\ & l_{31}u_{13} + l_{32}u_{23} + l_{33} = a_{33}, & \ldots\ldots \quad \ldots (e) \end{array}\right\}$$

Relation (b) $\Rightarrow u_{12} = a_{12}/l_{11} = a_{12}/a_{11}$ and $u_{13} = a_{13}/a_{11}$ ...(4)

Relation (c) $\Rightarrow l_{22} = a_{22} - l_{21}u_{12}, l_{32} = a_{32} - l_{31}u_{12}$ ...(5)

By these we can find remaining elements of the second column of L matrix.

Also relation $(d) \Rightarrow u_{23} = (a_{23} - l_{21}u_{13})/l_{22}$ ...(6)

From this, we can find third element of the second row of U matrix.

Finally relation (e) gives

$$l_{33} = a_{33} - l_{31}u_{13} - l_{32}u_{23}. \quad \ldots(7)$$

Thus, we can determine all the elements of L and U *i.e.*, they are completely determined.

To Find L^{-1} and U^{-1}.

Let $L^{-1} = X$, where X is also a lower triangular matrix.

$$\therefore \qquad LX = I$$

$$\begin{bmatrix} l_{11} & 0 & 0 \\ l_{21} & l_{22} & 0 \\ l_{31} & l_{32} & l_{33} \end{bmatrix} \begin{bmatrix} x_{11} & 0 & 0 \\ x_{21} & x_{22} & 0 \\ x_{31} & x_{32} & x_{33} \end{bmatrix} = \begin{bmatrix} 1 & 0 & 0 \\ 0 & 1 & 0 \\ 0 & 0 & 1 \end{bmatrix}$$

Proceeding as before, we again obtain

$$l_{11}\, x_{11} = 1,\ l_{22}\, x_{22} = 1,\ l_{33}\, x_{33} = 1 \qquad \ldots(8)$$

$$\left.\begin{aligned} & l_{21}\, x_{11} + l_{22}\, x_{21} = 0,\ l_{31}\, x_{11} + l_{32}\, x_{21} + l_{32}\, x_{31} = 0 \\ \text{and} \quad & l_{32}\, x_{22} + l_{33}\, x_{32} = 0 \end{aligned}\right\} \qquad \ldots(9)$$

Relation (8) $\Rightarrow x_{11} = (1/l_{11}),\ x_{22} = (1/l_{22}),\ x_{33} = (1/l_{33})$. $\qquad \ldots(10)$

In this way, the diagonal elements of the X matrix are determined.

$$\text{Relation (9)} \Rightarrow x_{21} = -\frac{l_{21} x_{11}}{l_{22}};\ x_{31} = -\left[\frac{(l_{31} x_{11} + l_{32} x_{21})}{l_{32}}\right] \qquad \ldots(11)$$

$$\text{and} \qquad x_{32} = -l_{32} x_{22} / l_{33}.$$

Hence, we can determine $X = L^{-1}$ completely.

To obtain the inverse of U, the upper triangular matrix, we use the following method. Suppose V is an upper triangular matrix and another upper triangular matrix Y is the inverse of V.

Then we easily note that $YV = I$.

$$\Rightarrow \begin{bmatrix} y_{11} & y_{12} & y_{13} \\ 0 & y_{22} & y_{23} \\ 0 & 0 & y_{33} \end{bmatrix} \begin{bmatrix} v_{11} & v_{12} & v_{13} \\ 0 & v_{22} & v_{23} \\ 0 & 0 & v_{33} \end{bmatrix} = \begin{bmatrix} 1 & 0 & 0 \\ 0 & 1 & 0 \\ 0 & 0 & 1 \end{bmatrix}$$

$$\left.\begin{aligned} \Rightarrow \quad & y_{11} v_{11} = 1,\quad y_{22} v_{22} = 1,\quad y_{33} v_{33} = 1 \\ \Rightarrow \quad & y_{11} = 1/v_{11},\ y_{22} = 1/v_{22},\ y_{33} = 1/v_{33} \end{aligned}\right\} \qquad \ldots(12)$$

Relation (12) determines the diagonal elements of Y. We also have

$$\left.\begin{aligned} & y_{11} v_{12} + y_{12} v_{22} = 0,\quad y_{11} v_{13} + y_{12} v_{23} + y_{13} v_{33} = 0 \\ \text{and} \quad & y_{22} v_{23} + y_{22} v_{33} = 0 \end{aligned}\right\} \qquad \ldots(13)$$

These imply

$$\left.\begin{aligned} & y_{12} = -y_{11} v_{12} / v_{22},\ y_{13} = -(y_{11} v_{13} + y_{12} v_{23}) / v_{33} \\ \text{and} \quad & y_{23} = -y_{22} v_{23} / v_{33} \end{aligned}\right\} \qquad \ldots(14)$$

From relations (12) and (14), we can easily compute $Y = V^{-1}$.

Example 8: *Apply Crout's method to obtain the inverse of*

$$\begin{pmatrix} 2 & -2 & 4 \\ 2 & 3 & 2 \\ -1 & 1 & -1 \end{pmatrix}$$

[Rohilkhand 2004, 2008]

Solution: Let $A = \begin{pmatrix} 2 & -2 & 4 \\ 2 & 3 & 2 \\ -1 & 1 & -1 \end{pmatrix}$

Then $A = LU$ and $A^{-1} = U^{-1}L^{-1}$, where L is a lower triangular matrix and U an upper triangular matrix.

Now, let $L = \begin{pmatrix} l_{12} & 0 & 0 \\ l_{21} & l_{22} & 0 \\ l_{31} & l_{32} & l_{33} \end{pmatrix}, U = \begin{pmatrix} 1 & u_{12} & u_{13} \\ 0 & 1 & u_{23} \\ 0 & 0 & 1 \end{pmatrix}$

$$A = L \Rightarrow \begin{pmatrix} 2 & -2 & 4 \\ 2 & 3 & 2 \\ -1 & 1 & -1 \end{pmatrix} = \begin{pmatrix} l_{11} & 0 & 0 \\ l_{21} & l_{22} & 0 \\ l_{31} & l_{32} & l_{33} \end{pmatrix} \begin{pmatrix} 1 & u_{12} & u_{13} \\ 0 & 1 & u_{23} \\ 0 & 0 & 1 \end{pmatrix}$$

Whence, by equality principle of matrices, we easily obtain

$$l_{11} = 2, l_{21} = 2, l_{22} = 5, l_{31} = -1, l_{32} = 0, l_{33} = 1$$

and $\quad u_{12} = -1, u_{13} = 2, u_{23} = -(2/5)$

$$\Rightarrow \quad L = \begin{pmatrix} 2 & 0 & 0 \\ 2 & 5 & 0 \\ -1 & 0 & 1 \end{pmatrix} \text{ and } U = \begin{pmatrix} 1 & -1 & 2 \\ 0 & 1 & -(2/5) \\ 0 & 0 & 1 \end{pmatrix}.$$

To Compute L^{-1} and U^{-1}.

Let the inverse of L (the lower triangular matrix) be X (a lower triangular matrix), then

$$LX = I.$$

$$\Rightarrow \begin{pmatrix} 2 & 0 & 0 \\ 2 & 5 & 0 \\ -1 & 0 & 1 \end{pmatrix} \begin{pmatrix} x_{11} & 0 & 0 \\ x_{21} & x_{22} & 0 \\ x_{31} & x_{32} & x_{33} \end{pmatrix} = \begin{pmatrix} 1 & 0 & 0 \\ 0 & 1 & 0 \\ 0 & 0 & 1 \end{pmatrix}$$

$$\Rightarrow \begin{pmatrix} 2x_{11} & 0 & 0 \\ 2x_{11} + 5x_{21} & 5x_{22} & 0 \\ -x_{11} + x_{31} & x_{32} & x_{33} \end{pmatrix} = \begin{pmatrix} 1 & 0 & 0 \\ 0 & 1 & 0 \\ 0 & 0 & 1 \end{pmatrix}$$

$$\Rightarrow \quad 2x_{11} = 1, 2x_{11} + 5x_{21} = 0, 5x_{22} = 1, x_{31} - x_{11} = 0, x_{32} = 0, x_{33} = 1$$

$$x_{11} = (1/2), x_{21} = -1/5, x_{22} = 1/5, x_{31} = \frac{1}{2}, x_{32} = 0, x_{33} = 1.$$

$$\therefore \quad X = \begin{pmatrix} 1/2 & 0 & 0 \\ -1/5 & 1/5 & 0 \\ 1/2 & 0 & 1 \end{pmatrix}$$

Similarly, let the inverse of U (the upper triangular matrix) by Y (an upper triangular matrix); then we have

$$UY = I \Rightarrow \begin{pmatrix} 1 & -1 & 2 \\ 0 & 1 & -2/5 \\ 0 & 0 & 1 \end{pmatrix} \begin{pmatrix} 1 & y_{12} & y_{13} \\ 0 & 1 & y_{23} \\ 0 & 0 & 1 \end{pmatrix} = \begin{pmatrix} 1 & 0 & 0 \\ 0 & 1 & 0 \\ 0 & 0 & 1 \end{pmatrix}$$

$$\Rightarrow \quad \begin{pmatrix} 1 & y_{12}-1 & y_{13}-y_{23}+2 \\ 0 & 1 & y_{23}-2/5 \\ 0 & 0 & 1 \end{pmatrix} = \begin{pmatrix} 1 & 0 & 0 \\ 0 & 1 & 0 \\ 0 & 0 & 1 \end{pmatrix}$$

$$\Rightarrow \quad y_{12}-1=0,\; y_{13}-y_{23}+2=0,\; y_{23}-(2/5)=0;$$

$$\Rightarrow \quad y_{12}=1,\; y_{13}=(2/5)-2=-(8/5),\; y_{23}=(2/5).$$

$$\therefore \quad Y = U^{-1} = \begin{pmatrix} 1 & 1 & -8/5 \\ 0 & 1 & 2/5 \\ 0 & 0 & 1 \end{pmatrix}.$$

Whence $A^{-1} = U^{-1}L^{-1}$

$$= \begin{pmatrix} 1 & 1 & -8/5 \\ 0 & 1 & 2/5 \\ 0 & 0 & 1 \end{pmatrix} \times \begin{pmatrix} 1/2 & 0 & 0 \\ -1/5 & 1/5 & 0 \\ 1/2 & 0 & 1 \end{pmatrix} = \begin{pmatrix} -1/5 & 1/5 & -8/5 \\ 0 & 1/5 & 2/5 \\ 1/2 & 0 & 1 \end{pmatrix}.$$

14.6 Doolittle Method

In this method, we write the given matrix $A = LU$, where

$$L = \begin{pmatrix} 0 & 0 & 1 \\ l_{21} & 1 & 0 \\ l_{31} & l_{32} & 1 \end{pmatrix} \quad \text{and} \quad U = \begin{pmatrix} u_{11} & u_{12} & u_{13} \\ 0 & u_{22} & u_{23} \\ 0 & 0 & u_{33} \end{pmatrix}$$

It is to be noted that in Crout's method, the diagonal elements of U were taken, to be unity, whereas in this method we take the diagonal elements of L to be unity. Again adopting the procedure as given in previous method, one can easily obtain A^{-1}.

14.7 Choleski's Method

In this method we write $A = TT'$, where T is a lower triangular matrix and T' is its transpose. It has been assumed that A is a symmetric matrix *i.e.* $A = A'$.

[Agra 2006; Patna 2008; Delhi (H) 2002, 2004, 2009]

Evidently, $$A^{-1} = (TT')^{-1} = (T')^{-1}T^{-1} = (T^{-1})'\,T^{-1} \qquad \ldots(1)$$

Now $$A = TT' \Rightarrow$$

$$\begin{pmatrix} a_{11} & a_{12} & a_{13} \\ a_{21} & a_{22} & a_{23} \\ a_{31} & a_{32} & a_{33} \end{pmatrix} = \begin{pmatrix} t_{11} & 0 & 0 \\ t_{21} & t_{22} & 0 \\ t_{31} & t_{32} & t_{33} \end{pmatrix} \begin{pmatrix} t_{11} & t_{21} & t_{31} \\ 0 & t_{22} & t_{32} \\ 0 & 0 & t_{33} \end{pmatrix}$$

Be equality principle of matrices, we get

$$\left.\begin{array}{c} t_{11}^2 = a_{11} \text{ or } t_{11} = \sqrt{a_{11}} \\ t_{11}t_{21} = a_{12} \text{ or } t_{21} = a_{12} / t_{11} \\ t_{11}t_{31} = a_{13} \text{ or } t_{31} = a_{13} / t_{11} \\ t_{21}^2 + t_{32}^2 = a_{22} \text{ or } t_{22} = \sqrt{(a_{32} - t_{21}^2)} \\ t_{21}t_{31} + t_{22}\,t_{32} = a_{23} \text{ or } t_{32} = (a_{23} - t_{21}t_{31}) / t_{22} \\ t_{31}^2 + t_{32}^2 + t_{33}^2 = a_{33} \text{ or } t_{33} = \sqrt{(a_{23} - t_{31}^2 = t_{32}^2)} \end{array}\right\}$$

Thus T is determined.

The diagonal elements are to be determined by taking square roots, it may yield some imaginary elements of T.

Note: In general, the formula for determining T are

$$t_{ii} = \left(a_{ii} - \sum_{k=1}^{n-1} t_{ik}^2\right)^{1/2} \quad ; \; i = 1, \ldots, n$$

$$t_{ij} = \left[\left(a_{ji} - \sum_{k=1}^{j-1} t_{ik}\, t_{jk}\right) \Big/ t_{jj}\right] \quad \begin{array}{c} t = 2, \ldots, n: \\ j < i \end{array}$$

$$t_{ij} = 0, \; i < j.$$

Example 9: *Find the inverse of*

$$A = \begin{bmatrix} 1 & 2 & 6 \\ 2 & 5 & 15 \\ 6 & 15 & 46 \end{bmatrix}, \textit{ using Choleski's method.}$$

[Meerut 2001, 2003; Rohilkhand 2008; Garhwal 2009; Kumaon 2003, 2005, 2010]

Solution: Evidently, the matrix A is a symmetric matrix, hence this method is applicable. Let us consider $A = TT'$, then proceeding as in the article we easily obtain

$$t_{11} = \sqrt{a_{11}} = \sqrt{1} = 1$$

$$t_{21} = 2/1 = 2, \; t_{31} = 6/1 = 6$$

$$t_{22} = \sqrt{(5 - 2^2)} = 1, \; t_{32} = (15 - 2.6)/1 = 3$$

$$t_{33} = \sqrt{(46 - 6^2 - 3^2)} = 1.$$

$$\therefore \text{ Lower triangular matrix, } T = \begin{bmatrix} 1 & 0 & 0 \\ 2 & 1 & 0 \\ 6 & 3 & 1 \end{bmatrix}.$$

To Compute T^{-1}. Let a lower triangular matrix X be the inverse of T, then proceeding as in Crout's method, we easily obtain

$$x_{11} = 1, x_{22} = 1, x_{33} = 1, x_{21} = -2, x_{31} = 0, x_{32} = -3.$$

$$\therefore \quad T^{-1} = \begin{bmatrix} 1 & 0 & 0 \\ -2 & 1 & 0 \\ 0 & -3 & 1 \end{bmatrix} \Rightarrow (T^{-1})' = \begin{bmatrix} 1 & -2 & 0 \\ 0 & 2 & -3 \\ 0 & 0 & 1 \end{bmatrix}$$

$$A^{-1} = (T^{-1})' T^{-1} = \begin{bmatrix} 1 & -2 & 0 \\ 0 & 1 & -3 \\ 0 & 0 & 1 \end{bmatrix} \begin{bmatrix} 1 & 0 & 0 \\ -2 & 1 & 0 \\ 0 & -3 & 1 \end{bmatrix} = \begin{bmatrix} 5 & -2 & 0 \\ -2 & 10 & -3 \\ 0 & -3 & 1 \end{bmatrix}$$

Example 10: *Apply Choleski's method to find the inverse of the matrix*

$$A = \begin{pmatrix} 1 & 2 & 0 & 0.5 \\ 2 & 5 & 0 & -2 \\ 0.5 & 0 & 2.25 & 7.5 \\ 1 & -2 & 7.5 & 27 \end{pmatrix} = \begin{pmatrix} a_{11} & a_{12} & a_{13} & a_{14} \\ a_{21} & a_{22} & a_{23} & a_{24} \\ a_{31} & a_{32} & a_{33} & a_{34} \\ a_{41} & a_{42} & a_{43} & a_{44} \end{pmatrix}$$

Solution: We have $A = TT'$

$$\text{Let } A = \underbrace{\begin{pmatrix} 1 & 2 & 0.5 & 1 \\ 2 & 5 & 0 & -2 \\ 0.5 & 0 & 2.25 & 7.5 \\ 1 & -2 & 7.5 & 27 \end{pmatrix}}_{\leftarrow \text{ Symmetric matrix } \rightarrow} = \underbrace{\begin{pmatrix} t_{11} & 0 & 0 & 0 \\ t_{21} & t_{22} & 0 & 0 \\ t_{31} & t_{32} & t_{33} & 0 \\ t_{41} & t_{42} & t_{43} & t_{44} \end{pmatrix}}_{\substack{\leftarrow T \rightarrow \\ \leftarrow \text{Lower triangular -matrix} \rightarrow}} \underbrace{\begin{pmatrix} t_{11} & t_{21} & t_{31} & t_{41} \\ 0 & t_{22} & t_{32} & t_{42} \\ 0 & 0 & t_{33} & t_{43} \\ 0 & 0 & 0 & t_{44} \end{pmatrix}}_{\leftarrow T' \rightarrow}$$

$$= \begin{pmatrix} t^2_{11} & t_{11}t_{21} & t_{11}t_{31} & t_{11}t_{41} \\ t_{21}t_{11} & t^2_{21} + t^2_{22} & t_{21}t_{31} + t_{22}t_{32} & t_{21}t_{41} + t_{22}t_{42} \\ t_{31}t_{11} & t_{31}t_{21} + t_{32}t_{22} & t^2_{31} + t^2_{32} + t^2_{33} & t_{31}t_{41} + t_{32}t_{42} + t_{33}t_{43} \\ t_{41}t_{11} & t_{41}t_{21} + t_{42}t_{22} & t_{41}t_{31} + t_{42}t_{32} + t_{43}t_{33} & t^2_{41} + t^2_{42} + t^2_{43} + t^2_{44} \end{pmatrix}$$

$$\Rightarrow \quad t^2_{11} = 1, t_{11}t_{21} = 2, t_{11}t_{31} = 0.5, t_{11}t_{41} = 1$$

$$t_{21}t_{11} = 2, t^2_{21} + t^2_{22} = 5, t_{21}\, t_{31} + t_{22}\, t_{32} = 0, t_{21}\, t_{41} + t_{22}\, t_{42} = -2$$

$$t^2_{31} + t^2_{32} + t^2_{33} = 2.25, \; t_{31}\, t_{41} + t_{32}\, t_{42} + t_{33}\, t_{43} = 7.5$$

$$t^2_{41} + t^2_{42} + t^2_{43} + t^2_{44} = 27$$

$$\Rightarrow \quad t_{11} = 1, t_{21} = 2, t_{31} = 0.5, t_{41} = 1, t_{22} = 1, t_{32} = -1, t_{42} = -4,$$

$$t_{33} = 1, t_{43} = 3, t_{44} = 1$$

$$\Rightarrow A = \begin{pmatrix} 1 & 2 & 0.5 & 1 \\ 2 & 5 & 0 & -32 \\ 0.5 & 0 & 2.25 & 7.5 \\ 1 & -2 & 7.5 & 27 \end{pmatrix} = \underbrace{\begin{pmatrix} 1 & 0 & 0 & 0 \\ 2 & 1 & 0 & 0 \\ 0.5 & -1 & 1 & 0 \\ 1 & -4 & 3 & 1 \end{pmatrix}}_{\leftarrow T \rightarrow} \underbrace{\begin{pmatrix} 1 & 2 & 0.5 & 1 \\ 0 & 1 & -1 & -4 \\ 0 & 0 & 1 & 3 \\ 0 & 0 & 0 & 1 \end{pmatrix}}_{\leftarrow T' \rightarrow}$$

$$\Rightarrow \quad A^{-1} = (TT')^{-1} = (T')^{-1}(T)^{-1} \qquad \ldots(1)$$

Now, $$T' = \begin{pmatrix} 1 & 0 & 0 & 0 \\ 2 & 1 & 0 & 0 \\ 0.5 & -1 & 1 & 0 \\ 1 & -4 & 3 & 1 \end{pmatrix} \quad \therefore \quad T^{-1} = \begin{pmatrix} 1 & 0 & 0 & 0 \\ -2 & 1 & 0 & 0 \\ -2.5 & 1 & 1 & 0 \\ -1.5 & 1 & -3 & 1 \end{pmatrix}$$

$$\Rightarrow \quad (T^{-1})' T^{-1} = (T')^{-1} T^{-1} = \begin{pmatrix} 1 & -2 & -2.5 & -1.5 \\ 0 & 1 & 1 & 1 \\ 0 & 0 & 1 & -3 \\ 0 & 0 & 0 & 1 \end{pmatrix} \begin{pmatrix} 1 & 0 & 0 & 0 \\ -2 & 1 & 0 & 0 \\ -2.5 & 1 & 1 & 0 \\ -1.5 & 1 & -3 & 1 \end{pmatrix}$$

$$\Rightarrow \quad (T')^{-1} T^{-1} = \begin{pmatrix} 13.5 & -6 & 2 & -1 \\ -6 & 3 & -2 & 1 \\ 2 & -2 & 10 & -3 \\ -1.5 & 1 & -3 & 1 \end{pmatrix} = A^{-1} \quad \text{using (1).}$$

14.8 Iterative Method

To obtain a more accurate inverse, if an approximate inverse is given.

Let B be the approximate inverse of A *i.e.* $A^{-1} = B$, then we have $R = I - BA$ *i.e.* $I - R = BA$, where R is the residual matrix and contains small numbers as its elements. Evidently, the matrices R^2, R^3, R^4 etc., will contain more and more smaller elements, hence the series $I + R + R^2 + R^3 + \ldots$ will definitely converge

$$\therefore \quad (I - R)(I + R + R^2 + \ldots) = I$$

$$\Rightarrow \quad (I + R + R^2 + \ldots) = (I - R)^{-1} = (BA)^{-1} = A^{-1}B^{-1}$$

$$\Rightarrow \quad (I + R + R^2 + \ldots) B = A^{-1}B^{-1}B = A^{-1}$$

i.e. $$A^{-1} = (I + R + R^2 + \ldots) B = B + RB + R^2 B + \ldots$$

Example 11: *Obtain a more accurate inverse, given*

$$A = \begin{bmatrix} 2 & 4 \\ 3 & 5 \end{bmatrix}, \; A^{-1} = B = \begin{bmatrix} -2.45 & 2.05 \\ 1.45 & -0.95 \end{bmatrix}.$$

[Agra 2002, 2006]

Solution: We have $BA = \begin{bmatrix} 1.25 & 0.45 \\ 0.05 & 1.05 \end{bmatrix}$

$$\Rightarrow \quad R = I - BA = \begin{bmatrix} 1 & 0 \\ 0 & 1 \end{bmatrix} - \begin{bmatrix} 1.25 & 0.45 \\ 0.05 & 1.05 \end{bmatrix} = \begin{bmatrix} -0.25 & -0.45 \\ -0.05 & -0.05 \end{bmatrix}$$

$$\therefore \quad RB = \begin{bmatrix} -0.25 & -0.45 \\ -0.05 & -0.05 \end{bmatrix} \begin{bmatrix} -2.45 & 2.05 \\ 1.45 & -0.95 \end{bmatrix} = \begin{bmatrix} -0.04 & -0.085 \\ 0.05 & -0.055 \end{bmatrix} \qquad \ldots(1)$$

$$\Rightarrow \quad B + RB = \begin{bmatrix} -2.49 & 1.965 \\ 1.50 & -1.005 \end{bmatrix} = \text{first approx} \qquad \ldots(2)$$

Again $R^2B = R(R\,B) = \begin{bmatrix} -0.25 & -0.45 \\ -0.05 & -0.05 \end{bmatrix}\begin{bmatrix} -0.04 & -0.085 \\ 0.05 & -0.055 \end{bmatrix}$

$$= \begin{bmatrix} -0.0125 & 0.04595 \\ -0.0005 & 0.00700 \end{bmatrix}$$

$$\therefore \quad B + RB + R^2B = \begin{bmatrix} -2.49 & 1.965 \\ 1.50 & -1.005 \end{bmatrix} + \begin{bmatrix} -0.0125 & 0.04595 \\ -0.0005 & 0.00700 \end{bmatrix}$$

$$= \begin{bmatrix} -2.50250 & 2.01095 \\ 1.49950 & -0.99800 \end{bmatrix} = \text{second approx.}$$

and $B + RB + R^2B + R^3B$ = third approximation etc.

Example 12: *Obtain a more accurate inverse, given*

$$A = \begin{pmatrix} 5 & 2 \\ 3 & -1 \end{pmatrix}, A^{-1} = B = \begin{pmatrix} .1 & .2 \\ .3 & -.4 \end{pmatrix}.$$

[Agra 2003; Meerut 2003, 2004, 2007]

Solution: We have $BA = \begin{pmatrix} .1 & .2 \\ .3 & -.4 \end{pmatrix}\begin{pmatrix} 5 & 2 \\ 3 & -1 \end{pmatrix} = \begin{pmatrix} 1.1 & 0 \\ .3 & 1 \end{pmatrix}$

$$\Rightarrow \quad R = I - BA = \begin{pmatrix} 1 & 0 \\ 0 & 1 \end{pmatrix} - \begin{pmatrix} 1.1 & 0 \\ 0.3 & 1 \end{pmatrix} = \begin{pmatrix} -.1 & 0 \\ -.3 & 0 \end{pmatrix}$$

$$\Rightarrow \quad RB = \begin{pmatrix} -.1 & 0 \\ -.3 & 0 \end{pmatrix}\begin{pmatrix} .1 & .2 \\ .3 & -.4 \end{pmatrix} = \begin{pmatrix} -.01 & -.02 \\ -.03 & -.06 \end{pmatrix}$$

$$\Rightarrow \quad B + RB = \begin{pmatrix} .1 & .2 \\ .3 & -.4 \end{pmatrix} + \begin{pmatrix} -.01 & -.02 \\ -.03 & -.06 \end{pmatrix} = \begin{pmatrix} .09 & .18 \\ .27 & -.46 \end{pmatrix} = \text{first approx.}$$

While second approx. $= B + RB + R^2B$

and third approx. $= B + RB + R^2B + R^3B$.

14.9 Escalator Method for Matrix Inversion

[Agra 2003, 2007, 2009]

This method is based on the principle of partitioning of matrices.

The philosophy of the method is that if the inverse of a matrix of order n is given, then we can easily obtain the inverse of the matrix of order $(n+1)\times(n+1)$.

Let the inverse of a $n \times n$ matrix (say A_1) be given and we want to determine the inverse of the $(n+1)\times(n+1)$ matrix (say A) which is obtained from A_1 by adding $(n+1)$ th row and $(n+1)$ th column to A_1.

$$\text{Now, let } A = \begin{bmatrix} A_1 & : & A_2 \\ \cdots & \cdots & \cdots \\ A_3^T & : & k \end{bmatrix} \text{ and } A^{-1} = \begin{bmatrix} B_1 & : & B_2 \\ \cdots & \cdots & \cdots \\ B_3^T & : & x \end{bmatrix},$$

Where A_2, B_2 are column vectors, A_3^T, B_3^T are row vectors and k, x are scalar numbers and B_1 is a $n \times n$ matrix.

Then, we have

$$A A^{-1} = I_{(n+1)} = \begin{bmatrix} I_n & : & 0_{n\times 1} \\ \dots & \dots & \dots \\ 0_{1\times n} & : & 1 \end{bmatrix}$$

$$= \begin{bmatrix} A_1 & : & A_2 \\ \dots & \dots & \dots \\ A_3^T & : & k \end{bmatrix} \begin{bmatrix} B_1 & : & B_2 \\ \dots & \dots & \dots \\ B_3^T & : & x \end{bmatrix},$$

Which given $\quad A_1 B_1 + A_2 B_3^T = I \quad$ ...(1)

$A_1 B_2 + A_2 x = 0 \quad$ ...(2)

$A_3^T B_1 + k B_3^T = 0 \quad$ ...(3)

$A_3^T B_2 + k x = 1 \quad$ ...(4)

Whence (2) $\Rightarrow \quad B_2 = -A_1^{-1} A_2 x$

$\Rightarrow \quad [k - A_3^T A_1^{-1} A_2] x = 1$ [making use of (2) in (4)] ...(5)

From here, x and hence B_2 can be determined. Now form (1), we obtain
$B_1 = A_1^{-1} (I - A_2 B_3^T)$

$\Rightarrow \quad (k - A_3^T A_1^{-1} A_2) B_3^T = - A_3^T A_1^{-1}$ [from (3)] ...(6)

and thus B_3^T can be obtained.

Finally, B_1 can be computed from (1) and hence A^{-1} can be obtained. Moreover this method is also used successively to increase the dimension.

Example 13: *Find the inverse of* $A = \begin{bmatrix} 1 & 3 & 3 & 2 \\ 1 & 4 & 3 & 4 \\ 1 & 3 & 4 & 5 \\ 2 & 5 & 3 & 2 \end{bmatrix}$, *given that if*

$$A_1 = \begin{bmatrix} 1 & 3 & 3 \\ 1 & 4 & 3 \\ 1 & 3 & 4 \end{bmatrix}, \quad \text{then} \quad A_1^{-1} = \begin{bmatrix} 7 & -3 & -3 \\ -1 & 1 & 0 \\ -1 & 0 & 1 \end{bmatrix}.$$

[Agra 2004, 2005, 2008, 2009]

Solution: Let $A = \begin{bmatrix} 1 & 3 & 3 & : & 2 \\ 1 & 4 & 3 & : & 4 \\ 1 & 3 & 4 & : & 5 \\ \dots & \dots & \dots & \dots & \dots \\ 2 & 5 & 3 & : & 2 \end{bmatrix} = \begin{bmatrix} A_1 & : & A_2 \\ \dots & \dots & \dots \\ A_3^T & : & k \end{bmatrix}$

Where $A_2 = [2 \ \ 4 \ \ 5]^T$, $A_3^T = [2 \ \ 5 \ \ 3]$, $k = 2$.

Now, let its inverse be $A^{-1} = \begin{bmatrix} B_1 & : & B_2 \\ \dots & \dots & \dots \\ B_3^T & : & x \end{bmatrix}$.

$$\Rightarrow \quad A_3^T A_1^{-1} A_2 = [2\,5\,3] \begin{bmatrix} 7 & -3 & -3 \\ -1 & 1 & 0 \\ -1 & 0 & 1 \end{bmatrix} \begin{bmatrix} 2 \\ 4 \\ 5 \end{bmatrix} = -7$$

Whence (5) $\Rightarrow [2-(-7)] . x = 1 \Rightarrow x = 1/9$

and (6) $\Rightarrow 9B_3^T = -A_2 A_1^{-1} = -[6\,-1\,-3]$

$\Rightarrow \quad B_3^T = -(1/9)[6\ -1\ -3]$.

Further, $B_2 = -A_1^{-1} A_2 x = -(1/9)(-13\ 2\ 3)^T$ [using (2)]

$$\Rightarrow \quad B_1 = A_1^{-1}(I - A_2 B_3^T) = A_1^{-1} - A_1^{-1} A_2 B_3^T$$

$$= \begin{bmatrix} 7 & -3 & -3 \\ -1 & 1 & 0 \\ -1 & 0 & 1 \end{bmatrix} + \begin{bmatrix} -13 \\ 2 \\ 3 \end{bmatrix} \begin{bmatrix} \frac{2}{3} & -\frac{1}{9} & -\frac{1}{3} \end{bmatrix}$$

$$= -\begin{bmatrix} -7 & +3 & +3 \\ +1 & -1 & 0 \\ +1 & 0 & -1 \end{bmatrix}$$

$$+ \begin{bmatrix} -26/3 & 13/9 & 13/3 \\ 4/3 & -2/9 & -2/3 \\ 2 & -1/3 & -1 \end{bmatrix} \begin{bmatrix} -5/3 & -14/9 & 4/3 \\ 1/3 & 7/9 & -2/3 \\ 1 & -1/3 & 3 \end{bmatrix}.$$

Whence, we get $A^{-1} = \begin{bmatrix} -5/3 & -14/9 & 4/3 & : & 13/9 \\ 1/3 & 7/9 & -2/3 & : & -2/9 \\ 1 & -1/3 & 0 & : & -1/3 \\ \dots & \dots & \dots & \dots & \dots \\ -2/3 & -1/9 & 1/3 & : & 1/9 \end{bmatrix}$

Example 14: *Find the inverse of* $A = \begin{pmatrix} 13 & 14 & 6 & 4 \\ 8 & -1 & 13 & 9 \\ 6 & 7 & 3 & 2 \\ 9 & 5 & 16 & 11 \end{pmatrix}$ *by Escalator method.*

Solution: We have

$$A = \begin{bmatrix} 13 & 14 & 6 & : & 4 \\ 8 & -1 & 13 & : & 9 \\ 6 & 7 & 3 & : & 2 \\ \dots & \dots & \dots & \dots & \dots \\ 9 & 5 & 16 & : & 11 \end{bmatrix} = \begin{bmatrix} A_1 & : & A_2 \\ \dots & \dots & \dots \\ A_3^T & : & k \end{bmatrix}$$

Where $A_1 = \begin{bmatrix} 13 & 14 & 6 \\ 8 & -1 & 13 \\ 6 & 7 & 3 \end{bmatrix}, A_2 = \begin{bmatrix} 4 \\ 9 \\ 2 \end{bmatrix},$

$A_3{}^T = [9 \ \ 5 \ \ 16]$ and $k = 11$.

Again, $A_1{}^{-1} = \dfrac{1}{94}\begin{bmatrix} 94 & 0 & -188 \\ -54 & -3 & 121 \\ -62 & 7 & 125 \end{bmatrix}.$

Next, we write $A^{-1} = \begin{bmatrix} B_1 & : & B_2 \\ \ldots & \ldots & \ldots \\ B_3{}^T & : & x \end{bmatrix}$. Then $A\,A^{-1} = I$.

Then, we readily obtain (proceeding as in article)

$$\left.\underset{\leftarrow(i)\rightarrow}{A_1 B_1 + A_2 B_3{}^T = I}, \underset{\leftarrow(ii)\rightarrow}{A_1 B_2 + A_2 x = 0}, \underset{\leftarrow(iii)\rightarrow}{A_3{}^T B_1 + k B_3{}^T = 0}, \underset{\leftarrow(iv)\rightarrow}{A_3{}^T B_2 + k x = 1}\right\} \quad \ldots(1)$$

$A_1 B_2 + A_2 x = 0 \Rightarrow A_1 B_2 = -A_2\, x$

$$\Rightarrow \quad B_2 = -A_1{}^{-1} A_2\, x = \frac{1}{94}\begin{bmatrix} 94 & 0 & -188 \\ -54 & -3 & 121 \\ -62 & 7 & 125 \end{bmatrix}_{3\times 3}\begin{pmatrix} 4 \\ 9 \\ 2 \end{pmatrix}_{3\times 3} x = -\frac{1}{94}\begin{pmatrix} 0 \\ -1 \\ 65 \end{pmatrix} x.$$

Now, $\quad A_3{}^T B_2 + k\,x = 1 \Rightarrow [9 \ \ 5 \ \ 16]\left(-\dfrac{1}{94}\right)\begin{pmatrix} 0 \\ -1 \\ 65 \end{pmatrix} x + 11x = 1$

$$\Rightarrow \quad -\frac{1}{94}(9.0 - 5 + 1040)\,x + 11\,x = 1$$

$$\Rightarrow \quad -\frac{1}{94}(1035)\,x + 11x = 1 \quad \Rightarrow \quad -1035x + 11\times 94x = 94$$

$$\Rightarrow \quad -1035x + 1034x = 94 \quad \Rightarrow \quad x = -94.$$

Hence $$B_2 = \frac{-94}{-94}\begin{pmatrix} 0 \\ -1 \\ 65 \end{pmatrix} = \begin{pmatrix} 0 \\ -1 \\ 65 \end{pmatrix} \quad \ldots(2)$$

Also $\quad B_1 = A_1{}^{-1}[I - A_2 B_3{}^T].$

Putting it in (iii), we get $A_3{}^T A_1{}^{-1}(I - A_2\, B_3{}^T) + k\, B_3{}^T = 0$

$$A_3{}^T A_1{}^{-1} - A_3{}^T \ A_1{}^{-1} A_2\, B_3{}^T + k\, B_3{}^T = 0$$

$$\Rightarrow \quad A_3{}^T A_1{}^{-1} = [A_3{}^T \ A_1{}^{-1} A_2\, k]\, B_3{}^T. \quad \ldots(3)$$

Now $$A_3{}^T A_1{}^{-1} = [9 \ \ 5 \ \ 16]_{1\times 3}\,\frac{1}{94}\begin{bmatrix} 94 & 0 & -1988 \\ -54 & -3 & 121 \\ -62 & 7 & 125 \end{bmatrix}_{3\times 3}$$

$$= (-416 \quad 97 \quad 913)_{1\times 3}\,\frac{1}{94}$$

and $A_3{}^T A_1{}^{-1} A_2 - k = \frac{1}{94}(-416 \quad 97 \quad 913)_{1\times 3}\begin{pmatrix}4\\9\\2\end{pmatrix}_{3\times 1} - 11$

$$= \frac{1}{94}(-1664 + 873 + 1826) - 11 = \frac{1035 - 11\times 94}{94}$$

$$= \frac{1035 - 1034}{94} = \frac{1}{94}.$$

Whence relation (3) gives

$$B_3{}^T = \frac{A_3{}^T A_1{}^{-1}}{[A_3{}^T A_1{}^{-1} A_2 - k]} = \frac{(1/94)(-416 \quad 97 \quad 913)}{1/94}$$

$$= (-416 \quad 97 \quad 913)_{1\times 3}.$$

Further $\quad B_1 = A_1{}^{-1}(I - A_2 B_3{}^T) = A_1{}^{-1} - A_1{}^{-1} A_2 B_3{}^T$

$$= \frac{1}{94}\begin{bmatrix}94 & 0 & -188\\-54 & -3 & 121\\-62 & 7 & 125\end{bmatrix}_{3\times 3} - \frac{1}{94}\begin{bmatrix}94 & 0 & -188\\-54 & -3 & 121\\-62 & 7 & 125\end{bmatrix}_{3\times 3} \times \begin{pmatrix}4\\9\\2\end{pmatrix}_{3\times 1} (-416 \quad 97 \quad 913)_{1\times 3}$$

$$= \frac{1}{94}\begin{bmatrix}94 & 0 & -188\\-54 & -3 & 121\\-62 & 7 & 125\end{bmatrix}_{3\times 3} - \frac{1}{94}\begin{bmatrix}94 & 0 & -188\\-54 & -3 & 121\\-62 & 7 & 125\end{bmatrix}_{3\times 3} \times \begin{pmatrix}-1664 & 388 & 3652\\-3744 & 873 & 821\\-832 & 194 & 1826\end{pmatrix}_{3\times 3}$$

$$= \frac{94}{94}\begin{bmatrix}1 & 0 & -2\\-5 & 1 & 11\\287 & -67 & -630\end{bmatrix}_{3\times 3} = \begin{bmatrix}1 & 0 & -2\\-5 & 1 & 11\\287 & -67 & -630\end{bmatrix}_{3\times 3}$$

$$\Rightarrow \quad A^{-1} = \begin{pmatrix}1 & 0 & -2 & : & 0\\-5 & 1 & 11 & : & -1\\287 & -67 & -630 & : & 65\\\cdots & \cdots & \cdots & \cdots & \cdots\\-416 & 97 & 913 & : & -94\end{pmatrix}$$

14.10 Complex Matrices and Inversion

Matrices having complex elements are said to be **complex matrices**. We shall show that it is easy to compute the inverse of the matrix $(A + iB)$ if at least one of the matrices A and B is non-singular. **[Agra 2004]**

Let the inverse of the matrix $(A + iB)$ be $(X - iY)$, so that we have

$$(A + iB)(X - iY) = I \quad \Rightarrow (AX - BY) + i(BX + AY) = I + i0$$

$$\Rightarrow \quad AX - BY = I \quad \text{(i)} \qquad \text{and} \quad AY + BX = 0 \quad \text{(ii)}$$

Now premultiplying by B^{-1} in (i), we get

$$B^{-1}AX - B^{-1}BY = B^{-1}I \Rightarrow B^{-1}AX - Y = B^{-1}I = B^{-1} \quad \ldots(1)$$

Also $\quad AY + BX = 0 \Rightarrow A^{-1}AY + A^{-1}BX = 0 \Rightarrow Y = -A^{-1}BX \quad \ldots(2)$

Adding (1) and (2), we get

$$B^{-1}AX = B^{-1} - A^{-1}BX \Rightarrow B^{-1}AX + A^{-1}BX = B^{-1}$$

$$\Rightarrow (B^{-1}A + A^{-1}B)X = B^{-1} \quad \ldots(3)$$

Premultiplying (3) by B, we get

$$(B\,B^{-1}A + B\,A^{-1}B)X = I \Rightarrow (A + B\,A^{-1}B)\,X = I$$

$$\Rightarrow \quad X = (A + B\,A^{-1}B)^{-1}I = A^{-1} + (BA^{-1}B)^{-1} = A^{-1} + B^{-1}AB^{-1} \quad \ldots(4)$$

Similarly when B^{-1} exists, we have

$$X = B^{-1}A\,[A\,B^{-1}\,A + B]^{-1} \quad \text{and} \quad Y = -(A\,B^{-1}A + B)^{-1}$$

In case A and B both are regular, the two expressions for X and Y are, of course, identical.

$$B^{-1}A\,(AB^{-1}A + B)^{-1} = (A^{-1}B)^{-1}.(AB^{-1}A + B)^{-1}$$

$$= \{[AB^{-1}A + B][A^{-1}B]\}^{-1} = [A + BA^{-1}B]^{-1}$$

Note: If A and B both are singular matrices but $A + iB$ is regular, then we proceed as follows:

Let $\quad F = A + rB \quad$ and $G = B - rA$ where r is real.

Then there must exist a number r such that for example, F becomes regular. To prove this, we write

det F = det $(A + rB) = f(r)$ where $f(r)$ is polynomial of degree n. Let $f(r) = 0, \forall r$, then we have $f(r) = 0$ against the assumption that $F = A + rB$ is regular.

Now $\quad F + iG = (A + rB) + i(B - rA) = (A + iB) - ir\,(A + iB) = (1 - ir)(A + iB)$

$$\Rightarrow \quad (F + iG)^{-1} = (1 - ir)^{-1}\,(A + iB)^{-1} \Rightarrow (A + iB)^{-1} = (1 - ir)\,(F + iG)^{-1} \quad \ldots(5)$$

$$\left[\because \quad (1 - ir)^{-1} = \frac{1}{1 - ir}\right]$$

Example 15: *Compute the inverse of the complex matrix*

$$M = \begin{pmatrix} 5 + i & 4 + 2i \\ 10 + 3i & 8 + 6i \end{pmatrix}.$$

[Agra 2004, 2006, 2009; Meerut 2002]

Solution: Let $M = A + iB = \begin{pmatrix} 5 + i & 4 + 2i \\ 10 + 3i & 8 + 6i \end{pmatrix} = \begin{pmatrix} 5 & 4 \\ 10 & 8 \end{pmatrix} + i\begin{pmatrix} 1 & 2 \\ 3 & 6 \end{pmatrix} \quad \ldots(1)$

Now $\det A = 40 - 40 = 0,\ \det B = 6 - 6 = 0$

$\Rightarrow$ A and B both are singular.

So we consider $F = A + rB$ and $G = B - rA$ where r is real.

Now $F + iG = (1 - ir)(A + iB) \Rightarrow (A + iB)^{-1} = (1 - ir)(F + iG)^{-1}$ ...(2)

$$\text{Again } F = \begin{pmatrix} 5 & 4 \\ 10 & 8 \end{pmatrix} + r\begin{pmatrix} 1 & 2 \\ 3 & 6 \end{pmatrix} = \begin{pmatrix} 5 & 4 \\ 10 & 8 \end{pmatrix} + \begin{pmatrix} r & 2r \\ 3r & 6r \end{pmatrix} = \begin{pmatrix} 5+r & 4+2r \\ 10+3r & 8+6r \end{pmatrix}.$$

$$\text{and } G = B - rA = \begin{pmatrix} 1 & 2 \\ 3 & 6 \end{pmatrix} - r\begin{pmatrix} 5 & 4 \\ 10 & 8 \end{pmatrix} = \begin{pmatrix} 1 & 2 \\ 3 & 6 \end{pmatrix} - \begin{pmatrix} 5r & 4r \\ 10r & 8r \end{pmatrix} = \begin{pmatrix} 1-5r & 2-4r \\ 3-10r & 6-8r \end{pmatrix}$$

Let us choose $r = 1$; so that

$$F = \begin{pmatrix} 6 & 6 \\ 13 & 14 \end{pmatrix} \text{ and } G = \begin{pmatrix} -4 & -2 \\ -7 & -2 \end{pmatrix} \Rightarrow \begin{matrix} \det F = 84 - 78 \neq 0, \\ \det G = 8 - 14 \neq 0. \end{matrix}$$

$\therefore$ F and G both are non-singular matrices.

We Now Proceed to Find the Inverse of F + iG.

Let Inverse of $(F + iG) = X + iY$ so that $(F + iG)^{-1} = X + iY$

As calculated in the article, we have

$$X = (F + GF^{-1}G)^{-1} \text{ and } Y = -F^{-1}G(F + GF^{-1}G)^{-1} \quad [\text{Assuming that } F^{-1} \text{ exists}]$$

$$\text{Now} \quad F = \begin{pmatrix} 6 & 6 \\ 13 & 14 \end{pmatrix} \Rightarrow F^{-1} = \begin{pmatrix} 7/3 & -1 \\ -13/6 & 1 \end{pmatrix}$$

$$\therefore \quad F^{-1}G = \begin{pmatrix} 7/3 & -1 \\ -13/6 & 1 \end{pmatrix}\begin{pmatrix} -4 & -2 \\ -7 & -2 \end{pmatrix} = \begin{pmatrix} -7/3 & -8/3 \\ 5/3 & 7/3 \end{pmatrix}$$

$$\text{And} \quad GF^{-1}G = \begin{pmatrix} -4 & -2 \\ -7 & -2 \end{pmatrix}\begin{pmatrix} -7/3 & -8/3 \\ 5/3 & 7/3 \end{pmatrix} = \begin{pmatrix} 6 & 6 \\ 13 & 14 \end{pmatrix}$$

$$\Rightarrow \quad F + GF^{-1}G = \begin{pmatrix} 6 & 6 \\ 13 & 14 \end{pmatrix} + \begin{pmatrix} 6 & 6 \\ 13 & 14 \end{pmatrix} = \begin{pmatrix} 12 & 12 \\ 26 & 28 \end{pmatrix}$$

$$\Rightarrow \quad [F + GF^{-1}G]^{-1} = \text{inverse of} \begin{pmatrix} 12 & 12 \\ 26 & 28 \end{pmatrix} = \begin{pmatrix} 7/6 & -1/2 \\ -13/12 & 1/2 \end{pmatrix} = X.$$

$$\text{Also } (F^{-1}G)(F + GF^{-1}G]^{-1} = \begin{pmatrix} -7/3 & -8/3 \\ 5/3 & 7/3 \end{pmatrix}\begin{pmatrix} 7/6 & -1/2 \\ -13/12 & 1/2 \end{pmatrix} = \begin{pmatrix} 1/6 & -1/6 \\ -7/12 & 1/3 \end{pmatrix}$$

$$\Rightarrow \quad Y = -(F^{-1}G)(F + GF^{-1}G]^{-1} = -\begin{pmatrix} 1/6 & -1/6 \\ -7/12 & 1/3 \end{pmatrix}$$

$$\Rightarrow \quad X + iY = \begin{Bmatrix} 7/6 & -1/2 \\ -13/12 & 1/2 \end{Bmatrix} + i(-1)\begin{Bmatrix} 1/6 & -1/6 \\ -7/12 & 1/3 \end{Bmatrix}$$

$$= \frac{1}{6}\begin{Bmatrix} 7-i & -3+i \\ -6.5+3.5i & 3-2i \end{Bmatrix}$$

Now $(A+iB)^{-1} = (1-ir)(F+iG)^{-1} = (1-i)(F+iG)^{-1}$

$$= (1-i)(X+iY) = \frac{1}{6}(1-i)\begin{Bmatrix} 7-i & -3+i \\ -6.5+3.5i & 3-2i \end{Bmatrix}$$

$$\Rightarrow \quad (A+iB)^{-1} = \frac{1}{6}\begin{Bmatrix} 6-8i & -2+4i \\ -3+10i & 1-5i \end{Bmatrix}$$

✦✦ Problem Set ✦✦

1. Find the inverse of the matrix $\begin{bmatrix} -2 & 4 & 8 \\ -4 & 18 & -16 \\ -6 & 2 & -20 \end{bmatrix}$ by

   (i) Crout's (ii) Doolittle method

2. Find A^{-1} if

   (i) $\begin{bmatrix} 2 & 1 & 0 \\ 4 & 3 & 1 \\ 1 & 1 & 1 \end{bmatrix}$, (ii) $A = \begin{bmatrix} 2 & -2 & 4 \\ 2 & 3 & 2 \\ -1 & 1 & -1 \end{bmatrix}$

   [Kumaon 2000, 2001, 2010]

3. Using Choleski's method, find the inverse of

   (i) $\begin{bmatrix} 1 & 2 & 0.5 & 1 \\ 2 & 5 & 0 & -2 \\ 0.5 & 0 & 2.25 & 7.5 \\ 1 & -2 & 7.5 & 27 \end{bmatrix}$ (ii) $\begin{bmatrix} 3 & -2 & 1 & 0 \\ -2 & 5 & -1 & 1 \\ 1 & -1 & -11 & -2 \\ 0 & 1 & -2 & -12 \end{bmatrix}$

4. Obtain a more accurate inverse of A, given

   (i) $A = \begin{bmatrix} 5 & 2 \\ 3 & -1 \end{bmatrix}$, $A^{-1} = B = \begin{bmatrix} 0.1 & 0.2 \\ 0.3 & -0.4 \end{bmatrix}$

   (ii) $A = \begin{pmatrix} 2 & 4 \\ 3 & 5 \end{pmatrix}$, $A^{-1} = B = \begin{pmatrix} -2.45 & 2.05 \\ 1.45 & -1.95 \end{pmatrix}$

5. Apply Jordan's method to find the inverse of

$$\begin{bmatrix} 0 & 2 & 4 \\ 2 & 4 & 6 \\ 6 & 2 & 2 \end{bmatrix}$$

[Agra 2009; Garhwal 2010]

6. Find the inverse of $A = \begin{bmatrix} 13 & 14 & 6 & 4 \\ 8 & -1 & 13 & 9 \\ 6 & 7 & 3 & 2 \\ 9 & 5 & 16 & 11 \end{bmatrix}$ using the Escalator method.

[Agra 2003; Meerut 2003]

7. Use Gauss-Jordan method to find the inverse of the following matrix:

$$\begin{bmatrix} 2 & 1 & 2 \\ 2 & 2 & 1 \\ 1 & 2 & 2 \end{bmatrix}$$

Use Factorization method, to find the inverse of the following matrices:

8. (i) $\begin{bmatrix} 1 & 2 & 3 \\ 3 & 2 & 1 \\ 2 & 1 & 3 \end{bmatrix}$ (ii) $\begin{bmatrix} 2 & -2 & 4 \\ 2 & 3 & 2 \\ -1 & 1 & -1 \end{bmatrix}$

Applying the Partition method to obtain inverse of the following matrices:

9. $\begin{bmatrix} 1 & 1 & 1 \\ 4 & 3 & -1 \\ 3 & 5 & -3 \end{bmatrix}$ 10. $\begin{bmatrix} 1 & 3 & 3 & 2 \\ 1 & 4 & 3 & 4 \\ 1 & 3 & 4 & 5 \\ 2 & 5 & 3 & 2 \end{bmatrix}$

11. Applying Iterative method to find more accurate inverse of $A = \begin{bmatrix} 1 & 10 & 1 \\ 2 & 0 & 1 \\ 3 & 3 & 2 \end{bmatrix}$,

assuming the initial inverse matrix to be $\begin{bmatrix} 0.43 & 2.43 & -1.43 \\ 0.14 & 0.14 & -0.14 \\ -0.85 & -3.85 & 2.85 \end{bmatrix}$

✦✦ Objective Type Question ✦✦

❖ Multiple Choice Questions

1. Which of the following methods can not be applied to find the inverse of matrix

(a) Choleski's Method (b) Escalator Method

(c) Relaxation Method (d) Gauss-Elimination Method

2. From which of the following methods, we can find the inverse of the matrix of the order $(n+1)\times(n+1)$:

(a) Escalator Method (b) Choleski's Method

(c) Crout's Method (d) Cayley-Hanilton Method

[Agra 2003, 2006]

3. Iterative Method is used to obtain

(a) Exact value of inverse of a matrix

(b) First approximate inverse of a matrix

(c) More accurate inverse of a matrix then a given inverse

(d) None of these. **[Agra 2004]**

4. Escalator Method is used to obtain inverse of a matrix of order n. If the inverse of a matrix of order ...... is given:

(a) n (b) $n-1$

(c) $n+1$ (d) n^2 **[Agra 2004]**

5. The Escalator Method is based on:

(a) Cayley Hamilton theorem (b) Partitioning of matrices

(c) Cramer's rule (d) None of these **[Agra 2004]**

6. Inverse of complex matrix $A+iB$ can not be obtained if:

(a) Either A or B is singular (b) Neither A or B is singular

(c) Both A and B are singular (d) None of these.

[Agra 2004, 2005, 2006, 2009]

7. Which one of the following is not used to obtain inverse of a matrix:

(a) Escalator Method (b) Jacobi's Method

(c) Iterative Method (d) Power Method **[Agra 2008]**

8. Escalator method for matrix inversion is based on:

(a) Addition of matrix (b) Subtraction of matrix

(c) Multiplication of matrix (d) Partition of matrix. **[Agra 2008]**

9. Choleski's Method is applicable only when the given matrix is:

(a) Complex symmetric matrix (b) Real symmetric matrix

(c) Real non-symmetric matrix (d) Skew symmetric matrix.

[Agra 2010]

10. In Crout's Method, the factorisation of a given matrix is a product of lower triangular matrix and upper triangular matrix with diagonal elements:

(a) 0 (b) 2

(c) 1 (d) 3. **[I.F.S. 2009]**

✦✦ Examination Question ✦✦

1. Solve the following system of linear equations by Doolittle's Method.

$$\begin{bmatrix} 10 & -7 & 3 & 5 \\ -6 & 8 & -1 & -4 \\ 3 & 1 & 4 & 11 \\ 5 & -9 & -2 & 4 \end{bmatrix} \begin{bmatrix} x_1 \\ x_2 \\ x_3 \\ x_4 \end{bmatrix} = \begin{bmatrix} 6 \\ 5 \\ 2 \\ 7 \end{bmatrix}.$$

[U.P.T.U. 2009; I.A.S. 2008]

✦✦ Answers ✦✦

❖ Problem Set

1.	$\begin{bmatrix} 4.1 & -0.8 & -1 \\ -0.2 & 7.1 & 0 \\ -1.25 & 0.25 & 0.25 \end{bmatrix}$	2. (i)	$\begin{bmatrix} 2 & -1 & 1 \\ -3 & 2 & -2 \\ 1 & -1 & 2 \end{bmatrix}$
(ii)	$\begin{bmatrix} -1/2 & 1/5 & -8/5 \\ 0 & 1/5 & 2/5 \\ 1/2 & 0 & 1 \end{bmatrix}$	3. (i)	$\begin{bmatrix} 13.5 & -6 & 2 & -1.5 \\ -6 & 3 & -2 & 1 \\ 2 & -2 & 10 & -3 \\ -1.5 & 1 & -3 & 1 \end{bmatrix}$
4. (i)	$\begin{bmatrix} 0.091 & 0.182 \\ 0.273 & -0.454 \end{bmatrix}$	(ii)	$\begin{bmatrix} -2.5025 & 2.0110 \\ 1.4995 & -0.9980 \end{bmatrix}$
5.	$\begin{bmatrix} 1/4 & -1/4 & 1/4 \\ -2 & 3/2 & -1/2 \\ 5/4 & -3/4 & 1/4 \end{bmatrix}$	6.	$\begin{bmatrix} 1 & 0 & -2 & 0 \\ -5 & 1 & 11 & -1 \\ 287 & -67 & -630 & 65 \\ -416 & 97 & 913 & -94 \end{bmatrix}$
7.	$\frac{1}{5}\begin{bmatrix} 2 & 2 & -3 \\ -2 & 2 & 2 \\ 2 & -3 & 2 \end{bmatrix}$	8. (i)	$\begin{bmatrix} -5/12 & 1/4 & 1/3 \\ 7/12 & 1/4 & -2/3 \\ 1/12 & -1/4 & 1/3 \end{bmatrix}$
(ii)	$\begin{bmatrix} -0.5 & 0.2 & -1.6 \\ 0 & 0.2 & 0.4 \\ 0.5 & 0 & 1 \end{bmatrix}$	9.	$\begin{bmatrix} 1.4 & 0.2 & -0.4 \\ -1.5 & 0 & 0.5 \\ 1.1 & -0.2 & -0.1 \end{bmatrix}$
10.	$\frac{1}{9}\begin{bmatrix} -15 & -14 & 12 & 13 \\ 3 & 7 & -6 & -2 \\ 9 & -3 & 0 & -3 \\ -6 & -1 & 3 & 1 \end{bmatrix}$	11.	$\begin{bmatrix} 0.429 & 2.429 & -1.429 \\ 0.143 & 0.143 & -0.143 \\ -0.857 & -3.857 & 2.857 \end{bmatrix}$

❖ Multiple Choice Questions

1.	(c)	**2.**	(a)	**3.**	(c)	**4.**	(c)	**5.**	(b)
6.	(b)	**7.**	(d)	**8.**	(d)	**9.**	(b)	**10.**	(c)

❖ Examination Question

1.	$x_1 = 5, x_2 = 4, x_3 = -7, x_4 = 1$

◆◆◆

Chapter 15

Eigen Values and Eigen Vectors

Eigen Values and Eigen Vectors, Power Series Method, Evaluation of all Eigen Values, Complex Eigen Values, Bounds for Eigen Values, Gerschgorin Bounds and Circles, Eigen Values of a Real Symmetric Matrix-Jacobi's, Given's, House Holder's Method, Eigen Values of Complex Matrices.

15.1 Introduction

Let $A = (a_{ij})_{n\times n}$ be any given square matrix and let there exist a number λ and non-zero Vector **x** such that $\mathbf{Ax} = \lambda \mathbf{x}$, then λ is called *Eigen value or latent root and* **x** is called *as the corresponding Eigen Vector or characteristic Vector of* the matrix **A**.

Now $\quad \mathbf{Ax} = \lambda\,\mathbf{x} \quad \Rightarrow (A - \lambda I)\,\mathbf{x} = \mathbf{0}$

$$\Rightarrow \begin{pmatrix} a_{11}-\lambda & a_{12} & \dots\ a_{1n} \\ a_{21} & a_{22}-\lambda & \dots\ a_{2n} \\ a_{31} & a_{32} & \dots\ a_{3n} \\ \dots & \dots & \dots\ \dots \\ a_{n1} & a_{n2} & \dots\ a_{nn}-\lambda \end{pmatrix} \mathbf{x} = \mathbf{0}. \qquad \dots(1)$$

Above is a homogeneous system of *n* linear equations and shall have a non-trivial solution, if and only if $\det(\mathbf{A} - \lambda\mathbf{I}) = 0$ and this on expansion yields

$$\lambda^n - (a_{11} + a_{22} + \dots + a_{nn})\,\lambda^{n-1} + \dots + (-1)^n \det \mathbf{A} = 0. \qquad \dots(2)$$

This is called **characteristic equation** and has n roots; say $\lambda_1, \lambda_2, \lambda_3, \dots \lambda_n$. These are the values of λ for which system (1) has non-trivial solution. These values of λ are also called as ***Eigen Values or latent roots or characteristics values of the matrix*** **A**. Also, the corresponding values of Vector **x** say $\mathbf{x_1}, \mathbf{x_2}, \dots, \mathbf{x_n}$ (corresponding to $\lambda_1, \lambda_2, \dots, \lambda_n$) such that $\mathbf{Ax_1} = \lambda_1\,\mathbf{x_1}, \mathbf{Ax_2} = \lambda_2\,\mathbf{x_2}, \dots, \mathbf{Ax_n} = \lambda_n\,\mathbf{x_n}$ are called **Eigen Vectors.** It is possible that out of n Eigen Values, some or all of them may coincide. From above it is obvious that

$$\sum_{i=1}^{n} \lambda_i = a_{11} + a_{22} + \dots + a_{nn} = \sum_{i=1}^{n} a_{ii} = \text{Sum of the diagonal values} \qquad \dots(3)$$

while $\prod_{i=1}^{n} \lambda_i = \det \mathbf{A}$.

From (1) it is obvious that a square matrix of order n has always n Eigen Values, special cases some or all of them may coincide. Now if the equation $\mathbf{A}\mathbf{x} = \lambda \mathbf{x}$ is premultiplied by A, we get $A^2 x = \lambda Ax = \lambda^2 x$ and analogously $A^m x = \lambda^m x$. Thus it is obvious that if **A** has the Eigen Values $\lambda_1, \lambda_2, \lambda_3, \ldots, \lambda_n$ then A^m has the Eigen Values $\lambda_1^m, \lambda_2^m, \lambda_3^m, \lambda_4^m, \ldots, \lambda_n^m$; while the Eigen Vectors remain the same.

Some Observations on Eigen Values

1. If $\lambda_1, \lambda_2, \ldots, \lambda_n$ are the Eigen Values of the matrix **A**, then $\lambda_1^r, \lambda_2^r, \lambda_3^r, \ldots, \lambda_n^r$ are the Eigen Values of the matrix A^r.
2. If $\mathbf{B} = \mathbf{P}^{-1}\mathbf{AP}$, then **B** is similar to the matrix **A** and Eigen Values of **A** and **B** are same, **P** being n^{th} order non-singular matrix.
3. Matrices **A** and $\mathbf{A}^T$ (*i.e.* transpose of **A**) have the same Eigen Values but Eigen Vectors are different.
4. The Eigen Values of the values matrix k **A**, k being scalar, are k times the Eigen Values of the matrix **A**.
5. If λ is any Eigen Value of the matrix A, then $\lambda + k$ is the Eigen Value of the matrix $\mathbf{A}+k\,\mathbf{I}$.
6. The Eigen Values of a triangular matrix are exactly the diagonal elements of the matrix.
7. If **A** is some non-singular square matrix, the Eigen Values of $\mathbf{A}^{-1}$ are the reciprocals of the Eigen Values of **A**.
8. If λ is an Eigen Value of the non-singular matrix **A**, then the Eigen Value of the matrix (adj. **A**) is (det **A** /λ).
9. The Eigen Values of a Hermitian matrix are all real.
10. The Eigen Values of a real symmetric matrix are all real.
11. The Eigen Values of a Skew Hermetian matrix is either zero or purely imaginary number.
12. If some Eigen Value, say λ_p, is repeated k times then there exist k orthonormal Eigen Vectors corresponding to λ_p.
13. Let **x** be the Eigen Vector corresponding to the Eigen Value λ of the matrix A, then $k\mathbf{x}$ (k being any scalar) is also the Eigen Vector corresponding to the some Eigen values. But corresponding to an Eigen Vector, there exists only one Eigen value.
14. Consider $f(A)$, as some rational function of the matrix **A** then the Eigen Values of $f(\mathbf{A})$ are $f(\lambda_1), f(\lambda_2), \ldots, f(\lambda_n)$ where λ_1 $(i = 1, 2, \ldots, n)$ are the Eigen Values of the matrix **A** and moreover det $[f(A)] = f(\lambda_1).\, f(\lambda_2), \ldots, f(\lambda_n)$.

15.2 Iterative Method for Dominant Latent Root (or Power Series Method)

[Meerut 2003, 2004, 2006; M.K.U. Tamil Nadu 2005, 2008; Agra 2003, 2007, 2009]

Consider $\mathbf{A} = (a_{ij})_{n \times n}$ and let its Eigen Values be $\lambda_1, \lambda_2, \ldots, \lambda_n$ such that $|\lambda_1| \geq |\lambda_2| \geq |\lambda_3| \geq \ldots \geq |\lambda_n|$ then we say that λ_1 is the dominant latent root of the matrix **A**.

Further, $\mathbf{x}_1, \mathbf{x}_2, \mathbf{x}_3, \ldots, \mathbf{x}_n$ be the corresponding Eigen Vectors then any arbitrary Vector $\mathbf{X}_0$ can be expressed as the linear combination of Eigen Vectors $\mathbf{x}_1, \mathbf{x}_2, \ldots, \mathbf{x}_n$, *i.e.*

$$\mathbf{X}_0 = \mathbf{a}_1 \mathbf{x}_1 + \mathbf{a}_2 \mathbf{x}_2 + \ldots + \mathbf{a}_n \mathbf{x}_n \text{ where } a_i\text{'s are scalars.}$$

Now

$$\begin{aligned} \mathbf{AX}_0 &= \mathbf{A}(\mathbf{a}_1 \mathbf{x}_1 + a_2 \mathbf{x}_2 + \ldots + \mathbf{a}_n \mathbf{x}_n) \\ &= a_1 \mathbf{Ax}_1 + a_2 \mathbf{Ax}_2 + \ldots + a_n \mathbf{Ax}_n \\ &= a_1 \lambda_1 \mathbf{x}_1 + a_2 \lambda_2 \mathbf{x}_2 + \ldots + a_n \lambda_n \mathbf{x}_n. \end{aligned}$$

Again

$$\begin{aligned} \mathbf{A}(\mathbf{AX}_0) &= \mathbf{A}(a_1 \lambda_1 \mathbf{x}_1 + a_2 \lambda_2 \mathbf{x}_2 + \ldots + a_n \lambda_n \mathbf{x}_n) \\ &= a_1 (\mathbf{A} \lambda_1 \mathbf{x}_1) + a_2 (\mathbf{A} \lambda_2 \mathbf{x}_2) + \ldots + a_n (\mathbf{A} \lambda_n \mathbf{x}_n) \\ &= a_1 \lambda_1^2 \mathbf{x}_1 + a_2 \lambda_2^2 \mathbf{x}_2 + \ldots + a_n \lambda_n^2 \mathbf{x}_n \end{aligned}$$

$$\Rightarrow \quad \mathbf{A}^2\mathbf{X}_0 = a_1 \lambda_1^2 \mathbf{x}_1 + a_2 \lambda_2^2 \mathbf{x}_2 + \ldots + a_n \lambda_n^2 \mathbf{x}_n$$

Continuing premultiplying by **A**, we get

$$\mathbf{A}^3\mathbf{X}_0 = a_1 \lambda_1^3 \mathbf{x}_1 + a_2 \lambda_2^3 \mathbf{x}_2 + a_n \lambda_n^3 \mathbf{x}_n$$

$$\ldots \quad \ldots \quad \ldots \quad \ldots \quad \ldots$$

$$\mathbf{A}^r\mathbf{X}_0 = a_1 \lambda_1^r \mathbf{x}_1 + a_2 \lambda_2^r \mathbf{x}_2 + \ldots + a_n \lambda_n^r \mathbf{x}_n$$

$$\Rightarrow \quad \mathbf{A}^r\mathbf{X}_0 = a_1 \lambda_1^r \mathbf{x}_1 + \lambda_1^r \sum_{i=2}^{n} a_i \left(\frac{\lambda_i}{\lambda_1}\right)^r \mathbf{x}_i.$$

When $r \to \infty$; $\left(\frac{\lambda_i}{\lambda_1}\right) \to 0 \quad (\because \lambda_2 < \lambda_1)$

$$\therefore \quad \mathbf{A}^r \mathbf{X}_0 = a_1 \lambda_1^r \mathbf{x}_1 = \text{scalar multiple of Eigen Vector.}$$

This shows that $\mathbf{A}^r \mathbf{X}_0$ is also the Eigen Vector corresponding to the largest Eigen Value λ_1. Let us assume $\mathbf{A}^r \mathbf{X}_0 = \mathbf{Y}_r$; then $\mathbf{Y}_r = a_1 \lambda_1^r \mathbf{x}_1$.

In practice, we generally take $\mathbf{Y}_1 = \mathbf{AX}_0 = k_1\mathbf{Z}_1$ or $\mathbf{Z}_1 = (1/k_1)\,\mathbf{Y}_1$. This is the method, how a Vector is normalised. Then the process is repeated as $\mathbf{Y}_{r+1} = \mathbf{AZ}_r = \mathbf{A}^{r+1}\mathbf{X}_0$. If $\mathbf{Y}_{r+1} = k_{r+1}\,\mathbf{Z}_{r+1}$ then k_{r+1} is the Eigen Value and $\mathbf{Z}_{r+1}$ is the Eigen Vector. This method is also defined as **Power Series Method.** The rate of convergence of this method depends upon the ratio (λ_i/λ_1) or say upon $\{|\lambda_i|/|\lambda_1|\}$. If λ_i and λ_1 are not much separated then we shall require more iterations and works rapidly if $|\lambda_i|/|\lambda_1|$ is very small.

The convergence also depends upon how large x_1 is as compared with other x_i which depends upon the choice of $\mathbf{X}_0$.

Note: For numerical calculations, the algorithm given above, can be formulated as follows:

Given a Vector $\mathbf{Z}_r$, we form two Vectors, $\mathbf{Z}_{r+1}$ and $\mathbf{Y}_{r+1}$:

$\mathbf{Y}_{r+1} = A\mathbf{Z}_r$; $\mathbf{Z}_{r+1} = \left\{\frac{\mathbf{Y}_{r+1}}{k_{r+1}}\right\}$ where k_{r+1} is the Eigen Value and $\mathbf{Z}_{r+1}$ **is the Eigen Vector**

k_{r+1} = max. of the elements ~ in $\mathbf{Z}_{r+1}$.

The initial Vector $\mathbf{X}_0$ should be chosen in a convenient way. Oftenly it is taken as a Vector with all components 1.

15.3 Evaluation of All the Eigen Values

The Iterative Method as discussed in 15.2 can also be used to obtain each Eigen Value in turn. Now, let $\mathbf{B} = \mathbf{A} - \mathbf{kI}$ and let λ be the Eigen Value of A; then we have

$AX=\lambda X \Rightarrow BX = (Ak - 1)\,X \Rightarrow BX = AX - k\,IX = \lambda X - kX = (\lambda - k)X$ and hence the latent roots of **B** are nothing but the latent roots of **A** diminished by k with the same Eigen Vectors. *If the matrix A is Hermitian and all Eigen values are distinct, then Eigen Vectors are orthogonal.*

Let **X** be the Vector obtained after r iterations, then we have

$$\mathbf{X} = a_1\,\mathbf{x}_1 + a_2\,(\lambda_2/\lambda_1)^r\,\mathbf{x}_2 + \ldots + a_n\left(\frac{\lambda_n}{\lambda_1}\right)^r = \mathbf{x_n}$$

$$= a_1\,x_1 + \varepsilon_2\,x_2 + \varepsilon_3\,x_3 + \ldots + \varepsilon_n\,\mathbf{x_n}\,.$$

Now let us assume all x_i's to be normalised such that $x_i^H\,x_k = \delta_{ik}$

where x_i^H is a matrix transposed and conjugated and $\delta_{ij} = \begin{cases} 0, & i \neq k \\ 1, & i = k \end{cases}$ and is defined as Kronecker delta

$$\Rightarrow \qquad \mathbf{AX} = a_1\,\mathbf{Ax}_1 + \varepsilon_2\,\mathbf{Ax}_2 + \ldots + \varepsilon_n\,\mathbf{Ax_n}$$

$$= a_1\,\lambda_1\,x_1 + \varepsilon_2\,\lambda_2\,x_2 + \ldots + \varepsilon_n\,\lambda_n\,x_n$$

and $\qquad \mathbf{X^H A X} = \lambda_1\,|a_1|^2 + \lambda_2\,|\varepsilon_2|^2 + \ldots + \lambda_n\,|\varepsilon_n|^2$

Further $\quad \mathbf{X^H}\,.\,\mathbf{X} = |a_1|^2 + |\varepsilon_2|^2 + \ldots + |\varepsilon_n|^2$

when $\qquad r \to \infty$, all $\varepsilon \to 0$ $\;\lambda_1 = \underset{r\to\infty}{\text{Limt}} \dfrac{\mathbf{X^H A X}}{\mathbf{X^H . X}}$.

Deductions: We know that if the matrix "A" has an Eigen Value λ, then the matrix $(A - q\,I)$ has an Eigen Value $\lambda - q$. Also when A^{-1} has an Eigen Value λ^{-1}, then the matrix $(A - qI)$ has an Eigen value $(\lambda - q)^{-1}$.

To obtain next largest Eigen Value:

Let a^T be the first row Vector of A and let $A_1 = A - x_1\,a^T$ where λ_1 is the Eigen value corresponding to the given Eigen Vector x_1 where of course x_1 is supposed to be normalised such that the first component of x_1 is 1. Hence the first row of A_1 must be zero. Further, let λ_2 and x_2 be the Eigen value and corresponding Eigen Vector with the first component of x_2 equal to 1.

$$\therefore \qquad A_1\,(x_1 - x_2) = (A - x_1\,a^T)\,(x_1 - x_2)$$

$$= A(x_1 - x_2) - (x_1\,a^T)(x_1 - x_2) = \lambda_1\,x_1 - \lambda_2\,x_2 - (\lambda_1 - \lambda_2)\,x_1$$

$$= \lambda_2\,(x_1 - x_2) \qquad (\because\ a^T\,x_1 = \lambda_1,\ a^T\,x_2 = \lambda_2)$$

This means that λ_2 is an Eigen value and $x_1 = x_2$ is as Eigen Vector of A_1. Again $x_1 - x_2$ has the first component equal to zero, the first column of A_1 is irrelevant. This leads to the $(n-1, n-1)$ matrix which is obtained when the first row and first column of A are deleted. Then we obtain an Eigen Vector of this matrix and by adding a zero first component, we get the Vector z and then we get

$$x_2 = x_1 + b\,z. \quad \Rightarrow a^T x_2 = a^T x_1 + ba^T z \quad \Rightarrow \lambda_2 = \lambda_1 + ba^T z$$

$$\Rightarrow \qquad b = [(\lambda_2 - \lambda_1)/(a^T z)]$$

The process is called ***Deflation*** and can be repeated further.

15.4 Complex Eigen Values

Let the Eigen values of a matrix be complex then taking the complex elements of **x**, the equation $(\mathbf{A} - \lambda\mathbf{I})\mathbf{x} = \mathbf{0}$ gives $2n$ equations in $2n$ unknowns.

$$\text{Let} \qquad \lambda = \alpha + i\beta \qquad \text{and} \qquad \mathbf{x} = \begin{pmatrix} a_1 + ib_1 \\ a_2 + ib_2 \\ \cdots\cdots \\ a_n + ib_n \end{pmatrix}$$

Now $(\mathbf{A} - \lambda\mathbf{I})\mathbf{x} = \mathbf{0} \Rightarrow$

$$\underbrace{\begin{bmatrix} a_{11}-\alpha & a_{12}\ldots & a_{1n} & \beta & 0\ldots & 0 \\ a_{21} & a_{22}-\alpha\ldots & a_{2n} & 0 & \beta\ldots & 0 \\ \ldots & \ldots\ \ldots\ \ldots & & \vdots & \vdots & \\ a_{n1} & a_{n2}\ldots & a_{nn}-\alpha & 0 & 0\ldots & \beta \\ -\beta & 0\ldots & 0 & a_{11}-\alpha & a_{12}\ldots & a_{1n} \\ 0 & -\beta\ldots & 0 & a_{21} & a_{22}-\alpha\ldots & a_{2n} \\ \vdots & \vdots & \vdots & \ldots & \ldots\ \ldots & \ldots \\ \vdots & \vdots & \vdots & & & \\ 0 & 0 & -\beta & a_{n1} & a_{n2}\ldots & a_{nn}-\alpha \end{bmatrix}}_{(\mathbf{A}-\lambda\mathbf{I})} \times \begin{bmatrix} x_1 \\ x_2 \\ \vdots \\ x_n \\ y_1 \\ y_2 \\ \ldots \\ y_n \end{bmatrix} = \begin{bmatrix} 0 \\ 0 \\ \vdots \\ 0 \\ 0 \\ 0 \\ \vdots \\ 0 \end{bmatrix} \qquad \ldots(1)$$

This matrix form yields $2n$ equations (in real numbers) in $2n$ unknowns which can be solved for a_i's and b_i's and hence Eigen Vector x is known corresponding to $\lambda = \alpha + i\beta$. But complex roots occur in pairs and hence $\lambda = \alpha - i\beta$ will also be its Eigen value. It is important to note that the Eigen Vector corresponding to $\lambda = \alpha - i\beta$ would be the complex conjugate of the Eigen Vector of λ. For this very reasons, we only need one Eigen Vector for each pair of complex Eigen Values.

15.5 Bounds for Eigen Values

If λ is the Eigen value of the matrix A, then for some $i\ (1 \le i \le n)$,

$|\lambda - a_{ii}| \le |a_{i1}| + |a_{i2}| + |a_{i3}| + \ldots + |a_{in}| = \rho_i$ *(say)*

OR

All the Eigen values of A lie in the union of the n circles with centers a_{ij} and radii ρ_i.

Proof: Let λ be the Eigen value of the squarematrix A and X be the corresponding Eigen Vector, Then we have $AX = \lambda X$

$$\Rightarrow \quad a_{11}x_1 + a_{12}x_2 + \ldots + a_{1n}x_n = \lambda x_1$$
$$a_{21}x_1 + a_{22}x_2 + \ldots + a_{2n}x_n = \lambda x_2$$
$$\ldots\ldots\ldots\ldots\ldots\ldots\ldots\ldots$$
$$\ldots\ldots\ldots\ldots\ldots\ldots\ldots\ldots$$
$$a_{i1}x_1 + a_{i2}x_2 + \ldots + a_{in}x_n = \lambda x_i$$
$$\ldots\ldots\ldots\ldots\ldots\ldots\ldots\ldots$$
$$a_{n1}x_1 + a_{n2}x_2 + \ldots + a_{nn}x_n = \lambda x_n$$

Let x_i be the largest component of **X**, then we can say that

$$|x_n / x_i| \leq 1 \qquad (n = 1, 2, \ldots, n) \qquad \ldots(1)$$

Form above, we have

$$a_{i1}x_1 + a_{i2}x_2 + \ldots + a_{ii}x_i + \ldots + a_{in}x_n = \lambda x_i$$
$$\Rightarrow \quad a_{i1}(x_1/x_i) + a_{i2}(x_2/x_i) + \ldots + a_{ii} + \ldots + a_{in}(x_n/x_i) = \lambda$$
$$\Rightarrow \quad a_{i1}(x_1/x_i) + a_{i2}(x_2/x_i) + \ldots + a_{in}(x_n/x_i) = \lambda - a_{ii}$$
$$\Rightarrow | \quad a_{i1}(x_1/x_i) + a_{i2}(x_2/x_i) + a_{i,\,i-1}(x_{i-1}/x_i) + \ldots + a_{in}(x_n/x_i)| = |\lambda - a_{ii}|$$
$$\Rightarrow \quad |\lambda - a_{ii}| \leq |a_{i1}| + |a_{i2}| + \ldots + |a_{i,\,i-1}| + \ldots + |a_{in}| = \rho_i$$

Which shows that all the Eigen values of A lie within or on the union of the circles with centers at a_{ii} and radii ρ_i. Such circles are known as **GERSCHGORIN CIRCLES.** All the Eigen values of A lie on the union of the above n circles. The bounds thus obtained are all independent. Hence the all Eigen values of A must lie in the intersection of these bounds. Such bounds are known that in case any of the **GERSCHGORIN** bound. It is to be noted that in case any of the **GERSCHGORIN** circles is isolated, then it has exactly one Eigen value.

Solved Examples

Example 1: *(**a**) Using Gerschgorin bounds, estimate the Eigen values of the matrix*

$$A = \begin{pmatrix} 13 & -1 & 1 \\ 01 & 10.5 & 2 \\ 02 & 1 & 14 \end{pmatrix}$$

*(**b**) Find the Eigen Values and Eigen Vectors of the matrix*

$$A = \begin{bmatrix} 1 & 2 & 3 \\ 0 & -4 & 2 \\ 0 & 0 & 7 \end{bmatrix}$$

[Bhopal 2002; Agra 2002, 2005, 2008]

*(**c**) Find the Eigen Values and Eigen Vector of the matrix*

$$A = \begin{bmatrix} 8 & -6 & 2 \\ -6 & 7 & -4 \\ 2 & -4 & 3 \end{bmatrix}$$

[M.K.U. (Tamil Nadu) 2005; 2007]

Solution: (a) By the theorem given above all the Eigen values of A lie in the union of the following three circles:

(i) C_1 : Centre at 13, radius $=|-1|+1=2$

(ii) C_2 : Centre at 10.5, radius $=1+2=3$,

(iii) C_3 : Center at 14, radius $=2+1=3$.

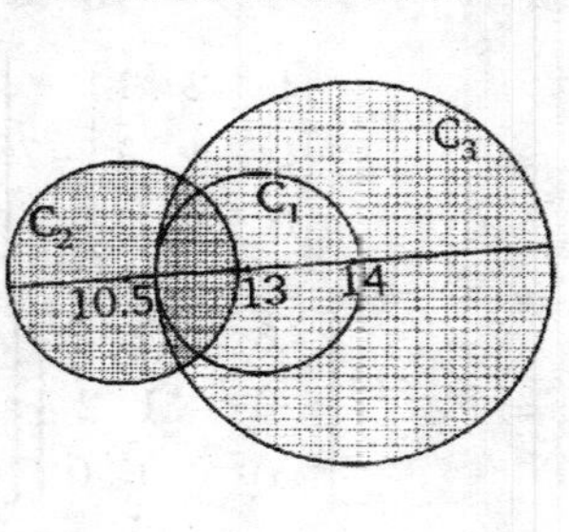

The intersection of these circles gives the result that the Eigen values of A are $10, 12.5, 15$.

(b) The characteristic equation of the given matrix is given by

$$\begin{vmatrix} 1-\lambda & 2 & 3 \\ 0 & -4-\lambda & 2 \\ 0 & 0 & 7-\lambda \end{vmatrix} = 0$$

$\Rightarrow$ $\lambda = 1, -4, 7$. Hence the Eigen values are $1, -4, 7$.

Case (i) When $\lambda = 1$ let the corresponding Eigen Vector be

$$\mathrm{x} = \begin{bmatrix} x_1 \\ x_2 \\ x_3 \end{bmatrix}; \Rightarrow \boldsymbol{Ax} = \lambda \boldsymbol{x} \Rightarrow (\boldsymbol{A} - \lambda \boldsymbol{I})\, \boldsymbol{x} = \boldsymbol{0}$$

$$\Rightarrow \left(\begin{bmatrix} 1 & 2 & 3 \\ 0 & -4 & 2 \\ 0 & 0 & 7 \end{bmatrix} - \begin{bmatrix} 1 & 0 & 0 \\ 0 & 1 & 0 \\ 0 & 0 & 1 \end{bmatrix} \right) \begin{bmatrix} x_1 \\ x_2 \\ x_3 \end{bmatrix} = \begin{bmatrix} 0 \\ 0 \\ 0 \end{bmatrix}$$

$$\Rightarrow \begin{bmatrix} 0 & 2 & 3 \\ 0 & -5 & 2 \\ 0 & 0 & 6 \end{bmatrix} \begin{bmatrix} x_1 \\ x_2 \\ x_3 \end{bmatrix} = \begin{bmatrix} 0 \\ 0 \\ 0 \end{bmatrix}$$

$\Rightarrow$ $2x_2 + 3x_3 = 0.\ \ -5x_2 + 2x_3 = 0,\ \ 6x_3 = 0$

$\Rightarrow x_2 = x_3 = 0. x_1$ is arbitrary (say k). Hence the corresponding Eigen Vector is $\begin{bmatrix} k \\ 0 \\ 0 \end{bmatrix}$.

Case (ii): When $\lambda = -4$, we get $\mathbf{Ax} = -4\mathbf{x} \Rightarrow (\mathbf{A} + 4\mathbf{I})\ \mathbf{x} = \mathbf{0}$

$$\Rightarrow \left(\begin{bmatrix} 1 & 2 & 3 \\ 0 & -4 & 2 \\ 0 & 0 & 7 \end{bmatrix} + 4 \begin{bmatrix} 1 & 0 & 0 \\ 0 & 1 & 0 \\ 0 & 0 & 1 \end{bmatrix} \right) \begin{bmatrix} x_1 \\ x_2 \\ x_3 \end{bmatrix} = \begin{bmatrix} 0 \\ 0 \\ 0 \end{bmatrix}$$

$$\Rightarrow \begin{bmatrix} 5 & 2 & 3 \\ 0 & 0 & 2 \\ 0 & 0 & 11 \end{bmatrix} \begin{bmatrix} x_1 \\ x_2 \\ x_3 \end{bmatrix} = \begin{bmatrix} 0 \\ 0 \\ 0 \end{bmatrix}$$

$\Rightarrow$ $5x_1 + 2x_2 + 3x_3 = 0, 2x_3 = 0, 11x_3 = 0.$

$\Rightarrow$ $x_3 = 0$ and taking $x_2 = k$, we get $x_1 = -(2k/5)$.

Hence the corresponding Eigen Vector is $\begin{bmatrix} -2k/5 \\ k \\ 0 \end{bmatrix}$.

Case (iii) When $\lambda = 7$, we get $\mathbf{Ax} = 7x \Rightarrow (\mathbf{A} - 7\mathbf{I})\,\mathbf{x} = \mathbf{0}$.

$$\Rightarrow \quad \left(\begin{bmatrix} 1 & 2 & 3 \\ 0 & -4 & 2 \\ 0 & 0 & 7 \end{bmatrix} - 7\begin{bmatrix} 1 & 0 & 0 \\ 0 & 1 & 0 \\ 0 & 0 & 1 \end{bmatrix}\right)\begin{bmatrix} x_1 \\ x_2 \\ x_3 \end{bmatrix} = \begin{bmatrix} 0 \\ 0 \\ 0 \end{bmatrix}$$

$$\Rightarrow \quad \begin{bmatrix} -6 & 2 & 3 \\ 0 & -11 & 2 \\ 0 & 0 & 0 \end{bmatrix}\begin{bmatrix} x_1 \\ x_2 \\ x_3 \end{bmatrix} = \begin{bmatrix} 0 \\ 0 \\ 0 \end{bmatrix}$$

$$\Rightarrow \quad -6x_1 + 2x_2 + 3x_3 = 0, \; -11x_2 + 2x_3 = 0.$$

Taking x_3 as arbitrary say k, we obtain $x_2 = 2k/11, \; x_1 = 37k/66$.

Hence the corresponding Eigen Vector is $\begin{bmatrix} 37k/66 \\ 2k/11 \\ k \end{bmatrix}$.

> **Note:** The Eigen Vector $x = \begin{bmatrix} x_1 \\ x_2 \\ x_3 \end{bmatrix}$ such that $x_1^2 + x_2^2 + x_3^2 = 1$, is termed as normalized or orthonormal Vector. Hence, when $\lambda = 1$, the corresponding Eigen Vector is $\begin{bmatrix} k \\ 0 \\ 0 \end{bmatrix}$. This Vector is orthonormal, since we have $k^2 + 0 + 0 = 1$ or $k = 1$. Hence the corresponding orthonormal Eigen Vector is $\begin{bmatrix} 1 \\ 0 \\ 0 \end{bmatrix}$.

(c) The characteristic equation is

$$|A - \lambda I| = \begin{bmatrix} 8-\lambda & -6 & 2 \\ -6 & 7-\lambda & -4 \\ 2 & -4 & 3-\lambda \end{bmatrix} = -\lambda^3 + 18\lambda^2 - 45\lambda = 0$$

$$\Rightarrow \quad \lambda(\lambda - 3)(\lambda - 15) = 0 \quad \therefore \; \lambda = 0, 3, 15.$$

Thus the Eigen values of A are 0, 3, 15.

If x, y, z be the components of an Eigen Vector corresponding to the Eigen value λ, we have

$$(A - \lambda I)\,X = \begin{bmatrix} 8-\lambda & -6 & 2 \\ -6 & 7-\lambda & -4 \\ 2 & -4 & 3-\lambda \end{bmatrix}\begin{bmatrix} x \\ y \\ z \end{bmatrix} = 0 \qquad \ldots(1)$$

Case (i): Putting $\lambda = 0$, we get $8x - 6y + 2z = 0$,

$$-6x + 7y - 4z = 0, \; 2x - 4y + 3z = 0.$$

These equations determine a single linearly independent solution and may be taken as (1, 2, 2). Hence every non-zero multiple of this Vector is an Eigen Vector corresponding to $\lambda = 0$ ...(2)

i.e. the corresponding Eigen Vector is $k\begin{pmatrix}1\\2\\2\end{pmatrix}$ *i.e.* $\begin{pmatrix}k\\2k\\2k\end{pmatrix}$.

Similarly, the Eigen Vectors corresponding to $\lambda = 3$ and $\lambda = 15$ are the arbitrary non-zero multiples of the Vectors (2, 1, −2) and (2, −2, 1) which are obtained from (1) and are

$$k\begin{pmatrix}2\\1\\-2\end{pmatrix} \quad \text{and} \quad k\begin{pmatrix}2\\-2\\1\end{pmatrix}.$$

Example 2: *Find the Eigen values and Eigen Vector of the matrix* $A = \begin{bmatrix}1&2&3\\0&2&3\\0&0&2\end{bmatrix}$.

Solution: The Eigen values of the given matrix are computed as 1, 2, 2; since the matrix is triangular.

Let $\lambda_1 = 1,\ \lambda_2 = \lambda_3 = 2.$

Now, the Eigen Vector corresponding to $\lambda_1 = 1$, is given by

$$\mathbf{Ax} = \boldsymbol{I}.\mathbf{x} \qquad \Rightarrow (\mathbf{A} - \mathbf{I})\mathbf{x} = \mathbf{0}$$

$$\Rightarrow \left(\begin{bmatrix}1&2&3\\0&2&3\\0&0&2\end{bmatrix} - \begin{bmatrix}1&0&0\\0&1&0\\0&0&1\end{bmatrix}\right)\begin{bmatrix}x_1\\x_2\\x_3\end{bmatrix} = \begin{bmatrix}0\\0\\0\end{bmatrix} \Rightarrow \begin{bmatrix}0&2&3\\0&1&3\\0&0&1\end{bmatrix}\begin{bmatrix}x_1\\x_2\\x_3\end{bmatrix} = \begin{bmatrix}0\\0\\0\end{bmatrix}$$

$$\Rightarrow \quad 2x_2 + 3x_3 = 0, x_2 + 3x_3 = 0, x_3 = 0 \Rightarrow x_2 = 0, x_3 = 0.$$

Now taking $x_1 = k$ arbitrarily, the corresponding Eigen Vector is $\begin{bmatrix}k\\0\\0\end{bmatrix}$

When $\lambda_2 = \lambda_3 = 2$, the Eigen Vector is given by $\mathbf{Ax} = \mathbf{2x} \Rightarrow (\mathbf{A} - \mathbf{2I})\,\mathbf{x} = \mathbf{0}$

Solving this, we get $x_1 = 2x_2$, $x_3 = 0$. Thus the Eigen Vector is $\begin{pmatrix}2k\\k\\0\end{pmatrix}$

Now, it will become an Orthonormal Vector if $4k^2 + k^2 + 0 = 1$

i.e. when $k = \pm\,(1/\sqrt{5})$.

$\Rightarrow$ The orthonormal Eigen Vector corresponding to Eigen value $\lambda_2 = 2$ is

$$(2/\sqrt{5}, 1/\sqrt{5}, 0)^T.$$

Example 3: *Find the dominant Eigen value and corresponding Eigen Vector of the matrix*

$$A = \begin{bmatrix} 1 & 6 & 1 \\ 1 & 2 & 0 \\ 0 & 0 & 3 \end{bmatrix}, \text{ taking } X_0 = \begin{bmatrix} 1 \\ 0 \\ 0 \end{bmatrix}$$

[Meerut 2002; Agra 2003]

Solution: Let the initial Eigen Vector be $X_0 = \begin{bmatrix} 1 \\ 0 \\ 0 \end{bmatrix}$, then we have

$$Y_1 = AX_0 = \begin{bmatrix} 1 & 6 & 1 \\ 1 & 2 & 0 \\ 0 & 0 & 3 \end{bmatrix} \begin{bmatrix} 1 \\ 0 \\ 0 \end{bmatrix} = \begin{bmatrix} 1 \\ 1 \\ 0 \end{bmatrix} = 1. \begin{bmatrix} 1 \\ 1 \\ 0 \end{bmatrix}$$

Here $\quad k_1 = 1$ and $Z_1 = \begin{bmatrix} 1 \\ 1 \\ 0 \end{bmatrix}$

Again $\quad Y_2 = AZ_1 = \begin{bmatrix} 1 & 6 & 1 \\ 1 & 2 & 0 \\ 0 & 0 & 3 \end{bmatrix} \begin{bmatrix} 1 \\ 1 \\ 0 \end{bmatrix} = \begin{bmatrix} 7 \\ 3 \\ 0 \end{bmatrix} = 7 \begin{bmatrix} 1 \\ .4 \\ 0 \end{bmatrix} = 7Z_2$

Then $\quad Y_3 = AZ_2 = \begin{bmatrix} 1 & 6 & 1 \\ 1 & 2 & 0 \\ 0 & 0 & 3 \end{bmatrix} \begin{bmatrix} 1 \\ .4 \\ 0 \end{bmatrix} = \begin{bmatrix} 3.4 \\ 1.4 \\ 0 \end{bmatrix} = (3.4) \begin{bmatrix} 1 \\ .52 \\ 0 \end{bmatrix} = (3.4) Z_3$

and $\quad Y_4 = AZ_3 = \begin{bmatrix} 1 & 6 & 1 \\ 1 & 2 & 0 \\ 0 & 0 & 3 \end{bmatrix} \begin{bmatrix} 1 \\ .52 \\ 0 \end{bmatrix} = \begin{bmatrix} 4.12 \\ 2.04 \\ 0 \end{bmatrix} = (4.12) \begin{bmatrix} 1 \\ .49 \\ 0 \end{bmatrix} = (4.12) Z_4$

Similarly, we have

$$Y_5 = AZ_4 = \begin{bmatrix} 1 & 6 & 1 \\ 1 & 2 & 0 \\ 0 & 0 & 3 \end{bmatrix} \begin{bmatrix} 1 \\ .49 \\ 0 \end{bmatrix} = \begin{bmatrix} 3.94 \\ 1.98 \\ 0 \end{bmatrix} = (3.94) \begin{bmatrix} 1 \\ .5 \\ 0 \end{bmatrix} = (3.94) Z_5$$

and $\quad Y_6 = AZ_5 = \begin{bmatrix} 1 & 6 & 1 \\ 1 & 2 & 0 \\ 0 & 0 & 3 \end{bmatrix} \begin{bmatrix} 1 \\ .50 \\ 0 \end{bmatrix} = \begin{bmatrix} 4 \\ 2 \\ 0 \end{bmatrix} = 4 \begin{bmatrix} 1 \\ .5 \\ 0 \end{bmatrix} = 4Z_6$

Thus dominant latent root is 4 and the corresponding Eigen Vector is $\begin{bmatrix} 1 \\ .5 \\ 0 \end{bmatrix}$.

Example 4: *(a) Find the dominant Eigen value and corresponding Eigen Vector of the matrix*

$A = \begin{pmatrix} 1 & -3 & 2 \\ 4 & 4 & -1 \\ 6 & 3 & 5 \end{pmatrix}$ *starting form* $X_0 = \begin{pmatrix} 1 \\ 1 \\ 1 \end{pmatrix}$.

[Meerut 2003; Agra 2007]

(b) *Determine the largest Eigen value and the corresponding Eigen Vector of the matrix.*

$$A = \begin{bmatrix} 2 & -1 & 0 \\ -1 & 2 & -1 \\ 0 & -1 & 2 \end{bmatrix}$$

[Agra 2008]

Solution: (a) $Y_1 = AX_0 = \begin{pmatrix} 1 & -3 & 2 \\ 4 & 4 & -1 \\ 3 & 6 & 5 \end{pmatrix}\begin{pmatrix} 1 \\ 1 \\ 1 \end{pmatrix} = \begin{pmatrix} 0 \\ 7 \\ 14 \end{pmatrix} = 14\begin{pmatrix} 0 \\ \frac{1}{2} \\ 1 \end{pmatrix} = k_1 \mathbf{Z}_1.$

Here $k_1 = 14,\ \mathbf{Z}_1 = \begin{pmatrix} 0 \\ \frac{1}{2} \\ 1 \end{pmatrix}.$

Then $\mathbf{Y}_2 = \mathbf{AZ}_1 = \begin{pmatrix} 1 & -3 & 2 \\ 4 & 4 & -1 \\ 6 & 3 & 5 \end{pmatrix}\begin{pmatrix} 0 \\ \frac{1}{2} \\ 0 \end{pmatrix} = \begin{pmatrix} \frac{1}{2} \\ 1 \\ 13/2 \end{pmatrix} = \begin{pmatrix} \frac{1}{2}/(13/2) \\ 1/(13/2) \\ (13/2)/(13/2) \end{pmatrix}(13/2) = k_2\,\mathbf{Z}_2$

$$k_2 = (13/2),\ \mathbf{Z}_2 = \begin{pmatrix} 1/13 \\ 2/13 \\ 1 \end{pmatrix}$$

$\Rightarrow \quad \mathbf{Y}_3 = \mathbf{AZ}_2 = \begin{pmatrix} 1 & -3 & 2 \\ 4 & 4 & -1 \\ 6 & 3 & 5 \end{pmatrix}\begin{pmatrix} 1/13 \\ 2/13 \\ 1 \end{pmatrix} = \begin{pmatrix} 21/13 \\ -1/13 \\ 77/13 \end{pmatrix} = (77/13)\begin{pmatrix} 21/77 \\ -1/77 \\ 1 \end{pmatrix} = k_3\,\mathbf{Z}_3$

$$k_3 = (77/13),\ \mathbf{Z}_3 = \begin{pmatrix} 21/77 \\ -1/77 \\ 1 \end{pmatrix}$$

$\Rightarrow \quad \mathbf{Y}_4 = \mathbf{AZ}_3 = \begin{pmatrix} 1 & -3 & 2 \\ 4 & 4 & -1 \\ 6 & 3 & 5 \end{pmatrix}\begin{pmatrix} 21/77 \\ -1/77 \\ 1 \end{pmatrix}\begin{pmatrix} 178/77 \\ 3/77 \\ 508/77 \end{pmatrix} = (508/77)\begin{pmatrix} 178/508 \\ 3/508 \\ 1 \end{pmatrix}$

$k_4\,\mathbf{Z}_4$ where $k_4 = (508/77)$ and $\mathbf{Z}_4 = \begin{pmatrix} 178/508 \\ 3/508 \\ 1 \end{pmatrix}$

$\Rightarrow \quad \mathbf{Y}_5 = \mathbf{AZ}_4 = \begin{pmatrix} 1 & -3 & 2 \\ 4 & 4 & -1 \\ 6 & 3 & 5 \end{pmatrix}\begin{pmatrix} 178/508 \\ 3/508 \\ 1 \end{pmatrix}$

$$\begin{pmatrix} 1185/508 \\ 216/508 \\ 3617/508 \end{pmatrix} = (3617/508)\begin{pmatrix} 1185/3617 \\ 216/3617 \\ 1 \end{pmatrix} = k_5\,\mathbf{Z}_5$$

Where $k_5 = (3617/508)$ and $\mathbf{Z}_5 = \begin{pmatrix} 1185/3617 \\ 216/3617 \\ 1 \end{pmatrix} = \begin{pmatrix} 0.3276 \\ 0.0597 \\ 1 \end{pmatrix}$.

Continuing in this way, we obtain

$$\mathbf{Z}_{11} = \begin{pmatrix} -0.3007 \\ 0.0661 \\ 1 \end{pmatrix}, \mathbf{Z}_{15} = \begin{pmatrix} -0.3000 \\ 0.0667 \\ 1 \end{pmatrix}, \mathbf{Z}_{16} = \begin{pmatrix} 2.0999 \\ 0.4668 \\ 7.0001 \end{pmatrix}.$$

The last element in $\mathbf{Z}_{16}$ is nearly 7. Hence rounding off $\lambda_1 = 7$.

Thus dominant latent root is 7 and the corresponding Eigen Vector is $\begin{pmatrix} 2.0999/7 \\ 0.4668/7 \\ 1 \end{pmatrix}$

Solution: (b) Let the initial Eigen Vector be $\mathbf{X_0} = \begin{pmatrix} 1 \\ 0 \\ 0 \end{pmatrix}$

Then $\quad \mathbf{Y}_1 = \mathbf{AX}_0 = \mathbf{A} = \begin{bmatrix} 2 & -1 & 0 \\ -1 & 2 & -1 \\ 0 & -1 & 2 \end{bmatrix} \begin{pmatrix} 1 \\ 0 \\ 0 \end{pmatrix}$

$$= \begin{pmatrix} 2 \\ -1 \\ 0 \end{pmatrix} = 2 \begin{pmatrix} 1 \\ -0.5 \\ 0 \end{pmatrix} = k_1 \mathbf{Z}_1, \text{ where } k_1 = 2, \mathbf{Z}_1 \begin{pmatrix} 1 \\ -0.5 \\ 0 \end{pmatrix}$$

Then $\quad \mathbf{Y}_2 = \mathbf{A}\,\mathbf{Z}_1 = \begin{bmatrix} 2 & -1 & 0 \\ -1 & 2 & -1 \\ 0 & -1 & 2 \end{bmatrix} \begin{pmatrix} 1 \\ -0.5 \\ 0 \end{pmatrix} = \begin{bmatrix} 2.5 \\ -2 \\ 0.5 \end{bmatrix} = 2.5 \begin{bmatrix} 1 \\ -0.8 \\ 0.2 \end{bmatrix} = k_2 \mathbf{Z}_2$

Repeating the above process, we get

$$\mathbf{Y}_3 = \mathbf{A}\,\mathbf{Z}_2 = 2.8 \begin{bmatrix} 1 \\ -1 \\ 0.43 \end{bmatrix} k_3 \mathbf{Z}_3 ; \mathbf{Y}_4 = \mathbf{A}\,\mathbf{Z}_3 = 3.43 \begin{bmatrix} 0.87 \\ -1 \\ 0.54 \end{bmatrix} = k_4 \mathbf{Z}_4$$

$$\mathbf{Y}_5 = \mathbf{A}\,\mathbf{Z}_4 = 3.14 \begin{bmatrix} 0.80 \\ -1 \\ 0.61 \end{bmatrix} k_5 \mathbf{Z}_5; \mathbf{Y}_6 = \mathbf{A}\,\mathbf{Z}_5 = 3.14 \begin{bmatrix} 0.76 \\ -1 \\ 0.65 \end{bmatrix} = k_6 \mathbf{Z}_6$$

$$\mathbf{Y}_7 = \mathbf{A}\,\mathbf{Z}_6 = 3.14 \begin{bmatrix} 0.74 \\ -1 \\ 0.67 \end{bmatrix} = k_7 \mathbf{Z}_7.$$

Hence the largest Eigen value is 3.14 and the corresponding Eigen-Vector is $[0.74, -1, 0.67]'$.

Example 5: *(a) Using the Gerschgorin bounds, estimate the Eigen value of the following matrices:*

(i) $\begin{bmatrix} 1 & 2 & 3 \\ 2 & 4 & 6 \\ 3 & 6 & 1 \end{bmatrix}$ (ii) $\begin{bmatrix} 1 & 2 & -1 \\ 1 & 1 & 1 \\ 1 & 3 & -1 \end{bmatrix}$

Ans: Eigen values lie within (i) the intersection of the circles with centers at 4, 1 and radii 8, 9; (ii) The circle having centre at 1 and radius 4.

(b) *Find, by power method, the largest Eigen value of the following matrices:*

(i) $\begin{bmatrix} 1 & 2 \\ 3 & 4 \end{bmatrix}$ **Ans.** 5.38, $\begin{pmatrix} .46 \\ 1 \end{pmatrix}$ (ii) $\begin{bmatrix} 4 & 1 \\ 1 & 3 \end{bmatrix}$ **Ans.** 4.618, $\begin{pmatrix} 1 \\ .618 \end{pmatrix}$

(c) *Find the largest Eigen value and the corresponding Eigen Vector of the matrices:*

(i) $\begin{bmatrix} 1 & 2 & 3 \\ 0 & -4 & 2 \\ 0 & 0 & 7 \end{bmatrix}$ (ii) $\begin{bmatrix} 1 & 3 & -1 \\ 3 & 2 & 4 \\ -1 & 4 & 10 \end{bmatrix}$

Ans. (i) 7, $\begin{pmatrix} 37k/66 \\ 2k/11 \\ k \end{pmatrix}$ (ii) 11.66, $\begin{pmatrix} .025 \\ .422 \\ 1 \end{pmatrix}$.

Solution: Solution of 5 (a), 5 (b), 5 (c) is same as the solution of example 4.

Example 6: *(a) Find all the latent roots of the matrix* $\mathbf{A} = \begin{bmatrix} 1 & 6 & 1 \\ 1 & 2 & 0 \\ 0 & 0 & 3 \end{bmatrix}$.

(b) *Find the Eigen values and Vectors of* $\begin{pmatrix} -1 & -5 \\ 1 & 3 \end{pmatrix}$.

Solution: (a) We have $\mathbf{B} = \mathbf{A} - 4\,\mathbf{I}$.

$$= \begin{bmatrix} 1 & 6 & 1 \\ 1 & 2 & 0 \\ 0 & 0 & 3 \end{bmatrix} - 4 \begin{bmatrix} 1 & 0 & 0 \\ 0 & 1 & 0 \\ 0 & 0 & 1 \end{bmatrix} = \begin{bmatrix} -3 & 6 & 1 \\ 1 & -2 & 0 \\ 0 & 0 & -1 \end{bmatrix}.$$

Let us assume $\mathbf{X_0} = \begin{bmatrix} 1 \\ 0 \\ 0 \end{bmatrix}$, then we get the following Iterative values;

$$\mathbf{Y_1} = \mathbf{B}\,\mathbf{X_0} = \begin{bmatrix} -3 & 6 & 1 \\ 1 & -2 & 0 \\ 0 & 0 & -1 \end{bmatrix} \begin{bmatrix} 1 \\ 0 \\ 0 \end{bmatrix} = \begin{bmatrix} -3 \\ 1 \\ 0 \end{bmatrix} = (-3) \begin{bmatrix} 1 \\ -.33 \\ 0 \end{bmatrix} = k_1 \mathbf{Z_1}$$

$$= -3\,\mathbf{Z_1} \qquad (k_1 = -3)$$

$$\mathbf{Y}_2 = \mathbf{B}\,\mathbf{Z}_1 = \begin{bmatrix} -3 & 6 & 1 \\ 1 & -2 & 0 \\ 0 & 0 & -1 \end{bmatrix}\begin{bmatrix} 1 \\ -.33 \\ 0 \end{bmatrix}$$

$$= \begin{bmatrix} -4.98 \\ 1.66 \\ 0 \end{bmatrix} = (-4.98)\begin{bmatrix} 1 \\ -.33 \\ 0 \end{bmatrix} = (-4.98)\ \mathbf{Z}_2 = k_2\,\mathbf{Z}_2$$

$$\mathbf{Y}_3 = \mathbf{B}\,\mathbf{Z}_2 = \begin{bmatrix} -3 & 6 & 1 \\ 1 & -2 & 0 \\ 0 & 0 & -1 \end{bmatrix}\begin{bmatrix} 1 \\ -.33 \\ 0 \end{bmatrix} = \begin{bmatrix} -4.98 \\ 1.66 \\ 0 \end{bmatrix} = (-4.98)\begin{bmatrix} 1 \\ -.33 \\ 0 \end{bmatrix} = k_3\,\mathbf{Z}_3$$

Thus the largest latent root of **B** is -4.98 and the corresponding Eigen Vector is $\begin{bmatrix} 1 \\ -.33 \\ 0 \end{bmatrix}$,

Which implies that the latent root of the matrix **A** is $(-4.98 + 4)$ or $-.98$.

Now, the remaining third latent root can be obtained as usual.

Thus third Eigen value is given by $4 + (-.98) + \lambda_3 = 1 + 2 + 3$ or $\lambda_3 = 2.98$.

Smallest Latent Root:

The smallest Eigen value of the matrix **A** is the reciprocal of the dominant Eigen value of $\mathbf{A}^{-1}$.

(b) The Eigen values are $\lambda = 1 + i, 1 - i$. Let $\mathbf{x} = \begin{bmatrix} x_1 + i\,y_1 \\ x_2 + i\,y_2 \end{bmatrix}$ be the Eigen Vector corresponding to $\lambda = 1 + i$. Then the 2×2 *i.e.* 4 equations in 4 unknowns x_1, y_1, x_2, y_2 are given by

$$\begin{bmatrix} -1-1 & -5 & 1 & 0 \\ 1 & 3-1 & 0 & 1 \\ -1 & 0 & -1-1 & -5 \\ 0 & -1 & 1 & 3-1 \end{bmatrix}\begin{bmatrix} x_1 \\ x_2 \\ y_1 \\ y_2 \end{bmatrix} = \begin{bmatrix} 0 \\ 0 \\ 0 \\ 0 \end{bmatrix} \Rightarrow \begin{bmatrix} -2 & -5 & 1 & 0 \\ 1 & 2 & 0 & 1 \\ -1 & 0 & -2 & -5 \\ 0 & -1 & 1 & 2 \end{bmatrix}\begin{bmatrix} x_1 \\ x_2 \\ y_1 \\ y_2 \end{bmatrix} = \begin{bmatrix} 0 \\ 0 \\ 0 \\ 0 \end{bmatrix}$$

$$\Rightarrow \begin{bmatrix} 1 & 2 & 0 & 1 \\ 0 & 1 & -1 & -2 \\ 0 & 0 & 0 & 0 \\ 0 & 0 & 0 & 0 \end{bmatrix}\begin{bmatrix} x_1 \\ x_2 \\ y_1 \\ y_2 \end{bmatrix} = \begin{bmatrix} 0 \\ 0 \\ 0 \\ 0 \end{bmatrix} \Rightarrow \left.\begin{matrix} x_1 + 2\,x_2 + y_2 = 0 \\ x_2 - y_1 - 2\,y_2 = 0 \end{matrix}\right\}$$

Let us take $x_1 = 0, y_1 = 1$, so that $x_2 = .2, y_2 = -.4$. Hence the Eigen Vector **x** is given by

$$\mathbf{x} = \begin{pmatrix} x_1 + i\,y_1 \\ x_2 + i\,y_2 \end{pmatrix} = \begin{pmatrix} i \\ .2 + .4\,i \end{pmatrix}.$$

This is the required Eigen Vector corresponding to Eigen value $1 + i$ and hence the Eigen Vector corresponding to $(1 - i)$ is $\begin{pmatrix} -i \\ .2 + .4i \end{pmatrix}$.

Example 7: *Find Eigen values and Eigen Vectors of* **A**, *when*

$$\mathrm{A} = \begin{pmatrix} 10 & 7 & 8 & 7 \\ 7 & 5 & 6 & 5 \\ 8 & 6 & 10 & 9 \\ 7 & 5 & 9 & 10 \end{pmatrix} \quad \textit{taking}\ \mathbf{X} = \begin{pmatrix} 1 \\ 1 \\ 1 \\ 1 \end{pmatrix}$$

[Agra 2008; Bihar 2006]

Solution: Let no of Iterations $= r = 1$.

$$\text{Then} \quad AX = \begin{pmatrix} 10+ & 7+ & 8+ & 7 \\ 7+ & 5+ & 6+ & 5 \\ 8+ & 6+10+ & 9 \\ 7+ & 5+ & 9+10 \end{pmatrix} = \begin{pmatrix} 32 \\ 23 \\ 33 \\ 31 \end{pmatrix}$$

$$\because \quad A = \text{given matrix}, X = \begin{pmatrix} 1 \\ 1 \\ 1 \\ 1 \end{pmatrix} \quad ...(1)$$

$$X^H = \text{Transposed conjugate of } X = [1 \ 1 \ 1 \ 1] \quad ...(2)$$

$$\text{and} \quad X^H AX = [32 + 23 + 33 + 31] = [119] \quad ...(3)$$

$$\Rightarrow \quad X^H X = [1 + 1 + 1 + 1] = [4] \quad ...(4)$$

$$\Rightarrow \quad \lambda_1 = \frac{X^H AX}{X^H X} = \frac{119}{4} = 29.75.$$

Let no. of iterations $= r = 2$. Now, we consider $X = \begin{pmatrix} 32/33 \\ 23/33 \\ 1 \\ 31/33 \end{pmatrix}$.

$$\text{Then} \quad AX = \begin{pmatrix} 10 & 7 & 8 & 7 \\ 7 & 5 & 6 & 5 \\ 8 & 6 & 10 & 9 \\ 7 & 5 & 9 & 10 \end{pmatrix}_{3\times3} \begin{pmatrix} 32/33 \\ 23/33 \\ 1 \\ 31/33 \end{pmatrix}_{3\times1} = \begin{pmatrix} 962/33 \\ 962/33 \\ 1003/33 \\ 946/33 \end{pmatrix}_{3\times1}$$

$$X^H = (32/33 \quad 23/33 \quad 1 \quad 31/33)$$

$$\Rightarrow \quad X^H X = \begin{pmatrix} \frac{32}{33} & \frac{23}{33} & 1 & \frac{31}{33} \end{pmatrix} \begin{pmatrix} 32/33 \\ 23/33 \\ 1 \\ 31/33 \end{pmatrix} = \left(\frac{32}{33}\right)^2 + \left(\frac{23}{33}\right)^2 + 1 + \left(\frac{31}{33}\right)^2$$

$$= [3603/1089]$$

$$\text{Also } X^H AX = \begin{pmatrix} \frac{32}{33} & \frac{23}{33} & 1 & \frac{31}{33} \end{pmatrix} \begin{pmatrix} 962/33 \\ 692/33 \\ 1003/33 \\ 946/33 \end{pmatrix}$$

$$= \left[\frac{32 \times 962 + 23 \times 692 + 33 \times 1003 + 31 \times 946}{33 \times 33}\right]$$

$$\text{whence} \quad \lambda_1 = \frac{X^H AX}{X^H X} = \frac{32 \times 962 + 23 \times 692 + 33 \times 1003 + 31 \times 946}{3603}$$

$$= \frac{115335}{3603} = 30.287.$$

Again proceeding for 3rd iteration, we get $\lambda_1 = 30.288662$.

To Obtain Eigen Vector

Let $AX = \lambda X \Rightarrow \begin{pmatrix} 10 & 7 & 8 & 7 \\ 7 & 5 & 6 & 5 \\ 8 & 6 & 10 & 9 \\ 7 & 5 & 9 & 10 \end{pmatrix} \begin{pmatrix} x_1 \\ x_2 \\ x_3 \\ x_4 \end{pmatrix} = 29.75 \begin{pmatrix} x_1 \\ x_2 \\ x_3 \\ x_4 \end{pmatrix}$

$$\Rightarrow \begin{pmatrix} 10x_1 + 7x_2 + 8x_3 + 7x_4 \\ 7x_1 + 5x_2 + 6x_3 + 5x_4 \\ 8x_1 + 6x_2 + 10x_3 + 9x_4 \\ 7x_1 + 5x_2 + 9x_3 + 10x_4 \end{pmatrix} = \begin{pmatrix} 29.75\ x_1 \\ 29.75\ x_2 \\ 29.75\ x_3 \\ 29.75\ x_4 \end{pmatrix}$$

$$\Rightarrow \begin{matrix} 10x_1 + 7x_2 + 8x_3 + 7x_4 = 29.75\ x_1 \\ 7x_1 + 5x_2 + 6x_3 + 5x_4 = 29.75\ x_2 \\ 8x_1 + 6x_2 + 10x_3 + 9x_4 = 29.75\ x_3 \\ 7x_1 + 5x_2 + 9x_3 + 10x_4 = 29.75\ x_4 \end{matrix} \quad \Rightarrow \begin{matrix} -19.75x_1 + 7x_2 + 8x_3 + 7x_4 = 0 \\ 7x_1 - 24.75x_2 + 6x_3 + 5x_4 = 0 \\ 8x_1 + 6x_2 - 19.75x_3 + 9x_4 = 0 \\ 7x_1 + 5x_2 + 9x_3 - 19.75x_4 = 0 \end{matrix}$$

These give $x_1 = 0.95761, x_2 = 0.68892, \ x_3 = 1, x_4 = 0.94379$.

$$\therefore \quad \text{Eigen Vector} = \mathbf{X} = \begin{pmatrix} x_1 \\ x_2 \\ x_3 \\ x_4 \end{pmatrix} = \begin{pmatrix} 0.95761 \\ 0.68892 \\ 1 \\ 0.94379 \end{pmatrix}$$

Example 8: *Obtain λ_2, λ_3 and the corresponding Eigen Vector of A, when*

$$A = \begin{pmatrix} -306 & -198 & 426 \\ 104 & 67 & -147 \\ -176 & -114 & 244 \end{pmatrix} \text{ given that } \lambda_1 = 6 \text{ and corresponding Eigen Vector} = \begin{pmatrix} 2 \\ -1 \\ 1 \end{pmatrix}$$

[Agra 2004]

Solution: Normalising $\begin{pmatrix} 2 \\ -1 \\ 1 \end{pmatrix}$, we have $\begin{pmatrix} 2/2 \\ -1/2 \\ 1/2 \end{pmatrix} = \mathbf{x}_1$ say.

Now, let $a^T = [-306 \quad -198 \quad 426]$

so that $x_1 a^T = \begin{pmatrix} 2/2 \\ -1/2 \\ 1/2 \end{pmatrix}_{3\times1} (-306 \quad -198 \quad 426)_{1\times3} = \begin{pmatrix} -306 & -198 & 426 \\ 153 & 99 & -213 \\ -153 & -99 & 213 \end{pmatrix}_{3\times3}$

$$\Rightarrow \quad \mathbf{A}_1 = A - x_1 a^T = \begin{pmatrix} -306 & -198 & 426 \\ 104 & 67 & -147 \\ -176 & -114 & 244 \end{pmatrix} - \begin{pmatrix} -306 & -190 & 426 \\ 153 & 99 & -213 \\ -153 & -99 & 213 \end{pmatrix}$$

$$= \begin{pmatrix} 0 & 0 & 0 \\ -44 & -32 & 66 \\ -23 & -15 & 31 \end{pmatrix}$$

We now consider only the matrix $\begin{pmatrix} -32 & 66 \\ -15 & 31 \end{pmatrix}$

[obtained by deleting R_1 and C_1 of A_1]

$$\begin{pmatrix} -32 & 66 \\ -15 & 31 \end{pmatrix}\begin{pmatrix} x_1 \\ x_2 \end{pmatrix} = \lambda\begin{pmatrix} x_1 \\ x_2 \end{pmatrix} = \begin{pmatrix} \lambda x_1 \\ \lambda x_2 \end{pmatrix}$$

$$\Rightarrow \quad \begin{pmatrix} -32x_1 + 66x_2 \\ -15x_1 + 31x_2 \end{pmatrix} = \begin{pmatrix} \lambda x_1 \\ \lambda x_2 \end{pmatrix} \Rightarrow \begin{matrix} -32x_1 + 66x_2 = \lambda x_1 \\ -15x_1 + 31x_2 = \lambda x_2 \end{matrix}$$

$$\Rightarrow \quad (-32 - \lambda)x_1 + 66x_2 = 0 \quad \text{and} \quad -15x_1 + (31 - \lambda)x_2 = 0$$

$$\therefore \quad \frac{-32 - \lambda}{-15} = \frac{66}{31 - \lambda} \Rightarrow \frac{32 + \lambda}{15} = \frac{66}{31 - \lambda} \Rightarrow \lambda^2 + \lambda - 2 = 0$$

$$\Rightarrow \quad (\lambda + 2)(\lambda - 1) = 0 \Rightarrow \lambda_2 = -2 \quad \text{and} \quad \lambda_3 = 1.$$

When $\lambda_2 = -2$, the Eigen Vector becomes $\begin{pmatrix} 11 \\ 5 \end{pmatrix}$

$$\Rightarrow \quad x_2 = x_1 + bz = \begin{pmatrix} 1 \\ -1/2 \\ -1/2 \end{pmatrix} + b\begin{pmatrix} 0 \\ 11 \\ 5 \end{pmatrix} \qquad \text{(adding zero).}$$

Also $\quad a^T z = (-306 \; -198 \; 426)_{1\times 3}\begin{pmatrix} 0 \\ 11 \\ 5 \end{pmatrix}_{3\times 1} = [-148 \times 11 + 426 \times 5] = -48$

$$b = \frac{\lambda_2 - \lambda_1}{a^T z} = \frac{-2-6}{-48} = \frac{1}{6}. \text{ Thus } x_2 = \begin{pmatrix} 1 \\ 4/3 \\ 4/3 \end{pmatrix} \text{ or } \begin{pmatrix} 3 \\ 4 \\ 4 \end{pmatrix}$$

With $\quad \lambda_3 = 1$, we obtain $x_3 = \begin{pmatrix} 1 \\ -1/2 \\ -1/2 \end{pmatrix} + b\begin{pmatrix} 0 \\ 2 \\ 1 \end{pmatrix}$

Where $a^T z = 30$ and $b = \dfrac{1-6}{30} = -\dfrac{1}{6}$

$$\Rightarrow \quad x_3 = \begin{pmatrix} 1 \\ -\frac{1}{2} + 2b \\ \frac{1}{2} + b \end{pmatrix} = \begin{pmatrix} 1 \\ -\frac{1}{2} - \frac{1}{3} \\ \frac{1}{2} - (1/6) \end{pmatrix} = \begin{pmatrix} 1 \\ -5/6 \\ 2/6 \end{pmatrix} \text{ or } \begin{pmatrix} 6 \\ -5 \\ 2 \end{pmatrix}$$

✦✦ Problem Set ✦✦

1. Find the Eigen values and Eigen Vectors of $A = \begin{pmatrix} 2 & 1 & 0 \\ 0 & 2 & 1 \\ 0 & 0 & 2 \end{pmatrix}$

2. Find the largest Eigen value and the corresponding Eigen Vector of the matrix,

$$A = \begin{pmatrix} -1 & 1 & 2 \\ 0 & 1 & -1 \\ 4 & -2 & -9 \end{pmatrix}$$

Find the largest Eigen value and the corresponding Eigen Vector of the matrix

3. $\begin{bmatrix} 10 & -2 & 1 \\ -2 & 10 & -2 \\ 1 & -2 & 10 \end{bmatrix}$ 4. $\begin{pmatrix} 1 & 3 & -1 \\ 3 & 2 & 4 \\ -1 & 4 & 10 \end{pmatrix}$

✦✦ Answers ✦✦

1. $\lambda_1 = \lambda_2 = \lambda_3 = 2; = x_1 = x_2 = x_3 = \begin{pmatrix} k \\ 0 \\ 0 \end{pmatrix}$

2. $\lambda = -10.099,\ \mathbf{x} = \begin{pmatrix} -0.2297 \\ 0.0901 \\ 1 \end{pmatrix}$

3. $\lambda = 9; \begin{pmatrix} 1 \\ 0 \\ -1 \end{pmatrix}$

4. $\lambda = 11.66; \begin{pmatrix} 0.025 \\ 0.422 \\ 1.0 \end{pmatrix}$

15.6 Eigen Values of Real Symmetric Matrix

The power method discussed earlier determines the largest/smallest Eigen value only. Now we proceed to discuss three new methods for obtaining all the Eigen values of a real symmetric matrix A. The Eigen values of A are given by the diagonal elements when A is reduced either to diagonal matrix D, or the lower triangular matrix L or the upper triangular matrix U. Hence the fundamental thing is simply to reduce the matrix A to D or L or U.

15.7 Jacobi's Method

[Agra 2004, 2006, 2009]

Let A be any real symmetric matrix whose Eigen values are real. Let there exist a real orthogonal matrix O, *such that* $O^{-1}AO$ is a diagonal matrix $\mathbf{D}$. This method consists of diagonalising $\mathbf{A}$ by applying a series of orthogonal transformations $O_1, O_2, O_3 ------ O_r$, such that their product $\mathbf{O} = O_1\ O_2\ O_3 \ldots . O_r$ satisfies the relation $O^{-1}AO = \mathbf{D}$. Let us now choose $A_1 = \begin{pmatrix} a_{ii} & a_{ij} \\ a_{ji} & a_{ji} \end{pmatrix}$

Where $a_{ij} = a_{ji}$ and the element a_{ij} is numerically largest non-deagonal element. Then A_1 can be diagonalised very easily. Now, we consider $O_1 = \begin{pmatrix} \cos\phi & -\sin\phi \\ \sin\phi & \cos\phi \end{pmatrix}$ so that

$$O_1^{-1} A_1 O_1 = \begin{pmatrix} \cos\phi & \sin\phi \\ -\sin & \cos\phi \end{pmatrix} \begin{pmatrix} a_{ii} & a_{ij} \\ a_{ji} & a_{jj} \end{pmatrix} \begin{pmatrix} \cos\phi & -\sin\phi \\ \sin\phi & \cos\phi \end{pmatrix}$$

$$= \begin{pmatrix} (a_{ii} \cos^2 \theta + a_{jj} \sin^2 \theta + a_{ij} \sin 2\theta) & a_{ij} \cos 2\theta + \frac{1}{2}(a_{jj} - a_{ii}) \sin 2\theta \\ a_{ij} \cos 2\theta + \frac{1}{2}(a_{jj} - a_{ii}) \sin 2\theta & a_{ii} \sin^2 \theta + a_{jj} \cos^2 \theta - a_{ij} \sin 2\theta \end{pmatrix}_{2\times 2} \quad \text{...(1)}$$

= **Diagonal Matrix**, provided we have $a_{ij} \cos 2\theta + \frac{1}{2}(a_{jj} - a_{ii}) \sin 2\theta = 0$

$$\Rightarrow \qquad \tan 2\theta = [2a_{ij} / (a_{ii} - a_{jj})] \quad \text{...(2)}$$

Above equation gives four values of θ but to obtain the least possible rotation, we choose $-(\pi/4) \le \theta \le (\pi/4)$. Further, the largest non-diagonal element (in magnitude) in the new rotated matrix is obtained and the above procedure is repeated using orthogonal matrix as O_2. Thus a series of such transformations are performed so as to annihilate the non diagonal elements. After using r transformations, we have

$O_r^{-1} O_{r-1}^{-1} ------ O_1^{-1} AO_1 \ldots O_{r-1} O_r = O^{-1} AO$. Now as $r \to \infty, O^{-1} AO$ approaches to a diagonal matrix whose diagonal elements are the Eigen values of **A**. The corresponding columns of $O = O_1 O_2 --- O_r$ are the Eigen Vectors. of **A**.

Example 9: *Using Jacobi's method, find all the Eigen values and the Eigen Vectors of the matrix*

$$\begin{pmatrix} 1 & \sqrt{2} & 2 \\ \sqrt{2} & 3 & \sqrt{2} \\ 2 & \sqrt{2} & 1 \end{pmatrix}$$

[Meerut 2003 (B.P.)]

Solution: The largest non-diagonal element is $a_{13} = a_{31} = 2$ and $a_{11} = 1, a_{33} = 1$.

$$\Rightarrow \qquad \tan 2\phi = \frac{2a_{13}}{a_{11} - a_{33}} = \frac{2 \times 2}{1-1} = \infty$$

$$\Rightarrow \qquad 2\phi = (\pi/2) \text{ or } \phi = (\pi/4)$$

$$\therefore \qquad O_1 = \begin{bmatrix} \cos\phi & 0 & -\sin\phi \\ 0 & 1 & 0 \\ \sin\phi & 0 & \cos\phi \end{bmatrix} = \begin{bmatrix} 1/\sqrt{2} & 0 & -1/\sqrt{2} \\ 0 & 1 & 0 \\ 1/\sqrt{2} & 0 & 1/\sqrt{2} \end{bmatrix}$$

Then the first transformation gives

$$D_1 = O_1^{-1} AO_1 = \begin{bmatrix} 1/\sqrt{2} & 0 & 1/\sqrt{2} \\ 0 & 1 & 0 \\ -1/\sqrt{2} & 0 & 1/\sqrt{2} \end{bmatrix} \begin{bmatrix} 1 & \sqrt{2} & 2 \\ \sqrt{2} & 3 & \sqrt{2} \\ 2 & \sqrt{2} & 1 \end{bmatrix} \begin{bmatrix} 1/\sqrt{2} & 0 & -1\sqrt{2} \\ 0 & 1 & 0 \\ 1/\sqrt{2} & 0 & 1/\sqrt{2} \end{bmatrix}$$

$$= \begin{bmatrix} 3 & 2 & 0 \\ 2 & 3 & 0 \\ 0 & 0 & -1 \end{bmatrix}$$

Further the largest non-diagonal element is $a_{12} = a_{21} = 2$ and $a_{11} = 3, a_{22} = 3$.

$$\Rightarrow \qquad \tan 2\phi = \frac{2a_{12}}{a_{11} - a_{22}} = \frac{2 \times 2}{0} = \infty.$$

$$\Rightarrow \qquad 2\phi = (\pi/2) \text{ or } \phi = (\pi/4)$$

$$\Rightarrow \quad O_2 = \begin{bmatrix} \cos\phi & -\sin\phi & 0 \\ \sin\phi & \cos\phi & 0 \\ 0 & 0 & 1 \end{bmatrix} = \begin{bmatrix} 1/\sqrt{2} & -1/\sqrt{2} & 0 \\ 1/\sqrt{2} & 1/\sqrt{2} & 0 \\ 0 & 0 & 1 \end{bmatrix}$$

Hence the second transformation gives

$$O_2^{-1} D_1 O_2 = \begin{bmatrix} 1/\sqrt{2} & 1/\sqrt{2} & 0 \\ -1/\sqrt{2} & 1/\sqrt{2} & 0 \\ 0 & 0 & 1 \end{bmatrix} \begin{bmatrix} 3 & 2 & 0 \\ 2 & 3 & 0 \\ 0 & 0 & -1 \end{bmatrix} \begin{bmatrix} 1/\sqrt{2} & -1/\sqrt{2} & 0 \\ 1/\sqrt{2} & 1/\sqrt{2} & 0 \\ 0 & 0 & 1 \end{bmatrix}$$

$$= \begin{bmatrix} 5 & 0 & 0 \\ 0 & 1 & 0 \\ 0 & 0 & -1 \end{bmatrix}$$

Thus the Eigen of the given matrix are 5, 1, −1 and the corresponding Eigen-Vectors are the columns of

$$O = O_1 O_2 = \begin{pmatrix} 1/\sqrt{2} & 0 & -1/\sqrt{2} \\ 0 & 1 & 0 \\ 1/\sqrt{2} & 0 & 1/\sqrt{2} \end{pmatrix} \begin{pmatrix} 1/\sqrt{2} & -1/\sqrt{2} & 0 \\ 1/\sqrt{2} & 1/\sqrt{2} & 0 \\ 0 & 0 & 1 \end{pmatrix}$$

$$= \begin{pmatrix} 1/2 & -1/2 & -1/\sqrt{2} \\ 1/\sqrt{2} & 1/\sqrt{2} & 0 \\ 1/2 & -1/2 & 1/\sqrt{2} \end{pmatrix}$$

Example 10: *Apply Jacobi's method to the Eigen values of the matrix* $A = \begin{bmatrix} 2 & 1 & 0 \\ 1 & 4 & 1 \\ 0 & 1 & 4 \end{bmatrix}$.

[Meerut 2003, 2004, 2006; Agra 2008, 2009]

Solution: Here matrix A is a symmetric matrix.

First Iteration: Consider the largest off diagonal element $a_{23} = 1$; since $a_{22} = a_{33}$ and $a_{23} > 0$, so $\phi = \pi/4$.

$$\Rightarrow \quad O_1 = \begin{bmatrix} 1 & 0 & 0 \\ 0 & \cos\phi & -\sin\phi \\ 0 & \sin\phi & \cos\phi \end{bmatrix} = \begin{bmatrix} 1 & 0 & 0 \\ 0 & .7071 & -7071 \\ 0 & .7071 & 7071 \end{bmatrix}$$

$$\Rightarrow \quad O_1^{-1} = \begin{bmatrix} 1 & 0 & 0 \\ 0 & .7071 & .7071 \\ 0 & -.7071 & .7071 \end{bmatrix}$$

Hence new value of A (say A_1) = $O_1^{-1} A O_1$

$$= \begin{bmatrix} 1 & 0 & 0 \\ 0 & .7071 & .7071 \\ 0 & -.7071 & .7071 \end{bmatrix} \begin{bmatrix} 2 & 1 & 0 \\ 1 & 4 & 1 \\ 0 & 1 & 4 \end{bmatrix} \begin{bmatrix} 1 & 0 & 0 \\ 0 & .7071 & -.7071 \\ 0 & .7071 & .7071 \end{bmatrix}$$

$$= \begin{bmatrix} 1 & 0 & 0 \\ 0 & .7071 & .7071 \\ 0 & -.7071 & .7071 \end{bmatrix} \begin{bmatrix} 2 & .7071 & -.7071 \\ 1 & 3.5355 & -2.1213 \\ 0 & 3.5355 & +2.1213 \end{bmatrix}$$

$$\Rightarrow \quad A_1 = \begin{bmatrix} 2 & .7071 & -.7071 \\ .7071 & 4.9999 & 0 \\ -.7071 & 0 & 2.9999 \end{bmatrix}$$

Let us now consider the annihilation of a_{12} (=.7071).

Since $a_{11} \neq a_{22}$, $\phi = \frac{1}{2} \tan^{-1}\left(\frac{2a_{12}}{a_{11} - a_{12}}\right)$

$$\Rightarrow \quad \phi = \frac{1}{2} \tan^{-1}\left(\frac{2 \times .7071}{2 - 2.9999}\right) = -27^0 22'.$$

$$\Rightarrow \quad \cos\phi = \cos(-27^0 22') = .8881, \sin\phi = -.4596.$$

Thus the transformation matrix $O_2 = \begin{bmatrix} \cos\phi & -\sin\phi & 0 \\ \sin\phi & \cos\phi & 0 \\ 0 & 0 & 1 \end{bmatrix} = \begin{bmatrix} .8881 & .4596 & 0 \\ -.4596 & .8881 & 0 \\ 0 & 0 & 1 \end{bmatrix}$

$$\therefore \quad O_2^{-1} = \begin{bmatrix} .8881 & -.4596 & 0 \\ .4596 & .8881 & 0 \\ 0 & 0 & 1 \end{bmatrix}$$

Again new value of $A = (A_2) = O_2^{-1} A_1 O_2$

$$= \begin{bmatrix} .8881 & -.4596 & 0 \\ .4596 & .8881 & 0 \\ 0 & 0 & 1 \end{bmatrix} \begin{bmatrix} 2 & .7071 & -.7071 \\ .7071 & 4.9999 & 0 \\ -.7071 & 0 & 2.9999 \end{bmatrix} \times \begin{bmatrix} .8881 & +.4596 & 0 \\ -.4596 & .8881 & 0 \\ 0 & 0 & 1 \end{bmatrix}$$

$$= \begin{bmatrix} .8881 & +.4596 & 0 \\ -.4596 & .8881 & 0 \\ 0 & 0 & 1 \end{bmatrix} \begin{bmatrix} 1.4512 & +1.5471 & -.7071 \\ -1.6699 & -4.7653 & 0 \\ -.6279 & .3249 & 2.999 \end{bmatrix}$$

$$= \begin{bmatrix} 2.0562 & -.8161 & -.6279 \\ -.8160 & 4.9431 & -.33249 \\ -.6279 & .3249 & 0 \end{bmatrix}$$

Then continuing the process 12 times, one may arrive at the diagonal matrix

$$A_{12} = \begin{bmatrix} 1.52 & 0 & 0 \\ 0 & 5.17 & 0 \\ 0 & 0 & 3.31 \end{bmatrix}.$$

Thus the Eigen values of matrix A are 1.52, 5.17, 3.31; and one may find the Eigen Vectors by multiplying the transformation matrices $O_1, O_2, \ldots, O_{12}$.

The characteristic equation of A is det $(A - I\lambda) = |A - \lambda I| = 0$ or $\lambda^3 - 10\lambda^2 + 30\lambda - 26 = 0$.

Obviously, sum of the Eigen roots is 10 and product 26.

Calculated sum of Eigen roots $= 1.52 + 5.17 + 3.31 = 10$; while product $= 1.52 \times 5.17 \times 3.31 = 26.0113$, which is very close to 26.

15.8 Given's Method

[Meerut 2003; M.K.U. (Tamil Nadu) Delhi (M.E) 2007]

The disadvantage to Jacobi's method is that the element annihiliated by a transformation, may not remain zero after the subsequent transformations. *Given's then suggested a reduction which does not disturb zeros already obtained. But instead of leading to a diagonal matrix, Given's method leads to a tri-diagonal matrix, The Eigen values and Eigen vector of the original matrix are to determined from those of the tri-diagonal matrix.*

Given's Method: Let A be real symmetric matrix, Given's method consists of the following steps:

Step 1: *Reduce A to a tri-diagonal symmetric matrix*:

Let us consider the matrix $A_1 = \begin{bmatrix} a_{11} & a_{12} & a_{13} \\ a_{12} & a_{22} & a_{23} \\ a_{13} & a_{23} & a_{33} \end{bmatrix}$ ...(1)

And let the orthogonal rotation matrix O_1 in the plane (2, 3) be

$$O_1 = \begin{bmatrix} 1 & 0 & 0 \\ 0 & \cos\theta & -\sin\theta \\ 1 & \sin\theta & \cos\theta \end{bmatrix}$$

$$\Rightarrow \quad O_1^{-1} A_1 O_1 = \begin{bmatrix} 1 & 0 & 1 \\ 0 & \cos\theta & \sin\theta \\ 0 & -\sin\theta & \cos\theta \end{bmatrix} \begin{bmatrix} a_{11} & a_{12} & a_{13} \\ a_{12} & a_{22} & a_{23} \\ a_{13} & a_{23} & a_{33} \end{bmatrix} \times \begin{bmatrix} 1 & 0 & 1 \\ 0 & \cos\theta & -\sin\theta \\ 1 & \sin\theta & \cos\theta \end{bmatrix}$$

Then in the resulting matrix, (1, 3) element is $-a_{12}\sin\theta + a_{13}\cos\theta$. Which will be zero, if $-a_{12}\sin\theta + a_{13}\cos\theta = 0 \Rightarrow \tan\theta = (a_{13}/a_{12})$. ...(2)

i.e. by this value of θ, the above transformation gives zero in (1, 3) and (3, 1) positions. Let us further perform rotation in the plane (2, 4) and put the resulting element $(1, 4) = 0$. This would not affect the zero obtained earlier. Then, the transformations are applied to the matrix inturn so as to annihilate the elements (1, 3), (1, 4), (1, 5) ...,(1, n); (2, 4), (2, 5) ,..., (2, n) and finally we arrive at the tri-diagonal matrix

$$P = \begin{bmatrix} p_1 & q_1 & 0 & 0 \ldots\ldots & 0 & 0 \\ q_1 & p_2 & q_2 & 0 \ldots\ldots\ldots & : & 0 \\ 0 & q_2 & p_3 & q_3 \ldots\ldots & : & 0 \\ \ldots\ldots\ldots\ldots & & & & P_{n-1} & q_{n-1} \\ 0 & 0 & 0 & 0 \ldots & q_{n-1} & p_n \end{bmatrix}$$

Step II: *To obtain the Eigen values of the tri-diagonal matrix.*

Let the resulting tri-diagonal matrix after first transformation be obtained as

$$\begin{bmatrix} \alpha_{11} & \alpha_{12} & 0 \\ \alpha_{12} & \alpha_{22} & \alpha_{23} \\ 0 & \alpha_{23} & \alpha_{33} \end{bmatrix} \quad ...(3)$$

Now, the Eigen values of (1) and (3) are the same. To find the Eigen values of (3), we consider

$$\begin{bmatrix} \alpha_{11} - \lambda & \alpha_{12} & 0 \\ \alpha_{12} & \alpha_{22} - \lambda & \alpha_{23} \\ 0 & \alpha_{23} & \alpha_{33} - \lambda \end{bmatrix} = 0 \text{ say } f_3(\lambda) = 0$$

Then we have $f_0(\lambda) = 1,\ f_1(\lambda) = \alpha_{11} - \lambda\ f_0(\lambda)$

and $$f_2(\lambda) = \begin{vmatrix} \alpha_{11} - \lambda & \alpha_{12} \\ \alpha_{12} & \alpha_{22} - \lambda \end{vmatrix} = (\alpha_{22} - \lambda)\ f_1(\lambda) - \alpha_{12}^2\ f_0(\lambda)$$

Now expanding $f_3(\lambda)$ in terms of the third row, we immediately obtain

$$f_3(\lambda) \equiv (\alpha_{33} - \lambda) \begin{vmatrix} \alpha_{11} - \lambda & \alpha_{12} \\ \alpha_{12} & \alpha_{22} - \lambda \end{vmatrix} - \alpha_{23} \begin{vmatrix} \alpha_{11} - \lambda & 0 \\ \alpha_{12} & \alpha_{23} \end{vmatrix}$$

$$\Rightarrow \quad f_3(\lambda) = (\alpha_{33} - \lambda)\ f_2(\lambda) - (\alpha_{23})^2\ f_1(\lambda)$$

The recurrence formula in general is

$$f_k(\lambda) = (\alpha_{kk} - \lambda)\ f_{k-1}(\lambda) - (\alpha_{k-1}, k)^2\ f_{k-2}(\lambda),\ 2 \le k \le n \quad ...(4)$$

Above is the characteristic equation which can be solved by any standard method. Thus the roots of (4) will be the Eigen values of the given symmetric matrix.

Step III: *To obtain the Eigen Vectors of the tri-diagonal matrix.*

Let Y be the Eigen Vector of the tri-diagonal matrix P and let $O_1, O_2 \ldots O_j$. be the orthogonal matrices employed in reducing the matrix **A** to the form **P**. The corresponding Eigen Vector of **A** is given by $X = O_1 O_2 \ldots O_j Y$.

***Special Points to Remember*:** 1. *The number of rotations needed for Given's Method are equivalent to the number of non-tri-diagonal elements of the matrix.* For a 3×3 matrix, only one rotation is required; whereas for 4×4 matrix, 3 rotations are required etc.

2. *The sequence of functions $f_0(\lambda), f_1(\lambda), f_2(\lambda), \ldots, f_k(\lambda)$ is known as the* ***Strum Sequence***. A table of the sequence for various λ is prepared and the number of changes in sign of the Strum sequence is noted, *the difference between the number of changes of sing for consecutive values of λ gives an approximate location of the Eigen values.* Knowing the location of the Eigen values, their exact values can be any Iterative method *e.g.* Newton-Raphson method.

Example 11: *Using Given's method, reduce the following matrix to the tri-diagonal form:*

$$A = \begin{bmatrix} 2 & 1 & 3 \\ 1 & 4 & 2 \\ 3 & 2 & 3 \end{bmatrix}$$

[M.K.U. (Tamil Nadu) 2005]

Solution: There is only one non-tri-diagonai element a_{13} (=3). This is to be reduced to zero, hence on rotation is required.

Now to annihilate a_{13}, we define the orthogonal matrix in the plane (2, 3) as:

$$O = \begin{bmatrix} 1 & 0 & 0 \\ 0 & \cos\theta & -\sin\theta \\ 0 & \sin\theta & \cos\theta \end{bmatrix}$$

Where θ is obtained by $\tan\theta = \dfrac{a_{13}}{a_{12}} = \dfrac{3}{2} = 3$

$\Rightarrow$ $\sin\theta = [3/\sqrt{10}]$ and $\cos\theta = [1/\sqrt{10}]$

Then, we have $A_1 = O^{-1}AO = \begin{bmatrix} \alpha_{11} & \alpha_{12} & 0 \\ \alpha_{12} & \alpha_{22} & \alpha_{23} \\ 0 & \alpha_{23} & \alpha_{33} \end{bmatrix}$

Here $\alpha_{11} = 2, \alpha_{12} = a_{12}\cos\theta + a_{13}\sin\theta = \sqrt{10} = 3.16,$

$\alpha_{22} = \alpha_{22}\cos^2\theta + 2a_{23}\sin\theta\cos\theta + a_{33}\sin^2\theta = 4.3$

$\alpha_{23} = (a_{33} - a_{22})\sin\theta\cos\theta + a_{23}(\cos^2\theta - \sin^2\theta) = -1.9$

and $\alpha_{33} = a_{22}\sin^2\theta + a_{33}\cos^2\theta = 3.9.$

Then A is reduced to the tri-diagonal matrix $\begin{bmatrix} 2 & 3.16 & 0 \\ 3.16 & 4.3 & -1.9 \\ 0 & -1.9 & 3.9 \end{bmatrix}$

15.9 House-Holder's Method

[Meerut 2002; M.K.U (Tamil Nadu) 2007]

The reduction of a symmetric matrix to the tri-diagonal form has been suggested by House-holders. This method requiers half as much computation, as the Given's method, but is complicated. As a matter of fact, it gives an improvement on the Given's procedure as it reduces an entire row and column by a single transformation. This method reduces the matrix to tri-diagonal form using elementary orthogonal transformations. We now describe this method. Let there exist an nth order real symmetric matrix $A = (a_{ij})$. This method consists of in pre and post-multiplying **A** by a real symmetric orthogonal matrix **O** such that **OAO** reduces to the tri-diagonal from.

Now, let the matrix **O** be written as $O = I - 2w\,w'$ ...(1)

Where w is a column matrix such that $ww' = w_2^1 + w_2^2 + \ldots + w_n^2 = 1$ ...(2)

Now $O' = (I - 2w\,w')' = I - 2w\,w' = O$

$\Rightarrow$ $O'O = (I - 2w\,w')'(I - 2w\,w') = I - 4w\,w' + 4\,w\,w'\,.w\,w' = I$

$\Rightarrow$ **O** is a symmetric orthogonal matrix.

Let us now take **w** with first $(k-1)$ zero components, so that

$$w_k' = [0, 0, \ldots, 0 x_k, \ldots, x_n] \quad \ldots(3)$$

But $w_k' w_k = 1$, so we get $x_k^2 + x_{k+1}^2 + \ldots x_n^2 = 1$

$\Rightarrow O_k^{-1} A\, O_k = O_k' A\, O_k = O_k A\, O_k$. We then form

$$A_k = O_k A_{k-1} O_k ; k = 2, 3 \ldots, n-1.$$

First, we determine x's so that zeros are created in the positions (1, 3), (1, 4),..., (1, n) and (3, 4), (4, 1), ..., (n, 1). Then on the second transformation, we find x's so that zeros are created in the positions (2, 4), (2, 5) ,..., (2, n) and (4, 2) (5, 2) ,..., (n, 2). Thus after $(n-2)$ such transformations, we arrive at a tri-diagonal matrix.

Example 12: *Using House-holder's Method, reduce the following matrix to the Tri-diagonal form:*

$$A = \begin{bmatrix} 1 & 4 & 3 \\ 4 & 1 & 2 \\ 3 & 2 & 1 \end{bmatrix}$$

[Pune 2002, 2004; M.K.U. (Tamil Nadu) 2008]

Solution: Let $A = \begin{bmatrix} a_{11} & a_{12} & a_{13} \\ a_{12} & a_{22} & a_{23} \\ a_{13} & a_{23} & a_{33} \end{bmatrix}$

Let us take $\quad w_2' = [0, x_2, x_3]$

$$\Rightarrow \qquad O = 1 - 2\, w_2\, w_2' = \begin{bmatrix} 1 & 0 & 0 \\ 0 & 1-2x_2^2 & -2x_2 x_3 \\ 0 & -2x_2 x_3 & 1-2x_3^2 \end{bmatrix}$$

Then the element (1, 3) of **OAO** is zero only when the corresponding element in **AO** is zero. The first row elements of **AO** are corresponding element in **AO** is zero. The first row elements of **AO** are

$$a_{11}, a_{12} - 2\, p_1 x_2, a_{13} - 2 p_1 x_3 \quad \text{where } p_1 = a_{12} x_2 + a_{13} x_3.$$

Then we require that $a_{13} - 2 p_1 x_3 = 0$ ...(1)

But the sum of the squares of the elements in any row is invariant under an orthoonal transformation, so we obtain $a_{11}^2 + a_{12}^2 + a_{13}^2 = a_{11}^2 + (a_{12} - 2\, p_1 x_2)^2 + 0$

$$\Rightarrow \qquad a_{12} - 2 p_1 x_2 = \pm \sqrt{(a_{12}^2 + a_{13}^2)} \quad \ldots(2)$$

Then for the given matrix, we have $3 - 2\, p_1 x_3 = 0$ ...(3)

$$4 - 2\, p_1 x_2 = \pm \sqrt{(4^2 + 3^2)} = \pm 5 \quad \ldots(4)$$

Where $p_1 = 4x_2 + 3x_3$ Now, multiplying (3) by x_3 and (4) by x_2 and then adding, we readily get $3x_3 + 4x_2 - 2p_1(x_3^2 + x_2^2) = \pm\, 5x_2$

$$\Rightarrow \quad p_1 - 2p_1 = \pm 5x_2 \Rightarrow p_1 = \mp 5\, x_2 \qquad [\because\ x_2^2 + x_3^2 = 1]$$

Putting in (4), we obtain $4 - 2(\mp 5x_2)x_2 = \pm 5$

$$\Rightarrow \quad x_2 = [1/\sqrt{10}] \quad \text{or} \quad x_2 = [3/\sqrt{10}] \qquad \therefore \quad x_3 = \frac{3}{2p_1} = \mp \frac{3}{10x_2}$$

But x_3 contains x_2 in the denominator, hence we obtain best accuracy, x_2 being large enough. Choosing $x_2 = \frac{3}{\sqrt{10}}$, $x_3 = \mp \frac{3}{10} \times \frac{\sqrt{10}}{3} = \mp \frac{1}{\sqrt{10}}$

Then taking $\div$ve sign, we get $x_2 = \frac{3}{\sqrt{10}}$ and $x_3 = \frac{1}{\sqrt{10}}$.

$$\Rightarrow \quad O = I - 2w_2 w_2'$$

$$= \begin{bmatrix} 1 & 0 & 0 \\ 0 & 1 & 0 \\ 0 & 0 & 1 \end{bmatrix} - 2\begin{bmatrix} 0 \\ 3/\sqrt{10} \\ 1/\sqrt{10} \end{bmatrix} [0, 3/\sqrt{10}, 1/\sqrt{10}] = \begin{bmatrix} 1 & 0 & 0 \\ 0 & -4/5 & -3/5 \\ 0 & -3/5 & -4/5 \end{bmatrix}$$

$$\Rightarrow \quad OAO = \begin{bmatrix} 1 & 0 & 0 \\ 0 & -4/5 & -3/5 \\ 0 & -3/5 & -4/5 \end{bmatrix} \begin{bmatrix} 1 & 4 & 3 \\ 4 & 1 & 2 \\ 3 & 2 & 1 \end{bmatrix} \times \begin{bmatrix} 1 & 0 & 0 \\ 0 & -4/5 & -3/5 \\ 0 & -3/5 & -4/5 \end{bmatrix}$$

$$= \begin{bmatrix} 1 & 0 & 0 \\ 0 & -4/5 & -3/5 \\ 0 & -3/5 & -4/5 \end{bmatrix} \begin{bmatrix} 1 & -5 & 0 \\ 4 & -2 & 1 \\ 3 & -11/5 & -2/5 \end{bmatrix}$$

$$= \begin{bmatrix} 1 & -5 & 0 \\ -5 & 73/25 & -14/25 \\ 0 & -14/25 & -11/25 \end{bmatrix}$$

This is the required tri-diagonal matrix.

✦✦ Problem Set ✦✦

1. Using Jacobi's Method, find all the Eigen values and the Eigen Vectors of the matrix

$$A = \begin{bmatrix} 5 & 0 & 1 \\ 0 & -2 & 0 \\ 1 & 0 & 5 \end{bmatrix}$$

2. Apply the Householder's Method, to find the Eigen values of the matrix

$$\begin{bmatrix} 2 & -1 & -1 \\ -1 & 2 & -1 \\ -1 & -1 & 2 \end{bmatrix}$$

[Meerut 2002]

3. Transform the matrix $\begin{bmatrix} 1 & 2 & 2 \\ 2 & 1 & 2 \\ 2 & 2 & 1 \end{bmatrix}$

   To the tri-diagonal form using Given's method. Hence find the langset Eigen value and corresponding Eigen Vector of the tri-diagonal matrix.

✦✦ Answers ✦✦

1. $4, -2, 6; [1/\sqrt{2}, 0, -1/\sqrt{2}]' \; [0,1,0]' \; [1/\sqrt{2}, 0, 1/\sqrt{2}]'$

2. $0, 3, 3$

3. $\begin{pmatrix} 1 & 2\sqrt{2} & 0 \\ 2\sqrt{2} & 3 & 0 \\ 0 & 0 & -1 \end{pmatrix}; 5, \begin{pmatrix} 1 \\ 1 \\ 1 \end{pmatrix}$

15.10 Eigen Values of Complex Matrices

To determine the Eigen values of the matrix $\boldsymbol{A}$ with complex elements we try to reduce the problem of determining the Eigen values of a real matrix. Let $\boldsymbol{A} = \boldsymbol{B} + i\mathbf{C}$. If λ is an Eigen value of $\boldsymbol{A}$ with Eigen Vector $\mathbf{u}$, then we have $(\boldsymbol{B} + i\boldsymbol{C})\boldsymbol{u} = \lambda \boldsymbol{u}$ ...(1)

$$\Rightarrow \quad (\boldsymbol{C} - i\boldsymbol{B})\, \mathbf{u} = -\lambda_1 \mathbf{u} \qquad \text{...(2)}$$

$$\text{(1) and (2)} \Rightarrow \begin{bmatrix} \boldsymbol{B} & -\boldsymbol{C} \\ \boldsymbol{C} & \boldsymbol{B} \end{bmatrix} \begin{bmatrix} \mathbf{u} \\ -i\mathbf{u} \end{bmatrix} = \lambda \begin{bmatrix} \mathbf{u} \\ -i\mathbf{u} \end{bmatrix} \qquad \text{...(3)}$$

This shows that λ is also an Eigen value of the real matrix $\boldsymbol{D} = \begin{bmatrix} \boldsymbol{B} - \boldsymbol{C} \\ \boldsymbol{C} \;\; \boldsymbol{B} \end{bmatrix}$ with Eigen Vector $[\mathbf{u} - i\mathbf{u}]^t$. Hence the problem is solved by obtaining the Eigen values of real matrix $\boldsymbol{D}$. But this method doubles the order of the matrix, so it involves more calculations.

Besides this, if $\boldsymbol{A}$ is Hermitian matrix, then the Jacobi's method can be adopted. Only by replacing the orthogonal matrix $\boldsymbol{O}$ by unitary matrix $\boldsymbol{U}$.

e.g. let $\quad A = \begin{bmatrix} a & b \\ c & d \end{bmatrix}$ and $U = \begin{bmatrix} p & -q \\ q & p \end{bmatrix}$, where p is real.

Now $\quad U^*U = I, \quad \Rightarrow \; p^2 + |q|^2 = 1$ and $U^{-1} = U^*$.

Further, let $\quad A_1 = U^{-1} AU = \begin{bmatrix} a_1 & b_1 \\ c_1 & d_1 \end{bmatrix}$

$$\Rightarrow \quad a_1 = d + (a - d)\, p^2 + p\,(bp + \overline{cq})$$

$$b_1 = bp^2 - \overline{cq^2} + (d - a)\, \overline{pq} \qquad c_1 = cp^2 + (d - a)\, pq - bq^2$$

$$d_1 = a + (d - a)\, p^2 - p\,(bq + \overline{cq}); \text{ where } a_1 + d_1 = a + d.$$

Now choosing $c_1 = 0$ and solving with $q = kp$, we readily obtain

$$bk^2 - (d - a)\, k - c = 0 \qquad \Rightarrow k = \frac{1}{2b}[(d - a) \pm \sqrt{\{(d - a)^2 + 4bc\}}] \qquad \text{...(4)}$$

Further, choosing the sign that makes k ; as small as we please and letting $p = \cos\theta$, $q = \sin\theta\, e^{i\theta}$, we get $\tan\theta = |k|$.

$$\therefore \quad \cos\theta = \frac{1}{1 + |k|^2} \qquad \Rightarrow p = (1 + |k|^2)^{-1/2}$$

Now, determining k from (4), one can obtain p, q by the relations

$$p = [1 + |k|^2]^{-1/2}, q = kp. \qquad ...(5)$$

Further, if A is Hermitian matrix, then a, d are real and $b = \bar{c}$ (or $\bar{b} = c$). Then, we have

$$\overline{c_1} = \overline{\{(cp^2 + (d - a)pq - bq^2)\}}$$

$$= \overline{cp^2} + (d - a)\,\overline{pq} - \overline{bp^2} = bp^2 + (d - a)\,\overline{pq} - \overline{cq^2} = b_1,$$

$$\therefore \quad c_1 = 0 \Rightarrow b_1 = \overline{c_1} = 0.$$

Hence A_1 will essentially be a diagonal matrix and hence the Eigen values can be obtained directly.

For higher order matrices, procedure is the same as that of Jacobi's method.

Example 13: *Find the Eigen values of the matrix* $A = \begin{bmatrix} 2 & -i & 0 \\ i & 2 & 0 \\ 0 & 0 & 3 \end{bmatrix}$ **[Agra 2006]**

Solution: Here A is Hermitian matrix. Let us annihilate a_{12} and a_{21}. Then the corresponding unitary sub-matrix is given by $U = \begin{bmatrix} p & -\bar{q} \\ q & p \end{bmatrix}$ where p, q, k are given by (5) and (4) and

$$a = 2,\ b = -i,\ c = i,\ d = 2.$$

Also (4) $\Rightarrow k = \dfrac{-1}{2i}[0 \pm \sqrt{\{0 + 4.(-i).i\}}] = \pm\dfrac{1}{i} = \pm i.$

Choosing, $k = +i$; we get $|k| = 1$.

$$\Rightarrow \qquad p = [1 + 1]^{-1/2} = 1/\sqrt{2} \quad \text{and} \quad q = (i/\sqrt{2}).$$

Hence corresponding unitary sub-matrix is given by

$$U_1 = \begin{bmatrix} 1/\sqrt{2} & i/\sqrt{2} \\ i/\sqrt{2} & 1/\sqrt{2} \end{bmatrix} \quad \text{as} -\bar{q} = i/\sqrt{2}.$$

Hence the matrix U s.t. $D = U^{-1}AU$, is given by

$$U_1 = \begin{bmatrix} 1/\sqrt{2} & i/\sqrt{2} & 0 \\ i/\sqrt{2} & 1/\sqrt{2} & 0 \\ 0 & 0 & 1 \end{bmatrix} \Rightarrow U^{-1} = U^* = \begin{bmatrix} 1/\sqrt{2} & -i/\sqrt{2} & 0 \\ -i/\sqrt{2} & 1/\sqrt{2} & 0 \\ 0 & 0 & 1 \end{bmatrix}$$

Where $\quad D = U^{-1}AU = \begin{bmatrix} 3 & 0 & 0 \\ 0 & 1 & 0 \\ 0 & 0 & 3 \end{bmatrix}$

Thus the Eigen values of D and hence of A are 3, 1, 3.

✦✦ Problem Set ✦✦

1. Can you find th smallest Eigen value by this method? If yes, then explain the method in brief

Hence find the smallest Eigen value of $\begin{bmatrix} 1 & 2 & -2 & 4 \\ 2 & 12 & 3 & 5 \\ 3 & 13 & 0 & 7 \\ 2 & 11 & 2 & 2 \end{bmatrix}$

Describe either Given's Method or House Holder's method for finding the Eigen values of a real and symmetric matrix. **[Meerut 2001, 2004]**

2. Obtain the Eigen values of the matrix $A = \begin{bmatrix} 2 & -1 & 0 \\ -1 & 2 & -1 \\ 0 & -1 & 0 \end{bmatrix}$ **[Agra 2003, 2007]**

3. Find Eigen values of (i) $\begin{bmatrix} 1 & 1-i \\ 1+i & 1 \end{bmatrix}$ (ii) $\begin{bmatrix} 8 & -5i & 3-5i \\ -5i & 3 & 0 \\ 3+5i & 0 & 2 \end{bmatrix}$

✦✦ Objective Type Question ✦✦

❖ Multiple Choice Questions

1. The characteristic equation of a homogeneous system of linear equation is:
   (a) $(A - \lambda) I = X$ (b) $(A - \lambda I) X = 0$
   (c) $AX - \lambda I = 0$ (d) $(A - \lambda X) I = 0$

2. The statement of Cayley-Hamilton Theorem is: **[Agra 2003]**
   (a) Every square matrix satisfy its characteristic equation
   (b) Every Eigen vector satisfy its characteristic equation
   (c) Every Eigen value satisfy its characteristic equation
   (d) None of these.

3. Characteristic matrix of the matrix $A = \begin{bmatrix} 2 & 0 & 1 \\ 0 & 2 & 0 \\ 1 & 0 & 2 \end{bmatrix}$ is **[Agra 2003]**

   (a) $\begin{bmatrix} 2-3\lambda & 0 & 1-\lambda \\ 0 & 2-\lambda & 0 \\ 1 & 0 & 2 \end{bmatrix}$ (b) $\begin{bmatrix} 2-\lambda & 0 & 1-\lambda \\ 0 & 2-\lambda & 0 \\ 1-\lambda & 0 & 2-\lambda \end{bmatrix}$

   (c) $\begin{bmatrix} 0 & 0 & 1 \\ 0 & 2-\lambda & 0 \\ 1-\lambda & 0 & 2-\lambda \end{bmatrix}$ (d) None of these

4. If λ is an Eigen value of the non-singular matrix A, the Eigen value of its adjoint *e.g.* adj A, will be: **[Agra 2004]**

(a) λ (b) $\frac{1}{\lambda}$ (c) $\lambda \det A$ (d) $\det A/\lambda$

5. The matrices A and A' (transpose of A) have: **[Agra 2004]**

(a) Same Eigen values but different Eigen Vectors

(b) Same Eigen Vectors but different Eigen values

(c) Same Eigen values and same Eigen Vectors

(d) Different Eigen values and different Eigen Vectors.

6. Let $A = (a_{ij})_{n \times n}$, $A = BC = (b_{ij})_{n \times k} (c_{ij})_{k \times n}$

Where a_{ij}, b_{ij}, c_{ij} are integers for every i and j, then $A^{-1} =$ **[Agra 2005]**

(a) $B^{-1} C^{-1}$ (b) $C^{-1} B^{-1}$ (c) $C^{-1} B$ (d) May not exist.

7. If λ^{-1} is an Eigen value of A^{-1}, then the Eigen value of $(A - kI)^{-1}$ is: **[Agra 2005, 2006]**

(a) $(\lambda - k)^{-1}$ (b) $(k - \lambda)^{-1}$ (c) $(\lambda^{-1} - k)$ (d) $(\lambda^{-1} - k^{-1})$

8. If matrix A a Hermitian and all Eigen values are distinct, then the Eigen Vectors are:

(a) Complex (b) Skew symmetric

(c) Orthonogonal (d) Hermitian.

9. The Eigen values of a symmetric matrix are: **[Agra 2005]**

(a) Real (b) Purely imaginary

(c) All of absolute values (d) None of these

10. Which of the following methods leads to the triagonal matrix:

(a) Jacobi's Method (b) Gauss-Method

(c) Power Series Method (d) Given's Method.

11. Which one of the following is not correct **[Agra 2007]**

(a) If A has an Eigen value λ, then $(A - qI)$ has an Eigen value $\lambda - q$.

(b) If A^{-1} has an Eigen value λ^{-1}, then $(\lambda - q)^{-1}$ is an Eigen value of $(A - qI)^{-1}$.

(c) If A has the Eigen values $\lambda_1, \lambda_2, \lambda_3$ ---- λ_n, then A^m has the Eigen values $\lambda_1^m, \lambda_2^m, \ldots, \lambda_n^m$.

(d) A and A^{-1} have same Eigen values.

12. If the Eigen value of A is λ, then the Eigen value of A^{-1} is:

(a) λ (b) λ^2 (c) $\frac{1}{\lambda}$ (d) λ^{-2}.

13. Dominant value can be obtained by using: **[Agra 2007, 2009]**

(a) Jordan Method (b) Choleski's Method

(c) Power Method (d) Escalator's Method

14. If A is an $m \times m$ matrix and $(A - \lambda I)$ is a characteristic matrix of A, then the order of $A - \lambda I$ is: **[Agra 2008]**

(a) $(m+1) \times m$ (b) $m \times (m+1)$ (c) $m \times m$ (d) $(m+1) \times (m+1)$

15. "Every square matrix $A_{n \times n}$ satisfies its characteristic equation is the statement of: **[Agra 2008]**

(a) Jacobi's Theorem (b) Cayley-Hamilton Theorem

(c) Taylor's Theorem (d) Runge-Kutta Theorem.

16. If $A = \begin{bmatrix} a & b \\ c & d \end{bmatrix}$, then A^{-1} is equal to: **[Agra 2008]**

(a) $\frac{1}{|A|}\begin{bmatrix} a & b \\ c & d \end{bmatrix}$ (b) $\frac{1}{|A|}\begin{bmatrix} -d & b \\ c & -a \end{bmatrix}$

(c) $\frac{1}{|A|}\begin{bmatrix} -d & b \\ -c & a \end{bmatrix}$ (d) $\frac{1}{|A|}\begin{bmatrix} d & -b \\ -c & a \end{bmatrix}$

17. The characteristic roots of the matrix $A = \begin{bmatrix} 8 & -6 & 2 \\ -6 & 7 & -4 \\ 2 & -4 & 3 \end{bmatrix}$ is **[Agra 2008]**

(a) 0, 4 and 12 (b) 0, 3 and 5 (c) 2, 3 and 4 (d) 0, 3 and 15

18. Which of the following methods for solving a system of equation is not an Iterative Method:

(a) Jacobi's Method (b) Choleski's Method

(c) Power Method (d) Gauss-Elimination Method.

19. House-Holder's Method is an improvement of:

(a) Given's Method (b) Jacobi's Method

(c) Power Method (d) Choleski's Method

20. If the Eigen value of a matrix A is λ then, the Eigen value of kA is:

(a) k/λ (b) λ^{κ} (c) $k\lambda$ (d) λ/k.

21. If the Eigen value of the matrix A is λ, then the Eigen value of $A + kI$ is

(a) $k\lambda$ (b) $\lambda - k$ (c) $k - \lambda$ (d) $\lambda + k$.

✦✦ Examination Questions ✦✦

1. Find the Eigen Values and Eigen Vectors of the following matrix:

(i) $A = \begin{bmatrix} 1 & 1 & 1 \\ -1 & -3 & -3 \\ 2 & 4 & 4 \end{bmatrix}$

(ii) $A = \begin{bmatrix} 2 & 2 & 0 \\ 2 & 1 & 1 \\ -7 & 2 & -3 \end{bmatrix}$ (iii) $A = \begin{bmatrix} 1 & 0 & -2 \\ 0 & 0 & 0 \\ -2 & 0 & 4 \end{bmatrix}$

2. Find the Eigen Values and Eigen Vector of the matrices given below:

(i) $\begin{bmatrix} 8 & -6 & 2 \\ -6 & 7 & -4 \\ 2 & -4 & 3 \end{bmatrix}$ (ii) $\begin{bmatrix} 2 & 2 & 1 \\ 1 & 3 & 1 \\ 1 & 2 & 2 \end{bmatrix}$

3. Find the roots of the equation $|xA - B| = 0$, where $A = \begin{bmatrix} 1 & 1 \\ 1 & 4 \end{bmatrix}$, $B = \begin{bmatrix} 0 & 3 \\ 3 & 0 \end{bmatrix}$.

4. Determine the Eigen values and Eigen Vectors of the matrix $A = \begin{bmatrix} 3 & 1 & 4 \\ 0 & 2 & 6 \\ 0 & 0 & 5 \end{bmatrix}$

Answers

Problem Set

2.	$2+\sqrt{2}, 2, 2-\sqrt{2}$.
3. (i)	$\lambda_1=\sqrt{2}+1,\ \lambda_2=1-\sqrt{2},\ u_1=(\sqrt{2}, 1+i)^t,\ u_2=(-\sqrt{2}, 1+i)^t$.
(ii)	Largest Eigen Value is 12.054.

Multiple Choice Questions

1.	(b)	2.	(a)	3.	(d)	4.	(d)	5.	(a)	6.	(b)	7.	(a)
8.	(c)	9.	(a)	10.	(d)	11.	(d)	12.	(c)	13.	(c)	14.	(c)
15.	(b)	16.	(d)	17.	(d)	18.	(d)	19.	(a)	20.	(c)	21.	(d)

❖ Examination Questions

1. (i)	$\lambda = 0, 0, 2$	(ii)	$\lambda = 1, 3, -4$
(iii)	$\lambda = 0, 0, 5 \quad X_1 = [2, 0, 1]', \ X_2 = [0, 1, 0]', \ X_3 = [1, 0, -2]'$		
2. (i)	$\lambda = 0, 3, 15, \ X_1 = [k_1, 2k_1, 2k_1]', \ X_2 = [2k_2, k_2, -2k_2]', \ X_3 = [2k_3, -2k_3, k_3]'$		
(ii)	$\lambda = 5, 1, 1, \ X_1 = [k, k, k]', \ X_2 = [k_1, 0, -k_1]', \ X_3 = [k_2, k_2, -3k_3]'$		
3.	$\lambda = 1, -3$		
4.	$\lambda = 3, 2, 5$		

◆◆◆

Theory | Solved Examples | Problem Set

Chapter 16

Bernoulli and Euler Polynomials

ϕ Polynomial, β Polynomial, Bernoulli's Polynomials and Numbers, Complementary Argument Theorem, Euler's Polynomials and Number.

16.1 Introduction

Bernoulli and Euler polynomials play an important role in calculus of finite differences and are developed by generalisation of some simplest polynomials as the powers of the variables.

16.2 The ϕ Polynomial

The ϕ polynomial of degree k and order n represented by $\phi_k^{(n)}(x)$ is defined by the relation

$$f_n(t)e^{xt+g(t)} = \sum_{k=0}^{\infty} \frac{t^k}{k!}\phi_k^{(n)}(x) \qquad \ldots(1)$$

where $f_n(t)$ and $g(t)$ are function of t such that in (1), R.H.S. is uniformly convergent series in t for particular range of x.

In case, we put $x = 0$ in (1) and write $\phi_k^{(n)}$ for $\phi_k^{(n)}(0)$, we get

$$f_n(t)e^{g(t)} = \sum_{k=0}^{\infty} \frac{t^k}{k!}\phi_k^{(n)}(0) = \sum_{k=0}^{\infty} \frac{t^k}{k!}\phi_k^{(n)} \qquad \ldots(2)$$

Now putting $x + y$ for x in (1), we get

$$\sum_{k=0}^{\infty} \frac{t^k}{k!}\phi_k^{(n)}(x+y) = f_n(t)e^{(x+y)t+g(t)} = e^{xt}\cdot f_n(t)e^{yt+g(t)}$$

$$= e^{xt}\sum_{k=0}^{\infty} \frac{t^k}{k!}\phi_k^{(n)}(y)^*$$

$$= \left(1 + tx + \frac{t^2x^2}{2!} + \ldots + \frac{t^kx^k}{k!} + \ldots\right) \times \left(\phi_0^{(n)}(y) + \frac{t}{1!}\phi_1^{(n)}(y) + \ldots + \frac{t^k}{k!}\phi_k^{(n)}(y) + \ldots\right)$$

*From (1), $f_n(t)e^{yt+g(t)} = \sum_{k=0}^{\infty} \frac{t^k}{k!}\phi_k^{(n)}(y)$.

On equating the coefficients of $\frac{t^k}{k!}$, we get

$$\phi_k^{(n)}(x+y) = \phi_k^{(n)}(y) + (x.\,^kC_1.\phi_{k-1}^{(n)}(y) + x^2.\,^kC_2.\phi_{k-2}^{(n)}(y) + \ldots + \ldots + x^k\,\phi_0^{(n)}(y).$$

Putting $y = 0$ here, we get

$$\phi_k^{(n)}(x) = \phi_k^{(n)}(0) + x.\,^kC_1\,\phi_{k-1}^{(n)}(0) + x^2.\,^kC_2\,\phi_{k-2}^{(n)}(0) + \ldots + x^k\phi_0^{(n)}(0). \qquad \ldots(3)$$

This is a polynomial in x of degree k provided $\phi_k^{(n)}(0) \neq 0$. From (3) we observe that

$$\phi_k^{(n)}(x) = [\phi^{(n)} + x]^k. \qquad \ldots(4)$$

Differentiating (4) w.r.t. x, get

$$\frac{d}{dx}\,\phi_k^{(n)}(x) = k\,[\phi^{(n)}(0) + x]^{k-1} = k\,\phi_{k-1}^{(n)}(x). \qquad \ldots(5)$$

We observe that the degree of the polynomial is reduced by one unit after differentiation. Now integrating (4) w.r.t. x, we get

$$\int \phi_k^{(n)}(x)\,dx = \frac{[\phi^{(n)}(0) + x]^{k+1}}{k+1} \qquad \ldots(6)$$

We observe that the degree of the polynomial is raised by one unit after integration. Operating Δ on (1), we have

$$\Delta\sum_{k=0}^{\infty}\frac{t^k}{k!}\,\phi_k{}^{(n)}(x) = \Delta[f_n(t)\,e^{xt+g(t)}]$$

$$= f_n(t)\,e^{(x+1)t+g(t)} - f_n(t)\,e^{xt+g(t)} = f_n(t)\,e^{xt+g(t)}[e^t - 1].$$

Again operating ∇ on (1), we have

$$\nabla\sum_{k=0}^{\infty}\frac{t^k}{k!}\,\phi_k{}^{(n)}(x) = f_n(t)\,e^{xt+g(t)}[1 - e^{-t}]$$

16.3 The β Polynomials

The β polynomials of degree k and order n represented by $\beta_k^{(n)}$ is defined by the relation

$$\frac{t^n}{(e^t-1)^n}\exp\{xt + g(t)\} = \sum_{k=0}^{\infty}\frac{t^k}{k!}\,\beta_k^{(n)}(x). \qquad \ldots(1)$$

Operating Δ on (1), we have

$$\sum_{k=0}^{\infty}\frac{t^k}{k!}\,\Delta\beta_k^{(n)}(x) = (e^t - 1)\,\frac{t^n}{(e^t-1)^n}\exp\ \{\mathrm{xt} + \mathrm{g(t)}\} = \frac{t^n}{(e^t-1)^{n-1}}\exp\ [\mathrm{xt} + \mathrm{g(t)}]$$

$$= t\sum_{k=0}^{\infty}\frac{t^k}{k!}\,\beta_k^{(n-1)}(x) = t\sum_{k=1}^{\infty}\frac{t^{k-1}}{(k-1)!}\,\beta_{k-1}^{(n-1)}(x).$$

On equating the coefficients of t^k, we have

$$\frac{\Delta\beta_k^{(n)}(x)}{k!} = \frac{\beta_{k-1}^{n-1}(x)}{(k-1)!} \quad\text{or}\quad \Delta\beta_k^{(n)}(x) = k\,\beta_{k-1}^{n-1}(x)$$

or

$$[\beta^{(n)} + x + 1]^k - [\beta^{(n)} + x]^k = k[\beta^{n-1} + x]^{k-1}$$

Putting $x = 0$ in above, we have

$$(\beta_k^{(n)} + 1)^k - \beta_k^{(n)} = k\,\beta_{k-1}^{(n-1)} \qquad \dots(2)$$

Relation (2) is the recurrence relation between the β numbers of order n and $n-1$.

16.4 Bernoulli's Polynomials and Bernoulli's Numbers

The β polynomials described in **16.3** are used to obtain some special type of polynomials known as **Bernoulli's polynomials.** Let us consider $f_n(t) = t^n (e^t - 1)^{-n}$, then for $n = 0$, we have $f_0(t) = 1$.

In the light of the above result, we can write

$$\sum_{k=0}^{\infty} \frac{t^k}{k!}\,\beta_k^{(0)}(x) = f_0(t)\,e^{xt+g(t)} = e^{xt}, \text{ if } g(t) = 0. \qquad \dots(1)$$

Hence for $n = 0$ and $g(t) = 0$, β polynomials of zero order can be simple expressed in successive power of x. These are also known as **Bernoulli's polynomials of order zero.**

$$\text{Now (1)} \Rightarrow \beta_0^{(0)}(x) + t\,\beta_1^{(0)}(x) + \frac{t^2}{2!}\beta_2^{(0)}(x) + \dots + \frac{t^k}{k!}\beta_k^{(0)}(x) + \dots$$

$$= 1 + xt + \frac{x^2t^2}{2!} + \dots + \frac{x^kt^k}{k!} + \dots \qquad \dots(2)$$

Whence comparing coefficients of t^k, we get

$$\beta_k^{(0)}(x) = x^k = \beta_k^0(x).$$

Thus Bernoulli's polynomials of order n can be derived from β-polynomials by putting

$$g(t) = 0 \text{ in } \frac{t^n}{(e^t - 1)^n}\,e^{xt+g(t)} = \sum_{k=0}^{\infty} \frac{t^k}{k!}\,\beta_k^{(n)}(x)$$

$$\frac{t^n e^{xt}}{(e^t - 1)^n} = \sum_{k=0}^{\infty} \frac{t^k}{k!}\,\beta_k^{(n)}(x) \qquad \dots(3)$$

Again putting $x = 0$ in (2), we get the corresponding **Bernoulli's numbers.**

$$\frac{t^n}{(e^t - 1)^n} = \sum_{k=0}^{\infty} \frac{t^k}{k!}\beta_k^{(n)} \qquad \dots(4)$$

$$\Rightarrow \beta_0^{(n)} + t\beta_1^{(n)} + \frac{t^2}{2!}\beta_2^{(n)} + \dots = t^n(e^t - 1)^{-n} = t^n\left(1 + t + \frac{t^2}{2!} + \frac{t^3}{3!} + \dots - 1\right)^{-n}$$

$$= t^n \,.\, t^{-n}\left(1 + \frac{t}{2!} + \frac{t^2}{3!} + \dots\right)^{-n}$$

$$= \left[1 - n\left(\frac{t}{2!} + \frac{t^2}{3!} + \dots\right) + \frac{n(n+1)}{2!}\left(\frac{t}{2!} + \frac{t^2}{3!} + \dots\right)^2 - \dots\right] \qquad \dots(5)$$

Comparing the coefficients of different powers of t, we get the **Bernoulli's number of Order n**, as given below:

$$B_0^{(n)} = 1, B_1^{(n)} = -(n/2), B_2^{(n)} = \frac{n(3n-1)}{2} \quad \text{...(6)}$$

$$B_3^{(n)} = -\frac{n^2}{8}(n-1) \quad \text{...(7)}$$

$$B_4^{(n)} = \frac{1}{240} n(15n^3 - 30n^2 + 5n + 2) \quad \text{...(8)}$$

$$B_5^{(n)} = -\frac{1}{96} n^2 (n-1)(3n^2 - 7n + 2) \quad \text{...(9)}$$

$$B_6^{(n)} = \frac{1}{4032} n(63n^5 - 315n^4 + 315n^3 + 91n^2 - 42n - 16). \quad \text{...(10)}$$

Again proceeding as in **16.2**, it can be shown that

$$\beta_k^{(n)}(x) = (\beta_k^{(n)} + x)^k \quad \text{...(11)}$$

$$\therefore \quad \Delta B_k^{(n)}(x) = k\, B_{k-1}^{(n-1)}(x) = k(k-1)\, B_{k-2}^{(n-2)}(x). \quad \text{...(12)}$$

... ...

Repeating this n times, where $k > n$, we get

$$\Delta^n B_k^{(n)}(x) = k(k-1)(k-2)\ldots(k-n+1) B^0{}_{k-n}.$$

$$= k(k-1)(k-2)\ldots(k-n+1)\, x^{k-n}. \quad \text{...(13)}$$

$$[\because B^0{}_{k-n} = x^{k-n}]$$

From (12), we can show that

$$B_k^{(n)}(x+1) = B_k^{(n)}(x) + k\, B_{k-1}^{(n-1)}(x). \quad \text{...(14)}$$

Putting, $x = 0$ in (14), we get

$$B_k^{(n)}(1) = B_k^{(n)}(0) + k\, B_{k-1}^{(n-1)}(0). \quad \text{...(15)}$$

Also $\displaystyle\int_x^{x+1} B_k^{(n)}(t)\, dt = \frac{1}{k+1} \Delta B_{k+1}^{(n)}(x) = B_k^{(n-1)}(x)$ ...(16)

and in particular, we have

$$\int_0^1 B_k^n(t)\, dt = B_k^{n-1} \quad \text{...(17)}$$

16.5 Bernoulli's Polynomials and Numbers of the First Order

Putting $n = 1$ in (8) of 16.4 and writing $B_k(x)$ for $B_k^{(1)}(x)$; we get

$$\frac{t\, e^{xt}}{(e^t - 1)} = \sum_{k=0}^{\infty} \frac{t^k}{k!} B_k(x). \quad \text{...(1)}$$

Putting $x = 0$ in (1), we get

$$\frac{t}{(e^t - 1)} = \sum_{k=0}^{\infty} \frac{t^k}{k!} B_k. \quad \text{...(2)}$$

Equations (1) and (2) are known as the generating functions of the Bernoulli's polynomials and Bernoulli's number B_k, of the first order.

On differentiating (1) with respect to x and then dividing by t, we get the relation

$$B_k^1\ (k) = k\, B_{k-1}(x). \qquad \ldots(3)$$

$$\Rightarrow \int_a^x B_k(x)\, dx = \frac{1}{k+1}\int_a^x B_k^{(1)}(x)\, dx = \frac{1}{k+1}\left[B_{k+1}^{(x)}\right]_a^x$$

$$= \frac{1}{k+1}[B_{k+1}(x) - B_{k+1}(a)].$$

Now, on putting $(1-x)$ for x in (1), we get

$$\frac{t\, e^{(1-x)t}}{e^t - 1} = \sum_{k=0}^{\infty} \frac{t^k}{k!} B_k(1-x). \qquad \ldots(4)$$

L.H.S. of (4)
$$= \frac{t\, e^{(1-x)t}}{e^t - 1} = \frac{t\, e^{-xt}}{1 - e^{-t}} = \frac{-t\, e^{-xt}}{e^{-t} - 1} = \sum_{k=0}^{\infty} \frac{(-t)^k}{k!} B_k(x). \qquad \ldots(5)$$

From (4) and (5) on equating the coefficients of t^k, we get

$$B_k(1-x) = (-1)^k\, B_k(x).$$

If $k = 2m$, then $B_{2m}(1-x) = B_{2m}(x)$.

First few Bernoulli's polynomials are deduced as below:

Multiply both sides of (1) by $(e^t - 1)$

$$\Rightarrow \quad t\, e^{xt} = (e^t - 1) \sum_{k=0}^{\infty} \frac{t^k}{k!} B_k(x)]$$

or
$$t\left(1 + tx + \frac{t^2 x^2}{2!} + \ldots\right) = \left(t + \frac{t^2}{2!} + \ldots\right) \times \left[B_0(x) + t\, B_1(x) + \frac{t^2}{2!} B_2(x) + \ldots\right]$$

Equating the coefficients of various powers of t, we get

$$B_0(x) = 1,\ B_1(x) = x - \frac{1}{2},\quad B_2(x) = x^2 - x + \frac{1}{6}$$

$$B_3(x) = x^3 - \frac{3}{2}x^2 + \frac{1}{2}x,\ B_4(x) = x^4 - 2x^3 + x^2 - \frac{1}{30}$$

$$B_5(x) = x^5 - \frac{5}{2}x^4 + \frac{5}{2}x^3 - \frac{1}{6}x$$

$$B_6(x) = x^6 - 3x^5 + \frac{5}{2}x^4 - \frac{1}{2}x^3 + \frac{1}{42};\ \text{etc.}$$

On putting $x = 0$, corresponding Bernoulli numbers are obtained which are

$$B_0 = 1, B_1 = -\frac{1}{2}, B_2 = \frac{1}{6}, B_3 = 0, B_4 = -\frac{1}{30}, B_5 = 0,$$

$$B_6 = \frac{1}{42} \text{ and so on.}$$

16.6 To Show That

$$B_k^{(n)}(n-x)=(-1)^k B_k^{(n)}(x).$$

In (3) of **16.4**, put $n-x$ for x; we have

$$\sum_{k=0}^{\infty}\frac{t^k}{k!}B_k^{(n)}(n-x)=\frac{t^n}{(e^t-1)^n}e^{(n-x)t}=t^n(e^t-1)^{-n}e^{(n-x)t}$$

or $$\sum_{k=0}^{\infty}\frac{t^k}{k!}B_k^{(n)}(n-x)=(-t)^n e^{-xt}(e^{-t}-1)^{-n}=\sum_{k=0}^{\infty}\frac{(-t^k)}{k!}B_k^{(n)}(x). \qquad \ldots(1)$$

On equating the coefficients of t^k from both sides of (1), we get

$$B_k^{(n)}(n-x)=(-1)^k B_k^{(n)}(x).$$

This is called **Complementary argument theorem.**

16.7 To Show That

$$B_k^{(n+1)}(x)=\left(1-\frac{k}{n}\right)B_k^{(n)}(x)+k\left(\frac{x}{n}-1\right)B_{k-1}^{(n)}(x).$$

Differentiating (3) of **16.4** with respect to t, we get

$$\sum_{k=1}^{\infty}\frac{k\,t^{k-1}}{k!}B_k^{(n)}(x)=\frac{(n\,t^{n-1}e^{xt}+xt^n e^{xt})(e^t-1)^n-n(e^t-1)^{n-1}e^t t^n e^{xt}}{(e^t-1)^{2n}}$$

Now multiplying both sides by t, we get

$$\sum_{k=0}^{\infty}\frac{t^k}{(k-1)!}B_k^{(n)}(x)=\frac{nt^n e^{xt}}{(e^t-1)^n}+\frac{xt^{n+1}e^{xt}}{(e^t-1)^n}-\frac{nt^{n+1}e^{(x+1)t}}{(e^t-1)^{n+1}} \qquad \ldots(1)$$

$$=n\sum_{k=0}^{\infty}\frac{t^k}{k!}B_k^{(n)}(x)+xt\sum_{k=0}^{\infty}\frac{t^k}{k!}B_k^{(n)}(x)-n\sum_{k=0}^{\infty}\frac{t^k}{k!}B_k^{(n+1)}(x+1).$$

On equating the coefficients of t^k from above, we get

$$k\,B_k^{(n)}(x)=n\,B_k^{(n)}(x)+k\,x\,B_{k-1}^{(n)}(x)-n\,B_k^{(n+1)}(x+1). \qquad \ldots(2)$$

Again, we know that

$$B_k^{(n)}(x+1)=B_k^{(n)}(x)+k\,B_{k-1}^{(n-1)}(x)$$

Putting $(n+1)$ for n, we get

$$B_k^{(n+1)}(x+1)=B_k^{(n+1)}(x)+k\,B_{k-1}^{(n)}(x). \qquad \ldots(3)$$

From (2) and (3), we get

$$B_k^{(n+1)}(x)=\left(1-\frac{k}{n}\right)B_k^{(n)}(x)+k\left(\frac{x}{n}-1\right)B_{k-1}^{(n)}(x) \qquad \ldots(4)$$

Corolary 1: Putting $x = 0$ in (4), we get

$$B_k^{(n+1)} = \left(1 - \frac{k}{n}\right) B_k^{(n)} - k\, B_{k-1}^{(n)} \qquad \ldots(5)$$

Again putting $x = 0$ in (3), we get

$$B_k^{(n+1)}(1) = \left(1 - \frac{k}{n}\right) B_k^{(n)}$$

On putting $(n + k)$ for n in above, we get

$$B_k^{(n+k+1)}(1) = \frac{n}{n+k} B_k^{(n+k)}. \qquad \ldots(6)$$

Corolary 2: Putting $k = n$, in (4), we get

$$\begin{aligned} B_n^{(n+1)}(x) &= (x - n)\, B_{n-1}^{(n)}(x) \\ &= (x - n)(x - n + 1)\, B_{n-2}^{(n-1)} = \ldots \\ &= (x - n)(x - n + 1)\ldots(x - 2)(x - 1)\, B_0^{(1)}(x) = (x - 1)^{(n)}. \end{aligned}$$

16.8 Euler Polynomials and Euler Numbers

$$\sum_{k=0}^{\infty} (t^k / k!)\, \phi_k^n(x) = f_n(t)\, e^{xt + gt} \qquad \ldots(1)$$

$$\Rightarrow \qquad \nabla \sum_{k=0}^{\infty} \frac{t^k}{k!} \phi_k^{(n)}(x) = f_n(t)\, e^{xt + g(t)} (e^t - 1) \qquad \ldots(2)$$

Whence putting $f_n(t) = 2^n (e^t + 1)^{-n}$, we immediately, obtain

$$\begin{aligned} \sum_{k=0}^{\infty} \frac{t^k}{k!} \nabla \phi_k^{(n)}(x) &= \frac{2^n (e^t + 1)}{2\, (e^t + 1)^n} e^{xt + g(t)} \\ &= \frac{2^{n-1}}{(e^t + 1)^{n-1}} e^{xt + g(t)} \\ &= \sum_{k=0}^{\infty} \frac{t^k}{k!} \phi_k^{(n-1)}(x). \end{aligned}$$

$$\Rightarrow \qquad \nabla \phi_k^{(n)}(x) = \phi_k^{(n-1)}(x) \qquad \ldots(3)$$

i.e., the operator ∇ depresses the order by one unit and leaves the degree unaltered.

Further, the polynomials of the form

$$\frac{2^n e^{xt + g(t)}}{(e^t + 2)^n} = \sum_{k=0}^{\infty} \frac{t^k}{k!} \eta_k^{(n)}(x). \qquad \ldots(4)$$

are known as η **polynomials**.

Also, we define **Euler polynomials** of order n, as follows:

$$\frac{2^n e^{xt}}{(e^t + 1)^n} = \sum_{k=0}^{\infty} \frac{t^k}{k!} E_k^{(n)}(x). \qquad \ldots(5)$$

And $E_k^{(n)}(x)$ for $x=0$ are known as **Euler numbers.** Using well known notation of Norlund for deriving Euler number, we write

$$E_k^{(n)} = 2^{-k} C_k^{(n)} \qquad \ldots(6)$$

where the generating function for C is given by putting $x=0$ and $E_k^{(n)}(0) = 2^{-k} C_k^{(n)}$ in (5)

i.e.
$$\frac{2^n}{(e^t+1)^n} = \sum_{k=0}^{\infty}\left[\left(\frac{t}{2}\right)^k / k!\right] C_k^{(n)} \qquad \ldots(7)$$

The values of $2^k\, E_k^{(n)}(x)$ for $x = \frac{1}{2} n$ are defined as Euler's numbers $E_k^{(n)}$ of order n.

16.9 Properties of Euler's Polynomials

It is evident from **5** of **16.8**, that Euler's polynomials are also some special forms of β and ϕ polynomials. Also, we can deduce that

$$\left.\begin{aligned} E_k^{(n)}(x) &= \left(E_k^{(n)} + x\right)^k \\ &= \left(\frac{1}{2} C^{(n)} + x\right)^k \\ \frac{d}{dx} E_k^{(n)}(x) &= k\, E_{k-1}^{(n)}(x) \\ \int_0^x E_k^{(n)}(t)\, dt &= \frac{1}{k+1}\left[E_{k+1}^{(n)}(x) - E_{k+1}^{(n)}(a)\right] \end{aligned}\right] \qquad \ldots(1)$$

$$\Rightarrow \qquad \nabla E_k^{(n)}(x) = E_k^{(n-1)}(x)$$

$$\vdots$$

$$\Delta^n E_k^{(n)}(x) = x^k \qquad \ldots(2)$$

16.10 Complementary Argument Theorem for Euler's Polynomials

Putting $n-x$ for x in **5** of **16.8**, we obtain

$$\sum_{k=0}^{\infty} \frac{t^k}{k!} E_k^{(n)}(n-x) = \frac{2^n e^{(n-x)t}}{(e^t+1)^n} = \frac{2^n e^{-xt}}{e^{-nt}(e^t+1)^n} = \frac{2^n e^{-xt}}{(e^{-t}+1)^n} \qquad \ldots(1)$$

Whence comparing the coefficients of t^k on both sides, we get

$$E_k^{(n)}(n-x) = (-1)^k E_k^{(n)}(x). \qquad \ldots(2)$$

Now putting $x=0$ and $2k$ for k in (2), we get

$$E_{2k}^{(n)}(n) = E_{2k}^{(n)}(0) = 2^{-2k} C_{2k}^{(n)}.$$

Further putting $x = (n/2)$ and $2k+1$ for k in (2), we get

$$E_{2k+1}^{(n)} = -E_{2k+1}^{(n)}$$

$$\Rightarrow \qquad E_{2k+1}^{(n)} = 0, \textit{ i.e., } \text{Euler's polynomials with an odd suffix vanish.}$$

16.11 Euler's Polynomials of Successive Orders

Differentiating **(5)** of **16.8, w.r.t.** t, we get

$$\sum_{k=1}^{\infty} \frac{k\,t^{k-1}}{k!} E_k^{(n)}(x) = \frac{2^n\, x\, e^{xt}}{(e^t+1)^n} - \frac{2^n . n e^{(x+t)t}}{(e^t+1)^{n+1}}$$

Now multiplying both sides by t, we obtain

$$\sum_{k=1}^{\infty} \frac{t^k}{(k-1)!} E_k^{(n)}(x) = \frac{2^n\, xt\, e^{xt}}{(e^t+1)^n} - \frac{2^n . nt\, e^{(x+t)t}}{(e^t+1)^{n+1}}$$

$$= x \sum_{k=1}^{\infty} \frac{t^k}{(k-1)!} E_{k-1}^{(n)}(x) - \frac{n}{2} \sum_{k=0}^{\infty} \frac{t^k}{(k-1)!} E_{(k-1)}^{(n+1)}(x+1).$$

Whence comparing coefficients of t^{k+1}, we get

$$E_{k+1}^{(n)}(x) = x\, E_k^{(n)}(x) - \frac{n}{2} E_k^{(n+1)}(x+1)$$

$$\Rightarrow \quad E_k^{(n+1)}(x+1) = \frac{2}{n} E_{k+1}^{(n)}(x) + \frac{2}{n}(n-x)\, E_k^{(n)}(x). \qquad \ldots (1)$$

16.12 Euler Polynomials and Euler's Number of First Order

Putting $n = 1$ in **5** of **16.8**, we obtain

$$\frac{2\,e^{xt}}{e^t+1} = \sum_{k=0}^{\infty} \frac{t^k}{k!} E_k(x). \qquad \ldots (1)$$

This relation can be used to find Euler's polynomials of first order by comparing the coefficients of t^k on both sides *i.e.*

$$E_0(x) = 1,\ E_1(x) = x - \frac{1}{2},\ E_2(x) = x(x-1),$$

$$E_3(x) = \left(x - \frac{1}{2}\right)\left(x^2 - x - \frac{1}{2}\right),$$

$$E_4(x) = x(x-1)(x^2 - x - 1),$$

$$E_5(x) = x\left(x - \frac{1}{2}\right)(x^4 - 2x^3 - x^2 + 2x + 1),$$

$$E_6(x) = x(x-1)(x^4 - 2x^3 - 2x^2 + 3x + 3).$$

Solved Examples

Example 1: *Show that*

(a) $1 + \frac{1}{2} + \frac{1}{3} + \ldots + \frac{1}{n} = \frac{(-1)^{n-1}}{(n-1)!} B_{n-1}^{n+1}(0).$

(b) $\frac{1}{t}\log(1+t) = \sum_{q=0}^{\infty} \frac{t^q}{(q+1)!} B_q^{(q+1)}(0).$

Solution: (a) We have

$$(1+t)^{x-1} = \sum_{k=0}^{\infty} \frac{(x-1)(x-2)\ldots(x-n)\,t^n}{n!} \text{ (using Binomial theorem)}$$

$$= \sum_{n=0}^{\infty} \frac{t^n}{n!} B^{(n+1)}(x) = \sum_{k=0}^{\infty} \frac{t^k}{k!} B_k^{(k+1)}(x). \qquad \ldots(1)$$

Differentiating both sides of (1) w.r.t. x, we obtain

$$(1+t)^{x-1} \log(1+t) = \sum_{k=1}^{\infty} \frac{t^k}{(k-1)!} B_{k-1}^{(k+1)}(x) \qquad \ldots(2)$$

$$[\because B'_k(x) = k.B_{k-1}(x)].$$

Putting $x = 0$, we obtain

$$[\log(1+t)](1+t)^{-1} = \sum_{k=1}^{\infty} \frac{t^k}{(k-1)!} B_{k-1}^{(k+1)}(0). \qquad \ldots(3)$$

Further, we have

$$\log(1+t) = \left[t - \frac{t^2}{2} \ldots + (-1)^{n-2} \frac{t^{n-1}}{(n-1)!} + \ldots\right] \qquad \ldots(4)$$

and $\quad (1+t)^{-1} = [1 - t + t^2 - \ldots].$

Making use of (4), equation (5) yields

$$\left[t - \frac{t^2}{2} + \ldots + (-1)^{k-2} \frac{t^{k-1}}{(k-1)!} + \ldots\right][1 - t + t^2 - \ldots] = \sum_{k=1}^{\infty} \frac{t^k}{(k-1)!} B_{k-1}^{(k+1)}(0). \qquad \ldots(5)$$

Equating coefficients t^n on both sides, we readily obtain

$$(-1)^{n-1}\left[\frac{1}{n} + \frac{1}{n-1} + \frac{1}{n-2} + \ldots + \frac{1}{2} + 1\right] = \frac{1}{(n-1)!} B_{n-1}^{(n+1)}(0)$$

$$\Rightarrow \qquad 1 + \frac{1}{2} + \frac{1}{3} + \ldots + \frac{1}{n} = \left[\frac{(-1)^{n-1}}{(n-1)!}\right] B_{n-1}^{(n+1)}(0)$$

(b) Differentiating (1), n times w.r.t. x, we get

$$(1+t)^{n-1}[\log(1+t)]^n = \sum_{p=n}^{\infty} \frac{t^p}{(p-n)!} B_{p-n}^{(p+1)'}(x). \qquad \left[\because \frac{d^n}{dx^n} B_p(x) = \frac{p!}{(p-n)!} B_{p-1}(x)\right]$$

Putting $x = 1$ and dividing by t^n, we get

$$\left[\frac{\log(1+t)}{t}\right]^n = \frac{1}{t^n} \sum_{p=n}^{\infty} \frac{t^p}{(p-n)!} B_{p-n}^{(p+1)}(1)$$

$$= \frac{1}{t^n} \sum_{q=0}^{\infty} \frac{t^{n+q}}{q!} B_q^{(n+q+1)}(1) \qquad [p - n = q \Rightarrow p = n + q]$$

$$= \sum_{q=0}^{\infty} \frac{t^q}{q!} B_q^{(n+q+1)}(1) = \sum_{q=0}^{\infty} \frac{t^q}{q!} \frac{n}{n+q} B_q^{(n+q)}(0)$$

$$\left[\because B_q^{(n+q+1)}(1) = \frac{n}{n+q} B_q^{(n+q)}(0)\right]$$

Putting $n = 1$, we atonce obtain

$$\log \frac{(1+t)}{t} = \sum_{q=0}^{\infty} \frac{t^q}{(q+1)!} B_k^{(q+1)}(0).$$

Example 2: *Prove that* $\Delta^n 0^k = \frac{k!}{(k-n)!} B_{k-1}^{(-n)}(0).$

Solution: $B_k^{(n)}(x+h) = B_k^{(n)}(h) + \sum_{s=1}^{k} x^{(s)} \Delta^s B_k^{(n)}(h).$ ...(1)

→ *Polynomial of degree n* → [using Newton's interpolation formula]

But $\Delta^s B_k^{(n)}(x) = k(k-1)(k-2)\ldots(k-s+1) B_{k-s}^{n-s}$

$$\therefore \quad B_k^{(n)}(x+h) = B_k^{(n)}(h) + \sum_{s=1}^{k} x^{(s)} \cdot {}^kC_s B_{k-s}^{(n-s)} = \sum_{s=0}^{k} x^{(s)} \cdot {}^kC_s B_{k-s}^{(n-s)}(h). \quad \ldots(2)$$

Putting $h = 0$ in (2), we get

$$2B_k^{(n)}(x) = \sum_{s=0}^{k} x^{(s)} \cdot {}^kC_s B_{k-s}^{(n-s)}(0). \quad \ldots(3)$$

Again substitution of $n = 0$ in (3) yields

$$B_k^{(0)}(x) = \sum_{s=0}^{k} x^{(s)} \cdot {}^kC_s B_{k-s}^{(-s)}(0). \quad \ldots(4)$$

Again $B_k^{(0)}(x) = x^k$, therefore (4)

$$\Rightarrow \quad x^k = \sum_{s=0}^{k} x^{(s)} \cdot {}^kC_s B_{k-s}^{(-s)}(0). \quad \ldots(5)$$

Finally operating with $\Delta^n, n \le k$ and then putting $x = 0$, we readily obtain

$$\Delta_n 0^k = \frac{k!}{(k-n)!} B_{k-n}^{(-n)}(0)$$

Example 3: *Prove that if $f_n(x)$ is a polynomial of degree n having the property that $Df_n(x) = f_{n-1}(x)$, then $f_n(x)$ must have the form*

$$f_n(x) = \frac{c_0 x^n}{n!} + \frac{c_1 x^{n-1}}{(n-1)!} + \ldots + c_{n-1} x + c_n,$$

where c's are constants independent of n.

Solution: Let

$$f_n(x) = A_0(n) x^n + A_1(n) x^{n-1} + \ldots + A_{n-1}(n) x + A_n(n) \quad \ldots(1)$$

Then using $Df_n(x) = f_{n-1}$, we obtain

$$nA_0(n)\,x^{n-1} + (n-1)\,A_1(n)\,x^{n-2} + \ldots + A_{n-1}(n)$$
$$= A_0(n-1)\,x^{n-1} + A_1(n-1)\,x^{n-2} + \ldots + A_{n-1}(n-1).$$

This should be an identity and hence we obtain

$$nA_0(n) = A_0(n-1),\ (n-1)\,A_1(n) = A_1(n-1), \ldots, A_{n-1}(n) = A_{n-1}(n-1).$$

From the first of these, we have $A_0(n) = \dfrac{A_0(n-1)}{n}$.

Putting $n-1$ for n etc. successively, we get

$$A_0(n) = \frac{A_0(n-1)}{n} = \frac{A_0(n-2)}{n(n-1)} = \ldots = \frac{A_0(0)}{n(n-1)\ldots 2.1} = \frac{c_0}{n!},$$

where $c_0 = A_0(0)$ is the constant independent of n.

Similarly from the second, we get

$$A_1(n) = \frac{A_1(n-1)}{n-1} = \frac{A_1(n-2)}{n(n-2)} = \ldots = \frac{A_1(0)}{(n-1)(n-2)\ldots 1} = \frac{c_1}{(n-1)!}$$

where $c_1 = A_1(0)$ is a constant independent of n.

Thus, we obtain

$$f_n(x) = \frac{c_0\,x^n}{n!} + \frac{c_1\,x^{n-1}}{(n-1)!} + \ldots + c_{n-1}\,x + c_n.$$

Example 4: *Prove that* $B_k(mx) = m^{k-1} \sum_{s=0}^{m-1} B_k\left(x + \frac{s}{m}\right)$.

Solution: We know that $\dfrac{t^n e^{xt}}{(e^t-1)^n} = \sum_{k=0}^{\infty} \dfrac{t^k}{k!} B_k^{(n)}(x)$.

Putting $n = 1$ and writing $B_k(x)$ for $B_k^{(1)}(x)$

$$\frac{t\,e^{xt}}{e^t - 1} = \sum_{k=1}^{\infty} \frac{t^k}{k!} B_k(x).$$

Writing $x + (s/m)$ for x in the above result and summing from $s = 0$ to $m-1$, we obtain

$$\sum_{s=0}^{m-1} \frac{t\,e^{\{x+(s/m)\}t}}{e^t - 1} = \sum_{s=0}^{m-1} \sum_{k=0}^{\infty} \frac{t^k}{k!} B_r\left(x + \frac{s}{m}\right)$$

i.e.
$$\sum_{s=0}^{m-1} \sum_{k=0}^{\infty} \frac{t^k}{k!} B_k\left(x + \frac{s}{m}\right) = \sum_{s=0}^{m-1} \frac{t\,e^{xt}}{e^t - 1} e^{(s/m)t}$$

$$= \frac{t\,e^{xt}}{(e^t - 1)} (1 + e^{t/m} + e^{2t/m} + \ldots + e^{(m-st/m)})$$

i.e. $$\sum_{k=0}^{\infty}\sum_{s=0}^{m-1} B_k\left(x+\frac{s}{m}\right) = \frac{t\,e^{xt}}{e^t-1}\frac{(e^t-1)}{(e^{t/m}-1)} = \frac{t\,e^{xt}}{e^{(t/m)}-1}$$

$$= \frac{m.(t/m)\;n^{mx.(t/m)}}{e^{(t/m)}-1}$$

$$= \sum_{k=0}^{\infty}\frac{m(t/m)^k}{k!}B_k(mx) = \sum_{k=0}^{\infty}\frac{t^k}{m^{k-1}.k!}B_k(mx)$$

$$\Rightarrow \quad \sum_{s=0}^{m-1}\frac{t^k}{k!}B_k\left(x+\frac{s}{m}\right) = \frac{t^k}{m^{k-1}.k!}B_k(mx)$$

$$\Rightarrow \quad B_k(mx) = m^{k-1}\sum_{s=0}^{m-1} B_k\left(x+\frac{s}{m}\right).$$

Example 5: *Evaluate $\sum_{s=1}^{n} s^k m$ by the use of Bernoulli's numbers.*

Solution: We have $\int_s^{s+1} B_k(x)\,dx = \int_s^{s+1}\frac{B'\,k+1}{k+1}dx$

$$= \frac{1}{k+1}[B_{k+1}(s+1) - B_{k+1}(s)] = s^k.$$

This gives $$\sum_{s=1}^{n} s^k = \int_0^{n+1} B_k(x)\,dx = \frac{1}{k+1}[B_{k+1}(n+1) - B_{k+1}(0)].$$

In particular, we have

$$\sum_{s=1}^{n} s^2 = \frac{1}{3}[B_3(n+1) - B_2(0)] = \frac{1}{3}\left[(n+1)^3 - \frac{3}{2}(n+1)^2 + \frac{1}{2}(n+1) - 0\right]$$

$$= \frac{1}{6}[n(n+1)(2n+1)] \text{ and similarly we can obtain } \sum_{1}^{n} s^3.$$

Example 6: *Prove that*

(a) $B_k^{(m+n)}(x+y) = [B^{(m)}(x) + B^{(n)}(y)]^k,$

(b) $B_k^{(n)}(x+y) = \sum_{p=0}^{n} {}^kC_p\, B_p^{(n)}(x)\, y^{k-p},$

(c) $B_k^{(n)}(x) = \sum_{p=0}^{k} {}^kC_p\, B_p^{(n)}\, B_{k-p}^{(n-1)}(x).$

Solution: (a) We know that

$$\sum_{k=0}^{\infty} B_k^{(n)}(x)\frac{t^k}{k!} = t^n (e^t-1)^{-n} e^{xt} \quad \text{...(1)}$$

Putting $m+n$ for n and $x+y$ for x in (1), we get

$$\sum_{k=0}^{\infty} B_k^{(m+n)}(x+y)\frac{t^k}{k!} = t^{m+n}(e^t-1)^{-(m+n)}e^{t(x+y)}$$

$$= \frac{t^{m+n}e^{(x+y)t}}{(e^t-1)^{m+n}} \qquad \ldots(2)$$

$$\Rightarrow \quad \sum_{k=0}^{\infty}\left(\frac{t^k}{k!}\right)B_k^{(m+n)}(x+y) = \frac{t^m.e^{tx}}{(e^t-1)^m}\,\frac{t^n.e^{ty}}{(e^t-1)^n} \qquad \ldots(3)$$

$$\Rightarrow \quad \sum_{k=0}^{\infty}\frac{t^k}{k!}B_k^{(m+n)}(x+y) = \left(\sum_{k=r}^{\infty}\frac{t^{k-r}}{(k-r)!}B_{k-r}^{(m)}(x)\right)\left(\sum_{p=0}^{\infty}\frac{t^p}{p!}B_p^{(n)}(y)\right). \qquad \ldots(4)$$

Now equating the coefficients of t^k on both sides, we have

$$B_k^{(m+n)}(x+y) = \sum_{r=0}^{r=k}\frac{k!}{(k-r)!}\frac{1}{r!}B_{k-r}^{(m)}(x)\,B_r^{(n)}(y) \qquad \ldots(5)$$

i.e. $\quad B_k^{(m+n)}(x+y) = [B^{(m)}(x)+B^{(n)}(y)]^k.$

(b) Putting $m=0$ and replacing x by y, y by x in (5), we get

$$B_k^{(n)}(x+y) = \sum_{r=0}^{k}\frac{k!}{(k-r)!}\frac{1}{r!}.B_{k-r}^{0}(y)\,B_r^{(n)}(x).$$

Again replacing r by p, we obtain

$$B_k^{(n)}(x+y) = \sum_{p=0}^{k}{}^kC_p\,B_{k-p}^{(0)}(y)\,B_p^{(n)}(x) = \sum_{p=0}^{k}{}^kC_p\,B_p^{(n)}(x)\,y^{k-p}$$

$$[\because\ B_{k-p}^{0}(y) = y^{k-p}].$$

(c) Putting $y=0$, $m=N-1$ and $n=1$ in (4), we obtain

$$\sum_{k=0}^{\infty}\frac{t^k}{k!}B_k^{(N)}(x) = \left(\sum_{k=r}^{\infty}\frac{t^{k-r}}{(k-r)!}B_{k-r}^{(N-1)}(x)\right)\left(\sum_{p=0}^{\infty}\frac{t^k}{k!}B_k^{(1)}(0)\right).$$

$$\Rightarrow \quad \sum_{k=0}^{\infty}\frac{t^k}{k!}B_k^{(N)}(x) = \left(\sum_{k=0}^{\infty}\frac{t^{k-p}}{(k-p)!}B_{k-p}^{(N-1)}(x)\right)\left(\sum_{p=0}^{\infty}\frac{t^p}{p!}B_p^{(1)}(0)\right).$$

On equating the coefficients of t^k on both the sides, we get

$$B_k^{(N)}(x)\frac{1}{k!} = \sum_{p=0}^{\infty}\frac{1}{(p)!\,(k-p)!}B_p^1(0)\,B_{(k-p)}^{(N-1)}(x)$$

$$\Rightarrow \quad B_k^{(N)}(x) = \sum_{p=0}^{\infty}{}^kC_p\,B_p^1(0)\,B_{(k-p)}^{(N-1)}(x).$$

Replacing N by n, we obtain

$$B_k^{(n)}(x) = \sum_{p=0}^{\infty}{}^kC_p\,B_p^1(0)\,B_{(k-p)}^{(n-1)}(x).$$

Example 7: *Prove that*

(a) $(x+y)^k = \sum_{p=0}^{\infty} {}^kC_p \, B_p^{(n)}(x) \, B_{(k-p)}^{(-n)}(y)$

(b) $\sum_{p=0}^{\infty} {}^kC_p \, B_p^{(n)}(x) \, B_{(k-p)}^{(-n)}(x) = 0, k > 0.$

Solution: (a) By example 6 equation (5), we have

$$B_k^{(m+n)}(x+y) = \sum_{r=0}^{\infty} \frac{k!}{(k-r)!} \frac{1}{r!} B_{(k-r)}^{(m)}(x) \, B_r^{(n)}(y).$$

Now changing m by $-n$, r by p and (x by y, y by x), we obtain

$$B_k^{(0)}(x+y) = \sum_{p=0}^{\infty} \frac{k!}{(k-p)!} \cdot \frac{1}{(p)!} B_{(k-p)}^{(-n)}(y) \, B_p^{(n)}(x)$$

$$(x+y)^k = \sum_{p=0}^{\infty} {}^kC_p \, B_p^{(n)}(x) \, B_{(k-p)}^{(-n)}(y)$$

(b) We have

$$\sum_{k=0}^{\infty} \frac{t^k}{k!} B_k^{(m+n)}(x+y) = \left(\sum_{r=k}^{\infty} \frac{t^{k-r}}{(k-r)!} B_{(k-r)}^{(m)}(x) \right) \left(\sum_{p=0}^{\infty} \frac{t^p}{p!} B_p^{(n)}(y) \right).$$

Putting $x = 0 = y$ and $m = -n$, r by p, we readily obtain

$$\sum_{k=0}^{\infty} \frac{t^k}{k!} B_k^{(0)}(0) = \left(\sum_{k=p}^{\infty} \frac{t^{k-p}}{(k-p)!} B_{(k-p)}^{(-n)}(0) \right) \left(\sum_{p=0}^{\infty} \frac{t^p}{p!} B_p^{(n)}(0) \right).$$

Now, equate coefficient of t^k on both the sides, we obtain

$$B_k^{(0)}(0) = \sum_{p=0}^{\infty} {}^kC_p \, B_p^{(n)}(0) \, B_{(k-p)}^{(-n)}(0)$$

and

$$B_k^0(0) = 0 \; \{B_k^0(0) = 0, k > 0\}.$$

Example 8: *Show that* $\dfrac{t}{e^t - 1} = \dfrac{\log(1+\Delta)}{\Delta} e^{0.t}$ *and hence deduce that*

$$B_{2n-1}(0) = (-1)^{n+1} \left\{ 1 - \frac{\Delta}{2} + \frac{\Delta^2}{3} - \ldots + \frac{\Delta^{2n}}{2n+1} \right\} 0^{2n}.$$

Solution: We have

$$\frac{t}{e^t - 1} = \frac{\log e^t}{e^t - 1} = \frac{\log E}{E - 1} e^{0.t} = \frac{\log(1+\Delta)}{E} e^{0.t} \quad \ldots(1)$$

$$\sum_{k=0}^{\infty} \frac{t_n}{k!} B_k(0) = \frac{\log(1+\Delta)}{\Delta} \sum_{k=0}^{\infty} \frac{0^k}{k!} t^k. \quad \ldots(2)$$

Equating coefficients of t^{2n} on both the sides, we get

$$\frac{1}{(2n)!}B_{2n}(0) = \frac{\log(1+\Delta)}{\Delta}\frac{0^{2n}}{(2n)!} \Rightarrow \frac{(-1)^{n+1}}{(2n)!}B_{2n-1}(0) = \frac{\log(1+\Delta)}{\Delta}\frac{0^{2n}}{(2n)!}$$

$$\Rightarrow \quad B_{2n-1}(0) = (-1)^{n+1}\left[\frac{\Delta}{\Delta} - \frac{\Delta^2}{2\Delta} + \frac{\Delta^3}{3\Delta} - \ldots + \frac{\Delta^{2n+1}}{(2n+1)\Delta}\right]0^{2n}$$

$$= (-1)^{n+1}\left[1 - \frac{\Delta}{2} + \frac{\Delta^2}{3} - \ldots + \frac{\Delta^{2n}}{2n+1}\right]0^{2n}$$

Example 9: *Prove that*

(*a*) $\sum_{s=1}^{m-1} B_k\left(\frac{s}{m}\right) = -\left(1 - \frac{1}{m^{k-1}}\right)B_k,$

(*b*) $B_k\left(\frac{1}{2}\right) = -\left(1 - \frac{1}{2^{k-1}}\right)B_k(0);\ k = 1, 2, \ldots$

Solution: (a) We know that

$$B_k(mx) = m^{k-1}\sum_{s=0}^{m-1} B_k\left(x + \frac{s}{m}\right).$$

Putting $x = 0$, we obtain

$$B_k(0) = m^{k-1}\sum_{s=0}^{m-1} B_k\left(\frac{s}{m}\right) = m^{k-1}B_k(0) + m^{k-1}\sum_{s=1}^{m-1} B_k\left(\frac{s}{m}\right)$$

$$\Rightarrow \quad \left(\frac{1-m^{k-1}}{m^{k-1}}\right)B_k(0) = \sum_{s=0}^{m-1} B_k\left(\frac{s}{m}\right)$$

$$\Rightarrow \quad -\left(x - \frac{1}{m^{k-1}}\right)B_k(0) = \sum_{s=1}^{m-1} B_k\left(\frac{s}{m}\right).$$

(b) By first part, we have

$$-\left(1 - \frac{1}{m^{k-1}}\right)B_k(0) = \sum_{s=0}^{m-1} B_k\left(\frac{s}{m}\right).$$

Putting $m = 2$, we have $-\left(1 - \frac{1}{2^{k-1}}\right)B_k(0) = B_k\left(\frac{1}{2}\right)$

$$\Rightarrow \quad B_k\left(\frac{1}{2}\right) = -\left(1 - \frac{2}{2^{k-1}}\right)B_k(0);\ k = 1, 2, \ldots$$

Example 10: *Prove that* $B_{2n-1} = (-1)^{n+1}\left(\Delta - \frac{\Delta^2}{2^2} + \frac{\Delta^3}{3^2} - \ldots\right)0^{2n+1}.$

Solution: By example 8, we known that

$$B_{2n-1}(0) = (-1)^{n+1}\left(1 - \frac{\Delta}{2} + \frac{\Delta^2}{3} - \ldots + \frac{\Delta^{2n}}{2n+1} - \ldots\right)0^{2n}.$$

Then using $\Delta^{n-1}0^{x-1} = \dfrac{\Delta^n 0^n}{n} - \Delta^n 0^{x-1}$; $\log(1+\Delta)0^{2n} = D0^{2n} = 0$,

we readily obtain

$$B_{2n-1} = (-1)^{n+1}\left\{\left(\Delta - \frac{\Delta^2}{2^2} + \frac{\Delta^3}{3^2} - \ldots\right)0^{2n+1} - \left(\Delta - \frac{\Delta^2}{2} + \frac{\Delta^3}{3} - \ldots\right)0^{2n}\right\}$$

$$= (-1)^{n+1}\left\{\left(\Delta - \frac{\Delta^2}{2^2} + \frac{\Delta^3}{3^2} - \ldots\right)0^{2n+1} - \log(1+\Delta).0^{2n}\right\}$$

$$= (-1)^{n+1}\left\{\Delta - \frac{\Delta^2}{2^2} + \frac{\Delta^3}{3^2} - \ldots\right\}0^{2n+1}$$

✦✦ Problem Set ✦✦

1. Obtain the Bernoulli Numbers B_4, B_6, B_8 without first finding the Bernoulli polynomials.

2. Prove that

(i) $B'_n(x) = nB_{n-1}(x)$,

(ii) $B_n = B_n(0) = B_n(1)$,

(iii) $B_{2n+1}\left(\frac{1}{2}\right) = (0)$,

(iv) $\int_0^1 B_n(x)\,dx = \begin{cases} 1 & n = 0 \\ 0 & n < 0, \end{cases}$

(v) $E_k^{(m+n)}(x+y) = [E^{(n)}(y) + E^{(m)}(x)]^k$,

(vi) $E_k^{(n+1)} = \dfrac{k!\,d^{n-k}}{n!\,d\,x^{n-k}}[(x-1)(x-2)\ldots(x-n)]$,

(vii) $(x+y))^k = \sum\limits_{p=0}^{p-1} {}^kC_p\, E_p^{(n)}(x)\, E_{k-p}^{(-n)}(y)$,

(viii) $\sum\limits_{p=1}^{\infty} (-1)^s s^k = \frac{1}{2}(-1)^n E_p(n+1) - \frac{1}{2}E_k(1)$,

(ix) $E_k^{(n)}(x) = \sum\limits_{p=0}^{k} \{E_p^{(n)}/2p\}.{}^kC_p\,(x - \frac{1}{2}n)^{k-p}$.

3. Prove that

(i) $B_{2n} = \dfrac{\Delta 0^{2n+1}}{1^2} - \dfrac{\Delta 0^{2n+1}}{2^2} + \ldots + \dfrac{\Delta^{2n+1} 0^{2n+1}}{(2n+1)^2}$,

(ii) $B_n = \sum_{m=0}^{n} \dfrac{(-1)^m}{m+1} \Delta^m \Delta^n$,

(iii) $B_{2n} = (-1)^{n-1}\left(\dfrac{1}{2} - \dfrac{1}{3}\Delta + \dfrac{1}{4}\Delta^2 - \ldots\right)0^{2n-1}$.

(iv) $B_{2n-1} = (-1)^{n-1}\left\{\dfrac{\Delta 0^{2n+1}}{1^2} - \dfrac{\Delta^2 0^{2n+1}}{2^2} + \ldots + \dfrac{\Delta^{2n+1} 0^{2n+1}}{(2n+1)^2}\right\}$,

4. Prove, for $E_k(x)$ Euler's polynomials of the first order

(i) $\dfrac{2e^{xt}}{e^t+1} = \sum_{k=1}^{\infty} \dfrac{t^k}{k!} E_k(x), \dfrac{2}{e^t+1} = \sum_{k=0}^{\infty} \dfrac{t^k}{2!} \dfrac{1}{2k} C_k$.

(ii) $\dfrac{2e^{(t/2)}}{e^t+1} = \sum_{k=0}^{\infty} \dfrac{t^k}{k!} \dfrac{E_k}{2^k}$.

(iii) $\nabla E_k^{(n)} = x^k, DE_k(x) = kE_{k-1}(x)$.

(iv) $E_k^{(1-n)} = (-1)^k E_k(x)$.

5. Obtain a recurrence formula for the Bernoulli's numbers of even order by equating like powers of x in the identity

$$\left\{B_0 - \sum_{k=1}^{n} B_{2k} \frac{(2x)^{2k}}{(2k)!}\right\} \sin h\, x = x \cos h\, x.$$

6. By means of Bernoulli's numbers or otherwise, prove that

$$\frac{1^3}{1^2+1} \cdot \frac{2^3}{2^2+1} \cdot \frac{3^3}{3^2+1} \ldots = \frac{2\pi}{e^{\pi} - e^{-\pi}}.$$

7. Prove that

$$1 - \frac{\pi^2}{2!} B_2 + \frac{\pi^4}{4!} B_4 - \ldots = 0.$$

✦✦ Answers ✦✦

❖ Problem Set

1.	$-\dfrac{1}{30}, \dfrac{1}{42}, \dfrac{1}{30}$

◆◆◆

Chapter 17

Curve Fitting and Principle of Least Squares

Scatter Diagram, Curve Fitting, Graphic Method, Laws Reducible to Linear Law, Method of Group Averages, Laws having Three Constants, Method of Least Squares, Most Plausible Solution for a System of Linear Equations, Fitting of Curves of Various Types, Method of Moments.

17.1 Scatter Diagram

Let there be two variables x and y which give us a set of n pairs of numerical values $(x_1, y_1)(x_2, y_2),(x_3, y_3),\ldots(x_n, y_n)$. In order to have an approximate idea about the relationship of these two variables, we plot these n-paired points on a graph, thus we get a diagram showing the simultaneous variation in values of both the variables.

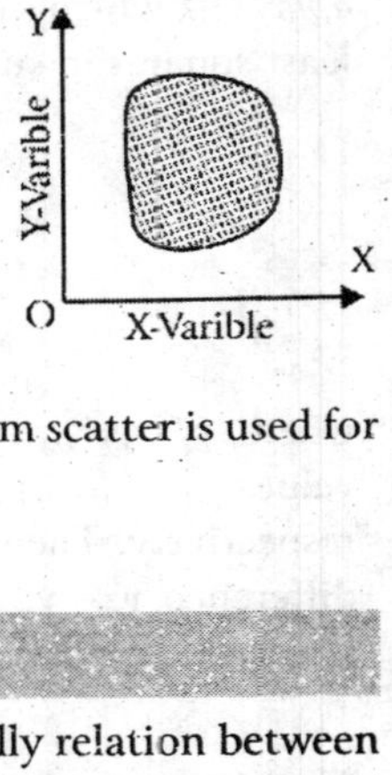

This diagram is called '**Scatter diagram**' or a '**Dot diagram**'. The term scatter is used for dispersion of the dots on the graph.

17.2 Curve Fitting

From scatter diagram, we get only an approximate nonmathematically relation between the two variables. Curve fitting means an exact relationship between two variables by Algebraic equations, in fact this relationship is the equation of the curve. Therefore curve fitting means to from an equation of the curve from the given data.

Curve fitting is considered of immense importance both from the point of view of theoretical and practical statistics. In theoretical statistics the lines of regression may be regarded as fitting of linear curves to the given bivariate values. In practical statistics it is requires to have a functional relationship between two variables x and y, where the dependent variable say, y is expressed as a function of the independent variable say x, involving integral powers upto n.

17.3 Method of Curve Fitting

There are two methods for fitting a curve. First is ***graphical*** and second is the ***method of least squares***.

17.3.1 Graphic Method is the simplest method of curve fitting. In this case, we draw a free hand curve passing through the maximum number of points in the scatter diagram, since in practice it is difficult to have all points falling on the line of definite curve without any sort of scattering or dispersion. The simplest curve that can be fitted to a number of points is the straight line for which $n = 1$, we can also find curves of second degree, third degree etc. giving the best representation of the points.

17.3.2 The Method of Least Squares

Let us have m-paired observations $(x_1, y_1), (x_2, y_2), \ldots, (x_m, y_m)$ of two variables x and y. It is required to fit a polynomial of degree n, of the type

$$y = a + bx + cx^2 + \ldots + kx^n \qquad \ldots (1)$$

of these values. We have to determine the constants $a, b, c, \ldots, k$ such that it represents the curve of best fit. In case $m = n$, then we have in general a unique set of values satisfying the given set of equations, but when $m > n$ then we get m equations by putting the different values of x and y in (1) and we have to find the values of only n constants. Thus there may be no such solution to satisfy all m equations. Therefore we try to find those values of $a, b, c, \ldots, k$ which satisfy all the equations as nearly as possible. We apply the principle of least squares in such in cases. Putting $x_1, x_2, \ldots, x_m$ for x in (1), we get

$$y_1' = a + bx_1 + cx_1^2 + \ldots + kx_1^n$$

$$y_2' = a + bx_2 + cx_2^2 + \ldots + kx_2^n$$

$$\ldots \quad \ldots \quad \ldots \quad \ldots \quad \ldots$$

$$y_m' = a + bx_m + cx_m^2 + \ldots + kx_m^n$$

where $y_1', y_2', \ldots, y_m'$ are the *expected values* of y for $x = x_1, x_2, \ldots, x_m$ respectively. The values $y_1, y_2, \ldots, y_m$ are called the observed values of y corresponding to $x = x_1, x_2, \ldots, x_m$ respectively. The expected values in general are different from the observed values, the difference $y_r - y_r'$, for different values of r, are called *residuals*. Introduce a new quantity U such that

$$U = \Sigma (y_r - y_r')^2 = \Sigma (y_r - a - bx_r - cx_r^2 \ldots - kx_r^n)^2.$$

The constant $a, b, c, \ldots k$ are choosen in such a way that the sum of the squares of residuals is maximum. Now the condition for U to be maximum or minimum is

$$\frac{\partial U}{\partial a} = 0 = \frac{\partial U}{\partial b} = \frac{\partial U}{\partial c} = \ldots = \frac{\partial U}{\partial k}.$$

On simplifying these relations, we get

$$\Sigma y = ma + b \Sigma x + \ldots + k \Sigma x^n$$

$$\Sigma xy = a \Sigma x + b \Sigma x^2 + \ldots + k \Sigma x^{n+1}$$

$$\Sigma x^2 y = a \Sigma x^2 + bx^3 + \ldots + k \Sigma x^{n+2}$$

$$\ldots \quad \ldots \quad \ldots \quad \ldots$$

$$\Sigma x^n y = a \Sigma x^n + b \Sigma x^{n+1} + \ldots + k \Sigma x^{2n}$$

These are known as ***Normal Equations*** and can be solved as simultaneous equations to give the values of the constants $a, b, c, \ldots, k$. These equations are $(n+1)$ in number. When second order partial derivatives are calculated and these values are put, they give a positive value of the function, so U is minimum.

This method does not help us to choose the degree of the curve to be fitted but helps us in finding the values of the constants when the form of the curve has already been chosen. To select the form of the curve is a matter of experience and practical considerations.

17.4 Particular Cases

In case $n = 1$, then the curve to be fitted is a straight line $y = a + bx$ and the normal equations are

$$\Sigma\, y = ma + b\,\Sigma\, x$$
$$\Sigma\, xy = a\,\Sigma\, x + b\,\Sigma\, x^2$$

In case $n = 2$, then the curve to be fitted is a second degree parabola $y = a + bx + cx^2$ and the normal equations are

$$\Sigma\, y = ma + b\,\Sigma\, x + c\,\Sigma\, x^2$$
$$\Sigma\, xy = a\,\Sigma\, x + b\,\Sigma\, bx^2 + c\,\Sigma\, x^3$$
$$\Sigma x^2\, y = a\,\Sigma\, x^2 + b\,\Sigma\, x^3 + c\,\Sigma\, x^4$$

which can be solved for a, b, c.

Exponential curve $y = ae^{bx}$.

Taking logarithms, the equation can be reduced to linear form $\log_{10} y = \log_{10} a + bx \log_{10} e$ which is of the form $Y = AX + B$, where $Y = \log_{10} y$, $A = b \log_{10} e$, $B = \log_{10} a$.

Applying the method for straight line, we can determine A, B and consequently a, b.

Solved Examples

Example 1: *The values of x and y obtained in an experiment are as follows*

x	2.30	3.10	4.00	4.92	5.91	7.20
y	33.0	39.1	50.3	67.2	85.6	125.0

The probable law is $y = a\,e^{bx}$. Text graphically the accuracy of this law and if the law holds good, find the best values of the constants.

Solution: $y = ae^{bx}$ ...(1)

Then taking logarithms to base 10, we get

$$\log_{10} y = \log_{10} a + (b \log_{10} e)\, x$$

Now putting $x = X$, $\log_{10} y = Y$, we have

$$Y = (b \log_{10} e)\, X + \log_{10} a \qquad \text{...(2)}$$

Table for the value of X and Y is as under:

$X = x$	2.30	3.10	4.00	4.92	5.91	7.20
$Y = y$	1.52	1.59	1.70	1.83	1.93	2.1

Then choosing 1 small division along $x-axis = 0.1, 10$ small divisions along $y-axis = 0.1$; we plot these points and draw the line of best fit. These points lie almost along a straight line, the given law is nearly accurate.

Then slope of this line $(= b\log_{10} e) = \frac{KN}{NK} = 0.12$

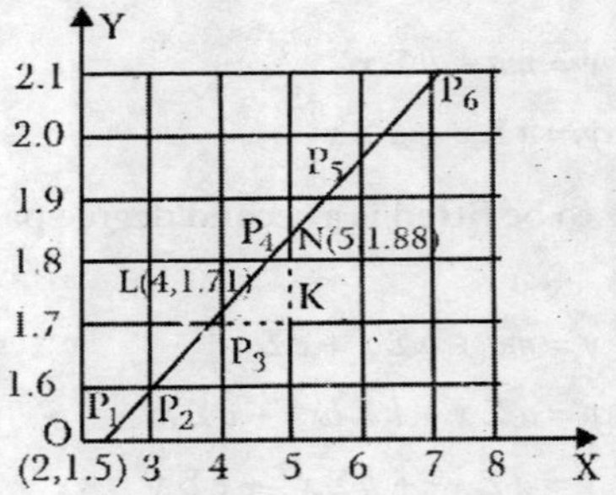

$$\Rightarrow \qquad b = \frac{0.12}{\log_{10} e} = 0.12 \times 2.303 = 0.276$$

But the point (4,1.71) lies on (2),

$\therefore \qquad 1.71 = 0.12 \times 4 + \log_{10} a \Rightarrow a = 17$ nearly.

Thus the curve of best fit is $y = 17e^{0.276x}$.

Example 2: *R is the resistance to motion of a train at speed V find a law of the type* $R = a + bV^2$ *connecting Rand V, using the following data:*

V (km/hr)	10	20	30	40	50
R (km/hr)	8	10	15	21	30

Solution: Law is $R = a + bV^2$ ...(1)

Taking $V^2 = x$ and R = y, we get $y = a + bx$ ...(2)

which is a linear law

x	100	400	900	1600	2500
y	8	10	15	21	30

The normal equations are

$$\Sigma y = ma + b\Sigma x, \Sigma xy = a\Sigma x + b\Sigma x^2$$

x	y	xy	x^2
100	8	800	10000
400	10	4000	160000
900	15	13500	810000
1600	21	33600	2560000
2500	30	75000	6250000
$\Sigma x = 5500$	$\Sigma y = 84$	$\Sigma xy = 126900$	$x^2 = 9790000$

Here $\quad m = 5, \Sigma x = 5500, \Sigma y = 84, \Sigma xy = 126900, \Sigma x^2 = 9790000$

$\Rightarrow \quad 84 = 5a + 5500b$ and $126900 = 5500a + 9790000b$

solving, we obtain $a = 6.68, b = .0092$

Hence the fitted equation is $y = 6.68 + .0092x$

Example 3: *The following values of x and y are supposed to follow the $y = ax^2 + b\log_{10} x$. Find graphically the most probable values of the constants a and b.*

x	2.85	3.88	4.66	5.69	6.65	7.77	8.67
y	16.7	26.4	35.1	47.5	60.6	77.5	93.4

Solution: Given law is $y = ax^2 + b\log_{10} x$

i.e. $$\frac{y}{\log_{10} x} = a\frac{x^2}{\log_{10} x} + b \qquad \ldots(1)$$

Putting $x^2/\log_{10} x = X$ and $y/\log_{10} x = Y$, in (1) becomes

$$Y = aX + b \qquad \ldots(2)$$

This is a linear law. Table for the values of X and Y is as follows:

$X = x^2/\log_{10} x$	17.93	25.56	32.49	42.87	53.75	67.80	80.83
$Y = y/\log_{10} x$	35.59	44.83	52.50	69.90	73.65	87.04	99.56

Let us plot these points and draw the straight line of best fit through these points

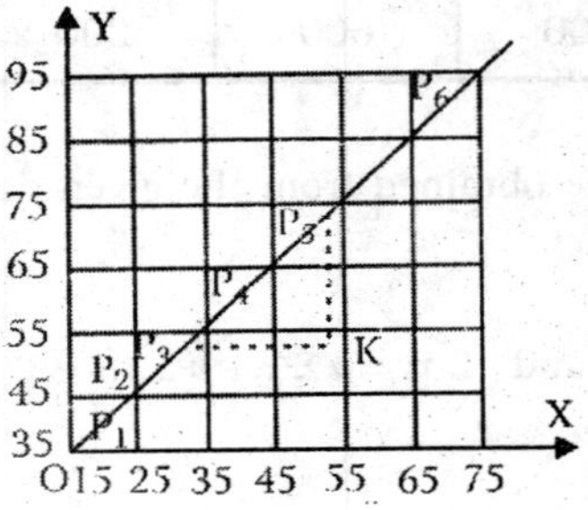

Slope of the line (= a) $= \frac{KP_5}{P_3K} = \frac{73.65-52.50}{53.75-32.49} = \frac{21.15}{21.26} = 0.99$

Now P_3 lies on (2), $\therefore\ 52.50 = 0.99 \times 32.49 + b \quad \Rightarrow b = 20.2$

Thus (1) becomes $y = (0.99)\,x^2 + (20.2)\log_{10} x$.

Example 4: *Fit a straight line to the following data regarding x as the independent variable*

x	0	1	2	3	4
y	1	1.8	3.3	4.5	6.3

Solution: Let the straight line obtained from the given data be

$$y = a + bx$$

then the normal equations are $\Sigma\, y = ma + b\,\Sigma\, x,\ \Sigma\, xy = a\,\Sigma\, x + b\,\Sigma\, x^2$

x	y	xy	x^2
0	1	0	0
1	1.8	1.8	1
2	3.3	6.6	4
3	4.5	13.5	9
4	6.3	25.2	16
$10 = \Sigma\, x$	$16.9 = \Sigma\, y$	$47.1 = \Sigma\, xy$	$30 = \Sigma\, x^2$

In this case $m = 5, \Sigma\, x = 10, \Sigma\, y = 16.9, \Sigma\, xy = 47.1$ and $\Sigma\, x^2 = 30$.

Putting these values in normal equations, we get $16.9 = 5a + 10b$

and $47.1 = 10a + 30b$.

Solving these equations, we get $a = 0.72, b = 1.33$.

Thus the required line is $y = 0.72 + 1.33x$.

Example 5: *Fit a straight line to the given data regarding x as the independent variable:*

x	1	2	3	4	5	6
y	1200	900	600	200	110	50

Solution: Let the straight line obtained from the given data be $y = a + bx$. Then the normal equations are

$$\Sigma\, y = ma + b\,\Sigma\, x \quad \text{and} \quad \Sigma\, xy = a\,\Sigma\, x + b\,\Sigma\, x^2.$$

Here $m = 6$.

x	y	x^2	xy
1	1200	1	1200
2	900	4	1800
3	600	9	1800
4	200	16	800
5	110	25	550
6	50	36	300
$\Sigma x = 21$	$\Sigma y = 3060$	$\Sigma x^2 = 91$	$\Sigma xy = 6450$

Substituting the values of Σx, Σy, Σx^2 and Σxy in the above equations from the Table, we get

$$3060 = 6a + 21b$$

$$6450 = 21a + 91b.$$

Solving these, we get $a = 1361.97$ and $b = -243.42$.

Hence the fitted equation is $y = 1361.97 - 243.42x$.

Example 6: *Fit a second degree parabola to the following data taking x as the independent variable:*

x	1	2	3	4	5	6	7	8	9
y	2	6	7	8	10	11	11	10	9

Solution: The equation of second degree parabola is given by $y = a + bx + cx^2$ and the normal equations are

$$\Sigma y = ma + b\Sigma x + c\Sigma x^2$$

$$\Sigma xy = a\Sigma x + \Sigma bx^2 + c\Sigma x^3 \quad \ldots(1)$$

$$\Sigma x^2 y = a\Sigma x^2 + b\Sigma x^3 + c\Sigma x^4$$

Here $m = 9$. The various sums are appearing in the table as follow:

x	y	xy	x^2	x^2y	x^3	x^4
1	2	2	1	2	1	1
2	6	12	4	24	8	16
3	7	21	9	63	27	81
4	8	32	16	128	64	256
5	10	50	25	250	125	625
6	11	66	36	396	216	1296
7	11	77	49	539	343	2401
8	10	80	64	670	512	4096
9	9	81	81	729	729	6561
$\Sigma x = 45$	$\Sigma y = 74$	$\Sigma xy = 421$	$\Sigma x^2 = 284$	$\Sigma x^2 y = 2771$	$\Sigma x^3 = 2025$	$\Sigma x^4 = 15333$

Putting these values of $\Sigma x, \Sigma y, \Sigma x^2, \Sigma x^2 y, \Sigma x^3$ and Σx^4 in (1) and solving the equations for a, b and c; we get

$$a = -0.923; \quad b = 3.520; \quad c = -0.267.$$

Hence the fitted equation is $y = -0.923 + 3.52x - 00.267x^2$.

17.5 Change of Origin and Scale for Simplifying the Calculations

Sometimes the magnitude of the variables in the given data is so big that the calculations become very much tedious. The size of the data can be considerably reduced by assuming some convenient origin for x and y series in the given data. The problem is further simplified by taking suitable scale when the values of x are given at equally spaced intervals.

Let h be the width of the interval at which the values of x are given and let the origins of x and y be taken at the point x_0, y_0 respectively, then putting $u = (x - x_0)/h$ and $v = y - y_0$; the equation

$y = a + bx + cx^2$ can be written in terms of v and u

$$\Rightarrow \quad v + y_0 = a + b(hu + x_0) + c(hu + x_0)^2 \quad \text{...(1)}$$

$$\Rightarrow \quad v = (a + bx_0 + cx_0)^2 + (bh + 2chx_0)u + ch^2u^2 \quad \text{...(2)}$$

$$= a' + b'u + c'u^2$$

where $\quad a' = a + bx_0 + cx_0^2, b' = bh + 2chx_0, c' = ch^2 \quad$ ...(3)

Now, we can get normal equations in terms of u and v by applying the usual least squares method on (2). After fitting (2) by calculating a', b' and c', u and v in fitted equation can be replaced by $\frac{x - x_0}{h}$ and $y - y_0$ to get the fitted equation in terms of x and y. Similar transformations can be applied to polynomials of higher degree.

Example 7: *Fit a second degree parabola to the following data by least squares method.*

x	1929	1930	1931	1932	1933	1934	1935	1936	1937
y	352	356	357	358	360	361	361	360	359

Solution: Taking $x_0 = 1933, h = 1$.

We have $u = x - 1933$ and $v = y - 357$, say $\left(\because u = \frac{x - x_0}{h}\right)$

and the equation $y = a + bx + cx^2$ is transformed to $v = a' + b'u + c'u^2$.

Now prepare the table.

x	$u = x - 1933$	y	$v = y - 357$	uv	u^2	u^2v	u^3	u^4
1929	−4	352	−5	20	16	−80	−64	256
1930	−3	356	−1	3	9	−9	−27	81
1931	−2	357	0	0	4	0	−8	16
1932	−1	358	1	−1	1	1	−1	1
1933	0	360	3	0	0	0	0	0
1934	1	361	4	4	1	4	1	1
1935	2	361	4	8	4	16	8	16
1936	3	360	3	9	9	27	27	81
1937	4	359	2	8	16	32	64	256
Total	$\Sigma u = 0$		$\Sigma v = 11$	$\Sigma uv = 11$	$\Sigma u^2 = 60$	$\Sigma u^2 v = -9$	$\Sigma u^3 = 0$	$\Sigma u^4 = 708$

Putting the values of $\Sigma u, \Sigma v, \Sigma uv, \Sigma u^2, \Sigma u^2 v, \Sigma u^3$ and Σu^4 form the table, in the normal equations; we get

$$9a' + 60c' = 11;\ 60b' = 51;\ 60a' + 708c' = -9$$

$$\Rightarrow \quad a' = 3, b' = 0.85 \text{ and } c' = -0.27.$$

Hence the fitted parabola in u and v is given by $v = 3 + 0.85\,u - 0.27\,u^2$.

Now putting $v = y - 357$ and $u = x - 1933$ in the fitted equation and simplifying, we obtain

$$y = 349 + 3.55x - 0.27x^2.$$

Example 8: *Show that the line of fit to the following data is given by*

$$y = .7x + 11.28.$$

x	0	5	10	15	20	25
y	12	15	17	22	24	30

Solution: There are six *i.e.* even values of x and are equidistant. Hence transfer the origin of x series to mean of 10 and 15 *i.e.* to 12.5 and take $\frac{5}{2}$ as the unit of measurement.

Putting $u = \dfrac{x-12.5}{2.5}$ and $v = y - 20$, we get

x	y	u	v	uv	u^2
0	12	−5	−8	40	25
5	15	−3	−5	15	9
10	17	−1	−3	3	1
15	22	1	2	2	1
20	24	3	4	12	9
25	30	5	10	50	25
		$\Sigma u = 0$	$\Sigma v = 0$	$\Sigma uv = 122$	$\Sigma u^2 = 70$

The normal equations are $0 = 6a + 0.b,\ 122 = 0.a + 70b$

which give $a = 0, b = 1.743$. Thus line of fit is $v = 1.743\,u$.

or $\quad y - 20 = (1.743)\left(\dfrac{x-12.50}{2.5}\right) = .7x - 8.715$

or $\quad y = .7x + 11.285$.

Example 9: *The weight of a calf taken at weekly intervals are given below. Fit a straight line using the method of least squares and calculate the average rate of growth per week.*

Age	1	2	3	4	5	6	7	8	9	10
Weight	52.5	58.7	65.0	70.2	75.4	81.1	87.2	95.5	102.2	108.4

Solution: Let us denote the variable age and weight by x and y respectively. In this case the number of values of x are 10, *i.e.* even and are equidistant at an interval of unity. Transfer the origin of x series to the means of 5 and 6 *i.e.* to 5.5 and take the unit of measurement as $\dfrac{1}{2}$. Introduce the new variable $u = (x - 5.5)/1/2$ *i.e.* $u = 2x - 11$.

The calculations are obtained as below:

x	y	u	uy	u^2
1	52.5	−9	−472.5	81
2	58.7	−7	−410.9	49
3	65.0	−5	−325.0	25
4	70.2	−3	−210.6	9
5	75.4	−1	−75.4	1
6	81.1	1	81.1	1
7	87.2	3	261.6	9
8	95.5	5	477.5	25
9	102.2	7	715.4	49
10	108.4	9	975.6	81
Total	796.2	$\Sigma u = 0$	$\Sigma uy = 1016.8$	$\Sigma u^2 = 330$

Let the line of fit be $y = a + bu$.

$$\Sigma y = na + b\Sigma u \text{ and } \Sigma uy = a\Sigma u + b\Sigma u^2.$$

i.e. $796.2 = 10a + 0.b +$ and $1016.8 = a.0 + 330b$.

Solving these, we get $a = 79.62$ and $b = 3.08$ approx.

Thus the line of fit is $y = 79.62 + 3.08u$

or $y = 79.62 + 3.08(2x - 11)$ or $y = 45.74 + 6.16x$

The calculations are obtained as below:

Example 10: *Fit second degree parabola to the following:*

x	0	1	2	3	4
y	1	1.8	1.3	2.5	6.3

Solution: Since the number of values of x are odd and are equidistant, transfer the origin for the x series at the middle valuc 2.

Now let $u = x - 2$ and $v = y$ and the curve of fit be $v = a + bu + cu^2$

x	y	u	v	uv	u^2	u^2v	u^3	u^4
0	1	−2	1	−2	4	4	−8	16
1	1.8	−1	1.8	−1.8	1	1.8	−1	1
2	1.3	0	1.3	0	0	0	0	0
3	2.5	1	2.5	2.5	1	2.5	1	1
4	6.3	2	6.3	12.6	4	25.2	8	16
Total		$\Sigma u = 0$	$\Sigma v =$ 12.9	$\Sigma uv =$ 11.3	$\Sigma u^2 = 10$	$\Sigma u^2 v =$ 33.5	$\Sigma u^3 = 0$	$\Sigma u^4 = 34$

$$\Sigma v = 5a + b\Sigma u + c\Sigma u^2$$

Hence the normal equations are: $\Sigma uv = a\Sigma u + b\Sigma u^2 + c\Sigma u^3$

$$\Sigma u^2 v = a\Sigma u^2 + b\Sigma u^3 + c\Sigma u^4.$$

Putting the values of $\Sigma u, \Sigma v$ etc. from the table in these, we get

$$12.9 = 5a + 10c, \quad 11.3 = 10b, \quad 33.5 = 10a + 34c.$$

On solving these equations, we get $a = 1.48, b = 1.13, c = 0.55$.

Therefore the required equation is $v = 1.48 + 1.13u + 0.55u^2$

Again changing the origin *i.e.* substituting $u = x - 2, v = y$, we get $y = 1.48 + 1.13(x - 2) + 0.55(x - 2)^2$ or $y = 1.42 - 1.07x + 0.55x^2$.

Example 11: *The profit of a certain company in the xth year of its life are given by*

x	1	2	3	4	5
y	1250	1400	1650	1850	2300

Taking $u = x - 3$ *and* $v = \dfrac{y - 1650}{50}$, *show that the parabola of the second degree of v on u is* $v + 0.086 = 5\ 30\,u + 0.643\,u^2$ *and deduce that the parabola of the second degree of y on x is*

$$y = 1144 + 72x + 32.15x^2.$$

Solution: With given conditions, the calculations are as shown in the table:

x	y	u	v	uv	u^2	$u^2 v$	u^3	u^4
1	1250	−2	−8	16	4	−32	−8	16
2	1400	−1	−5	5	1	−5	−1	1
3	1650	0	0	0	0	0	0	0
4	1950	1	6	6	1	6	1	1
5	2300	2	13	26	4	52	8	16
		$\Sigma u = 0$	$\Sigma v = 6$	$\Sigma uv = 53$	$\Sigma u^2 = 10$	$\Sigma u^2 v = 21$	$\Sigma u^3 = 0$	$\Sigma u^4 = 34$

Let $v = a + bu + cu^2$ be the second degree parabola. The normal

equations are

$$\Sigma v = 5a + b\,\Sigma u + c\,\Sigma u^2$$
$$\Sigma uv = a\,\Sigma u + b\,\Sigma u^2 + c\,\Sigma u^3$$
$$\Sigma u^2 v = a\,\Sigma u^2 + b\,\Sigma u^3 + c\,\Sigma u^4$$

i.e. $6 = 5a + b.0 + 10c$ i.e. $6 = 5a + 10c$ ...(1)

$53 = 0.a + b.10 + c.0$ i.e. $b = 5{,}30$

$21 = 10a + b.0 + 34c$ i.e. $21 = 10a + 34c$ ...(2)

Solving (1) and (2), we get $c = .643$ and $a = -0.086$

Therefore putting these values of a, b, c in $v = a + bu + cu^2$, we get

$$v = -0.086 + 5.30\,u + .643\,u^2 \text{ or } v + 0.086 = 5.30\,u + .643\,u^2$$

Again putting $u = x - 3$ and $v = \dfrac{y - 1650}{50}$, we get

$$\frac{y - 1650}{50} + 0.086 = 5.30\,(x - 3) + .643\,(x - 3)^2$$

or $$y - 1650 + .43 = 265\,(x - 3) + 32.15\,(x^2 - 6x + 9)$$

or $$y = 1144 + 72x + 32.15x^2.$$

Example 12: *Fit a parabolic curve to the following data:*

x	1	2	3	4	5
y	1090	1220	1390	1625	1915

Solution: Changing the origin by $u = x - 3$, $v = (y - 1450)/5$. Suppose the curve of best fit be $v = a + bu + cu^2$. The normal equations are given

by
$$\left.\begin{aligned}\Sigma v &= 5a + \Sigma u + c\,\Sigma u^2\\ \Sigma uv &= a\,\Sigma u + b\,\Sigma u^2 + c\,\Sigma u^3\\ \Sigma u^2 v &= a\,\Sigma u^2 + b\Sigma u^3 + c\,\Sigma u^4\end{aligned}\right]$$

x	y	u	v	u^2	u^3	u^4	uv	$u^2 v$
1	1090	−2	−72	4	−8	16	144	−288
2	1220	−1	−46	1	−1	1	46	−46
3	1390	0	−12	0	0	0	0	0
4	1625	1	35	1	1	1	35	35
5	1915	2	93	4	8	16	186	372
Total		$\Sigma u = 0$	$\Sigma v = -2$	$\Sigma u^2 = 10$	$\Sigma u^3 = 0$	$\Sigma u^4 = 34$	$\Sigma uv = 411$	$\Sigma u^2 v = 73$

Putting the value in the normal equations, we have

$$-2 = 5a + 10c,\ 411 = 10b,\ 73 = 10a + 34c.$$

Solving these, we get $a = -11.4, b = 41.1, c = 5.5$.

Therefore the curve of best fit is given by

$$v = -11.4 + 41.1u + 5.5u^2.$$

Now changing the origin back *i.e.*, putting $u = x - 3$ and $v = (y - 1450)/5$, the required curve of best fit is given by

$$\frac{1}{5}(y - 1450) = -11.4 + 41.1(x - 3) + 5.5\,(x - 3)^2$$

or
$$y = 1024 + 40.5x + 27.5\,x^2.$$

17.6 Most Plausible Solution of a System of Linear Equations

Let us consider a number of independent linear equations in variables, $x, y, z, \ldots, t$.

$$\left.\begin{aligned}a_1 x + b_1 y + c_1 z + \ldots + k_1 t &= l_1\\ a_2 x + b_2 y + c_2 z + \ldots + k_2 t &= l_2\\ \ldots\quad \ldots\quad \ldots\quad &\ldots\quad \ldots\\ a_m x + b_m y + c_m z + \ldots + k_m t &= l_m\end{aligned}\right\} \quad \ldots(1)$$

where *a's*, *b's*,..., *l's* are constants.

In case $m = n$ then we can solve (1) uniquely with the help of algebra. In case $m > n$ *i.e.* the number of equations is greater than the number of unknown, it may not be possible to determine a unique solution $x, y, z, \ldots, t$ satisfying (1). In such cases, we find the values of $x, y, z, \ldots, t$ which will satisfy the given system of equations as nearly as possible.

The principle of least squares asserts in minimizing the sum of the squares of the residues or the errors. Let

$$E_i = a_i x + b_i y + c_i z + \ldots + k_i t - l_i$$

where $i = 1, 2, \ldots m$, be the residual for *ith* equation, then we have to find those values $x, y, z, \ldots, t$ which makes

$$U = \sum_{i=1}^{m} E_i^2 = \sum_{i=1}^{m} (a_i x + b_i y + c_i z + \ldots + k_i t - l_i)^2 \text{ to be minimum.}$$

Applying the conditions of maxima or minima, we should have

$$\frac{\partial U}{\partial x} = 0 = \sum_{i=1}^{m} a_i (a_i x + b_i y + c_i z + \ldots + k_i t - l_i)$$

$$\frac{\partial U}{\partial y} = 0 = \sum_{i=1}^{m} b_i (a_i x + b_i y + c_i z + \ldots + k_i t - l_i)$$

$$\ldots \quad \ldots \quad \ldots \quad \ldots \quad \ldots \quad \ldots$$

$$\frac{\partial U}{\partial t} = 0 = \sum_{i=1}^{m} k_i (a_i x + b_i y + c_i z + \ldots + k_i t - l_i)$$

These are known as the ***normal equations*** for $x, y, z, \ldots, t$ respectively. On solving these equations simultaneously they give the values of $x, y, z, \ldots, t$; these are known as the best or most plausible values.

On calculating the second order partial derivative and substituting the values of $x, y, z, \ldots, t$ so obtained we will observe that the expression will be positive *i.e.* U is minimum.

Example 13: *Find the most plausible values of x and y from the following equations:*

$$x - 5y + 4 = 0, \; 2x - 3y + 5 = 0,$$

$$x + 2y - 3 = 0, \; 4x + 3y + 1 = 0.$$

[Meerut 2003]

Solution: Let $U = (x - 5y + 4)^2 + (2x - 3y + 5)^2 + (x + 2y - 3)^2 + (4x + 3y + 1)^2$

The values of x, y which make U a minimum are called most plausible values and are given by $\frac{\partial U}{\partial x} = 0 = \frac{\partial U}{\partial y}$

i.e. $\quad (x - 5y + 4).1 + (2x - 3y + 5).2 + (x + 2y - 3).1 + (4x + 3y + 1).4 = 0$

or $\quad 22x + 3y + 15 = 0 \qquad \ldots (1)$

and $(x-5y+4).(-5)+(2x-3y+5).(-3)+(x+2y-3).2+(4x+3y+1).3=0$

i.e. $3x+47y-38=0$ ...(2)

Solving (1) and (2), we get

$$x=-0.799 \text{ approx and } y=0.86 \text{ approx}$$

These are the most plausible values of x and y.

Example 14: *Drive the least square equations for fitting a curve of the type $y=ax^2+(b/x)$ to a set of n points. Hence fit a curve of this type to the data:* **[Meerut 2005]**

x	1	2	3	4
y	-1.51	0.99	3.88	7.66

Solution: Let the n points are given by $(x_1, y_1), (x_2, y_2), ..., (x_n, y_n)$.

The error of estimate for the *ith* point (x_i, y_i)

$$E_i=\{y_i-ax_i^2-(b/x_i)\}.$$

By the principle of least squares, the values of a and b are such so that the sum of the squares of error U, *viz.*,

$$U=\sum_{i=1}^{n}E_i^2=\sum_{i=1}^{n}\left(y_i-ax_i^2-\frac{b}{x_i}\right)^2 \text{ is minimum.}$$

Therefore the normal equations are given by $\frac{\partial U}{\partial a}=0$ and $\frac{\partial U}{\partial b}=0$

or $$\sum_{i=1}^{n}y_ix_i^2=a\sum_{i=1}^{n}x_i^4+b\sum_{i=1}^{n}x_i, \sum_{i=1}^{n}\frac{y_i}{x_i}=a\sum_{i=1}^{n}x_i+b\sum_{i=1}^{n}\frac{1}{x_i^2}$$

These are the required least square equations.

x	y	x^2	x^4	$\frac{1}{x}$	$\frac{1}{x^2}$	yx^2	$\frac{y}{x}$
1	-1.51	1	1	1	1	-1.51	-1.51
2	0.99	4	16	.5	.25	3.96	.495
3	3.88	9	81	.3333	.1111	34.92	1.2933
4	3.66	16	256	.25	.0625	122.56	2.9150
10			354		1.4236	159.93	1.1933

Putting the values in the above least square equations we get

$$159.93=354a+10b \text{ and } 2.1933=10a+1.4236b.$$

Solving these, we have $a=0.509, b=-2.04$. Therefore the equation of the curve fitted to the above data is $y=0.509x^2-\frac{2.04}{x}$.

Example 15: *Fit an exponential curve of the form $y = ab^x$ to the following data:*

x	1	2	3	4	5	6	7	8
y	1.0	1.2	1.8	2.5	3.6	4.7	6.6	9.1

Solution: $y = ab^x$ takes the form $Y = A + Bx$,

where $Y = \log y$, $A = \log a$ and $B = \log b$.

Hence the normal equations are given by

$$\Sigma Y = nA + B\,\Sigma x \text{ and } \Sigma xY = A\,\Sigma x + B\,\Sigma x^2.$$

x	y	$Y = \log y$	xY	x^2
1	1.0	0.0000	0.000	1
2	1.2	0.0792	0.1584	4
3	1.8	0.2553	0.7659	9
4	2.5	0.3979	1.5916	16
5	3.6	0.5563	2.7815	25
6	4.7	0.6721	4.0326	36
7	6.6	0.8195	5.7365	49
8	9.1	0.9590	7.6720	64
36	30.5	3.7393	22.7385	204

Putting the value in the normal equations, we obtain

$$3.7393 = 8A + 36B \text{ and } 22.7385 = 36A + 204B.$$

$$\Rightarrow \quad B = 0.1406,\ A = \bar{1}.8336.$$

$$\Rightarrow \quad b = \text{antilog } B = 1.38 \text{ and } a = \text{antilog } A = 0.68.$$

Thus the required curve of best fit is $y = (0.68)(1.38)^x$.

Example 16: *Find the most plausible values of x, y and z from the following equations:*

$x - y + 2z = 3,\ \ 3x + 2y - 5z = 5,\ \ 4x + y + 4z = 21,\ \ -x + 3y + 3z = 14.$ **[Meerut 2002]**

Solution: Normal equation for x is

$$(x - y + 2z - 3) + 3(3x + 2y - 5z - 5) + 4(4x + y + 4z - 21) - 1(-x + 3y + 3z - 14) = 0$$

$$\Rightarrow \quad 27x + 6y = 88. \qquad \ldots(1)$$

Normal equation for y is

$$-(x - y + 2z - 3) + 2(3x + 2y - 5z - 5) + (4x + y + 4z - 21) + 3(-x + 3y + 3z - 14) = 0$$

$$\Rightarrow \quad 6x + 15y + z = 70. \qquad \ldots(2)$$

While normal equation for z is

$$2(x-y+2z-3)-5(3x+2y-5z-5)+4(4x+y+4z-21)$$
$$+3(-x+3y+3z-14)=0$$

$$y+54z=107. \quad \ldots(3)$$

Solving the equations (1), (2) and (3), we get

$$x=2.47, \quad y=3.55, \quad z=1.92.$$

Hence the most plausible values of x, y and z are $2.47, 3.55, 1.92$ respectively.

17.7 Fitting of the Curve of the Type $y = ab^x$ and $y = ax^b$

The following procedure is adopted in fitting the curve of these types. Let the curve to be fitted be $y = ab^x$.

Taking log, we have $\log y = \log a + x \log b$ or $Y = A + Bx$,

[where $Y = \log y$, $A = \log a$ and $B = \log b$]

Fitting of (1) will be done just like the case of straight line, the normal equations in this case are

$$\Sigma Y = nA + B\Sigma x \text{ i.e., } \Sigma \log y = n \log a + \log b \, \Sigma x$$

and $$\Sigma xY = A\Sigma x + B\Sigma x^2 \text{ i.e., } \Sigma x \log y = \log a \, \Sigma x + \log b \, \Sigma x^2.$$

These equations are solved for $\log a$ and $\log b$ and then on taking antilogs, we can find the values of a and b.

Example 17: *Fit a curve $y = ab^x$ to the following data:*

x	2	3	4	5	6
y	144	172.8	207.4	248.8	298.5

Solution: $y = ab^x$ reduces to $Y = A + Bx$,

where $Y = \log y$, $A = \log a$ and $B = \log b$.

The normal equations are $\Sigma \log y = n \log a + \log b \, \Sigma x$

$$\Sigma x \log y = \log a \, \Sigma x + \log b \, \Sigma x^2.$$

The calculation of Σx, $\Sigma \log y$, Σx^2 and $\Sigma x \log y$ are put in the following tabular form

x	y	x^2	$\log y$	$x \log y$
2	144	4	2.1584	4.3168
3	172.8	9	2.2375	6.7125
4	207.4	16	2.3168	9.2672
5	248.8	25	2.3959	11.9795
6	298.5	36	2.4749	14.8494
20		90	11.5835	47.1254

Putting these values in the normal equations, we have

$$11.5835 = 5 \log a + 20 \log b$$

and $$47.1254 = 20 \log a + 90 \log b.$$

Solving these equations and taking antilogs, we have $a = 100, b = 1.2$ approx. Therefore equation of the curve is $y = 100\,(1.2)^x$

17.8 Fitting of the Curve $pv^r = k$

Taking p as the independent variable

$$p\,v^r = k \quad \text{or} \quad v = \left(\frac{k}{p}\right)^{1/r} = k^{1/r} p^{-1/r}.$$

On taking log, we get $\log v = \frac{1}{r} \log k - \frac{1}{r} \log p$

which is of the form $Y = A + BX$, where $a = \frac{1}{r} \log k$

$$B = -\frac{1}{r},\ X = \log p \text{ and } Y = \log v.$$

We can determine A and B by proceeding in the same way as in the case of fitting of a straight line. Once A and B are calculated the values of r and k can be obtained from the above relations.

17.9 Fitting of the Curve of Type $xy = b + ax$

$$xy = b + ax,$$

$$\therefore \quad y = \frac{b}{x} + a \qquad y = bX + a, \qquad \ldots(1)$$

where $X = \frac{1}{x}$. We have fitted equation (1) like a straight line.

Example 18: *Fit the curve $p\,v^r = k$ to the following data:*

$p\,(kg/cm^2)$	0.5	1.0	1.5	2.0	2.5	3.0
v *(litres)*	1.62	1.00	0.75	0.62	0.52	0.46

Solution: Proceeding like 17.8, the equation to be fitted is

$$Y = A + BX$$

where $$A = \frac{1}{r} \log k,\ B = -\frac{1}{r},\ X = \log p \text{ and } Y = \log v.$$

Put the calculations in following form taking v in $c.c.$

p	v in $c.c.$	$X = \log p$	$Y = \log v$	XY	X^2
0.5	1620	$\bar{1}.698$*	3.209	–.9691	0.0912
1.0	1000	.000	3.000	0.0000	0.0000
1.5	750	.176	2.875	.5060	0.0309
2.0	620	.301	2.792	.8403	0.0906
2.5	520	.397	2.716	1.0782	0.1576
3.0	460	.477	2.662	1.2697	0.2286
Total		1.049	17.254	1.7251	0.5989

Thus the normal equations are

$$\Sigma Y = nA + B\Sigma X \text{ i.e. } 17.254 = 6A + 1.049B$$

$$\Sigma XY = A\Sigma X + B\Sigma X^2, 2.7251 = 1.049A + .5989B.$$

Solving these, we get $A = 3, B = -.71$.

$$\therefore \qquad r = -\left(-\frac{1}{.71}\right) = \frac{1}{.71} = 1.41 \text{ approx.}$$

Again $\log k = Ar = 3.(1.41) = 4.23$

$$= 10^5 \times (.16980) = 16980.$$

Therefore the required curve $y_v^{1.41} = 16980.$

Example 19: *For the data given below, find the equation to the best fitting exponential curve of the form* $y = ae^{bx}$

x	1	2	3	4	5	6
y	1.6	4.5	13.8	40.2	125	300

Solution: $y = ae^{bx}$, taking log, we get

Note: $\bar{1}.698 = -1 + .698 = -.302$

$\log y = \log a + bx \log_{10} e$ which is of the form

$Y = A + Bx$, where $Y = \log y$, $A = \log a$ and $\log_{10} e$.

Put the calculation in the following tabular form, also transfer the origin of x series to 3, so that $u = x - 3$:

x	y	$\log y = Y$	$x - 3 = u$	uY	u^2
1	1.6	.204	−2	−.408	4
2	4.5	.653	−1	−.653	1
3	13.8	1.140	0	1.604	0
4	40.2	1.604	1	.0	1
5	125.0	2.094	2	4.194	4
6	300.0	2.477	3	7.431	9
Total		8.175	3	12.168	19

In case $Y = A' + B'.u$, then normal equations are given by

$$\sum Y = nA' + B' \sum u \text{ i.e. } 8.175 = 6A' + 3B' \quad \text{...(1)}$$

and $$\sum uY = A' \sum u + B' \sum u^2 \text{ i.e. } 12.168 = 3A' + 19B' \quad \text{...(2)}$$

Solving (1) and (2), we get $A' = 1.13$ and $B' = .46$.

Thus equation is $Y = 1.13 + .46\,u$, i.e. $Y = 1.13 + .46(x - 3)$

or $\qquad Y = .46x - .25$

which gives $\log a = -.25$ i.e. $a = \text{antilog}(-.25) = \text{antilog}(\bar{1}.75) = .557$

$$b = \frac{B}{\log_{10} e} = \frac{64}{.4343} = 1.06.$$

Hence the required equation of the curve is $y = (.577)e^{1.6X}$.

17.10 Method of Group Averages

Let the straight line $y = a + bx$ ...(1)

fit the set of n observations $(x_1, y_1), (x_2, y_2), \ldots, (x_n, y_n)$ quite closely. When $x = x_1$, the *observed value* of $y = y_1 = R_1P_1$ and from (1), $y = a + bx_1 = R_1M_1$. This is known as the *expected* (or *calculated*) *value of* y at R_1. Now

e_1 = observed value at R_1 − expected value at R_1 $P_1 = y_1 - (a + bx_1) = M_1P_1$.

This is called the *error* (or *residual*) at x_1. Similarly the errors for the other observations are given by $e_2 = y_2 - (a + bx_2) = M_2P_2, \ldots\ldots; e_n = y_n - (a + bx_n) = M_n P_n$. Some of these errors may be positive and others negative. The basic idea of the method of group averages is based on the assumption that the sum of the residuals is zero. To find the constants a and b, we require two equations. For this, we divide the data into two groups:

(i) First containing k observations $(x_1, y_1), (x_2, y_2) \ldots (x_k, y_k)$;

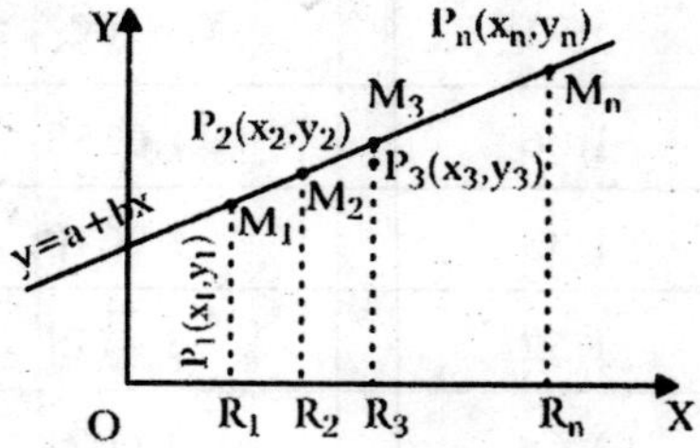

(ii) The second group having the remaining $n-k$ observations

$(x_{k+1}, y_{k+1}), (x_{k+2}, y_{k+2}), \ldots, (x_n, y_n)$.

Let the sum of the errors in each group be zero, then we get

$$\{y_1 - (a + bx_1)\} + \{y_2 - (a + bx_2)\} + \ldots + \{y_k - (a + bx_k)\} = 0$$

$$\{y_{k+1} - (a + bx_{k+1})\} + \{y_{k+2} - (a + bx_{k+2})\} + \ldots + \{y_n - (a + bx_n)\} = 0$$

Then on simplification, we readily get

$$\frac{y_1 + y_2 + \ldots y_k}{k} = a + b\frac{x_1 + x_2 + \ldots + x_k}{k} \quad \ldots(2)$$

$$\frac{y_{k+1} + y_{k+2} + \ldots + y_n}{n-k} = a + b\frac{x_{k+1} + x_{k+2} + \ldots + x_n}{n-k} \quad \ldots(3)$$

But $\frac{1}{k}(x_1 + x_2 + \ldots + x_k)$ and $\frac{1}{k}(y_1 + y_2 + \ldots y_k)$ are simply the average values of x's and y's of the first group. Thus the equations (2) and (3) are obtained from (1) by replacing x and y by their respective averages of the group. Solving (2) and (3), we get a and b.

> **Note:** The drawback of this method is that the different grouping of the observations will give different values of a and b. In practice, we divide the data in such a way that each group contains almost an equal number of observations.

Example 20: *The observations in the following table fit a law of the form $y = x^n$. Estimate a and n by the method of group averages.*

x	10	20	30	40	50	60	70	80
y	1.06	1.33	1.52	1.68	1.81	1.91	2.01	2.11

Solution: $y = ax^n$, taking logarithms, $\log_{10} y = \log_{10} a + n \log_{10} x$

$$\Rightarrow \quad Y = A + nX \quad \ldots(1)$$

where $X = \log_{10} x, Y = \log_{10} y, A \log_{10} a$

Let us now divide the data into two groups such that each contains four pairs of values:

x	y	$X = \log_{10} x$	$Y = \log_{10} y$
10	1.06	1.0253	0.0253
20	1.33	1.3010	0.1238
30	1.52	1.4771	0.1818
40	1.68	1.6021	0.2253
		$\Sigma X = 5.4055$	$\Sigma Y = 0.5562$

x	y	$X = \log_{10} x$	$Y = \log_{10} y$
50	1.81	1.6990	0.2577
60	1.91	1.7782	0.2810
70	2.01	1.8451	0.3032
80	2.11	1.9031	0.3243
		$\Sigma X = 7.2254$	$\Sigma Y = 1.1662$

Then substituting the averages of X's and Y's of the two groups in (1), we get

$$\frac{0.5562}{4} = A + n\frac{5.4055}{4} \quad i.e.\ 0.1390 = A + 1.3514\, n \qquad \ldots(2)$$

$$\frac{1.1662}{4} = A + n\frac{7.2254}{4} \quad i.e.\ 0.2916 = A + 1.8064\, n \qquad \ldots(3)$$

Solving (2) and (3), we get $n = 0.3354$

and $\quad A = -0.3142 \quad \Rightarrow \log_{10} a = -0.3142$

i.e. $\quad a = \text{antilog}\,(-0.3142) = 0.4851.$

Example 21: *The latent heat of vaporisation of steam r, is given in the following table at different temperatures t:*

t	40	50	60	70	80	90	100	110
F	1069.1	1063.6	1058.2	1052.7	1049.3	1041.8	1036.3	1030.8

For this range of temperature, a relation of the form $r = a + bt$ is known to fit the data. Find the values of a and b by the method of group averages.

Solution: Let the whole data be divided into two groups such that each contains four readings. Then we have two groups as follows:

t	r	t	r
40	1069.1	80	1049.3
50	1063.6	90	1041.8
60	1058.2	100	1036.3
70	1052.7	110	1030.8
$\Sigma t = 220$	$\Sigma r = 4243.6$	$\Sigma t = 380$	$\Sigma r = 4158.2$

Then substituting the averages of t's and r's of the two groups in the given relation, we have

$$\frac{4243.6}{4} = a + b\frac{220}{4} \quad i.e. \; 1060.9 = a + 55b \qquad \ldots (1)$$

and $$\frac{4158.2}{2} = a + b\frac{380}{4} \quad i.e. \; 1039.55 = a + 95\,b \qquad \ldots (2)$$

Then solving (1) and (2), we get

$$a = 1090.26, b = -0.534.$$

17.11 Laws Containing Three Constants

So far we have the above methods to fit the data to laws involving two constants only. But some times we come across laws of the form

$$y = a + bx + cx^2,\ y = a + bx^c \text{ and } y = a + be^{cx}$$

each of which contains three constants. To fit such laws to a set of observations, we device the following procedure.

(1) Equation $y = a + bx + cx^2$

Let (x_1, y_1) be a point on the curve satisfying the given data, then we have

$y_1 = a + bx_1 + cx_1^2 \Rightarrow y - y_1 = b(x - x_1) + c(x^2 - x_1^2)$

$$\Rightarrow \qquad \frac{y - y_1}{x - x_1} = b + c(x + x_1)$$

Now putting $x + x_1 = X$ and $(y - y_1)/(x - x_1) = Y$, we get

$Y = b + cX$. Then b and c can be found by the graphical method or the method of averages.

(2) Equation $y = a + bx^c$

We have $$y - a = bx^c \quad \text{...(1)}$$

To find a, let $(x_1, y_1), (x_2, y_2)(x_3, y_3)$ be three particular points on the curve (1) such that x_1, x_2, x_3 are in geometric progression

i.e. $$x_1 x_3 = x_2^2 \quad \text{...(2)}$$

Then we have $y_1 - a = bx_1^c$, $y_2 - a = bx_2^c$, and $y_3 - a = bx_3^c$

$$\Rightarrow \quad (y_1 - a)(y_3 - a) = b^2 (x_1 x_3)^c = b^2 (x_2^2)^c = (bx_2^c)^2 = (y_2 - a)^2$$

$$\Rightarrow \quad a(y_1 + y_3 - 2y_2) = y_1 y_3 - y_2^2$$

This gives a, then (1) reduce to a relation containing two constants b and c only.

Now taking logarithms, (1), $\Rightarrow \log_{10}(y - a) = \log_{10} b + c \log_{10} x$

$$\Rightarrow \quad Y = B + cX \quad \text{...(3)}$$

where $X = \log_{10} x, Y = \log_{10}(y - a), B = \log_{10} b$.

Thus we can find b and c.

(3) Equation $y = a + be^{cx}$

We have $$y - a = be^{cx} \quad \text{...(1)}$$

To find a, let $(x_1, y_1), (x_2, y_2)(x_3, y_3)$ be three particular points on the curve (1) such that x_1, x_2, x_3 are in arithmetic progression, then we have

$$x_1 + x_3 = 2x_2,\ y_1 - a = be^{cx_1},\ y_2 - a = be^{cx_2},\ y_3 - a = be^{cx_3},$$

$$\Rightarrow \quad (y_1 - a)(y_3 - a) = b^2 e^{c(x_1 + x_3)} = (be^{cx_2})^2 = (y_2 - a)^2$$

$$\Rightarrow \quad a(y_1 + y_3 - 2y_2) = y_1 y_3 - y_2^2$$

This gives a. Now (1) reduces to a law containing two constants b and c only.

Taking logarithms, (1) yields $\log_{10}(y - a) = \log_{10} b + cx \log_{10} e$

$$\Rightarrow \quad Y = B + Cx \quad \text{...(2)}$$

where $Y = \log_{10}(y - a), B = \log_{10} b, C = c \log_{10} e$.

Hence b and c as can be obtained as before.

Example 22: *The train resistance R(lbs/ton) is measured for the following values of its velocity $v\,(km/hr)$:*

V	20	40	60	80	100
R	5	9	14	25	36

If R is related to V by formula $R = a + bV^n$, find a, b and n.

Solution: To find a, we consider the following three values of v:

$$v_1 = 20,\ v_2 = 40,\ v_3 = 80 \quad \textbf{(in G.P)}$$

Then $R_1 = 5, R_2 = 9, R_3 = 25 \Rightarrow (R_1 - a)(R_3 - a) = (R_2 - a)^2$

$$\therefore \quad a = \frac{R_1 R_3 - R_2^2}{R_1 + R_3 - 2R_2} = 3.67 \quad \Rightarrow \quad R - 3.67 = bV^n$$

$$\Rightarrow \quad \log_{10}(R - 3.67) = \log_{10} b + n \log_{10} V \Rightarrow Y = k + nX \quad \ldots(1)$$

where $X = \log_{10} V, Y = \log_{10}(R - 3.67), k = \log_{10} b.$

Now from the following table of values:

V	R	$X = \log_{10} V$	$Y = \log_{10}(R - 3.67)$
20	5	1.3010	0.1238
40	9	1.6021	0.7267
60	14	1.7782	1.0141
		$\Sigma X = 4.6813$	$\Sigma Y = 1.8646$
80	25	1.9031	1.3290
100	36	2.000	1.5096
		$\Sigma X = 3.9031$	$\Sigma Y = 2.8386$

Then putting the averages of X's and Y's in (1)

$$\Rightarrow \quad \frac{1.8646}{2} = k + n\frac{4.6813}{2} \quad i.e.\ 0.6215 = k + 1.5604\,n \quad \ldots(2)$$

$$\text{and} \quad \frac{2.8366}{2} = k + n\frac{3.9031}{2} \quad i.e.\ 1.493 = k + 1.9516\,n \quad \ldots(3)$$

Solving we get $n = 2.04, k = -2.56,$

$$b = \text{antilog}(-2.56) = 0.0028$$

Example 23: *The corresponding values of x and y are given by the following table:*

x	87.5	84.0	77.8	63.7	46.7	36.9
y	292	283	270	235	197	181

Fit a parabola of the form $y = a + bx + cx^2$, by the method of group averages.

Solution: Taking $x = 84, y = 283$ as a particular point on the curve we readily get

$$y = a + bx + cx^2,\ 283 = a + b(84) + c(84)^2 \quad \ldots(1)$$

$$\Rightarrow \quad y - 283 = b(x - 84) + c[x^2 - (84)^2]$$

$$\Rightarrow \quad \frac{y - 283}{x - 84} = b + c(x + 84) \Rightarrow Y = b + cX \quad \ldots(2)$$

where $X = x + 84, Y = (y - 283)/(x - 84).$

Then we have the table:

x	y	$X = x + 84$	$Y = (y - 283)/(x - 84)$
87.5	292	171.5	2.571
84.0	283	–	–
77.8	270	161.8	2.097
		$\Sigma X = 333.3$	$\Sigma Y = 4.668$
63.7	235	147.7	2.364
46.7	197	130.7	2.306
36.9	181	120.9	2.166
		$\Sigma X = 399.3$	$\Sigma Y = 6.836$

Now substituting the averages of X and Y in (2), we get

$$\frac{4.688}{2} = b + c\,\frac{333.3}{2} \quad i.e.\ 2.33 = b + 165.65\,c \qquad \ldots(3)$$

and $$\frac{6.836}{3} = b + c\,\frac{399.3}{3} \quad i.e.\ 2.28 = b + 131.1c \qquad \ldots(4)$$

Solving, we get $c = 0.0014$, and $b = 2.0967 = 2.1$ nearly

From (1), we get $a = 96.9988 = 97$ nearly.

Hence the parabola of fit is $y = 97 + 2.1x + .0014x^2$.

17.12 Method-Moments

Let $(x_1, y_1), (x_2, y_2), \ldots (x_n, y_n)$ be the set of n observations and

$x_2 - x_1 = x_3 - x_2 = x_4 - x_3 = \ldots = x_n - x_{n-1} = h$ say. Then we define the *moments of the observed values of y as*

m_1 = the 1st moment $= h\,\Sigma\, y$

m_2 = the 2nd moment $= h\,\Sigma\, xy$

m_3 = the third moment $= h\,\Sigma\, x^2 y$ etc.

Further, let the curve fitting the given data be $y = f(x)$; then the *moments of the calculated values of y are*

μ_1 = the 1st moment $= \int y\,dx$

μ_2 = the 2nd moment $= \int xy\,dx$

μ_3 = the 3rd moment $= \int x^2 y\,dx$ etc. As a matter of fact, *this method is based on the assumption that the moments of the observed values are respectively equal to the moments of the calculated values of y i.e.,*

$m_1 = \mu_1,\ m_2 = \mu_2,\ m_3 = \mu_3$ etc.

Such equations are known as *observation equations* and are used to determine the constants in $f(x)$.

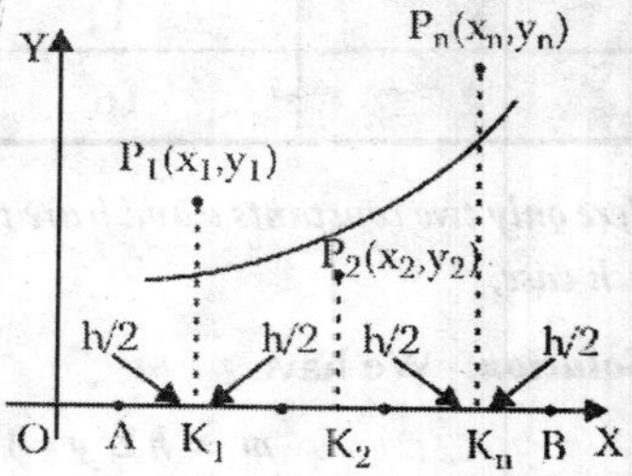

Now m's can be calculated from the tabulated values of x and y where as μ's are computed as given below:

Let y_1 be the ordinate of $P_1(x = x_1)$. It can be taken as the value of y at the mid-point of the interval $(x_1 - h/2, x_1 + h/2)$.

Similarly y_n, the ordinate of $P_n(x = x_n)$, can be taken as the value of y at the mid-point of the interval $(x_n - h/2, x_n + h/2)$.

Now $\quad OA = x_1 - (h/2)$ and $OB = x_n + (h/2)$

$$\mu_1 = \int y\,dx = \int_{x_1-(h/2)}^{x_n+(h/2)} f(x)\,dx$$

$$\mu_2 = \int_{x_1-(h/2)}^{x_n+(h/2)} xf(x)\,dx$$

$$\mu_3 = \int_{x_1-(h/2)}^{x_n+(h/2)} x^2 f(x)\,dx; \text{etc.}$$

Example 24: *In the following data, find the parabola of best fit by the method of moments.*

x	0	1	2	3	4
y	1	5	10	22	38

Solution: Let the parabola of best fit be $y = a + bx + cx^2$ ...(1)

Three constants are to be found, so we calculate the first three moments in each case.

$\therefore \quad m_1 = h\Sigma y = (1 + 5 + 10 + 22 + 38) = 76,$

$m_2 = h\Sigma xy = 1(0 + 5 + 20 + 66 + 152) = 243,$

and $\quad m_3 = h\Sigma x^2 y = 1(0 + 5 + 40 + 198 + 608) = 851 \quad (\because h = 1)$

Then $\quad \mu_1 = \int_{-.5}^{4.5} (a + bx + cx^2)\,dx = 5a + 10b + 30.4c,$

$$\mu_2 = \int_{-.5}^{4.5} x(a + bx + cx^2)\,dx = 10a + 30.4b + 102.5c,$$

$$\mu_3 = \int_{-.5}^{4.5} x^2(a + bx + cx^2)\,dx = 30.4a + 102.5b + 369.1c,$$

Then $\quad m_r = \mu_r \ (r = 1,2,3)$

$\Rightarrow \quad 5a + 10b + 30.4c = 76, \quad 10a + 30.4b + 102.5c = 243,$

and $\quad 30.4a + 102.5b + 369.1c = 851.$

Solving these equations, we get $a = 0.4, b = 3.15, c = 1.4$.

Thus the parabola of best fit is $y = 0.4 + 3.15x + 1.4x^2$.

Example 25: *Fit a straight line $y = a + bx$ to the following data by the method of moments:*

x	1	2	3	4
y	16	19	23	26

Here only two constants a and b are to be obtained so, it is sufficient to calculate first two moments in each case,

Solution: We have

$$m_1 = h\Sigma y = 1(16 + 19 + 23 + 26) = 84$$

and $$m_2 = h\Sigma xy = 1(1\times16 + 2\times19 + 3\times22 + 4\times26) = 227$$

where $h = 1$. To compute the moments of calculated values of $y = a + bx$, the limits of integration will be $1 - (h/2)$ and $4 + (h/2)$ *i.e.*, 0.5 and 4.5

Now $$\mu_1 = \int_{1-(h/2)}^{4+(h/2)} y dx = \int_{.5}^{4.5} (a + bx)\, dx = \left[ax + b\frac{x^2}{2}\right]_{.5}^{4.5}$$

$$= 4a + 10b \qquad (\because h = 1)$$

$$\mu_2 = \int_{.5}^{4.5} x(a + bx)\, dx = 10a + \frac{91}{3}b.$$

Then $$m_r = \mu_r (r = 1, 2) \Rightarrow 4a + 10b = 84$$

and $10a + \frac{91}{3}b = 227 \Rightarrow a = 13.02$ and $b = 3.19$.

$\therefore$ Required equation is $y = 13.02 + 3.19x$.

✦✦ Problem Set ✦✦

1. How do you define the term 'Line of best fit'? Give the normal equation generally used to obtain such a line. Fit a straight line and parabolic curve to the following data:

x	1.0	1.5	2.0	2.5	3.0	3.5	4.0
y	1.1	1.3	1.6	2.6	2.7	3.4	4.1

2. Show that the line of best fit to following data is given by

$$y = -0.5x + 8.$$

x	6	7	7	8	8	8	9	9	10
y	5	5	4	5	4	3	4	3	3

3. Fit a straight line to the following data treating y as the dependent variable.

x	1	2	3	4	5
y	5	7	9	10	11

4. Fit a second degree parabola to the following data, x as the independent variable.

x	1	2	3	4	5	6	7	8	9
y	2	6	7	8	10	11	11	10	9

5. Fit a parabolic curve of regression of y on x to the seven pairs of values.

x	1.0	1.5	2.0	2.5	3.0	3.5	4.0
y	1.1	1.3	1.6	2.0	2.7	3.4	4.1

6. Fit a curve $y = ax^b$ to the following data:

x	1	2	3	4	5	6
y	2.98	4.26	5.21	6.10	6.80	7.50

7. Fit a curve $y = ae^x$ to the following data:

x	1	2	3	4	5	6	7	8
y	15.3	20.5	27.4	36.6	49.1	65.6	87.3	117.6

8. Find the most plausible values of x and y from the following equations:

$$x + y = 3.01, \quad 2x - y = 0.03, \quad x + 3y = 7.03, \quad 3x + y = 4.97$$

9. Find the most plausible values of x and y from the following equations:

$$x - y + 2z = 3, \quad 3x + 2y - 5z = 5, \quad 4x + y + 4z + 21, \quad -x + 3y + 3z = 14$$

10. Fit the curve $y = ax^2 + (b/x)$ to the following data:

x	1	2	3	5
y	−1.51	0.99	3.88	7.66

[Meerut 2003]

11. The profit of a certain company in the xth year of its life are given by:

x	1	2	3	4	5
y	1250	1400	1650	1950	2300

Taking $u = x - 3$ and $v = \dfrac{y - 1650}{50}$, show that the parabola of second degree of v on u is $v = 5.30\,u + 0.643\,u^2 - 0.086$ and deduce that the parabola of second degree of y on x is

$$y = 1144 + 72x + 32.15x^2.$$

12. Find the most plausible values of x and y from the following equations:

$$x - 5y + 4 = 0, \quad 2x - 3y + 5 = 0,$$
$$x + 2y - 3 = 0, \quad 4x + 3y + 1 = 0.$$

13. Find the most plausible values of x and y from the following equations:

$$x + y = 3.01, \quad 2x - y = 0.33,$$
$$x + 3y = 7.03, \quad 3x + y = 4.97.$$

14. By using the method of moments, fit a parabola to the following data:

x	1	2	3	4
y	0.30	0.64	1.32	5.40

[Madras (Chennai) B.E., 2003]

15. Fit parabola of the form $y = a + bx + cx^2$ to the data:

x	1	2	3	4
y	1.7	1.8	2.3	3.2

by the method of moments.

16. Fit a straight line to the following data, using the method of moments:

x	1	3	5	7	9
y	1.5	2.8	4.0	4.7	6.0

✦✦ Objective Type Question ✦✦

❖ Multiple Choice Questions

1. The simplest method of curve fitting is:
   (a) Method of least squares (b) Graphic method
   (c) Scatter diagram (d) None of these.

2. In the method of least square, the constants are choosen in such a way that the sum of the squares of residuals is:
   (a) Minimum (b) Maximum
   (c) Optimum (d) Averages.

3. Which of the following is incorrect:

(a) The method of least squares does not help us to choose the degree of the curve

(b) The method of least squares helps us in finding the values of the constants when the form of the curve has already been chosen

(c) To select the form of the curve is a matter of experience and practical considerations

(d) None of these.

4. Which of the following about the method of least square is incorrect:

(a) It can fit the curves of the form $y = ab^x$ and $y = ax^b$

(b) It can fit the straight lines

(c) It cannot fit curves of the form $pv^r = k$, taking p as independent variable

(d) It can fit the curves of the form $xy = b + ax$.

5. The method of group averages is based on the assumption that the sum of the residuals is:

(a) Zero (b) Unity (c) Constant (d) None of these.

6. If the sum of equations is U, then the most plausible values of a system of equations are found:

(a) By putting $\frac{\partial^2 U}{\partial x^2} = 0, \frac{\partial^2 U}{\partial y^2} = 0$

(b) By putting $\frac{\partial U}{\partial x} = 0 = \frac{\partial U}{\partial y}$

(c) By putting $\frac{\partial U}{\partial x} \neq 0 \neq \frac{\partial U}{\partial y}$

(d) By putting $U = 0$.

Answers

Problem Set

1.	$y = 1.04 - .198x + 0.24x^2$	3.	$y = 3.9 + 1.5x$
4.	$y = -1 + 3.35x - .27x^2$	5.	$y = 1.04 - .198x + 0.24x^2$
6.	$y = 2.978e^{-0.5444}$	7.	$y = 11.58e^{-0.2888x}$
8.	$x = 1.0003,\ y = 2.0007$	9.	$x = 2.47,\ y = 3.55,\ z = 1.92$
10.	$y = 0.509x^2 - (2.04/x)$	12.	$x = -0.8,\ y = 0.86$
13.	$x = 1.0003,\ y = 2.0007$	14.	$y = 0.485 + 0.397x + 0.124x^2$
15.	$y = 1.53 + 0.063x + 0.074x^2$	16.	$y = 1.184 + 0.523x$

Multiple Choice Questions

1.	(b)	2.	(a)	3.	(d)	4.	(c)	5.	(a)	6.	(b)

◆◆◆

Theory | Solved Examples | Problem Set

Chapter 18

Numerical Solution of Partial Differential Equations

Introduction, Classification of Second Order Equations, Finite Difference Approximations to Partial Derivatives, Elliptic Equations, Solution of Laplace's Equation, Solution of Poisson's Solutions of Elliptic Equation by Various Methods, Parabolic Equations, Solution of One Dimensional Heat Equation, Solution of Two Dimensional Heat Equation, Hyperbolic Equations, Wave Equation.

Before proceeding further, we would like to study boundary-value problems.

18.1 Boundary-Value Problems

Consider simple examples of two-point linear boundary-value problems as follows:

(i) $$\frac{d^2 y}{dx^2} + f(x)\frac{dy}{dx} + g(x)\ y(x) = r(x) \quad ...(1)$$

With the boundary conditions: $y(x_0) = a$ and $y(x_n) = b$ ...(2)

(ii) $$\frac{d^4 y}{dx^4} + p(x)\ y(x) = q(x) \quad ...(3)$$

with $y(x_0) = y'(x_0) = A$ and $y(x_n) = y''(x_n) = B$ ...(4)

The second problem which involves fourth order differential equation is much more complicated and shall not be discussed here. As far as first problem is concerned, there exist a number of methods to solve second order boundary-value problems. One of these is the finite difference method, which is most popular and shall be discussed here only in brief. The finite difference method for the solution of a two-point boundary-value problem consists in replacing the derivatives present in the differential equation and the boundary conditions with the help of finite difference approximations and then solving the resulting linear system of equation by a standard method.

Using Taylor's series, we have

$$y(x+h) = y(x) + hy'(x) + \frac{h^2}{2!}y''(x) + \frac{h^3}{3!}y'''(x) + \dots \quad ...(5)$$

$$y(x-h) = y(x) - h\,y'(x) + \frac{h^2}{2!}y''(x) - \frac{h^3}{3!}y'''(x) + \dots \quad ...(6)$$

$$\therefore \quad y'(x) = \frac{y(x+h) - y(x)}{h} - \frac{h}{2!} y''(x) \ldots\ldots$$

$$= \frac{y(x+h) - y(x)}{h} + 0(h) \qquad \ldots(7)$$

This is the forward difference approximation for $y'(x)$.

Also, we have $\quad y'(x) = \dfrac{y(x) - y(x-h)}{h} + 0(h) \qquad \ldots(8)$

This gives the back-ward difference approximation for $y'(x)$. Then the central difference approximation for $y'(x)$ is obtained by subtracting (6) from (5); viz.,

$$y(x+h) - y(x-h) = 2h\, y'(x) + \frac{2h^3}{3!} y'''(x) + \ldots$$

$$\Rightarrow \quad y'(x) = \frac{y(x+h) - y(x-h)}{2h} - \frac{h^2}{3!} y'''(x) \ldots$$

$$= \frac{y(x+h) - y(x-h)}{2h} + 0(h^2) \ldots \qquad \ldots(9)$$

This gives us a better approximation to $y'(x)$ as compared to (7) or (8), Further adding (5) and (6), we get $y(x+h) + y(x-h) = 2\,y(x) + h^2\, y''(x) + \dfrac{2h^4}{4!} y^{iv}(x) + \ldots$

$$\Rightarrow \quad \frac{y(x+h) - 2\,y(x) + y(x-h)}{h^2} = y''(x) + \frac{2}{4!} h^2 y^{iv}(x) + \ldots$$

$$\Rightarrow \quad y''(x) = \frac{y(x-h) - 2\,y(x) + y(x+h)}{h^2} + 0(h^2) \qquad \ldots(10)$$

Similarly, we can obtain finite-difference approximations of higher derivatives. Now to solve the boundary-value problem given by (1) and (2), we divide the range $[x_0, x_n]$ into n equal sub intervals of width h so that $x_i = x_0 + ih\ (i = 1, 2, 3, \ldots, n)$.

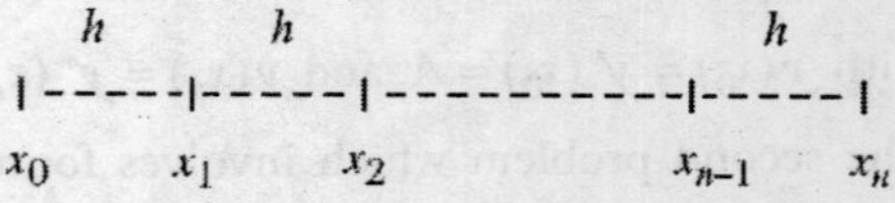

The corresponding value of y are then given by $y(x_i) = y_i = y(x_0 + ih)$; $i = 0, 1, 2, \ldots, n$. Now using equations (9), (10); values of $y'(x)$ and $y''(x)$ at the points $x = x_i$ can be written as

$$y_i' = \frac{y_{i+1} - y_{i-1}}{2h} + 0(h^2) \quad \text{and} \quad y_i'' = \frac{y_{i-1} - 2\,y_i + y_{i+1}}{h^2} + 0(h^2)$$

Then satisfying the differential equations at the point $x = x_i$.

$$y = y_i; \text{ we get } y_i'' + f_i\, y_i' + g_i\, y_i = r_i \qquad \ldots(11)$$

Now substituting the values of y_i' and y_i'' in (11), we get

$$\frac{y_{i-1} - 2\,y_i + y_{i+1}}{h^2} + f_i \frac{y_{i+1} - y_{i-1}}{2h} + g_i\, y_i = r_i;\ i = 1, 2, 3, \ldots, (n-1)$$

Where $y_i = y(x_i)$, $g_i = g(x_i)$, etc.

Multiplying throughout by h^2 and then simplifying, we get

$$\left(1-\frac{h}{2}f_i\right)y_{i-1} + (-2 + g_i h_i^2)\, y_i + \left(1+\frac{h}{2}f_i\right)y_{i+1} = r_i h^2 \; [i = 1, 2, 3, \ldots, n-1] \qquad \ldots(12)$$

Where $y_0 = a$ and $y_n = b$. ...(13)

Now equation (12) under the conditions (13) give rise to a *tridiagonal system* which can be easily solved by the methods discussed earlier. We shall illustrate this method by the following example.

Solved Examples

Example 1: *Solve numerically the equation $y'' + y + 1 = 0$, with boundary conditions $y = 0$ when $x = 0$ and $y = 0$ when $x = 1$.*

Solution: Here $nh = 1$. Choosing $n = 2$, we get $h = \frac{1}{2}$. Now $y_i'' = \frac{y_{i-1} - 2y_i + y_{i+1}}{h^2}$. Putting this value in the given equation, we get

$$\frac{y_{i-1} - 2y_i + y_{i+1}}{h^2} + y_i + 1 = 0$$

• ------• -----•

(x_0, y_0) (x_1, y_1) (x_2, y_2)

$$\Rightarrow \quad y_{i-1} - (2 - h^2)\, y_i + y_{i+1} = -h^2,\; i = 1, 2, \ldots, (n-1)$$

Putting $n = 2$, we get $i = 1 \Rightarrow y_0 - \left(2 - \frac{1}{4}\right) y_1 + y_2 = -\frac{1}{4}$

But $y_0 = 0$ and $y_2 = 0$. $\therefore -\left(\frac{7}{4}\right) y_1 = -\frac{1}{4}$

$$\Rightarrow \quad y_1 = \frac{1}{7} = 0.14285\ldots \text{ But } y_1 = y(0.5) = 0.14285\ldots \qquad \ldots(1)$$

Again, solving the given equation analytically by standard method, we get

$$y\left(\frac{1}{2}\right) = 0.13949 \qquad \ldots(2)$$

Inspection of (1) and (2) shows that the finite-difference solution for $y\left(\frac{1}{2}\right)$ is about 2.4% too large. Further, when we choose $n = 4$, we get $nh = 1 \Rightarrow h = .25$; and in this situation we have

$$\begin{cases} y_0 - (13/16)\, y_1 + y_2 = (-1/16);\; y_1 - (31/16)\, y_2 + y_3 = -(1/16) \\ \text{and} \quad y_2 = -(31/16)\, y_3 + y_4 = (-1/16) \quad \text{where } y_0 = y_4 = 0 \end{cases} \qquad \ldots(3)$$

Then solving the system, we have $y_2 = y(0.5) = (63/449) = 0.14031\ldots$. This is again 0.58%. These results show that the accuracy obtained by the finite difference method depends on the width of the subinterval chosen. Reduction of h increases the accuracy but the number of equations to be solved also increase.

18.2 Introduction

Partial differential equations mostly occur in various branches of applied mathematics; viz. hydrodynamics magneto-hydrodynamics; elasticity, eqantum-mechanics electromagnetic theory etc. The solution of these equations are obtained by standard methods as given in various texts of differential equations. On the other hand, it is generally easier to obtain sufficiently approximate solutions by simple and efficient numerical methods. Many numerical methods have been proposed to obtain sufficiently approximate solutions of partial differential equations. But, only the methods of finite differences have become most popular and hence are used more gainfully than others. We will therefore study such methods involving finite differences to obtain approximate solutions, numerically, of various simple problems occurring in partial differential equations. A general second-order linear partial differential equation is of the type:

$$A\frac{\partial^2 u}{\partial x^2} + B\frac{\partial^2 u}{\partial x \partial y} + C\frac{\partial^2 u}{\partial y^2} + D\frac{\partial u}{\partial x} + E\frac{\partial u}{\partial y} + Fu = G \qquad \text{...(1)}$$

Where A, B, C, D, E, F, G are all functions of x and y. This equation can be classified with respect to the sign of the discriminant $\Delta s = B^2 - 4AC$.

(i) If $\Delta s < 0$, at a point (x, y) in the plane, the equation is said to be of ***elliptic-type.***

(ii) If $\Delta s > 0$, at a point (x, y) in the plane, the equation is said to be of ***hyperbolic-type.***

(iii) If $\Delta s = 0$, at a point (x, y) in the plane, the equation is said to be of ***parabolic-type.***

We now consider the following partial differential equations:

$\frac{\partial^2 u}{\partial x^2} + \frac{\partial^2 u}{\partial y^2} = 0$ **(Laplace's equation)**, (i)

$\frac{\partial^2 u}{\partial x^2} = \frac{1}{c^2}\frac{\partial^2 u}{\partial t^2}$ **(Wave equation)** (ii)

and $\frac{\partial^2 u}{\partial x^2} = \frac{\partial u}{\partial t}$ **(Heat conduction equation)** (iii)

Where (x, y) are the space co-ordinates and t is the time co-ordinate. In equation (i) we have $A = 1, \; B = 0, \; C = 1; \Rightarrow \; \Delta s = B^2 - 4AC = -4 =$ **Neg.**

Hence Laplace's equation is of elliptic type. In equation (ii) we also have $\Delta s =$ positive *i.e.* $\Delta s > 0$ and hence the equation is *hyperbolic type.* On the other hand, in equation (iii) we have $\Delta s = 0$ and hence the *heat equation is parabolic type.* While studying partial differential equations, we come across usually with three types of problems.

Type 1: Dirichlet's Problem

Let there exist a continuous function f *on the boundary* C *of a region* R. *To find the function u satisfying Laplace's equation* $\frac{\partial^2 u}{\partial x^2} + \frac{\partial^2 u}{\partial y^2} = 0$ *in* R *and* $u = f$ on C.

Type 2: Cauchy's Problem

To find the function u satisfying the equation $\frac{\partial^2 u}{\partial t^2} - \frac{\partial^2 u}{\partial x^2} - 0;\ t > 0,\ u(x, 0) = f(x)$ *and* $[\partial u / \partial t]_{x,0} = g(x)$ *where* $f(x)$ *and* $g(x)$ *are arbitrary.*

Type 3: $(\partial u / \partial t) - (\partial^2 u / \partial x^2) = 0,\ t > 0, u(x, 0) = f(x)$. **To find u(x, t)**

It has been discussed in various texts of partial differential equations that these equations possess unique solutions.

18.3 To Obtain Finite-Difference Approximations of Partial Derivatives

Let the $x - y$ plane be divided into a network of rectangles of side $\Delta_x = h$ and $\Delta_y = k$ by drawing the set of lines $x = ih\ (i = 0, 1, 2, ...)$ and $y = jk\ (j = 0, 1, 2, ...)$. The points of intersection of these lines are called *mesh points (lattice points or grid-points)*

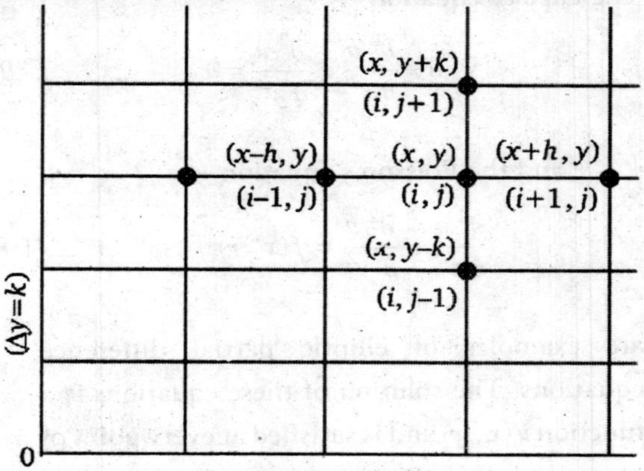

Then we have the finite difference approximations for the partial derivatives in x-direction, as

$$\frac{\partial u}{\partial x} = \frac{u(x+h, y) - u(x, y)}{h} + O(h)$$

$$= \frac{u(x, y) - u(x-h, y)}{h} + O(h) = \frac{u(x+h, y) - u(x-h, y)}{2h} + O(h^2)$$

$$\frac{\partial^2 u}{\partial x^2} = \frac{u(x-h, y) - 2u(x, y) + u(x+h, y)}{h^2} + O(h^2)$$

Further writing $u(x, y) = u(ih, jk)\ [i, j = 1, 2, 3, ...]$ as simply u_{ij} the above approximations are reduced to

$$u_x = \frac{u_{i+1,j} - u_{i,j}}{h} + O(h) \qquad ...(1)$$

$$= \frac{u_{i,j} - u_{i-1,j}}{h} + O(h) \qquad ...(2)$$

$$= \frac{u_{i+1,j} - u_{i-1,j}}{2h} + O(h^2) \qquad ...(3)$$

and $$u_{xx} = \frac{u_{i-1,j} - 2u_{i,j} + u_{i+1,j}}{h^2} + O(h^2) \qquad ...(4)$$

And similarly we have the approximations for the derivative w.r.t y:

$$u_y = \frac{u_{i,j+1} - u_{i,j}}{k} + O(k) \qquad ...(5)$$

$$= \frac{u_{i,\,j} - u_{i,\,j-1}}{k} + O(k) \qquad \text{...(6)}$$

$$= \frac{u_{i,\,j+1} - u_{i,\,j-1}}{2k} + O(k^2) \qquad \text{...(7)}$$

and $$u_{yy} = \frac{u_{i,\,j-1} - 2\,u_{i,\,j} + u_{i,\,j+1}}{k^2} + O(k^2) \qquad \text{...(8)}$$

18.3.1 Elliptic Equations

The Laplace equation

$$\nabla^2 u \equiv \frac{\partial^2 u}{\partial x^2} + \frac{\partial^2 u}{\partial y^2} = 0 \qquad \text{...(9)}$$

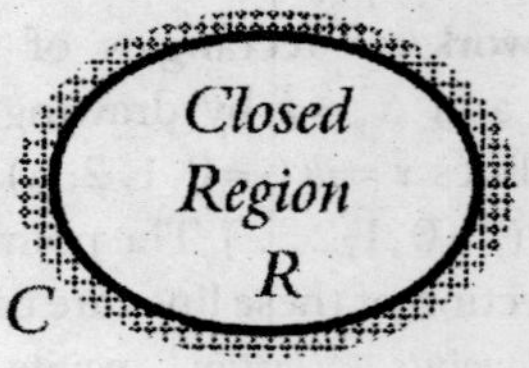

and the Poisson's equation

$$\frac{\partial^2 u}{\partial x^2} + \frac{\partial^2 u}{\partial y^2} = f(x, y) \qquad \text{...(10)}$$

are examples of elliptic partial difference equations. The solution of these equations is a function $u(x, y)$ and is satisfied at every point of a region R subject to certain boundary conditions

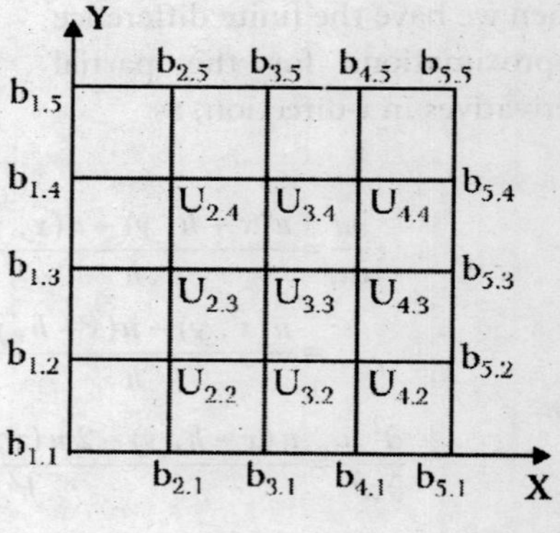

[A] Solution of Laplace's equation: $\dfrac{\partial^2 u}{\partial x^2} + \dfrac{\partial^2 u}{\partial y^2} = 0$ ...(11)

Let us consider a rectangular region R for which $u(x, y)$ is known on the boundary. Divide this region into a network of square meshes of side h (*i.e.* $k = h$) assuming that an exact aub-division of R is possible. Replacing the derivatives by their difference approximations, we readily obtain

$$\frac{1}{h^2}[u_{i-1,\,j} - 2\,u_{i,\,j} + u_{i+1,\,j}] + \frac{1}{h^2}[u_{i,\,j-1} - 2\,u_{i,\,j} + u_{i,\,j+1}] = 0$$

$$\Rightarrow \qquad u_{ij} = \frac{1}{4}[u_{i-1,\,j} + u_{i+1,\,j} + u_{i,\,j+1} + u_{i,\,j-1}] \qquad \text{...(12)}$$

$\Rightarrow$ the value of u at any interior mesh point is the average of its values at four neighbouring points to the left, right above and below. This is also called the ***standard 5-point formula***.

Sometimes a formula similar to (12) is used and is given by

$$u_{i,j} = \frac{1}{4}\,(u_{i-1,\,j+1} + u_{i+1,\,j-1} + u_{i+1,\,j+1} + u_{i-1,\,j-1}) \qquad \text{...(13)}$$

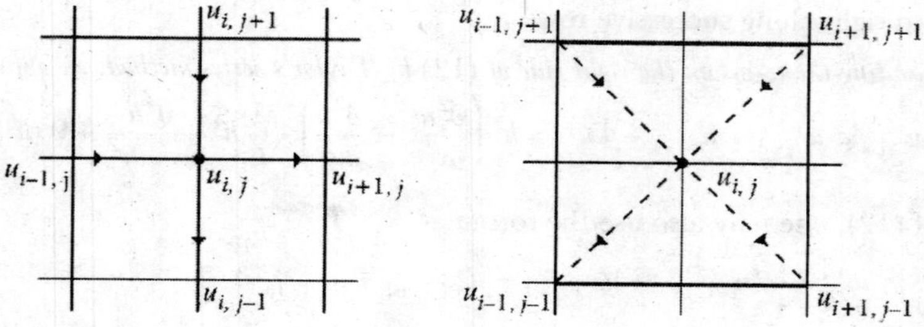

i.e. the value of $u_{i,j}$ is the average of its values at the four neighbouring diagonal mesh points. This is called the diagonal ***5-point formula***. Although (13) is less accurate than (12) yet it serves a reasonably good approximation to obtain the starting values at the mesh points.

Then to find the initial values of u at the interior mesh points, first we use the diagonal five point formula and compute $u_{3,3}, u_{2,4}, u_{4,4}, u_{4,2}$ and $u_{2,2}$, in this order

$$\Rightarrow \quad u_{3,3} = \frac{1}{4}(b_{1,5} + b_{5,1} + b_{5,5} + b_{1,1});\ u_{2,4} = \frac{1}{4}(b_{1,5} + u_{3,3} + b_{3,5} + b_{1,3})$$

$$u_{4,4} = \frac{1}{4}(b_{3,5} + b_{5,3} + b_{3,5} + u_{3,3});\ u_{4,2} = \frac{1}{4}(u_{3,3} + b_{5,1} + b_{3,1} + b_{5,3})$$

$$u_{2,2} = \frac{1}{4}(b_{1,3} + b_{3,1} + u_{3,3} + b_{1,1})$$

Also, the values at the remaining interior points *i.e.* $u_{2,3}, u_{3,4}, u_{4,3}$ and $u_{3,2}$ are computed by ***standard five-point formula***.

$$\Rightarrow \quad u_{2,3} = \frac{1}{4}(b_{1,3} + u_{3,3} + u_{2,4} + u_{2,2}),\ u_{3,4} = \frac{1}{4}(u_{2,4} + u_{4,4} + b_{3,5} + u_{3,3})$$

$$u_{4,3} = \frac{1}{4}(u_{3,3} + b_{5,3} + u_{4,4} + u_{4,2}),\ u_{3,2} = \frac{1}{4}(u_{2,2} + u_{4,2} + u_{3,3} + u_{3,1})$$

Having obtained all the nine values of $u_{i,j}$, their accuracy is improved by either of the following iterative methods. The method is repeated till the difference between two consecutive values becomes negligible.

Iterative Methods

(i) Jacobi's Method

Denoting the nth iterative value of $u_{i,j}$ by $u^{(n)}{}_{i,j}$, the iterative formula is:

$$u^{(n+1)}{}_{i,j} = \frac{1}{4}\left[u^{(n)}{}_{i-1,j} + u^{(n)}{}_{i+1,j} + u^{(n)}{}_{i,j+1} + u^{(n)}{}_{i,j-1}\right]. \qquad \text{...(14)}$$

It gives improved values of $u_{i,j}$ at the interior mesh points and is called the ***Point Jacobi's Formula***.

(ii) Gauss-Seidal Method

In this method, the iteration formula is

$$u_{i,j}^{(n+1)} = \frac{1}{4}[u^{(n+1)}{}_{i-1,j} + u^{(n)}{}_{i+1,j} + u^{(n+1)}{}_{i,j+1} + u^{(n)}{}_{i,j-1}] \quad ...(15)$$

It utilises the latest iterative value available and scans the mesh points symmetrically from left to right along successive rows.

Again, expanding the terms on the right side of (12) *by Taylor's series method, we obtain*

$$u_{i+1,j} - u_{i-1,j} + u_{i,j+1} + u_{i,j-1} - 4u_{i,j} = h^2\left(\frac{\partial^2 u}{\partial x^2} + \frac{\partial^2 u}{\partial y^2}\right) - \frac{1}{6}h^4 \frac{\partial^4 u}{\partial x^2\, \partial y^2} + 0\,(h^6) \quad ...(16)$$

Instead of (12), one may also use the formula

$$u_{i,j} = \frac{1}{4}\{u_{i-1,j-1} + u_{i+1,j-1} + u_{i+1,j+1} + u_{i-1,j+1}\} \quad ...(17)$$

This formula uses the functional values at the *diagonal-points* and hence is known as the *diagonal-point* formula. We know that the Laplace equation is invariant when the axes are turned through an angle of 45° and hence (13) is perfectly valid. Further expanding the R.H.S of (13) by Taylor's series method, we obtain

$$u_{i-1,j-1} + u_{i+1,j-1} + u_{i+1,j+1} + u_{i-1,j+1} - 4u_{i,j} = \frac{2}{3}h^4 \frac{\partial^4 u}{\partial x^2\, \partial y^2} + 0\,(h^6) \quad ...(18)$$

If we neglect the terms of the order h^6, then form (16) and (18) it is obvious that the error in the diagonal formula is four times as compared to the standard formula. *This suggests us that in all computations, we should prefer standard five-point formula.*

Eliminating the term containing h^4 from (16) and (18), we obtain **Nine-point Formula;**

$$u_{i-1,j-1} + u_{i+1,j-1} + u_{i+1,j+1} + u_{i-1,j+1} + 4(u_{i+1,j} + u_{i-1,j} + u_{i,j+1} + u_{i,j-1}) - 20\,u_{i,j} = 0 \quad ...(19)$$

This formula consists of the error of order h^6. On the same lines, we can obtain the *finite-difference analogues* of the wave equation $\left(\frac{\partial^2 u}{\partial x^2} - \frac{1}{c^2}\frac{\partial^2 u}{\partial t^2} = 0\right)$ and the heat conduction equation $\left(\frac{\partial^2 u}{\partial x^2} - \frac{\partial u}{\partial t} = 0\right)$.

18.4 To Solve Laplace's Equation $(\partial^2 u/\partial x^2) + (\partial^2 u/\partial y^2) = 0$ in the Bounded Region R with Boundary C

[Bhopal 2007; Bangaluru 2002, 2004, 2005, 2007]

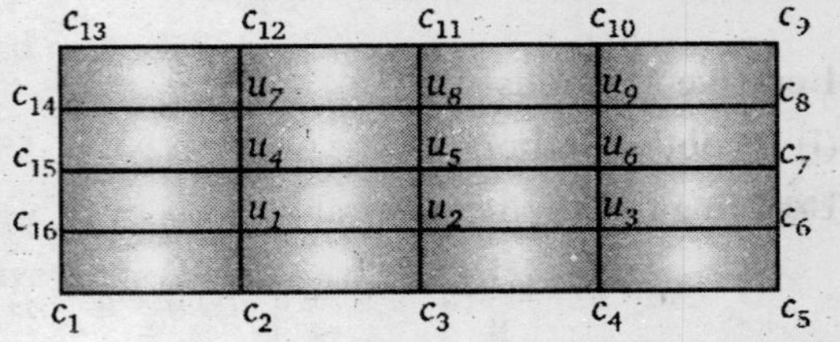

Just like Dirichlet's Problem, let u be specified everywhere on C. For the sake of convenience, let R denote the square region so that it can be divided into a network of small squares of side h. Further, let the values of u (x, y) on the boundary C be C_i and further let the interior mesh points and boundary points be as shown in the following figure.

Then Laplace's equation $\frac{\partial^2 u}{\partial x^2}+\frac{\partial^2 u}{\partial y^2}=0$ can be either replaced by *standard five-point* formula or by the diagonal five-point formula. Using diagonal five-point formula, the approximate function values at the interior mesh points can be easily computed. We thus compte u_5, u_7, u_9, u_1 and u_3 in this order as follows:

$$u_5=\frac{1}{4}(c_1+c_5+c_9+c_{13});\ u_7=\frac{1}{4}(c_{15}+u_5+c_{11}+c_{13})$$

$$u_9=\frac{1}{4}(u_5+c_7+c_9+c_{11});\ u_1=\frac{1}{4}(c_1+c_3+u_5+c_{15})$$

$$u_3=\frac{1}{4}(c_3+c_5+c_7+u_5).$$

Then we proceed to compute in order, the remaining quantities; viz u_8, u_4, u_6, u_2 *by the standard point formula* (11) and thus we have

$$u_8=\frac{1}{4}(u_5+u_9+c_{11}+c_7);\ u_4=\frac{1}{4}(u_1+u_5+u_7+c_{15})$$

$$u_6=\frac{1}{4}(u_3+c_7+u_9+u_5);\ u_2=\frac{1}{4}(c_3+u_3+u_5+u_1)$$

When all u_i' s $(i=1,2,3,\ldots 9)$ are calculated, their accuracy is improved by any of the following iterative methods.

(i) Point-Jacobi Iterative Method **[Bhopal 2007]**

If $u_{i,j}^{(n)}$ denotes the nth -iterative value of $u_{i,j}$ then an iterative procedure to solve

$$u_{i+1,j}+u_{i-1,j}+u_{i,j+1}+u_{i,j-1}-4u_{i,j}=0 \text{ is given by}$$

$$u_{i,j}^{(n+1)}=\frac{1}{4}\left[u_{i-1,j}^{(n)}+u_{i+1,j}^{(n)}+u_{i,j-1}^{(n)}+u_{i,j+1}^{(n)}\right]$$

For the interior mesh points and is known as *point Jacobi's* method.

(ii) Gauss-Seidel Method **[Bhopal 2007]**

The iterative formula is

$$u_{i,j}^{(n+1)}=\frac{1}{4}\left[u_{i-1,j}^{(n+1)}+u_{i+1,j}^{(n)}+u_{i,j-1}^{(n+1)}+u_{i,j+1}^{(n)}\right]$$

And this method uses the latest iterative values available. It scans the mesh points systematically from left to right along successive rows. This method converges twice as fast as the **Jacobi's Scheme.**

(iii) Successive-Over-Relaxation Method (S.O.R.)

By Gauss-Seidel method, we have $u_{i,j}^{(n+1)}=\frac{1}{4}\left[u_{i-1,j}^{(n+1)}+u_{i+1,j}^{(n)}+u_{i,j-1}^{(n+1)}+u_{i,j+1}^{(n)}\right]$

$$=\frac{1}{4}\left[\left(4u_{i,j}^{(n)}+u_{i-1,j}^{(n+1)}+u_{i+1,j}^{(n)}+u_{i,j-1}^{(n+1)}+u_{i,j+1}^{(n)}\right)-4u_{i,j}^{(n)}\right]$$

$$= u_{i,j}^{n} + \frac{1}{4}\left[u_{i-1,j}^{(n+1)} + u_{i+1,j}^{(n)} + u_{i,j-1}^{(n+1)} + u_{i,j+1}^{(n)} - 4u_{i,j}^{(n)}\right]$$

$$= u_{i,j}^{(n)} + \frac{1}{4}R_{i,j} \qquad \text{...(1)}$$

$$\text{Where } R_{i,j} = \left[u_{i-1,j}^{(n+1)} + u_{i+1,j}^{(n)} + u_{i,j-1}^{(n+1)} + u_{i,j+1}^{(n)} - 4u_{i,j}^{(n)}\right] \qquad \text{...(2)}$$

This clearly shows that $R_{i,j}$ is nothing but the change in the value of $u_{i,j}$ for ***Gauss-Seidel Iteration.*** In **S.O.R.** Method a larger change than the above is given to $u_{i,j}^{(n)}$ and the corresponding iteration formula becomes

$$u_{i,j}^{(n+1)} = u_{i,j}^{(n)} + \frac{1}{4}\omega R_{i,j}$$

$$= u_{i,j}^{(n)} + \frac{1}{4}\omega\left[u_{i-1,j}^{(n+1)} + u_{i+1,j}^{(n)} + u_{i,j-1}^{(n+1)} + u_{i,j+1}^{(n)} - 4u_{i,j}^{(n)}\right]$$

$$= u_{i,j}^{(n)}, (1-\omega) + \frac{\omega}{4}\left[u_{i-1,j}^{(n+1)} + u_{i+1,j}^{(n)} + u_{i,j-1}^{(n+1)} + u_{i,j+1}^{(n)}\right] \qquad \text{...(3)}$$

The rate of convergence of the formula (3) depends upon the choice of ω, which is called the **accelerating factor** an lies between 1 and 2.

> **Note:** For $\omega = 1.875$, it was shown by B.A. Carr'e that the rate convergence of (3) is twice as great as when $\omega = 1$. For $\omega = 1.9$, the rate of convergence is 40 times greater as when $\omega = 1$. As a matter of fact, it is very difficult to estimate the value of ω.

Example 2: *Solve the partial differential equation; (viz. Laplace's equation)* $(\partial^2 u / \partial x^2) + (\partial^2 u / \partial y^2) = 0$ *for the figure given below.*

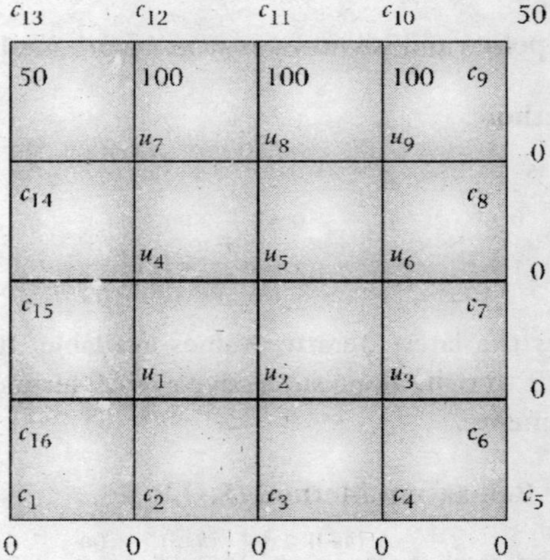

Elliptic Type

[P.T.U. (Punjab) 2005, 200?; Chennai (B.E.) 2001, 2003, 2004, 2008; Raipure (B.E.) 2007, 2009; U.P.T.U. (B.E.) 2008; Rohilkhand (M.Sc.) 2007; Bangaluru 2005, 2008]

Solution: Using digonal five point formula; *viz*

$$u_{i,j} = \frac{1}{4}[u_{i-1,j-1} + u_{i+1,j-1} + u_{i+1,j+1} + u_{i-1,j+1}]\text{; we obtain}$$

$$u_5 = \frac{1}{4}(c_1 + c_5 + c_9 + c_{13}) = \frac{1}{4}(0 + 0 + 50 + 50) = 100/4 = 25,$$

$$u_7 = \frac{1}{4}(c_{15} + u_5 + c_{11} + c_{13}) = \frac{1}{4}(0 + 25 + 100 + 50) = 43.75,$$

Then, we proceed to compute in order, the remaining quantities; viz, u_8, u_4, u_6, u_2 by the standard point formula and

Thus all u_i^s $(i = 1, 2, 3, \ldots, 9)$ are calculated, their accuracy is then improved, say by **Gauss-Seidel Method**

First approximations of all the nine mesh points are given by

$$u_5^{(1)} = 25.00, u_7^{(1)} = 43.75, u_9^{(1)} = 43.75, u_1^{(1)} = 6.25, u_3^{(1)} = 6.25$$

$$u_8^{(1)} = 53.12, u_4^{(1)} = 18.75, u_6^{(1)} = 18.75, u_2^{(1)} = 9.38.$$

Now G.S. method gives $u_{i,j}^{(n+1)} = \frac{1}{4}\left[u_{i-1,j}^{(n+1)} + u_{i+1,j}^{(n)} + u_{i,j-1}^{(n+1)} + u_{i,j+1}^{(n)}\right]$

$$\Rightarrow u_1^{(2)} = \frac{1}{4}[c_{16} + u_2^{(1)} + c_2 + u_4^{(1)}] = \frac{1}{4}(0 + 9.38 + 0 + 18.75) = 7.03$$

$$u_2^{(2)} = \frac{1}{4}(u_1^{(2)} + u_3^{(1)} + c_3 + u_5^{(1)}) = \frac{1}{4}(7.03 + 6.25 + 0 + 25) = 9.57$$

$$u_3^{(2)} = \frac{1}{4}(u_2^{(2)} + c_6 + c_4 = u_6^{(1)}) = \frac{1}{4}(9.57 + 0 + 0 + 18.75) = 7.08$$

$$u_4^{(2)} = \frac{1}{4}(c_{15} + u_5^{(1)} + u_1^{(2)} + u_7^{(1)}) = 18.94$$

$$u_5^{(2)} = \frac{1}{4}(u_4^{(2)} + u_6^{(1)} + u_2^{(2)} + u_8^{(1)}) = \frac{1}{4}(18.94 + 18.75 + 9.57 + 53.12)$$

$$= (100.38/4) = 2.10,$$

$$u_6^{(2)} = \frac{1}{4}(u_5^{(2)} + c_7 + u_3^{(2)} + u_9^{(1)}) = \frac{1}{4}(25.10 + 0 + 7.08 + 43.75) = 18.98$$

$$u_7^{(2)} = \frac{1}{4}(c_{14} + u_8^{(1)} + u_4^{(2)} + c_{12}) = \frac{1}{4}(0 + 53.12 + 18.94 + 100) = \frac{172.06}{4} = 43.02$$

$$u_8^{(2)} = \frac{1}{4}(u_7^{(2)} + u_9^{(1)} + u_5^{(2)} + c_{11}) = \frac{1}{4}(43.02 + 43.75 + 25.10 + 100) = 52.97$$

$$u_9^{(2)} = \frac{1}{4}(u_8^{(2)} + c_8 + u_6^{(2)} + c_{10}) = \frac{1}{4}(52.97 + 0 + 18.98 + 100) = \frac{171.95}{4} = 42.99$$

These are the first iterations due to G.S. method

Further, we have

$$u_{i,j} = \frac{1}{4}\left[u_{i-1,j}^{(3)} + u_{i+1,j}^{(2)} + u_{i,j-1}^{(3)} + u_{i,j+1}^{(2)}\right]$$

$$u_1^{(3)} = \frac{1}{4}[c_{16} + u_2^{(2)} + c_2 + u_4^{(2)}] = \frac{1}{4}(0 + 9.57 + 0 + 18.94) = 7.13,$$

$$u_2^{(3)} = \frac{1}{4}[u_1^{(3)} + u_3^{(2)} + c_3 + u_5^{(2)}] = \frac{1}{4}(7.13 + 7.08 + 0 + 25.10) = 9.83,$$

$$u_3^{(3)} = \frac{1}{4}[u_2^{(3)} + c_6 + c_4 + u_6^{(2)}]\frac{1}{4}(9.83 + 0 + 0 + 18.98) = 7.20,$$

$$u_4^{(3)} = \frac{1}{4}[c_{15} + u_5^{(2)} + u_1^{(3)} + u_7^{(2)}] = \frac{1}{4}(0 + 25.10 + 7.13 + 43.02) = 18.81,$$

$$u_5^{(3)} = \frac{1}{4}[u_4^{(3)} + u_6^{(2)} + u_2^{(3)} + u_8^{(2)}] = \frac{1}{4}(18.81 + 18.89 + 9.83 + 52.97) = 25.15,$$

$$u_6^{(3)} = \frac{1}{4}[u_5^{(3)} + c_7 + u_3^{(3)} + u_9^{(2)}] = \frac{1}{4}(25.15 + 0 + 7.20 + 42.99) = 18.84,$$

$$u_7^{(3)} = \frac{1}{4}[c_{14} + u_8^{(2)} + u_4^{(3)} + c_{12}] = \frac{1}{4}(0 + 52.97 + 18.81 + 100) = 25.04,$$

$$u_8^{(3)} = \frac{1}{4}[u_7^{(3)} + u_9^{(2)}\ u_5^{(3)} + c_{11}] = \frac{1}{4}(42.94 + 42.99 + 25.15 + 100) = 52.77,$$

$$u_9^{(3)} = \frac{1}{4}[u_8^{(3)} + c_8 + u_6^{(3)} + c_{10}] = \frac{1}{4}(52.77 + 0 + 18.84 + 100) = 42.90.$$

These give the second iterations due to G.S. method. To find the third iterations due to G.S. method, we again consider:

$$u_{i,j}^4 = \frac{1}{4}[u_{i-1,j}^{(4)} + u_{i+1,j}^{(3)} + u_{i,j-1}^{(4)} + u_{i,j+1}^{(3)}]$$

Whence;

$$u_1^{(4)} = \frac{1}{4}(c_{16} + u_2^{(3)} + c_2 + u_4^{(3)}) = \frac{1}{4}(0 + 9.38 + 0 + 18.81) = 7.16,$$

$$u_2^{(4)} = \frac{1}{4}(u_1^{(4)} + u_3^{(3)} + c_3 + u_5^{(3)}) = \frac{1}{4}(7.16 + 7.20 + 0 + 25.15) = 9.88,$$

$$u_3^{(4)} = \frac{1}{4}(u_2^{(4)} + c_6 + c_4 + u_6^{(3)}) = \frac{1}{4}(9.88 + 0 + 0 + 18.84) = 7.18,$$

$$u_4^{(4)} = \frac{1}{4}(c_{15} + u_5^{(3)} + u_1^{(4)} + u_7^{(3)}) = \frac{1}{4}(0 + 25.15 + 7.16 + 42.94) = 18.81,$$

$$u_5^{(4)} = \frac{1}{4}(u_4^{(4)} + u_6^{(3)} + u_2^{(4)} + u_8^{(3)}) = \frac{1}{4}(18.81 + 18.84 + 9.88 + 52.77) = 25.08,$$

$$u_6^{(4)} = \frac{1}{4}(u_5^{(4)} + c_7 + u_3^{(4)} + u_9^{(3)}) = \frac{1}{4}(25.08 + 0 + 7.18 + 42.90) = 18.79,$$

$$u_7^{(4)} = \frac{1}{4}(c_{14} + u_8^{(3)} + u_4^{(4)} + c_{12}) = \frac{1}{4}(0 + 52.77 + 18.81 + 100) = 42.89,$$

$$u_8^{(4)} = \frac{1}{4}(u_7^{(4)} + u_9^{(3)} + u_5^{(4)} + c_{11}) = \frac{1}{4}(42.89 + 42.90 + 25.08 + 100) = 52.72,$$

$$u_9^{(4)} = \frac{1}{4}(u_8^{(4)} + c_8 + u_6^{(4)} + c_{10}) = \frac{1}{4}(52.72 + 0 + 18.79 + 100) = 42.88,$$

and the fourth iterations due to **G.S. method** are given as

$$u_1^{(5)} = \frac{1}{4}(c_{16} + u_2^{(4)} + c_4 + u_4^{(4)}) = \frac{1}{4}(0 + 9.88 + 0 + 18.81) = 7.17,$$

$$u_2^{(5)} = \frac{1}{4}(u_1^{(5)} + u_3^{(4)} + c_3 + u_5^{(4)}) = \frac{1}{4}(7.17 + 7.18 + 0 + 25.08) = 9.86,$$

$$u_3^{(5)} = \frac{1}{4}(u_2^{(5)} + c_6 + c_4 + u_6^{(4)}) = \frac{1}{4}(9.86 + 0 + 0 + 18.79) = 7.16,$$

$$u_4^{(5)} = \frac{1}{4}(c_{15} + u_5^{(4)} + u_1^{(5)} + u_7^{(4)}) = \frac{1}{4}(0 + 25.08 + 7.17 + 42.89) = 18.78,$$

$$u_5^{(5)} = \frac{1}{4}(u_4^{(5)} + u_6^{(4)} + u_2^{(5)} + u_8^{(4)}) = \frac{1}{4}(18.78 + 18.79 + 9.86 + 52.72) = 25.04,$$

$$u_6^{(5)} = \frac{1}{4}(u_5^{(5)} + c_7 + u_3^{(5)} + u_9^{(4)}) = \frac{1}{4}(25.04 + 0 + 7.16 + 42.88 = 18.77,$$

$$u_7^{(5)} = \frac{1}{4}(c_{14} + u_8^{(4)} + u_4^{(5)} + c_{12}) = \frac{1}{4}(0 + 52.72 + 18.78 + 100) = 42.88,$$

$$u_8^{(5)} = \frac{1}{4}(u_7^{(5)} + u_9^{(4)} + u_5^{(5)} + c_{11}) = \frac{1}{4}(42.88 + 42.88 + 25.04 + 100) = 52.70,$$

$$u_9^{(5)} = \frac{1}{4}(u_8^{(5)} + c_8 + u_6^{(5)} + c_{10}) = \frac{1}{4}(52.70 + 0 + 18.77 + 100) = 42.87.$$

Also, we have

$$u_1^{(6)} = \frac{1}{4}(c_{16} + u_2^{(5)} + c_2 + u_4^{(5)}) = \frac{1}{4}(0 + 9.86 + 0 + 18.78) = 7.16,$$

$$u_2^{(6)} = \frac{1}{4}(u_1^{(6)} + u_3^{(5)} + c_3 + u_5^{(5)}) = \frac{1}{4}(7.16 + 7.16 + 0 + 25.04) = 9.84,$$

$$u_3^{(6)} = \frac{1}{4}(u_2^{(6)} + c_6 + c_4 + u_6^{(5)}) = \frac{1}{4}(9.48 + 0 + 0 + 18.77) = 7.15,$$

$$u_4^{(6)} = \frac{1}{4}(c_{15} + u_5^{(5)} + u_1^{(6)} + u_7^{(5)}) = \frac{1}{4}(0 + 25.04 + 7.16 + 42.88) = 18.77,$$

$$u_5^{(6)} = \frac{1}{4}(u_4^{(6)} + u_6^{(5)} + u_2^{(6)} + u_8^{(5)}) = \frac{1}{4}(18.77 + 18.77 + 9.84 + 52.70) = 25.02,$$

$$u_6^{(6)} = \frac{1}{4}(u_5^{(6)} + c_7 + u_3^{(6)} + u_9^{(5)}) = \frac{1}{4}(25.02 + 0 + 7.15 + 42.87) = 18.76,$$

$$u_7^{(6)} = \frac{1}{4}(c_{14} + u_8^{(5)} + u_4^{(6)} + c_{12}) = \frac{1}{4}(0 + 52.70 + 18.77 + 100) = 42.87,$$

$$u_8^{(6)} = \frac{1}{4}(u_7^{(6)} + u_9^{(5)} + u_5^{(6)} + c_{11}) = \frac{1}{4}(42.87 + 42.87 + 25.02 + 100) = 52.69$$

$$u_9^{(6)} = \frac{1}{4}(u_8^{(6)} + c_8 + u_6^{(6)} + c_{10}) = \frac{1}{4}(52.69 + 0 + 18.76 + 100) = 42.86,$$

These are the fifth iterations due to **G.S. method.** We now give below the first five iterates obtained by G.S. method.

u_1	u_2	u_3	u_4	u_5	u_6	u_7	u_8	u_9
7.03	9.57	7.08	18.94	25.10	18.98	43.02	52.97	42.99
7.13	9.83	7.20	18.81	25.15	18.84	42.94	52.77	42.90
7.16	9.88	7.18	18.81	25.08	18.79	42.89	52.72	42.88
7.17	9.86	7.16	18.78	25.04	18.77	42.88	52.70	42.87
7.16	9.84	7.15	18.77	25.02	18.76	42.87	52.69	42.86

Example 3: *Solve the partial difference equation* $\dfrac{\partial^2 u}{\partial x^2} + \dfrac{\partial^2 u}{\partial y^2} = 0$ *for figure given below, by* **(a)** *Jacob's method,* **(b)** *Gauss-Seidel's method,* **(c)** *S.O.R. method* **(Elliptic Type)**

[(B.E.) Chennai 2005; Roorkee (B.E.) 2006; Bangaluru 2005; Andhra (B.E.) 2002, 2004, 2008; Bhopal (B.E.) 2009]

Solution: The approximate values of u_1, u_2, u_3, u_4 are calculated as follows:

$$u_1 = \frac{1}{4}(0+0+0+1) = 0.25,$$

$$u_2 = \frac{1}{4}(0+0+0+1) = 0.25;$$

$$u_3 = \frac{1}{4}(1+1+0+0) = 0.5,$$

$$u_4 = \frac{1}{4}(1+1+0+0) = 0.50.$$

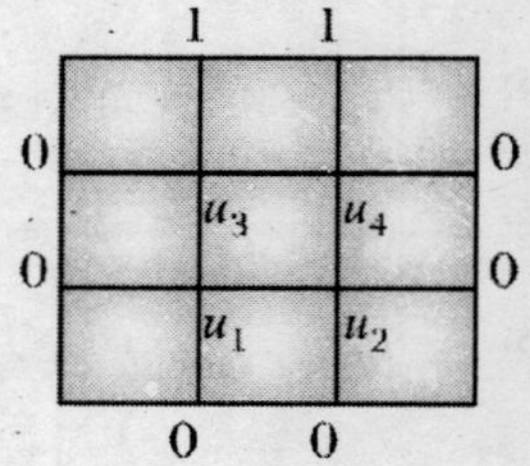

Let these value be denoted by $u_1^{(1)}, u_2^{(1)}, u_3^{(1)}$ and $u_4^{(1)}$ respectively; so that we may get

$$u_1^{(1)} = 0.25, u_2^{(1)} = 0.25, u_3^{(1)} = 0.50 \text{ and } u_4^{(1)} = 0.50.$$

(a) Using formula **"Jacobi's Method"**, viz.

$$u_{i,j}^{(n+1)} = \frac{1}{4}[u_{i-1,j}^{(n)} + u_{i+1,j}^{(n)} + u_{i,j-1}^{(n)} + n_{i,j+1}^{(n)}], \text{ we get}$$

$$u_1^{(2)} = \frac{1}{4}(0 + u_2^{(1)} + 0 + u_3^{(1)}) = \frac{1}{4}(.25 + .50) = .1875,$$

$$u_2^{(2)} = \frac{1}{4}(u_1^{(1)} + 0 + 0 + u_4^{(1)}) = \frac{1}{4}(0.25 + 0.50) = .1875,$$

$$u_3^{(2)} = \frac{1}{4}(0 + u_4^{(1)} + u_1^{(1)} + 1) = \frac{1}{4}(0.50 + 0.25 + 1) = .4375,$$

$$u_4^{(2)} = \frac{1}{4}(u_3^{(1)} + 0 + u_2^{(1)} + 1) = \frac{1}{4}(.50 + 25 + 1) = .4375,$$

$$u_1^{(3)} = \frac{1}{4}(0 + u_2^{(2)} + 0 + u_3^{(2)}) = \frac{1}{4}(.1875 + 4375) = .15625,$$

$$u_2^{(3)} = \frac{1}{4}(u_1^{(2)} + 0 + 0 + u_4^{(2)}) = \frac{1}{4}(.1875 + .4375) = .15625,$$

$$u_3^{(3)} = \frac{1}{4}(0 + u_4^{(2)} + u_1^{(2)} + 1) = \frac{1}{4}(0 + .4375 + .1875 + 1) = .40625,$$

$$u_4^{(3)} = \frac{1}{4}(u_3^{(2)} + 0 + u_2^{(2)} + 1) = \frac{1}{4}(.4375 + 0 + .1875 + 1) = .40625,$$

$$u_1^{(4)} = \frac{1}{4}(0 + u_2^{(3)} + 0 + u_3^{(3)}) = \frac{1}{4}(.15625 + .40625) = .14062,$$

$$u_2^{(4)} = \frac{1}{4}(u_1^{(3)} + 0 + 0 + u_4^{(3)}) = \frac{1}{4}(.15625 + .40625) = .14062,$$

$$u_3^{(4)} = \frac{1}{4}(0 + u_4^{(3)} + u_1^{(3)} + 1) = \frac{1}{4}(.40625 + .15625 + 1) = .39062,$$

$$u_4^{(4)} = \frac{1}{4}(u_3^{(3)} + 0 + u_2^{(3)} + 1) = \frac{1}{4}(.40625 + .15625 + 1) = .39062,$$

$$u_1^{(5)} = \frac{1}{4}(0 + u_2^{(4)} + 0 + u_3^{(4)}) = \frac{1}{4}(.14062 + 39062) = .13281,$$

$$u_2^{(5)} = \frac{1}{4}(u_1^{(4)} + 0 + 0 + u_4^{(4)}) = \frac{1}{4}(.14062 + .39062) = .13281,$$

$$u_3^{(5)} = \frac{1}{4}(0 + u_4^{(4)} + u_1^{(4)} + 1) = \frac{1}{4}(.39062 + .14062 + 1) = .38281,$$

$$u_4^{(5)} = \frac{1}{4}(u_3^{(4)} + 0 + u_2^{(4)} + 1) = \frac{1}{4}(.39062 + 0 + .14062 + 1) = .38281,$$

$$u_1^{(6)} = \frac{1}{4}(0 + u_2^{(5)} + 0 + u_3^{(5)}) = \frac{1}{4}(.13281 + .38281) = .12891,$$

$$u_2^{(6)} = \frac{1}{4}(u_1^{(5)} + 0 + 0 + u_4^{(5)}) = \frac{1}{4}(.13281 + .38281) = .12891,$$

$$u_3^{(6)} = \frac{1}{4}(0 + u_4^{(5)} + u_1^{(5)} + 1) = \frac{1}{4}(.38281 + .13281 + 1) = .37891,$$

$$u_4^{(6)} = \frac{1}{4}(u_3^{(5)} + 0 + u_2^{(5)} + 1) = \frac{1}{4}(.38281 + 0 + .13281 + 1) = .37891.$$

These are five successive iterates by *Jacobi's scheme*.

(b) Using **Gauss-Seidel Method**, the five successive iterates are given as below:

$$\left[u_{i,j}^{(n+1)} = \frac{1}{4}\left(u_{i-1,j}^{(n+1)} + u_{i+1,j}^{(n)} + u_{i,j-1}^{(n+1)} + u_{i,j+1}^{(n)}\right)\right]$$

$$u_1^{(1)} = .25,\ u_2^{(1)} = .3125,\ u_3^{(1)} = .5625,\ u_4^{(1)} = .46875,$$

$$u_1^{(2)} = \frac{1}{4}(0 + u_2^{(1)} + 0 + u_3^{(1)}) = \frac{(.3125 + .5625)}{4} = .21875,$$

$$u_2^{(2)} = \frac{1}{4}(u_1^{(2)} + 0 + 0 + u_4^{(1)}) = \frac{1}{4}(.21875 + 0 + .46875) = 0.17187,$$

$$u_3^{(2)} = \frac{1}{4}(0 + u_4^{(1)} + u_1^{(2)} + 1) = \frac{1}{4}(.468750 + .21875 + 1) = .42187,$$

$$u_4^{(2)} = \frac{1}{4}(u_3^{(2)} + 0 + u_2^{(2)} + 1) = \frac{1}{4}(.42187 + 0.17187 + 1) = 0.39844,$$

$$u_1^{(3)} = \frac{1}{4}(u_2^{(2)} + u_3^{(2)}) = \frac{1}{4}(.17187 + .42187) = .14844,$$

$$u_2^{(3)} = \frac{1}{4}(u_1^{(3)} + u_4^{(2)}) = \frac{1}{4}(.14844 + .39844) = .13672,$$

$$u_3^{(3)} = \frac{1}{4}(u_4^{(2)} + u_1^{(3)} + 1) = \frac{1}{4}(.39844 + .14844 + 1) = .38672,$$

$$u_4^{(3)} = \frac{1}{4}(u_3^{(3)} + u_2^{(3)} + 1) = \frac{1}{4}(.38672 + .13672 + 1) = .38086,$$

$$u_1^{(4)} = \frac{1}{4}(u_2^{(3)} + u_3^{(3)}) = \frac{1}{4}(.13672 + .38672) = .13086,$$

$$u_2^{(4)} = \frac{1}{4}(u_1^{(4)} + u_4^{(3)}) = \frac{1}{4}(.13086 + .38086) = .12793,$$

$$u_3^{(4)} = \frac{1}{4}(u_4^{(3)} + u_1^{(4)} + 1) = \frac{1}{4}(.38086 + .13086 + 1) = 0.37793,$$

$$u_4^{(4)} = \frac{1}{4}(u_3^{(4)} + u_2^{(4)} + 1) = \frac{1}{4}(.37793 + .12793 + 1) = 0.37646,$$

$$u_1^{(5)} = \frac{1}{4}(u_2^{(4)} + u_3^{(4)}) = \frac{1}{4}(.12793 + .37793) = .12646,$$

$$u_2^{(5)} = \frac{1}{4}(u_1^{(5)} + u_4^{(4)}) = \frac{1}{4}(.12646 + .37646) = .12573,$$

$$u_3^{(5)} = \frac{1}{4}(u_4^{(4)} + u_1^{(5)} + 1) = \frac{1}{4}(.37646 + .12646 + 1) = .37573,$$

$$u_4^{(5)} = \frac{1}{4}(u_3^{(5)} + u_2^{(5)} + 1) = \frac{1}{4}(.37573 + .12573 + 1) = .37537,$$

$$u_1^{(6)} = \frac{1}{4}(u_2^{(5)} + u_3^{(5)}) = \frac{1}{4}(.12573 + .37573) = .12536,$$

$$u_2^{(6)} = \frac{1}{4}(u_1^{(6)} + u_4^{(5)}) = \frac{1}{4}(.12536 + .37537) = .12518,$$

$$u_3^{(6)} = \frac{1}{4}(u_4^{(5)} + u_1^{(6)} + 1) = \frac{1}{4}(.37537 + .12536 + 1) = .37518,$$

$$u_4^{(6)} = \frac{1}{4}(u_3^{(6)} + u_2^{(6)} + 1) = \frac{1}{4}(.37518 + .12518 + 1) = .37509.$$

(c) **S.O.R. Method**

The iteration formula is

$$u_{i,j}^{(n+1)} = \frac{\omega}{4}\left[u_{i-1,j}^{(n+1)} + u_{i+1,j}^{(n)} + u_{i,j-1}^{(n+1)} + u_{i,j+1}^{(n)}\right] + (1-\omega)\, u_{i,j}^{(n)}$$ where ω lies between 1 and 2.

Let us choose $\omega = 1.1$, so that above formula is

$$u_{i,j}^{(n+1)} = \frac{1.1}{4}\left[u_{i-1,j}^{(n+1)} + u_{i+1,j}^{(n)} + u_{i,j-1}^{(n+1)} + u_{i,j+1}^{(n)}\right] - (.1)\, u_{i,j}^{(n)}$$

we have $u_1^{(1)} = 0.275$, $u_2^{(1)} = 0.35062$, $u_3^{(1)} = 0.35062$, $u_4^{(1)} = 0.35062$,

$$u_1^{(2)} = \frac{1.1}{4}(0 + u_2^{(1)} + 0 + u_3^{(1)}) - \frac{1}{10}u_1^{(1)} = \frac{1.1}{4}(.35062 + .35062) - \frac{.275}{10} = .16534,$$

$$u_2^{(2)} = \frac{1.1}{4}(u_1^{(2)} + 0 + 0 + u_4^{(1)}) - (.1)\, u_2^{(1)}$$

$$= \frac{1.1}{4}(.16534 + 0 + 0 + 0.35062) - \frac{1}{10} \times 0.35062 = .10683,$$

$$u_3^{(2)} = \frac{1.1}{4}(0 + u_4^{(1)} + u_1^{(2)} + 1) - \frac{1}{10}u_3^{(1)} = \frac{1.1}{4}(.35062 + 1 + .16534) - 0.35062 = 0.38183,$$

$$u_4^{(2)} = \frac{1.1}{4}(u_3^{(2)} + 0 + u_2^{(2)} + 1) - \frac{1}{10}u_4^{(1)} = \frac{1.1}{4}(.38183 + .10683 + 1) - \frac{1}{10}(.35062)$$

$$= .40938 - .03506 = .37432,$$

$$u_1^{(3)} = \frac{1.1}{4}(u_2^{(2)} + u_3^{(2)}) - \frac{1}{10}u_1^{(2)} = \frac{1.1}{4}(.10683 + .38183) - .016534 = 0.11785,$$

$$u_2^{(3)} = \frac{1.1}{4}(u_1^{(3)} + u_4^{(2)}) - \frac{u_2^{(2)}}{10} = \frac{1.1}{4}(0.11785 + .37432) - .010683 = 0.12181,$$

$$u_3^{(3)} = \frac{1.1}{4}(u_4^{(2)} + u_1^{(3)} + 1) - \frac{u_3^{(2)}}{10} = \frac{1.1}{4}(.37432 + .11785 + 1) - .038183 = .37216,$$

$$u_4^{(3)} = \frac{1.1}{4}(u_3^{(3)} + u_2^{(3)} + 1) - \frac{u_4^{(2)}}{10} = \frac{1.1}{4}(.37216 + .12181 + 1) - .037432 = .37341,$$

$$u_1^{(4)} = \frac{1.1}{4}(u_2^{(3)} + u_3^{(3)}) - \frac{1}{10}u_1^{(3)} = \frac{1.1}{4}(.12181 + .37216) - .011785 = .12413,$$

$$u_2^{(4)} = \frac{1.1}{4}(u_1^{(4)} + u_4^{(3)}) - \frac{u_2^{(3)}}{10} = \frac{1.1}{4}(.12413 + .37341) - .012181 = .12464,$$

$$u_3^{(4)} = \frac{1.1}{4}(u_4^{(3)} + u_1^{(4)} + 1) - \frac{u_3^{(3)}}{10} = \frac{1.1}{4}(.37341 + .12413 + 1) - .037216 = .37460,$$

$$u_4^{(4)} = \frac{1.1}{4}(u_3^{(4)} + u_2^{(4)} + 1) - \frac{u_4^{(3)}}{10} = \frac{1.1}{4}(.37460 + .12464 + 1) - .037341 = 0.37495,$$

$$u_1^{(5)} = \frac{1.1}{4}(u_2^{(4)} + u_3^{(4)}) - \frac{1}{10}u_1^{(4)} = \frac{1.1}{4}(.12464 + .37460) - .012413 = .12488,$$

$$u_2^{(5)} = \frac{1.1}{4}(u_1^{(5)} + u_4^{(4)}) - \frac{u_2^{(4)}}{10} = \frac{1.1}{4}(.12488 + .37495) - .012464 = .12499,$$

$$u_3^{(5)} = \frac{1.1}{4}(u_4^{(4)} + u_1^{(5)} + 1) - \frac{u_3^{(4)}}{10} = \frac{1.1}{4}(.37495 + .12488 + 1) - .03746 = .37499,$$

$$u_4^{(5)} = \frac{1.1}{4}(u_3^{(5)} + u_2^{(5)} + 1) - \frac{u_4^{(4)}}{10} = \frac{1.1}{4}(.37499 + .12499 + 1) - .03749 = 0.375.$$

Example 4: ***(a)*** *Solve the elliptic equation* $u_{xx} + u_{yy} = 0$ *for the following square mesh with boundary values as shown.*

[R.G.V.P. (M.P.) 2009; Bangaluru (B.E.) 2007; Bangaluru 2006]

(b) *Given the values of u* (x, y) *on the boundary of the square in the Figure and evaluate the function u* (x, y) *satisfying the Laplace equation* $\nabla^2 u = 0$ *at the pivotal points of this figure by*

(i) Jacobi's Method **[Channai B.E. 2004]**

(ii) Gauss-Seidal Method. **[V.T.U. (B.E.) 2007; Andhra 2000, 2006]**

Solution: (a) We have

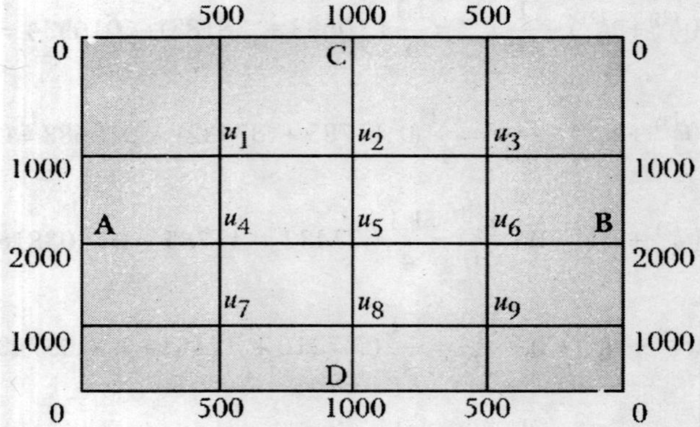

Let $u_1, u_2, \ldots, u_9$ be the values of u at the interior mesh-points. But the boundary values of u are symmetrical about AB, so we have $u_7 = u_1, u_8, = u_2, u_9 = u_3$. Also the values of *u are* symmetrical about *CD*, $\Rightarrow u_3 = u_1, u_6 = u_4, u_9 = u_7$.

Hence it is sufficient to find the values u_1, u_2, u_4 and u_5.

Now we find their initial values in the following order:

$$u_5 = \frac{1}{4}(2000 + 2000 + 1000 + 1000) = 1500 \qquad \textbf{(Std. formula)}$$

$$u_1 = \frac{1}{4}(0 + 1500 + 1000 + 2000) = 1125 \qquad \textbf{(Diag. formula)}$$

$$u_2 = \frac{1}{4}(1125 + 1125 + 1000 + 1500) = 1188 \qquad \textbf{(Std. formula)}$$

$$u_4 = \frac{1}{4}(2000 + 1500 + 1125 + 1125) = 1438 \qquad \textbf{(Std. formula)}$$

Then we carry out the iteration process using the formulae:

$$u_1^{(n+1)} = \frac{1}{4}[1000 + u_2^{(n)} + 500 + u_4^{(n)}]$$

$$u_2^{(n+1)} = \frac{1}{4}[u_1^{(n+1)} + u_1^{(n)} + 1000 + u_5^{(n)}]$$

$$u_4^{(n+1)} = \frac{1}{4}[2000 + u_5^{(n)} + u_1^{(n+1)} + u_1^{(n)}]$$

$$u_5^{(n+1)} = \frac{1}{4}[u_4^{(n+1)} + u_4^{(n)} + u_2^{(n+1)} + u_2^{(n)}]$$

For first iteration: (put $n = 0$)

$$u_1^{(1)} = \frac{1}{4}(1000 + 1188 + 500 + 1438) = 1032$$

$$u_2^{(1)} = \frac{1}{4}(1032 + 1125 + 1000 + 1500) = 1164$$

$$u_4^{(1)} = \frac{1}{4}(2000 + 1500 + 1032 + 1125) = 1414$$

$$u_5^{(1)} = \frac{1}{4}(1414 + 1438 + 1164 + 1188) = 1301$$

For second iteration: (put $n = 1$)

$$u_1^{(2)} = \frac{1}{4}(1000 + 1164 + 500 + 1414) = 1020$$

$$u_2^{(2)} = \frac{1}{4}(1020 + 1032 + 1000 + 1301) = 1088$$

$$u_4^{(2)} = \frac{1}{4}(2000 + 1301 + 1020 + 1032) = 1338$$

$$u_5^{(2)} = \frac{1}{4}(1338 + 1414 + 1088 + 1164) = 1251$$

For third iteration:

$$u_1^{(3)} = \frac{1}{4}(1000 + 1088 + 500 + 1338) = 982$$

$$u_2^{(3)} = \frac{1}{4}(982 + 1020 + 1000 + 1251) = 1063$$

$$u_4^{(3)} = \frac{1}{4}(2000 + 1251 + 982 + 1020) = 1313$$

$$u_5^{(3)} = \frac{1}{4}(1313 + 1338 + 1063 + 1088) = 1201$$

For fourth iteration:

$$u_1^{(4)} = \frac{1}{4}(1000 + 1063 + 500 + 1313) = 969$$

$$u_2^{(4)} = \frac{1}{4}(969 + 982 + 1000 + 1201) = 1038,$$

$$u_4^{(4)} = \frac{1}{4}(2000 + 1201 + 989 + 982) = 1288,$$

$$u_5^{(4)} = \frac{1}{4}(1288 + 1313 + 1038 + 1063) = 1176,$$

For fifth iteration:

$$u_1^{(5)} = \frac{1}{4}(1000 + 1038 + 500 + 1288) = 957,$$

$$u_2^{(5)} = \frac{1}{4}(957 + 969 + 1000 + 1176) \approx 1026,$$

$$u_4^{(5)} = \frac{1}{4}(2000 + 1176 + 957 + 969) \approx 1276,$$

$$u_5^{(5)} = \frac{1}{4}(1276 + 1288 + 1026 + 1038) = 1157,$$

Similarly, $u_1^{(6)} = 951, u_2^{(6)} = 1016, u_4^{(6)} = 1266, u_5^{(6)} = 1146,$

$$u_1^{(7)} = 946,\ u_2^{(7)} = 1011,\ u_4^{(7)} = 1260,\ u_5^{(7)} = 1138,$$

$$u_1^{(8)} = 943,\ u_2^{(8)} = 1007,\ u_4^{(8)} = 1257,\ u_5^{(8)} = 1134,$$

$$u_1^{(9)} = 941,\ u_2^{(9)} = 1005,\ u_4^{(9)} = 1255,\ u_5^{(9)} = 1131,$$

$$u_1^{(10)} = 940,\ u_2^{(10)} = 1003,\ u_4^{(10)} = 1253,\ u_5^{(10)} = 1129,$$

$$u_1^{(11)} = 939,\ u_2^{(11)} = 1002,\ u_4^{(11)} = 1252,\ u_5^{(11)} = 1126,$$

$$u_1^{(12)} \approx 939,\ u_2^{(12)} \approx 1001,\ u_4^{(12)} \approx 1251,\ u_5^{(12)} \approx 1126,$$

Hence there is negligible difference between the values obtained in the 11th and 12th iterations implying that $u_1 = 939$, $u_2 = 1001$, $u_4 = 1251$ and $u_5 = 1126$.

Solution: (b) To get the initial values of u_1, u_2, u_3, u_4 we assume that $u_4 = 0$.

$$u_1 = \frac{1}{4}(1000 + 0 + 1000 + 2000) = 1000 \qquad \textbf{(Diag. formula)}$$

$$u_2 = \frac{1}{4}(1000 + 500 + 1000 + 0) = 625 \qquad \textbf{(Std. formula)}$$

$$u_3 = \frac{1}{4}(2000 + 0 + 1000 + 500) = 875 \qquad \textbf{(Std. formula)}$$

$$u_4 = \frac{1}{4}(875 + 0 + 625 + 0) = 375 \qquad \textbf{(Std. formula)}$$

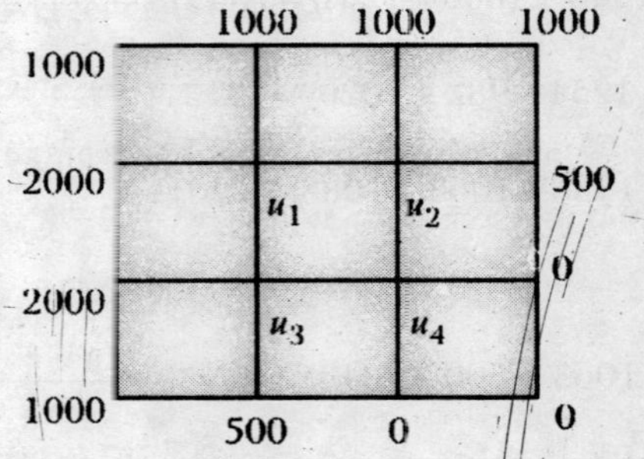

(i) We carry out the successive iterations, using Jacobi's formulae:

$$u_1^{(n+1)} = \frac{1}{4}[2000 + u_2^{(n)} + 1000 + u_3^{(n)}], \quad u_2^{(n+1)} = \frac{1}{4}[u_1^{(n)} + 500 + 1000 + u_4^{(n)}]$$

$$u_3^{(n+1)} = \frac{1}{4}[2000 + u_4^{(n)} + u_1^{(n)} + 500], \quad u_4^{(n+1)} = \frac{1}{4}[u_3^{(n)} + 0 + u_2^{(n)} + 0]$$

For first iteration: (put $n = 0$)

$$u_1^{(1)} = \frac{1}{4}(2000 + 625 + 1000 + 875) = 1125, \quad u_2^{(1)} = \frac{1}{4}(1000 + 500 + 1000 + 375) \approx 719,$$

$$u_3^{(1)} = \frac{1}{4}(2000 + 375 + 1000 + 500) \approx 969, \quad u_4^{(1)} = \frac{1}{4}(875 + 0 + 625 + 0) \approx 375.$$

For second iteration: (put $n = 1$)

$$u_1^{(2)} = \frac{1}{4}(2000 + 719 + 1000 + 969) = 1172, \quad u_2^{(2)} = \frac{1}{4}(1125 + 500 + 1000 + 375) = 750,$$

$$u_3^{(2)} = \frac{1}{4}(2000 + 375 + 1125 + 500) = 1000, \quad u_4^{(2)} = \frac{1}{4}(969 + 0 + 719 + 0) = 422.$$

Similarly, we have

$$u_1^{(3)} \approx 1188, \quad u_2^{(3)} \approx 774, \quad u_3^{(3)} \approx 1024, \quad u_4^{(3)} \approx 438,$$

$$u_1^{(4)} \approx 1200, \quad u_2^{(4)} \approx 782, \quad u_3^{(4)} \approx 1032, \quad u_4^{(4)} \approx 450,$$

$$u_1^{(5)} \approx 1204,\ u_2^{(5)} \approx 788,\ u_3^{(5)} \approx 1038,\ u_4^{(5)} \approx 454,$$

$$u_1^{(6)} \approx 1206.5,\ u_2^{(6)} \approx 790,\ u_3^{(6)} \approx 1040,\ u_4^{(6)} \approx 456.5$$

$$u_1^{(7)} \approx 1208,\ u_2^{(7)} \approx 791,\ u_3^{(7)} \approx 1041,\ u_4^{(7)} \approx 458$$

and $u_1^{(8)} = 1208,\ u_2^{(8)} = 791.5,\ u_3^{(8)} = 1041.5,\ u_4^{(8)} = 458,$

Hence there is no significant difference between the seventh and eight iteration values.

Thus $u_1 = 1208, u_2 = 792, u_3 = 1042$ and $u_4 = 458$.

(ii) We carry out the successive iterations, using Gauss-Seidal formulae

$$u_1^{(n+1)} = \frac{1}{4}[2000 + u_2^{(n)} + 1000 + u_3^{(n)}]$$

$$u_2^{(n+1)} = \frac{1}{4}[u_1^{(n+1)} + 500 + 1000 + u_4^{(n)}]$$

$$u_3^{(n+1)} = \frac{1}{4}[2000 + u_4^{(n)} + u_1^{(n+1)} + 500]$$

$$u_4^{(n+1)} = \frac{1}{4}[u_3^{(n+1)} + 0 + u_2^{(n+1)} + 0]$$

For first iteration: (put $n = 0$)

$$u_1^{(1)} = \frac{1}{4}(2000 + 625 + 1000 + 875) = 1125,$$

$$u_2^{(1)} = \frac{1}{4}(1125 + 500 + 1000 + 375) = 750,$$

$$u_3^{(1)} = \frac{1}{4}(2000 + 375 + 1125 + 500) = 1000,$$

$$u_4^{(1)} = \frac{1}{4}(1000 + 0 + 750 + 0) \approx 438,$$

For second iteration: (put $n = 1$)

$$u_1^{(2)} = \frac{1}{4}(2000 + 750 + 1000 + 1000) \approx 1188$$

$$u_2^{(2)} = \frac{1}{4}(1188 + 500 + 1000 + 438) \approx 782$$

$$u_3^{(2)} = \frac{1}{4}(2000 + 438 + 1188 + 500) \approx 1032$$

$$u_4^{(2)} = \frac{1}{4}(1032 + 0 + 782 + 0) \approx 454$$

Similarly $u_1^{(3)} \approx 1204,\ u_2^{(3)} \approx 789,\ u_3^{(3)} \approx 1040,\ u_4^{(3)} \approx 458$

$$u_1^{(4)} \approx 1207,\ u_2^{(4)} \approx 791,\ u_3^{(4)} \approx 1041,\ u_4^{(4)} \approx 458$$

and $u_1^{(5)} = 1208,\ u_2^{(5)} \approx 791.5,\ u_3^{(5)} \approx 1041.5,\ u_4^{(5)} \approx 458.25$

Hence there is no significant difference between the fourth and fifth iteration values. Thus $u_1 = 1208, u_2 = 792, u_3 = 1042$ and $u_4 = 458$.

18.5 Parabolic Equations

Consider, the heat conduction equation; viz $\frac{\partial u}{\partial t}=\frac{\partial^2 u}{\partial x^2}$ where $u=u(x,t)$ ...(1)

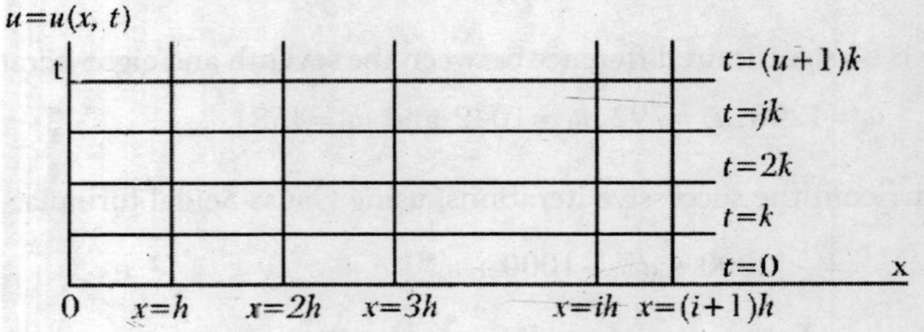

Let us divide the $x-t$ plane into a number of smaller rectangles by means of the lines $x=0, x=h, x=2h,$ (*i.e.* $x=ih; i=0,1,2,3,...$) and $t=0,k,2k,...$

(*i.e.* $t=jk$; $j=0,1,2,...$). Then by relations (4) and (7) we readily obtain $\frac{\partial^2 u}{\partial x^2}=\frac{1}{h^2}[u_{i-1,j}-2u_{i,j}+u_{i+1,j}]$ and $\frac{\partial u}{\partial t}=\frac{1}{k}[u_{i,j+1}-u_{i,j}]$. Putting these values in (1), we get $\frac{1}{k}[u_{i,j+1}-u_{i,j}]=\frac{1}{h^2}[u_{i-1,j}-2u_{i,j}+u_{i+1,j}]$

$$\Rightarrow \quad u_{i,j+1}-u_{i,j}=r(u_{i-1,j}-2u_{i,j}+u_{i+1,j}) \text{ where } r=(k/h^2)$$

$$\Rightarrow \quad u_{i,j+1}=u_{i,j}+r[u_{i-1,j}-2u_{i,j}+u_{i+1,j}] \quad ...(2)$$

This formula (2) gives the value of the unknown function at the $(i, j+1)$ the interior point in terms of the known functional values and hence is known as *explicit formula* and remains valid only for $0<r\le(1/2)$. It is important to note here that for the approximation of $(\partial^2 u/\partial x^2)$, we have used the functional values along the jth row only. In 1947 **CRANK** and **NICOLSON** suggested the method according to which $(\partial^2 u/\partial x^2)$ is replaced by the average value of its finite-difference approximations on the jth and $(j+1)$th rows implying.

$$\frac{\partial^2 u}{\partial x^2}=\frac{1}{2}\left[\frac{u_{i-1,j}-2u_{i,j}+u_{i+1,j}}{h^2}+\frac{u_{i-1,j+1}-2u_{i,j+1}+u_{i+1,j+1}}{h^2}\right]$$

Now putting this value of $\frac{\partial^2 u}{\partial x^2}$ and $\frac{\partial u}{\partial t}$ in equation (1), we get

$$\frac{1}{k}\{u_{i,j+1}-u_{i,j}\}=\frac{1}{2h^2}\{u_{i-1,j}-2u_{i,j}+u_{i+1,j}+u_{i-1,j+1}-2u_{i,j+1}+u_{i+1,j+1}\}$$

$$\Rightarrow \quad -r\,u_{i-1,j+1}+(2+2r)\,u_{i,j+1}-r\,u_{i+1,j+1}$$

$$=r\,u_{i-1,j}+2(1-r)\,u_{i,j+1}+r\,u_{i+1,j} \text{ where } r=(k/h^2) \quad ...(3)$$

On the L.H.S. of this equation we have three unknowns while on R.H.S. all the three are known. The implicit formula (3) is known as *Crank Nicolson formula* and remains convergent for all finite values of r. If in each row, we have "*m*" internal mesh points then the above formula gives "*m*" simultaneous equations for "*m*" unknowns in terms of known boundary values. On the same lines, one can calculate the internal mesh points on all rows.

Example 5: *Solve the heat equation* $\frac{\partial u}{\partial t}=\frac{\partial^2 u}{\partial x^2}$ *subject to the boundary and initial conditions as follows:* $u(x,0)=0,\ u(0,t)=0,\ u(1,t)=t.$

[Meerut 2003; Rohilkhand (M.Sc.) 2006, 2009; Bhopal 2007; Bangaluru 2004]

Solution: By **18.4**, relation (3), we have

$$-r\,u_{i-1,j+1}+(2+2r)\,u_{i,j+1}-r\,u_{i+1,j+1}$$
$$=r\,u_{i-1,j}+2(1-r)\,u_{i,j}+r\,u_{i+1,j}\quad \text{where } r=(k/h^2) \text{ and } u\equiv u(x,t) \qquad ...(1)$$

(i) Let us choose $h=\frac{1}{2}$ and $k=\frac{1}{8}$ so that $r=\frac{1}{2}$. Then (1) can be re-written as

$$-u_{i-1,j+1}+6\,u_{i,j+1}-u_{i+1,j+1}=u_{i-1,j}+2\,u_{i,j}+u_{i+1,j} \qquad ...(2)$$

Let $OA=h=\frac{1}{2}$, $OB=k=\frac{1}{8}$. Then co-ordinates of P are given by $\left(\frac{1}{2},\frac{1}{8}\right)$. Let the value of u at P be u_1. Now applying **Crank Nicolson** scheme (2) at P, we get

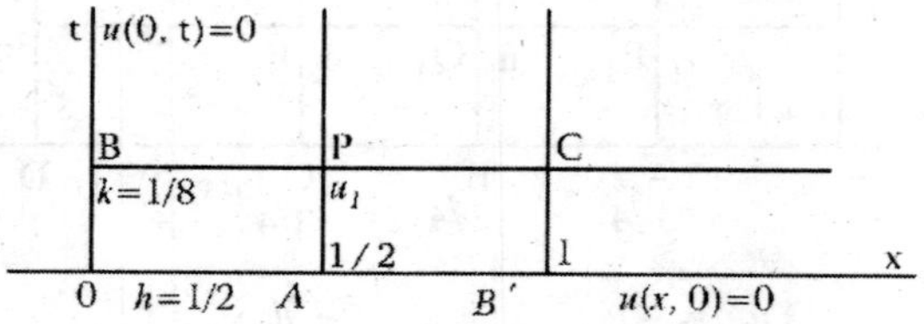

$$-u_B+6\,u_P-u_C=u_O+2\,u_A+u_{B'}$$

$$\Rightarrow\quad -0+6\,u_1-u\left(1,\frac{1}{8}\right)=0+2\,u\left(\frac{1}{2},0\right)+u(1,0)$$

$$\Rightarrow\quad -0+6\,u_1-\frac{1}{8}=0+2.0+0 \qquad (\because\ u(x,0)=0)$$

$$\Rightarrow\quad 6\,u_1=1/8\ \Rightarrow\ u_1=(1/48)=0.02083.$$

(ii) Let us choose $k=\frac{1}{8}$ and $h=\frac{1}{2}$ so that $r=(k/h^2)=2$. It is worth noting that **C – N** scheme is convergent for all finite values of r. For $r=2$, equation (1) implies

$$-u_{i-1,j+1}+3\,u_{i,j+1}-u_{i+1,j+1}=u_{i-1,j}-u_{i,j}+u_{i+1,j} \qquad ...(3)$$

Applying this equation for the mesh point P in the diagram, we have

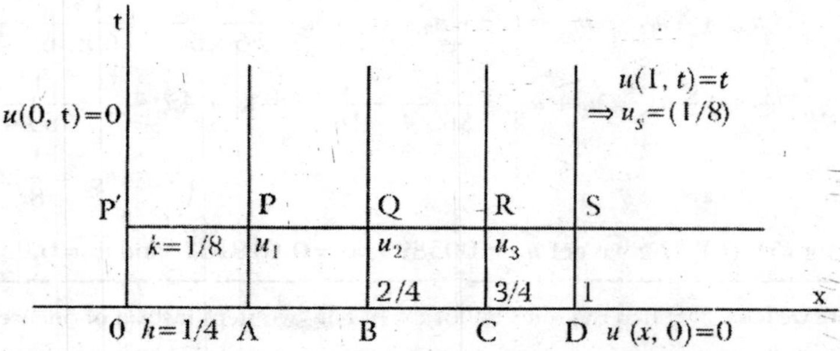

$$-u_{p'} + 3u_p - u_Q = u_O - u_A + u_B \text{ where } u_{i,j+1} \equiv u_1$$

$$\Rightarrow \quad -0 + 3u_1 - u_2 = 0 - 0 + 0 = 0 \quad \Rightarrow 3u_1 = u_2$$

Again, applying the same scheme at Q and R respectively, we obtain

$$-u_P + 3u_Q - u_R = u_A - u_B + u_C = 0 \quad \Rightarrow -u_1 + 3u_2 - u_3 = 0$$

Thus we have three unknowns and three equations. Solving these, one may get

$$u_1 = .00595,\ u_2 = 0.01785 \text{ and } u_3 = 0.04760$$

(iii) We now consider $k = \frac{1}{16}$ and $h = \frac{1}{4}$ so that $r = 1$. For $r = 1$, **C – N** Scheme can be written as

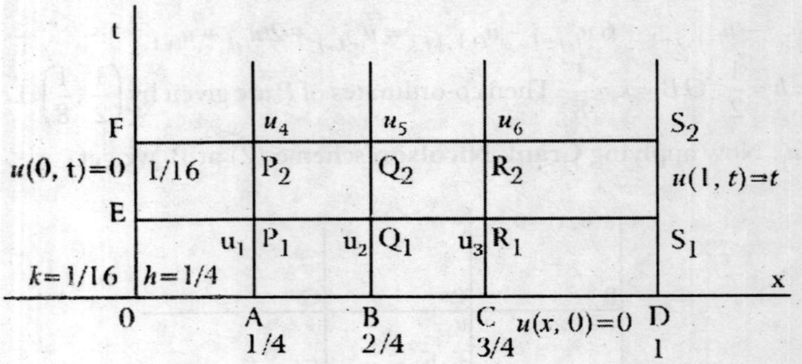

$$-u_{i-1,j+1} + 4u_{i,j+1} - u_{i+1,j+1} = u_{i-1,j} + u_{i+1,j}$$

Applying this scheme at P_1, Q_1, R_1, we get $-u_E + 4u_{P_1} - u_{Q_1} = u_O + u_B$ where $u_{i,j+1} \equiv u_1$

i.e $\quad -0 + 4u_1 - u_2 = 0 \quad$ ...(1)

$-u_{P_1} + 4u_{Q_1} - u_{R_1} = u_A + u_C = 0 \Rightarrow -u_1 + 4u_2 - u_3 = 0 \quad$ ...(2)

and $\quad -u_{Q_1} + 4u_{R_1} - u_{S_1} = u_B + u_D = 0 \Rightarrow -u_2 + 4u_3 - u_{S_1} = 0 \quad$ ...(3)

But $\quad u_{S_1} = [t]_{t=(1/16)} = \frac{1}{16} \Rightarrow -u_2 + 4u_3 - \frac{1}{6} = 0 \quad$ ...(4)

Solving (1), (2) and (4) for u_1, u_2, u_3; we get

$$u_1 = \frac{1}{16 \times 56} = .001116,\ u_2 = \frac{1}{56 \times 4} = .004464 \text{ and } u_3 = \frac{15}{16 \times 56} = .016740.$$

Again applying the scheme at P_2, Q_2, R_2; we get

$$-u_F + 4u_{P_2} - u_{Q_2} = u_E + u_{Q_1} \Rightarrow 4u_4 - u_5 = u_2 = \frac{1}{56 \times 4} \quad \text{...(5)}$$

$$-u_{P_2} + 4u_{Q_2} - u_{R_2} = u_{P_1} + u_{R_1} = u_1 + u_3 = \frac{1}{16 \times 56} + \frac{15}{16 \times 56} = \frac{1}{56} \quad \text{...(6)}$$

and $\quad -u_{Q_2} + 4u_{R_2} - u_{S_2} = u_2 + u_{S_1} = \frac{1}{56 \times 4} + \frac{1}{16} \Rightarrow -u_5 + 4u_6 - \frac{1}{8} = \frac{1}{56 \times 4} + \frac{1}{16} \quad$ ...(7)

$$\left(\because \quad u_{S_2} = \frac{1}{8} \text{ and } u_{S_1} = \frac{1}{6}\right)$$

Now solving (5), (6), (7); we get $u_4 = .005899$, $u_5 = 0.019132$ and $u_6 = 0.052771$.

Note: Here we have obtained the solution for $t = 1/8$ in two steps instead of one step.

(iv) As our final choice, we choose $k = 1/24, h = 1/4$ so that

$r = (k/h^2) = \left(\frac{1}{24} \Big/ \frac{1}{16}\right) = (2/3)$. Thus we now propose to find the solution at $t = (1/8)$ in 3 steps insted of one step.

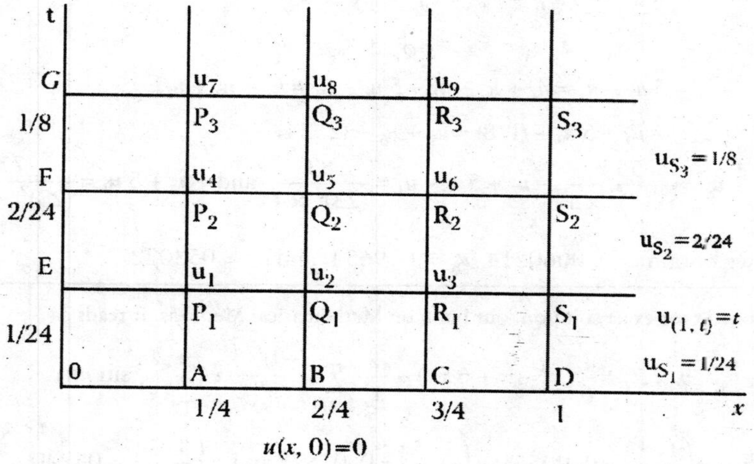

For $r = (2/3)$, C – N, scheme can be written as

$$-\frac{2}{3}u_{i-1,j+1} + \frac{10}{3}u_{i,j+1} - \frac{2}{3}u_{i+1,j+1} = \frac{2}{3}u_{i-1,j} + \frac{2}{3}u_{i,j} + \frac{2}{3}u_{i+1,j}$$

$$\Rightarrow \quad -u_{i-1,j+1} + 5u_{i,j+1} - u_{i+1,j+1} = u_{i-1,j} + u_{i,j} + u_{i+1,j} \qquad ...(1)$$

Applying this equation for the mesh points P_1, Q_1, R_1 respectively; we get

$$-u_E + 5u_{P_1} - u_{Q_1} = U_O + u_A + u_B \qquad ...(2)$$

$$-u_{P_1} + 5u_{Q_1} - u_{R_1} = u_A + u_B + u_C \qquad ...(3)$$

$$-u_{Q_1} + 5u_{R_1} - U_{S_1} = u_B + u_C + u_D \qquad ...(4)$$

$$\Rightarrow \quad 5u_1 - u_2 = 0, -u_1 + 5u_2 - u_3 = 0, -u_2 + 5u_3 - \frac{1}{24} = 0$$

Solving these we get $u_1 = \frac{1}{115 \times 24}, u_2 = \frac{1}{23 \times 24}, u_3 = \frac{1}{115}$.

Applying C.N. scheme at P_2, Q_2, R_2; we get $-u_F + 5u_{P_2} - u_{Q_2} = u_E + u_{P_1} + u_{Q_1}$

$$-u_{P_2} + 5u_{Q_2} - u_{R_2} = u_{P_1} + u_{Q_1} + u_{R_1}$$

$$-u_{Q_2} + 5u_{R_2} - u_{S_2} = u_{Q_1} + u_{R_1} + u_{S_1}$$

$$\Rightarrow \quad -0 + 5u_4 - u_5 = u_1 + u_2 = \frac{1}{4 \times 115},$$

$$-u_4 + 5u_5 - u_6 = u_1 + u_2 + u_3 = 1/92,$$

and $$-u_5 + 5u_6 = \frac{2}{24} + u_2 + u_3 + \frac{1}{24} = \frac{374}{24 \times 115}$$

Solving these, we get $u_4 = \dfrac{668}{24 \times (115)^2}$, $u_5 = \dfrac{53}{12 \times (23)^2}$, $u_6 = \dfrac{761}{(115)^2 \times 2}$.

Applying **C.N.** Scheme again at P_3, Q_3, R_3; we get

$$-u_G + 5\,u_{P_3} - u_{Q_3} = u_F + u_{P_2} + u_{Q_2}$$

$$-u_{P_3} + 5\,u_{Q_3} - u_{R_3} = u_{P_2} + u_{Q_2} + u_{R_2}$$

and $$-u_{Q_3} + 5\,u_{R_3} - u_{S_3} = u_{Q_2} + u_{R_2} + u_{S_2}$$

$\Rightarrow$ $$5\,u_7 - u_8 = u_4 + u_5 - u_7 + 5\,u_8 - u_9 = u_4 + u_5 + u_6$$

and $$-u_8 + 5\,u_9 - (1/8) = u_5 + u_6 + (2/24)$$

$$\Rightarrow 5u_7 - u_8 = \frac{553}{(115)^2 \times 4}, -u_7 + 5u_8 - u_9 = \frac{83}{(23)^2 \times 4} \text{ and } -u_8 + 5\,u_9 = \frac{77907}{(23)^2 \times 24 \times 25}$$

Solving, we obtain $u_7 = .0060214$, $u_8 = .019654$ and $u_9 = .053022$

Note: Consult for exact solution, our book on Mathematical Methods. It reads as

$$u(x,t) = \frac{1}{6}(x^3 - x + 6\,x\,t) + \frac{2}{\pi^3}\sum_{n=1}^{\infty}\frac{(-1)^{n-1}}{n^3}e^{-n^2\pi^2 t}\sin n\pi x$$

$$\Rightarrow \quad u\left(\frac{1}{4}, \frac{1}{8}\right) = 0.00541, u\left(\frac{1}{2}, \frac{1}{8}\right) = 0.01878 \text{ and } u\left(\frac{3}{4}, \frac{1}{8}\right) = .05240.$$

18.6 Iterative Methods

Iterative methods, discussed earlier can be used to solve finite difference equation:

$$-r\,u_{i-1,j+1} + (2 + 2\,r)\,u_{i,j+1} - r\,u_{i+1,j+1} = r\,u_{i-1,j} + (2 - 2r)\,u_{i,j} + r\,u_{i+1,j}$$ where

$r = (k/h^2)$ [*Crank-Nicolson Formula*] obtained by the heat conduction equation $\dfrac{\partial u}{\partial t} = \dfrac{\partial^2 u}{\partial x^2}$.

The Crank-Nicolson Formula can be further written as

$$(1 + r)\,u_{i,j+1} = u_{i,j} + (r/2)\{u_{i-1,j+1} + u_{i+1,j} + u_{i+1,j+1} + u_{i-1,j} - 2\,u_{i,j}\}$$ where

$$r = (k/h^2) \qquad ...(1)$$

In this equation, the unknowns are $u_{i,j+1}$, $u_{i-1,j+1}$ and $u_{i+1,j+1}$ and all others are known as these were computed at the j-th step. Keeping this in view, we drop the j's and then

setting $P_i = u_{i,j} + \dfrac{r}{2}\{u_{i-1,j} - 2\,u_{i,j} + u_{i+1,j}\}$ ...(2)

in (1), we have obtained $(1 + r)\,u_i = p_i + \dfrac{r}{2}(u_{i-1} + u_{i+1})$ ...(3)

$$\Rightarrow \quad u_i = \frac{p_i}{1 + r} + \frac{r}{2(1 + r)}\{u_{i-1} + u_{i+1}\} \qquad ...(4)$$

Form (4), we obtain the iterative formula as follows:

$$u_i^{(n+1)} = \frac{p_i}{1 + r} + \frac{r}{2(1 + r)}\{u_{i-1}^{(n)} + u_{i+1}^{(n)}\} \qquad ...(5)$$

Formula (5) gives the $(n+1)$ th iterate in terms of the nth iterates only and is known as ***Jacobi's Iteration Formula***. By (5), it can be seen easily that while computing $u_i^{(n+1)}$, the latest value of u_{i-1} namely $u_{i-1}^{(n+1)}$ is known already. Thus the convergence of the ***Jacobi's Iteration Formula*** can be improved by putting $u_{i-1}^{(n+1)}$, for $u_{i-1}^{(n)}$ and accordingly we obtain the formula

$$u_i^{(n+1)} = \frac{p_i}{1+r} + \frac{r}{2(1+r)} \{u_{i-1}^{(n+1)} + u_{i+1}^{(n)}\} \quad \text{...(6)}$$

This formula (6) is known as ***Gauss-Seidel Iteration Formula*** and is convergent for all finite values of r. *This formula converges twice as fast as* ***Jacobi's Scheme***. Equation (6) can also be written as

$$u_{(i)}^{(n+1)} = u_i^{(n)} + \left\{\frac{r}{2(1+r)} (u_{(i-1)}^{(n+1)} + u_{i+1}^{(n)}) + \frac{p_i}{1+r} - u_i^{(n)}\right\} \quad \text{...(7)}$$

From (7), it is clear that the expression within the curly brackets is the difference between the *n*th and $(n+1)$ th iterates. If this difference is taken as ω times the above expression, then we have

$$u_i^{(n+1)} = u_i^{(n)} + \omega \left\{\frac{r}{2(1+r)} \cdot (u_{i-1}^{(n+1)} + u_{i+1}^{(n)}) + \frac{p_i}{1+r} - u_i^{(n)}\right\} \quad \text{...(8)}$$

This formula is known as *Successive-Over Relaxation method* (**S.O.R.** method) while ω is called the **relaxation factor** and generally lies in between 1 and 2.

Example 6: *Solve the heat conduction equation* $\frac{\partial u}{\partial t} = \frac{\partial^2 u}{\partial x^2}$ *under the boundary and initial conditions:*

(*a*) $u(x, t) = 0$ at $x = 0$ and $x = 1$ for $t > 0$, **[Kurukshetra (M.E.) 2002, 2003, 2006, 2008]**

(*b*) $u(x, t) = \sin \pi x$ *at* $t = 0$ for $0 \le x \le 1$, *by* **Gauss-Seidel Method.**

[Madurai (B.E.) 2004; Bilaspur 2006, 2009]

Solution:

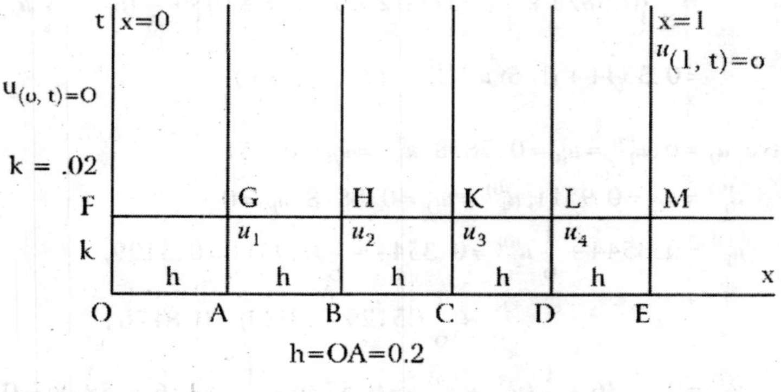

h=OA=0.2

Let us choose $h = .2$ and $k = .02$ so that we have $r = (k/h^2) = (.20/.04) = 1/2$.

Form 18.5, relation (6) [**G.S.** *iteration formula*], we then have

$$u_i^{(n+1)} = \frac{p_i}{1+r} + \frac{r}{2(1+r)} \{u_{i-1}^{(n+1)} + u_{i+1}^{(n)}\} \quad \text{...(1)}$$

$$\Rightarrow u_i^{(n+1)} = \frac{2}{3} p_i + \frac{1}{6}(u_{i-1}^{(n+1)} + u_{i+1}^{(n)}) = \frac{2}{3}\left\{u_{i,j} + \frac{1}{4}(u_{i-1,j} + 2u_{i,j} + u_{i+1,j})\right\} + \frac{1}{6}(u_{i-1}^{(n+1)} + u_{i+1}^{(n)})$$

Now $u_O = [\sin \pi x]_{x=0} = 0$, $u_A = [\sin \pi x]_{x=.2} = 0.5878$,

$u_B = [\sin \pi x]_{x=.4} = 0.9511$, $u_C = [\sin \pi x]_{x=.6} = 0.9511$,

$u_D = [\sin \pi x]_{x=0.8} = 0.5878$, $u_E = \sin \pi = 0$.

Whence applying the **G.S.** formula at *G, H, K, L,* respectively, we get

$$u_1^{(n+1)} = \frac{2}{3}\left\{u_A + \frac{1}{4}(u_0 - 2u_A + u_B)\right\} + \frac{1}{6}(u_F + u_2^{(n)})$$

$$= \frac{2}{3}\left(.5878 + \frac{1}{4}(0 - 2 \times .5878 + 0.9511)\right) + \frac{1}{6}(0 + u_2^{(n)}) = 0.3544 + \frac{1}{6}u_2^{(n)} \quad ...(2)$$

$$u_2^{(n+1)} = \frac{2}{3}\left\{u_B + \frac{1}{4}(u_A - 2u_B + u_C)\right\} + \frac{1}{6}(u_G^{(n+1)} + u_3^{(n)})$$

$$= \frac{2}{3}\left\{0.9511 + \frac{1}{4}(0.5878 - 2 \times 0.9511 + 0.9511)\right\} + \frac{1}{6}(u_1^{(n+1)} + u_3^{(n)})$$

$$= 0.5736 + \frac{1}{6}(u_1^{(n+1)} + u_3^{(n)}) \quad ...(3)$$

$$u_3^{(n+1)} = \frac{2}{3}\left\{u_C + \frac{1}{4}(u_B - 2u_C + u_D)\right\} + \frac{1}{6}(u_2^{(n+1)} + u_4^{(n)})$$

$$= \frac{2}{3}\left\{0.9511 + \frac{1}{4}(0.9511 - 2 \times 0.9511 + 0.5878)\right\} + \frac{1}{6}(u_2^{(n+1)} + u_4^{(n)})$$

$$= 0.5736 + \frac{1}{6}(u_2^{(n+1)} + u_4^{(n)}) \quad ...(4)$$

and $$u_4^{(n+1)} = \frac{2}{3}\left\{u_D + \frac{1}{4}(u_C - 2u_D + u_E)\right\} + \frac{1}{6}(u_3^{(n+1)} + u_M^{(n)})$$

$$= \frac{2}{3}\left\{0.5878 + \frac{1}{4}(.9511 - 2 \times 0.5878 + 0)\right\} + \frac{1}{6}(u_3^{(n+1)} + u_M^{(n)})$$

$$= 0.3544 + (1/6)\, u_3^{(n+1)} \quad (\because \ u_M = 0) \quad ...(5)$$

We have $u_0 = 0, u_1^{(0)} = u_A = 0.5878, u_2^{(0)} = u_B = 0.9511,$

$u_3^{(0)} = u_C = 0.9511, u_4^{(0)} = u_D = 0.5878, u_E = 0$

$$\Rightarrow \quad u_1^{(1)} = 0.3544 + \frac{1}{6}u_2^{(0)} = 0.3544 + \frac{1}{6}0.9511 = 0.5129,$$

$$+ \frac{1}{6}(.5129 + .9511) = 0.8176,$$

$$u_3^{(1)} = 0.5736 + \frac{1}{6}(u_2^{(1)} + u_4^{(0)}) = 0.5736 + \frac{1}{6}(.8176 + .5878) = 0.8078,$$

$$u_4^{(1)} = 0.3544 + \frac{1}{6}u_3^{(1)} = 0.3544 + \frac{0.8078}{6} = 0.4890$$

$$u_1^{(2)} = 0.3544 + \frac{1}{6}u_2^{(1)} = 0.3544 + \frac{1}{6} \times .8176 = 0.4907,$$

$$u_2^{(2)} = 0.5736 + \frac{1}{6}(u_1^{(2)} + u_3^{(1)}) = 0.5736 + \left(\frac{.4907 + .8078}{6}\right) = 0.7900,$$

$$u_3^{(2)} = 0.5736 + (u_2^{(2)} + u_4^{(1)}) = 0.5736 + \left(\frac{0.7900 + 0.4890}{6}\right) = 0.7868,$$

$$u_4^{(3)} = 0.3544 + \frac{u_3^{(2)}}{6} = 0.3544 + \frac{7868}{6} = 0.4855,$$

$$u_1^{(3)} = 0.3544 + \frac{u_2^{(2)}}{6} = 0.3544 + \frac{0.7900}{6} = 0.4861,$$

$$u_2^{(3)} = 0.5736 + \frac{1}{6}(u_1^{(3)} + u_3^{(2)}) = 0.5736 + \frac{.4861 + 7868}{6} = 0.7858$$

$$u_3^{(3)} = 0.5736 + \frac{1}{6}(u_2^{(3)} + u_4^{(2)}) = .5736 + \left(\frac{.7858 + .4855}{6}\right) = 0.7855.$$

$$u_4^{(3)} = 0.3544 + \frac{1}{6}u_3^{(3)} = 0.3544 + \frac{.7855}{6} = 0.4853,$$

$$u_1^{(4)} = 0.3544 + \frac{1}{6}u_2^{(3)} = 0.3544 + \frac{1}{6}(.7858) = 0.4854,$$

$$u_2^{(4)} = 0.5736 + \frac{1}{6}(u_1^{(4)} + u_3^{(3)}) = 0.5736 + \frac{1}{6}(.4854 + .4853) = .7854,$$

$$u_3^{(4)} = .5736 + \frac{1}{6}(u_2^{(4)} + u_4^{(3)}) = .5736 + \frac{1}{6}(.7854 + .4853) = .7854,$$

$$u_4^{(4)} = 0.3544 + \frac{1}{6}u_3^{(4)} = .3544 + \frac{1}{6}(.7854) = 0.4853,$$

$$u_1^{(5)} = 0.3544 + \frac{1}{6}u_2^{(4)} = .3544 + \frac{1}{6}(.7854) = 0.4853,$$

$$u_2^{(5)} = .5736 + \frac{1}{6}(u_1^{(5)} + u_3^{(4)}) = .5736 + \frac{1}{6}(.4853 + .7854) = .7854$$

$$u_3^{(5)} = .5736 + \frac{1}{6}(u_2^{(5)} + u_4^{(4)}) = .5736 + \frac{1}{6}(.7854 + .4853) = .7854,$$

$$u_4^{(5)} = .3544 + \frac{1}{6}u_3^{(5)} = 0.3544 + \frac{1}{6}(.7854) = 0.4853$$

$$u_1^{(6)} = 0.3544 + \frac{1}{6}u_2^{(5)} = .3544 + \frac{.7854}{6} = 0.4853,$$

$$u_2^{(6)} = .5736 + \frac{1}{6}(u_1^{(6)} + u_3^{(5)}) = .5736 + \left(\frac{.4853 + .7854}{6}\right) = 0.7854,$$

$$u_3^{(6)} = .5736 + \frac{1}{6}(u_2^{(6)} + u_4^{(5)}) = .5736 + \left(\frac{.7854 + .4853}{6}\right) = .7854,$$

$$u_4^{(6)} = .3544 + \frac{1}{6}u_3^{(6)} = .3544 + \frac{.7854}{6} = 0.4853.$$

Above gives the successive iterates of u_1, u_2, u_3, and u_4 corresponding to $t = 0\ 02$. A close inspection of this reveals that there exists a solution symmetry about $x = 0.5$.

TABULAR FORM OF RESULTS

x	0.0	0.2	0.4	0.6	0.8	1.0
$u(x)$	0.0	0.5878	0.9511	0.9511	0.5878	0.0
$n=0$	0.0	0.5878	0.9511	0.9511	0.5878	0.0
$n=1$	0.0	0.5129	0.8176	0.8078	0.4890	0.0
$n=2$	0.0	0.4907	0.7900	0.7868	0.4855	0.0
$n=3$	0.0	0.4861	0.7858	0.7855	0.4853	0.0
$n=4$	0.0	0.4854	0.7854	0.7854	0.4853	0.0
$n=5$	0.0	0.4853	0.7854	0.7854	0.4853	0.0
$n=6$	0.0	0.4853	0.7854	0.7854	0.4853	0.0

18.7 Solution of Laplace's Equation by Iteration (Leibmann's Process)

[Rohilkhand (M.Sc.) 2007, 2008; Bangaluru 2008]

Refer Figure given below: to solve $(\partial^2 u / \partial x^2) + (\partial^2 u / \partial y^2) = 0$, in the bounded square region with boundary C, let region R be divided in to a net work of small squares of each side h. Let the values of $u(x, y)$ on the boundary C be given by C_i.

We know that $u(x, y)$ satisfying Laplace's equation can be replaced either by standard five point formula or the diagonal 5-pt formula. To obtain initial values at the interior points of the network, we first compute u_5 at the centre of the square by taking the mean of the four boundary values of the horizontal and vertical lines passing through it implying $u_5 = \frac{1}{4}(c_{15} + c_3 + c_7 + c_{11})$, where of course we have obtained u_5 in **example 2** by diagonal five point formula. Next, we find the initial values at the centers of the four large inner squares by taking the means at the ends of the diagonals passing through them.

$$u_1 = \frac{1}{4}(c_1 + u_5 + c_3 + c_{15}),$$

$$u_3 = \frac{1}{4}(c_3 + c_7 + u_5 + c_5),$$

$$u_7 = \frac{1}{4}(c_{15} + c_{11} + u_5 + c_{13}),$$

$$u_9 = \frac{1}{4}(u_5 + c_9 + c_7 + c_{11}).$$

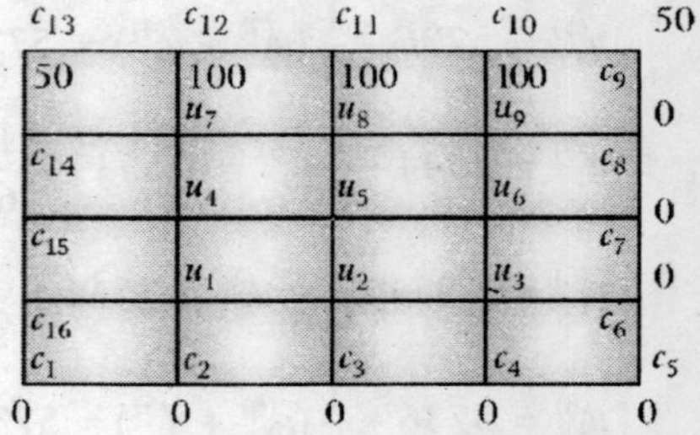

Elliptic Type

The values of u at the remaining points are calculated by taking the means of the values at the four adjacent points. This implies:

$$u_2 = \frac{1}{4}(u_1 + c_3 + u_3 + u_5), \quad u_4 = \frac{1}{4}(c_{15} + u_1 + u_5 + u_7)$$

$$u_6 = \frac{1}{4}(u_5 + u_3 + c_7 + u_9), \quad u_8 = \frac{1}{4}(u_7 + u_5 + u_9 + c_{11}).$$

Thus, calculating all the boundary values for the network and rough values at the interior mesh points, we proceed to obtain their accuracy by the iteration process. We start with u_7 and iterate it by using the latest available values at the four ***adjacent points***. In this way, we iterate all the mesh points systematically from left to right along successive rows using ***Leibmann's Iteration Scheme*** given by

$$u_{i,j}^{n+1} = \frac{1}{4}\left(u_{i-1,j}^{n+1} + u_{i+1,j}^{(n)} + u_{i,j-1}^{(n)} + u_{i,j+1}^{(n+1)}\right).$$

Example 7: *Determine by iteration method the values at the interior mesh points of a square region of the harmonic function u whose boundary values are given as shown in the figure.*

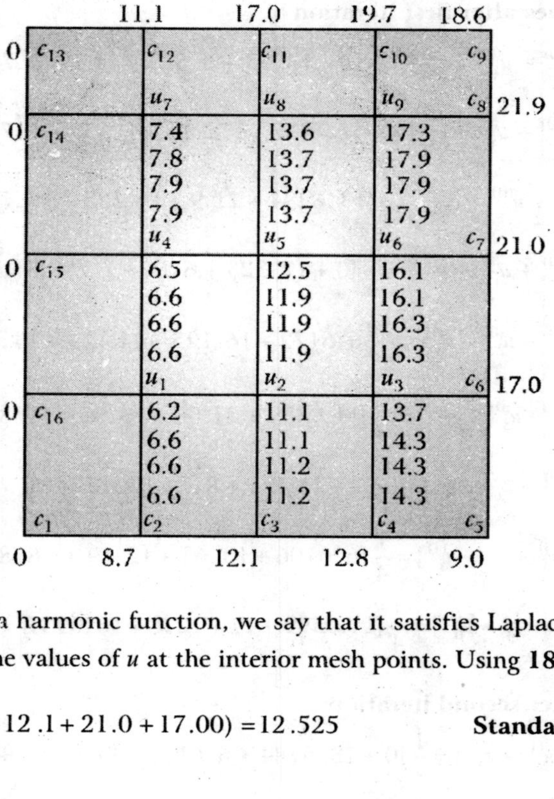

Solution: As u is a harmonic function, we say that it satisfies Laplaces's equation. Let $u_1, u_2, u_3, \ldots, u_9$ be the values of u at the interior mesh points. Using **18.4**, we have

$$u_5 = \frac{1}{4}(0 + 12.1 + 21.0 + 17.00) = 12.525 \qquad \textbf{Standard – 5 pt formula}$$

(S.P.F. in Short)

Next we find the initial values at the centres of the four large inner squares by taking the means at the ends of the diagonals passing through them; *i.e.* we have

$$u_1 = \frac{1}{4}(0 + 12.5 + 12.1) = 6.15\,; \; u_3 = \frac{1}{4}(12.1 + 21.0 + 12.5 + 9.0) = 13.65$$

$$u_7 = \frac{1}{4}(0 + 12.5 + 0 + 17.0) = \frac{29.5}{4} = 7.375,\; u_9 = \frac{1}{4}(12.5 + 18.6 + 17.0 + 21)$$

$$= \frac{69.1}{4} = 17.275,$$

The values of u at the remaining points are calculated by taking the means of the values at the four adjacent points. This implies

$$u_2 = \frac{1}{4}(6.2 + 12.5 + 13.7 + 12.1) = \frac{44.5}{4} = 11.125,$$

$$u_4 = \frac{1}{4}(0 + 7.4 + 12.5 + 6.2) = \frac{26.1}{4} = 6.525,$$

$$u_6 = \frac{1}{4}(12.5 + 17.3 + 21.0 + 13.7) = \frac{64.5}{4} = 16.125,$$

$$u_8 = \frac{1}{4}(7.4 + 17.0 + 17.3 + 12.5) = \frac{54.2}{4} = 13.55.$$

To obtain the values after first iteration

$$u_7^{(1)} = \frac{1}{4}[c_{14} + u_8^{(0)} + u_4^{(0)} + c_{12}] = \frac{1}{2}[0 + 13.55 + 6.525 + 11.1] = 7.7937,$$

$$u_8^{(1)} = \frac{1}{4}[u_7^{(1)} + u_9^{(0)} + u_5^{(0)} + c_{11}] = \frac{1}{4}[7.7937 + 17.275 + 12.525 + 17] = 13.6484,$$

$$u_9^{(1)} = \frac{1}{4}[u_8^{(1)} + c_8 + u_6^{(0)} + c_{10}] = \frac{1}{4}[13.6484 + 21.9 + 16.125 + 19.7] = 17.8434,$$

$$u_4^{(1)} = \frac{1}{4}[c_{15} + u_5^{(0)} + u_1^{(0)} + u_7^{(1)}] = \frac{1}{4}[0 + 12.525 + 6.15 + 7.7937] = 6.6172,$$

$$u_5^{(1)} = \frac{1}{4}\left[u_4^{(1)} + u_6^{(0)} + u_2^{(0)} + u_8^{(1)}\right] = \frac{1}{4}\left[6.6172 + 16.125 + 11.125 + 13.6484\right] = 11.8789,$$

$$u_6^{(1)} = \frac{1}{4}[u_5^{(1)} + c_7 + u_3^{(0)} + u_9^{(1)}] = \frac{1}{4}[11.8789 + 21.00 + 13.65 + 17.8434] = 16.0931,$$

$$u_1^{(1)} = \frac{1}{4}[c_{16} + u_2^{(0)} + c_2 + u_4^{(1)}] = \frac{1}{4}[0 + 11.125 + 8.7 + 6.6172] = 6.6106,$$

$$u_2^{(1)} = \frac{1}{4}[u_1^{(1)} + u_3^{(0)} + c_3 + u_5^{(1)}] = \frac{1}{4}[6.6106 + 13.65 + 12.1 + 11.8789] = 11.0599,$$

$$u_3^{(1)} = \frac{1}{4}[u_2^{(1)} + c_6 + c_4 + u_6^{(1)}] = \frac{1}{4}[11.0599 + 17 + 12.8 + 16.0931] = 14.2383,$$

To compute *u's* after second iteration

$$u_7^{(2)} = \frac{1}{4}[c_{14} + u_8^{(1)} + u_4^{(1)} + c_{12}] = \frac{1}{4}[0 + 13.6484 + 6.6172 + 11.1] = 7.8414,$$

$$u_8^{(2)} = \frac{1}{4}[u_7^{(2)} + u_9^{(1)} + u_5^{(1)} + c_{11}] = \frac{1}{4}[7.8414 + 17.8434 + 11.8789 + 17] = 13.6409,$$

$$u_9^{(2)} = \frac{1}{4}[u_8^{(2)} + u_6^{(1)} + c_{10}] = \frac{1}{4}[13.6409 + 21.9 + 16.0931 + 19.7] = 17.8335,$$

$$u_4^{(2)} = \frac{1}{4}(c_{15} + u_5^{(1)} + u_1^{(1)} + u_7^{(2)}) = \frac{1}{4}(0 + 11.8789 + 6.6106 + 7.8414) = 6.5827,$$

$$u_5^{(2)} = \frac{1}{4}(u_4^{(2)} + u_6^{(1)} + u_2^{(1)} + u_8^{(2)}) = \frac{1}{4}(6.5827 + 16.0931 + 11.0599 + 13.6409) = 11.8442,$$

$$u_6^{(2)} = \frac{1}{4}(u_5^{(2)} + c_7 + u_3^{(1)} + u_9^{(2)}) = \frac{1}{4}(11.08442 + 21.00 + 14.2383 + 17.8335) = 16.229,$$

$$u_1^{(2)} = \frac{1}{4}(c_{16} + u_2^{(1)} + c_2 + u_4^{(2)}) = \frac{1}{4}(0 + 11.0599 + 8.7 + 6.5827) = 6.5857,$$

$$u_2^{(2)} = \frac{1}{4}(u_1^{(2)} + u_3^{(1)} + c_3 + u_5^{(2)}) = \frac{1}{4}(6.5857 + 14.2383 + 12.1 + 11.8442) = 11.1915,$$

$$u_3^{(2)} = \frac{1}{4}(u_2^{(2)} + c_6 + c_4 + u_6^{(2)}) = \frac{1}{4}(11.1915 + 17.00 + 12.8 + 16.229) = 14.3051,$$

To compute *u's* after third iteration

$$u_7^{(3)} = \frac{1}{4}[c_{14} + u_8^{(2)} + u_4^{(2)} + c_{12}] = \frac{1}{4}[0 + 13.6409 + 6.5827 + 11.1] = 7.8309,$$

$$u_8^{(3)} = \frac{1}{4}(u_7^{(3)} + u_9^{(2)} + u_5^{(2)} + c_{11}) = \frac{1}{4}(7.8309 + 17.8335 + 11.8442 + 17) = 13.6271,$$

$$u_9^{(3)} = \frac{1}{4}(u_8^{(3)} + c_8 + u_6^{(2)} + c_{10}) = \frac{1}{4}(13.6271 + 21.9 + 16.229 + 19.7) = 17.8640,$$

$$u_4^{(3)} = \frac{1}{4}(c_{15} + u_5^{(2)} + u_1^{(2)} + u_7^{(3)}) = \frac{1}{4}(0 + 11.8442 + 6.5857 + 7.8309) = 6.5652,$$

$$u_5^{(3)} = \frac{1}{4}(u_4^{(3)} + u_6^{(2)} + u_2^{(2)} + u_8^{(2)}) = \frac{1}{4}(6.5652 + 16.229 + 11.1915 + 13.6271) = 11.9032,$$

$$u_6^{(3)} = \frac{1}{4}(u_5^{(3)} + c_7 + u_3^{(2)} + u_9^{(3)}) = \frac{1}{4}(11.9032 + 21 + 14.3051 + 17.8640) = 16.2681,$$

$$u_1^{(3)} = \frac{1}{4}(c_{16} + u_2^{(2)} + c_2 + u_4^{(3)}) = \frac{1}{4}(0 + 11.1915 + 8.7 + 6.5652) = 6.6142,$$

$$u_2^{(3)} = \frac{1}{4}(u_1^{(3)} + u_3^{(2)} + c_3 + u_5^{(3)}) = \frac{1}{4}(6.6142 + 14.3051 + 12.1 + 11.9032) = 11.2306,$$

$$u_3^{(3)} = \frac{1}{4}(u_2^{(3)} + c_6 + c_4 + u_6^{(3)}) = \frac{1}{4}(11.2306 + 17 + 12.8 + 16.2681) = 14.3247,$$

To compute *u's* after fourth iteration

$$u_7^{(4)} = \frac{1}{4}(c_{14} + u_8^{(3)} + u_4^{(3)} + c_{12}) = \frac{1}{4}(0 + 13.6271 + 6.5652 + 11.1) = 7.8231,$$

$$u_8^{(4)} = \frac{1}{4}(u_7^{(4)} + u_9^{(3)} + u_5^{(3)} + c_{11}) = \frac{1}{4}(7.8231 + 17.8640 + 11.9032 + 17) = 13.6476,$$

$$u_9^{(4)} = \frac{1}{4}(u_8^{(4)} + c_8 + u_6^{(3)} + c_{10}) = \frac{1}{4}(13.6476 + 21.9 + 16.2681 + 19.7) = 17.8789,$$

$$u_4^{(4)} = \frac{1}{4}(c_{15} + u_5^{(3)} + u_1^{(3)} + u_7^{(4)}) = \frac{1}{4}(0 + 11.9032 + 6.6142 + 7.8231) = 6.5851,$$

$$u_5^{(4)} = \frac{1}{4}(u_4^{(4)} + u_6^{(3)} + u_2^{(3)} + u_8^{(4)}) = \frac{1}{4}(6.5851 + 16.2681 + 11.2306 + 13.6476) = 11.9329,$$

$$u_6^{(4)} = \frac{1}{4}(u_5^{(4)} + c_7 + u_3^{(3)} + u_9^{(4)}) = \frac{1}{4}(11.9329 + 21 + 14.3247 + 17.8789) = 16.2841,$$

$$u_1^{(4)} = \frac{1}{4}(c_{16} + u_2^{(3)} + c_2 + u_4^{(4)}) = \frac{1}{4}(11.2306 + 8.7 + 6.5851) = 6.6289,$$

$$u_2^{(4)} = \frac{1}{4}(u_1^{(4)} + u_3^{(3)} + c_3 + u_5^{(4)}) = \frac{1}{4}(6.6289 + 14.3247 + 12.1 + 11.9329) = 11.2466,$$

$$u_3^{(4)} = \frac{1}{4}(u_2^{(4)} + c_6 + c_4 + u_6^{(4)} = \frac{1}{4}(11.2466 + 12.8 + 17 + 1.62841) = 14.3327,$$

To compute *u's* after fifth iteration

$$u_7^{(5)} = \frac{1}{4}(c_{14} + u_8^{(4)} + u_4^{(4)} + c_{12}) = \frac{1}{4}(0 + 11.1 + 13.6476 + 6.5851) = 7.8332$$

$$u_8^{(5)} = \frac{1}{4}(u_7^{(5)} + u_9^{(4)} + u_5^{(4)} + c_{11}) = \frac{1}{4}(17 + 7.8332 + 17.8789 + 11.9329) = 13.6613,$$

$$u_9^{(5)} = \frac{1}{4}(u_8^{(5)} + c_8 + u_6^{(4)} + c_{10}) = \frac{1}{4}(21.9 + 19.7 + 13.6613 + 16.2841) = 17.8864,$$

$$u_4^{(5)} = \frac{1}{4}(c_{15} + u_5^{(4)} + u_1^{(4)} + u_7^{(5)}) = \frac{1}{4}(0 + 11.9329 + 6.6289 + 7.8332) = 6.5988$$

$$u_5^{(5)} = \frac{1}{4}(u_4^{(5)} + u_6^{(4)} + u_2^{(4)} + u_8^{(5)}) = \frac{1}{4}(6.5988 + 16.2841 + 11.2466 + 13.6613) = 11.9477$$

$$u_6^{(5)} = \frac{1}{4}(u_5^{(5)} + c_7 + u_3^{(4)} + u_9^{(5)}) = \frac{1}{4}(11.9477 + 21 + 47.3327 + 17.8864) = 16.2917,$$

$$u_1^{(5)} = \frac{1}{4}(c_{16} + u_2^{(4)} + c_2 + u_4^{(5)}) = \frac{1}{4}(11.2466 + 8.7 + 6.5988) = 6.6394,$$

$$u_2^{(5)} = \frac{1}{4}(u_1^{(5)} + u_3^{(4)} + c_3 + u_5^{(5)}) = \frac{1}{4}(6.6364 + 14.3327 + 12.1 + 11.9477) = 11.2542,$$

$$u_3^{(5)} = \frac{1}{4}(u_2^{(5)} + c_6 + c_4 + u_6^{(5)}) = \frac{1}{4}(11.2542 + 17 + 12.8 + 16.2917) = 14.3365,$$

To compute *u's* after sixth iteration

$$u_7^{(6)} = \frac{1}{4}[c_{14} + u_8^{(5)} + u_4^{(5)} + c_{12}] = \frac{(11.1 + 13.6613 + 0 + 6.5988)}{4} = 7.8400,$$

$$u_8^{(6)} = \frac{1}{4}[u_7^{(6)} + u_9^{(5)} + u_5^{(5)} + c_{11}] = \frac{1}{4}[7.84 + 17.8864 + 11.9477 + 17] = 13.6685,$$

$$u_9^{(6)} = \frac{1}{4}[u_8^{(6)} + c_8 + u_6^{(5)} + c_{10}] = \frac{1}{4}[13.6685 + 21.9 + 16.2917 + 19.7] = 17.8900,$$

$$u_4^{(6)} = \frac{1}{4}[c_{15} + u_5^{(5)} + u_1^{(5)} + u_7^{(6)}] = \frac{1}{4}[11.9477 + 6.6364 + 7.84] = 6.6060,$$

$$u_5^{(6)} = \frac{1}{4}[u_4^{(6)} + u_6^{(5)} + u_2^{(5)} + u_8^{(6)}] = \frac{6.6060 + 16.2917 + 11.2542 + 13.6685}{4} = 11.9551,$$

$$u_6^{(6)} = \frac{1}{4}[u_5^{(6)} + c_7 + u_3^{(5)} + u_9^{(6)}] = \frac{1}{4}[11.9551 + 21 + 14.3365 + 17.89] = 16.2954,$$

$$u_1^{(6)} = \frac{1}{4}[c_{16} + u_2^{(5)} + c_2 + u_4^{(6)}] = \frac{1}{4}[11.2542 + 8.7 + 6.6060] = 6.6400,$$

$$u_2^{(6)} = \frac{1}{4}[u_1^{(6)}\ u_3^{(5)} + c_3 + u_5^{(6)}] = \frac{1}{4}[6.64 + 14.3365 + 12.1 + 11.9551] = 11.2579,$$

$$u_3^{(6)} = \frac{1}{4}[u_2^{(6)} + c_6 + c_4 + u_6^{(6)}] = \frac{1}{4}[11.2579 + 12.8 + 17 + 16.2954] = 14.3383,$$

To compute *u's* after seventh iteration

$$u_7^{(7)} = [c_{14} + u_8^{(6)} + u_4^{(6)} + c_{12}] = \frac{1}{4}[11.1 + 13.6685 + 6.6060] = 7.8436,$$

$$u_8^{(7)} = \frac{1}{4}[u_7^{(7)} + u_9^{(6)} + u_5^{(6)} + c_{11}] = \frac{1}{4}[7.8436 + 17.89 + 11.9551 + 17] = 13.6722,$$

$$u_9^{(7)} = \frac{1}{4}[u_8^{(7)} + c_8 + u_6^{(6)} + c_{10}] = \frac{1}{4}[13.6722 + 21.9 + 16.2954 + 19.7] = 17.8919,$$

$$u_4^{(7)} = \frac{1}{4}[c_{15} + u_5^{(6)} + u_1^{(6)} + u_7^{(7)}] = \frac{1}{4}[11.9551 + 6.64 + 7.8436] = 6.6097,$$

$$u_5^{(7)} = \frac{1}{4}[u_4^{(7)} + u_6^{(6)} + u_2^{(6)} + u_8^{(7)}] = \frac{1}{4}(6.6097 + 16.2954 + 11.2579 + 13.6722) = 11.9588,$$

$$u_6^{(7)} = \frac{1}{4}[u_5^{(7)} + c_7 + u_3^{(6)} + u_9^{(7)}] = \frac{1}{4}(11.9588 + 21 + 14.3383 + 17.8919) = 16.2973,$$

$$u_1^{(7)} = \frac{1}{4}[c_{16} + u_2^{(6)} + c_2 + u_4^{(7)}] = \frac{1}{4}(11.2579 + 8.7 + 6.6097) = 6.6419,$$

$$u_2^{(7)} = \frac{1}{4}[u_1^{(7)} + u_3^{(6)} + c_3 + u_5^{(7)}] = \frac{1}{4}(6.6419 + 14.3383 + 21.1 + 11.9588) = 11.2598,$$

$$u_3^{(7)} = \frac{1}{4}[u_2^{(7)} + c_6 + c_4 + u_6^{(7)}] = \frac{1}{4}(11.2598 + 17 + 12.8 + 16.2973) = 14.3393,$$

Thus we see that $u_1 = 6.64, u_2 = 11.25, u_3 = 14.33, u_4 = 6.60, u_5 = 11.95, u_6 = 16.29$, $u_7 = 7.84, u_8 = 13.67$ and $u_9 = 17.89$; correct to two places of decimal.

Example 8: *For the following figure, evaluate u (x, y) satisfying Laplace's equation* $\frac{\partial^2 u}{\partial x^2} + \frac{\partial^2 y}{\partial y^2} = 0$ *at the pivotal points of the figure.*

[Mumbai (M.Sc.) 2005, 2009; U.P.T.U. (B.E.) 2007; M.K.U.C.T. (Tamil Nadu) 2008]

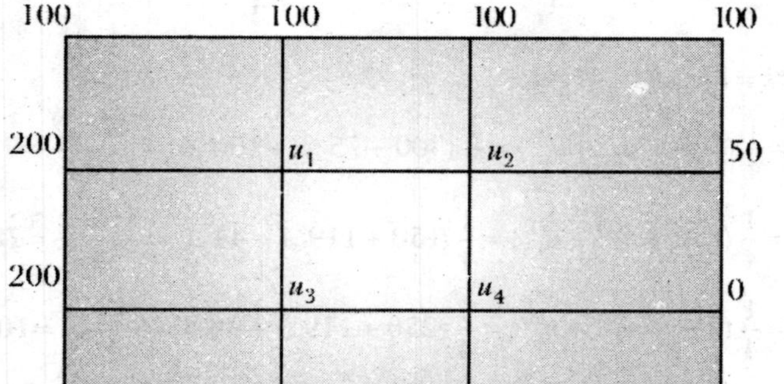

Solution: Let the values of u the pivotal points 1 to 4 be u_1, u_2, u_3, u_4 respectively. Initially, we start by taking $u_4 = 0$. Then

$$u_1 = \frac{1}{4}(100 + 200 + 0) = 100; \text{ by } \textit{diagonal averaging}$$

$$u_2 = \frac{1}{4}(u_3 + 50 + 100 + u_2) = \frac{1}{4}(100 + 50 + 100 + 0) = 62.5 = 60$$

by Cross-averaging

$$u_3 = \frac{1}{4}(u_2 + 200 + u_3 + 50) = \frac{1}{4}(250 + 100) = 87.50 \approx 90,$$

$$u_4 = \frac{1}{4}(u_1 + 0 + 0 + u_4 + 0) = \frac{1}{4}(87.5 + 62.5) = 37.5 \approx 40 \text{ by Cross-averaging}$$

Then we start the iteration process by using the formula given below

$$\left.\begin{aligned} u_1^{(k+1)} &= \frac{1}{4}(200 + 100 + u_2^{(k)} + u_3^{(k)}) \\ u_2^{(k+1)} &= \frac{1}{4}(100 + 50 + u_1^{(k+1)} + u_4^{(k)}) \\ u_3^{(k+1)} &= \frac{1}{4}(200 + 50 + u_1^{(k+1)} + u_4^{(k)}) \\ u_4^{(k+1)} &= \frac{1}{4}(0 + 0 + u_3^{(k+1)} + u_2^{(k+1)}) \end{aligned}\right\} \quad \text{(A)}$$

Now putting $k = 0$ in the above results, we get

$$u_1^{(1)} = \frac{1}{4}(300 + u_2^{(0)} + u_3^{(0)}) = \frac{1}{4}(300 + 60 + 90) = \frac{450}{4} = 112.5,$$

$$u_2^{(1)} = \frac{1}{4}(150 + u_1^{(1)} + u_4^{(0)}) = \frac{1}{4}(150 + 112.5 + 40) = \frac{302.5}{4} = 75.6,$$

$$u_3^{(1)} = \frac{1}{4}(250 + u_1^{(1)} + u_4^{(0)}) = \frac{1}{4}(250 + 112.5 + 40) = \frac{402.5}{4} = 100.6,$$

$$u_4^{(1)} = \frac{1}{4}(u_3^{(1)} + u_2^{(1)}) = \frac{1}{4}(75.6 + 100.6) = \frac{176.2}{4} = 44.1$$

Again putting $k = 1$ in (A), we get

$$u_1^{(2)} = \frac{1}{4}(300 + u_2^{(1)} + u_3^{(1)}) = \frac{1}{4}(300 + 75.6 + 100.6) = \frac{476.2}{4} = 119.1,$$

$$u_2^{(2)} = \frac{1}{4}(150 + u_1^{(2)} + u_4^{(1)}) = \frac{1}{4}(150 + 119.1 + 44.1) = \frac{313.2}{4} = 78.3,$$

$$u_3^{(2)} = \frac{1}{4}(250 + u_1^{(2)} + u_4^{(1)}) = \frac{1}{4}(250 + 119.1 + 44.1) = \frac{413.2}{4} = 103.3,$$

$$u_4^{(2)} = \frac{1}{4}(u_3^{(2)} + u_2^{(2)}) = \frac{1}{4}(103.3 + 78.3) = \frac{181.6}{4} = 45.4,$$

Further putting $k = 2$ in (A), we obtain

$$u_1^{(3)} = \frac{1}{4}(300 + u_2^{(2)} + u_3^{(2)}) = \frac{1}{4}(300 + 78.3 + 103.3) = \frac{481.6}{4} = 120.4,$$

$$u_2^{(3)} = \frac{1}{4}(150 + u_1^{(3)} + u_4^{(2)}) = \frac{1}{4}(150 + 120.4 + 45.4) = \frac{315.8}{4} = 79.0,$$

$$u_3^{(3)} = \frac{1}{4}(250 + u_1^{(3)} + u_4^{(2)}) = \frac{1}{4}(250 + 120.4 + 45.4) = \frac{481.6}{4} = 104.0,$$

$$u_4^{(3)} = \frac{1}{4}(u_3^{(3)} + u_2^{(3)}) = \frac{1}{4}(104.0 + 79.0) = \frac{183.0}{4} = 45.8,$$

For $k = 3$, we also obtain

$$u_1^{(4)} = \frac{1}{4}(300 + u_2^{(3)} + u_3^{(3)}) = \frac{1}{4}(300 + 79 + 104) = \frac{483}{4} = 120.8,$$

$$u_2^{(4)} = \frac{1}{4}(150 + u_1^{(4)} + u_4^{(3)}) = \frac{1}{4}(150 + 120.8 + 45.8) = \frac{316.6}{4} = 79.2,$$

$$u_3^{(4)} = \frac{1}{4}(250 + u_1^{(4)} + u_4^{(3)}) = \frac{1}{4}(250 + 120.8 + 45.8) = \frac{416.6}{4} = 104.2,$$

$$u_4^{(4)} = \frac{1}{4}(u_3^{(4)} + u_2^{(4)}) = \frac{1}{4}(104.2 + 79.2) = \frac{183.4}{4} = 45.9,$$

Finally putting $k = 4$ in (A), we get

$$u_1^{(5)} = \frac{1}{4}(300 + u_2^{(4)} + u_3^{(4)}) = \frac{1}{4}(300 + 79.2 + 104.2) = \frac{483.4}{4} = 120.9,$$

$$u_2^{(5)} = \frac{1}{4}(150 + u_1^{(5)} + u_4^{(4)}) = \frac{1}{4}(150 + 120.9 + 45.9) = \frac{316.8}{4} = 79.2,$$

$$u_3^{(5)} = \frac{1}{4}(250 + u_1^{(5)} + u_4^{(4)}) = \frac{1}{4}(250 + 120.9 + 45.9) = \frac{416.8}{4} = 104.2,$$

$$u_4^{(5)} = \frac{1}{4}(u_3^{(5)} + u_2^{(5)}) = \frac{1}{4}(104.2 + 79.2) = \frac{183.4}{4} = 45.9.$$

Inspection of the above results reveals that there is practically no difference between the values obtained in the fifth and fourth iterations and hence we have $u_1 = 120.9$, $u_2 = 79.2$, $u_3 = 104.2$, $u_4 = 45.9$.

In tabular form the results are as follows:

Iteration u_i	0	1	2	3	4	5
u_1	100	112.5	119.1	120.4	120.8	120.9
u_2	60.0	75.6	78.3	79.0	79.2	79.2
u_3	90.0	100.6	103.3	104.0	104.2	104.2
u_4	40	44.1	45.3	45.8	45.9	45.9

18.8 Poisson's Equation

The partial differential equation $\nabla^2 u = F(x, y)$

i.e.
$$\frac{\partial^2 u}{\partial x^2} + \frac{\partial^2 u}{\partial y^2} = F(x, y) \qquad ...(1)$$

Where $F(x, y)$ is a given function of x and y, is known as **poisson's equation.**

We can solve it numerically at the points of a square mesh, by replacing the derivatives by difference expressions at the points $x = ih$, $y = jk$ (here $k = h$), and then substituting in (1), we get
$$\frac{u_{i-1,j} - 2u_{i,j} + u_{i+1,j}}{h^2} + \frac{u_{i,j-1} - 2u_{i,j} + u_{i,j+1}}{h^2} = F(ih, jh)$$

$$\Rightarrow \quad (u_{i-1,j} + u_{i+1,j}) + (u_{i,j-1} + u_{i,j+1}) - 4_{i,j} = h^2 F(ih, jh) \qquad ...(2)$$

Using replacement formula at each mesh point, we can obtain similar equations in i, j and then such equations can be solved by iteration techniques. By replacing $\frac{\partial^2 u}{\partial x^2}$ with the difference expression we get an error or the order $O(h^2)$ and also there exist and error of order $O(h^2)$, when we replace $\frac{\partial^2 u}{\partial x^2}$ by its difference expression. Hence the error in solving Poissons's equation by difference methods is of the order $O(h^2)$.

Example 9: *Solve the partial differential equation*

$\nabla^2 u = -10(x^2 + y^2 + 10)$ *over the square with sides* $x = 0 = y, x = 3 = y$ *with* $u = 0$ *on the boundary and mesh length* $= 1$.

[M.K.U. (Tamil) Nadu 2005, 2008; Roorkee (M.E.) 2002, 2005, 2007]

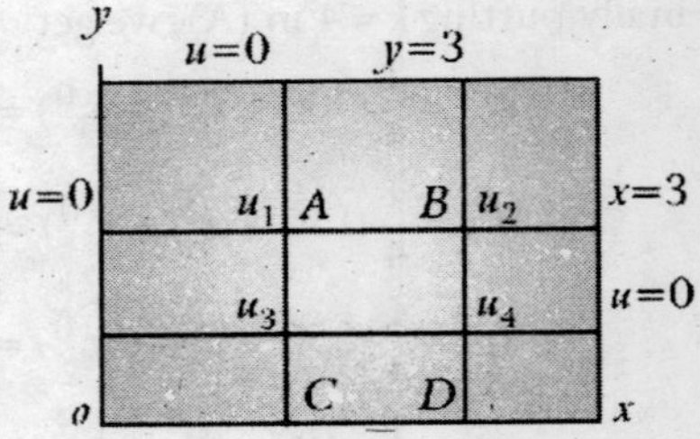

Solution: Let the values of u at the four mesh points be u_1, u_2, u_3, u_4 respectively. The differential equation is given by

$$(\partial^2 u/\partial x^2) + (\partial^2 u/\partial y^2) = -10(x^2 + y^2 + 10) \quad ...(1)$$

Now putting $(\partial^2 u/\partial x^2) + (\partial^2 u/\partial y^2)$ in the form of finite difference expressions and putting $x = ih, y = ih\ (h = 1)$ in (1), we get

$$u_{i-1,j} - 2u_{i,j} + u_{i+1,j} + u_{i,j} - 1\} - 2u_{i,j} + 2u_{i,j+1} = -10(i^2 + j^2 + 10) \quad ...(2)$$

Using this formula at A, where $i - 1$ and $j = 2$ we get $0 + 0 + u_2 + u_3 - 4u_1 = -10(1 + 4 + 10)$

$$\Rightarrow \quad u_2 + u_3 - 4u_1 = -150 \quad ...(3)$$

Also, applying the formula at B, where $i = 2$ and $j = 2$; we obtain

$$u_1 + 0 + 0 + u_4 - 4u_2 = -10(4 + 4 + 10)$$

$$\Rightarrow \quad u_1 + u_4 - 4u_2 = -180 \quad ...(4)$$

Again applying the formula at C, where $i = 1$ and $j = 1$;

we obtain $0 + u_1 + u_4 + 0 - 4u_3 = -10(1 + 1 + 0)$

$$\Rightarrow \quad u_1 + u_4 - 4u_3 = -120 \quad ...(5)$$

Finally, applying the formula at D, where $i = 2$ and $j = 1$;

we get $u_3 + u_2 + 0 + 0 - 4u_2 = -10(4 + 1 + 10)$

$$\Rightarrow \quad u_3 + u_2 - 4u_4 = -150 \quad ...(6)$$

We now solve equations (3) to (6) by Gauss-Siedel iteration technique (G.S.method). The process of iteration will converge, if in each equation of the system, the abs value of the largest coefficient is greater than the sum of the absolute values of all the remaining coefficients.

This condition holds good in equation (3) to (6).

Now writing the equations in the form:

$$u_1 = \frac{1}{4}(u_2 + u_3 + 150) \quad ...(7)$$

$$u_2 = \frac{1}{4}(u_1 + u_4 + 180) \quad ...(8)$$

$$u_3 = \frac{1}{4}(u_1 + u_4 + 120) \quad ...(9)$$

$$u_4 = \frac{1}{4}(u_2 + u_3 + 150) \quad ...(10)$$

We obtain $u_4 = u_1$. So it is enough if we can find u_1, u_2, u_3. Now, let us start the iteration by putting $u_2 = 0 = u_3$ in (7).

$$\Rightarrow \quad u_1^{(1)} = \frac{150}{4} = 37.5 = u_4^{(1)}$$

Putting $u_1 = 37.5 = u_4^{(1)}$ in (8) and (9), we obtain $u_2^{(1)} = \frac{1}{4}(75 + 180) = \frac{255}{4} = 63.75$

and $\quad u_3^{(1)} = \frac{1}{4}(75 + 120) = \frac{195}{4} = 48.75.$

For the second iteration, we write

$$u_4^{(2)} = u_1^{(2)} = \frac{1}{4}(63.75 + 48.75 + 150) = \frac{262.5}{4} = 65.6250,$$

$$u_2^{(2)} = \frac{1}{4}(65.625 + 65.625 + 180) = \frac{310}{4} = 77.8125,$$

$$u_3^{(2)} = \frac{1}{4}(65.625 + 65.625 + 120) = \frac{250}{4} = 62.8125.$$

Proceeding for the third iteration, we get

$$u_4^{(3)} = u_1^{(3)} = \frac{1}{4}(77.8125 + 62.8125 + 150) = 72.6563,$$

$$u_2^{(3)} = \frac{1}{2}(72.6563 + 72.6563 + 180) = 81.3282,$$

$$u_3^{(3)} = \frac{1}{4}(72.6563 + 72.6563 + 120) = 66.3282,$$

And then for the fourth iteration, we get

$$u_4^{(4)} = u_1^{(4)} = \frac{1}{4}(81.3282 + 66.3282 + 150) = 74.4141,$$

$$u_2^{(4)} = \frac{1}{4}(74.4141 + 74.4141 + 180) = 82.2071,$$

$$u_3^{(4)} = \frac{1}{4}(74.4141 + 74.4141 + 120) = 67.2071.$$

For the fifth iteration, we obtain

$$u_1^{(5)} = \frac{1}{4}(82.2071 + 67.2071 + 150) = 74.8536 = u_4^{(5)}$$

$$u_2^{(5)} = \frac{1}{4}(74.8536 + 74.8536 + 180) = 82.4268$$

$$u_3^{(5)} = \frac{1}{4}(74.8536 + 74.8536 + 120) = 67.4268$$

For the sixth iteration, we have

$$u_1^{(6)} = u_4^{(6)} = \frac{1}{4}(u_2^{(5)} + u_3^{(5)} + 150) = \frac{1}{4}(82.4268 + 67.4268 + 150) = 74.9634,$$

$$u_2^{(6)} = \frac{1}{4}(74.8536 + 74.8536 + 150) = 67.4268,$$

and $u_3^{(6)} = \frac{1}{4}(74.8536 + 74.8536 + 150) = 67.4268.$

For the seventh iteration, we have

$$u_1^{(7)} = u_4^{(7)} = \frac{1}{4}(u_2^{(6)} + u_3^{(6)} + 150) = \frac{1}{4}(82.4268 + 67.4268 + 150) = 74.9634$$

$$u_2^{(7)} = \frac{1}{4}(u_1^{(6)} + u_4^{(6)} + 180) = \frac{1}{4}(74.9634 \times 2 + 180) = 82.4817,$$

$$u_3^{(7)} = \frac{1}{4}(u_1^{(6)} + u_4^{(6)} + 120) = \frac{1}{4}(74.9634 \times 2 + 120) = 67.4817.$$

For the eighth iteration, we have

$$u_1^{(8)} = u_4^{(8)} = \frac{1}{4}(u_2^{(7)} + u_3^{(7)} + 150) = \frac{1}{4}(82.4817 + 67.4817 + 150) = 74.99085$$

$$u_2^{(8)} = \frac{1}{4}(2\,u_1^{(7)} + 180) = \frac{1}{4}(2 \times 74.9634 + 180) = 82.4817$$

$$u_3^{(8)} = \frac{1}{4}(2\,u_1^{(7)} + 120) = \frac{1}{4}(2 \times 74.9634 + 120) = 67.4817$$

For the ninth iteration, we have

$$u_1^{(9)} = u_4^{(9)} = \frac{1}{4}(u_2^{(8)} + u_3^{(8)} + 150) = \frac{1}{4}(82.4817 + 67.4817 + 150) = 74.99085$$

$$u_2^{(9)} = \frac{1}{4}(2\,u_1^{(8)} + 180) = (2 \times 74.99058 + 180) = 82.4954$$

$$u_3^{(9)} = \frac{1}{4}(2\,u_1^{(8)} + 120) = \frac{1}{4}(2 \times 74.99085 + 120) = 67.4954$$

For the tenth iteration, we have

$$u_1^{(10)} = u_3^{(10)} = \frac{1}{4}(u_2^{(9)} + u_3^{(9)} + 150) = \frac{1}{4}(82.454 + 67.4954 + 150) = 74.9977$$

$$u_2^{(10)} = \frac{1}{4}(2u_1^{(9)} + 180) = \frac{1}{4}(2 \times 74.99085 + 180) = 82.4954$$

$$u_3^{(10)} = \frac{1}{4}(2u_1^{(9)} + 120) = \frac{1}{4}(2 \times 74.990 + 120) = 67.4954$$

Hence $u_1 = u_4 = 74.99, u_2 = 82.49, u_3 = 67.49$;

correct to two places of decimal.

18.9 Parabolic Equations [Solution by Bender Schmidt Recurrence Relation]

[R.G.V.P. (M.P.) 2007, 2008]

One dimensional heat equation is given by

$\frac{\partial u}{\partial t}=\alpha^2 \frac{\partial^2 u}{\partial x^2}$ where $\alpha^2 = \frac{k}{c\rho}$, where c is the specific heat of the material, ρ is the density and k is the thermal conductivity. This implies $u_t=\alpha^2 u_{xx}$ or $u_{xx}-au_t=0$ where

$$a=(1/\alpha^2). \quad ...(1)$$

Here $A=1, B=0, C=0$ and hence we have $\Delta S=B^2-4AC=0-0=0 \Rightarrow$ the equation is parabolic.

Let us solve it by the method of finite differences, under the boundary conditions:

$$u(0,t)=T_0 \quad ...(2)$$

$$u(l,t)=T_l \quad ...(3)$$

and initial condition: $u(x,0)=f(x)$

We have $u_{xx}=\frac{u_{i+1,j}-2u_{i-1,j}}{h^2}$, $u_t=\frac{u_{i,j+1}-u_{i,j}}{k}$

Putting these values in (1), we get $\frac{u_{i+1,j}-2u_{i-1,j}}{h^2}, -a.\left(\frac{u_{i,j+1}-u_{i,j}}{k}\right)=0$

$$\Rightarrow u_{i,j+1}-u_{i,j}=\frac{k}{h^2 a}(u_{i+1,j}-2u_{i,j}+u_{i-1,j})$$

$$=\lambda(u_{i+1,j}-2u_{i,j}+u_{i-1,j}) \text{ where } \lambda=\frac{k}{h^2 a}$$

$$\Rightarrow \quad u_{i,j+1}=\lambda u_{i+1,j}+(1-2\lambda)u_{i,j}+\lambda u_{i-1,j} \quad ...(4)$$

The boundary conditions (2) can be put in different form as $\left.\begin{matrix} u_{0,j}=T_0 \\ u_{n,j}=T_l\end{matrix}\right\} j=1,2,\ldots$ ...(5)

Where $nh=l$

The initial conditions (3) can be written as $u_{i,0}=f(ih) \quad i=1,2,\ldots$ ...(6)

Now equation (4) gives the value of u at $x=ih$, and t_j+k in terms of values of u at $x=(i-1)j, ih$ and $x=(i+1)h$ at a time t_j.

But $u(x,0)=f(x)$,

Hence the re-currence relation (4) gives u at each pivotal point x_i at any time t_j. Furthermore, the equation (4) becomes simple, if for a given h, k; we choose

$$1-2\lambda=0 \quad \Rightarrow \quad \lambda=\frac{1}{2} \quad i.e. \quad \frac{k}{h^2 a}=\frac{1}{2} \quad \text{or} \quad k=\frac{h^2 a}{2}$$

Now equation (4) can be written as $u_{i,j+1}=\frac{1}{4}(u_{i+1,j}+u_{i-1,j})$ ...(7)

i.e. u at $x=x_i$ at a time t_{j+1} is equal to the average of the values of u at the surrounding points x_{i+1} and x_{i-1} at the previous time t_j *I*. ***Relation*** (7) is called the ***Bender-Schmidt Recurrence Relation.***

Example 10: *Find the solution of the parabolic equation* $\frac{\partial^2 u}{\partial x^2} - 2\frac{\partial u}{\partial t} = 0$ *when* $u(0,t) = 0, u(4,t) = 0, u(x,0) = x(4-x)$. *The values upto* $t = 5$.

[Andhra (M.E.) 2007, 2008; Bhopal 2006; Bangaluru 2003]

Solution: The general heat equation is $u_{xx} = a \cdot u_t$

Here $a = 2, h = 1;\ \lambda = \frac{k}{h^2 a} = \frac{1}{2}k$.

Let us choose $\lambda = \frac{1}{2}$, then k must be $= 1$.

j \ i	0	1	2	3	4
0	0	3	4	3	0
1	0	2	3	2	0
2	0	1.5	2	1.5	0
3	0	1	1.5	1	0
4	0	.75	1	.75	0
5	0	5	.75	.5	0

Range for x is 4, so we put $x = ih, x_i = ih = i \quad (\because h = 1)$

and $t = jh,\ t_j = jk = j \quad (\because k = 1)$

Also, $u(x,0) = x(4-x) = i(4-i)$

Now for various values of $i\ (i = 0,1,2,3,4)$ at time $t = 0$, values of $u(x,0)$ are $0,3,4,3,0$ and are written in the first row of the table. Again $u(0,t) = 0$ for all values of t, so $u(0,j) = 0$ for all values of j. Thus the entries in the first column of the table are all zero. Similarly, $u(4,t) = 0$ for all values if t *i.e.*

$u(4,j) = 0$ for all j, hence all the entries in the last column are again zero. Further, by Bender Schmidt's recurrence relation,

We have $$u_{i,j+1} = \frac{1}{2}[u_{i+1,j} + u_{i-1,j}] \quad ...(1)$$

Now, putting $j = 0$ in (1), we readily obtain $$u_{i,1} = \frac{1}{2}[u_{i+1,0} + u_{i-1,0}] \quad ...(2)$$

$$\Rightarrow \quad u_{1,1} = \frac{1}{2}(u_{2,0} + u_{0,0}) = \frac{1}{2}(4+0) = 2,$$

$$u_{2,1} = \frac{1}{2}(u_{3,0} + u_{1,0}) = \frac{1}{2}(3+3) = 3,$$

and $$u_{3,1} = \frac{1}{2}(u_{4,0} + u_{2,0}) = \frac{1}{2}(0+4) = 2,$$

Thus the second row is complete.

Again putting $j = 1,2,3,4$ the other rows can be easily completed.

18.10 Derive the Crank Nicholson Difference Scheme for the Parabolic Equation $u_{xx} = au_t$ with Boundary Conditions as $u(0,t) = T_0$, $u(l,t) = T_1$ and the Initial Condition as $u(x,0) = f(x)$

The given equation is $u_{xx} = au_t$. By **18.4** we have

$$u_{xx} = \frac{u_{i+1,j+1} - 2u_{i,j+1} + u_{i-1,j+1} + u_{i+1,j} - 2u_{i,j} + u_{i-1,j}}{2h^2} \text{ and } u_i = \frac{u_{i,j+1} - u_{i,j}}{k}$$

Then substituting in (1), we obtain

$$u_{xx} = \frac{u_{i+1,j+1} - 2u_{i,j+1} + u_{l-1,j+1} + u_{i+1,j} - 2u_{i,j} + u_{i-1,j}}{2h^2} = \frac{a(u_{i,j+1} - u_{i,j})}{k}$$

$$\Rightarrow \quad \frac{k}{2h^2 a}(u_{i+1,j+1} - 2u_{i,j+1} + u_{i-1,j+1} + u_{i+1,j} - 2u_{i,j} + u_{i-1,j}) = u_{i,j+1} - u_{i,j}$$

Putting $\frac{k}{h^2 a} = r$, we have

$$\frac{1}{2} r u_{i+1,j+1} - r u_{i,j+1} + \frac{1}{2} r u_{i-1,j+1} - u_{i,j+1} = r u_{i,j} - \frac{1}{r u_{i+1,j}} - \frac{1}{2} r u_{i-1,j} - u_{i,j}$$

$$\Rightarrow \quad \frac{1}{2} r u_{i-1,j+1} - (r+1) u_{i,j+1} + \frac{1}{2} r u_{i+1,j+1} = -\frac{1}{2} r u_{i-1,j} + (r-1) u_{i,j} - \frac{1}{2} r u_{i+1,j} \quad \text{...(I)}$$

$$\Rightarrow \quad -r u_{i-1,j+1} + 2(r+1) u_{i,j+1} - r u_{i+1,j+1} = r u_{i-1,j} + 2(1-r) u_{i,j} + r u_{i+1,j}$$

This is called C.N. difference scheme.

Example 11: *Find the value of $u(x,t)$ satisfying the parabolic equation $\frac{\partial u}{\partial t} = 4\frac{\partial^2 u}{\partial x^2}$ and the boundary conditions $u(0,t) = 0 = u(8,t)$ and $u(x,0) = 4x - \frac{1}{2}x^2$ at the points*

$$x = i : i = 0, 1, 2, \ldots 7 \text{ and } t = \frac{1}{8} j : j = 0, 1, 2, \ldots, 5.$$

Solution: Here $\alpha^2 = 4, h = 1, k = \frac{1}{8}, a = \frac{1}{\alpha^2} = \frac{1}{4}. \lambda = \frac{k}{ah^2} = \frac{1}{2}$.

We have Bendre-Schmidit's recurrence relation

$$u_{i,j+1} = 2(u_{i-1,j} + u_{i+1,j}) \text{ But } u(0,t = 0 = u(8,t)$$

$\Rightarrow u_{0,j} = 0$ and $u_{8,j} = 0$ for all values of j, *i.e.* the entries in the first and last column are zero.

Again $\quad u(x,0) = 4x - \frac{1}{2}x^2 \qquad \therefore \quad u_{i,0} = 4i - \frac{1}{2}i^2$

$$= 0, 3.5, 6, 7.5, 8, 7.5, 6, 3.5$$

for $\quad i = 0, 1, 2, 3, 4, 5, 6, 7$ at $t = 0$

These are entries of the first row.

j \ i	0	1	2	3	4	5	6	7	8
0	0	3.5	6	7.5	8	7.5	6	3.5	0
1	0	3	5.5	7	7.5	7	5.5	3	0
2	0	2.75	5	6.5	7	6.5	5	2.75	0
3	0	2.5	4.625	6	6.5	6	4.625	2.5	0
4	0	2.3125	4.25	5.5625	6	5.5625	4.25	2.3125	0
5	0	2.125	3.9375	5.125	5.5625	5.125	3.9375	2.125	0

Putting $j=0$ in (1), we get $u_{i,1}=\frac{1}{2}(u_{i-1,0}+u_{i+1,0})$

Taking $i=1,2,\ldots,7$ successively, we get $u_{1,1}=\frac{1}{2}(u_{0,0}+u_{2,0})=\frac{1}{2}(0+6)=3$

$$u_{2,1}=\frac{1}{2}(u_{1,0}+u_{3,0})=\frac{1}{2}(3.5+7.5)=5.5$$

$$u_{3,1}=\frac{1}{2}(u_{2,0}+u_{4,0})=\frac{1}{2}(6+8)=7$$

$$u_{4,1}=7.5,\ u_{5,1}=7,\ u_{6,1}=5.5,\ u_{7,1}=3.$$

These are the entries in the second row.

Putting $j=1$ in (1), the entries of the third row are then $u_{i,2}=\frac{1}{2}(u_{i-1,i}+u_{i+1,1})$. Then putting $j=2,3,4$ successively in (1), the entries of the fourth, fifth and sixth rows are obtained.

Hence the values of $u_{i,j}$ are as given in the above table.

Example 12: *Solve the equation* $\frac{\partial u}{\partial t}=\frac{\partial^2 u}{\partial x^2}$ *subject to the conditions*

$$u(x,0)=\sin \pi x,\ 0\le x\le 1;\ u(0,t)=u(1,t)=0.$$

Carry out computations for two levels, taking $h=(1/3),\ k=(1/36)$. **[Chennai (M.E.) 2003]**

Solution: Here $\alpha^2=1.h=(1/3),\ k=(1/36)$ so that $\alpha=1$, and $\lambda=\frac{k}{ah^2}=\frac{1}{4}$.

Also $u_{1,0}=\sin(\pi/3)=(\sqrt{3}/2),\ u_{2,0}=\sin(2\pi/3)=(\sqrt{3}/2)$

and all other boundary values are zero as shown in Fig.

Again, we have $u_{i,j+1}=\alpha\, u_{i-1,j}+(1-2\alpha)\, u_{i,j}+\alpha\, u_{i+1,j}$

$\Rightarrow \quad u_{i,j+1}=\frac{1}{4}[u_{i-1,j}+2\,u_{i,j}+u_{i+1,j}]$ Putting $i=1,2;\ j=0;$ we get

$$u_{1,1} = \frac{1}{4}[u_{0,0} + 2u_{1,0} + u_{2,0}\}] = \frac{1}{4}(0 + 2 \times \sqrt{3}/2 + 3/2) = 0.65$$

$$u_{2,1} = \frac{1}{4}[u_{1,0} + 2u_{2,0} + u_{3,0}] = \frac{1}{4}(\sqrt{3}/2 + 2 \times \sqrt{3}/2 + 0) = 0.65$$

Putting $i = 1, 2, j = 1$; we get $u_{1,2} = \frac{1}{4}(u_{0,1} + 2u_{1,1} + u_{2,1}) = 0.49$

$$u_{2,2} = \frac{1}{4}(u_{1,1} + 2u_{2,1} + u_{3,1}) = 0.49$$

Illustration 1: *Solve the equation* $\frac{\partial^2 u}{\partial x^2} = \frac{\partial u}{\partial t}$ *with the conditions* $u(0, t) = 0$, $u(x, 0) = x(1 - x)$ *and* $u(1, t) = 0$. *Assume* $h = 0.1$. *Tabulate* u *for* $t = k, 2k$ *and* $3k$ *choosing an appropriate value of* k.

Illustration 2: *Solve the boundary value problem* $u_t = u_{xx}$ *under the conditions:* $u(0, t) = u(1, t) = 0$ *and* $u(x, 0) = \sin \pi x, 0 \le x \le 1$, *by the Gauss-Seidal method. (Take* $h = 0.2$ *and* $x = \frac{1}{2}$*).*

Illustration 3: *Solve the equation* $\partial u / \partial t = \partial^2 u / \partial x^2$ *subject to the conditions* $u(0, t) = u(1, t) = 0$ *and* $u(x, 0) = \begin{cases} 2x \text{ for } 0 \le x \le 1/2 \\ 2(1 - x) \text{ for } 1/2 \le x \le 1 \end{cases}$.

Take $h = (1/4)$ and k according to Bendre-Schmidt equations.

18.11 Hyperbolic Equations

[R.G.V.P. Bhopal 2008]

One dimensional wave equation is given by $a^2 \frac{\partial^2 u}{\partial x^2} - \frac{\partial^2 u}{\partial t^2} = 0 \quad \Rightarrow a^2 u_{xx} - u_{tt} = 0$.

Where $A = a^2, B = 0, C = -1$

$\therefore \quad B^2 - 4AC = 0 - 4a^2 \times -1 = 4a^2 + ve$

$\Rightarrow$ The equation is hyperbolic.

Let us solve, by the method of finite differences, the equation $a^2 u_{xx} - u_{tt} = 0$ ...(1)

Under the boundary conditions: $u(0, t) = 0$ ...(i) $u(l, t) = 0$ ...(ii)

And the initial conditions : $u(x, 0) = f(x)$ ...(iii) $u_t(x, 0) = 0$ ...(iv)

Now, selecting the spacing h for the variable x and a spacing k for t; we have

$$u_{xx} = \frac{u_{i+1,j} - 2u_{i,j} + u_{i-1,j}}{h^2}; \quad u_{tt} = \frac{u_{i,j+1} - 2u_{i,j} + u_{i,j-1}}{k^2}; \text{ and } u_t = \frac{u_{i,j+1} - u_{i,j}}{k}$$

Thus equation (1)

$$\Rightarrow \quad a^2 \frac{(u_{i+1,j} - 2u_{i,j} + u_{i-1,j})}{h^2} - \frac{(u_{i,j+1} - 2u_{i,j} + u_{i,j-1})}{k^2} = 0$$

$$\Rightarrow \quad u_{i+1,j} - 2u_{i,j} + u_{i-1,j} - \frac{h^2}{k^2 a^2}(u_{i,j+1} - 2u_{i,j} + u_{i,j+1}) = 0$$

Now assuming $r = (k/h)$, we have

$$r^2 a^2 (u_{i+1,j} - 2u_{i,j} + u_{i-1,j}) - u_{i,j+1} + 2u_{i,j} - u_{i,j-1} = 0$$

$$\therefore \quad u_{i,j+1} = 2(1 - r^2 a^2) u_{i,j} + r^2 a^2 (u_{i+1,j} + u_{i-1,j}) - u_{i,j-1} \quad ...(2)$$

Again, the boundary conditions (i) and (ii) can be put in difference form as

$$u_{0,j} = 0 = u_{n,j} \quad j = 1, 2, 3, (nh = l) \quad ...(3)$$

Also, the initial condition (iii) can be as $u_{i,0} = f(ih)\ i = 1, 2, ...$ ...(4)

and (iv) can be written as $\dfrac{u_{1,j+1} - u_{i,j}}{k} = 0$ when $t = 0$ *i.e.* $j = 0 \Rightarrow u_{i,1} - u_{i,0} = 0$ ...(5)

i.e. $\quad u_{i,1} = u_{i,0} = f(ih)$ using (4) ...(6)

Whence (4) and (5) give the values of u on the first two rows $i = 0$ and $j = 1$. Further, putting $j = 1$ in (2), we get $u_{i,2} = 2(1 - r^2 a^2) u_{i,1} + r^2 a^2 (u_{i+1,1} + u_{i-1,1}) - u_{i,0}$ ...(7)

Obviously, the terms on the R.H.S. of (7) involve the values of u on the first two rows ($j = 0$ and $j = 1$) and these are known from the initial conditions (4) and (6), hence $u_{i,2}$ is calculated explicitly. Then knowing $u_{i,2}$ we can calculate $u_{i,3}$ by putting $j = 2$ in (2) so on. Hence (2) gives an explicit scheme for the solution of one dimensional wave equation. When $k < h$, the solution (2) is convergent. And the coefficient of $u_{i,j}$ in (2) will be zero if we take $1 - r^2 a^2 = 0$

$$\Rightarrow \quad r^2 = \frac{1}{a^2} \quad \Rightarrow \quad \frac{k^2}{h^2} = \frac{1}{a} \quad \Rightarrow \quad k = \frac{h}{a}$$

Then, the recurrence relation (2) takes the simplified form as:

$$u_{i,j+1} = u_{i+1,j} + u_{i-1,j} - u_{i,j-1} \quad ...(8)$$

Hence the value of u at $x = x_i$ at time $t = t_i + k$ equals to the sum of the values of u at the surrounding points $x = x_{i-1}$ and $x = x_{i+1}$ at the previous time $t = t_j$ minus the value of at $x = x_j$ at time $t = t_j - k$.

Example 13: *Evaluate the pivotal values of the following equation taking h = 1 and upto one half of the period of vibration* $16\dfrac{\partial^2 u}{\partial x^2} = \dfrac{\partial^2 u}{\partial t^2}$ *given that* $u(0,t) = u(5,t) = 0; u(x,0) = x^2(5 - x)$ *given that* $u(0,t) = u(5,t) = 0; u(x,0) = x^2(5-x)$ *and* $u_t(x,0) = 0$

[Meerut 2002; Chennai (B.E.) 2007; R.G.V.P. (M.P.) (B.E.) 2006]

Solution: $\dfrac{\partial^2 u}{\partial t^2} = a^2 \dfrac{\partial^2 u}{\partial x^2}$, is the equation of the vibrating string of length 1, whose period of vibration $= \left(\dfrac{2l}{a}\right)$

Here $l = 5$ and $a^2 = 16$ *i.e.* $a = 4$ $\quad \therefore$ period $= 2 \times \dfrac{5}{4} = \dfrac{5}{2}$ secs,

Now, we want values of u upto $t = \dfrac{5}{4}$ seconds.

The given equation is $\quad 16\, u_{xx} = u_{tt} \quad$ ...(1)

$$\Rightarrow \quad \frac{16\,(u_{i+1,j} - 2\,u_{i,j} + u_{i-1,j})}{h^2} = \frac{u_{i,j+1} - 2\,u_{i,j} + u_{i,j-1}}{k^2}$$

(in terms of difference expression)

Now, taking $h = 1$, we get $16\,k^2\,(u_{i+1,j} - 2\,u_{i,j} + u_{i-1,j}) = u_{i,j+1} - 2\,u_{i,j} + u_{i,j-1}$

$$\Rightarrow \quad u_{i,j+1} = 2\,(1 - 16\,k^2)\,u_{i,j} + 16\,k^2\,(u_{i+1,j} + u_{i-1,j}) - u_{i,j-1}$$

If we choose k, so that coefficient of $u_{i,j} = 0$; then the above gives

$$1 - 16\,k^2 = 0 \quad \Rightarrow k^2 = \frac{1}{6} \quad \Rightarrow k = \frac{1}{4}$$

Then the above equation takes the form:

$$u_{i,j+1} = u_{i+1,j} + u_{i-1,j} - u_{i,j-1} \quad \text{...(2)}$$

As $k = \dfrac{1}{4} < h = 1$, so the solution (2) is convergent.

Also, the initial conditions $u(0, t) = 0 = u(5, t)$ become $u_{0,j} = 0$ *and* $u_{n,j} = 0$ ...(3)

for all values of j.

Thus the first and last column entries giving the values of $u_{i,j}$ are all zero. The condition $u_t(x, 0) = 0$

$$\Rightarrow \quad \frac{u_{i,j+1} - u_{i,j}}{k} = 0 \text{ when } t = 0 \quad \textit{i.e.} \text{ when } j = 0$$

$$\Rightarrow \quad u_{i,1} - u_{i,0} = 0 \quad \text{or} \quad u_{i,1} = u_{i,0}$$

Also the initial condition $u(x, 0) = x^2\,(5 - x)$ implies $u_{i,0} = i^2\,(5 - i)$ ...(4)

The putting $i = 1, 2, 3, 4$ in (4), we get $u_{1,0} = 1\,(5 - 1) = 4$; $u_{2,0} = 2^2\,(5 - 2) = 12$;

$u_{3,0} = 3^2\,(5 - 3) = 18$ and $u_{4,0} = 4^2\,(5 - 4) = 16$.

Thus the first row is now complete.

But $u_{i,1} = u_{i,0}$, so the second row is the same as the first row.

Again putting $j = 1$ in (2) we readily obtain $u_{i,2} = u_{i+1,1} + u_{i-1,1} - u_{i,0}$ ...(5)

Now putting $i = 1, 2, 3, 4$ successively, in (5), we get

$$u_{1,2} = u_{2,1} + u_{0,1} - u_{1,0} = u_{2,0} + 0 - 4 = 12 - 4 = 8$$

$$u_{2,2} = u_{3,1} + u_{1,1} - u_{2,0} = u_{3,0} + u_{1,0} - 12 = 18 + 4 - 12 = 10$$

$$u_{3,2} = u_{4,1} + u_{2,1} - u_{3,0} = u_{4,0} + u_{2,0} - 18 = 16 + 12 - 18 = 10$$

$$u_{4,2} = u_{5,1} + u_{3,1} - u_{4,0} = u_{5,0} + u_{3,0} - u_4 ,0) = 0 + 18 - 16 = 2.$$

This completes the third row. In a similar manner, all the rows can be completed. The values of $u_{i,j}$ are given in the following table.

j \ i	0	1	2	3	4	5
0	0	4	12	18	16	0
1	0	4	12	18	16	0
2	0	0+12−4	4+18−12	12+16−18	18+0−16	0
		=8	=10	=10	=2	
3	0	0+10−4	8+10−12	10+2−18	10+0−16	0
		=6	=6	=−6	=−6	
4	0	−2	−10	−10	−8	0
5	0	−16	−18	−12	−4	0

18.12 Solution of Elliptic Equations by Relaxation Method

[Delhi (M.E) 2006; Chennai (M.E.) 2008]

Let us consider Laplace equation

$$\frac{\partial^2 u}{\partial x^2} + \frac{\partial^2 u}{\partial y^2} = 0 \qquad \text{...(1)}$$

We take a square region and divide it into a square net of mesh size h. Let the value of u at A be u_0 and its values at the four adjacent points be u_1, u_2, u_3, u_4. Then we have

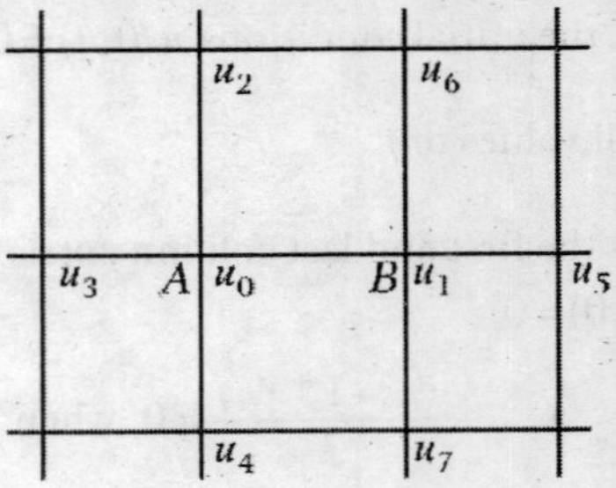

Fig. (a)

$$\frac{\partial^2 u}{\partial x^2} \approx \frac{u_1 + u_4 - 2u_0}{h^2}; \quad \frac{\partial^2 u}{\partial y^2} \approx \frac{u_2 + u_4 - 2u_0}{h^2}$$

If (1) is satisfied at A. Then we have

$$\frac{u_1 + u_3 - 2u_0}{h^2} + \frac{u_2 + u_4 - 2u_0}{h^2} \approx 0 \quad \Rightarrow u_1 + u_2 + u_3 + u_4 - 4u_0 \approx 0$$

Let r_0 be the residual (discrepency) at the mesh point A, then we have

$$r_0 = u_1 + u_2 + u_3 + u_4 - 4u_0 \qquad \text{...(2)}$$

Similarly the residual at the point *B*, is given by

$$r_1 = u_0 + u_5 + u_6 + u_7 - 4\,u_1 \text{ etc.} \qquad \ldots(3)$$

As a matter of fact, the main aim of the relaxation method is to reduce all the residuals to zero by making them as small as possible step by step. Hence we try to adjust the value of *u* at an internal mesh point so as to make the residual thereat zero. But when the value of *u* is changing at a mesh point, the values of the residuals at the neighbouring interior points will also change. If u_0 is given an increment 1, then

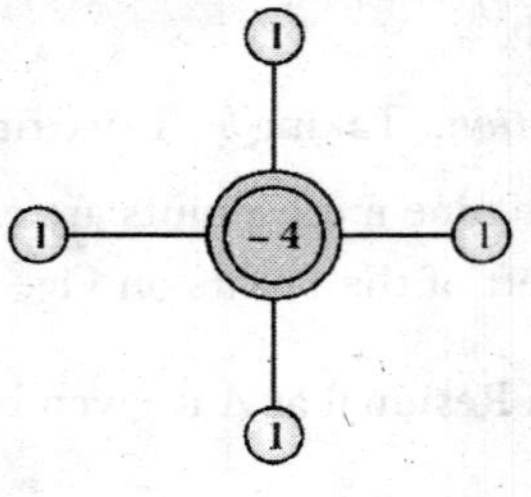

Fig. (b)

(i) (2) shows that r_0 is changed by – 4 .

(ii) (3) shows that r_1 is changed by 1.

Thus if the value of the fun*ction is increased by* 1 *at a mesh point (shown by a double ring), the residual at that point is decreased by* 4 *while the residuals at the adjacent interior points (shown by a single ring), get increased each by* 1. This relaxation pattern is shown in the figure given above:

Working Method

1. Write down, by trial, the initial values of *u* at the interior mesh points by diagonal-averaging or cross-averaging.

2. Calculate the residuals at each of these points by (2) above. In case we apply this formula at a point near the boundary, on or more end points get chopped of as there are no residuals at the boundary.

3. Write the residuals at a mesh-point on the right of this point and the value of *u* on its left.

4. Find the solution by reducing the residuals to zero. One by one, by giving suitable increments to *u* using Fig. (b). At each step, we reduce the numerically largest residual to zero and record the increment of *u* on the left (below the earlier value thereat) and the right (below the earlier residual).

5. When a round of relaxation is completed, the value of u and its increments are added at each point. Using these values we then calculate all the residuals afresh. If some of the recalculated residuals are large, these are again liquidated.

6. Stop the relaxation process, when the current values of the residuals are very very small and the solution will be the current value of *u* at each of the nodes.

Note: Relaxation method combines simplicity with the speed of convergence. But the drawback is of its unsuitability for computer calculations.

Example 14: *Solve by relaxation method, the Laplace equation* $\frac{\partial^2 u}{\partial x^2} + \frac{\partial^2 u}{\partial y^2} = 0$.

Inside the square bounded by lines $x = 0, x = 4, y = 0, y = 4$, *given that* $u = x^2 y^2$ *on the boundary.*

[Karnataka (M.E.) 2007; Bhopal 2006; Bangaluru 2004]

Solution: Taking $h = 1$, we find u on the boundary from $u = x^2 y^2$. The initial values of u at the nine mesh-points are estimated as 24, 56, 104; 16, 32, 56; 8, 16, 24 as shown on the left of the points on Fig.

Then Residual at A is given by $r_A = 0 + 56 + 16 + 16 - 4 \times 24 = -8$

and similarly $r_B = 0, r_C = -16, r_D = 0, r_E = 16, r_F = 0, r_G = 0, r_H = 0, r_I = -8$

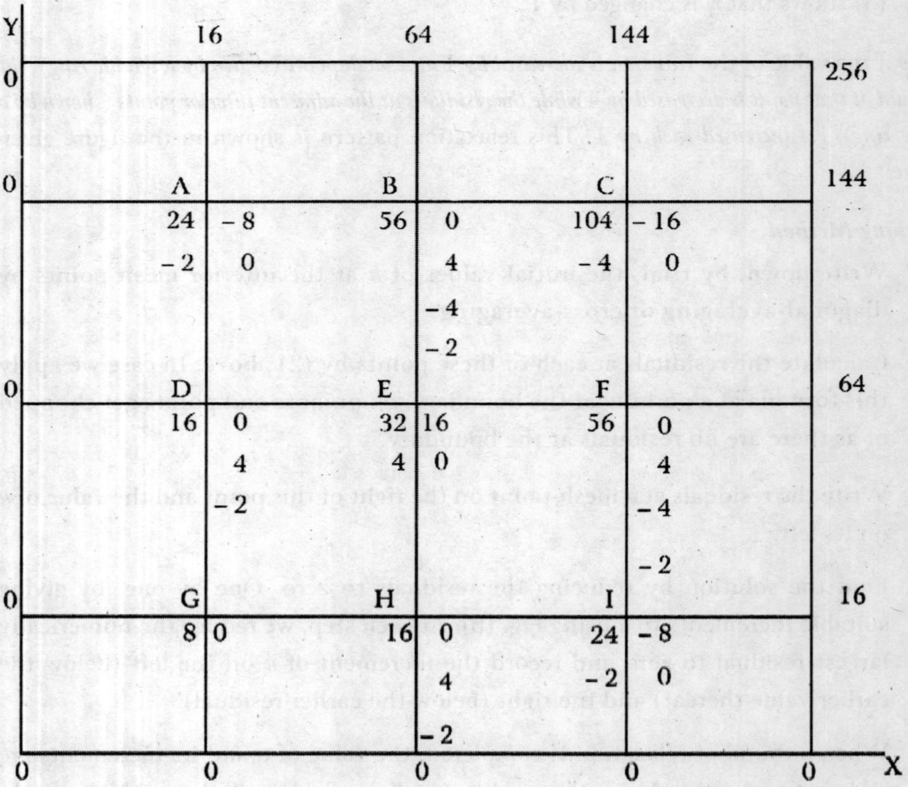

(i) Now the numerically largest residual is 16 at E so to liquidate it, we increase u by 4 so that the residual becomes zero and the residuals at neighbouring nodes get increased by 4.

(ii) The numerically largest residual is -16 at C, so to reduce it to zero, we increase u by -4 implying that the residuals at the adjacent nodes are increased by -4.

(iii) Now, the numerically largest residual is – 8 at A. To liquidate it, we increase u by – 2 so that the residuals at the adjacent nodes are again increased by – 2.

(iv) Finally, the largest residual is – 8 at I. To liquidate it, we increase u by – 2 so that the residuals at the adjacent points are increased by – 2.

(v) The numerically largest current residual is 2, then we stop the relaxation process. Hence the final values of u are given as

$$u_A = 22,\ u_B = 56,\ u_C = 100;$$
$$u_D = 16,\ u_E = 36,\ u_F = 56;$$
$$u_G = 8,\ u_H = 16,\ u_I = 22.$$

Example 15: *Solve by relaxation method Example 4(b) Page 670.*

[Roorkee (M.E.) 2009]

Solution: (i) The initial values of u at A, B, C and D are estimated as 1000, 625, 875 and 375 [Fig. a] Hence

$r_A = 500, r_B = 375, r_C = 375, r_D = 0$. Then to liquidate r_A, increase u by 125, to liquidate r_B, increase u by 94; to liquidate r_C, increase u by 94.

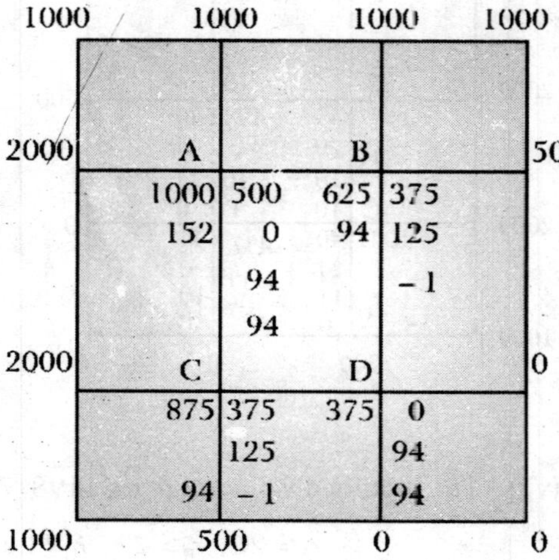

(a)

(ii) The modified values of u are 1125, 719, 969, 37 [Fig. b]

$\Rightarrow$ $r_A = 188,\ r_B = 124,\ r_C = 124,\ r_D = 188.$

Then to liquidate r_A, r_D, r_B, r_C let us increase u by 47, 47, 31, 31 in turn.

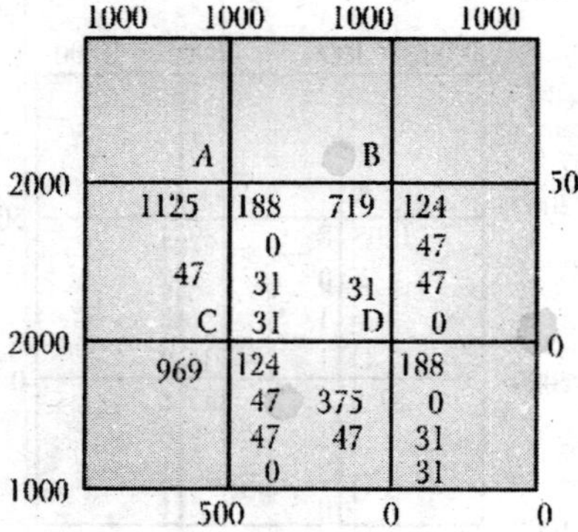

(b)

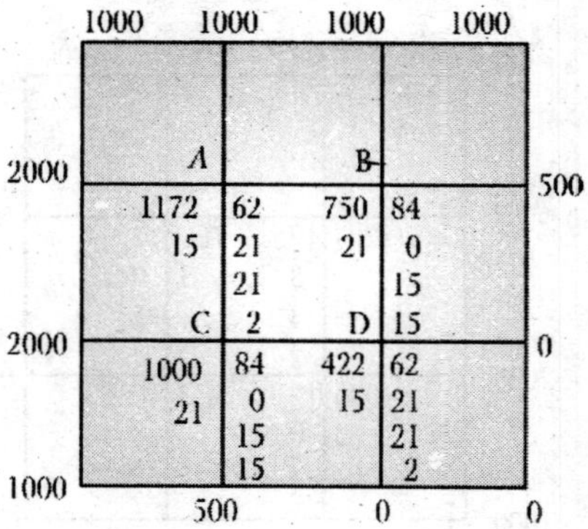

(c)

(iii) The revised values of u are 1172, 750, 1000, 422 [Fig. c]

$$\Rightarrow \qquad r_A = 62, r_B = 84, r_C = 84, r_D = 62$$

Further, to liquidate r_B, r_C, r_A, r_D let us again increase u by 21, 21, 15, 15 respectively.

(iv) Improved values of u are 1187, 771, 1021, 437 [Fig. d]

$$\Rightarrow \qquad r_A = 44, \; r_B = 40, \; r_C = 40, \; r_D = 44.$$

Then to liquidate r_A, r_D, r_B, r_C let us increase u by 11, 11, 10, 10 respectively.

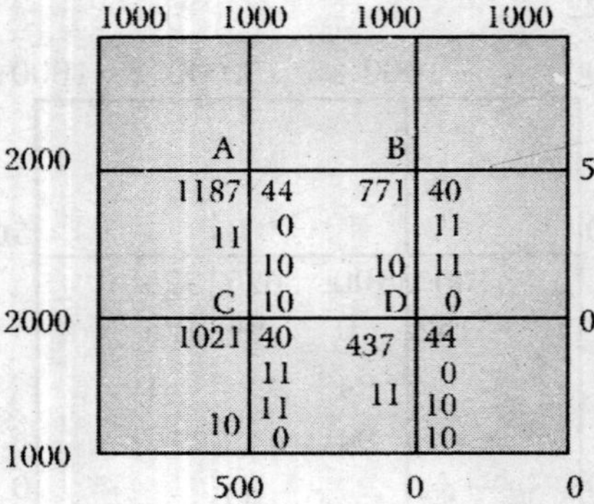

(d)

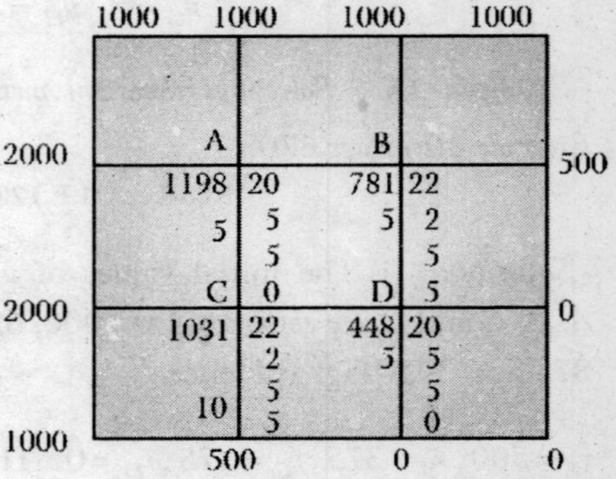

(e)

(v) The modified values of u are 1198, 781, 1031, 488 [Fig. (e)]

$$\Rightarrow \qquad r_A = 20, \; r_B = 22, \; r_C = 22, \; r_D = 20.$$

Then to liquidate r_B, r_C, r_A, r_D let us increase u by 5, 5, 5, 5 respectively.

(vi) Revised values of u are 1203, 786, 1036, 453 [Fig. (f)]

$$\Rightarrow \qquad r_A = 10, \; r_B = 12, \; r_C = 12, \; r_D = 10$$

Then to liquidate r_B, r_C, r_A, r_D increase u by 3, 3, 2, 2 respectively.

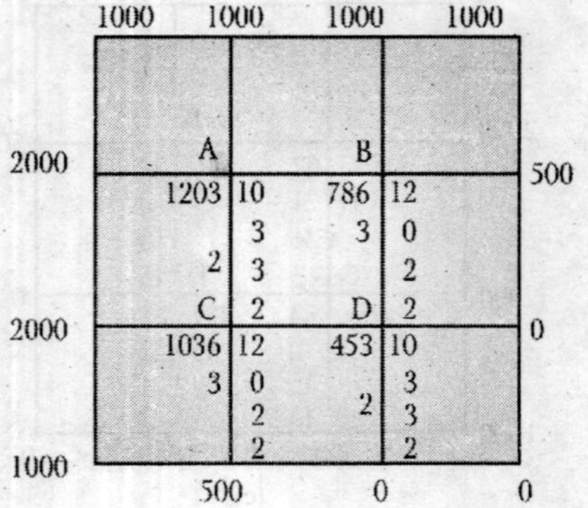

(f)

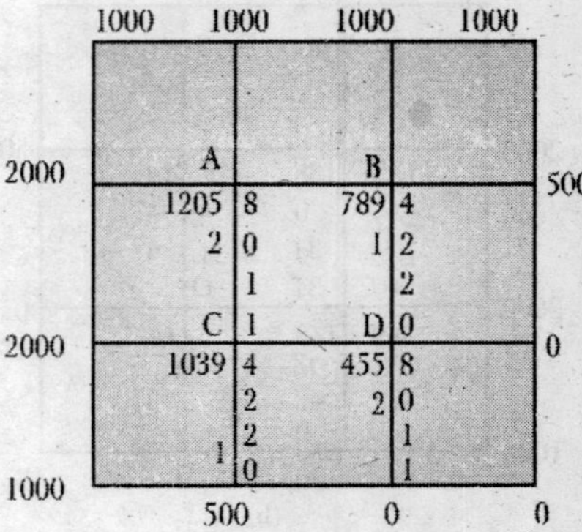

(g)

(vii) Improved values of u are 1205, 789, 1039, 455, [Fig. (g)]

$$\Rightarrow \qquad r_A = 8, r_B = 4, r_C = 4, r_D = 8.$$

Then to liquidate r_A, r_D, r_B, r_C increase u by 2, 2, 1, 1.

(viii) Finally the current residuals are 1, 0, 0, 1; so we stop the relaxation process.

Hence the values of u at A, B, C, D are 1207, 790, 1040, 457.

✦✦ Problem Set ✦✦

1. Solve the elliptic equation $u_{xx} + y_{yy} = 0$ for the following square mesh with boundary values as shown, using Leibmann method. Iterate until the maximum difference between successive values at any point is less than .005.

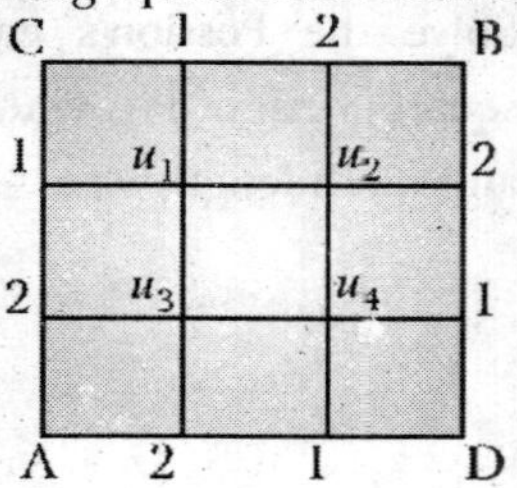

2. Solve the equation $u_{xx} + y_{yy} = 0$ for the following square mesh with the boundary values as shown. Iterate until the maximum difference between the successive values at any point is less than 0.005.

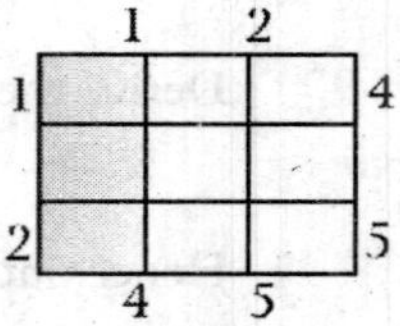

3. By iteration method, solve the elliptic equation $\partial^2 u/\partial x^2 + \partial^2 u/\partial y^2 = 0$ over the square region of side 4, satisfying the boundary conditions
(i) $u(0, y) = 0$ for $0 \le y \le 4$,
(ii) $u(4, y) = 12 + y$ for $0 \le y \le 4$,
(iii) $u(4, 0) = 3x$ for $0 \le x \le 4$, (iv) $u(x, 4) = x^2$ for $0 \le x \le 4$.
By dividing the square into 16 square meshes of side 1 and always correcting the computed values to two places of decimals, obtain the values of u at 9 interior pivotal points.

4. Solve the elliptic equation $u_{xx} + u_{yy} = 0$ for the following square mesh with boundary values as shown, using Leibmann's iteration procedure.

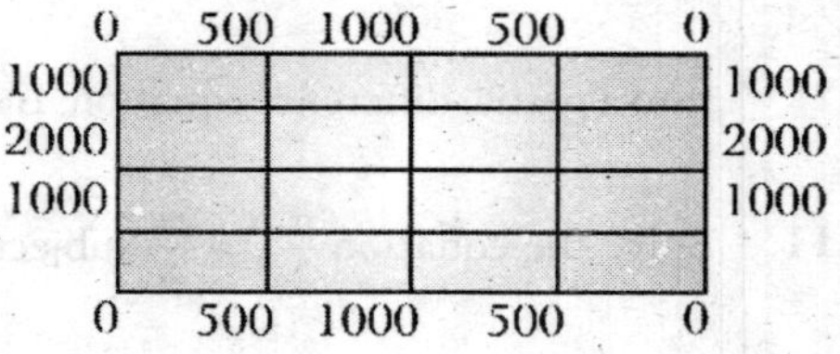

5. Solve the elliptic equation $u_{xx} + u_{yy} = 0$ for the following square mesh with boundary values as shown. Iterate until the maximum difference between successive values at any point is less than .005.

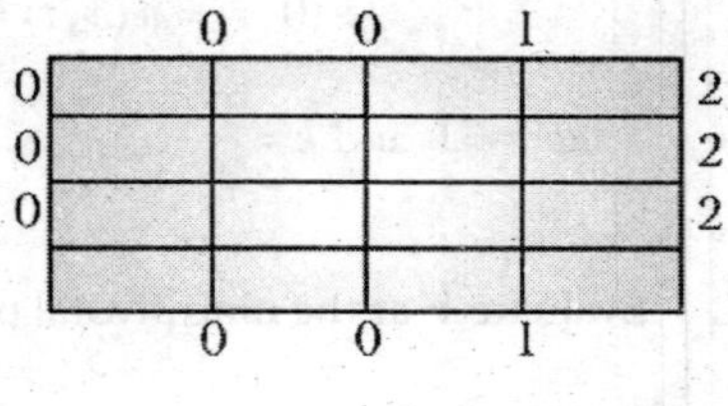

6. Using forward difference approximation to derivatives, express the one dimensional heat flow equation $\dfrac{\partial^2 u}{\partial x^2} = \dfrac{c\rho}{k}\dfrac{\partial u}{\partial t}$ as a difference equation.

If the ratio of $\dfrac{\Delta t}{(\Delta x)^2}$ is chosen so that $\dfrac{k.\Delta t}{c\rho(\Delta x)^2} = \dfrac{1}{2}$ where Δt and Δx are the time and distance steps, show that the difference equation can be simplified.

7. Show by suitable changes of variable transformation, the equation $u_{xx} - a^2 u_{tt} = 0$ can be reduced to the normalised form of the wave equation $u_{xx} - u_{tt} = 0$.

8. Solve the Possion's equation $\nabla^2 u = 8x^2 y^2$ for the square mesh of Fig. with $u(x, y) = 0$ on the boundary and mesh length $= 1$.

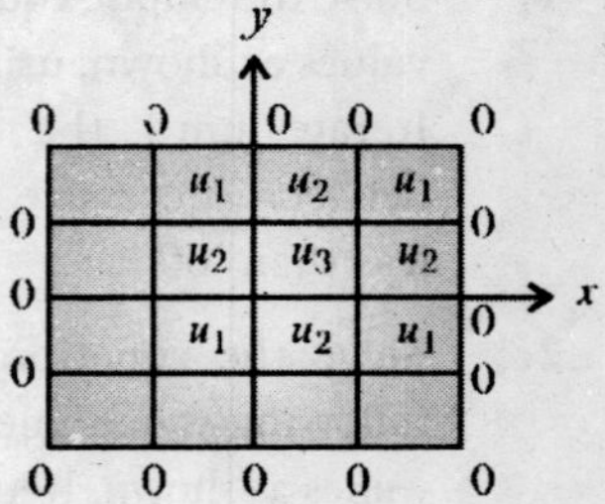

9. Derive the 'difference equation' corresponding the equation $\dfrac{\partial^2 u}{\partial x^2} + \dfrac{\partial^2 u}{\partial y^2} = \phi(x, y)$.

Hence outline a method of evaluating u at the pivotal points of a unit square, if u satisfies the equation $\dfrac{\partial^2 u}{\partial x^2} + \dfrac{\partial^2 u}{\partial y^2} = -10(x^2 + y^2 + 10)$ inside the square and the conditions $u = 0$ on the boundary of the square, $x = 0 = y, x = 3 = y$. (Assume the origin at the centre of the square and divide the square into 16 equal parts).

10. Express the harmonic equation $\dfrac{\partial^4 u}{\partial x^4} + 2\dfrac{\partial^4 u}{\partial x^2 \partial y^2} + \dfrac{\partial^4 u}{\partial y^4} = \phi(x, y)$ into a partial difference equation. Indicate briefly how will you solve this equation?

11. Solve the equation $\dfrac{\partial^2 u}{\partial x^2} = \dfrac{\partial u}{\partial t}$ subject to the conditions

$$u(0, t) = u(5, t) = 1 \quad \text{and} \quad u(x, 0) = x^2(25 - x^2)$$

Take $h = 1$ and $k = \dfrac{1}{2}$.

12. Evaluate V at the nine pivotal points of a unit square when $\dfrac{\partial^2 V}{\partial x^2} + \dfrac{\partial^2 V}{\partial y^2} = -4\pi(x^2 + y^2)$ and $V = 0$ on the boundary.

13. Evaluate u at the nine pivotal points of a unit square when $\frac{\partial^2 u}{\partial x^2}+\frac{\partial^2 u}{\partial y^2}=x^2\ y^2$ and $u=0$ on the boundary. (Assume the origin at the centre of the square and divide the square into 16 equal parts.)

14. Obtain the values of $u_1, u_2, u_3, \ldots, u_8, u_9$ at the nine internal mesh points of the square given below

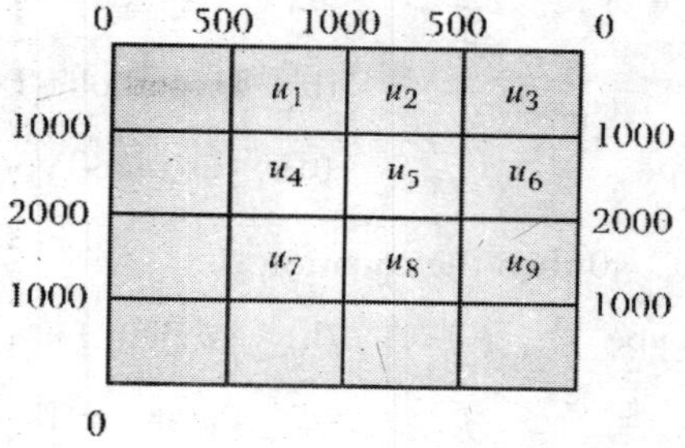

15. Let $\frac{\partial^2 \phi}{\partial x^2}+\frac{\partial^2 \phi}{\partial y^2}+400=0$ and $\phi=0$ on the boundary of a square having each side equal to 4 units. Evaluate ϕ at the nine pivotal points of the square.

16. Solve the equation $\frac{\partial^2 u}{\partial x^2}+\frac{\partial^2 u}{\partial y^2}=0$

[Bangaluru 2007]

for the region boundary by the square $0 \le x \le 4$ and $0 \le y \le 4$, subject to the bcs

$$u=0 \text{ at } x=0;$$

$$u=8+2y \text{ at } x=4$$

$$u=\frac{1}{2}x^2 \text{ at, } y=0$$

$$u=x^2 \text{ at } y=4$$

Choose $h=k=0.1$ and use Gauss-Siedal method to compute u at the internal mesh points.

✦✦ Objective Type Question ✦✦

❖ Multiple Choice Questions

1. If $B^2 - 4\,A\,C < 0$, then the equation

$$A\frac{\partial^2 u}{\partial x^2} + B\frac{\partial^2 u}{\partial x\,\partial y} + C\frac{\partial^2 u}{\partial\,y^2} + D\frac{\partial y}{\partial\,x} + E\frac{\partial u}{\partial y} + Fu = G \text{ is:}$$

(a) Elliptic-Type (b) Hyperbolic-Type

(c) Parabolic-Type (d) Circular-Type.

2. If in Q1. $B^2 - 4\,A\,C = 0$ then the equation is:

(a) Hyperbolic-Type (b) Straight Line

(c) Circle (d) Parabolic-Type

3. If in Q1. $B^2 - 4\,A\,C > 0$, then the equation is:

(a) Parabolic-Type (b) Circle

(c) Hyperbolic-Type (d) Elliptic-Type.

4. The equation $\frac{\partial^2 u}{\partial x^2} = \frac{1}{c^2}\frac{\partial^2 u}{\partial t^2}$ is known as:

(a) Laplace's Equaiton (b) Wave-Equation

(c) Heat Equation (d) None of these

5. The Heat Conduction Equation is:

(a) $\frac{\partial^2 u}{\partial x^2} + \frac{\partial^2 u}{\partial y^2} = 0$ (b) $\frac{\partial^2 u}{\partial x^2} = \frac{\partial u}{\partial t}$

(c) $\frac{\partial^2 u}{\partial x^2} = \frac{1}{c^2}\frac{\partial^2 u}{\partial t^2}$ (d) None of these

6. Which of the following are iterative formula/formulae:

(a) Jacobi's Method (b) Gauss-Seidal Method

(c) Relaxation Method (d) All the above.

7. Which of the following methods for solving a system of equations is not an iterative method: **[Agra 2007]**

(a) Relaxation Method (b) Gauss-Elimination Method

(c) Gauss-Seidal Method (d) Jacobi Method.

8. The Laplace's equations is:

(a) Elliptic (b) Parabolic

(c) Hyperbolic (d) None of these.

9. The rate of convergence of Gauss-seidal method is

(a) Less than Jacobi's Method (b) Equal to Jacobi's Method

(c) Greater than Jacobi's Method (d) None of these

10. In S.O.R. Method $u_{i,j}^{(n+1)} = u_{i,j}^{(n)} .(1-\omega) + \frac{\omega}{4}\left[u_{i-1,j}^{(n+1)} + u_{i+1,j}^{(n)} + u_{i,j-1}^{n+1} + u_{i,j+1}^{(n)}\right]$ the rate of convergence depends:

(a) Upon the choice of $u_{i,j}^{(n+1)}$ (b) Upon the choice of $u_{i,j}^{(r)}$

(c) Upon the choice of $u_{i,j+1}^{(n)}$ (d) Upon the choice of ω.

11. In S.O.R. method the accelerating factor ω lies between:

(a) 0 and 1 (b) 1 and 2

(c) 3 and 2 (d) 4 and 5.

12. The heat conduction equation $\frac{\partial u}{\partial t} = \frac{\partial^2 u}{\partial x^2}$ is:

(a) Elliptic (b) Parabolic

(c) Hyparabolic (d) All of the above.

✦✦ Answers ✦✦

❖ Problem Set

1.	$u_1 = 1.333 = u_4;\ u_2 = 1.667 = u_2$
2.	1.999, 2.999, 3.999
3.	2.37, 5.59, 9.87, 2.88, 6.13, 9.88, 3.01, 6.16, 9.51
4.	939, 1001, 1251, 1126
5.	.18756, .5000, 1.1875, .2500, .6250, 1.2500
8.	$u_1 = -3, u_2 = u_3 = -2$
9.	$u_1 = 75, u_2 = 82.5, u_3 = 67.5, u_4 = 75$

11.

$j \downarrow$ \ $i \rightarrow$	0	1	2	3	4	5
0	0	24	84	144	144	0
1	0	42	84	114	72	0
2	0	42	78	78	57	0
3	0	39	60	67.5	39	0
4	0	30	53.25	49.5	33.75	0
5	0	26.625	39.75	43.5	24.75	0
6	0	19.875	35.06	32.25	21.75	0

12.	$v = -2\pi x^2 y^2$
13.	$u_1 = -3, u_2 = u_3 = -2$
14.	$u_1 = u_3 = u_7 = u_9 = 938; u_2 = 1001, u_4 = u_6 = 1251, u_5 = 1126, u_8 = 1001$
15.	$\phi_1 = 620.9, \phi_2 = 479.2, \phi_3 = 504.2, \phi_4 = 445.9$
16.	$u_1 = 1208, u_2 = 782, u_3 = 1042, u_4 = 458$

❖ Multiple Choice Questions

1.	(a)	2.	(d)	3.	(c)	4.	(b)	5.	(b)	6.	(d)
7.	(b)	8.	(a)	9.	(c)	10.	(d)	11.	(b)	12.	(b)

◆◆◆

Theory | Solved Examples | Problem Set

Chapter

19

Computer Fundamentals with Programming in C

19.1 Introduction

A digital computer manipulates discrete elements of information and that these elements are represented in the binary (0s and Is) form. Other discrete elements, including octal numbers, Hexadecimal numbers, and decimal digits, are represented in binary codes. Data processing is carried out by means of binary logic elements **(GATES)** using binary signals. Quantities are stored in binary storage elements (**Flip-Flop**, Registers).

(i) Binary Numbers

A decimal number such as 7392 represents a quantity equal to 7 thousands plus 3 hundreds, plus 9 tens, plus 2 units. The thousands, hundreds, etc. are powers of 10 implied by the position of the coefficients. To be more exact, 7392 should be written as

$$7\times10^3+3\times10^2+9\times10^1+2\times10^0$$

In general, a number with a decimal point is represented as follows

$a_n\,a_{n-1}\ldots a_2\,a_1\,a_0\,.\,a_{-1}\,a_{-2}\ldots a_{m-1}\,a_{-m}$ where a_j is an integer such that $0\le a_j\le 9$. Above number can be written as

$$a_n\times10^n+a_{n-1}\times10^{n-1}+\ldots+a_2\times10^2+a_1\times10^1+a_0\times10^0$$

$$+\,a_{-1}\times10^{-1}+a_{-2}\times10^{-2}+\ldots a_{-m}\times10^{-m}$$

The decimal number system is said to be of base, or radix 10 because it uses ten digits (0, 1, ..., 9) and coefficients (a_s) are multiplied by powers of 10. Any numbers system is said to be of base, or ***radix*** r if its coefficients use r possible values (0, 1, ... $r-1$) and coefficients are multiplied by powers of r. Any numbers in base r is written as follows

$(a_n\,a_{n-1}\ldots a_1\,a_0\,.\,a_{-1}\,a_{-2}\ldots a_{-m})_r$ is equivalent to $a_n\,r^n+a_{n-1}\times r^{n-1}+\ldots+a_1\,r^1$

$+\,a_0\,r^0+a_{-1}\,r^{-1}+a_{-2}\,r^{-2}+\ldots a_{-m}\,r^{-m}$ in decimal number system.

As an example of base 4, the number is:

$$(301.2)_4=3\times4^2+0\times4^1+1\times4^0+2\times4^{-1}=(49.5)_{10}$$

A binary number system is a number system whose radix is 2. *i.e.* whose coefficients can have only two possible values: 0 and 1 and each coefficient a_j is multiplied by 2^j. For example

$$(1011.101)_2 = 1\times 2^3 + 0\times 2^2 + 1\times 2^1 + 1\times 2^0 + 1\times 2^{-1} + 0\times 2^{-2} + 1\times 2^{-3} = (11.625)_{10}$$

Similarly, ***Octal*** and ***Hexadecimal*** number systems are the number systems that use base or radix 8 and 16 respectively.

The first 16 numbers in the decimal, binary, octal and hexadecimal systems are listed in following table:

S.No.	Decimal (Base 10)	Binary (Base 2)	Octal (Base 8)	Hexadecimal (Base 16)
1.	00	0000	00	0
2.	01	0001	01	1
3.	02	0010	02	2
4.	03	0011	03	3
5.	04	0100	04	4
6.	05	0101	05	5
7.	06	0110	06	6
8.	07	0111	07	7
9.	08	1000	10	8
10.	09	1001	11	9
11.	10	1010	12	A
12.	11	1011	13	B
13.	12	1100	14	C
14.	13	1101	15	D
15.	14	1110	16	E
16.	15	1111	17	F

(ii) Number Base Conversions

A binary number can be converted to decimal by forming the sum of the powers of 2 of those coefficients whose values is 1. For example:

$$(10111011.011010)_2 = 2^7 + 2^5 + 2^4 + 2^3 + 2^1 + 2^0 + 2^{-2} + 2^{-3} + 2^{-5}$$

$$= (187.40625)_{10}$$

Similarly, a number expressed in base r can be converted to its decimal equivalent by multiplying each coefficient with the corresponding power of r and adding. For example

$$(201.2)_8 = 2\times 8^2 + 1\times 8^0 + 2\times 8^{-1} = 129.25$$

$$(C14A)_{16} = 12\times 16^3 + 1\times 16^2 + 4\times 16^1 + 10\times 16^0 = (49482)_{10}$$

To convert any integer decimal number into any radix r number, there are two points to remember: (i) Keep dividing by r until you reach a zero quotient (ii) Use remainder in reverse order.

For example to convert $(187)_{10}$ into binary system:

2	187	
2	93	1
2	46	1
2	23	0
2	11	1
2	5	1
2	2	1
2	1	0
2	0	1

$(187)_{10} = (10111011)_2$

To convert $(4823)_{10}$ to base 8

8	4823	
8	602	7
8	75	2
8	9	3
8	1	1
	0	1

$(4823)_{10} = (11327)_8$

The conversion of a decimal fraction to base-r is accomplished by a method similar to that used for integer. However, multiplication is used instead of division, and integers are accumulated instead of remainder.

For Example: To convert $(0.5125)_{10}$ to binary system:

$$0.5125 \times 2 = 0.025 + 1$$
$$0.025 \times 2 = 0.05 + 0$$
$$0.05 \times 2 = 0.1 + 0$$
$$0.1 \times 2 = 0.2 + 0$$
$$0.2 \times 2 = 0.4 + 0$$

$$0.4\times 2 = 0.8 + 0$$
$$0.8\times 2 = 1.6 + 1$$
$$0.6\times 2 = 0.2 + 1$$

$\therefore \quad (0.5125)_{10} = (0.10000011....)_2$. To convert $(0.625)_{10}$ into octal

$0.625\times 8 = 0.000+5 \qquad \therefore \quad (0.625)_{10} = (0.5)_8$

Note: The conversion from one base to another is more convenient, if the number is separated into an integral part and a fractional part and the conversion of each part is done separately.

Since $2^3 = 8$ and $2^4 = 16$, each octal digit corresponds to three binary digits and each Hexadecimal digit corresponds to four binary digits. The conversion from binary to octal is easily accomplished by partitioning the binary number into groups of three digits each, starting from the binary point and proceeding to the left and to the right. The corresponding octal digit is then assigned to each group. For example:

$$(\underbrace{10}_{2}\ \underbrace{111}_{7}\ \underbrace{110}_{6}\ \underbrace{100}_{4}\ .\ \underbrace{101}_{5}\ \underbrace{110}_{6})_2 = (2764.56)_8$$

Conversion form binary to hexadecimal is similar, except that the binary number is divided into groups of four digits

$$(\underbrace{11}_{3}\ \underbrace{1101}_{D}\ \underbrace{0111}_{7}\ .\ \underbrace{1100}_{C}\ \underbrace{1110}_{E})_2 = (3D7.CE)_{16}$$

Conversion from octal or hexadecimal to binary is done by a procedure revers to the above. For example

$$(745.46)_8 = (\underbrace{111}_{7}\ \underbrace{100}_{4}\ \underbrace{101}_{5}\ .\ \underbrace{100}_{4}\ \underbrace{110}_{6})_2$$

$$(A3.6D)_{16} = (\underbrace{1010}_{A}\ \underbrace{0011}_{3}.\ \underbrace{0110}_{6}\ .\ \underbrace{1101}_{D})_{16}$$

Arithmetic operations with numbers in base r follow the same rule as for decimal numbers. When other then base 10 is used, one must be careful to use only the r allowable digits. For example: addition, subtraction and multiplication in binary is done according to the following rule:

x	y	$x + y$		$x - y$		$x\times y$
		C	S	B	D	
0	0	0	0	0	0	0
0	1	0	1	1	1	0
1	0	0	1	0	1	0
1	1	1	0	0	0	1

C : Carry, S : Sum, B : Borrow, D : Difference.

(iii) Complements

There are two types of complements for each base - r system (1) the r's complement and (2) the $(r-1)$'s complement.

Complements are used to represent negative numbers, to simplify the subtraction operation and for logical manipulations.

The r's complement:

Given a positive number N in base r with an integer of n digits, the r's complement of N is defined as $r^n - N$ for $N \neq 0$ and 0 for $n = 0$, For example:

The 10's complement of $(4276)_{10}$ is $10^4 - 4276 = 5724$

The 10's " " " $(76.8)_{10}$ is $10^2 - 76.8 = 23.2$

The 2's " " " $(110.01)_2$ is $(2^3)_{10} - 110.01 = (001.11)_2$

The **$(r-1)$'s complement: Given a positive number** N is base r with an integer part of n digits and a fraction part of m digit, the $(r-1)$'s complement of N is defined as $r^n - r^{-m} - N$. For example:

The 9's complement of $(736.54)_{10} = 10^3 - 10^{-2} - 736.54$

$= 999.99 - 736.54 = (263.45)_{10}$

The *I's complement of* $(0.01110)_2 = (1-2^{-5})_{10} - (0.01110)_2$

$= (0.11111)_2 - (0.01110)_2 = (0.10001)_2$

Note: r's complement can be obtained from the $(r-1)$'s complement after the addition or r^{-m} to the least significant digit. This is because of the definition of the complements.

(iv) Subtraction with r's Complement The subtraction of two positive numbers M and N *i.e.* $(M-N)$ both of base r, may be done as follows

Step 1: Add M to the r's complement of N.

Step 2: Inspect the result obtained in step 1 for an end carry

(i) If an end carry occurs, discard it.

(ii) If an end carry does not occur, take the r's complement of the number obtained in step 1 and place a negative sign in front.

Illustration 1: $M = (1010100)_2$, $N = (1000100)_2$ **[I.P.S. 2003]**

M		1010100
		+
2' s complement of N		0111100
End carry	←------ 1	0010000

∴ Discard the carry, hence answer is 10000

Illustration 2: $M = (1000100)_2$, $N = (1010100)_2$

M	1000100
	+
2's complement of N	0101100
no carry	1110000

As no carry is generated hence answer will be – (2's complement of 1110000) Answer :-10000

(v) Subtraction with (*r* – 1)'*s* Complement

The subtraction of M and N $(M - N)$, where M and N both are positive and with same base r can be done using $(r-1)$'s complement as follows:

Step 1: Add M to the $(r-1)$'s complement of N

Step 2: Inspect the result obtained in step1 for an end carry

(i) If an end carry occurs, add 1 to the least significant digit.

(ii) If an end carry does not occur, take the $(r-1)$'s complement of the number obtained in step *l* and place a negative sing in front.

Illustration 3: $M = (1010100)_2$, $N = (1000100)_2$

M	1010100
	+
I's complement of N	0111011
End carry	0001111
	+
	1
	0010000

Ans: 0010000

Illustration 4: $M = (1000100)_2$ and $N = (1010100)_2$

M	1000100
	+
I's complement of N	0101011
No carry	1101111

∴ **Ans:** = – (I's complement of 1101111)

= – 0010000

19.2 Floating Points Numbers

Excess-K representation: In Excess K representation a number is stored as the sum of itself and K. For example, for excess 127, a number is stored as its true value plus 127. Therefore -4 becomes $-4+127=123$ and -4 represented by the $8-$ bit binary number for 123 (01111011). In this way numbers from -127 to $+128$ are mapped onto 0 to 255, all of which are expressible as an $8-$ bit positive integer. Until about 1980, each computer manufacturer had its own floating-point format. To standardize floating-point arithmetic IEEE set up a committee in late 1970s, the resulting work led to IEEE standard 754. Most CPUs these days (including the Intel, and JVM) have floating point instructions that confirm to the IEEE floating-point standard.

The standard defines mainly two formats: single precision (32 bits), and double precision (64 bits). Both the single and double precision formats use radix 2 for fractions and excess

SINGLE PRECISION

	1	8	23
Bits	SIGN	EXPONENT	FRACTION

DOUBLE PRECISION

		11	52
Bits	SIGN	EXPONENT	FRACTION

notation for exponents. The formats are shown below: Both formats start with a sign bit for the number as a whole, 0 being positive and 1 being negative. Next comes the exponent, using excess 127 for single precision and excess 1023 for double precision. *The minimum* 0 *and maximum* (255 *and* 2047) *exponents are not used for normalized number they have special uses. Finally we have fractions,* 23 *and* 52 *bits, respectively. According to the standard, the fraction consists of an implied I bit, an implied binary point, and then either* 23 *or* 52 *arbitrary bits. If all* 23 *or* 52 *fraction bits are* 0_s, *the fraction has the numerical value* 1.0; *If all of them are* 1_s, *the fraction is numerically slightly less then* 2.0. *To avoid confusion with a conventional fraction, the combination of the implied* 1, *and implied binary point, and the* 23 *or* 53 *explicits bits is called a significant instead of a fraction or mantissa. All normalized number have a significant, s, in the range* $1 \le s \le 2$. *i.e. if binary equivalent of* 23 *or* 52 *bit fraction is* M, $S=1.M$ *in case of normalized floating point representation.*

For example: **To represent 0.5 according to the IEEE standard 754**

Binary equivalent of $0.5=(0.1)_2$

$$(0.1)_2=(0.1)_2\times(2^0)_{10}=(1.0)_2\times(2^{-1})_{10}$$

$\therefore$ In a single precision, **sing bit** $=0$ ($+ve$)

Exponent $=(-1+127)_{10}=(126)_{10}=(01111110)_2$

$\therefore$ fraction = 00000000000000000000000

1 8 23

$\therefore$ 0.5 = 0 011 1111 0000 0000 0000 0000 0000 0000

$=(3F000000)_{16}=3F000000\,H$ (**H**: For Hexadecimal)

To represent 1.5: Binary equivalent of $(1.5) = (1.1)_2, (1.1)_2 = (1.1) \times (2^0)_{10}$

∴ In single precision representation

Sing bit $= 0\ (+ ve)$

Exponent $= (0 + 127)_{10} = (01111111)_2$

Fraction $= 10000000000000000000000000$

$$\therefore 1.5 = \underbrace{0}_{1}\ \underbrace{01111111}_{8}\ \underbrace{10000000000000000000000000}_{23 \text{ bits}}$$

$$= (3FC00000)_{16} = 3FC00000\,H$$

The numerical characteristics of the IEEE floating -point numbers are given in following table.

Item	Single Precision	Double Precision
Bits in Sing	1	1
Bits in Exponent	8	11
Bits in Fraction	23	52
Bits, Total	32	64
Exponent System	Excess 127	Excess 1023
Exponent Range	−126 to +127	− 1022 to + 1023
Smallest normalized number	2^{-126}	2^{-1022}
Largest normalized number	approx 2^{128}	approx 2^{1024}
Decimal range	approx 10^{-38} to 10^{38}	approx 10^{-308} to 10^{308}
Smallest denormalized number	approx 10^{-45}	approx 10^{-324}

In addition to normalized numbers, the standard has four other numerical types.

19.3 Denormalized Number

These number have an exponent of *0* and a fraction given by the following 23 or 52 bits. The implicit 1 bit to the left of the binary point now becomes a *0*. Denormalized number can be distinguished from normalized ones because the latter are not permitted to have an exponent of *0*. The smallest normalized single precision number has a 1 as exponent and *0 as a fraction, and represents* 1.0×2^{-126}. *The largest denormalized number has a 0* as exponent and all Is in the fraction, and represents about $0.9999999 \times 2^{-127}$. The smallest non zero denormalized number consists of a1 in the right most, with the rest being *0*. The exponent represents 2^{-127} and the fraction represents 2^{-23} so the value is 2^{-150} . Two zeros are presented in this scheme, positive and negative, determined by the ***sign bit***. Both have an exponent of *0 and a fraction of 0*. Here two bits to the left of the binary point is implicitly *0* rather than 1. According to the representation, a special representation is provided for infinity, consisting of an ***exponent*** will all is (not for normalized numbers), and a fraction of *0*.

What about zero divided by zero? The result is undefined. To handle this case, another format is provided, called **NaN** (not a number).

Basic Operations: Followings are the four basic arithmetic operations for floating point numbers.

[Meerut 2002]

Addition: $X + Y = (X_M \, .2^{X_E - Y_E} + Y_M) \times 2^{Y_E}$,

Subtraction: $(X - Y) = (X_M \, 2^{X_E - Y_E} - Y_M) \times 2^{Y_E}$; where $X_E \le Y_E$

Multiplication: $(X \times Y) = X_M \times Y_M \times 2^{X_E + Y_E}$

IEEE NUMERICAL TYPES

Normalized	±	0 < exp.< max	Any bit pattern
Denormalized	±	0	Any non zero bit pattern
Zero	±	0	0
Infinity	±	111.....1	0
Not a number	±	111.....1	Any non zero bit patten

Division: $(X / Y) = (X_M / Y_M) \times 2^{X_E - Y_E}$

Where X is represented as (X_M, X_E) and has numerical value $X_M \times B^{X_E}$ and Y represented as (Y_M, Y_E) and has numerical value $Y_M \times B^{Y_E}$

19.4 Representation Error

Machine computation often deals with mathematical models of actual situations that exist in the physical world. The values that are used in these models can be either computed theoretically or obtained by making measurement of physical parameters. In both cases accuracy is concern. There are at least three possible types of errors that relate to the representation of numerical values.

(a) Measurement of Errors: It happens when the method or device used to get the values is not completely accurate. For example a customer orders an item with code 512 and the sales order is written as 521 by the person or by mistake another key is pressed.

(b) Scaling Errors: It happens when the number system can not exactly represent each of the values. It is generally under the control of the user or the programmer who choose how the variables in the models should be represented. Let us assume that an actual number falls between, two integer points on the scale and value has to be represented as an integer, the best we can do is to represent that value by the closest integer. This representation contains an error, whose magnitude varies as follows.

So the maximum error is a closest value and is one half the length of the space between representable points on the number scale.

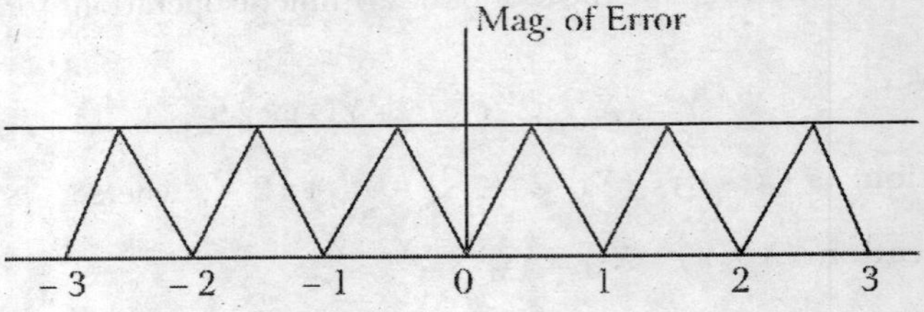

(c) Truncation and Rounding off Errors: It happens when the word length is not long enough to store the needed number of digits. Following three specific procedures have been commonly used to store the value in the word.

(i) **Truncation:** The simplest is truncation, but it introduces the most error. It consists of cutting or chopping off the word as the stated length and ignoring all lower order bits or digits.

(ii) **Half Adjusting:** It is done by first adding one half of the digits or bits to the right of the desired least significant digit or bit and then truncating number, For example

Decimal half-adjusting

1823	5105
	5000
1824	0105
↓ 1824	

(iii) **Statistical Rounding:** It is most accurate and is recommended in the IEEE floating point standard. It is similar to half adjusting except it teats the exact middle case differently. Half the time the value is rounded to the larger representable number and half the time it is rounded to the lower. It is usually done in a manner that results in the desired least significant position being even or odd as chosen by the programmer.

(d) Classification of Errors: The error may be classified into the following types

(i) **Inherent Error:** It is the quantity that is already present in the statement of the problem before its solution. This error arise either due to the simplified assumptions in the mathematical formulation of the problem or due to the physical measurements of the parameters of the problem.

(ii) **Round Off Error:** It is the quantity which must be added to the finite representation of the computer number in order to make it the true representation of that number.

(iii) **Truncation Error:** It is the quantity which must be added to the true representation of the quantity in order that the result be exactly equal to the quantity we are seeking to generate.

The quantity true value-Appx. value is called error.

Absolute error = |error|

Relative error = {|error|}/{|True value|}

Percentage error = {|error|× 100}/{|True value|}

19.5 Introduction to C Language

C is a general purpose, structured programming language, originally developed in the 1970s by Dennis Ritchie at Bell Telephone Laboratories, Inc. The American National Standards Institute (ANSI) developed a standardized definition of the C language known as ANSI C. C is a multipurpose programming language suitable for systems programming as well as for application programming.

1. Keywords and Identifiers: Every C word is classified as either a keyword or an identifier. All keywords have fixed meaning and there meanings can not be changed. For example ***auto, double, int, if, for, void*** etc are some C keywords.

Identifiers refer to the names of variables, functions and arrays. These are user-defined names and consist of a sequence of letters and digits with a letter as a first chacacter.

2. Constants: Constants in C refer to fixed values that do no change during the execution of a program. These may be of following types

Constant type	valid	Invalid
Integer Constants	123, −321, 0	15750, 20,000 $400
Floating point (real)	0.073, −1.42, 3.18 *E*3	7.3 *e* 5, 1.5 *E*2.5
Single character const	'5', '*x*', '*a*'	*a*, "*b*", 4
String constant	"yahow", "*a*"	*b*, 5

3. Variables: A variable is a data name that may be used to store a data value. Unlike constants that remain unchanged during the execution of a program, a variable may take different values at different times during execution. A variable name can be chosen by the programmer following are the valid variable names.

john, value, x_1, X_1, markm, sum

Invalid examples include 123, (area), %, 2nd following are the rules for naming C variables

(i) They must begin with a letter

(ii) Upper case and lower case are significant

(iii) The variable name should not be a keyword

(iv) White space is not allowed

(v) ANSI standard recognizes a length of first 31 characters.

Data type: *C* supports several different types of data, each of which may be represented differently within the computers memory.

Following is the description of basics data types

Data type	Description	Range
Char	Single character	-128 to 127
Int	Integer Quantity	-32768 to 32767
Float	Floating point number	$3.4e-38$ to $3.4e+38$
Double	Double precision floating-point number	$1.7e-308$ to $1.7e+308$

4. Declaration of Variables: The syntax for declaring a variable is as follows data-type $v_1, v_2, \ldots, v_n$;

for example: **int count, sum, char ch;**

5. Storage Class: There are four storage classes explained in following table

Storage class	Meaning
Auto	Local variable known to only to the function in which it is declared Default is auto.
Static	Local variable which exists and retains its value even after the control is transferred to the calling function.
Extern	Global variable known to all functions in the file.
Register	Local variable which is stored in the microprocessor registers (If available)

6. Assignment Statement: Values can be assigned to variables using the assignment operator = as follows

variable-name = constant; variable-name = exp;

For example sum $=0$; aveg $=3+5$;

7. Comments: Comment is *C* starts with "/*" and end with "*/" for example /* program for Bisection method */ comments have nothing to do with the execution of program.

8. Reading Value from Keyboard: To read data from keyboard scanf function is used as follows

scanf ("control string", & v_1, & v_2, ... & v_n);

& symbol is used before each variable name. For Example scanf ("% *d*", & size);

control string contains the format of the data being input by the user It contains

% *c* for data item is a single character

% *d* for data item is a decimal integer

% *f* for data item is a floating point value.

For example scanf ("%*d*%*f*",&*c*,&*d*); reads one integer value and then a floating point value from the key board and these values are assigned to variables *c* and *d* respectively.

9. Writing Result on the Monitor Screen: To write the result printf function is used. In general terms printf function is written as

printf ("control string", $v_1, v_2, \ldots v_n$);

Where control string has same meaning as in the case of scanf and $v_1, v_2, \ldots v_n$ are variables that represents the value you want to print on the screen. Note that "&" is not used in printf function.

> **Note:** To work with printf and scanf; one must include "stdio.h" file in the program.

10. Escape Sequences: Certain nonprinting characters, as well as back slash (\) and the appostrophe ('). Can be expressed in terms of escape sequences. An escape sequence always begins with a backward slash and is followed by one or more special character. Some of the escape sequences are listed below.

back spaces	\b
horizontal tab	\t
vertical tab	\v
newline	\n
carriage return	\r
back slash	\\
null	\0

11. Arithmetic Operators: *C* provieds all the basic arithmatic operators (listed below)

[Meerut 2002]

+	addition
–	subtraction
*	multiplication
/	Division
%	modulo division

For Example: If $a = 8$, and $b = 4$

$$a - b = 4, a + b = 12, a * b = 32$$

$$a / b = 2, a \% b = 0, - a * b = -32$$

> **Note:** C does not have an operator for exponentiation.

12. Relational Operators: *C* supports six relational-operators in all.

$<$	is less than
$<=$	is less than or equal to
$>$	is greater than
$>=$	is greater than or equal to
$=$	is equal to
$!=$	is not equal to

A simple relational expression contains only one relational-operator and takes the following form.

Exp 1 Relational-operatos Exp 2

For Example, $3.5 <= 11$ true

$3.5 < -11$ false

$9 < 7+6$ true

13. Logical Operators: *C* has following three logical operators

&&	logical AND
||	logical OR
!	logical NOT

14. Assignment Operators: '=' is called assignment operator as studied above. Used as: $x = a + b;\ \ y = a + b/z - c;$

15. Short Hand Assignment Operators:

Statements with Simple Assignment Operator	Statement with Shorthand Operator
$a = a + 2$	$a += 2$
$b = b - 2$	$b -= 2$
$a = a * b$	$a *= b$
$b = b / c$	$b /= c$
$n = n \% a$	$n \%= a$

16. Increment and Decrement Operators: The operator ++ is called increment operator and adds 1 to the operand while -- is called decrement operator and subtracts 1. Both are unary operators and take the following form $++n$ or $n++;$ $--m$ or $m--$

For Example: $m = 5;\ \ y = ++m;$

In this case value of y & m will be 6.

While incase of $m = 5;\ \ y = m++;$

Values of y will be 5 and value of m will be 6.

17. Conditional Operators: A ternary operator pair"?:" is available in C to construct conditional expressions of the form Exp 1 ? Exp 2: Exp 3;

For Example: $x = (a > b)\ ?\ a : b$.

If a, is greater than b, value assigned to x will be a else value assigned to x will be equal to the values of b.

18. Arithmetic Expressions:

Algebraic Expression	C Expression
$a \times b - c$	$a * b - c$
$(m + n)(x + y)$	$(m + n) * (x + y)$
$3x^2 + 2x + 1$	$3 * x * x + 2 * x + 1$
$(x / y) + c$	$(x / y) + c$

In C *, / and % are given higher precedence over the + and – operators in evaluating an arithmetic expression.

19. Mathematical Function: To use mathematical functions such as sin, cos, sqrt, log etc one must include the following line in the program #include<math.h>
Some such functions are given below in the table.

Function	Meaning
$a\cos(x)$	Arc cosine of x
$a\sin(x)$	Arc sin of x
$a\tan(x)$	Arc tangent of x
$\cos(x)$	cosine of x
$\sin(x)$	sine of x
$\tan(x)$	Tangent of x
$\cosh(x)$	Hyperbolic cosine of x
$\sinh(x)$	Hyperbolic sine of x
$\tanh(x)$	Hyperbolic tangent of x
$\log(x)$	Natural log of $x, x > 0$
$\log_{10}(x)$	Base 10 log of $x, x > 0$
pow (x, y)	x to the power $y (x^y)$
sqrt (x)	square root of $x, x >= 0$

Note: (1) x and y should be declared as double.

(2) In trignometric and hyperbolic functions, x and y are in radians

(3) All the above functions return a double.

20. Decision Making Statement: If statement: It is used as follows

if (exp 1) {statements 1}

else {statements 2}

Statements 1 are *C* statements and are executed if value of exp 1 is TRUE (non-zero).

Statements 2 are *C* statements and are executed if value of exp 1 is FALSE (zero).

If statements are used to control the flow of execution of statements. In **If** statements ***else*** part is optional.

21. LOOPS: (i) While loop: Syntax of while loop is as follows

While (exp) {statements}

Above loop, cause execution of statements while value of exp is TRUE (non-zero).

(ii) Do-while loop: syntax

Do {statements} while (exp);

In this loop, statements will be executed at least once and will be executed iteratively while value of exp is True (non-zero) and control will be transfered out of loop when value of exp is FALSE (zero).

For loop: The **for** loop is another loop that provides a more concise loop control structure. The general form of the **for** loop is

```
for (initialization ; condition ; increment or decrement)
        {
          statements
         /* (Body of loop) */
        }
```

The flow chart for loop is given below

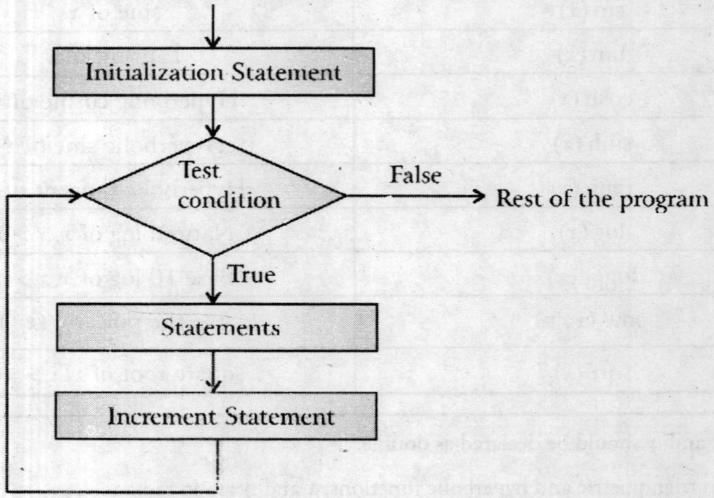

22. Break Statement: When a ***break*** statement is encountered inside a loop, that loop is excited, irrespective of the value of test-condition or exp, and program continues with the statement immediately following the loop. The syntax of break statement is as follows.

```
break;
```

23. Arrays: An array is a group of data items that share a common name. An array is an aggregate of elements of the array. The following statements declares arrays in *c* :

```
int a[10];
float b[5][5];
```

The first statement creates an one dimensional array named as a having 10 elements of type int. each element being refered by an appropriate subscript in rectangular brackets *i.e.* a[0], a[1], ... a[9];

The second statement creates a two dimentional array named as *b* having 25 (5×5) elements of type float, individual element can be represented as b[i][j], $0 \le i \le 4$ and $0 \le j \le 4$.

In case of arrays, Individual element can be processed, assigned a value, modified, and accessed independent of the other. For Example following are valid *C* statements involving array elements.

$a =$ num[0] + 10;

num[5] = num[2]+ num[3];

num[2] = x[3] + y[4];

val [6] = num [5] $\times$ 3;

Array can be initialized (*i.e.* values to the array elements can be assigned at the time of declaration) as follows

float total[5] = {0.0, 0.11, 0.2, 1.0, 1.7}

In this way array elements total[0], total[1], total[2], total[3] and total[4] get values 0.0, 0.11, 0.2, 1.0 and 1.7 respectively.

24. Function: *C* function can be classified into two categories, namely library function such as ***printf***, ***sqrt*** and ***user-defined function.***

A function is a self contained block of code that performs a particular task. Once a function has been designed and packed. It can be treated as a 'black box' that takes some data from calling position and returns a value.

A function definition has two principal components:

The first line (including the argument declarations), and the body of the function. In general terms, the first line can be written as [data-type name (type1 arg1, type2 arg2, ... type*n* arg*n*)] where data-type represents the data type of the item that is returned by the function, name represents the function name, and type1, type2, ... type*n* represent the data type of arguments arg1, arg2.

The arguments are called formal arguments, because they represent the names of data items that are transferred into the function from the calling portion of the program. (The corresponding arguments in the function reference are called actual arguments).

The function body consists of C statements that defines the action to be taken by the function. To return some value from the function the return statement is used as follows. ***return exp***; The value of exp is returned to the calling portion of the program. To return nothing from a function ***void*** is used instead of data-type in the function definition.

A function can be accessed (*i.e.* called) by specifying its name, followed by a list of arguments enclosed in parentheses and separated by commas. For example $y =$ **fact**(x); is a call to function "***fact***". The value of actual argument of x is copied into the formal argument of the function ***fact*** and then after the execution of function ***fact***, return value is assigned to y.

25. Preprocessor Directives: The lines in a *c* program that begin with a hash # sign are called preprocessor directives. The two most commonly used are #define and #include.

(i) # define

syntax # define name replacement

It instructs the computer to replace all occurances of name with the replacement even before the program is processed *i.e.* checked for syntax. For example:

```
# define N 2    /*(NOTE No semicolon at the end)*/
int  a[N];
```

Before the program is processed by the computer, the second line ie,int a[N]; is changed to int a[2]; and the first line is removed. Hence the resulting statement that is processed is int a[2].

(iii) # include

syntax

```
# include< header-file-name>
# include"header-file-name"
```

This instructs the computer to insert the contents of the mentioned header file at the place to where the directive appeared.

Note: The header file contains declarations of various function.

26. Basic Structure of a C Program: A *C* program can be viewed as a group of building blocks called functions. A function is subroutine that may include one or more statements designed to perform a specific task. To write a program in *C*, we first create functions and then put them together. Basic structure of a *C* program is as follows.

Every C program must have one main() function section because execution of program starts with this function.

All sections, except the main function section, may be absent when they are not required.

Documentation Section (Comments)
Link Section (# include<XYZ.h>)
Definition Section (# define........)
Global Declaration Section

Function Sector
Main ()
{
Declaration Part
Excutable Part
}

Subprogram Section Function 1 Function 2 | | | | Function n (User-defined functions)

SOME PROGRAMS IN C

1. (a) FLOW CHART FOR BISECTION METHOD

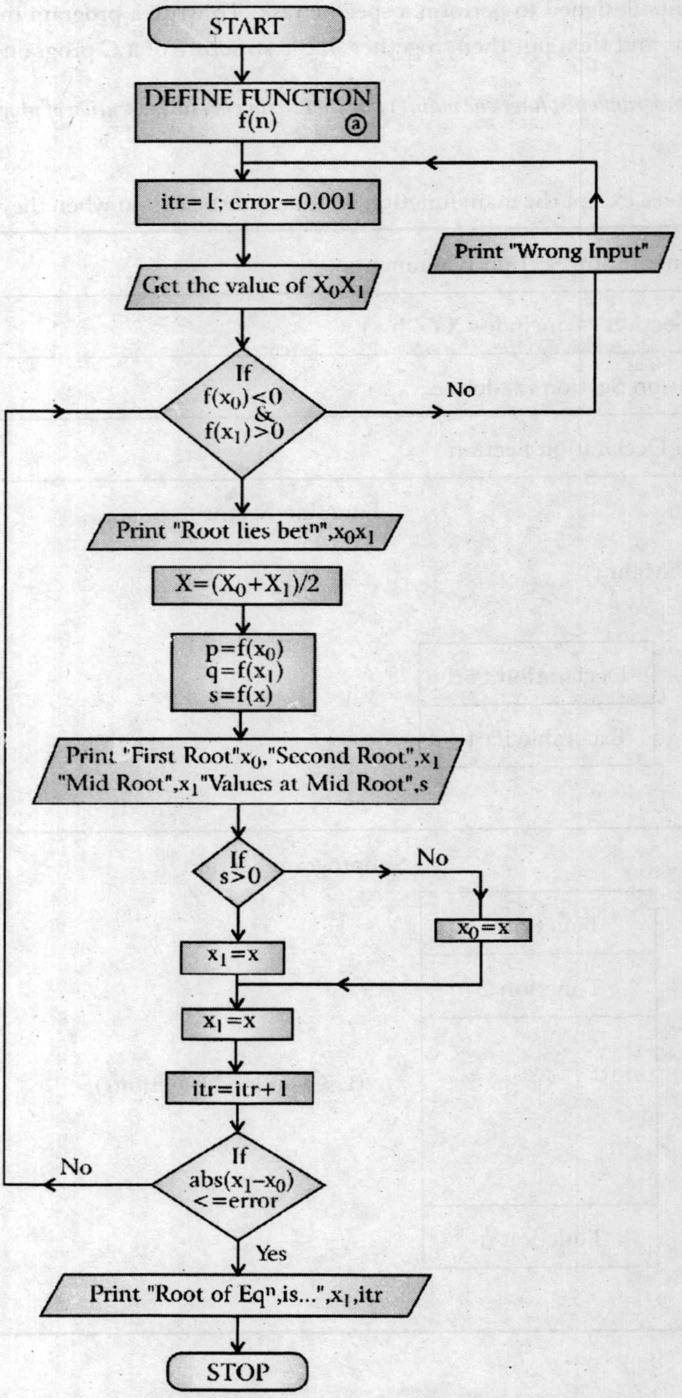

1. (b) BISECTION METHOD PROGRAM

/ *TO FIND THE ROOT USING BISECTION METHOD*/

Used formula: $x = \frac{x_0 + x_1}{2}$

```
# include< stdio.h>
#include<math.h>
# include<conio.h>
#include<process.h>
float fun (float);
void main ()
{
        clrscr ( );
        long float x 0, x, x1, p, q, s;
        int d = l;
        l:
        printf ("\ n ENTER THE FIRST VALUE OF x 0");
        scanf (" % 1 f ", &x 0);
        printf (" \n ENTER THE SECOND VALUE OF xl ");
        scanf (" % 1f",&x1);
        if ((fun(x0)<0)&&(fun (x1) > 0))
        {
    printf ("\ n THE ROOT LIES BETWEEN %1 f AND %1 f",x 0,x1);
            printf ("\ nn         a              b
            x                    f (x)");
            b:
            x= (x 0+ x 1) /2 . 0 ;
            p= fun (x 0);
            q= fun (x1);
            s= fun (x);
            printf ("\ n%d\t%1f\t%1f\t%1f\t%1f",d,x 0,x1,x,s);
            if (s >0);
            xl = x;
            else
            x 0= x;
            d++ ;
            if (fabs (xl – x 0) <= 0.0001)
            {
            printf ("\ n\ nTHE ROOT OF THE EQUATION IS = ");
```

```
            printf ("%1f",x);
            getch();
            exit (0);
        }
        else
        goto b;
    }
    else
    {
        printf ("\ n WRONG VALUES ENTERED. ENTER AGAIN");
        goto 1;
    }
}
float fun (float m)
{
        float f;
        f = m * exp(m) – 1;
        return (f);
}
```

ENTER THE FIRST VALUE OF x 0 0

ENTER THE SECOND VALUE OF x1 1

THE ROOT LIES BETWEEN 0.000000 AND 1.000000

n	a	b	x	$f(x)$
1	0.000000	1.000000	0.500000	−0.175639
2	0.500000	1.000000	0.750000	0.587750
3	0.500000	0.750000	0.625000	0.167654
4	0.500000	0.625000	0.562500	−0.012782
5	0.562500	0.625000	0.593750	0.075142
6	0.562500	0.593750	0.578125	0.030619
7	0.562500	0.578125	0.570312	0.008780
8	0.562500	0.570312	0.566406	−0.002035
9	0.566406	0.570312	0.568359	0.003364
10	0.566406	0.568359	0.567383	0.000662
11	0.566406	0.567383	0.566895	−0.000687
12	0.566895	0.567383	0.567139	−0.000013
13	0.567139	0.567383	0.567261	0.000325
14	0.567139	0.567261	0.567200	0.000156

THE ROOT OF THE EQUATION IS 0.567200

2. (a) FLOW CHART FOR FALSE POSITION METHOD **[Meerut 2002]**

/* The given function is $f(m) = m^3 - 2m - 5$ */

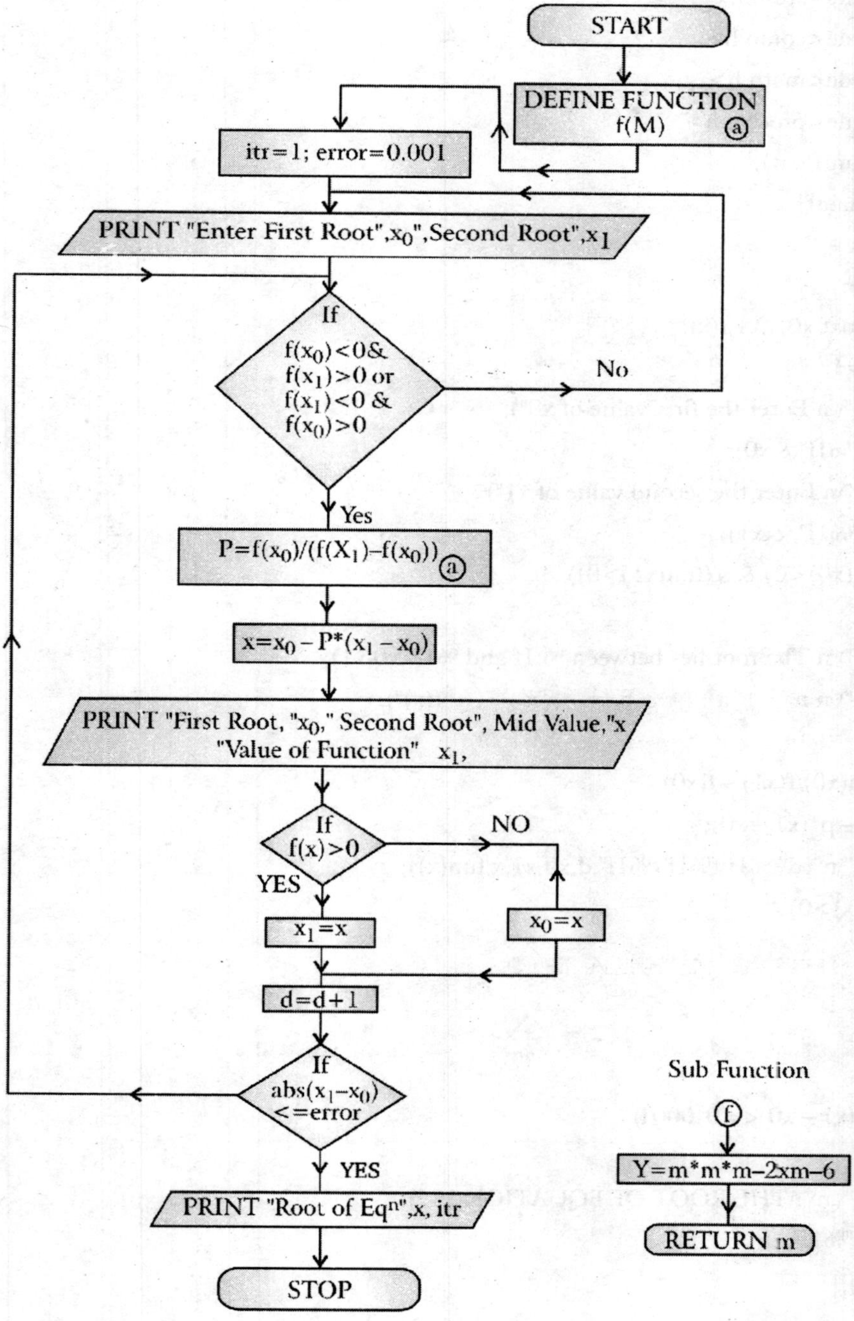

2. (b) /*TO FIND THE ROOT USING FALSE POSITION METHOD*/

Used formula: $x_2 = x_0 - \dfrac{f(x_0)(x_1 - x_0)}{f(x_1) - (f(x_0))}$

```
#include<stdio.h>
#include<conio.h>
#include<math.h>
#include<process.h>
float fun(float);
void main()
{
clrscr();
long float x0,x,x1,f(x);
int d=1;
printf("\ n Enter the first value of x0");
scanf("%1f",&x0);
printf("\n Enter the second value of x1");
scanf("%1f", &x1);
if((fun(x0)<0) &&(fun(x1)>0))
{
printf("\ n The root lies between % 1f and %1f",x0,x1);
printf("\ n n        a        b        x        f(x)");
b:
p = fun(x0)/f(x1) – f(x0)
x = x0 – p*(x1 – x0);
printf("\n%d\t%1f\t%1f\t%1f",d,x0,x1,x,fun(x));
if(fun(x)>0)
x1=x;
else
x0=x;
d ++;
if(fabs(x1 – x0)<=0.0001)
{
printf("\ n\ nTHE ROOT OF EQUATION IS ");
printf("%1f",x);
getch();
```

```
exit(0);
}
else
goto b;
}
        else
        {
        printf("\ n WRONG VALUES ENTERED. ENTER AGAIN");
        goto 1;
        }
        }
        float fun (float m)
        {
        long float f;
        f = m * m * m – 2 * m – 5;
        return (f);
enter the value of x0  2
enter the value of x1  3
```

The root lies between 2.000000 AND 3.000000

n	a	b	x	$f(x)$
1	2.000000	3.000000	2.058824	–0.390799
2	2.058824	3.000000	2.081264	–0.147205
3	2.081264	3.000000	2.089639	–0.054677
4	2.089639	3.000000	2.092740	–0.020203
5	2.092740	3.000000	2.093884	–0.007450
6	2.093884	3.000000	2.094305	–0.002745
7	2.094305	3.000000	2.094461	–0.001013
8	2.094461	3.000000	2.094518	–0.000372
9	2.094538	3.000000	2.094839	–0.000137
10	2.094539	3.000000	2.094547	–0.000050
11	2.094547	3.000000	2.094550	–0.000020
12	2.094550	3.000000	2.094551	–0.000007
13	2.094551	3.000000	2.094551	–0.000002
14	2.094551	3.000000	2.094551	–0.000002
15	2.094551	3.000000	2.094552	–0.000001

THE ROOT OF EQUATION IS 2.094552

3. (a) FLOW CHART FOR NEWTON RAPHSON METHOD

*/*The function is* $f(a) = a * a * a - 2 * a - 5 *$ /

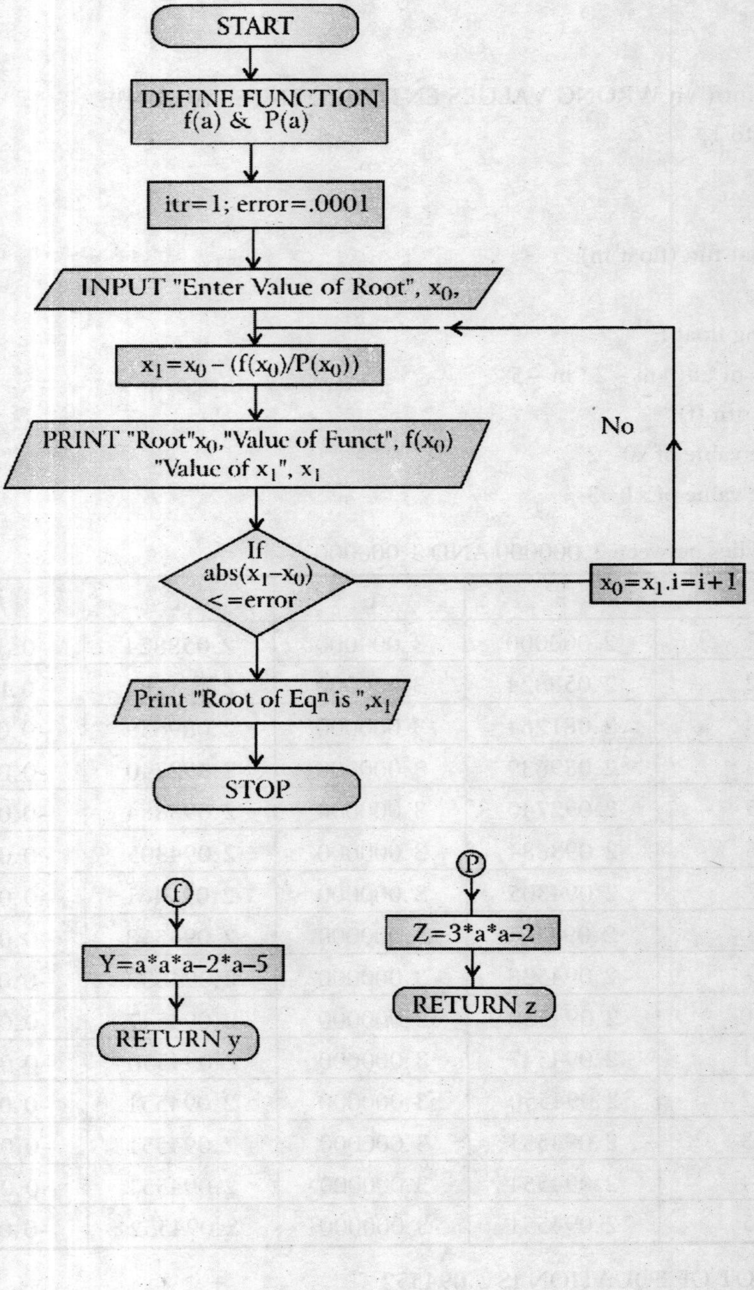

3. (b) /*TO FIND THE ROOT USING NEWTON RAPHSON METHOD*/

[Indore 2007]

Used formula: $\phi(x) = x - \dfrac{f(x)}{f'(x)}$

```
#include<stdio.h>
#include<conio.h>
#include<math.h>
#include<process.h>
float f (float);
float p (float);
void main ( )
{
    clrscr ( );
    int i = 1;
    float x0, x1;
    printf ("\ nENTER THE  INITIAL VALUE OF x0");
    scanf (" %f ",&x0);
    printf ("\ nn          x(n)      f(x)       x(n + 1)");
    1:
    x1 =x0 – (f(x0)/p(x0));
    printf("\n%d\t%f\t%f\t%f ", i, x0, f(x0), x1);
    if (fabs (x1 – x0)< =0.0001)
    {
      printf ("\ n\ nTHE ROOT OF EQUATION IS % f ", x0);
      getch ( );
      exit (0);
    }
    else
    {
      x0 =x1;
```

```
        i++;
        goto 1;
    }
}
float f(float a)
{
float f1;
f1 = a*a*a - 2*a - 5;
return (f1);
}
float p  (float a)
{
    float p1;
    p1 = 3*a*a-2;
    return (p1);
}
```

ENTER THE INITIAL VALUE OF x0   1

n	x (n)	f (x)	x (n + 1)
1	1.000000	–6.000000	7.000000
2	7.000000	324.000000	4.765517
3	4.765517	93.694595	3.348703
4	3.348703	25.854309	2.531600
5	2.531600	6.161812	2.173916
6	2.531600	0.925899	2.097884
7	2.097884	0.037262	2.094558
8	2.094558	0.000070	2.094552

THE ROOT OF EQUATION IS 2.094558

4. (a) FLOW CHART FOR TRAPEZOIDAL RULE

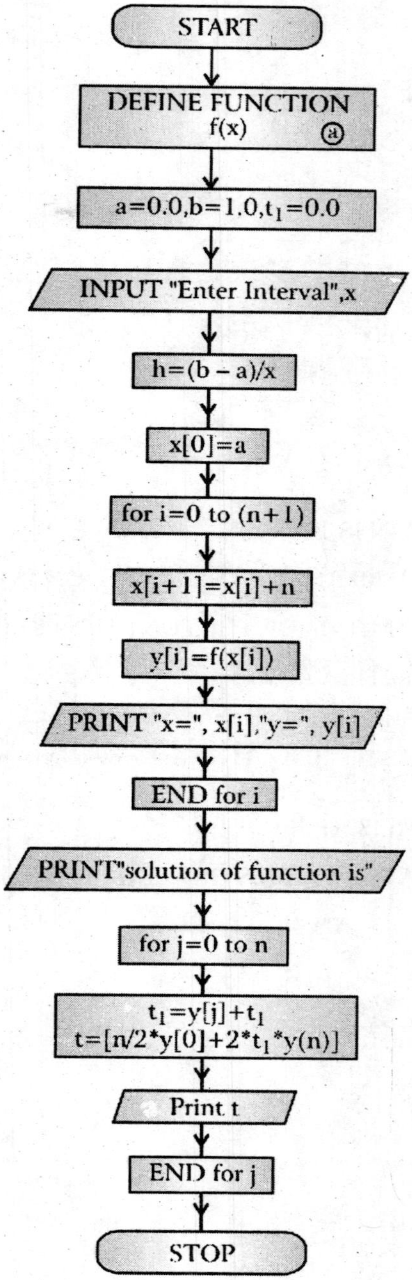

4. (b) /*TRAPEZOIDAL RULE*/

Used formula: $\int_a^b y\,dx = (h/2)\,[y_0 + 2(y_1 + y_2 + \dots y_{n-1}) + y_n]$.

```
#include<stdio.h>
#include<math.h>
#include<conio.h>
float f(float);
void main()
{
float  h,x[10],y[10],t,t1 =0.0;
int n,i;
float  a = 0.0, b = 1.0;
clrscr();
printf("\nTHE FUNCTION IS 1/(1+X)");
printf("\nTHE LOWER LIMIT (a) OF THE FUNCTION IS 0");
printf("\nTHE UPPER LIMIT (b) OF THE FUNCTION IS 1");
printf("\nENTER THE INTERVALS");
scanf(" %d", &n);
h = (b - a)/n;
printf ("THE VALUE OF h IS %f",h);
printf("\n THE TABULATED VALUES OF X AND Y ARE ");
printf("\n          X               Y");
X[0]= a;
for      (i = 0,; i<n +1;i ++)
{
x[i + 1]= x[i] + h;
y[i] =  f(x[i]);
printf ("\n %f\t%f",x[i],y[i]);
}
printf("\nTHE SOLUTION OF THE FUNCTION USING TRAPEZOIDIAL RULE ");
```

```
for(i = 1; i<n;i ++)
t1 =y[i] + t1;
t = (h/2)*(y[0] + 2*t1 + y[n]);
printf(" %f",t);
getch();
}
float f(float a)
{
        float f1;
f1 = 1/(1 + a);
return(f1);
}
```

THE FUNCTION IS 1/(1 + X)

THE LOWER LIMIT (a) OF THE FUNCTION IS 0

THE UPPER LIMIT (b) OF THE FUNCTION IS 1

ENTER THE INTERVALS 6

THE VALUES OF h IS 0.166667

THE TABULATED VALUES OF X AND Y ARE

X	Y
0.000000	1.000000
0.166667	0.857143
0.333333	0.750000
0.500000	0.666667
0.666667	0.600000
0.8333333	0.545455
1.000000	0.500000

THE VALUE OF THE INTEGRAL USING TRAPEZOIDAL RULE IS 0.694877

5. (a) FLOW CHART FOR SIMPSON'S 1/3rd RULE

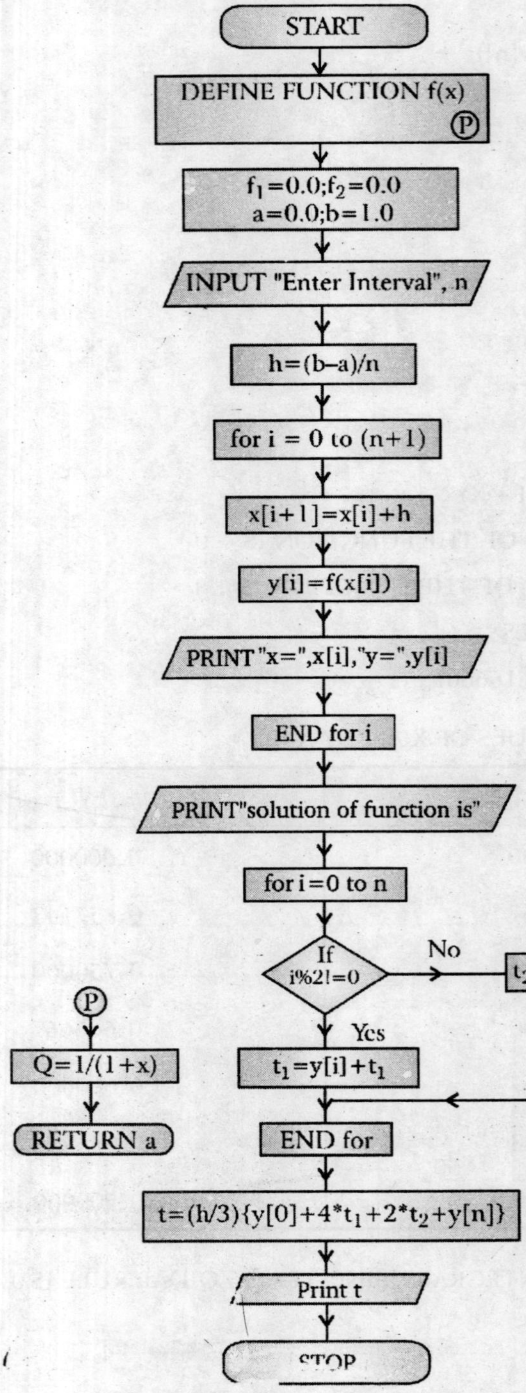

5. (b) /*SIMPSON'S 1/3rd RULE*/

Used formula: $\int_a^b y\,dx = (h/3)[y_0 + 4(y_1 + y_3 + y_5 + \ldots + y_{n-1}) + 2(y_2 + y_4 + y_6 + \ldots + y_{n-2}) + y_n]$

```
#include<stdio.h>
#include<conio.h>
#include<math.h>
float f(float);
void main ( )
{
float  h,x[10],y[10],t,t1 =0.0,t2 =0.0;
int n,i;
float  a =0.0, b  =1.0;
clrscr();
printf("\ nTHE  FUNCTION IS      1/(1 + X)");
printf("\ nTHE LOWER LIMIT (a) OF THE FUNCTION IS 0");
printf("\ nTHE UPPER LIMIT (b) OF THE FUNCTION IS  1");
printf("\ nENTER THE INTERVAL (MUST BE EVEN)  ");
scanf("%d",&n);  h = (b – a)/n;
printf('THE VALUE OF h IS  %f",h);
printf("THE TABULATED VALUES OF X AND Y ARE ");
printf("\ n          X          Y");
X[0] = a;
for(i = 0;i<n + 1;i + +)
{
x[i + 1] = x[i] + h;        y[i] = f(x[i]);
printf("\ n%f\t%f",x[i],y[i]);
}
printf("\ nTHE VALUE OF THE INTEGRAL USING SIMPSON'S 1/3rd RULE");
for(i = 1;i<n;i + + )
{
```

```
if(i%2)
t1 =y[i] + t1;
else
t2 =  y[i] + t2;
}
t = (h/3)*(y[0] + 4*t1 + 2*t2 + y[n]);
printf("%f",t);     getch();
}
float f(float a)
{
float f1
f1 = 1/(1 + a);
return(f1);
}
```

THE FUNCTION IS 1/(1 + X)

THE LOWER LIMIT (a) OF THE FUNCTION IS 0

THE UPPER LIMIT (b) OF THE FUNCTION IS 1

ENTER THE INTERVAL (MUST BE EVEN) 4

THE VALUE OF h IS 0.250000

THE TABULATED VALUES OF X AND Y ARE

X	Y
0.000000	1.000000
0.250000	0.000000
0.500000	0.666667
0.750000	0.571429
1.000000	0.500000

THE SOLUTION OF THE FUNCTION USING SIMPSON'S (1/3)rd RULE IS 0.693254

6. (a) FLOW CHART FOR GAUSS ELIMINATION METHOD

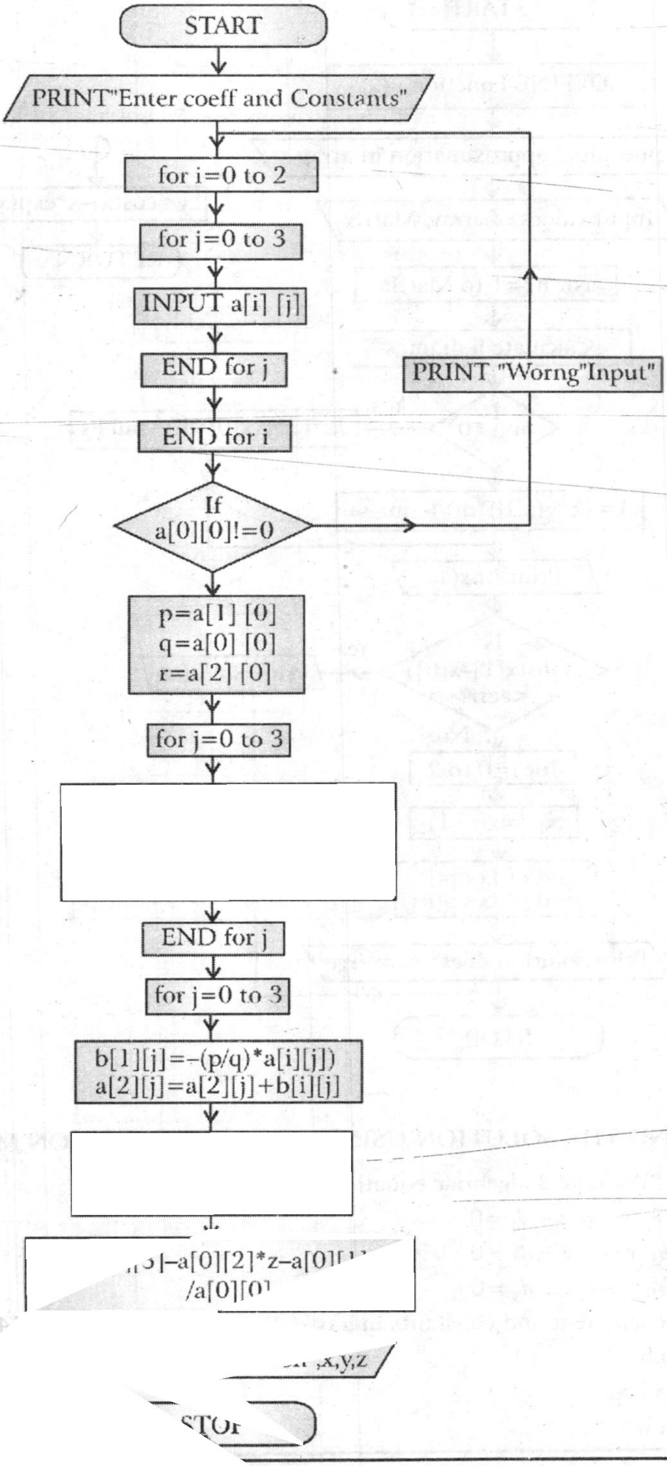

6. (a′) FLOW CHART FOR MULLER'S METHOD

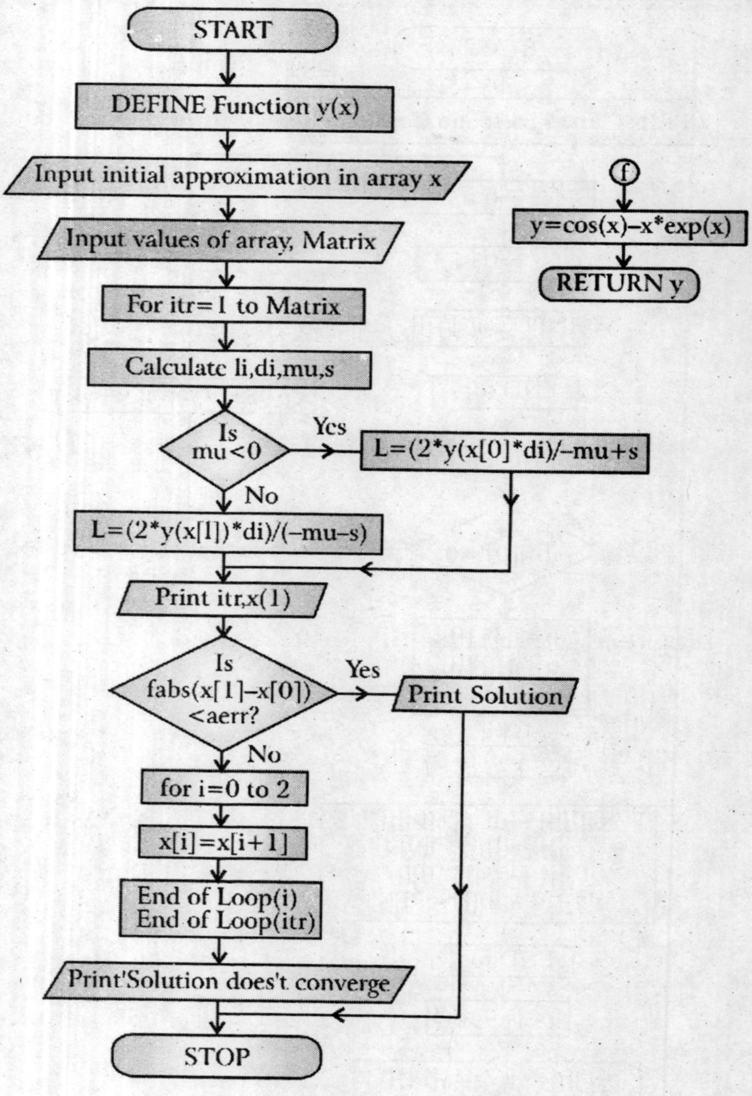

6. (b) /*TO FIND THE SOLUTION USING GAUSS ELIMINATION METHOD*/

Used formula: /*We take 3 algebraic equations in the format

i.e.
$$a_1 x + b_1 y + c_1 z + d_1 = 0$$
$$a_2 x + b_2 y + c_2 z + d_2 = 0$$
$$a_3 x + b_3 y + c_3 z + d_3 = 0$$

and store their coefficient and constants in a two dimensional matrix [illegible][4]*/

```
#include<stdio.h>
#include<conio.h>
#include<math.h>
```

```
void main ( )
{
        clrscr ( );
        int i,j;
        float a [3][4], b[3][4], c[4][4];
        float x,y,z,p,q,r;
        1:
        printf ("\ nENTER THE COEFFICIENTS\N");
        for (i = 0;i<3;i + +)
        for (j = 0;j<3;j + +)
        scanf ("%f",&a[i] [J] );
        printf ("ENTER THE CONSTANTS\N");
        for (i= 0; i< 3; i+ + )
        scanf("% f", &a[i] [3] );
        printf ("\ nTHE SYSTEM IS ");
        for (i = 0; i<3; i + +)
    printf("\ n%f*x + %f*y + %f*z = %f",a[i][0], a[i][1], a[i][2], a[i][3];
    if (a[0][0] ! =0.0)
        {
            p = a[1][0];
            q = a[0][0];
            r = a[2][0];
            for (j = 0:j< =3;j + +  )
            {
                b[0][j] =- (p/q)*a[0][j];
                a[1][j] = a[1][j] + b[0][j];
                c[0][j] = -(r/q)*a[0][j];
                a[2][j] = a[2][j] + c[0][j];
            }
          p = a[2] [1];
          q = a[1][1];
          for (j = 0; j< = 3; j + + )
            {
                b[1][j] =- (p/q)*a[1][j];
                a[2][j] = a[2][j] + b[1][j];
            }
      printf ("\n\nTHE MATRIX BECOMES\N");
      for (i = 0; i<3; i + +)
            {
                for (j=0; j<4; j + +)
```

```
            printf ("%f\t",a[i][j]);
            printf ("\n");
        }
    z = a[2][3]/a[2][2];
    y = (a[1][3] – a[1][2] *z)/a[1][1];
    x = (a[0][3] – a[0][2] *z – a[0][1]*y)/a[0][0];
    printf (" \ n THE SOLUTION IS");
    printf ("\ nx = %f, y = %f, z = %f", x,y,z);
  }
  else
  printf("\ nTHE FIRST COFFICIENT MUST NOT BE EQUAL TO ZERO. ENTER
  AGAIN");
        goto 1;
    }
    getch ( );
}
1
1
3
2
3
1
4
9
ENTER THE CONSTANTS
10
18
16

THE SYSTEM IS
2.000000 * x + 1.000000 * y + 1.000000 * z = 10.000000
3.000000 * x + 2.000000 * y + 3.000000 * z = 18.000000
1.000000 * x + 4.000000 * y + 9.000000 * z = 16.000000

THE MATRIX BECOMES
    2.000000        1.000000        1.000000        10.000000
    0.000000        0.500000        1.500000         3.000000
    0.000000        0.000000       –2000000        –10.00000

THE SOLUTION IS
X = 7.000000, Y = – 9.000000, Z = 5.000000
```

7. (a) FLOW CHART FOR GAUSS JORDAN METHOD

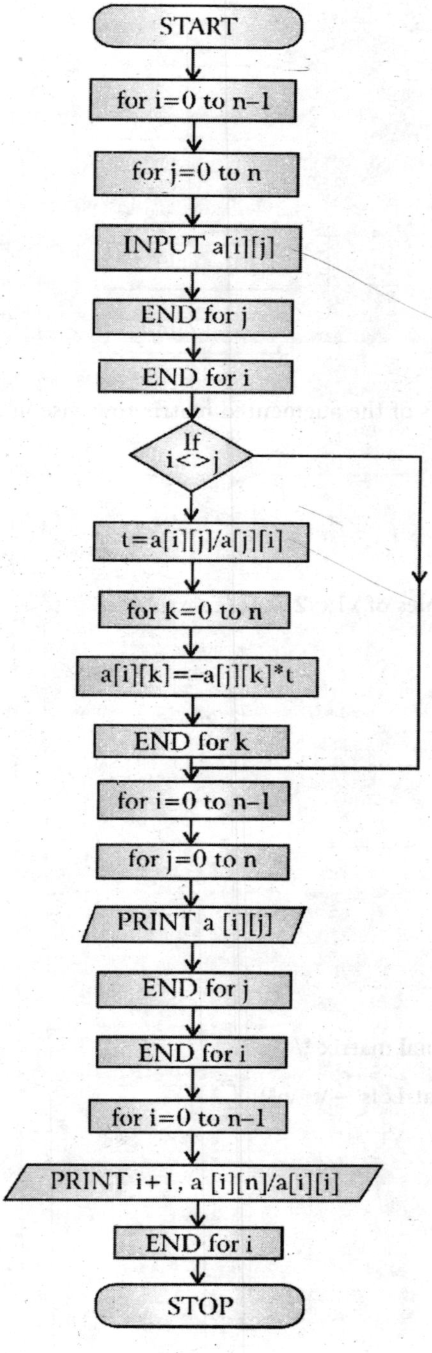

7. (b) /*GAUSS JORDAN METHOD*/

```
#include<stdio.h>
#include<conio.h>
#include<math.h>
#define n   4
void main ( )
{
float a[n] [n+l], t;
int i,j,k;
clrscr();
printf("enter the elements of the augmented matrix row wise \n");
for(i = 0;i<n;i+ +)
for(j = 0;j<n + l;j + +)
scanf("%f",&a[i][j]);
/*now calculating the values of x1, x2,...........xn */
for (j = 0;     j<n;j + +)
for(i = 0;1<n;i + +)
if(i! = j)
{
t=(a[i][j])/(a[j][j]);
for(k = 0;k<n + 1;k + +)
a[i][k] -= a[j][k]*t;
}
/*now printing the diagonal matrix */
printf("\t the diagonal matrix is :- \t \n");
for(i = 0;i<n;i++)
{
for(j = 0;j<n+1;j ++)
printf ("%f",a[i][j]);
printf ("\n");
}
```

```
/*now printing the results */
printf("\t the solution is :-  \t\n");
for(i = 0;i<n;i + +)
printf("x[%d] = %f\n",i + 1,a[i][n]/a[i][i];
}
getche ( );
```

Enter the elements of the augmented matrix row wise

10	–7	3	5	6
–6	8	–1	–4	–5
3	1	4	1	2
5	–9	–2	4	7

The digonal matrix is :-

10.000001 – 0.000000 – 0.000000 – 0.0000006.121344

0.0000003.800000 – 0.0000000.000000 – 0.403467

–0.0000000.0000002.4473680.000000 – 2.044335

0.000000 – 0.000000 – 0.0000009.9247313.258065

Hence the solution is:-

$x[1] = 0.612134$

$x[2] = -0.106175$

$x[3] = -0.835320$

$x[4] = 0.328277$

Enter the elements of the augmented matrix row wise.

8. (a) FLOW CHART FOR GAUSS SIEDAL METHOD

(Iterative Method)

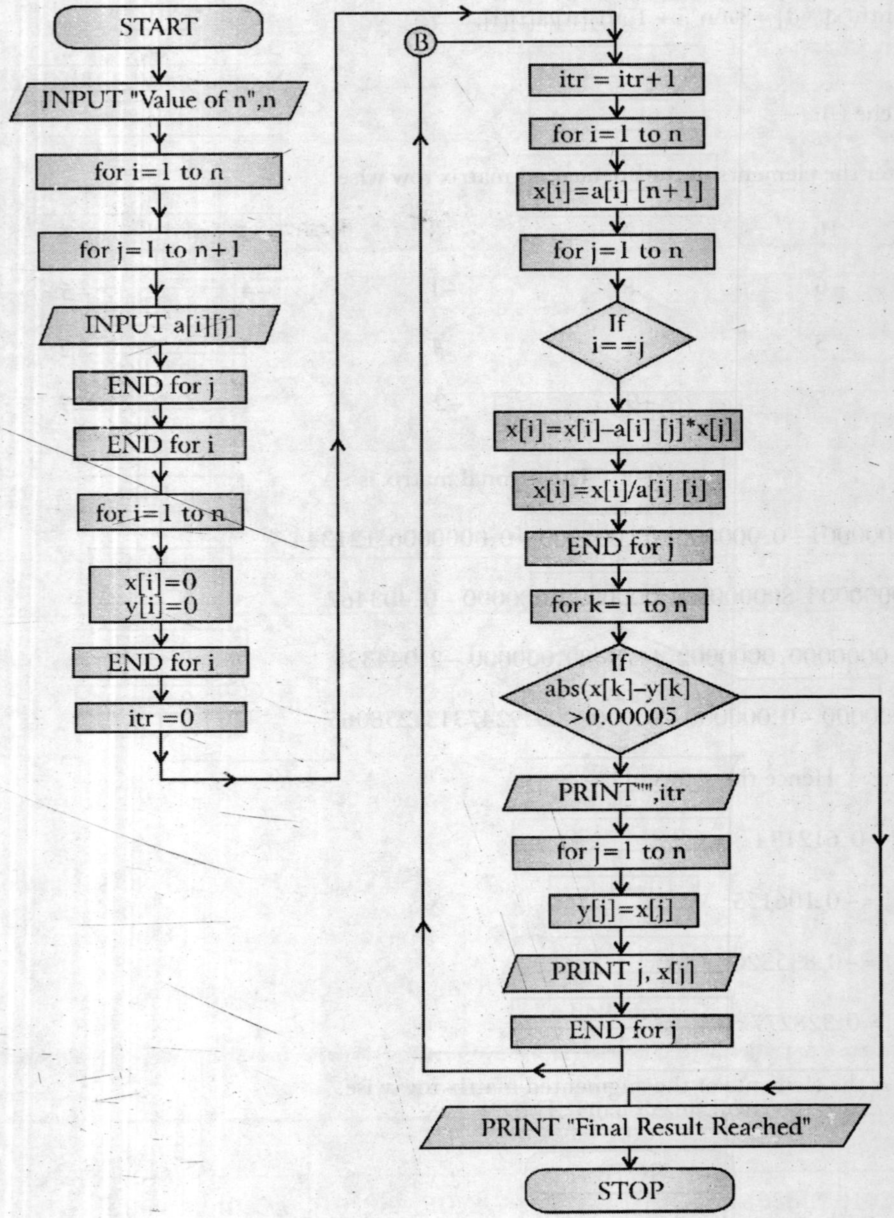

8. (b) /*GAUSS SIEDAL ITERATIVE METHOD */

```
#include<stdio.h>
#include<conio.h>
#include<math.h>
void main ( )
{
float x[10],y[10],a[10][10];
int i,j,n,k iteration;
printf("\ nENTER THE VALUE FOR n......\n");
scanf("%d",&n);
printf("\ENTER THE COEFFICIENTS AND RHS \n");
{
for   (i = l;  i<=n;   i++)
for   (j=1;  j<=n+l;  j++)
scanf("%f", &a[i][j];
printf("\n");
}
for(i = l;   i < = n;   i+ +)
{
x[i] =0.0;
y[i] =0.0;
}
iteration =0;
step1:iteration   + +;
for   (i = l;   i < = n;   i+ +)
{
x[i] = a[i] [n + 1];
for(j = l;   j< = n;   j+ +)
{
if     (i = = j)
continue;
x[i] = x[i] - a[i][j] *x[j];
}
x[i] = x[i]/a[i] [i];
```

```
}
for(k = l;  k< = n;  k + +)
{
if(fabs (x[k] - y[k])> 0 .00005)
{
printf ("\ITERATION = %d\n\n",  iteration);
for    (i= l;   i< = n;    i + +)
{
y[i] = x[i];
printf ("\x[%d] = %f",i,x[i]);
}
goto step l;
}
}
printf("\ n FINAL RESULT REACHED");
}
```

ENTER THE VALUE FOR N . . . . . .

3

ENTER THE COEFFICIENTS AND RHS

83	11	−4	95
7	52	13	104
3	8	29	71

ITERATION = l

x [l] = 1.144578 x [2] = 1.845922 x [3] = 1.820651 ITERATION = 2

x [l] = 0.987680 x [2] = 1.411880 x [3] = 1.956618 ITERATION = 3

x [l] = 1.051756 x [2] = 1.369263 x [3] = 1.961746 ITERATION = 4

x [l] = 1.057652 x [2] = 1.367187 x [3] = 1.961708 ITERATION = 5

x [l] = 1.057925 x [2] = 1.367160 x [3] = 1.961688

9. (a) FLOW CHART FOR PREDICTOR-CORRECTOR METHOD

The function is $f(y) = 1 + y^2$

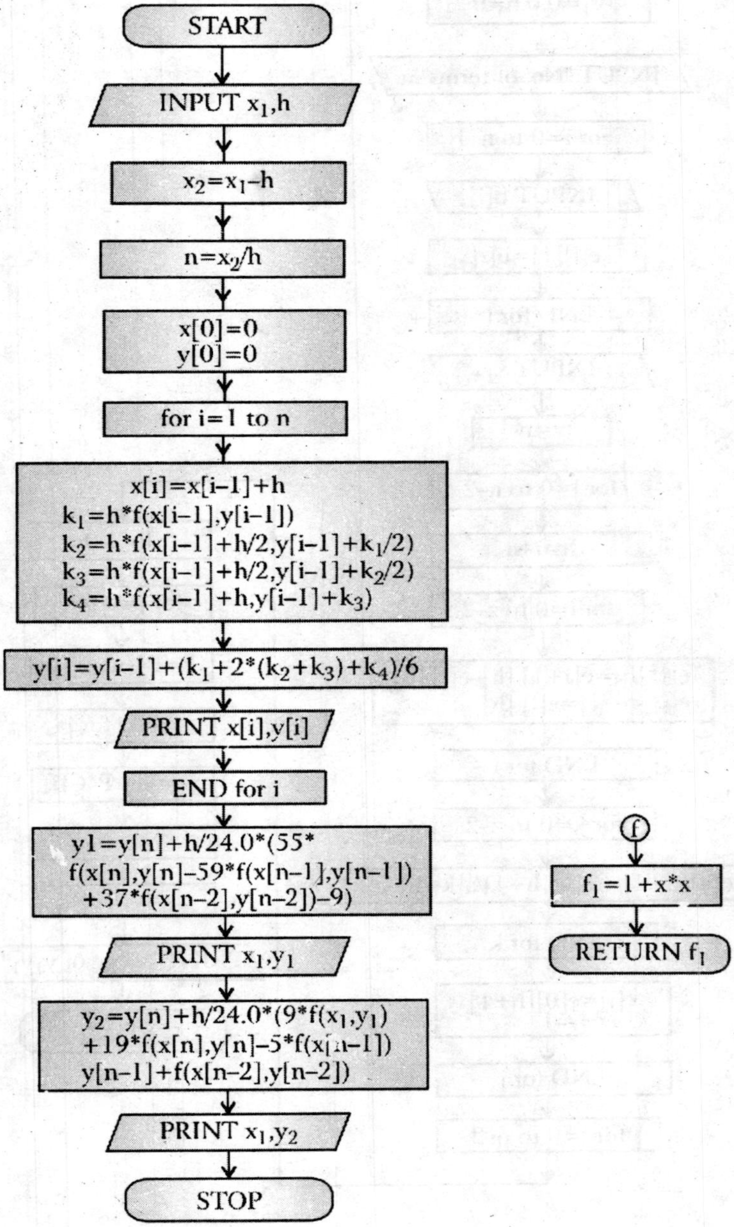

9. (a') FLOW CHART FOR NEWTON DIVIDED INTERPOLATION FORMULA

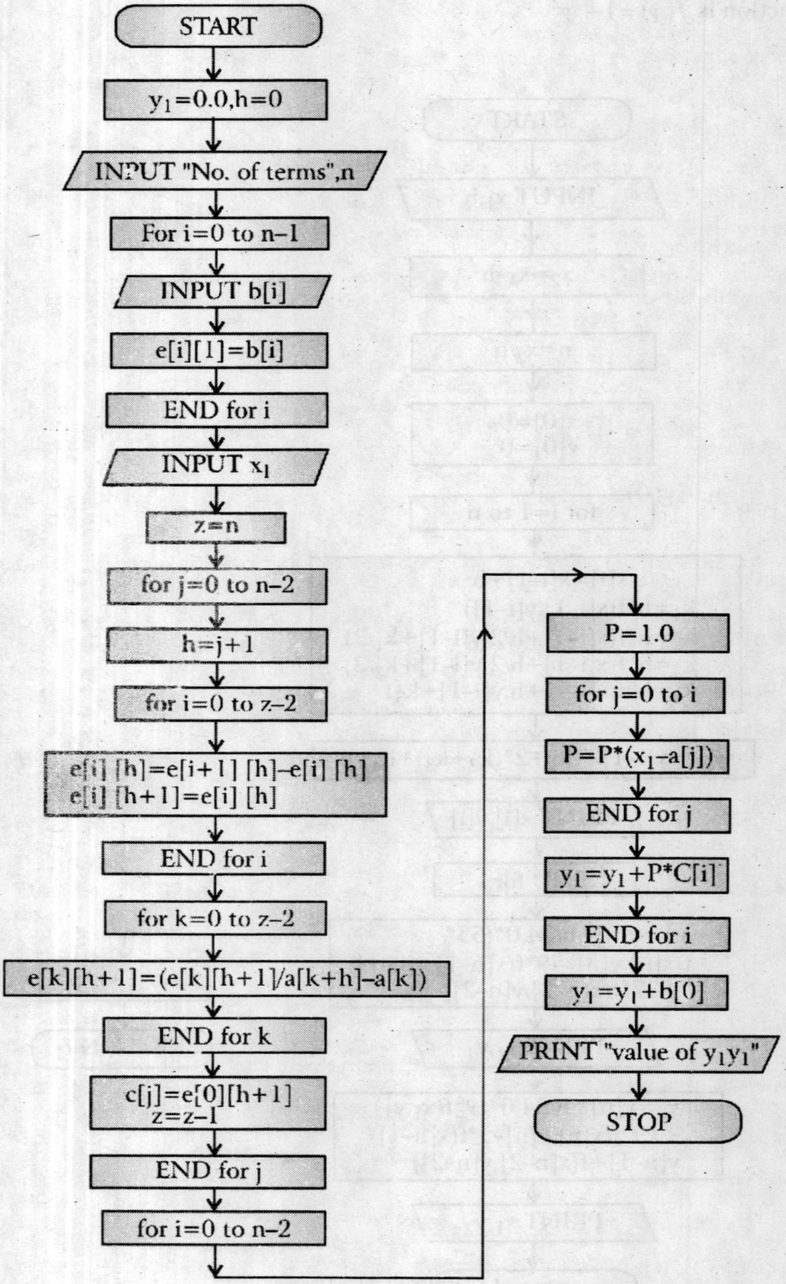

9. (b) /*PREDICTOR-CORRECTOR METHOD*/

Used formula: $y_1^p = y_0 + \frac{h}{24}[55 f_0 - 59 f_{-1} + 37 f_{-2} - 9 f_{-3}]$

$$y_1^c = y_0 + \frac{h}{24}[9 f_1^p + 19 f_0 - 5 f_{-1} + f_{-2}]$$

```
#include<stdio.h>
#include<math.h>
#include<conio.h>
float f(float, float);
void main ( )
{
    float x1, h, x[10],y[10], k1, k2, k3, k4, x2, y1, y2;
    int i,n, j;
    clrscr ( );
    printf("\ nTHE FUNCTION IS 1+Y^2");
    printf ("AND THE CONDITION IS Y (0) = 0");j
    printf("\ nENTER THE VALUE OF X FOR COMPUTING ");
    scanf("%f",&x1);
    x2 = x1- h;
    n = x2/h;
    x[0] = 0.0 ;
    y[0] = 0.0;
    printf ("\ n THE TABULATED VALUES");
    for(i = 1; i< = n; i + +)
    {
        x[i] = x[i- 1] + h;
        k1 = h*f(x[i - 1],y[i - 1];
        k2 = h*f(x[i - 1] + h/2,y[i - 1] + k1/2);
        k3 = h*f(x[i - 1] + h/2,y[i - 1] + k2/2);
        k4 = h*f(x[i - 1] + h,y[i - 1] + k3);
        y[i] = y[i - 1] + (k1 + 2*(k2 + k3) + k4/6;
```

```
        printf("\ nY[%f] = %f",x[i],y[i]);
    }
y1 =y[n] + h/24.0*(55*f(x[n],y[n]) – 59*f(x[n – 1],y[n –1]) + 37*f(x[n – 2] –
y[n – 2] – 9;
printf("\ n\ nTHE PREDICTED VALUE OFYAT X=%f IS %f" x1, y1);
y2 =y[n] + (h/24).0*(9*f(x1,y1) + 19*f(x[n],y[n]  – 5*f(x[n – 1],
y[n – 1] + f(x[n – 2],y[n – 2]));
printf("\ n\ nTHE CORRECTED VALUE OF Y AT X = %f IS %f", x1,y2);
getch( );  }
float f(float a, float b)
{
float f1;
f1     = 1 + b*b;
return  (f1);
}
```

THE FUNCTION IS 1 = Y ^2 AND THE CONDITION IS $y(0) = 0$

ENTER THE VALUE OF X FOR COMPUTING 0.8

ENTER THE VALUE OF H 0.2

THE TABULATED VALUES

Y [0.200000] = 0.202707

Y [0.400000] = 0.422789

Y [0.600000] = 0.684133

THE PREDICTED VALUE OF Y AT X = 0.800000 is 1.023435

THE CORRECTED VALUE OF Y AT X = 0.800000 is 1.029690

10. (a) FLOW CHART FOR NUMERICAL DIFFERENTIATION

(Backward Method)

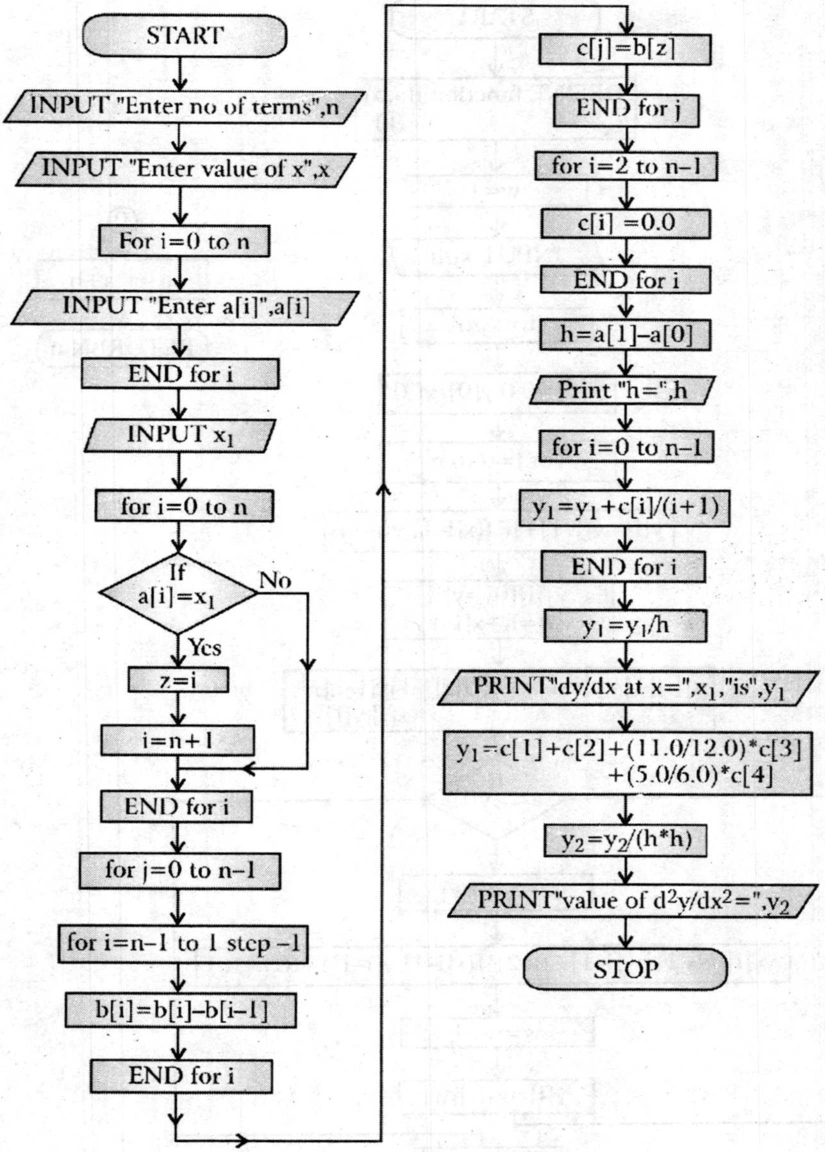

10. (a′) FLOW CHART FOR EULER'S MODIFIED METHOD

Aliter: (Refer Page 839)

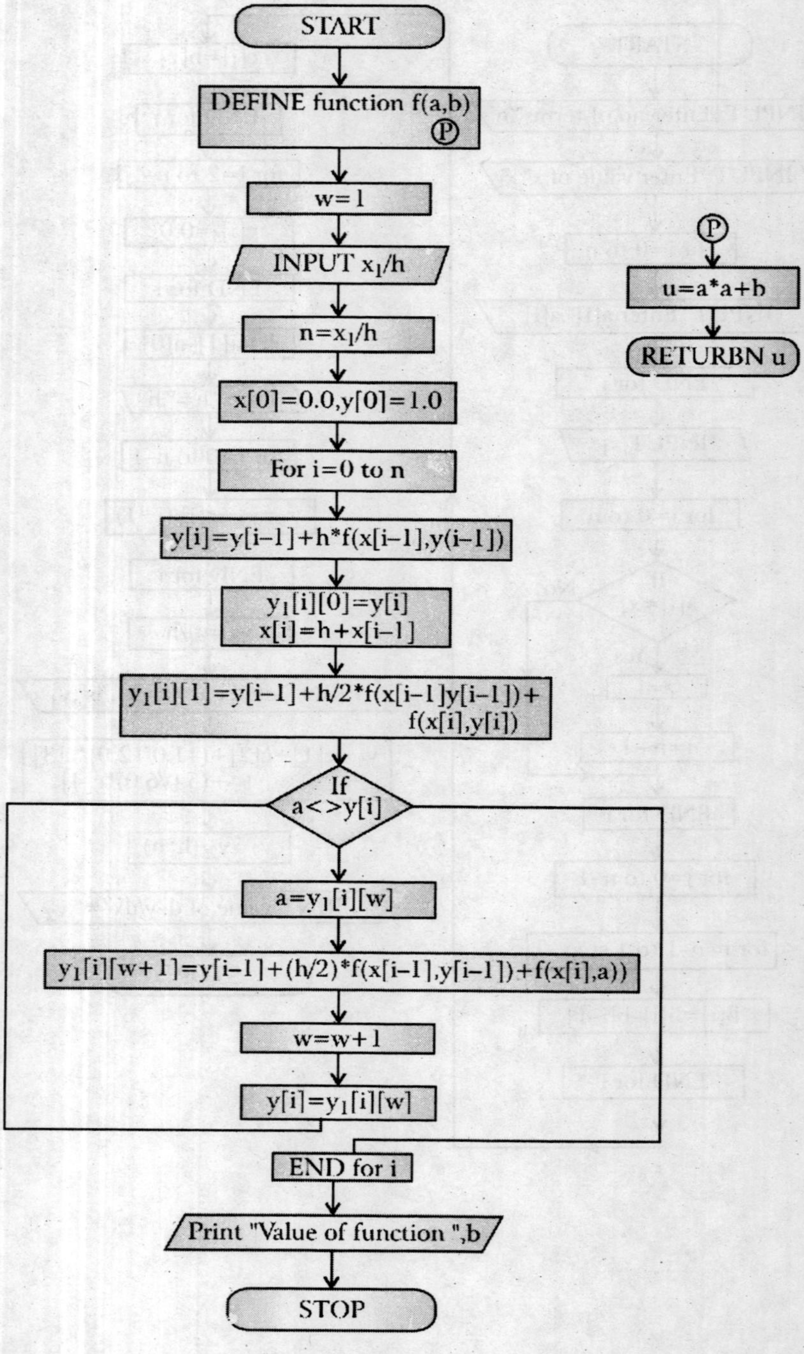

10. (b) /*NUMERICAL DIFFERENTIATION (backward) METHOD*/

Used formula: $[(d^2 y / dx^2)] = (1/h^2)[\nabla^2 y_n + \nabla^3 y_n + \frac{11}{12} \nabla^n y_4 + \frac{5}{6} \nabla^5 y_n]$

```
#include<stdio.h>
#include<conio.h>
#include<math.h>
void main ( )
{
    float a[20].b[20],c[20],e[20][20],x1,h,y1 =0.0,y2 =0.0;
    int i,n,j,z,k,w;
    clrscr ( )
    printf("\ nENTER THE NUMBER OF TERMS");
    scanf("%d",& n);
    printf("ENTER THE VALUES OF X\n");
    for(i = 0;i< n;i + +)
      {
         prinf("X[%d] = ",i+1);
         scanf("%f",& b[i]);
      }
     printf("\ nENTER THE VALUE OF X FOR COMPUTING
          (backward)");
     scanf("%f",&x1);
     for(i = 0;i< n;i + +)
   {
     if (a[i] =x1)
       {
          z = i;
          break;
       }
   }
   for(j= 0;j< n– 1;j+ +)
   {
     for(i = n– 1;i> 0;i--)
       {
```

```
        b[i] = b[i] – b[i – 1];
     }
     c[j] = b[z];
   }
   for (i = z;i< n – 1;i+ +)
   c[i] =0 .0;
   h = a[1] – a[0];
   printf("h = %f",h);
   for(i = 0;i< n – 1;i + +)
   y1+ = c[i]/(i + 1);
   y1 = y1/h;
   printf("\ n\ nTHE VALUE OF dY/dX at X = %f IS: %f ",x1,y1);
   y2 = c[1] + c[2] + (11.0 /12.0) *c[3] + (5 .0 /6 .0)*c[4];
   y2 = y2/(h*h);
   printf("\ n\ nTHE VALUE OF d ^ 2Y/dX ^ 2AT  X = %f IS :%f",x1,y2);
   getch ( );
ENTER THE NUMBER OF TERMS     7
ENTER THE VALUES OF   X
X[1] = 1
X[2]1.2
X[3] =1.4
X[4] =1.6
X[5] =1.8
X[6] =2
X[7] =2 .2
ENTER THE VALUE OF Y
Y[1] =2 .7183
Y[2] =3 .3201
Y[3] =4 .0552
Y[4] =4 .9530
Y[5] =6 .0496
Y[6] =7 .3891
Y[7] =9 .0250
ENTER THE VALUE OF X FOR COMPUTING (backward) 2 .2   h =0 .200000
THE VALUE OF dY/dX at X =2 .200000 IS : 9 .022895
THE VALUE OF d ^ 2Y/dX ^ 2 AT   X =2 .200000 IS : 8 .992064
```

10. (c) FLOW CHART FOR NUMERICAL DIFFERENTIATION (forward) METHOD

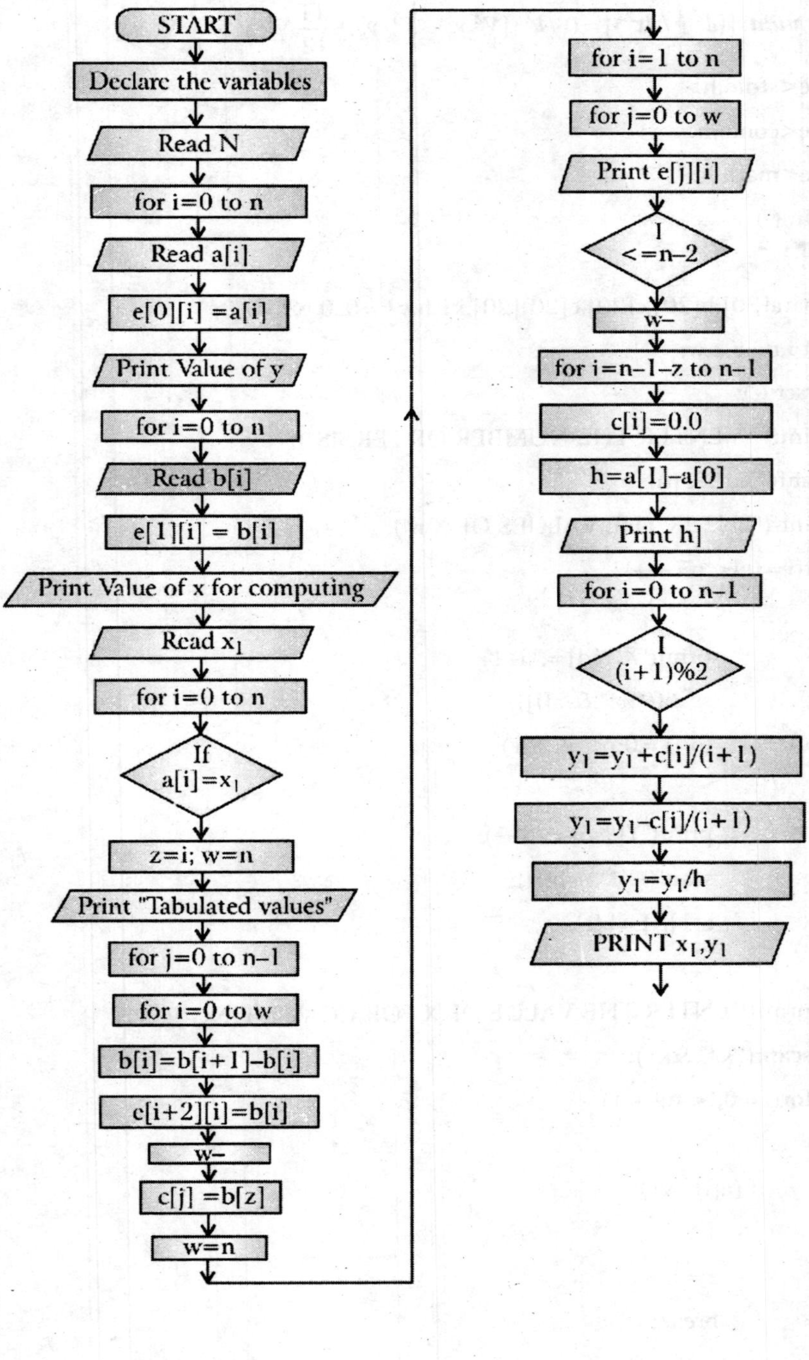

10. (d) /*NUMERICAL DIFFERENTIATION (forward) METHOD*/

Used formula: $[(d^2 y / dx^2)] = (1/h^2)[\nabla^2 y_n - \nabla^3 y_n + \frac{11}{12}\nabla^n y_n - \frac{5}{6}\nabla^5 y_n]$

```
#include<stdio.h>
#include<conio.h>
#include<math.h>
void main ( )
{
    floata[20],b[20],c[20],e[20][20],x1,h,y1 =0.0,y2 =0.0;
    int i,n,j,z,k,w;
    clrscr ( );
    printf("\ nENTER THE NUMBER OF TERMS");
    scanf("%d",& n);
    printf("ENTER THE VALUES OF X\n");
    for(i = 0;i< n;i + +)
    {
            prinf("X[%d] = ",i+1);
            scanf("%f",& a[i]);
            for(i = 0;i< n;i + +)
      {
            prinf("Y[%d] = ",i+1);
            scanf("%f",& b[i]);
            e[1][i] = b[i];
      }
     printf("ENTER THE VALUE OF X FOR COMPUTING");
     scanf("%f",&x1);
     for(i = 0;i< n;i + +)
    {
         if (a[i] =x1)
            {
            z = i;
            break;
         }
     }
```

```
  w = n;
  printf("TABULATED VALUES ARE:");
  printf ("\ nX      Y");
  printf ("\ n");
            for(j = 0;j<n - 1;j + +)
            {
            for(i = 0;i< w;i + +)
            {
                    b[i] = b[i + 1] - b[i]; e[j + 2][i] = b[i];
             }
             w - - ; c[j] = b[z];
            }
           w = n;    for(i = 0;i<n;i + +)
        {
                 for(j= 0;j< = w; j+ +)
                 printf("%f",e[j][i]); if(i< = n - 2)
                 w - - ;    printf("\n");
        }
     for(i = n - 1 - z;i< n - 1;i + + )
     c[i] =0.0;         h = a[1] - a[0];
     printf("h = %f",h);
     for(i = 0;i<n - 1;i + +)
   if(i + l)% 2)
 yl + = c[i]/(i + l);
   else
 yl- = c[i]/(i + l);
   }
  yl = yl/h;
 printf("THE VALUES OF dY/dX AT X = % f IS : %f",xl,yl);
  y2 = c[1] - c[2] + (11.0 /12.0)*c[3] - (5.0 /6.0)*c[4];
y2 = y2/(h*h);
printf("\ nTHE VALUE OF d ^ 2Y/dX ^ 2  AT  X = %f IS :  %f",xl,y2);
getch ( );
}
```

```
ENTER THE VALUES OF  X
X[1] =1.0
X[2] =1.2
X[3] =1.4
X[4] =1.6
X[5] =1.8
X[6] =2
X[7] =2.2
ENTER THE VALUE OF Y
Y[1] =2.7183
Y[2] =3.3201
Y[3] =4.05521
Y[4] =4.9530
Y[5] =6.0496
Y[6] =7.3891
Y[7] =9.0250
ENTER THE VALUE OF X FOR COMPUTING 1.2
TABULATED VALUES ARE :
X                    Y
1.0000002.7183000.6018000.1333100.0293700.0067600.0011990.000251
1.2000003.3201000.7351100.1626800.0361300.0079600.001450
1.4000004.0552100.8977900.1988100.0440900.009410
1.6000004.9530001.096600.2429000.053500
1.8000006.0496001.3395000.296400
2.0000007.3891001.635900
2.2000009.025000
h =0.200000 THE VALUE OF dY/dX AT  X =1.200000 IS : 3.320567
THE VALUE OF d ^2Y/dX ^2 AT  X =1.200000  IS : 3.315934
```

11. (a) FLOW CHART FOR NEWTON DIVIDED INTERPOLATION FORMULAE (general)

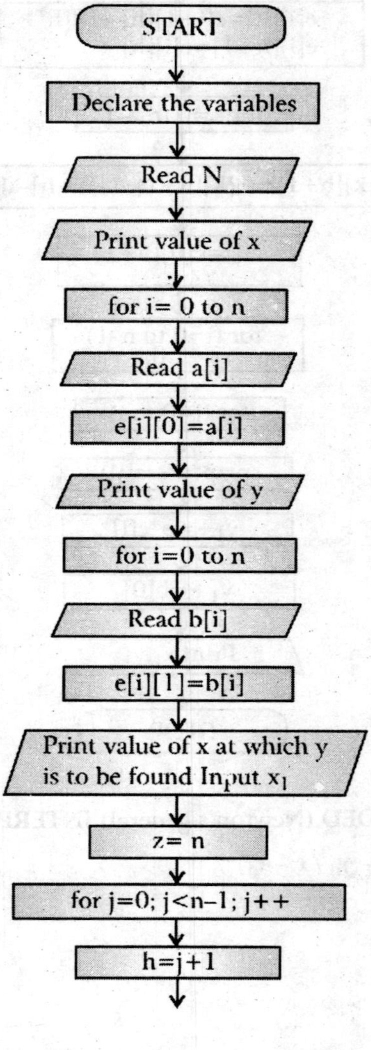

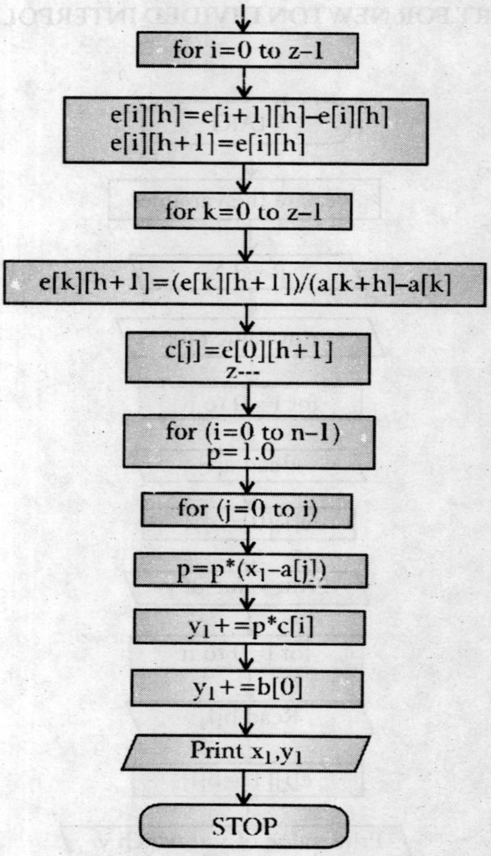

11. (b) /*NEWTON-DIVIDED (Newton's general) INTERPOLATION FORMULAE*/

Used formula $[x, x_0] = (y - y_0 / x - x_0)$

```
#include<stdio.h>
#include<conio.h>
void main ( )
{
	float a[20],b[20],c[20],x1,y1 =0.0, p;
	floate[20][20];
	int i,n,j,z,h = 0,k;
	clrscr();
	printf("\ nENTER THE NUMBER OF TERMS ");
	scanf("%d",&n);
	printf("\ nENTER THE VALUES OF X\N");
	for(i = 0;i< n;i + +)
```

```
{
 printf("X[%d] = ",i + 1);
 scanf("%f",&a[i]);
 e[i][0] = a[i];
 }
 printf("\ nENTER THE VALUES OF Y\n");
 for(i = 0;i< n;i + +)
 {
 printf("Y[%d] = ",i + 1);
 scanf("%f",&b[i]);
 e[i][1] = b[i];
 }
printf("\ nENTER THE VALUES OF X AT WHICH Y IS TO BE FOUND");
 scanf("%f",&x1);
 z = n;
 for(j = 0;j< n - l;j + +)
 {
  h = j + l;
  for(i = 0;i< z - 1;i + +)
     {
     e[i][h] = e[i + 1][h] - e[i][h];
     e[i][h + 1] = e[i][h];
     }
     for(k = 0;k< z - 1;k + +)
     e[k][h + 1] = (e[k][h + 1])/(a[k + h] - a[k]);
     c[j] = e[0][h + 1];
     z - -;
  }
  for(i = 0;i< n - 1;i + +)
     {
```

```
            p = 1.0;
            for(j = 0;j< = i;j + +)
                {
                p = p*(x1 - a[j]);
        }
    y1 + = p*c[i]; }
    y1 + = b[0];
  printf("\n\nTHE VLAUE OF Y AT  X = % f IS :%f",x1,y1);
  getch();
}
```

```
ENTER THE NUMBER OF TERMS    5
ENTER THE VALUES OF       X
X[1] = -1
X[2] = 0
X[3]  = 3
X[4]  = 6
X[5] = 7
ENTER THE VALUES OF Y
Y[1] = 3
Y[2] = -6
Y[3] = 39
Y[4] = 822
Y[5] = 1611
ENTER THE VALUE OF X AT WHICH Y IS TO BE FOUND   1
THE VALUE OF Y AT Z = 1.000000  IS : -3.000000
```

12. (a) FLOW CHART FOR LAGRANGE'S INTERPOLATION FORMULA

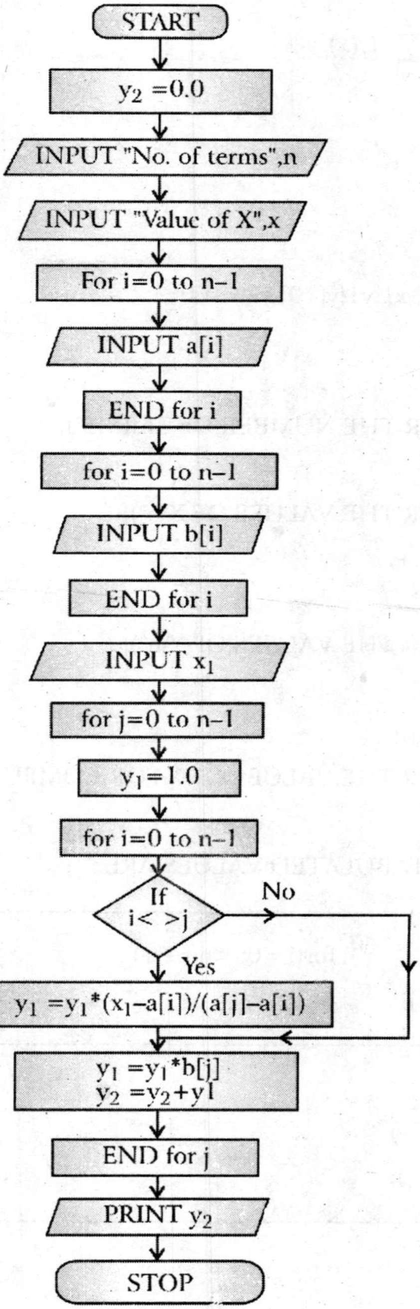

12. (b) /*LAGRANGE'S INTERPOLATION FORMULA*/

Used formula: $L_n(x) = \sum_{i=0}^{n} l_i(x)\, y_1$

```
#include<stdio.h>
#include<conio.h>
void main ( )
{
    float a[10],b[10],x1,y1,y[10],y2 =0.0;
    intn,i,j;
    clrscr();
    printf("\ nENTER THE NUMBER OF TERMS');
    scanf("% d",&n);
    printf("\ nENTER THE VALUES OF X\n");
    for(i = 0;i< n;i + +)
    scanf("% f",&a[i]);
    printf("\ nENTER THE VALUES OF Y\n");
    for(i = 0;i< n;i + +)
    scanf("% f",&b[i]);
    printf("\ nENTER THE VALUES OF X FOR COMPUTING");
    scanf("% f",&x1);
    printf("\ nTHE TABULATED VALUES ARE :");
    printf("\ n------------------------------------------------------------------------------");
    printf("\ nX          :"); for(i = 0;i<n;i + +)
    printf("\t% f",a[i]);
    printf("\ n------------------------------------------------------------------------------");
    printf("\ nY:");
    for(i = 0;i< n;i ++)
    printf("\t% f",b[i]);
    printf("\ n------------------------------------------------------------------------------");
    for(j = 0;j< n;j + +)
    {
    Y1 =1.0; for(i = 0;i<n;i + +)
      {
```

```
            if(j! = i)
            Y1* = (x1 - a[i])/(a[j] - a[i]);
        }
      Y1* = b[j];
      Y2 + = Y1;
    }
    printf("\ n\ nTHE VALUE OF Y AT  X = %f IS : %f",x1,y2);
    getch();
}
```

```
ENTER THE NUMBER OF TERMS    3
ENTER THE VALUES OF X
2
2.5
3
ENTER THE VALUES OF Y
.69315
.91629
1.09861
ENTER THE VALUE OF X FOR COMPUTING 2.7
X :            2.000000      2.500000      3.000000
Y :            0.693150      0.916290      1.098610
THE VALUE OF Y AT  X = 2.700000 IS : 0.994116
```

13. (a) FLOW CHART FOR EULER'S METHOD

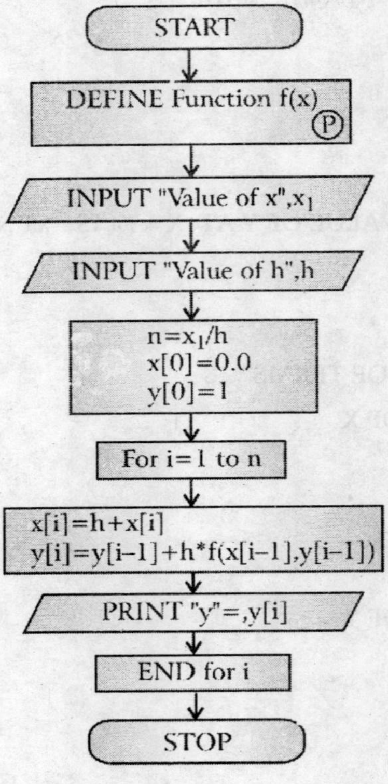

13. (b) /*EULER'S METHOD*/

Used formula $y_{n+1} = y_n + h f(x_n, y_n), n = 0, 1, 2 ---$

```
#include<stdio.h>
#include<math.h>
#include<conio.h>
float f(float,float);
void main ()
{
      float x[10],y[10],h,x1;
      int  i,n;
      clrscr();
      printf("\ nTHE FUNCTION IS – Y");
      printf("\ nAND THE CONDITION IS Y(0) = 1");
```

```
printf("\ nENTER THE VALUES OF X  ");
scanf("% f",&x1);
printf("\ENTER THE VALUE OF H ");
scanf("% f",&h);
printf("\ nTHE TABULATED VALUES OF X AND Y ARE ");
n = x1/h;
x[0] = 0.0;
y[0] = 1;
for (i = 1;i< = n;i + +)
{
    x[i] = h + x[i];
    y[i] = y[i - 1] + h*f(x[i - 1], y[i - 1]);
    printf("\ nY(%f) = %f",x[i],y[i]);
}
printf("\ n\ nTHE VALUE AT X = %f IS %f", x1,y[n]);
getch();
}
float f(float a, float b)
{
        float f1;
        f1 = - b;
        return(f1);
}
```

```
THE FUNCTION IS - Y AND THE CONDITION IS Y(0) = 1
ENTER THE VALUE OF  X 0.04
ENTER THE VALUE OF  H .01
THE TABULATED VALUES OF X AND Y ARE
Y(- NAN) =0.990000
Y(0.010000) = 0.980100
Y(0.010000) = 0.970299
Y(0.010000) = 0.960596
THE VALUE AT X= 0.040000 IS 0.960596
```

14. (a) FLOW CHART FOR EULER'S MODIFIED METHOD

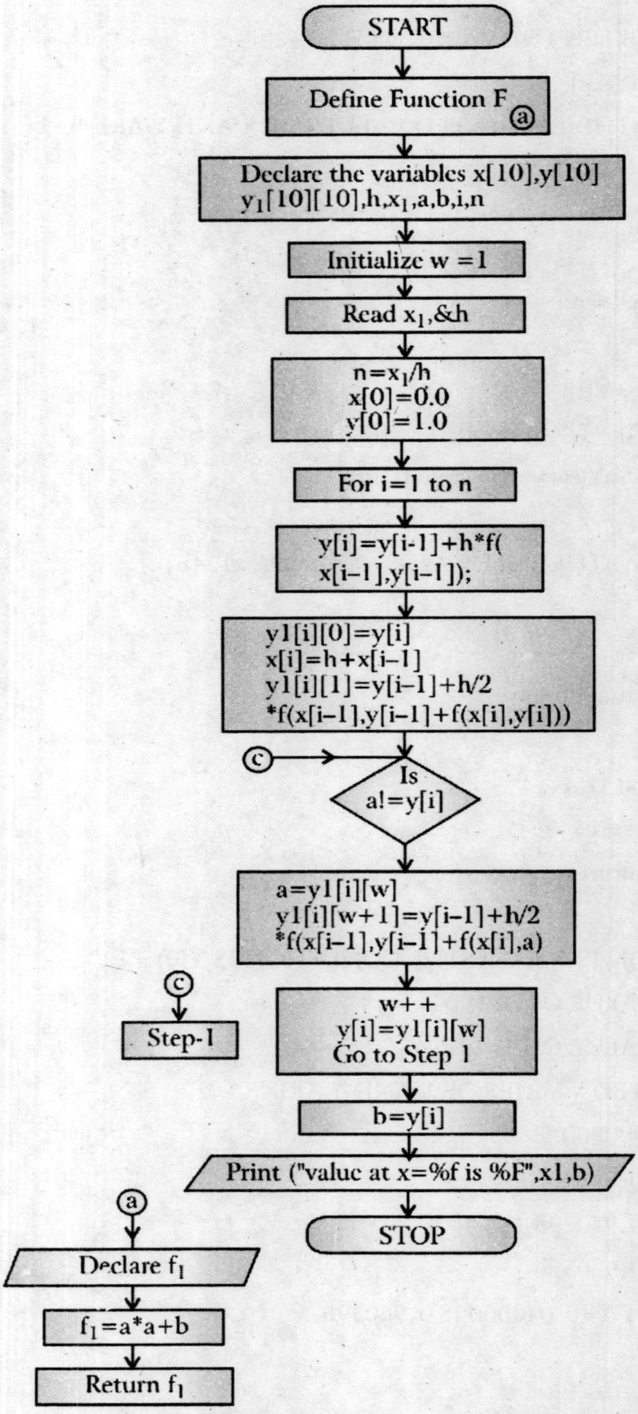

14. (b) /*EULER'S MODIFIED METHOD*/

Used formula $y_1 = y_0 + (h/2)\,[f(x_0, y_0) + f(x_1, y_1)]$

```
#include<stdio.h>
#include<conio.h>
#include<math.h>
float f(float,float);
void main ( )
{
    float x[10],y[10],y1[10][10],h,x1,a,b;
    int  i,n,w =1;
    clrscr();
    printf("\ n THE FUNCTION IS X ^ 2 + Y");
    printf("\ AND THE CONDITION IS Y(0) = 1");
    printf("\ nENTER THE VALUES OF X FOR COMPUTING ");
    scanf("% f",&x1);
    printf("\ENTER THE VALUES OF H ");
    scanf("% f",&h);
    n = x1/h;
    x[0] =0.0 ;
    y[0] = 1.0;
      for (i = 1;i< = n;i + +)
    {
      y[i] = y[i – 1] + h*f(x[i – 1], y[i – 1]);
      y1[i][0] = y[i];
      x[i] = h + x[i – 1];
      y1[i][1] = y[i – 1] + (h/2)*f(x[i – 1], y[i – 1]) + f(x[i],y[i]));
      1:
      if(a! = y[i])
      {
      a = y1[i][w];
```

```
    y[i][w + 1] = y[i – 1] + (h/2)*f(x[i – 1], y[i – 1]) + f(x[i],a))
    w + + ;
    y[i] = y1[i][w];
    goto 1;
   }
   b = y[i];
  }
  printf("\ n\ nTHE VALUE AT  X = % f IS % f ",x1,b);
  getch();
}
  float f(float a, float b)
   {
      float f1;
  f1 = a*a + b;
      return(f1);
}
```

THE FUNCTION IS X ^ 2 + Y AND THE CONDITION IS Y(0) = 1

ENTER THE VALUE OF X FOR COMPUTING .1

ENTER THE VALUE OF H .05

THE VALUE AT X = 0.100000 IS1.105582

15. (a) FLOW CHART FOR RUNGA KUTTA (SECOND ORDER) METHOD FOR EQUATION $f_1 = x - y$

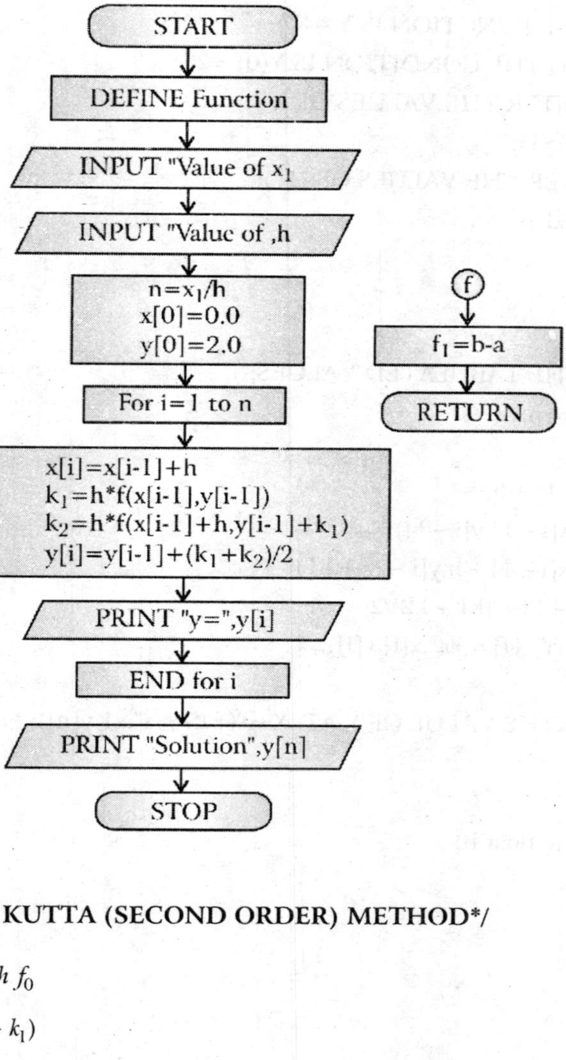

15. (b) /*RUNGA KUTTA (SECOND ORDER) METHOD*/

Used formula: $k_1 = h\, f_0$

$k_2 = h\, f(x_0 + h, y_0 + k_1)$

$y_1 = y_0 + \frac{1}{2}(k_1 + k_2)$

```
#include<stdio.h>
#include<math.h>
#include<conio.h>
float f(float, float);
void main ( )
{
```

```
float x1,h,x[10],y[10],k1,k2;
int  i,n;
clrscr();
printf("\ nTHE FUNCTION IS Y – X");
printf("\ AND THE CONDITION IS Y(0) = 2");
printf("\ nENTER THE VALUES OF X");
scanf("% f",&x1);
printf("\ENTER THE VALUES OF H ");
scanf("% f",&h);
n = x1/h;
n[0] = 0.0;
y[0] = 2;
printf("\ n THE TABULATED VALUES:");
for (i = 1;i< = n;i + +)
{
   x[i] = x[i–1] + h;
   k1 = h*f(x[i – 1],y[i – 1]);
   k2 = h*f(x[i – 1] + h,y[i – 1] + k1);
   y[i] = y[i – 1] + (k1 + k2)/2;
   printf("\ nY[%f] = %f",x[i],y[i]);
}
printf("\ n\ nTHE VALUE OF Y AT  X = %f IS % f",x1,y[n]);
getch();
}
float f(float a, float b)
{
   float f1;
   f1 = b – a;
   return(f1);
}
```

THE FUNCTION IS *Y* – *X* AND THE CONDITION IS Y (0) = 2

ENTER THE VALUES OF X 0.2

ENTER THE VALUE OF H 0.1

THE TABULATED VALUES

Y[0.100000] = 2.205171

Y[0.200000] = 2.421403

N THE VALUE OF Y AT X = 0.200000 IS 2.421025

16. (a) FLOW CHART FOR RUNGA KUTTA (FOURTH ORDER) METHOD

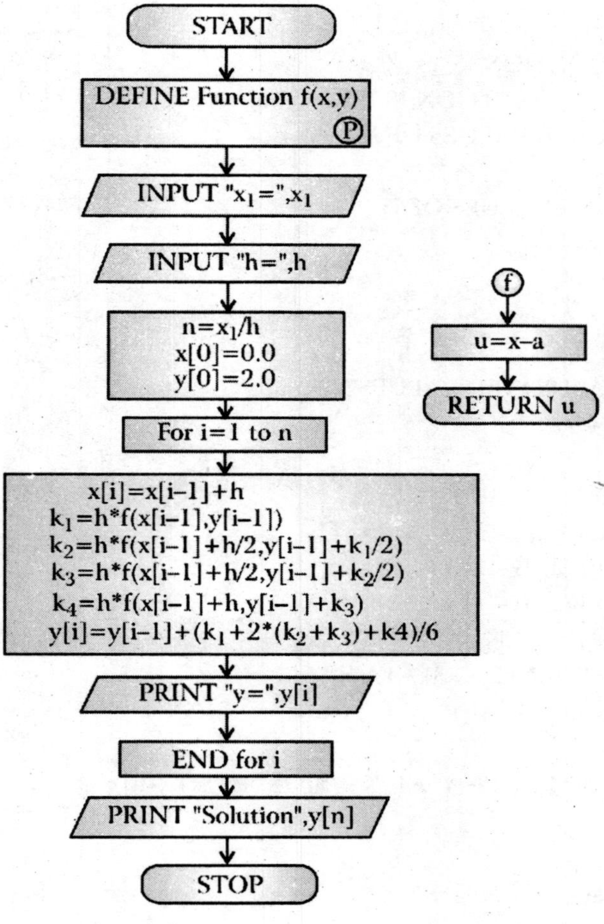

16. (b) /* RUNGA KUTTA (FOURTH ORDER) METHOD*/

Used formula: $k_1 = h\, f(x_0, y_0)$

$$k_2 = h\, f(x_0 + \frac{1}{2}h, y_0 + \frac{1}{2}k_1)$$

$$k_3 = h\, f(x_0 + \frac{1}{2}h, y_0 + \frac{1}{2}k_2)$$

$$k_4 = h\, f(x_0 + h, y_0 + k_3)$$

$$y_1 = y_0 + \frac{1}{6}(k_1 + 2\,k_2 + 2\,k_3 + k_4).$$

```
#include<stdio.h>
#include<math.h>
float f(float, float);
void main ( )
{
```

```
float x1,h,x[10],y[10],k1,k2,k3,k4;
int i,n,;
clrscr();
printf("\ nTHE FUNCTION IS Y – X");
printf("\ AND THE CONDITION IS Y(0) = 2");
printf("\ nENTER THE VALUES OF X");
scanf("% f",&x1);
printf("\ENTER THE VALUES OF H ");
scanf("% f",&h);
n = x1/h;
x[0] = 0.0;
y[0] = 2;
printf("\ nTHE TABULATED VALUES");
for (i = 1;i< = n;i + +)
{
x[i] = x[i – 1] + h;
k1 = h*f(x[i – 1],y[i – 1]);
k2 = h*f(x[i – 1] + h/2,y[i – 1] + k1/2);
k3 = h*f(x[i – 1] + h/2,y[i – 1] + k2/2);
k4 = h*f(x[i – 1] + h,y[i – 1] + k3);
y[i] = y[i – 1] + (k1 + 2*(k2 + k3) + k4/6;
printf("\ nY[%f] = %f",x[i],y[i]);
}
printf("\ n\ nTHE VALUE OF Y AT X = %f IS % f",x1,y[n]);
getch();
}
float f(float a, float b)
{
float f1;
f1 = b – a;
return(f1);
}
```

THE FUNCTION IS *Y* – *X* AND THE CONDITION IS Y (0) = 2

ENTER THE VALUE OF X 0.1

ENTER THE VALUE OF H 0.1

THE TABULATED VALUES

Y[0.100000] = 2.205171

Y[0.200000] = 2 /421403

Y[0.300000] = 2.649859

Y[0.400000] = 2.891824

THE VALUE OF Y AT X = 0.400000 IS 2.891824

17. (a) FLOW CHART FOR GAUSS SEIDEL METHOD

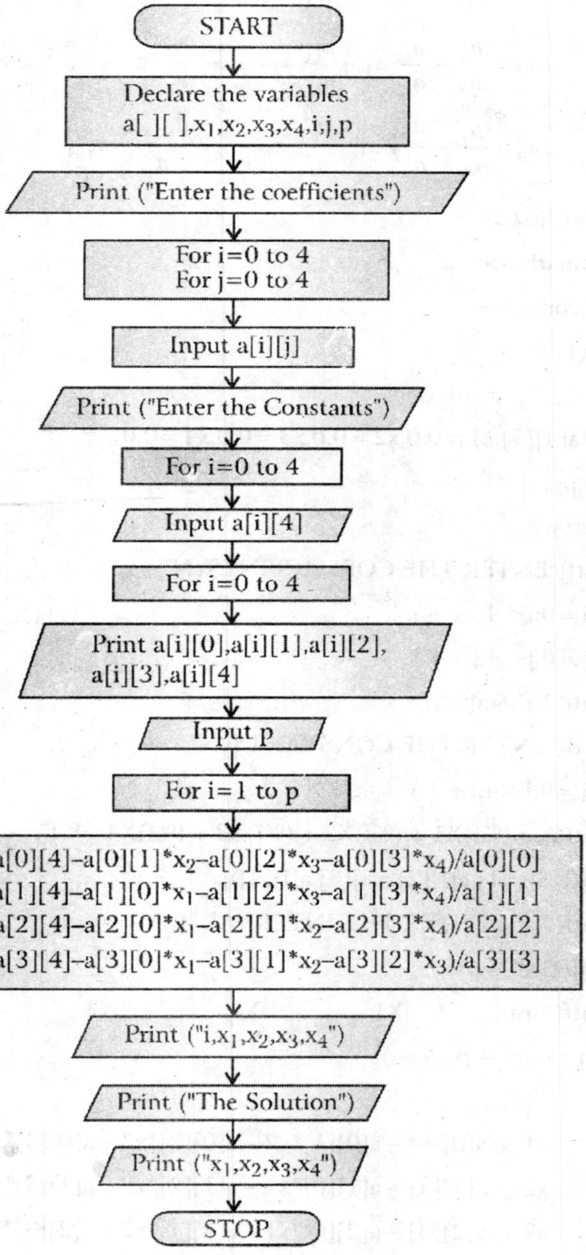

17. (b) /*GAUSS SEIDEL METHOD*/

Used formula: $x_1 = \frac{b_1}{a_{11}} - \frac{a_{12}}{a_{11}} x_2 - \frac{a_{13}}{a_{11}} x_3 - \ldots - \frac{a_{1n}}{a_{11}} x_n$

$$x_2 = \frac{b_2}{a_{22}} - \frac{a_{21}}{a_{22}} x_1 - \frac{a_{23}}{a_{22}} x_2 - \ldots - \frac{a_{2n}}{a_{22}} x_n$$

$$x_n = \frac{b_n}{a_{nn}} - \frac{a_{n1}}{a_{nn}} x_1 - \frac{a_{n2}}{a_{nn}} x_2 - \ldots - \frac{a_{n,n-1}}{a_{nn}} x_{n-1}$$

```
#include<stdio.h>
#include<math.h>
#include<conio.h>
void main()
{
    floata[4][5],x1 = 0.0,x2 = 0.0,x3 = 0.0,x4 = 0.0;
    int i,j,p;
    clrscr();
    printf("ENTER THE COEFFICIENTS\ N");
    for(i = 0;i< 4;i + + )
    for(j = 0;j< 4;j + + )
    scanf("%f",&a[i][j]);
    printf("ENTER THE CONSTANTS\ N");
    for(i = 0;i< 4;i + + )
    printf("\ n (%f)X1 + (%f)X2 + (%f)X3 + (%f)X4 = %f",
    a[i][0],a[i][1],a[i][2],a[i][3],a[i][4]);
    printf("\ n\ nENTER THE INTERVAL ");
    scanf("%d",&p);
    printf("\ nn          X1          X2          X3          X4");
    for(i = 1;i< = p;i + + )
  {
        x1 = (a[0][4] – a[0][1]*x2 – a[0][2]*x3 – a[0][3]*x4)/a[0][0];
        x2 = (a[1][4] – a[1][0]*x1 – a[1][2]*x3 – a[1][3]*x4)/a[1][1];
        x3 = (a[2][4] – a[2][0]*x1 – a[2][1]*x2 – a[2][3]*x4)/a[2][2];
        x4 = (a[3][4] – a[3][0]*x1 – a[3][1]*x2 – a[3][2]*x3)/a[3][3];
        printf("\ n%d\ t%f\ t%f\ t%f\ t%f",1,x1,x2,x3,x4);
  }
```

```
    printf("\ nTHE SOLUTION :");
    printf("\ nX1 = %f,  X2 = %f,  X3 = %f,  X4 = %f",  x1,x2,x3,x4);
    getch();
}
}
```

ENTER THE CONSTANTS
3
15
27
-9

THE EQUATIONS
(10.000000)X1 + (-2.000000)X2 + (- 1.000000)X3 + (- 1.000000)X4 = 3.000000
(-2.000000)X1 + (10.000000)X2 + (- 1.000000)X3 + (- 1.000000)X4 = 15.000000
(- 1.000000)X1 + (- 1.000000)X2 + (-2,000000)X3 + (10.000000)X4 =-9.000000

ENTER THE INTERVAL 7

n	X1	X2	X3	X4
1	0.300000	1.560000	2.886000	- 0.136800
2	0.886920	1.952304	2.956562	- 0024765
3	0.983640	1.989908	2.992402	- 0.004165
4	0.996805	1.998135	2.998666	- 0.000768
5	0.999427	1.999675	2.999757	- 0.000138
6	0.999897	1.999941	2.999956	- 0.000025
7	0.999981	1.999989	2.999992	- 0.000005

18. (a) FLOW CHART FOR NEWTON BACKWARD INTERPOLATION METHOD

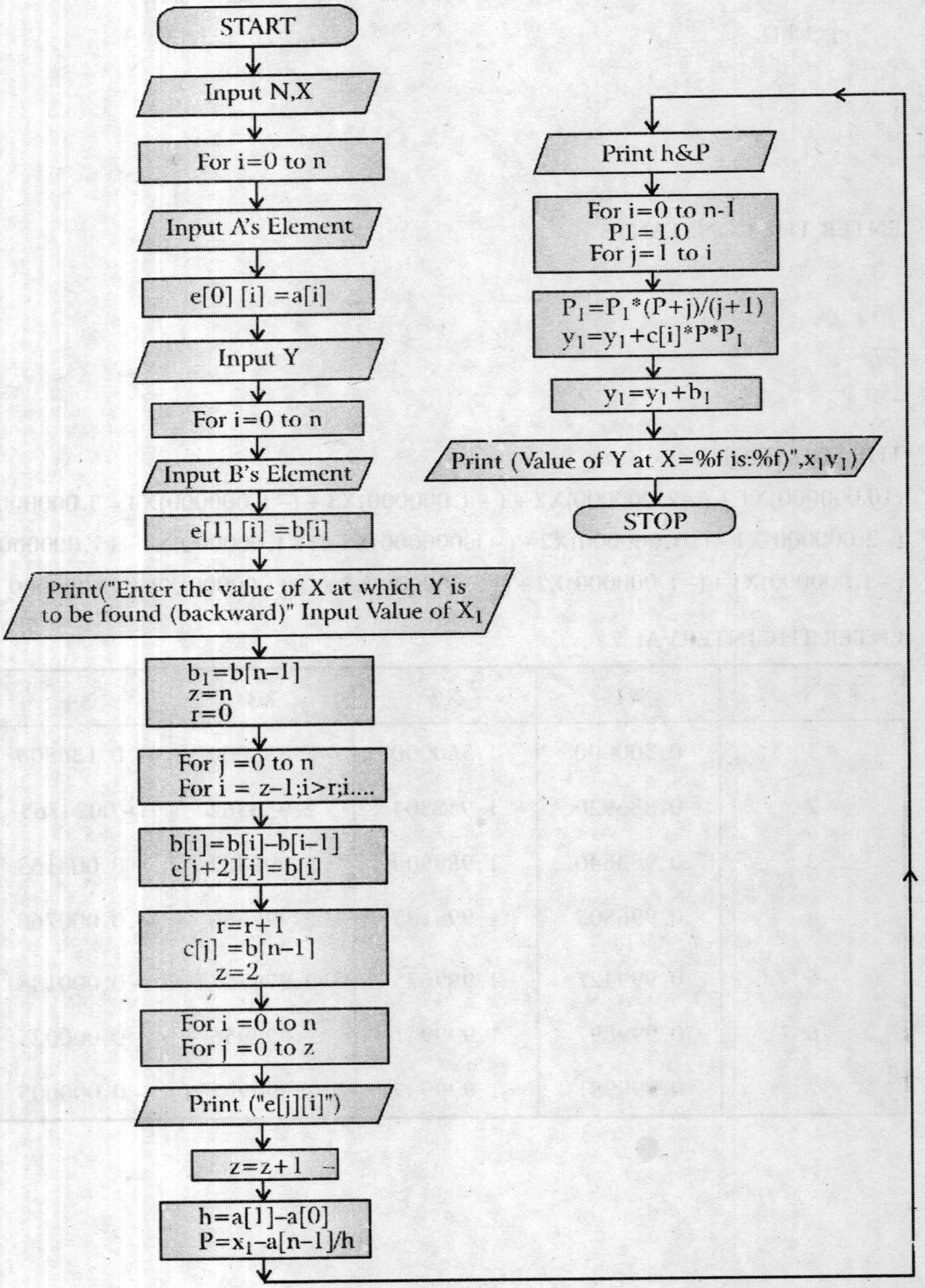

18. (b) /*NEWTON BACKWARD INTERPOLATION METHOD*/

Used formula:

$$y_n(x) = y_n + p\nabla y_n + \frac{p(p-1)}{!2}\nabla^2 y_n + \ldots + \frac{p(p+1)(p+n-1)}{!n}\nabla^n y_n$$

```
#include<stdio.h>
#include<conio.h>
#include<math.h>
void main()
{
      float a[20],b[20],c[20],e[20][20],x1,p,h,p1,y1 = 0.0,b1;
        int i,n,j,z,r;
        clrscr();
        printf("\ nENTER THE NUMBER OF TERMS");
        scanf("%d",&n);
        printf("ENTER THE VALUE OF X\ n");
        for(i = 0;i< n;i + + )
        {
              printf("x[%d] = ",i + 1);
              scanf("%f",&a[i]);
              e[0][i] = a[i];
        }
        printf("ENTER THE VALUES OF Y\ n");
        for(i = 0;i< n;i + + )
        {
       printf("Y[%d] = ",i + 1);
       scanf("%f",&b[i]);
       e[1][i] = b[i];
       }
  printf("\nENTER THE VALUE OF X AT WHICH Y IS TO BE FOUND (backward");
       scanf("%f",&x1);
       b1 = b[n – 1];
       z = n;
       r = 0;
            for(j = 0;j< n;j + + )
            {
                  for(i = z – 1;i> r;i – – )
                        {
                        b[i] = b[i] – b[i – 1];
                        e[j + 2][i] = b[i];
                  }
                  r + + ;
                  c[j] = b[n – 1];
    }
```

```
printf("\ nX          Y     ");
for(i = 0;i< n-1;i + + )
printf(" # [%d]\ t",i + 1);
printf("\ n");
z = 2;
   for(i = 0;i< n;i + + )
   {
       for(j = 0;j< z;j + + )
       printf("%f ",e[j][i]); z + + ;
       printf("\ n");
   }
   h = a[1] - a[0];
   p = (x1 - a[n -1])/h;
   printf("\ nh = %f",h);
   printf("\ np = %f",p);
   for(i = 0;i< n - 1;i + + )
   {
       p1 = 1.0;
       for(j = 1;j< = i;j + + )
       p1 = p1*((p + j)/(j + 1));
       y1 + = c[i]*p*p1;
}
```

```
X[1] = 1891
X[2] = 1901
X[3] = 1911
X[4] = 1921
X[5] = 1931
ENTER THE VALUES OF Y
Y[1] = 46
Y[2] = 66
Y[3] = 81
Y[4] = 93
Y[5] = 101
ENTER THE VALUE OF X AT WHICH Y IS TO BE FOUND (backward)1925
THE TABULATED VALUES ARE :
X        Y          # [1]          # [2]          # [3]          # [4]
1891.000000 46.000000
1901.000000 66.000000 20.000000
1911.000000 81.000000 15.000000 - 5.000000
1921.000000 93.000000 12.000000 - 3.0000002.000000
1931.000000 101.000000 8.000000 - 4.000000 - 1.000000 - 3.000000
h = 10.000000
p = - 0.600000
THE VALUE OF Y AT X - 1925.000000 IS : 96.836800
```

19. (a) FLOW CHART FOR NEWTON FORWARD INTERPOLATION METHOD

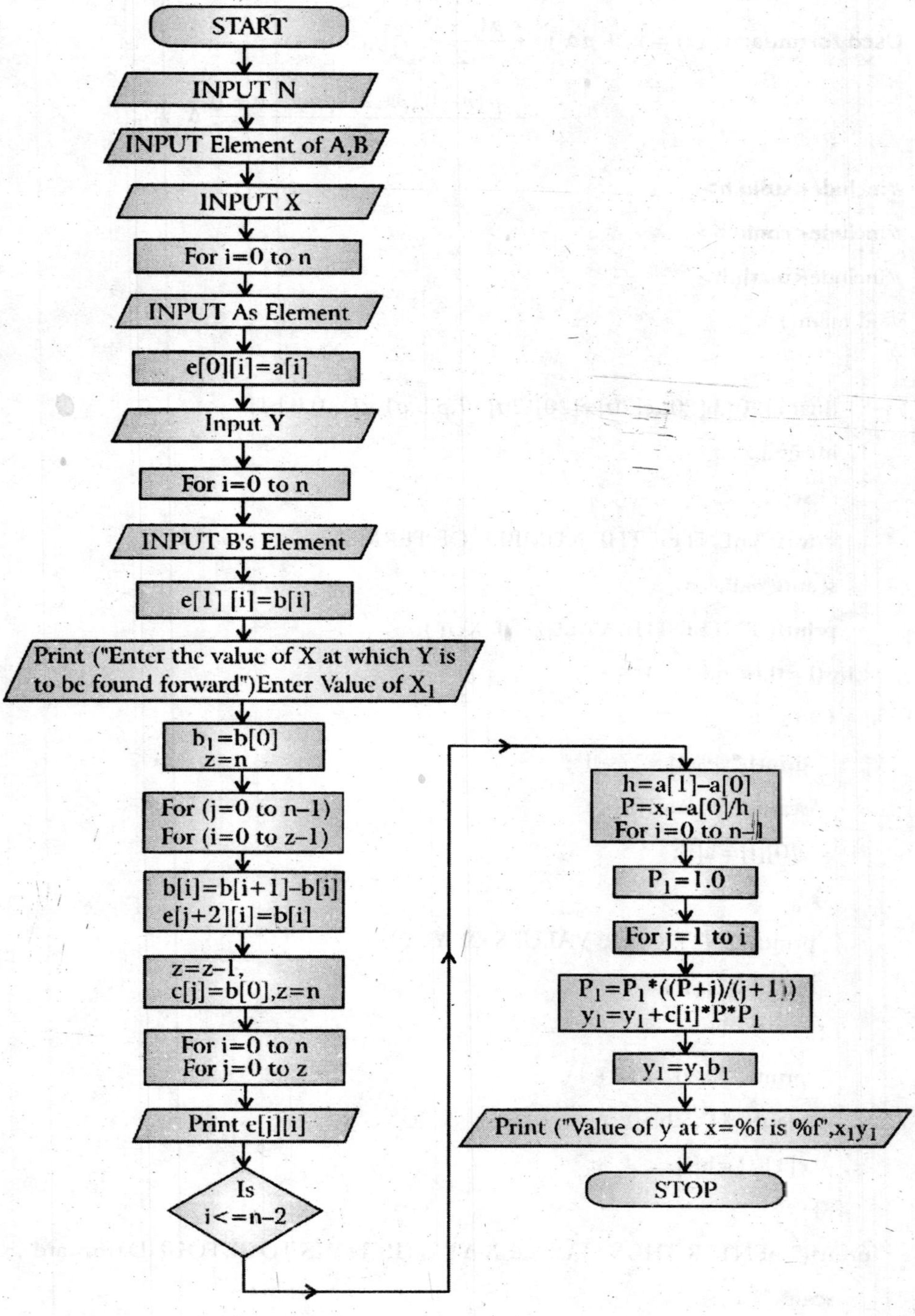

19. (b) /*NEWTON FORWARD INTERPOLATION METHOD*/

Used formula: $y_n(x) = y_0 + p\Delta y_0 + \frac{p(p-1)}{!2}\Delta^2 y_0 + \ldots$

$$+ \frac{p(p-1)(p-2)\ldots.(p-n+1)}{!2}\Delta^n y_0$$

```
#include<stdio.h>
#include<conio.h>
#include<math.h>
void main()
{
    float a[20],b[20],c[20],e[20][20],x1,p,h,p1,y1 =0.0,b1;
    int i,n,j,z;
    clrscr();
    printf("\ nENTER THE NUMBER OF TERMS");
    scanf("%d",&n);
    printf("ENTER THE VALUE OF X\ n");
  for(i = 0;i< n;i + + )
    {
      printf("x[%d] = ",i + 1);
      scanf("%f",&a[i]);
      e[0][i] = a[i];
    }
     printf("ENTER THE VALUES OF Y\ n");
     for(i = 0;i< n;i + + )
    {
      printf("y[%d] = "',i + 1);
      scanf("%f",&b[i]);
      e[1][i] = b[i];
    }
 printf("\ nENTER THE VALUE OF X AT WHICH Y IS TO BE FOUND (forward");
    scanf("%f",&x1);
    b1 = b[0];
```

```
z = n;
printf("\ nTHE TABULATED VALUES ARE:");
    for(j = 0;j< n - 1;j + + )
      {
        for(i = 0;i< z - 1;i + + )
        {
        b[i] = b[i + 1] - b[i];
        e[j + 2][i] = b[i];
        }
        z - - ;
          c[j] = b[0];
        }
    printf("\ nX                    Y    ");
    for(i = 0;i< n - 1;i + + )
    printf(" # [%d]\ t",i + 1);
    printf("\ n");
    z = n;
  for(i = 0;i< n;i + + )
    {
        for(j = 0;j< z;j + + )
        printf("%f ",e[j][i]);
        if(i< = n - 2)
        z - - ;
        printf("\ n");
    }
    h = a[1] - a[0];
    p = (x1  - a[0])/h;
    printf(h = %f",p);
    printf("\ np = %f",p);
    for(i = 0;i< n - 1;i + + )
    {
```

```
        p1 = 1.0;
        for(j = 1;j< = i;j + + )
        p1 =p1*((p + j)/(j + 1));
        y1 + = c[i]*p*p1;
      }
      y1 + =b1;1
      printf("\ n\ nTHE VALUE OF Y AT  X =  % f  IS : %f",x1,y1);
      getch();
      }
X[1] = 1891
X[2] = 1901
X[3] = 1911
X[4] = 1921
X[5] = 1931
ENTER THE VALUES OF Y
Y[1] = 46
Y[2] = 66
Y[3] = 81
Y[4] = 93
Y[5] = 101
ENTER THE VALUE OF X AT WHICH Y IS TO BE FOUND (forward)1895
THE TABULATED VALUES ARE :
X         Y         # [1]         # [2]         # [3]         # [4]
1891.00000046.00000020.000000 – 5.000000 2.000000 – 3.000000
1901.00000066.00000015.000000 – 3.000000 – 1.000000
1911.000000 81.000000 12.000000 – 4.000000
1921.00000093.0000008.000000
1931.000000101.000000
h = 10.000000
p =  0.00000
THE VALUE OF Y AT X = 1895.000000 IS : 54.852789
```

20. (a) FLOW CHART FOR EULER RICHARDSON METHOD

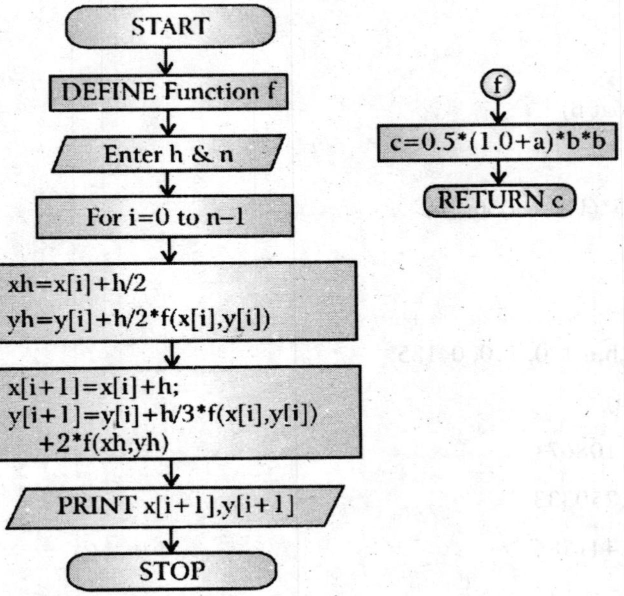

20. (b) /*PROGRAM FOR EULER RICHARDSON METHOD */

```
#include<stdio.h>
#include<conio.h>
void main()
{
float x[20],y[20]f(float,float),h,xh,yh;
int i,n;
printf("\ n enter   x(0),y(0),h,n");
scanf("%f,%f,%d", &x[0], &y[0],&h,&n); print("\ nx(i) y(i)");
for(i = 0; i< = n –1;     i + +)
{
xh = x[i] + h/2.0;
yh = y[i] + h/2.0*f(x[i],y[i]);
x[i + 1] = x[i] + h;
y[i + 1] = y[i] + h/3.0*(f(x[i]y[i] + 2.0*f(xh,yh));
```

```
printf("\ n%f%f",x[i + 1],y[i + 1]);
}
}
floatf(float a,float b)
{
float  c;  c = 0.5*(1.0 + a)*b  *b;
return  (c);
}
```

enter x(0),y(0),h,n 1.0, 1.0, 0.1, 5

x(i)	y(i)
1.100000	1.108671
1.200000	1.250333
1.300000	1.441586
1.400000	1.712145
1.500000	2.120517

enter x(0),y(0), h,n 1.0, 1.0, 0.2, 5

x(i)	y(i)
1.200000	1.236067
1.400000	1.650420
1.600000	2.519940
1.800000	5.084853
2.000000	22.147118

21. (a) FLOW CHART FOR MILNE'S PREDICTOR-COORRECTOR METHOD

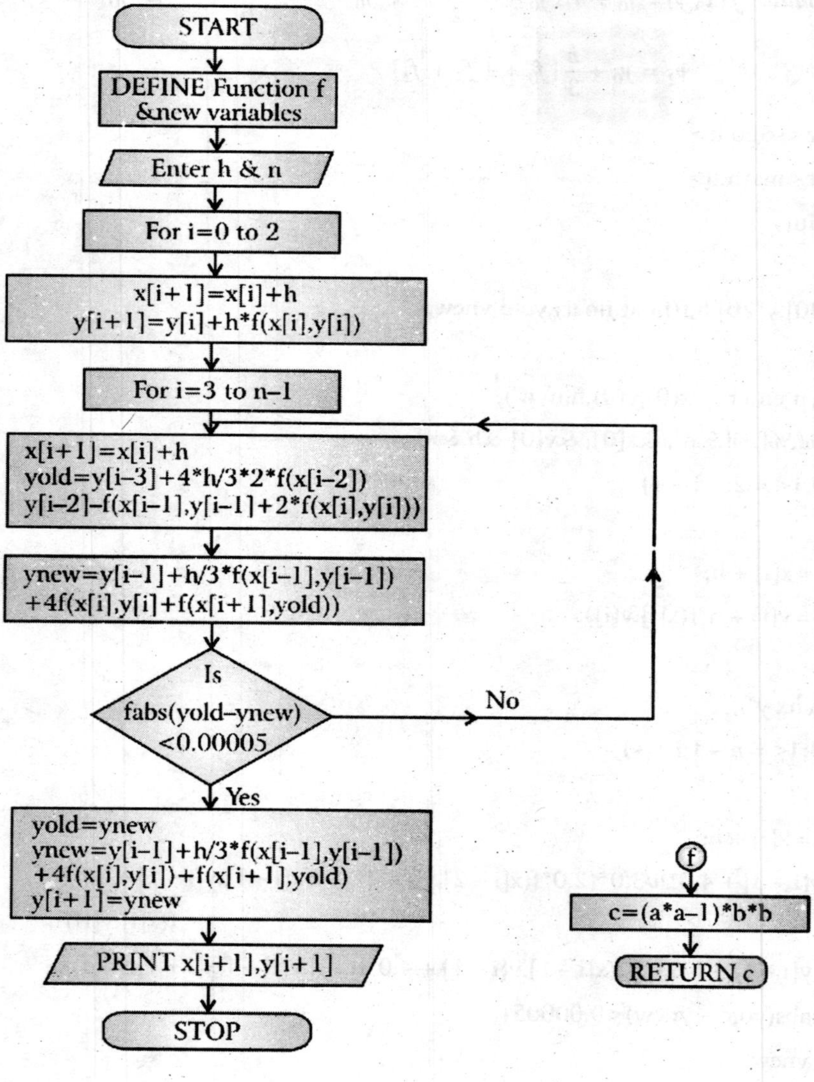

21. (b) /* MILNE'S PREDICTOR-CORRECTOR METHOD*/

Used formula: $f(x, y) = f_0 + n\Delta f_0 + \frac{n(n-1)}{2}\Delta^2 f_0 + \frac{n(n-1)(n-2)}{6}\Delta^3 f_0 + \ldots$

$$y_2 = y_0 + \frac{h}{3}[f_0 + 4f_1 + f_2]$$

```
#include<stdio.h>
#include<math.h>
void main()
{
float x[20],y[20],h,f(float,float),yold,ynew;
int i,n;
printf("\ n enter    x(0),y(0),h,n\ n");
scanf("%f,%f,%f,%d", &x[0], &y[0],&h,&n);
for(i = 0; i< = 2;   i + +)
{
x[i + 1] = x[i] + h;
y[i + 1] = y[i] + h*f(x[i],y[i]);
}
printf("\ nx y");
for(i = 3; i< = n – 1;i + +)
{
x[i + 1] = x[i] + h;
yold = y[i – 3] + 4.0*h/3.0*(2.0*f(x[i – 2],y[i – 2]) – f(x[i – 1],y[i – 1] + 2.0*
                                                                    f(x[i],y[i]));

ynew = y[i – 1] + h/3.0*(f(x[i – 1],y[i – 1] + 4.0*f(x[i],y[i] + f(x[i + 1],yold));
while (fabs(yold – ynew)<0.00005)
{yold = ynew;
ynew = y[i – 1] + h/3.0*(f(x[i – 1],y[i – 1] + 4.0*f(x[i],y[i] + f(x[i + 1],yold));

step 2:}  y[i + 1] = ynew;
printf("\ n    %f  %f",x[i + 1],y[i + 1]);
}
}
float f (float a, float b)
{
```

```
float (c);
c = (a*a – 1)*b*b;
return c;
}
enter x(0),y(0),h,n
0.0,2.0,0.05,10
x       y
0.20000001.412726
0.2500001.312902
0.3000001.249164
0.3500001.171336
0.4000001.127313
0.4500001.065127
0.5000001.035706
enter  x(0),y(0),h,n
1.0,2.0,0.05,10
x       y
1.2000002.161194
1.2500002.272713
1.3000002.458393
1.3500002.699059
1.4000003.078099
1.4500003.649036
1.5000004.650804
enter  x(0),y(0),h,n
```

22. (a) FLOW CHART FOR ADAMS-MOULTON METHOD

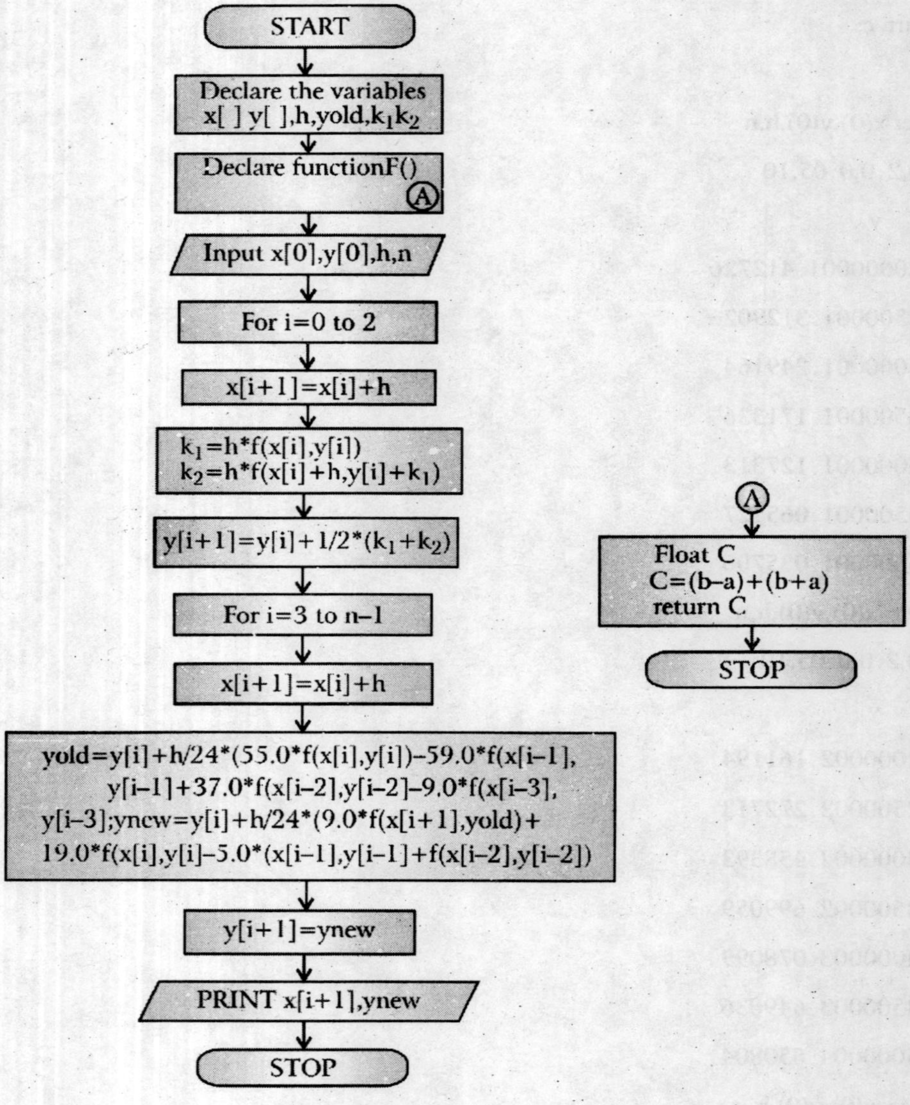

22. (b) /*ADAMS-MOULTON METHOD*/

Used formula: $y_1^p = y_0 + \frac{h}{24}(55\, f_0 - 59\, f_{-1} + 37 f_{-2} - 9 f_{-3})$

$$y_1^c = y_0 + \frac{h}{24}(9\, f_1^p + 19\, f_0 - 5\, f_{-1} + f_{-2})$$

```
#include<stdio.h>
#include<conio.h>
#include<math.h>
void main()
{
float f(float,float),h,x[20],y[20],yold,ynew,k1,k2;
int i,n;
clrscr();
print f("THE INPUT VALUES ARE \ n");
printf("\ nX(0),y(0),h,n\ n");
scanf("%f,%f,%f,%d",&x[0],&y[0],&h,&n);
for(i = 0;i< = 2;i + +)
{
x[i + 1] = x[i] + h;
k1 = h*f(x[i],y[i]);
k2 = h*f(x[i] + h,y[i] +k1);
y[i +1] = y[i] + 0.5*(k1 + k2);
}
printf("\ n the out put values are\ n");
printf("\ nx        y         \ n");
for(i = 3;i<n  - 1;i + +)  h;
{
x[i + 1] = x[i]+h;
yold = y[i] + h/24.0*(55.0*f(x[i],y[i] – 59.0*f(x[i – 1],y[i – 1])
+ 37.0*f(x[i – 2],y[i – 2] – 9.0*f(x[i – 3],y[i – 3));
ynew = y[i] + h/24.0*(9.0*f(x[i + 1],yold)+ 19.0*f(x[i],y[i]
```

```
- 5.0*f(x[i - 1],y[i - 1]) + f(x[i - 2],y[i - 2]));
y[i + 1] =ynew;
printf("\ n%f,%f",x[i + 1],ynew);
}
getche();
}
float f(float a, float b)
{
float c;
c = (b - a)/    (b + a);
return   (c);
}
```

THE INPUT VALUES ARE

x(0), y(0), h, n

0.0, 1.0, 0.2, 6

THE OUT PUT VALUES ARE

x y

0.800000, 1.456850

1.000000, 1.505934

1.200000, 1.538336

THE INPUT VALUES ARE

x(0),y(0),h,n

0.0,2.0,0.1,6

THE OUT PUT VALUES ARE

x y

0.400000, 2.336047

0.500000, 2.404166

0.600000, 2.467351

23. (a) FLOW CHART FOR ADAMS-BASHFORTH METHOD

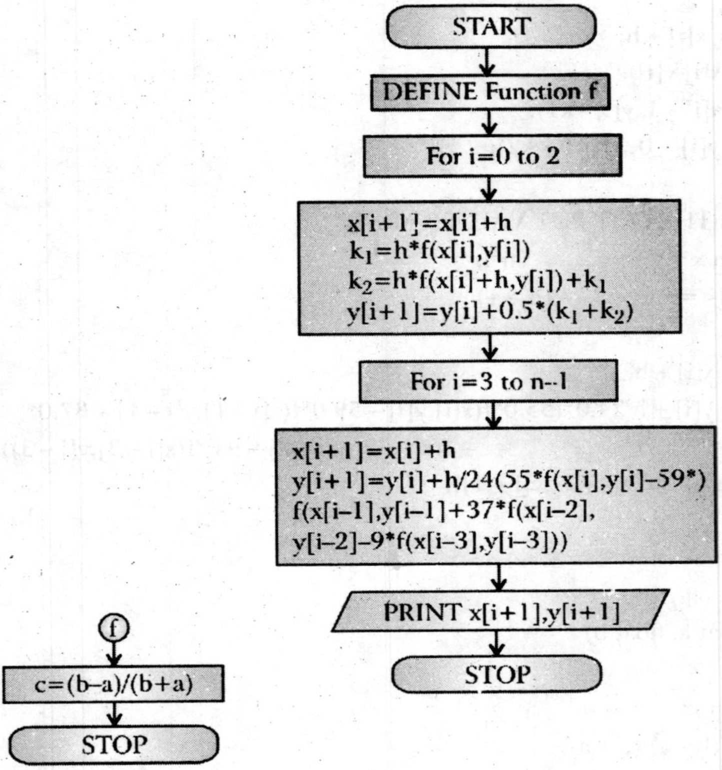

23. (b) /*ADAMS-BASHFORTH METHOD*/

Used formula: $y_1^p = y_0 + \frac{h}{24}[55\, f_0 - 59\, f_{-1} + 37\, f_{-2} - 9\, f_{-3}]$

```
#include<stdio.h>
#include<conio.h>
#include<math.h>
void main()
{
float f(float,float),h,x[20],y[20],k1,k2;
int i,n;
clrscr();
printf("\nTHE INPUT VALUES ARE\N");
printf("\ nx(0),y(0),h,n\ n");
scanf("%f,%f,%f,%d",&x[0],&y[0],&h,&n);
```

```
for    (i = 0;i< = 2;i + +)
{
x[i + 1] =  x[i] + h;
k1 = h*f(x[i],y[i]);
k2 = h*f(x[i] + h,y[i] +k1);
y[i +1] = y[i] + 0.5*(k1 + k2);
}
printf("\ nTHE OUT PUT VALUES ARE\N");
printf("\ n x         y          \ n");
for(i = 3;i<=n          - 1;i + +)
{
x[i + 1] = x[i] + h;
y[i + 1] = y[i] + h/24.0*(55.0*f(x[i],y[i] – 59.0*f(x[i – 1],y[i – 1] + 37.0*
                          f(x[i – 2],y[i – 2] = 9.0*f(x[i – 3],y[i – 3));
printf("\ n%f,%f",x[i + 1],y[i + 1]);
}
getche();
}
float f(float a, float b)
{
    float c;
    c = (b – a)/(b + a);
    return (c);
}
```

THE INPUT VALUES ARE

x(0), y(0), h, n

0.0, 1.0, 0.05, 6

THE OUT PUT VALUES ARE

x y

0.200000, 1.168000

0.250000, 1.202044

0.300000, 1.233627

THE INPUT VALUES ARE

x(0), y(0), h, n

1.0, 2.0, 0.1, 6

THE OUT PUT VALUES ARE

x y

1.400000, 2.106076

1.500000, 2.124751

1.600000, 2.140584

24. (a) FLOW CHART FOR EIGEN VECTOR

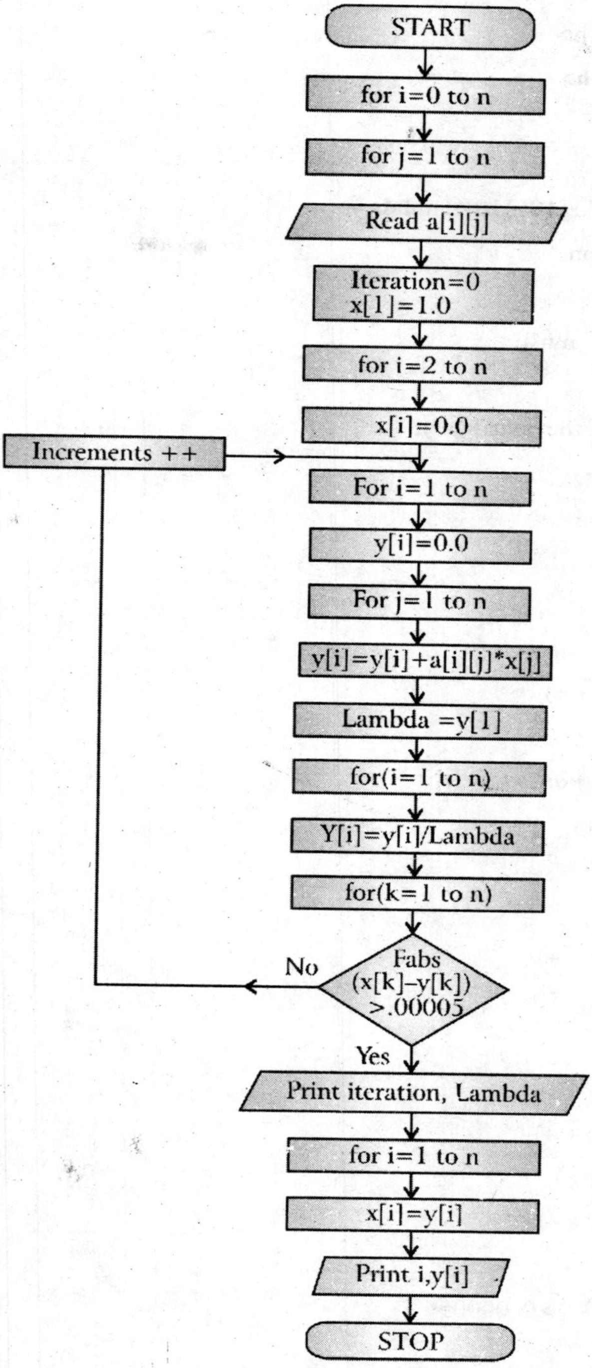

24. (b) /*--------EIGEN VECTOR ----------------------- */

```
#include<stdio.h>
#include<conio.h>
#include<math.h>
void main()
{
float x[20],y[20],a[10],[10], lambda;
int i,j,k,n iteration;
clrscr();
printf("\ n  enter  n\n");
scanf("%d",&n);
printf("\n  enter  the  matrix\n");
for(i=1;i<=n;i++)
for(j=1;i<=n;j++)
scanf("%f",&a[i][j]);
iteration=0;
x[1] = 1.0;
for(i = 2;i<= n;i + +)
x[i]=0.0;
increment:  iteration  ++;
for(i=1;i<=n;i++)
{
y[i] = 0.0;
for(j = 1;j< = n;j + +)
y[i] = y[i]+a[i][j]*x[j];
}
lambda = y[i];
for(i = 1;i< = n;i + +)
y[i] = y[i]/lambda;
for(k = 1;k< = n;k + +)
{
if(fabs(x[k] – y[k])>0.00005)
{
printf("\n\n iteration = %d lambda=%f",  iteration,      lambda);
```

```
for(i = 1;i< = n;i + +)
{
x[i] = y[i];
printf("\ nx[%d] = %g",i,y[i]);
}
goto increment;
}
}
getche();
}
```

```
enter the matrix
1  2
2  1
        iteration = 1 lambda 1.000000
        x[1] = 1
        x[2] = 2  iteration = 2 lambda 5.000000
        x[1] = 1
        x[2] = 0.8 iteration = 3 lambda 2.600000
        x[1] = 1
        x[2] = 1.07692 iteration = 4 lambda 3.153946
        x[1] = 1
        x[2] = 0.97561  iteration 5 lambda 2.951220
        x[1] = 1
        x[2] = 1.00826 iteration = 6 lambda 3.016529
        x[1] = 1
        x[2] = 0.99726 iteration = 7 lambda 2.994521
        x[1] = 1
        x[2] = 1.00091 iteration = 8 lambda 2.999391
        x[1] = 1
        x[2] = 0.999695 iteration = 9 lambda 2.999391
        x[1] = 1
        x[2] = 1.0001 iteration = 10 lambda 3.000203
        x[1] = 1
        x[2] = 0.999966
```

25. (a) FLOW CHART FOR PARABOLIC FIT BY LEAST SQUARES METHOD

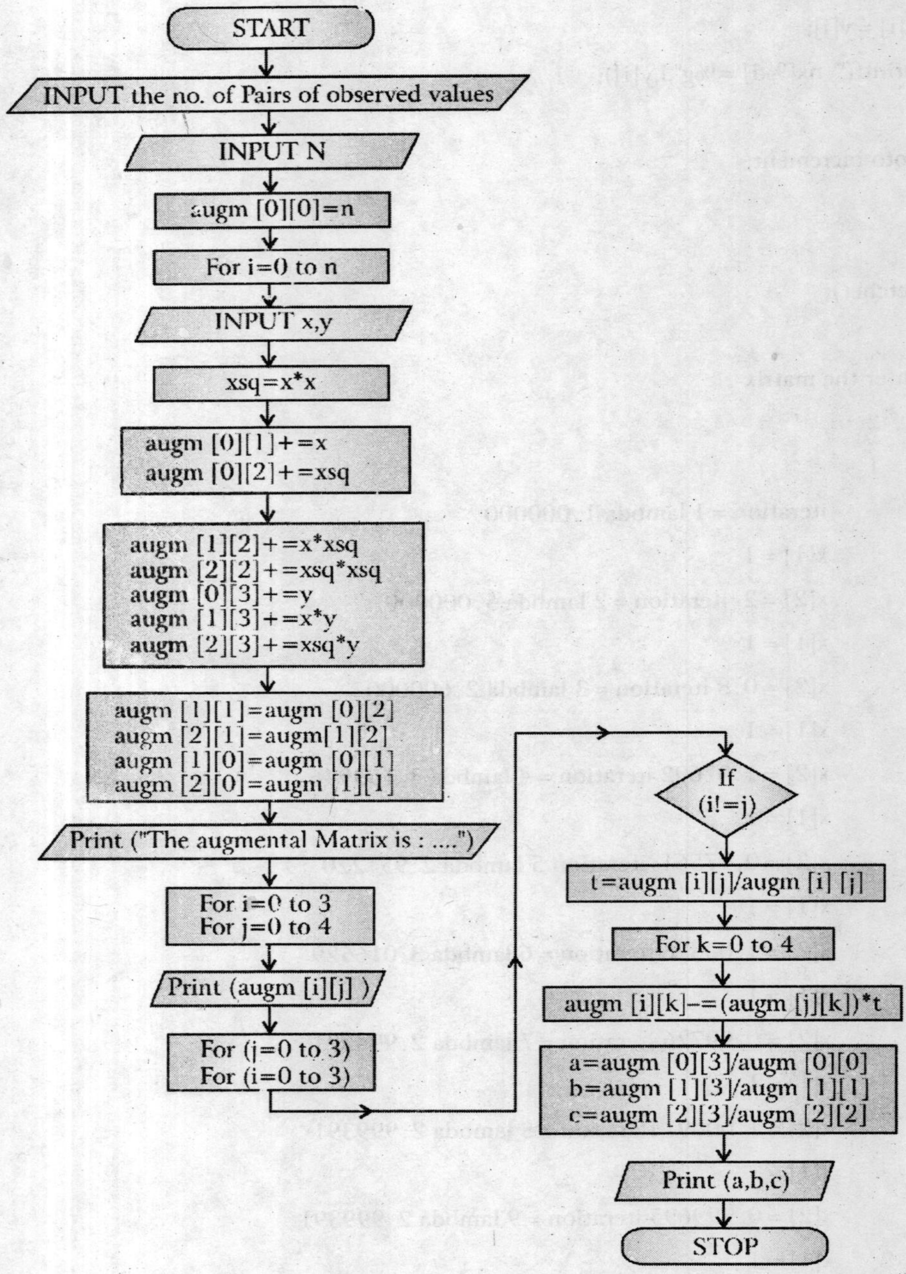

25. (b) /*PARABOLIC FIT BY LEAST SQUARES METHOD */

Used formula: $m\,a_0 + a_1 \sum_{i=1}^{m} x_i = \sum_{i=1}^{m} y_i$

$$a_0 + \sum_{i=1}^{m} x_i + a_1 \sum_{i=1}^{m} x_i^2 = \sum_{i=1}^{m} x_i\, y_i$$

```
#include<stdio.h>
#include<conio.h>
#include<math.h>
void main()
{
float augm[3][4]={{0,0,0,0}, {0,0,0,0}, {0,0,0,0}};
float t,a,b,c,x,y,xsq;
int i,j,k,n;
puts("enter the no. of pairs of "" observed values");
scanf("%d",&n);
augm[0][0] = n;
for(i = 0;i<n;i + +){
printf("pair   no.  %d\ n",i + 1);
scanf("%f%f",&x,&y);
xsq = x*x;
augm[0][1] + = x;
augm[0][2] + = xsq;
augm[1][2] + = x*xsq;
augm[2][2] + = xsq*xsq;
augm[0][3] + = y;
augm[1][3] + = x*y;
augm[2][3] + = xsq*y;
}
augm[1][1] + = augm[0][2];
augm[2][1] + = augm[1][2];
augm[1][0] = augm[0][1];
augm[2][0] = augm[1][1];
puts("the augmental matrix is : – ");
for(i = 0;i<3;i + +)
{
for(j = 0;j<4;j + +)
printf("%f",augm[i] [j]);
```

```
printf("\ n "); }
/*now solving for a, b, c by Gauss Jorden method*/
for(j = 0;j<3;j + +)
for(i = 0;i<3;i + +)
if(i ! = j)
{
t = (augm[i][j]/(augm[j][j]);
for(k = 0;k<4;k + +)
augm[i][k] – = (augm[j][k])*t;
}
a = augm[0][3]/augm[0][0];
b = augm[1][3]/augm[1][1];
c = augm[2][3]/augm[2][2];
printf("a = %8.4f     b = %8.4f     c = %8.4f\ n",a,b,c);
}     }
getche ();
}
enter the no. of pairs of observed values
7
pair no. 1
1      1.1
pair no.2
1.5   1.3
pair no.3
2      1.6
pair no.4
2.5   2
pair no.5
3.0   2.7
pair no.6
3.5   3.4
pair no.7
4.0   4.1
the augmental matrix is :-
7.000000, 17.500000, 50.750000, 16.200001
17.500000, 50.750000, 161.875000, 47.650002
50.750000, 161.875000, 548.187500, 154.475006
a = 1.0357  b =–0.1929   c = 0.2429
enter the no. of pairs of observed values
```

26. (a) FLOW CHART FOR THE LAPLACE'S EQUATION

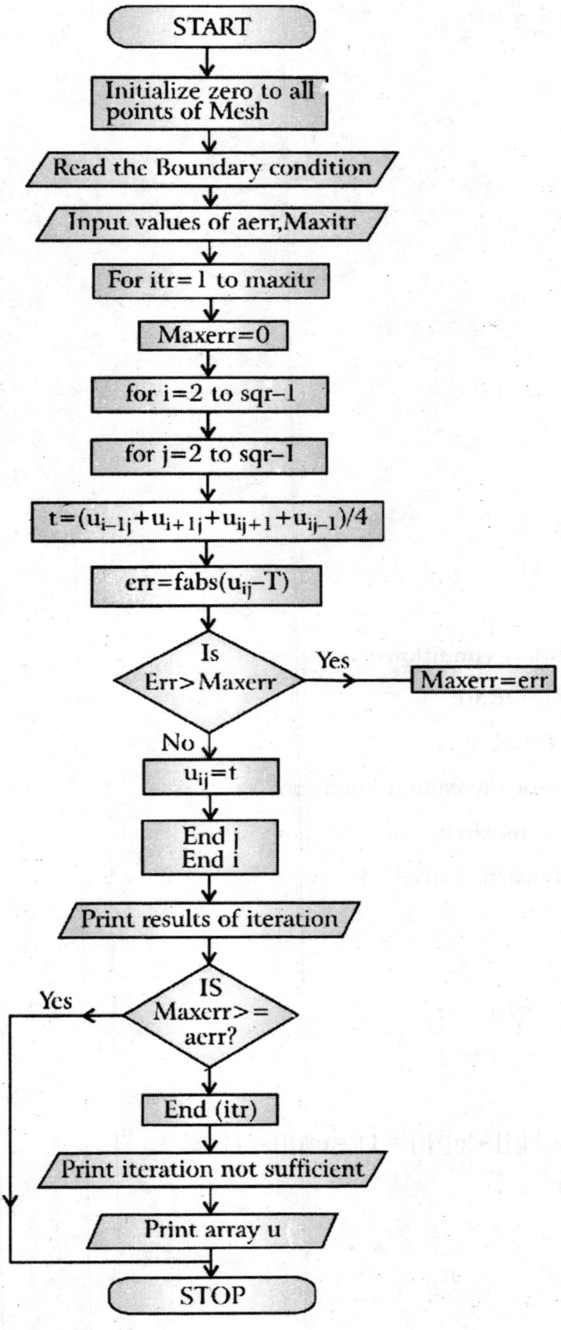

26. (b) Program: /*Laplace's equation*/

Used formula: $\frac{\partial^2 u}{\partial x^2}+\frac{\partial^2 u}{\partial y^2}=0$

```
#inculde<stdio.h>
#include<conio.h>
#include<math.h>
#include <process.h>
#define SQR  4
void main()
{
float  maxerr,  aerr,  err,  t;
int  i,j,itr,maxitr;
array  u;
for(i = 1;i<= SQR;i + +)
for(j = 1;j<= SQR;j + +)
u[i][j] = 0;
puts("Enter the boundary conditions:");
getrow (1,u); getrow (SQR,u);
getcol  (1,u); getcol  (SQR,u);
puts("Enter allowed eror","maximum iterations");
scanf("%f%f",&aerr,  &maxitr);
for     (itr = 1;itr< = maxitr;       itr + +)
{
maxerr = 0;
for(i = 2;i<= SQR       - 1;i + +)
for(j = 2;j<= SQR       - 1;j + +)
{
t = (u[i - 1][j] + u[i + 1][j] + u[i][j + 1] + u[i][j - 1]/4;
err = fabs(u[i][j]  - t);
if      (err>maxerr)
maxerr = err;
u[i][j] = t;
}
printf("Iteration  No.  %d\ n",itr);
```

```
printf("Iteration No. %d\ n",itr);
printarr(u,9,2);
if(maxerr< = aerr)
{
printf("After%d iterations\ n"  "The solution:     \ n",itr);
printarr(u,8,1);
return 0;
}
}
puts("Iterations not sufficient.");
return 1;
}
typedef float array [SQR+1][SQR+1];
void getrow(int i, array u)
{
int j;
printf("Enter the values of u[%d,j]","j = 1, %d\ n",i,SQR);
for(j = 1;j<= SQR;j + +)
scanf("%f",&u[i][j]);
}
void getcol (int j , array u)
{
int i;
printf("Enter the values of u[i,%d]",i = 2, %d\ n",j,SQR – 1);
for(i = 2;i<= SQR     – 1;i + +)
scanf("%f",&u[i][j]);
}
void printarr (array u, int width, int precision)
{
{int i,j;
for(i = 1;i<= SQR;i++)
{
for(j = 1;j<= SQR;j + +)
printf("%*.*f",width, precision,u[i][j]);
```

```
printf("\ n");
}
}
```

Enter the boundary conditions

Enter the values of u[1,j],j = 1,4

1000 1000 1000 1000

Enter the values of u [4,j],j = 1,4

1000 500 0 0

Enter the values of u[i,1],i = 2,3

2000 2000

Enter the values of u[i,4],i = 2,3

500 0

Enter allowed error, maximum iterations

.1 3

Iteration No. 1

1000.00	1000.00	1000.00	1000.00
2000.00	750.00	562.50	500.00
2000.00	812.50	343.75	0.00
1000.00	500.00	0.00	0.00

Iteration No. 2

1000.00	1000.00	1000.00	1000.00
2000.00	1093.75	734.38	500.00
2000.00	984.38	429.69	0.00
1000.00	500.00	0.00	0.00

Iteration No. 3

1000.00	1000.00	1000.00	1000.00
2000.00	1179.69	777.34	500.00
2000.00	1027.34	451.17	0.00
1000.00	500.00	0.00	0.00

27. (a) FLOW CHART FOR HEAT EQUATION

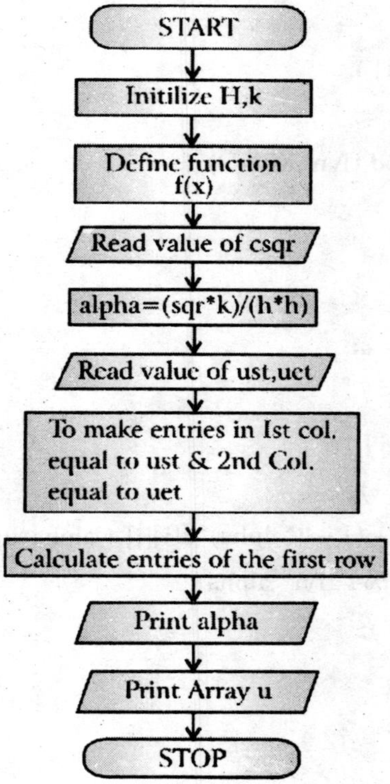

27. (b) *PARABOLIC EQUATION BY BENDRE SCHMIDT METHOD*/

Used formula: $\frac{\partial u}{\partial t} = c^2 \frac{\partial^2 u}{\partial x^2}$

```
#include<stdio.h>
#define XEND 8
#define TEND 5
float f(intx)
{
return 4*x – (x*x)/2.0;
}
main()
{
float u(XEND + 1][TEND + 1],h = 1.0,k = 0.125,csqr,alpha,ust,uet;
int i,j;
```

```
puts("Enter the square of 'C'");
scanf("%f" &csqr);
alpha = (csqr*k)/(h*h);
puts("Enter the value of u[0,t]");
scanf("%f"&ust);
printf("Enter the value ofu[%d,t]\ n",XEND);
scanf("%f",&uet);
for(j = 0;j< = TEND;j + +)
u[0][j] = u[XEND][j] = ust;
for(i=1;i<XEND          - 1;i + +)
u[i][0] = f(i);
for(j = 0;j<=TEND     - 1;j + +)
for(i = 1;i< = XEND   - 1;i + +)
u[i][j + 1] = alpha*u[i – 1][j] + (1 – 2*alpha)*u[i][j] + alpha*u[i + 1][j];
printf("The value of alpha is  %4.2f\n ",alpha);
puts("The values of u[i,j]are:-");
for(j = 0;j<TEND;j + +)
{
for(i= 0;i<XEND;i + +)
printf("%7.4f",u[i][j];
printf("\ n");
}
}
```

```
Enter the sq.  of  "C"
4
Enter value of  u(0,t)
0
Enter value of  u(8,t)
0
The value of alpha is  0.50
The values of u(i,j) are
0.0000       3.5000       6.0000
7.5000       8.0000       7.5000
6.0000       3.5000       0.0000
```

28. (a) FLOW CHART FOR WAVE EQUATION

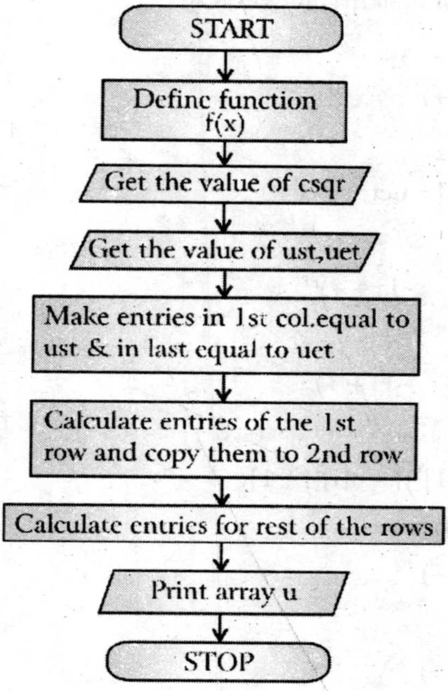

28. (b) /*SOLUTION OF HYPERBOLAIC EQUATION*/

Used formula: $\frac{\partial^2 u}{\partial t^2} = c^2 \frac{\partial^2 u}{\partial x^2}$

```
#include<stdio.h>
#define XEND  5
#define TEND  5
float f(int x)
{
return x*x*(5 – x);
}
main()
{
floatu[XEND + 1][TEND + 1],csqr,ust,uet;
int i,j;
puts("Enter the square of 'C'");
scanf("%d",&csqr);
printf("Enter the value of u[0][t]\n");
```

```
scanf("%f",&ust);
printf("Enter the value of u[%d][t]\n",XEND);
scanf("%f",&uet);
for(j = 0;j< = TEND;j + +)
{
u[0][j] = ust;u[XEND][j] = uet;
}
for(i = 1;i<XEND          -1;i + +)
u[i][1] = u[i][0] = f(i);
for(j = 1;j< = TEND          -1;j + +)
for(i = 1;i< = XEND          - 1;i + +)
u[i][j+1]=u[i-1][j]+u[i+1][j] - u[i][j - 1];
puts("The values of u[i][j]are:-");
for(j = 0;j< = TEND;j + +)
{
for(i = 0;i< = XEND;i + +)
print("%6.1f",u[i][j]);
printf("\n");
}
}
Enter the square of "C"
16
Enter value of  u(0,t)
0
Enter value of  u(5,t)
0
The values of  u(i,j) are:-
    0.0       4.0      12.0      18.0      16.0      0.0
    0.0       4.0      12.0      18.0      16.0      0.0
    0.0       8.0      10.0      10.0       2.0      0.0
    0.0       6.0       6.0      -6.0      -6.0      0.0
    0.0      -2.0     -10.0     -10.0      -8.0      0.0
    0.0     -16.0     -18.0     -12.0      -4.0      0.0
```

✦✦ Objective Type Question ✦✦

❖ Multiple Choice Questions

1. Data processing is carried out by means of binary logic elements using:
   (a) Decimal numbers (b) Hexadecimal numbers
   (c) Binary numbers (d) Stirling numbers.

2. The base or radix used for decimal numbers is
   (a) 2 (b) 10
   (c) 8 (d) 4

3. The base 2 is used for: **[I.A.S. 2000 (Pre)]**
   (a) Decimal numbers (b) Octal numbers
   (c) Hexadecimal numbers (d) Binary numbers

4. The binary equivalent of $(11.625)_{10}$ is
   (a) $(1101.110)_2$ (b) $(1011.001)_2$
   (c) $(1011.101)_2$ (d) $(111.101)_2$

5. The decimal equivalent to the Binary number $(10111011.011010)_2$ is
   (a) $(817.40625)_{10}$ (b) $(187.40625)_{10}$
   (c) $(188)_{10}$ (d) $(189.265)_{10}$

6. $(C14A)_{16}$ corresponds to:
   (a) $(49482)_{10}$ (b) $(44982)_{10}$
   (c) $(42894)_{10}$ (d) $(48492)_{10}$

7. Quantities are stored in:
   (a) Flip-Flop (b) Registers
   (c) Both (d) None of the these

8. $(1010100)_2 + (1000100)_2$ equals to:
   (a) 11001000 (b) 1001100
   (c) 1110001 (d) 1010100

9. (1100)*(1010) is equivalent to:
   (a) 1111000 (b) 110100
   (c) 111001 (d) 111100

10. (1.01) * (10.1) equals to:
    (a) 11.001 (b) 10.111
    (c) 101.01 (d) 100.11

11. The Hexadecimal number F F is equivalent to the decimal number:

[I.A.S. 2000 (Pre)]

(a) 4080 (b) 625

(c) 552 (d) 255

12. The Octal sums of $670 + 255$, $267 + 531$ and $671 + 265$ are respectively:

[I.A.S. 2000 (Pre)]

(a) 1020, 1145 and 1156

(b) 1020, 1156 and 1145

(c) 1145, 1020 and 1156

(d) 1145, 1156 and 1020

13. A combination of bits used to represent a character is known as:

[I.A.S. 2000 (Pre)]

(a) Byte (b) Binary digit

(c) Word (d) Code

14. In a flow chart, a Parallelogram box is used as: **[I.A.S. 2000 (Pre)]**

(a) Terminal box (b) A processing box

(c) An input or output box (d) A connector box

15. The Decimal number corresponding to the Binary number $(111000.0101)_2$ is:

[I.A.S. 2001 (Pre)]

(a) $(5.6312)_{10}$ (b) $(56.3125)_{10}$

(c) $(563.125)_{10}$ (d) $(5631.2)_{10}$

16. The Octal number corresponding to the decimal number $(372.21875)_{10}$ is:

[I.A.S. 2001 (Pre)]

(a) $(564.16)_{10}$ (b) $(56.416)_8$

(c) $(5.6416)_8$ (d) $(56.641)_8$

17. The product of the two numbers 0.3541E11 and 0.2672 E –09 is:

[I.A.S. 2001 (Pre)]

(a) 0.9460 E 02 (b) 0.9460 E 01

(c) 0.9460 E –99 (d) 0.9460 E 20

18. Consider the algorithm:

1. $i \leftarrow 10$
2. $i \leftarrow (i - 1)$
3. if $i > 0$, go to step 2
4. print i

The looping of the statements 2 – 3 during execution, occurs: **[I.A.S. 2003 (Pre)]**

(a) 9 times (b) 10 times

(c) 11 times (d) 12 times

19. 51 letters of a certain language are to be uniquely coded using strings of 6 bits. In this system, how many possible non-printable control characters can be uniquely coded:

[I.A.S. 2003 (Pre)]

(a) 0 (b) 8

(c) 13 (d) 77

20. What is the decimal equivalent of the hexadecimal number $(\underbrace{100\text{----}001}_{23\text{ zeros}})_{16}$:

[I.A.S. 2004]

(a) $2^{23}+1$ (b) $2^{24}+1$

(c) $2^{92}+1$ (d) $2^{96}+1$

21. If the decimal number 2^{111} is written in the Octal system, then what is its unit place digit: **[I.A.S. 2004 (Pre)]**

(a) 0 (b) 1

(c) 2 (d) 3

22. Consider the following statements regarding algorithm of a problem:

1. It begins with instructions to accept inputs.

2. The processing rules specified in the algorithm must be precise and unambiguous.

3. Total time to carry out all the steps must be infinite.

4. It must produce one or more outputs which of the statements given above are correct: **[I.A.S. 2004 (Pre)]**

(a) 1 and 4 (b) 1 and 2

(c) 2 and 3 (d) 1, 2 and 4.

23. Which one of the following is not a merit of a flow chart? **[I.A.S. 2004 (Pre)]**

(a) It aids in communicating the facts of a problem due to pictorial representation

(b) It begins at the inter-relationship of different steps involved

(c) Larger number of decision paths make the system analysis simple

(d) With the help of flow chart all the steps can be checked.

24. Which one of the following number systems results in the largest storage requirements? **[I.A.S. 2005]**

(a) Hexadecimal system (b) Octal system

(c) Decimal system (d) Binary system.

25. What is the maximum number of different characters that an 8-bit code represents? **[I.A.S. 2005]**

(a) 16 (b) 64

(c) 128 (d) 256.

26. Which of the following is correct: **[I.A.S. 2005]**

(a) The storage device are both input and output devices

(b) The program, during execution, can read data stored in auxiliary memory for input and write the output of the program into the auxiliary memory.

(c) Both are correct

(d) None of these.

27. The range of single character is:

(a) –128 to 127 (b) 127 to 150

(c) 0 to 1 (d) –1 to 1

28. To write the result on monitor screen, one use:

(a) "stdio.h" (b) printf

(c) scanf (d) None

29. Which of the following is not an arithmetic operator:

(a) '+' (b) *

(c) % (d) < =

30. The equivalent c expression to the arithmetic expression $5x^3 + 3x^3 + x + 1$ is:

(a) $5 \times x \times x \times x + 3 \times x \times x + 1 \times x + 1$

(b) $5 * x * x * x + 3 * x * x + 1 * x + 1$

(c) $c \,.\, x \,.\, x \,.\, x + 3 \,.\, x \,.\, x + 1 \,.\, x + 1$

(d) None of these

Examination Questions

1. Express the area of the triangle having sides of lengths $6\sqrt{2}, 12, 6\sqrt{2}$ units in binary number system.

   [I.A.S. 2001]

2. Convert $(100.85)_{10}$ into its binary equivalent. **[I.A.S. 2002]**

3. Multiply the binary numbers $(1111.01)_2$ and $(1101.11)_2$ and check with its decimal equivalent. **[I.A.S. 2002]**

4. Convert the following binary number into octal and hexadecimal systems:

   101110010.10010 **[I.A.S. 2003]**

5. Find the multiplication of the following binary numbers:

   11001.1 and 101.1 **[I.A.S. 2003]**

6. If $(ABCD)_{16} = (x)_2 = (y)_8 = (z)_{10}$ then find x, y and z. **[I.A.S. 2004]**

7. Find the hexadecimal equivalent of $(41819)_{10}$ and decimal equivalent of $(111011.10)_2$.

   [I.A.S. 2005]

8. Given the number 59.625 in decimal system. Write its binary equivalent.

   [I.A.S. 2006]

9. Given the number 3898 in decimal system. Write its equivalent in system base 8.

   [I.A.S. 2006]

10. **Convert:**

    (i) 46655 given to be in the decimal system into one in base 6. **[I.A.S. 2007]**

    (ii) $(11110.01)_2$, into a number in the decimal system. **[I.A.S. 2007]**

11. Convert the decimal number $(1479.25)_{10}$ to the binary and the hexadecimal numbers.

    [I.F.S. 2001]

12. Convert $(135.34)_8$ to decimal number and then convert the resulting decimal number to binary number. **[I.F.S. 2002]**

13. (i) Convert $(ABCD)_{16}$ and $(76543)_8$ to decimal. **[I.F.S. 2003]**

    (ii) Convert $(39870)_{10}$ to octal and hexadecimal. **[I.F.S. 2003]**

14. **Convert:**

(i) The decimal number 412 to octal, to binary and finally to hexadecimal number. **[I.F.S. 2004]**

(ii) The hexadecimal number F9A.BC3 to a decimal number. **[I.F.S. 2004]**

15. **Convert:**

(i) $(266.375)_{10}$ to base 8 **[I.F.S. 2008]**

(ii) $(341.24)_5$ to base 10 **[I.F.S. 2008]**

(iii) $(43.3125)_{10}$ to base 2 **[I.F.S. 2008]**

✦✦ Answers ✦✦

❖ Multiple Choice Questions

1.	(c)	**2.**	(b)	**3.**	(d)	**4.**	(c)	**5.**	(b)
6.	(a)	**7.**	(c)	**8.**	(b)	**9.**	(d)	**10.**	(a)
11.	(d)	**12.**	(c)	**13.**	(a)	**14.**	(c)	**15.**	(b)
16.	(a)	**17.**	(b)	**18.**	(a)	**19.**	(b)	**20.**	(d)
21.	(a)	**22.**	(d)	**23.**	(c)	**24.**	(d)	**25.**	(d)
26.	(c)	**27.**	(a)	**28.**	(b)	**29**	(d)	**30.**	(b)

◆◆◆

LOGARITHMS

	0	1	2	3	4	5	6	7	8	9	1 2 3	4 5 6	7 8 9
10	0000	0043	0086	0128	0170	0212	0253	0294	0334	0374	5 9 13 4 8 12	17 21 26 16 20 24	30 34 38 28 32 36
11	0414	0453	0492	0531	0569	0607	0645	0682	0719	0775	4 8 12 4 7 11	16 20 23 15 18 22	27 31 35 26 29 33
12	0792	0828	0864	0899	0934	0969	1004	1038	1072	1106	3 7 11 3 7 10	14 18 21 14 17 20	25 28 32 24 27 31
13	1139	1173	1206	1239	1271	1303	1335	1367	1399	1430	3 6 10 3 7 10	13 16 19 13 16 19	23 26 29 22 25 29
14	1461	1492	1523	1551	1584	1614	1644	1673	1703	1732	3 6 9 3 6 9	12 15 19 12 14 17	22 25 28 20 23 26
15	1761	1790	1818	1847	1875	1903	1932	1959	1987	2014	3 6 9 3 6 8	11 14 17 11 14 17	20 23 26 19 22 25
16	2041	2068	2095	2122	2148	2175	2201	2227	2253	2279	3 6 8 3 5 8	11 14 16 10 13 16	19 22 24 18 21 23
17	2304	2330	2355	2380	2405	2430	2455	2480	2504	2529	3 5 8 3 5 8	10 13 15 10 12 15	18 20 23 17 20 22
18	2533	2577	2601	2625	2648	2672	2695	2718	2742	2765	2 5 7 2 4 7	9 12 14 9 11 14	17 19 21 16 18 21
19	2788	2810	2833	2856	2878	2900	2923	2945	2967	2989	2 4 7 2 4 6	9 1i 13 8 11 13	16 18 20 15 17 19
20	3010	3032	3054	3075	3096	3118	3139	3160	3181	3201	2 4 6	8 11 13	15 17 19
21	3222	3243	3263	3284	3304	3324	3345	3365	3385	3404	2 4. 6	8 10 12	14 16 18
22	3424	3444	3464	3483	3502	3522	3541	3560	3579	3598	2 4 6	8 10 12	14 15 17
23	3617	3636	3655	3674	3692	3711	3729	3747	3766	3784	2 4 6	7 9 11	13 15 17
24	3802	3820	3838	3856	3874	3892	3909	3927	3945	3962	2 4 5	7 9 11	12 14 16
25	3979	3997	4014	4031	4048	4065	4082	4099	4116	4133	2 3 5	7 9 10	12 14 15
26	4150	4166	4183	4200	4216	4232	4249	4265	4281	4298	2 3 5	7 8 10	11 13 15
27	4314	4330	4346	4302	4378	4393	4409	4425	4440	4456	2 3 5	6 8 9	11 13 14
28	4472	4487	4502	4518	4533	4548	4564	4579	4594	4609	2 3 5	6 8 9	11 12 14
29	4624	4639	4654	4669	4683	4698	4713	4728	4742	4757	1 3 4	6 7 9	10 12 13
30	4771	4786	4800	4814	4829	4843	4857	4871	4886	4900	1 3 4	6 7 9	10 11 13
31	4914	4928	4942	4955	4969	4983	4997	5011	5024	5038	1 3 4	6 7 8	10 11 12
32	5051	5065	5079	5092	5105	5119	5132	5145	5159	5172	1 3 4	5 7 8	9 11 12
33	5185	5198	5211	5224	5237	5250	5263	5276	5289	5302	1 3 4	5 6 8	9 10 12
34	5315	5328	5340	5353	5366	5378	5391	5403	5416	5428	1 3 4	5 6 8	9 10 11
35	5441	5453	5456	5478	5490	5502	5514	5527	5539	5551	1 2 4	5 6 7	9 10 11
36	5563	5557	5587	5599	5611	5623	5635	5647	5658	5670	1 2 4	5 6 7	8 10 11
37	5682	5694	5705	5717	5729	5740	5752	5763	5775	5786	1 2 3	5 6 7	8 9 10
38	5798	5309	5821	5832	5843	5855	5866	5877	5888	5899	1 2 3	5 6 7	8 9 10
39	5911	5922	5933	5944	5955	5966	5977	5988	5999	6010	1 2 3	4 5 7	8 9 10
40	6021	6031	6042	6053	6064	6075	6085	6096	6107	6117	1 2 3	4 5 6	8 9 10
41	6128	6138	6149	6160	6170	6180	6191	6201	6212	6222	1 2 3	4 5 6	7 8 9
42	6232	6243	6253	6263	6274	6284	6294	6304	6314	6325	1 2 3	4 5 6	7 8 9
43	6335	6345	6355	6365	6375	6385	6395	6405	6415	6425	1 2 3	4 5 6	7 8 9
44	6435	6444	6454	6464	6474	6484	6493	6503	6513	6522	1 2 3	4 5 6	7 8 9
45	6532	6542	6551	6561	6571	6580	6590	6599	6609	6618	1 2 3	4 5 6	7 8 9
46	6628	6637	6646	6656	6665	6675	6684	6693	6702	6712	1 2 3	4 5 6	7 7 8
47	6721	6730	6739	6749	6758	6767	6776	6785	6794	6803	1 2 3	4 5 6	6 7 8
48	6812	6821	6830	6839	6848	6857	6866	6875	6884	6893	1 2 3	4 5 6	6 7 8
49	6902	6911	6920	6928	6937	6946	6955	6964	6972	6981	1 2 3	4 5 6	6 7 8

LOGARITHMS

	0	1	2	3	4	5	6	7	8	9	1 2 3	4 5 6	7 8 9
50	6990	6998	7007	7016	7024	7033	7042	7050	7059	7067	1 2 3	3 4 5	6 7 8
51	7076	7084	7093	7101	7110	7118	7126	7135	7143	7152	1 2 3	3 4 5	6 7 8
52	7160	7168	7177	7185	7193	7202	7210	7218	7226	7235	1 2 2	3 4 5	6 7 7
53	7243	7251	7259	7267	7275	7284	7292	7300	7308	7316	1 2 2	3 4 5	6 6 7
54	7324	7332	7340	7348	7356	7364	7372	7380	7388	7396	1 2 2	3 4 5	6 6 7
55	7404	7412	7419	7427	7435	7443	7451	7459	7466	7474	1 2 2	3 4 5	5 6 7
56	7482	7490	7497	7505	7513	7520	7528	7536	7543	7551	1 2 2	3 4 5	5 6 7
57	7559	7566	7574	7582	7589	7597	7604	7612	7619	7627	1 2 2	3 4 5	5 6 7
58	7634	7642	7649	7657	7664	7672	7679	7686	7694	7701	1 1 2	3 4 4	5 6 7
59	7709	7716	7723	7731	7738	7745	7752	7760	7767	7774	1 1 2	3 4 4	5 6 7
60	7782	7789	7796	7803	7810	7818	7825	7832	7839	7846	1 1 2	3 4 4	5 6 6
61	7853	7860	7868	7875	7882	7889	7896	7903	7910	7917	1 1 2	3 4 4	5 6 6
62	7924	7931	7938	7945	7952	7959	7966	7973	7980	7987	1 1 2	3 3 4	5 6 6
63	7993	8000	8007	8014	8021	8028	8035	8041	8048	8055	1 1 2	3 3 4	5 5 6
64	8062	8069	8075	8082	8089	8096	8102	8109	8116	8122	1 1 2	3 3 4	5 5 6
65	8129	8136	8142	8149	8156	8162	8269	8176	8182	8189	1 1 2	3 3 4	5 5 6
66	8195	8202	8209	8215	8222	8228	8235	8241	8248	8254	1 1 2	3 3 4	5 5 6
67	8261	8267	8274	8280	8287	8293	8299	8306	8312	8319	1 1 2	3 3 4	5 5 6
68	8325	8331	8338	8344	8351	8357	8363	8370	8376	8382	1 1 2	3 3 4	4 5 6
69	8388	8395	8401	8407	8414	8420	8426	8432	8439	8545	1 1 2	2 3 4	4 5 6
70	8451	8457	8463	8470	8476	8482	8488	8494	8500	8506	1 1 2	2 3 4	4 5 6
71	8513	8519	8525	8531	8537	8543	8549	8555	8561	8567	1 1 2	2 3 4	4 5 6
72	8573	8579	8585	8591	8597	8603	8609	8615	8621	8627	1 1 2	2 3 4	4 5 5
73	8633	8639	8645	8651	8557	8663	8669	8675	8681	8686	1 1 2	2 3 4	4 5 5
74	8692	8698	8704	8710	8716	8722	8727	8733	8739	8745	1 1 2	2 3 4	4 5 5
75	8751	8756	8762	8768	8774	8779	8785	8791	8797	8802	1 1 2	2 3 3	4 5 5
76	8808	8814	8820	8825	8832	8837	8842	8848	8854	8859	1 1 2	2 3 3	4 5 5
77	8865	8871	8876	8882	8887	8893	8899	8904	8910	8915	1 1 2	2 3 3	4 4 5
78	8921	8927	8932	8938	8943	8949	8954	8960	8965	8971	1 1 2	2 3 3	4 4 5
79	8976	8982	8987	8993	8998	9004	9009	9015	9020	9025	1 1 2	2 3 3	4 4 5
80	9031	9036	9042	9047	9053	9058	9063	9069	9074	9079	1 1 2	2 3 3	4 4 5
81	9085	9090	9096	9101	9106	9112	9117	9122	9128	9133	1 1 2	2 3 3	4 4 5
82	9138	9143	9149	9154	9159	9165	9170	9175	9180	9186	1 1 2	2 3 3	4 4 5
83	9191	9196	9201	9206	9212	9217	9222	9227	9232	9238	1 1 2	2 3 3	4 4 5
84	9243	9248	9253	9258	9263	9269	9274	9279	9284	9289	1 1 2	2 3 3	4 4 5
85	9294	9299	9304	9309	9315	9320	9325	9330	9335	9340	1 1 2	2 3 3	4 4 5
86	9345	9350	9335	9360	9365	9370	9375	9380	9385	9390	1 1 2	2 3 3	4 4 5
87	9395	9400	9405	9410	9415	9420	9425	9430	9435	9440	0 1 1	2 2 3	3 4 4
88	9445	9450	9455	9460	9465	9469	9474	9479	9484	9489	0 1 1	2 2 3	3 4 4
89	9494	9499	9504	9509	9513	9518	9523	9528	9533	9538	0 1 1	2 2 3	3 4 4
90	9542	9547	9552	9557	9562	9566	9571	9576	9581	9586	0 1 1	2 2 3	3 4 4
91	9590	9595	9600	9605	9609	9614	9616	9624	9628	9633	0 1 1	2 2 3	3 4 4
92	9638	9643	9647	9652	9657	9661	9666	9671	9675	9680	0 1 1	2 2 3	3 4 4
93	9685	9689	9694	9699	9703	9708	9713	9717	9722	9727	0 1 1	2 2 3	3 4 4
94	9731	9736	9741	9745	9750	9754	9759	9763	9768	9773	0 1 1	2 2 3	3 4 4
95	9777	9782	9786	9791	9795	9800	9805	9809	9814	9818	0 1 1	2 2 3	3 4 4
96	9823	9827	9832	9836	9841	9845	9850	9854	9859	9863	0 1 1	2 2 3	3 4 4
97	9868	9872	9877	9881	9886	9890	9894	9899	9903	9908	0 1 1	2 2 3	3 4 4
98	9912	9917	9921	9926	9930	9934	9939	9943	9948	9952	0 1 1	2 2 3	3 4 4
99	9956	9961	9965	9969	9974	9978	9983	9987	9991	9996	0 1 1	2 2 3	3 3 4

ANTILOGARITHMS

	0	1	2	3	4	5	6	7	8	9	1 2 3	4 5 6	7 8 9
.00	1000	1002	1005	1007	1009	1012	1014	1016	1019	1021	0 0 1	1 1 1	2 2 2
.01	1023	1026	1028	1030	1033	1035	1038	1040	1042	1045	0 0 1	1 1 1	2 2 2
.02	1047	1050	1052	1054	1057	1059	1062	1064	1067	1069	0 0 1	1 1 1	2 2 2
.03	1072	1074	1076	1079	1081	1084	1086	1089	1091	1094	0 0 1	1 1 1	2 2 2
.04	1096	1099	1102	1104	1107	1109	1112	1114	1117	1119	0 1 1	1 1 2	2 2 2
.05	1122	1125	1127	1130	1132	1135	1138	1140	1143	1146	0 1 1	1 2 2	2 2 2
.06	1148	1151	1153	1156	1159	1161	1164	1167	1169	1172	0 1 1	1 2 2	2 2 2
.07	1175	1178	1180	1183	1186	1189	1191	1194	1197	1199	0 1 1	1 2 2	2 2 2
.08	1202	1205	1208	1211	1213	1216	1219	1122	1225	1227	0 1 1	1 2 2	2 2 3
.09	1230	1233	1236	1139	1242	1245	1247	1250	1253	1256	0 1 1	1 2 2	2 2 3
.10	1259	1262	1256	1268	1271	1274	1276	1279	1282	1285	0 1 1	1 2 2	2 2 3
.11	1288	1291	1294	1297	1300	1303	1306	1309	1312	1315	0 1 1	1 2 2	2 2 3
.12	1318	1321	1324	1327	1330	1334	1337	1340	1343	1346	0 1 1	1 2 2	2 2 3
.13	1349	1352	1355	1358	1361	1365	1368	1371	1374	1377	0 1 1	1 2 2	2 3 3
.14	1380	1384	1387	1390	1393	1396	1400	1403	1406	1409	0 1 1	1 2 2	2 3 3
.15	1413	1416	1419	1422	1426	1429	1432	1435	1439	1442	0 1 1	1 2 2	2 3 3
.16	1445	1449	1452	1455	1459	1462	1466	1469	1472	1476	0 1 1	1 2 2	2 3 3
.17	1479	1483	1486	1489	1493	1496	1500	1503	1507	1510	0 1 1	1 2 2	2 3 3
.18	1514	1517	1521	1524	1528	1531	1535	1538	1542	1545	0 1 1	1 2 2	2 3 3
.19	1549	1552	1556	1560	1563	1567	1570	1574	1578	1581	0 1 1	1 2 2	3 3 3
.20	1585	1589	1592	1596	1600	1603	1607	1611	1614	1618	0 1 1	1 2 2	3 3 3
.21	1622	1626	1629	1633	1637	1641	1644	1648	1652	1656	0 1 1	2 2 2	3 3 3
.22	1660	1663	1667	1671	1675	1679	1683	1687	1690	1694	0 1 1	2 2 2	3 3 3
.23	1698	1702	1706	1710	1714	1718	1722	1726	1730	1734	0 1 1	2 2 2	3 3 4
.24	1738	1742	1746	1750	1754	1758	1762	1766	1770	1774	0 1 1	2 2 2	3 3 4
.25	1778	1782	1786	1791	1795	1799	1803	1807	1811	1816	0 1 1	2 2 2	3 3 4
.26	1820	1824	1828	1832	1837	1841	1845	1849	1854	1858	0 1 1	2 2 3	3 3 4
.27	1862	1866	1871	1875	1879	1884	1888	1892	1897	1901	0 1 1	2 2 3	3 3 4
.28	1905	1910	1914	1919	1923	1928	1932	1936	1941	1945	0 1 1	2 2 3	3 4 4
.29	1950	1954	1959	1963	1968	1972	1977	1982	1986	1991	0 1 1	2 2 3	3 4 4
.30	1995	2000	2004	2009	2014	2018	2023	2028	2032	2037	0 1 1	2 2 3	3 4 4
.31	2042	2046	2051	2056	2061	2065	2070	2075	2080	2084	0 1 1	2 2 3	3 4 4
.32	2089	2094	2099	2104	2109	2113	2118	2123	2128	2133	0 1 1	2 2 3	3 4 4
.33	2138	2143	2148	2153	2158	2163	2168	2173	2178	2183	0 1 1	2 2 3	3 4 4
.34	2188	2193	2198	2203	2208	2213	2218	2223	2228	2234	1 1 2	2 3 3	4 4 5
.35	2239	2244	2249	2254	2259	2265	2270	2275	2280	2286	1 1 2	2 3 3	4 4 5
.36	2291	2296	2301	2307	2312	2317	2323	2328	2333	2339	1 1 2	2 3 3	4 4 5
.37	2344	2350	2355	2360	2366	2371	2377	2382	2388	2393	1 1 2	2 3 3	4 4 5
.38	2399	2404	2410	2415	2421	2427	2432	2438	2443	2449	1 1 2	2 3 3	4 4 5
.39	2455	2460	2466	2472	2477	2483	2489	2495	2500	2506	1 1 2	2 3 3	4 5 5
.40	2512	2518	2523	2529	2535	2541	2547	2553	2559	2564	1 1 2	2 3 4	4 5 5
.41	2570	2576	2582	2588	2594	2600	2606	2612	2618	2624	1 1 2	2 3 4	4 5 5
.42	2630	2636	2642	2649	2655	2661	2667	2673	2679	2685	1 1 2	2 3 4	4 5 6
.43	2692	2698	2704	2710	2716	2723	2729	2735	2742	2748	1 1 2	3 3 4	4 5 6
.44	2754	2761	2767	2773	2780	2786	2793	2799	2805	2812	1 1 2	3 3 4	4 5 6
.45	2818	2825	2831	2838	2844	2851	2858	2864	2871	2877	1 1 2	3 3 4	5 5 6
.46	2884	2891	2897	2904	2911	2917	2924	2931	2938	2944	1 1 2	3 3 4	5 5 6
.47	2951	2958	2965	2972	2979	2985	2992	2999	3006	3013	1 1 2	3 3 4	5 5 6
.48	3020	3027	3034	3041	3048	3055	3062	3069	3076	3083	1 1 2	3 4 4	5 6 6
.49	3090	3097	3105	3112	3119	3126	3133	3141	3148	3155	1 1 2	3 4 4	5 6 6

ANTILOGARITHMS

	0	1	2	3	4	5	6	7	8	9	1	2	3	4	5	6	7	8	9
.50	3162	3170	3177	3184	3192	3199	3206	3214	3221	3228	1	1	2	3	4	5	5	6	7
.51	3236	3243	3251	3258	3266	3273	3281	3289	3296	3304	1	2	2	3	4	5	5	6	7
.52	3311	3319	3327	3334	3342	3350	3357	3365	3373	3381	1	2	2	3	4	5	5	6	7
.53	3388	3396	3404	3412	3420	3428	3436	3443	3451	3459	1	2	2	3	4	5	6	6	7
.54	3467	3475	3483	3491	3499	3508	3516	3524	3532	3540	1	2	2	3	4	5	6	6	7
.55	3548	3556	3565	3573	3581	3589	3597	3606	3614	3622	1	2	2	3	4	5	6	7	7
.56	3631	3639	3648	3656	3664	3673	3681	3690	3698	3707	1	2	3	3	4	5	6	7	8
.57	3715	3724	3733	3741	3750	3758	3767	3776	3784	3793	1	2	3	3	4	5	6	7	8
.58	3802	3811	3819	3828	3837	3846	3855	3864	3873	3882	1	2	3	4	4	5	6	7	8
.59	3890	3899	3908	3917	3926	3936	3945	3959	3963	3972	1	2	3	4	5	6	6	7	8
.60	3981	3990	3999	4009	4018	4027	4036	4046	4055	4064	1	2	3	4	5	6	6	7	8
.61	4074	4083	4093	4102	4111	4121	4130	4140	4150	4159	1	2	3	4	5	6	7	8	9
.62	4169	4178	4188	4198	4207	4217	4227	4236	4246	4256	1	2	3	4	5	6	7	8	9
.63	4266	4276	4285	4295	4305	4315	4325	4335	4345	4355	1	2	3	4	5	6	7	8	9
.64	4365	4375	4385	4395	4406	4416	4426	4436	4446	4457	1	2	3	4	5	6	7	8	9
.65	4467	4477	4487	4498	4508	4519	4529	4539	4550	4560	1	2	3	4	5	6	7	8	9
.66	4571	4581	45)2	4603	4613	4624	4634	4645	4556	4667	1	2	3	4	5	6	7	9	10
.67	4677	4688	4699	4710	4721	4732	4742	4753	4764	4675	1	2	3	4	5	7	8	9	10
.68	4786	4797	4808	4819	4831	4842	4853	4864	4875	4887	1	2	3	5	6	7	8	9	10
.69	4898	4909	4920	4932	4943	4955	4966	4977	4989	5000	1	2	3	5	6	7	8	9	10
.70	5012	5023	5035	5047	5058	5070	5082	5093	5105	5117	1	2	4	5	6	7	8	9	11
.71	5129	5140	5152	5164	5176	5188	5200	5212	5224	5236	1	2	4	5	6	7	8	10	11
.72	5248	5260	5272	5284	5297	5309	5321	5333	5346	5358	1	2	4	5	6	7	9	10	11
.73	5370	5383	5395	5408	5420	5433	5445	5458	5470	5483	1	3	4	5	6	8	9	10	11
.74	5495	5508	5521	5534	5546	5559	5572	5585	5598	5610	1	3	4	5	6	8	9	10	12
.75	5623	5636	5649	5662	5675	5689	5702	5715	5728	5741	1	3	4	5	7	8	9	10	12
.76	5754	5768	5781	5794	5808	5821	5834	5848	5861	5875	1	3	4	5	7	8	9	11	12
.77	5888	5902	5916	5929	5943	5957	5970	5984	5998	6012	1	3	4	5	7	8	10	11	12
.78	6026	6039	6053	6067	6081	6095	6109	6124	6138	6152	1	3	4	6	7	8	10	11	13
.79	6166	6180	6194	6209	6223	6237	6252	6266	6281	6295	1	3	4	6	7	9	10	11	13
.80	6310	6324	6339	63)3	6308	6383	6397	6412	6427	6442	1	3	4	6	7	9	11	12	13
.81	6457	6471	6486	6501	6516	6431	6546	6561	6577	6592	2	3	5	6	8	9	11	12	14
.82	6607	6622	6637	6653	6668	6683	6699	6714	6730	6745	2	3	5	6	8	9	11	12	14
.83	6761	6776	6792	6803	6823	6839	6855	6871	6887	6902	2	3	5	6	8	9	11	13	14
.84	6918	6934	6950	6966	6982	6998	7015	7031	7047	7063	2	3	5	6	8	10	11	13	15
.85	7079	7096	7112	7129	7145	7161	7178	7194	7211	7228	2	3	5	7	8	10	12	13	15
.86	7244	7261	7278	7295	7311	7328	7345	7362	7379	7396	2	3	5	7	8	10	12	13	15
.87	7413	7430	7447	7464	7482	7499	7516	7534	7551	7568	2	3	5	7	9	10	12	14	16
.88	7686	7603	7621	7638	7656	7674	7691	7709	7727	7745	2	4	5	7	9	11	12	14	16
.89	7762	7780	7798	7816	7834	7852	7870	7889	7907	7825	2	4	5	7	9	11	13	14	16
.90	7943	7962	7980	7998	8017	8035	8054	8072	8091	8110	2	4	6	7	9	11	13	15	17
.91	8128	8147	8166	8185	8204	8222	8241	8260	8279	8299	2	4	6	8	9	11	13	15	17
.92	8318	8337	8356	8375	8395	8414	8433	8453	8472	8492	2	4	6	8	10	12	14	15	17
.93	8511	8531	8551	8570	8590	8610	8630	8650	8670	8690	2	4	6	8	10	12	14	16	18
.94	8710	8730	8750	8770	8790	8810	8831	8851	8872	8892	2	4	6	8	10	12	14	16	18
.95	8913	8933	8954	8974	8995	9016	9036	9057	9078	9099	2	4	6	8	10	12	15	17	19
.96	9120	9141	9162	9183	8204	9226	9247	9208	9290	9311	2	4	6	8	11	13	15	17	19
.97	9333	9354	9376	9307	9419	9441	9462	9484	9596	9528	2	4	7	9	11	13	15	17	20
.98	9550	9572	9594	9616	9638	9661	9683	9705	9727	9750	2	4	7	9	11	13	16	18	20
.99	9772	9795	9817	9840	9863	9886	9908	9931	9954	9977	2	5	7	9	11	13	16	18	20

POWERS, ROOTS AND RECIPROCALS

n	n^2	n^3	$\sqrt{n}$	$\sqrt[3]{n}$	$\sqrt{10n}$	$\sqrt[3]{10n}$	$\sqrt[3]{100n}$	$1/n$
1	1	1	1.000	1.000	3.162	2.154	4.642	1.000
2	4	8	1.414	1.260	4.472	2.714	5.848	.5000
3	9	27	1.732	1.472	5.477	3.107	6.694	.3333
4	16	64	2.000	1.587	6.325	3.420	7.368	.2500
5	25	125	2.236	1.710	7.071	3.684	7.937	.2000
6	36	216	2.449	1.817	7.746	3.915	8.434	.1667
7	49	343	2.646	1.913	8.367	4.121	8.879	.1429
8	64	512	2.828	2.000	8.944	4.309	9.283	.1250
9	81	729	3.000	2.080	9.487	4.481	9.655	.1111
10	100	1000	3.162	2.154	10.000	4.642	10.000	.1000
11	121	1331	3.317	2.224	10.488	4.791	10.323	.09091
12	144	1728	3.464	2.289	10.954	4.932	10.627	.08333
13	169	2197	3.606	2.351	11.402	5.066	10.914	.07692
14	196	2744	3.742	2.410	11.832	5.192	11.187	.07143
15	225	3375	3.873	2.466	12.247	5.313	11.447	.06667
16	256	4096	4.000	2.520	12.649	5.429	11.696	.06250
17	289	4913	4.123	2.571	13.038	5.540	11.935	.05882
18	324	5832	4.243	2.621	13.416	5.646	12.164	.05556
19	361	6859	4.359	2.668	13.784	5.749	12.386	.05263
20	400	8000	4.472	2.714	14.142	5.848	12.599	.0500
21	441	9261	4.583	2.759	14.491	5.944	12.806	.04762
22	484	10648	4.690	2.802	14.832	6.037	13.006	.04545
23	529	12167	4.796	2.844	15.166	6.127	13.200	.04348
24	576	13824	4.899	2.884	15.492	6.214	13.389	.04167
25	625	15625	5.000	2.924	15.811	6.300	13.572	.0400
26	676	17576	5.099	2.962	16.125	6.383	13.751	.03846
27	729	19683	5.196	3.000	16.432	6.463	13.925	.03704
28	784	21952	5.292	3.037	16.733	6.542	14.095	.03571
29	841	24389	5.385	3.072	17.029	6.619	14.260	.03448
30	900	27000	5.477	3.107	17.321	6.694	14.422	.03333
31	961	29791	5.568	3.141	17.607	6.768	14.581	.03226
32	1024	32768	5.657	3.175	17.889	6.840	14.736	.03125
33	1089	35937	5.745	3.208	18.166	6.910	14.888	.03030
34	1156	39304	5.831	3.240	18.439	6.980	15.037	.02941
35	1225	42875	5.916	3.271	18.708	7.047	15.183	.02857
36	1296	46656	6.000	3.302	18.974	7.114	15.326	.02778
37	1369	50653	6.083	3.332	19.235	7.179	15.467	.02703
38	1444	54872	6.164	3.362	19.494	7.243	15.605	.02632
39	1521	59319	6.245	3.391	19.748	7.306	15.741	.02564
40	1600	64000	6.325	3.420	20.00	7.368	15.874	.02500
41	1681	68921	6.403	3.448	20.248	7.429	16.005	.02439
42	1764	74088	6.481	3.476	20.494	7.489	16.134	.02381
43	1849	79507	6.557	3.503	20.736	7.548	16.261	.02326
44	1936	85184	6.633	3.530	20.976	7.606	16.386	.02273
45	2025	91125	6.708	3.557	21.213	7.663	16.510	02222
46	2116	97336	6.782	3.583	21.448	7.719	16.631	.02174
47	2209	103823	6.856	3.609	21.679	7.775	16.751	.02128
48	2304	110592	6.928	3.634	21.909	7.830	16.869	.02083
49	2401	117649	7.000	3.659	22.136	7.884	16.985	.02041
50	2500	125000	7.071	3.684	22.361	7.937	17.100	.02000

POWERS, ROOTS AND RECIPROCALS

n	n^2	n^3	$\sqrt{n}$	$\sqrt[3]{n}$	10n	$\sqrt[3]{10n}$	$\sqrt[3]{100n}$	1/n
51	2601	132651	7.141	3.708	22.583	7.990	17.213	.01961
52	2704	140608	7.211	3.733	22.804	8.041	17.325	.01923
53	2809	148877	7.280	3.756	23.022	8.093	17.435	.01887
54	2916	157464	7.348	3.780	23.238	8.143	17.544	.01852
55	3025	166375	7.416	3.803	23.452	8.193	17.652	.01818
56	3136	175616	7.483	3.826	23.664	8.243	17.758	.01786
57	3249	185193	7.550	3.849	23.875	8.291	17.863	.01754
58	3364	195112	7.616	3.871	24.083	8.340	17.967	.01724
59	3481	205379	7.681	3.893	24.290	8.387	18.070	.01695
60	3600	216000	7.746	3.915	24.495	8.434	18.171	.01667
61	3721	226981	7.810	3.936	24.698	8.481	18.272	.01639
62	3844	238328	7.874	3.958	24.900	8.527	18.371	.01613
63	3969	250047	7.937	3.979	25.100	8.573	18.469	.01587
64	4096	262144	8.000	4.000	25.298	8.618	18.566	.01562
65	4225	274625	8.062	4.021	25.495	8.662	18.663	.01538
66	4356	287496	8.124	4.041	25.690	8.707	18.758	.01515
67	4489	300763	8.185	4.062	25.884	8.750	18.852	.01493
68	4624	314432	8.246	4.082	26.077	8.794	18.945	.01471
69	4761	328509	8.307	4.102	26.268	8.837	19.038	.01449
70	4900	343000	8.367	4.121	26.458	8.879	19.129	.01429
71	5041	357911	8.426	4.141	26.646	8.921	19.220	.01408
72	5184	373248	8.485	4.160	26.833	8.963	19.310	.01389
73	5329	389017	8.544	4.179	27.019	9.004	19.399	.01370
74	5476	405224	8.602	4.198	27.203	9.045	19.487	.01351
75	5625	421875	8.660	4.217	27.386	9.086	19.574	.01333
76	5776	438976	8.718	4.236	27.568	9.126	19.661	.01316
77	5929	456533	8.775	4.254	27.749	9.166	19.747	.01299
78	6084	474552	8.832	4.273	27.928	9.205	19.832	.01282
79	6241	493039	8.888	4.291	28.107	9.244	19.916	.01266
80	6400	512000	8.944	4.309	28.284	9.283	20.000	.01250
81	6561	531441	9.000	4.327	28.460	9.322	20.083	.01235
82	6724	551368	9.055	4.344	28.636	9.360	20.165	.01220
83	6889	571787	9.110	4.362	28.810	9.398	20.247	.01205
84	7056	592704	9.165	4.380	28.983	9.435	20.328	.01190
85	7225	614125	9.220	4.397	29.155	9.473	20.408	.01176
86	7396	636056	9.274	4.414	29.326	9.510	20.488	.01163
87	7569	658503	9.327	4.431	29.496	9.546	20.567	.01149
88	7744	681472	9.381	4.448	29.665	9.583	20.646	.01136
89	7921	704969	9.434	4..465	29.833	9.619	20.724	.01124
90	8100	729000	9.487	4.481	30.000	9.655	20.801	.01111
91	8281	753571	9.539	4..498	30.166	9.691	20.878	.01099
92	8464	778688	9.592	4.514	30.332	9.726	20.954	.01087
93	8649	804357	9.644	4.531	30.496	9.761	21.029	.01075
94	8836	830584	9.695	4.547	30.659	9.796	21.105	.01064
95	9025	857375	9.747	4.563	30.822	9.830	21.179	.01053
96	9216	884736	9.798	4.579	30.984	9.865	21.253	.01042
97	9409	912673	9.849	4.595	31.145	9.899	21.327	.01031
98	9604	941192	9.899	4.610	31.305	9.933	21.400	.01020
99	9801	970299	9.950	4.626	31.464	9.967	21.472	.01010
100	10000	1000000	10.000	4.642	31.623	10.000	21.544	.01000

NATURAL TANGENTS

Degrees	0'	6'	12'	18'	24'	30'	36'	42'	48'	54'	Mean Differences				
	0'.0	0'.1	0'.2	0'.3	0'.4	0'.5	0'.6	0'.7	0'.8	0'.9	1	2	3	4	5
0	.0000	0017	0035	0052	0070	0087	0105	0122	0140	0157	3	6	9	12	15
1	.0175	0192	0209	0227	0244	0262	0279	0297	0314	0332	3	6	9	12	15
2	.0349	0367	0384	3402	0419	0437	0454	0472	0489	0507	3	6	9	12	15
3	.0524	0542	0559	0577	0594	0612	0629	0647	0664	0682	3	6	9	12	15
4	.0699	0717	0734	0752	0769	0787	0805	0822	0840	0857	3	6	9	12	15
5	.0875	0892	0910	0928	0945	0963	0981	0998	1016	1033	3	6	9	12	15
6	.1051	1069	1086	1104	1122	1139	1157	1175	1192	1210	3	6	9	12	15
7	.1128	1246	1263	1281	1299	1317	1334	1353	1370	1388	3	6	9	12	15
8	.1405	1423	1441	1459	1477	1495	1512	1530	1548	1566	3	6	9	12	15
9	.1584	1602	1620	1638	1655	1673	1691	1709	1727	1745	3	6	9	12	15
10	.1763	1781	1799	1817	1835	1853	1871	1890	1908	1926	3	6	9	12	15
11	.1944	1962	1980	1998	2016	2035	2053	2071	2039	2107	3	6	9	12	15
12	.2126	2144	2162	2180	2199	2217	2235	2254	2272	2290	3	6	9	12	15
13	.2309	2327	2345	2364	2382	2401	2419	2438	2456	2475	3	6	9	12	15
14	.2493	2512	2530	2549	2568	2586	2605	2623	2642	2661	3	6	9	12	16
15	.2679	2698	2717	2736	2754	2773	2792	2811	2830	2849	3	6	9	13	16
16	.2867	2886	2905	2924	2943	2962	2981	3000	3019	3038	3	6	9	13	16
17	.3057	3076	3096	3115	3134	3153	3172	3191	3211	3230	3	6	10	13	16
18	.3249	3269	3288	3307	3327	3346	3365	3385	3404	3424	3	6	10	13	16
19	.3443	3463	3482	3502	3522	3541	3561	3581	3600	3620	3	7	10	13	16
20	.3640	3659	3679	3699	3719	3739	3759	3779	3799	3819	3	7	10	13	17
21	.3839	3859	3879	3899	3919	3939	3959	3979	4000	4020	3	7	10	13	17
22	.4040	4061	4081	4101	4122	4142	4163	4183	4204	4224	3	7	10	14	17
23	.4245	4265	4286	4307	4327	4348	4369	4390	4411	4431	3	7	10	14	17
24	.4452	4473	4494	4515	4536	4557	4578	4599	4621	4642	4	7	11	14	18
25	.4663	4684	4706	4727	4748	4770	4791	4813	4834	4856	4	7	11	14	18
26	.4877	4899	4921	4942	4964	4986	5008	5029	5051	5073	4	7	11	15	18
27	.5095	5117	5139	5161	5184	5206	5228	5250	5272	5295	4	7	11	15	18
28	.5317	5340	5362	5384	5407	5430	5452	5475	5498	5520	4	8	11	15	19
29	.5543	5566	5589	5612	5635	5658	5681	5704	5727	5750	4	8	12	15	19
30	.5774	5797	5820	5844	5867	5890	5914	5938	5961	5985	4	8	12	16	20
31	.6009	6032	6056	6030	6104	6128	6152	6176	6200	6224	4	8	12	16	20
32	.6249	6273	6297	6322	6346	6371	6395	6420	6445	6469	4	8	12	16	20
33	.6494	6519	6544	6569	6594	0619	6644	6669	6694	6720	4	8	13	17	21
34	.6745	6771	6796	6822	6847	6873	6899	6924	6950	6976	4	9	13	17	21
35	.7002	7028	7054	7080	7107	7133	7159	7186	7212	7239	4	9	13	18	22
36	.7265	7292	7319	7346	7373	7400	7427	7454	7481	7508	5	9	14	18	23
37	.7536	7563	7590	7618	7646	7673	7701	7729	7757	7785	5	9	14	18	23
38	.7813	7841	7869	7898	7926	7954	7983	8012	8040	8069	5	9	14	19	24
39	.8098	8127	8156	8185	8214	8243	8273	8302	8332	8361	5	10	15	20	24
40	.8391	8421	8451	8481	8511	8541	8571	8601	8632	8662	5	10	15	20	25
41	.8693	8724	8754	8785	8816	8847	8878	8910	8941	8972	5	10	16	21	26
42	.9004	9036	9067	9099	9131	9163	9195	9228	9260	9293	5	11	16	21	27
43	.9325	9358	9391	9424	9457	9490	9523	9556	9590	9623	5	11	17	22	28
44	.9657	9691	9725	9759	9793	9827	9861	9896	9930	9965	5	11	17	23	29

NATURAL TANGENTS

Degrees	0'	6'	12'	18'	24'	30'	36'	42'	48'	54'	Mean Differences				
	0'.0	0'.1	0'.2	0'.3	0'.4	0'.5	0'.6	0'.7	0'.8	0'.9	1	2	3	4	5
45	1.0000	0035	0070	0105	0141	0176	0212	0247	0283	0319	6	12	18	24	30
46	1.0355	0392	0428	0464	0501	0538	0575	0612	0649	0686	6	12	18	25	31
47	1.0724	0761	0799	0837	0875	0913	0951	0990	1028	1067	6	13	19	25	32
48	1.1106	1145	1184	1224	1263	1303	1343	1383	1423	1463	7	13	20	27	33
49	1.1504	1544	1585	1626	1667	1708	1750	1792	1833	1875	7	14	21	28	34
50	1.1918	1960	2002	2045	2088	2131	2174	2218	2261	2305	7	14	22	29	36
51	1.2349	2393	2437	2482	2527	2572	2617	2662	2708	2753	8	15	23	30	38
52	1.2799	2846	2892	2938	2985	3032	3079	3127	3175	3222	8	16	24	31	39
53	1.3270	3319	3367	3416	3465	3514	3564	3613	3663	3713	8	16	25	33	41
54	1.3764	3814	3865	3916	3968	4019	4071	4124	4176	4229	9	17	26	34	43
55	1.4281	4335	4388	4442	4496	4550	4605	4659	4715	4770	9	18	27	36	45
56	1.4826	4882	4938	4994	5051	5108	5166	5224	5282	5340	10	19	29	38	48
57	1.5399	5458	5517	5577	5637	5697	5757	5818	5880	5941	10	20	30	40	50
58	1.6003	6066	6128	6191	6255	6319	6383	6447	6512	6577	11	21	32	43	53
59	1.6643	6709	6775	6842	6909	6977	7045	7113	7182	7251	11	23	34	45	56
60	1.7321	7391	7461	7532	7603	7675	7747	7820	7893	7966	12	24	36	48	60
61	1.8040	8115	8190	8265	8341	8418	8495	8572	8650	8728	13	26	38	51	64
62	1.8807	8887	8967	9047	9128	9210	9292	9375	9458	9542	14	27	41	55	68
63	1.9626	9711	9797	9883	9970	2.0057	2.0145	2.0233	2.0323	2.0413	15	29	44	58	73
64	2.0503	0594	0686	0778	0872	0965	1060	1155	1251	1348	16	31	47	63	78
65	2.1445	1543	1642	1742	1842	1943	2045	2148	2251	2355	17	34	51	68	85
66	2.2460	2566	2673	2781	2889	2998	3109	3220	3332	3445	18	37	55	73	92
67	2.3559	3673	3789	3906	4023	4142	4262	4383	4504	4627	20	40	60	79	99
68	2.4751	4876	5002	5129	5257	5386	5517	5040	5782	5016	22	43	65	87	108
69	2.6051	6187	6325	6464	6605	6746	6889	7034	7179	7326	24	47	71	95	119
70	2.7475	7625	7776	7929	8083	8239	8397	8556	8716	8878	26	52	78	104	131
71	2.9042	9208	9375	9544	9714	9887	3.0061	3.0237	3.0415	3.0595	29	58	87	116	145
72	3.0777	0961	1146	1334	1524	1716	1910	2106	2305	2506	32	64	96	129	161
73	3.2709	2914	3122	3332	3544	3759	3977	4197	4420	4646	36	72	108	144	180
74	3.4874	5105	5339	5576	5816	6059	6305	6554	6806	7062	41	81	122	163	204
75	3.7321	7583	7848	8118	8391	8667	8947	9232	9520	9612	46	93	139	186	232
76	4.0108	0406	0713	1022	1335	1653	1976	2303	2635	2972	53	107	160	213	267
77	4.3315	3662	4015	4374	4737	5107	5483	5864	6252	6646					
78	4.7046	7453	7867	8288	8716	9152	9594	5.0045	5.0504	5.0970					
79	5.1446	1929	2422	2924	3435	3955	4486	5026	5578	6140					
80	5.6713	7297	7894	8502	9124	9758	6.0405	6.1066	6.1742	6.2432					
81	6.3138	3859	4596	5330	6122	6912	7720	8548	9395	7.0264					
82	7.1154	2066	3002	3962	4947	5958	6996	8062	9158	8.0285					
83	8.1444	2636	3863	5126	6427	7769	9152	9.0579	9.2052	9.3572	Mean differences cease to be sufficiently accurate				
84	9.5144	9.677	9.845	10.02	10.20	10.39	10.58	10.78	10.99	11.20					
85	11.43	11.66	11.91	12.16	12.43	12.71	13.00	13.30	13.62	13.95					
86	14.30	14.67	15.06	15.46	15.89	16.35	16.83	17.34	17.89	18.46					
87	19.08	19.74	20.45	21.20	22.02	22.90	23.86	24.90	26.03	27.27					
88	28.64	30.14	31.82	33.69	35.80	38.19	40.92	44.07	47.74	52.08					
89	57.29	63.66	71.62	81.85	95.49	114.6	143.2	191.0	286.5	573.0					

NATURAL SINES

Degrees	0'	6'	12'	18'	24'	30'	36'	42'	48'	54'	Mean Differences				
	0'.0	0'.1	0'.2	0'.3	0'.4	0'.5	0'.6	0'.7	0'.8	0'.9	1	2	3	4	5
0	.0000	0017	0035	0052	0070	0087	0105	0122	0140	0157	3	6	9	12	15
1	.0175	0192	0209	0227	0244	0262	0279	0297	0314	0332	3	6	9	12	15
2	.0349	0366	0384	3401	0419	0436	0454	0471	0488	0506	3	6	9	12	15
3	.0523	0541	0558	0576	0593	0610	0628	0645	0663	0680	3	6	9	12	15
4	.0698	0715	0732	0750	0767	0785	0802	0819	0837	0854	3	6	9	12	15
5	.0872	0889	0906	0924	0941	0958	0976	0993	1011	1028	3	6	9	12	14
6	.1045	1063	1080	1097	1115	1132	1149	1167	1184	1201	3	6	9	12	14
7	.1219	1236	1253	1271	1288	1305	1323	1340	1357	1374	3	6	9	12	14
8	.1392	1409	1426	1444	1461	1478	1495	1513	1530	1547	3	6	9	12	14
9	.1564	1582	1599	1616	1633	1650	1668	1685	1702	1719	3	6	9	12	14
10	.1736	1754	1771	1788	1805	1822	1840	1857	1874	1891	3	6	9	12	14
11	.1908	1925	1942	1959	1977	1994	2011	2028	2045	2062	3	6	9	11	14
12	.2079	2096	2113	2130	2147	2164	2181	2198	2215	2232	3	6	9	11	14
13	.2250	2267	2284	2300	2317	2334	2351	2368	2385	2402	3	6	8	11	14
14	.2419	2436	2453	2470	2487	2504	2521	2538	2554	2571	3	6	8	11	14
15	.2588	2605	2622	2639	2656	2672	2689	2706	2723	2740	3	6	8	11	14
16	.2756	2773	2790	2807	2823	2840	2857	2874	2890	2907	3	6	8	11	14
17	.2924	2940	2957	2974	2990	3007	3024	3040	3057	3074	3	6	8	11	14
18	.3090	3107	3123	3140	3156	3173	3190	3206	3223	3239	3	6	8	11	14
19	.3256	3272	3289	3305	3322	3338	3355	3371	3387	3404	3	5	8	11	14
20	.3420	3437	3453	3469	3486	3502	3518	3535	3551	3567	3	5	8	11	14
21	.3584	3600	3616	3633	3649	3665	3681	3697	3714	3730	3	5	8	11	14
22	.3746	3762	3778	3795	3811	3827	3843	3859	3875	3891	3	5	8	11	14
23	.3907	3923	3939	3955	3971	3987	4003	4019	4035	4051	3	5	8	11	14
24	.4067	4083	4099	4115	4131	4147	4163	4197	4195	4210	3	5	8	11	13
25	.4226	4242	4258	4274	4289	4305	4321	4337	4352	4368	3	5	8	11	13
26	.4384	4399	4415	4431	4446	4462	4478	4493	4509	4524	3	5	8	10	13
27	.4540	4555	4571	4586	4602	4617	4633	4648	4664	4679	3	5	8	10	13
28	.4695	4710	4726	4741	4756	4772	4787	4802	4818	4833	3	5	8	10	13
29	.4848	4863	4879	4894	4909	4924	4939	4955	4970	4985	3	5	8	10	13
30	.5000	5015	5030	5045	5060	5075	5090	5105	5120	5135	3	5	8	10	13
31	.5150	5165	5180	5195	5210	5225	5240	5255	5270	5284	2	5	7	10	12
32	.5299	5314	5329	5344	5358	5373	5388	5402	5417	5432	2	5	7	10	12
33	.5446	5461	5476	5490	5505	5519	5534	5548	5563	5577	2	5	7	10	12
34	.5592	5606	5621	5635	5650	5664	5678	5693	5707	5721	2	5	7	10	12
35	.5736	5750	5764	5779	5793	5807	5821	5835	5850	5864	2	5	7	10	12
36	.5878	5892	5906	5920	5934	5948	5962	5976	5990	6004	2	5	7	9	12
37	.6018	6032	6046	6060	6074	6088	6101	6115	6129	6143	2	5	7	9	12
38	.6157	6170	6184	6198	6211	6225	6239	6252	6266	6280	2	5	7	9	11
39	.6293	6307	6320	6334	6347	6361	6374	6388	6401	6414	2	4	7	9	11
40	.6428	6441	6455	6468	6481	6494	6508	6521	6534	6547	2	4	7	9	11
41	.6561	6574	6587	6600	6613	6626	6639	6652	6665	6678	2	4	7	9	11
42	.6691	6704	6717	6730	6743	6756	6769	6782	6794	6807	2	4	6	9	11
43	.6820	6833	6845	6858	6871	6884	6896	6909	6921	6934	2	4	6	8	11
44	.6947	6959	6972	6984	6997	7009	7022	7034	7046	7059	2	4	6	8	10

NATURAL SINES

Degrees	0'	6'	12'	18'	24'	30'	36'	42'	48'	54'	Mean Differences	
	0'. 0	0'. 1	0'. 2	0'. 3	0'. 4	0'. 5	0'. 6	0'. 7	0'. 8	0'. 9	1 2 3	4 5
45	.7071	7083	7096	7108	7120	7133	7145	7157	7169	7181	2 4 6	8 10
46	.7193	7206	7218	7230	7242	7254	7266	7278	7290	7302	2 4 6	8 10
47	.7314	7325	7337	7349	7361	7373	7385	7396	7408	7420	2 4 6	8 10
48	.7431	7443	7455	7466	7478	7490	7501	7513	7524	7536	2 4 6	8 10
49	.7547	7558	7570	7581	7593	7604	7615	7627	7638	7649	2 4 6	8 9
50	.7660	7672	7683	7694	7705	7716	7727	7738	7749	7760	2 4 6	7 9
51	.7771	7782	7793	7804	7815	7826	7837	7848	7859	7869	2 4 5	7 9
52	.7880	7891	7902	7912	7923	7934	7944	7955	7965	7976	2 4 5	7 9
53	.7986	7997	8007	8018	8028	8039	8049	8059	8070	8080	2 3 5	7 9
54	.8090	8100	8111	8121	8131	8141	8151	8161	8171	8181	2 3 5	7 8
55	.8192	8202	8211	8221	8231	8241	8251	8261	8271	8281	2 3 5	7 8
56	.8290	8300	8310	8320	8329	8339	8348	8358	8368	8377	2 3 5	6 8
57	.8387	8396	8406	8415	8425	8434	8443	8453	8462	8471	2 3 5	6 8
58	.8480	8490	8499	8508	8517	8526	8536	8545	8554	8563	2 3 5	6 8
59	.8572	8581	8590	8599	8607	8616	8625	8634	8643	8652	1 3 4	6 7
60	.8660	8669	8678	8686	8695	8704	8712	8721	8729	8738	1 3 4	6 7
61	.8746	8755	8763	8771	8780	8788	8796	8805	8813	8821	1 3 4	6 7
62	.8829	8838	8846	8854	8862	8870	8878	8886	8894	8902	1 3 4	5 7
63	.8910	8918	8926	8934	8942	8949	8957	8965	8973	8980	1 3 4	5 6
64	.8988	8996	9003	9011	9018	9026	9033	9041	9048	9056	1 3 4	5 6
65	.9063	9070	9078	9085	9092	9100	9107	9114	9121	9128	1 2 4	5 6
66	.9135	9143	9150	9157	9164	9171	9178	9184	9191	9198	1 2 3	5 6
67	.9205	9212	9219	9225	9232	9239	9245	9252	9259	9265	1 2 3	4 6
68	.9272	9278	9285	9291	9298	9304	9311	9317	9323	9330	1 2 3	4 5
69	.9336	9342	9348	9354	9361	9367	9373	9379	9385	9391	1 2 3	4 5
70	.9397	9403	9409	9415	9421	9426	9432	9438	9444	9449	1 2 3	4 5
71	.9455	9461	9466	9472	9478	9483	9489	9494	9500	9505	1 2 3	4 5
72	.9511	9516	9521	9527	9532	9537	9542	9548	9553	9558	1 2 3	3 4
73	.9563	9568	9573	9578	9583	9588	9593	9598	9603	9608	1 2 2	3 4
74	.9613	9617	9622	9627	9632	9636	9641	9646	9650	9655	1 2 2	3 4
75	.9659	9664	9668	9673	9677	9681	9686	9690	9694	9699	1 1 2	3 4
76	.9703	9707	9711	9715	9720	9724	9728	9732	9736	9740	1 1 2	3 3
77	.9744	9748	9751	9755	9759	9763	9767	9770	9774	9778	1 1 2	3 3
78	.9781	9785	9789	9792	9796	9799	9803	9806	9810	9813	1 1 2	2 3
79	.9816	9820	9823	9826	9829	9833	9836	9839	9842	9845	1 1 2	2 3
80	.9848	9851	9854	9857	9860	9863	9866	9869	9871	9874	0 1 1	2 2
81	.9877	9880	9882	9885	9888	9890	9893	9895	9898	9900	0 1 1	2 2
82	.9903	9905	9907	9910	9912	9914	9917	9919	9921	9923	0 1 1	2 2
83	.9925	9928	9930	9932	9934	9936	9938	9940	9942	9943	0 1 1	1 2
84	.9945	9947	9949	9951	9952	9954	9956	9957	9959	9960	0 1 1	1 2
85	.9962	9963	9965	9966	9968	9969	9971	9972	9973	9974	0 0 1	1 1
86	.9976	9977	9978	9979	9980	9981	9982	9983	9984	9985	0 0 1	1 1
87	.9986	9987	9988	9980	9990	9990	9991	9992	9993	9993	0 0 0	1 1
88	.9994	9995	9995	9996	9996	9997	9997	9997	9998	9998	0 0 0	0 0
89	.9998	9999	9999	9999	9999	1.000	1.000	1.000	1.000	1.000	0 0 0	0 0
90	1.000											

NATURAL COSINES

Degrees	0'	6'	12'	18'	24'	30'	36'	42'	48'	54'	Mean Differences				
	0'.0	0'.1	0'.2	0'.3	0'.4	0'.5	0'.6	0'.7	0'.8	0'.9	1	2	3	4	5
0	1.000	1.000	1.000	1.000	1.000	1.000	.9999	9999	9999	9999	0	0	0	0	0
1	.9998	9998	9998	9997	9997	9997	9996	9996	9995	9995	0	0	0	0	0
2	.9994	9993	9993	9992	9991	9990	9990	9989	9988	9987	0	0	0	1	1
3	.9986	9985	9984	9983	9982	9981	9980	9979	9978	9977	0	0	1	1	1
4	.9976	9974	9973	9972	9971	9969	9968	9966	9965	9963	0	0	1	1	1
5	.9962	9960	9959	9957	9956	9954	9952	9951	9949	9947	0	1	1	1	2
6	.9945	9943	9942	9940	9938	9936	9934	9932	9930	9928	0	1	1	1	2
7	.9925	9923	9921	9919	9917	9914	9912	9910	9907	9905	0	1	1	2	2
8	.9903	9900	9898	9895	9893	9890	9888	9885	9882	9880	0	1	1	2	2
9	.9877	9874	9871	9869	9866	9863	9860	9857	9854	9851	0	1	1	2	2
10	.9848	9845	9842	9839	9836	9833	9829	9826	9823	9820	1	1	2	2	3
11	.9816	9813	9810	9806	9803	9799	9796	9792	9789	9785	1	1	2	2	3
12	.9781	9778	9774	9770	9767	9763	9759	9755	9751	9748	1	1	2	3	3
13	.9744	9740	9736	9732	9728	9724	9720	9715	9711	9707	1	1	2	3	3
14	.9703	9699	9694	9690	9686	9681	9677	9673	9668	9664	1	1	2	3	4
15	.9659	9655	9650	9646	9641	9636	9632	9627	9622	9617	1	2	2	3	4
16	.9613	9608	9603	9598	9593	9588	9583	9578	9573	9568	1	2	2	3	4
17	.9563	9558	9553	9548	9542	9537	9532	9527	9521	9516	1	2	3	3	4
18	.9511	9505	9500	9494	9489	9483	9478	9472	9466	9461	1	2	3	4	5
19	.9455	9449	9444	9438	9432	9426	9421	9415	9409	9403	1	2	3	4	5
20	.9397	9391	9385	9879	9373	9367	9361	9354	9348	9342	1	2	3	4	5
21	.9336	9330	9323	9317	9311	9304	9298	9291	9285	9278	1	2	3	4	5
22	.9272	9265	9259	9252	9245	9239	9232	9225	9219	9212	1	2	3	4	6
23	.9205	9198	9191	9184	9178	9171	9164	9157	9150	9143	1	2	3	5	6
24	.9135	9128	9121	9114	9107	9100	9092	9085	9078	9070	1	2	4	5	6
25	.9063	9056	9048	9041	9033	9026	9018	9011	9003	8996	1	3	4	5	6
26	.8988	8980	8973	8965	8957	8949	8942	8934	8926	8918	1	3	4	5	6
27	.8910	8902	8894	8886	8878	8870	8862	8854	8846	8838	1	3	4	5	7
28	.8829	8821	8813	8805	8769	8788	8780	8771	8763	8755	1	3	4	6	7
29	.8746	8738	8729	8721	8712	8704	8695	8686	8678	8669	1	3	4	6	7
30	.8660	8652	8643	8654	8625	8616	8607	8599	8590	8581	1	3	4	6	7
31	.8572	8563	8554	8543	8536	8526	8517	8508	8499	8490	2	3	5	6	8
32	.8480	8471	8462	8453	8443	8434	8425	8415	8406	8396	2	3	5	6	8
33	.8387	8377	8368	8358	8348	8339	8329	8320	8310	8300	2	3	5	6	8
34	.8290	8281	8271	8261	8251	8241	8231	8221	8211	8202	2	3	5	7	8
35	.8192	8181	8171	8161	8151	8141	8131	8121	8111	8100	2	3	5	7	8
36	.8090	8080	8070	8059	8049	8039	8028	8018	8007	7997	2	3	5	7	9
37	.7986	7976	7965	7955	7944	7934	7923	7912	7902	7801	2	4	5	7	9
38	.7880	7869	7859	7848	7837	7826	7815	7804	7793	7782	2	4	5	7	9
39	.7771	7760	7749	7738	7727	7716	7705	7694	7683	7672	2	4	6	7	9
40	.7660	7649	7638	7627	7615	7604	7593	7581	7570	7559	2	4	6	8	9
41	.7547	7536	7524	7513	7501	7490	7478	7466	7455	7443	2	4	6	8	10
42	.7431	7420	7408	7396	7385	7373	7361	7349	7337	7325	2	4	6	8	10
43	.7314	7302	7290	7278	7266	7254	7242	7230	7218	7205	2	4	6	8	10
44	.7193	7181	7169	7157	7145	7133	7120	7108	7096	7083	2	4	6	8	10

NATURAL COSINES

Degree	0'	6'	12'	18'	24'	30'	36'	42'	48'	54'	Mean Differences	
	0'. 0	0'. 1	0'. 2	0'. 3	0'. 4	0'. 5	0'. 6	0'. 7	0'. 8	0'. 9	1 2 3	4 5
45	.7071	7059	7046	7034	7022	7009	6997	6984	6972	6959	2 4 6	8 10
46	.6947	6934	6921	6909	6896	6884	6871	6858	6845	6833	2 4 6	8 11
47	.6820	6807	6794	6782	6769	6756	6743	6730	6717	6704	2 4 6	9 11
48	.6691	6678	6665	6652	6639	6626	6613	6600	6587	6574	2 4 7	9 11
49	.6561	6547	6534	6521	6508	6494	6481	6468	6455	6441	2 4 7	9 11
50	.6428	6414	6401	6388	6374	6361	6347	6334	6320	6307	2 4 7	9 11
51	.6293	6280	6266	6252	6239	6225	6211	6198	6184	6170	2 5 7	9 11
52	.6157	6143	6129	6115	6101	6088	6074	6060	6046	6032	2 5 7	9 12
53	.6018	6004	5990	5976	5962	5948	5934	5920	5906	5892	2 5 7	9 12
54	.5878	5864	5850	5835	5821	5807	5793	5779	5764	5750	2 5 7	9 12
55	.5736	5721	5707	5693	5678	5664	5650	5635	5621	5606	2 5 7	10 12
56	.5592	5577	5563	5548	5534	5519	5505	5490	5476	5461	2 5 7	10 12
57	.5446	5432	5417	5402	5388	5373	5358	5344	5329	5314	2 5 7	10 12
58	.5299	5284	5270	5255	5240	5225	5210	5195	5180	5165	2 5 7	10 12
59	.5150	5135	5120	5105	5090	5075	5060	5045	5030	5015	3 5 8	10 13
60	.5000	4985	4970	4955	4939	4924	4909	4894	4879	4863	3 5 8	10 13
61	.4848	4833	4818	4802	4787	4772	4756	4741	4726	4710	3 5 8	10 13
62	.4695	4679	4664	4648	4633	4617	4602	4586	4571	4555	3 5 8	10 13
63	.4540	4524	4509	4493	4478	4462	4446	4431	4415	4399	3 5 8	10 13
64	.4384	4368	4352	4337	4321	4305	4289	4274	4258	4242	3 5 8	11 13
65	.4226	4210	4195	4179	4163	4147	4131	4115	4099	4083	3 5 8	11 13
66	.4067	4051	4035	4019	4003	3987	3971	3955	3939	3923	3 5 8	11 14
67	.3907	3891	3875	3859	3843	3827	3811	3795	3778	3762	3 5 8	11 14
68	.3746	3730	3714	3697	3681	3665	3649	3633	3616	3600	3 5 8	11 14
69	.3584	3567	3551	3535	3518	3502	3486	3469	3453	3437	3 5 8	11 14
70	.3420	3404	3387	3371	3355	3338	3322	3305	3289	3272	3 5 8	11 14
71	.3256	3239	3223	3206	3190	3173	3156	3140	3123	3107	3 6 8	11 14
72	.3090	3074	3057	3040	3024	3007	2990	2974	2957	2940	3 6 8	11 14
73	.2924	2907	2890	2874	2857	2840	2823	2807	2790	2773	3 6 8	11 14
74	.2756	2740	2723	2706	2689	2672	2656	2639	2622	2605	3 6 8	11 14
75	.2588	2571	2554	2538	2521	2504	2487	2470	2453	2436	3 6 8	11 14
76	.2419	2402	2385	2368	2351	2334	2317	2300	2284	2267	3 6 8	11 14
77	.2250	2233	2215	2198	2181	2164	2147	2130	2113	2096	3 6 9	11 14
78	.2079	2062	2045	2028	2011	1994	1977	1959	1942	1925	3 6 9	11 14
79	.1908	1891	1874	1857	1840	1822	1805	1788	1771	1754	3 6 9	11 14
80	.1736	1719	1702	1685	1668	1650	1633	1616	1599	1582	3 6 9	12 14
81	.1564	1547	1530	1513	1495	1478	1461	1444	1426	1409	3 6 9	12 14
82	.1392	1374	1357	1340	1323	1305	1288	1271	1253	1236	3 6 9	12 14
83	.1219	1201	1184	1167	1149	1132	1115	1097	1080	1063	3 6 9	12 14
84	.1045	1028	1011	0993	0976	0958	0941	0924	0906	0889	3 6 9	12 14
85	.0872	0854	0837	0819	0882	0785	0767	0750	0732	0715	3 6 9	12 15
86	.0698	0680	0663	0645	0628	0610	0593	0576	0558	0541	3 6 9	12 15
87	.0523	0506	0488	0471	0454	0436	0419	0401	0384	0366	3 6 9	12 15
88	.0349	0332	0314	0297	0279	0262	0244	0227	0209	0192	3 6 9	12 15
89	.0175	0157	0140	0122	0105	0087	0070	0052	0035	0017	3 6 9	12 15
90	.0000											

WEIGHTS AND ABSCISSAE OF LEGENDRE-GAUSS QUADRATURE FORMULA

i	$\pm \mu_i$	w_i
	$n = 1$	
0	0.0000000000	2.0000000000
	$n = 2$	
1	0.57735 02692	1.00000 00000
	$n = 3$	
0	0.00000 00000	0.88888 88889
1	0.77459 66692	0.55555 55556
	$n = 4$	
1	0.33998 10436	0.65214 51549
2	0.86113 63116	0.34785 48451
	$n = 5$	
0	0.00000 00000	0.56888 88889
1	0.53846 93101	0.47862 36705
2	0.90617 98459	0.23692 68851
	$n = 6$	
1	0.23861 91861	0.46791 39346
2	0.66120 93865	0.36076 15730
3	0.93246 95142	0.17132 44924
	$n = 7$	
0	0.00000 00000	0.41795 91837
1	0.40584 51514	0.38183 00505
2	0.74153 11856	0.27970 53915
3	0.94910 79123	0.12948 49662
	$n = 8$	
1	0.18343 46425	0.36268 37834
2	0.52553 24099	0.31370 66459
3	0.79666 64774	0.22238 10345
4	0.96028 98565	0.10122 85363
	$n = 9$	
0	0.00000 00000	0.33023 93550
1	0.32425 34234	0.31234 70770
2	0.61337 14327	0.26061 06964
3	0.83603 11073	0.18064 81607
4	0.96816 02395	0.08127 43834
	$n = 10$	
1	0.14887 43390	0.29552 42247
2	0.43339 53941	0.26926 67193
3	0.67940 95683	0.21908 63625
4	0.86506 33667	0.14945 13492
5	0.97390 65285	0.06667 13443

i	$\pm \mu_i$	w_i
	$n = 11$	
0	0.00000 00000	0.27292 50868
1	0.26954 31560	0.26280 45445
2	0.51909 61291	0.23319 37646
3	0.73015 20056	0.18629 02109
4	0.88706 25998	0.12558 03695
5	0.97822 86581	0.05566 85671
	$n = 12$	
1	0.12533 34085	0.24914 70458
2	0.36783 14989	0.23349 25365
3	0.58731 79543	0.20316 74267
4	0.76990 26742	0.16007 83285
5	0.90411 72564	0.10693 93260
6	0.98156 06342	0.04717 53364
	$n = 13$	
0	0.00000 00000	0.23255 15532
1	0.23045 83160	0.22628 31803
2	0.44849 27510	0.20781 60475
3	0.64234 93394	0.17814 59808
4	0.80157 80907	0.13887 35102
5	0.91759 83992	0.09212 14998
6	0.98418 30547	0.04048 40048
	$n = 14$	
1	0.10805 49487	0.21526 38535
2	0.31911 23689	0.20519 84637
3	0.51524 86364	0.18553 83975
4	0.68729 29048	0.15720 31672
5	0.82720 13151	0.12151 85707
6	0.92843 48837	0.08015 80872
7	0.98628 38087	0.03511 94603
	$n = 15$	
0	0.00000 00000	0.20257 82419
1	0.20119 40940	0.19843 14853
2	0.39415 13471	0.18616 10000
3	0.57097 21726	0.16626 92058
4	0.72441 77314	0.13957 06779
5	0.84820 65834	0.10715 92205
6	0.93727 33924	0.07036 60475
7	0.98799 25180	0.03075 32420
	$n = 16$	
1	0.09501 25098	0.18945 06105
2	0.28160 35508	0.18260 34150
3	0.45801 67777	0.16915 65194
4	0.61787 62444	0.14959 59888
5	0.75540 44084	0.12462 89713
6	0.86563 12024	0.09515 85117
7	0.94457 50231	0.06225 35239
8	0.98940 09350	0.02715 24594

NATURAL SECANTS

Degrees	0′ 0°.0	6′ 0°.1	12′ 0°.2	18′ 0°.3	24′ 0°.4	30′ 0°.5	36′ 0°.6	42′ 0°.7	48′ 0°.8	54′ 0°.9	Mean Differences 1	2	3	4	5
0	1.0000	0000	0000	0000	0000	0000	0001	0001	0001	0001	0	0	0	0	0
1	1.0002	0002	0002	0003	0003	0003	0004	0004	0005	0006	0	0	0	0	0
2	1.0006	0007	0007	0008	0009	0010	0010	0011	0012	0013	0	0	0	0	0
3	1.0014	0015	0016	0017	0018	0019	0020	0021	0022	0023	0	0	1	1	1
4	1.0024	0026	0027	0028	0030	0031	0032	0034	0035	0037	0	0	1	1	1
5	1.0038	0040	0041	0043	0045	0046	0048	0050	0051	0053	0	1	1	1	1
6	1.0055	0057	0059	0061	0063	0065	0067	0069	0071	0073	0	1	1	1	2
7	1.0075	0077	0079	0082	0084	0086	0089	0091	0093	0096	0	1	1	2	2
8	1.0098	0101	0103	0106	0108	0111	0114	0116	0119	0122	0	1	1	2	2
9	1.0125	0127	0130	0133	0136	0139	0142	0145	0148	0151	0	1	1	2	2
10	1.0154	0157	0161	0164	0167	0170	0174	0177	0180	0184	1	1	2	2	3
11	1.0187	0191	0194	0198	0201	0205	0209	0212	0216	0220	1	1	2	2	3
12	1.0223	0227	0231	0235	0239	0243	0247	0251	0255	0259	1	1	2	3	3
13	1.0263	0267	0271	0276	0280	0284	0288	0293	0297	0302	1	1	2	3	4
14	1.0306	0311	0315	0320	0324	0329	0334	0338	0343	0348	1	2	2	3	4
15	1.0353	0358	0363	0367	0372	0377	0382	0388	0393	0398	1	2	3	3	4
16	1.0403	0408	0413	0419	0424	0429	0435	0440	0446	0451	1	2	3	3	4
17	1.0457	0463	0468	0474	0480	0485	0491	0497	0503	0509	1	2	3	4	5
18	1.0515	0521	0527	0533	0539	0545	0551	0557	0564	0570	1	2	3	4	5
19	1.0576	0583	0589	0595	0602	0608	0615	0622	0628	0635	1	2	3	4	5
20	1.0642	0649	0655	0662	0669	0676	0683	0690	0697	0704	1	2	3	5	6
21	1.0711	0719	0726	0733	0740	0748	0755	0763	0770	0778	1	2	4	5	6
22	1.0785	0793	0801	0808	0816	0824	0832	0840	0848	0856	1	3	4	5	6
23	1.0864	0872	0880	0888	0896	0904	0913	0921	0929	0938	1	3	4	6	7
24	1.0946	0955	0963	0972	0981	0989	0998	1007	1016	1025	1	3	4	6	7
25	1.1034	1043	1052	1061	1070	1079	1089	1098	1107	1117	2	3	5	6	8
26	1.1126	1136	1145	1155	1164	1174	1184	1194	1203	1213	2	3	5	6	8
27	1.1223	1233	1243	1253	1264	1274	1284	1294	1305	1315	2	3	5	7	9
28	1.1326	1336	1347	1357	1368	1379	1390	1401	1412	1423	2	4	5	7	9
29	1.1434	1445	1456	1467	1478	1490	1501	1512	1524	1535	2	4	6	8	9
30	1.1547	1559	1570	1582	1594	1606	1618	1630	1642	1654	2	4	6	8	10
31	1.1666	1679	1691	1703	1716	1728	1741	1753	1766	1779	2	4	6	8	10
32	1.1792	1805	1818	1831	1844	1857	1870	1883	1897	1910	2	4	7	9	11
33	1.1924	1937	1951	1964	1978	1992	2006	2020	2034	2048	2	5	7	9	12
34	1.2062	2076	2091	2105	2120	2134	2149	2163	2178	2193	2	5	7	10	12
35	1.2208	2223	2238	2253	2268	2283	2299	2314	2329	2345	3	5	8	10	13
36	1.2361	2376	2392	2408	2424	2440	2456	2472	2489	2505	3	5	8	11	13
37	1.2521	2538	2554	2571	2588	2605	2622	2639	2656	2673	3	6	8	11	14
38	1.2690	2708	2725	2742	2760	2778	2796	2813	2831	2849	3	6	9	12	15
39	1.2868	2886	2904	2923	2941	2960	2978	2997	3016	3035	3	6	9	12	16
40	1.3054	3073	3093	3112	3131	3151	3171	3190	3210	3230	3	7	10	13	16
41	1.3250	3270	3291	3311	3331	3352	3373	3393	3414	3435	3	7	10	14	17
42	1.3456	3478	3499	3520	3542	3563	3585	3607	3629	3651	4	7	11	14	18
43	1.3673	3696	3718	3741	3763	3786	3809	3832	3855	3878	4	8	11	15	19
44	1.3902	3925	3949	3972	3996	4020	4044	4069	4093	4118	4	8	2	16	20

NATURAL SECANTS.

Degrees	0′ 0°. 0	6′ 0°. 1	12′ 0°. 2	18′ 0°. 3	24′ 0°. 4	30′ 0°. 5	36′ 0°. 6	42′ 0°. 7	48′ 0°. 8	54′ 0°. 9	Mean Differences 1	2	3	4	5
45	1.4142	4167	4192	4217	4242	4267	4293	4318	4344	4370	4	8	13	17	21
46	1.4396	4422	4448	4474	4501	4527	4554	4581	4608	4635	4	9	13	18	22
47	1.4663	4690	4718	4746	4774	4802	4830	4859	4887	4916	5	9	14	19	23
48	1.4945	4974	5003	5032	5062	5092	5121	5151	5182	5212	5	10	15	20	25
49	1.5243	5273	5304	5335	5366	5398	5429	5461	5493	5525	5	10	16	21	26
50	1.5557	5590	5622	5655	5688	5721	5755	5788	5822	5856	6	11	17	22	28
51	1.5890	5925	5959	5994	6029	6064	6099	6135	6171	6207	6	12	18	24	29
52	1.6243	6279	6316	6353	6390	6427	6464	6502	6540	6578	6	12	19	25	31
53	1.6616	6655	6694	6733	6772	6812	6852	6892	6932	6972	7	13	20	26	33
54	1.7013	7054	7095	7137	7179	7221	7263	7305	7348	7391	7	14	21	28	35
55	1.7434	7478	7522	7566	7610	7655	7700	7745	7791	7837	7	15	22	30	37
56	1.7883	7929	7976	8023	8070	8118	8166	8214	8263	8312	8	16	24	32	40
57	1.8361	8410	8460	8510	8561	8612	8663	8714	8766	8818	7	17	26	34	43
58	1.8871	8924	8977	9031	9084	9139	9194	9249	9304	9360	9	18	27	36	45
59	1.9416	9473	9530	9587	9645	9703	9762	9821	9880	9940	10	19	29	39	49
60	2.000	0061	0122	0183	0245	0308	0371	0434	0498	0562	10	21	31	42	52
61	2.0627	0692	0757	0824	0890	0957	1025	1093	1162	1231	11	22	34	45	56
62	2.1301	1371	1441	1513	1584	1657	1730	1803	1877	1952	12	24	36	48	61
63	2.2027	2103	2179	2256	2333	2412	2490	2570	2650	2730	13	26	39	52	66
64	2.2812	2894	2976	3060	3144	3228	3314	3400	3486	3574	14	28	43	57	71
65	2.3662	3751	3841	3931	4022	4114	4207	4300	4395	4490	15	31	46	62	77
66	2.4586	4683	4780	4879	4978	5078	5180	5282	5384	5488	17	34	50	67	84
67	2.5593	5699	5805	5913	6022	6131	6242	6354	6466	6580	18	37	55	73	92
68	2.6695	6811	6927	7046	7165	7285	7407	7529	7653	7778	20	40	60	81	101
69	2.7904	8032	8161	8291	8422	8555	8688	8824	8960	9099					
70	2.9238	9379	9521	9665	9811	9957	3.0106	3.0256	3.0407	3.0561	Mean Differences cease to be sufficiently accurate				
71	3.0716	0872	1030	1190	1352	1515	1681	1848	2017	2188					
72	3.2361	2535	2712	2891	3072	3255	3440	3628	3817	4009					
73	3.4203	4399	4598	4799	5003	5209	5418	5629	5843	6060					
74	3.6280	6502	6727	6955	7186	7420	7657	7897	8140	8387					
75	3.8637	8890	9147	9408	9672	9939	4.0211	4.0486	4.0765	4.1048					
76	4.1336	1627	1923	2223	2527	2837	3150	3469	3792	4121					
77	4.4454	4793	5137	5486	5841	6202	6569	6942	7321	7706					
78	4.8097	8496	8901	9313	9732	5.0159	5.0593	5.1034	5.1484	5.1942					
79	5.2408	2883	3367	3860	4362	4874	5396	5928	6470	7023					
80	5.7588	8164	8751	9351	9963	6.0589	6.1227	6.1880	6.2546	6.3228					
81	6.3925	4637	5366	6111	6874	7655	8454	9273	7.0112	2.0972					
82	7.1853	2757	3684	4635	5611	6613	7642	8700	9787	8.0905					
83	8.2055	3238	4457	5711	7004	8337	9711	9.1129	9.2593	9.4105					
84	9.5668	9.728	9.895	10.07	10.25	10.43	10.63	10.83	11.03	11.25					
85	11.47	11.71	11.95	12.20	12.47	12.75	13.03	13.34	13.65	13.99					
86	14.34	14.70	15.09	15.50	15.93	16.38	16.86	17.37	17.91	18.49					
87	19.11	19.77	20.47	21.23	22.04	22.93	23.88	24.92	26.05	27.29					
88	28.65	30.16	31.84	33.71	35.81	38.20	40.93	44.08	47.75	52.09					
89	57.30	63.66	71.62	81.85	95.49	114.6	143.2	191.0	286.5	573.0					

EXPONENTIAL AND HYPERBOLIC FUNCTIONS

x	e^x	e^{-x}	sin h x	cos h x	x	e^x	e^{-x}	sin h x	cos h x
.02	1.0202	.9802	.0200	1.0002	**1.0**	2.7183	.3679	1.1752	1.5431
.04	1.0408	.9608	.0400	1.0008	1.1	3.0042	.3329	1.3356	1.6685
.06	1.0618	.9418	.0600	1.0018	1.2	3.3201	.3012	1.5095	1.8107
.08	1.0833	.9231	.0801	1.0032	1.3	3.6693	.2725	1.6984	1.9709
.10	1.1052	.9048	.1002	1.0050	1.4	4.0552	.2466	1.9043	2.1509
.11	1.1163	.8958	.1102	1.0061	**1.5**	4.4817	.2231	2.1293	2.3524
.12	1.1275	.8869	.1203	1.0072	1.6	4.9530	.2019	2.3756	2.5775
.13	1.1388	.8781	.1304	1.0085	1.7	5.4739	.1827	2.6456	2.8283
.14	1.1503	.8694	.1405	1.0098	1.8	6.0497	.1653	2.9422	3.1075
.15	1.1618	.8607	.1506	1.0113	1.9	6.6859	.1496	3.2682	3.4177
.16	1.1735	.8521	.1607	1.0128	**2.0**	7.3891	.1353	3.6269	3.7622
.17	1.1853	8437	.1708	1.0145	2.1	8.1662	.1225	4.0219	4.1443
.18	1.1972	8353	.1810	1.0162	2.2	9.0250	.1108	4.4571	4.5679
.19	1.2092	.8270	.1911	1.0181	2.3	9.9742	.1003	4.9370	5.0372
.20	1.2214	.8187	.2013	1.0201	2.4	11.023	.0907	5.4662	5.5569
.21	1.2337	8106	.2115	1.0221	**2.5**	12.182	.0821	6.0502	6.1323
.22	1.2461	.8025	.2218	1.0243	2.6	13.464	.0743	6.6947	6.7690
.23	1.2586	.7945	.2320	1.0266	2.7	14.880	.0672	7.4063	7.4735
.24	1.2712	.7866	.2423	1.0289	2.8	16.445	.0608	8.1919	8.2527
.25	1.2840	.7788	.2526	1.0314	2.9	18.174	.0550	9.0596	9.1146
.26	1.2969	.7711	.2629	1.0340	**3.0**	20.085	.0498	10.018	10.068
.27	1.3100	.7634	.2733	1.0367	3.1	22.198	.0450	11.076	11.121
.28	1.3231	.7558	.2837	1.0395	3.2	24.532	.0408	12.246	12.287
.29	1.3364	.7483	.2941	1.0423	3.3	27.113	.0369	13.538	13.575
.30	1.3499	.7408	.3045	1.0453	3.4	29.964	.0334	14.965	14.999
.31	1.3634	.7335	.3150	1.0484	**3.5**	33.115	.0302	16.543	16.573
.32	1.3771	.7261	.3255	1.0516	3.6	36.598	.0273	18.285	18.313
.33	1.3910	.7189	.3360	1.0550	3.7	40.447	.0247	20.211	20.236
.34	1.4050	.7118	.3466	1.0584	3.8	44.701	.0224	22.339	22.362
.35	1.4191	.7047	.3572	1.0619	3.9	49.402	.0202	24.691	24.711
.36	1.4333	.6977	.3678	1.0655	**4.0**	54.598	.0183	27.290	27.308
.37	1.4477	.6907	.3785	1.0692	4.1	60.340	.0166	30.162	30.178
.38	1.4623	.6839	.3892	1.0731	4.2	66.686	.0150	33.336	33.351
.39	1.4770	6771	.4000	1.770	4.3	73.700	.0136	36.843	36.857
.40	1.4918	.6703	.4107	1.0811	4.4	81.451	.0123	40.719	40.732
.41	1.5068	.6636	.4216	1.0852	**4.5**	90.017	.0111	45.003	45.014
.42	1.5220	.6570	.4325	1.0895	4.6	99.484	.0100	49.737	49.747
.43	1.5373	.6505	.4434	1.0939	4.7	109.95	.00910	54.969	54.978
.44	1.5527	.6440	.4543	1.0984	4.8	121.51	.00823	60.751	60.759
.45	1.5683	.6376	.4653	1.1030	4.9	134.29	.00745	67.141	67.149
.46	1.5841	.6313	.4764	1.1077	**5.0**	148.41	.00674	74.203	74.210
.47	1.6000	.6250	.4875	1.1125	5.1	164.02	.00610	82.008	82.014
.48	1.6161	.6188	.4986	1.1174	5.2	181.27	.00552	90.633	90.639
.49	1.6323	.6126	.5098	1.1225	5.3	200.34	.00499	100.17	100.17
.50	1.6487	.6065	.5211	1.1276	5.4	221.41	.00452	110.70	110.71
.60	1.8221	.5488	.6367	1.1855	**5.5**	244.69	.00409	122.34	122.35
.70	2.0138	.4966	.7586	1.2552	5.6	270.43	.00370	135.21	135.21
.80	2.2255	.4493	.8881	1.3374	5.7	298.87	.00335	149.43	149.43
.90	2.4596	.4066	1.0265	1.4331	5.8	330.30	.00303	165.15	165.15
					5.9	365.04	.00274	182.52	182.52
					6.0	403.43	.00248	201.71	201.72

$$\cos h\, x = \frac{1}{2}(e^x + e^{-x}), \sin h\, x = \frac{1}{2}((e^x - e^{-x})$$